COMPENDIUM

OF METHODS

FOR THE

MICROBIOLOGICAL

EXAMINATION

OF FOODS

Third Edition

Edited by:

Carl Vanderzant, PhD
Don F. Splittstoesser, PhD

Compiled by the
APHA Technical
Committee on
Microbiological
Methods for Foods

American Public Health Association

American Public Health Association
1015 Fifteenth Street, NW
Washington, DC 20005

William H. McBeath, MD, MPH
Executive Director

Printed and bound in the United States of America

Design: Linda Sherman Design, Gaithersburg, MD

Typesetting: EPS Group Inc., Hanover, MD

Set in: Times Roman

Printing and Binding: Edwards Brothers, Ann Arbor, MI

ISBN 0-87553-173-3

3M 3/92

COMPENDIUM FOR THE MICROBIOLOGICAL EXAMINATION OF FOODS
3RD EDITION

EDITORIAL COMMITTEE

STEPHANIE DOORES
Department of Food Science
Pennsylvania State University
University Park, PA 16802

DAMIEN A. GABIS
Silliker Laboratories
1304 Halsted Street
Chicago Heights, IL 60411

KEITH A. ITO
National Food Processors Association
6363 Clark Avenue
Dublin, CA 94568

GEORGE JACKSON
Division of Microbiology
Center for Food Safety & Applied Nutrition
US Food and Drug Administration
Washington, DC 20204

DON F. SPLITTSTOESSER
Department of Food Science and Technology
New York State Agricultural Experiment Station
Geneva, NY 14456

JOHN A. TROLLER
Procter & Gamble Company
6071 Center Hill Road
Cincinnati, OH 45224

CARL VANDERZANT
Animal Science Department
Texas A&M University
College Station, TX 77843

APHA REPRESENTATIVE

HOWARD L. BODILY
P.O. Box 69
Midway, UT 84049

AUTHORS

CARLOS ABEYTA, JR.
Food & Drug Administration, 22201 23rd Drive S.E., Bothell, WA 98041-3012

G. R. ACUFF
Department of Animal Science, Texas A&M University, College Station, TX 77843

WALLACE H. ANDREWS
Division of Microbiology, Center for Food Safety & Applied Nutrition, Food and Drug Administration, Washington, DC 20204

DAVID H. ASHTON
Beatrice/Hunt-Wesson, 1645 W Valencia Drive, Fullerton, CA 92633

J. STAN BAILEY
USDA—ARS, R.B. Russell Agricultural Research Center, P.O. Box 5677, Athens, GA 30613

J. A. BAROSS
School of Oceanography, Oregon State University, Corvallis, OR 97331

R. W. BENNETT
Division of Microbiology, Center for Food Safety & Applied Nutrition, Food and Drug Administration, Washington, DC 20204

DANE T. BERNARD
National Food Processors Association, 1401 New York Ave. N.W., Washington, DC 20005

LARRY R. BEUCHAT
Department of Food Science & Technology, University of Georgia, Griffen, GA 30223

JEFFREY W. BIER
Division of Microbiology, Center for Food Safety and Applied Nutrition, Food and Drug Administration, Washington, DC 20204

ROBERT E. BRACKETT
Department of Food Science & Technology, University of Georgia, Griffen, GA 30223

R. L. BUCHANAN
Eastern Regional Research Center, U.S. Department of Agriculture, 600 E Mermaid Lane, Philadelphia, PA 19118

LLOYD B. BULLERMAN
Department of Food Science, University of Nebraska, Lincoln, N.E. 68583

V. KELLY BUNNING
Division of Microbiology, Center for Food Safety & Applied Nutrition, Food and Drug Administration, Washington, DC 20204

FRANCIS F. BUSTA
Department of Food Science and Nutrition, University of Minnesota, 1334 Eckles Ave., St. Paul, MN 55108

MICHAEL C. CIRIGLIANO
Thomas J. Lipton Co., 800 Sylvan Ave., Englewood Cliffs, NJ 07632

DEAN O. CLIVER
Food Research Institute, University of Wisconsin, 1925 Willow Drive, Madison, WI 53706

DAVID COLLINS-THOMPSON
Department of Environmental Biology and Food Science, University of Guelph, Guelph, Ontario, Canada N1G 2W1

DONALD A. CORLETT
ESCAgenetics Corp., 830 Branston Rd., San Carlos, CA 94070

M. A. COUSIN
Department of Food Science, Purdue University, W Lafayette, IN 47907

SARAH COWMAN
Sparkletts Drinking Water Corp., 4500 York Blvd., Los Angeles, CA 90041

NELSON A. COX
USDA-ARS, R.B. Russell Agricultural Research Center, P.O. Box 5677, Athens, GA 30613

MICHAEL S. CURIALE
Silliker Laboratories, Inc., 1304 Halsted St., Chicago Heights, IL 60411

M. A. DAESCHEL
Department of Food Science & Technology, Oregon State University, Corvallis, OR 97331-6602

JEAN-Yves D'AOUST
Banting Research Center, Health Protection Branch, Health and Welfare Canada, Tunney's Pasture, Ottawa, Ontario, Canada K1A OL2

KURT E. DEIBEL
Gerber Products Co., 45 State St., Fremont, MI 49412

R. H. DEIBEL
Deibel Lab. Inc., 845 E Johnson St., Madison, WI 53703

CLEVE B. DENNY
National Food Processors Association, 1401 New York Ave., NW, Washington, DC 20005

CATHERINE W. DONNELLY
Department of Animal Science, University of Vermont, Burlington, VT 05405

L. SCOTT DONNELLY
Wyeth Nutritionals, Inc., P.O. Box 815, Milton, VT 05468

STEPHANIE DOORES
Department of Food Science, Pennsylvania State University, University Park, PA 16802

MICHAEL P. DOYLE
Department of Food Science & Technology, University of Georgia, Griffin, GA 30223

JOHN M. DRYER
Heinz USA, P.O. Box 57, Pittsburgh, PA 15270

R. D. ELLENDER
Department of Microbiology, University of Southern Mississippi, Box 5153, Southern Station, Hattiesburg, MS 39401

GEORGE M. EVANCHO
Campbell Soup Co., Campbell Place, Camden, NJ 08101

RONALD FAYER
Animal Parasitology Institute, U.S. Department of Agriculture, Beltsville, MD 20705

GUNNAR FINNE
Applied Microbiological Services, Inc., P.O. Box 10280, College Station, TX 77840

RUTH FIRSTENBERG-EDEN
DIFCO Laboratories, R & D Center, 1180 Ellsworth Rd., Ann Arbor, MI 48108

HENRY P. FLEMING
USDA-ARS, Department of Food Science, North Carolina State University, Raleigh, NC 27695

RUSSELL S. FLOWERS
Silliker Laboratories, Inc., 1304 Halsted Street, Chicago Heights, IL 60411

PEGGY M. FOEGEDING
    Department of Food Science, North Carolina State University, Box 7624, Raleigh, NC 27695-7624

G. SHAY FOUT
    Environmental Monitoring & Support Laboratory, U.S. Environmental Protection Agency, 26 W Martin Luther King Jr. Drive, Cincinnati, OH 45268

JOSEPH F. FRANK
    Department of Food Sciences and Technology, 204 Dairy Science Bldg., University of Georgia, Athens, GA 30632

GLENN W. FRONING
    Department of Food Science and Technology, University of Nebraska, Lincoln, NE 68583-0919

DANIEL Y. C. FUNG
    Department of Animal Sciences and Industry, Kansas State University, Manhattan, KS 66506

H. R. GAMBLE
    Animal Parasitology Institute, U.S. Department of Agriculture, Beltsville, MD 20705

JOHN S. GECAN
    Division of Microbiology, Center for Food Safety & Applied Nutrition, Food and Drug Administration, Washington, DC 20204

BONITA A. GLATZ
    Department of Food Technology, Iowa State University, Ames, IA 50010

J. M. GOEPFERT (Deceased)
    Canada Packers Ltd., Toronto, Ontario, Canada M6N 1K4

MILLICENT C. GOLDSCHMIDT
    University of Texas, Health Science Center at Houston, Dental Science Institute, P.O. Box 20068, Houston, TX 72225

RICHARD R. GRAVES
    American-National Can Co., 433 N Northwest Highway, Barrington, IL 60010

R. J. H. GRAY
    Hercules, Inc., Hercules Plaza, Medical Dept. 2465, Wilmington, DE 19894

PHILIP A. GUARINO
    McCormick & Co., 11104 McCormick Road, Hunt Valley, MD 20131

MICHAEL J. HAAS
Animal Biomaterials Unit, USDA-ERRC, 600 E Mermaid Lane, Philadelphia, PA 19118

LESTER HANKIN
Department of Biochemistry and Genetics, The Connecticut Agricultural Experiment Station, 123 Huntington St., Box 1106, New Haven, CT 06504

STANLEY M. HARMON
Division of Microbiology, Center for Food Safety & Applied Nutrition, Food and Drug Administration, Washington, DC 20204

PAUL H. HARTMAN
Department of Microbiology, Iowa State University, Ames, IA 50011

WILLIAM S. HATCHER
The Coca-Cola Co., P.O. Box 2079, Houston, TX 77252

E. C. HILL
Florida Dept. Citrus, Box 1088, Lake Alfred, FL 33850

ANTHONY D. HITCHINS
Division of Microbiology, Center for Food Safety & Applied Nutrition, Food and Drug Administration, Washington, DC 20204

GARY A. HOUGHTBY
Laboratory Quality Assurance Branch, Food & Drug Administration, 1090 Tusculum Avenue, Cincinnati, OH 45226

D. A. HUNT (Retired)
Shellfish Branch, Food and Drug Administration, Washington, DC 20204

AMY IZAT
Department of Animal & Poultry Sciences, University of Arkansas, Fayetteville, AK 72701

J. M. JAY
Department of Biological Science, Wayne State University, Detroit, MI 48202

MICHAEL G. JOHNSON
Department of Food Science, University of Arkansas, 272 Young Ave., Fayetteville, AR 72703

R. W. JOHNSTON
Microbiology Division, Meat and Poultry Inspection Program, Food Safety and Inspection Service, U.S. Department of Agriculture, Washington, DC 20250

DONALD A. KAUTTER
  Division of Microbiology, Center for Food Safety & Applied Nutrition, Food and Drug Administration, Washington, DC 20204

CHARLES A. KAYSNER
  Food and Drug Administration, 22201 23rd Drive SE, Bothell, WA 98041-3012

ROBERT KELSEY
  Perrier Group of America, 1566 E. Washington Blvd., Los Angeles, CA 90021

A. DOUGLAS KING, JR.
  USDA, 800 Buchanan St., Berkeley, CA 94710

J. A. KOBURGER
  Department of Food Science and Human Nutrition, University of Florida, Gainesville, FL 32611

PATRICK J. KONKEL
  Nestle, S.A., Carnation Co., Oconomowoc, WI 53066

A. A. KRAFT
  Department of Food Science, Iowa State University, Ames, IA 50011

EDWARD P. KRYSINSKI
  Campbell Soup Co., Campbell Place, Camden, NJ 08103-1799

RONALD G. LABBE
  Department of Food Science & Nutrition, University of Massachusetts, Amherst, MA 01003

G. H. LACY
  Laboratory for Molecular Biology of Plant Stress, Virginia Polytechnic Institute and State University, Blacksburg, VA 24061-0330

DON E. LAKE
  American-National Can Co., 433 N Northwest Highway, Barrington, IL 60010

GAYLE A. LANCETTE
  Food and Drug Administration, 60 8th St., NE, Atlanta, GA 30309

R. A. LEDFORD
  Department of Food Science, Stocking Hall, Cornell University, Ithaca, NY 14853

JONG S. LEE
  University of Alaska, 202 Center St., Kodiak, AK 99615

WEI H. LEE
  USDA, FSIS, Building 322, ARC East. Beltsville, MD 20705

Lawrence M. Lenovich
: Tech. Ctr.—Hershey Foods Corp., 1025 Reese Ave., Hershey, PA 17033

J. R. Lichtenfels
: Animal Parasitology Institute, U.S. Department of Agriculture, Beltsville, MD 20705

M. B. Liewen
: General Mills Inc., 9000 Plymouth Ave. N, Minneapolis, MN 55427

L. Duane Lindsay
: R&D Walnut Division, Sun-Diamond Growers of California, P.O. Box 1727, Stockton, CA 95201

Joseph H. Lovett
: Division of Microbiology, Food & Drug Administration, 1090 Tusculum Ave., Cincinnati, OH 45226

John P. Lucas
: Division of Emergency & Epidemiology Operations, Office of Regulatory Affairs, U.S. Food and Drug Administration, 5600 Fischers Lane, Rockville, MD 20857

Howard Magwire
: Egg Products Grading Branch, Poultry Division, Agriculture Marketing Service, U.S. Department of Agriculture, Washington, DC 20250

Joe Mayou
: The Pillsbury Co., 311 Second St., S.E., Minneapolis, MN 55414

Barbara A. McCardell
: Division of Microbiology, Center for Food Safety & Applied Nutrition, Food & Drug Administration, Washington, DC 20204

R. F. McFeeters
: USDA-ARS, Department of Food Science, North Carolina State University, Raleigh, NC 27695

James W. Messer
: Laboratory Quality Assurance Branch, Division of Microbiology, Food and Drug Administration, 1090 Tusculum Ave., Cincinnati, OH 45226

Thaddeus F. Midura
: Microbial Diseases Laboratory, Department of Health Services, 2151 Berkeley Way, Berkeley, CA 94704

J. J. Miescier
: Shellfish Branch, Food and Drug Administration, Washington, DC 20204

DANIEL C. MILLS
California State Health Department, 2151 Berkeley Way, Berkeley, CA 94704

PHILIP B. MISLIVEC
Microanalytical Branch, Center for Food Safety & Applied Nutrition, Food and Drug Administration, Washington, DC 20204

LLOYD J. MOBERG
General Mills, Inc., J. F. B. Technical Center, 9000 Plymouth Ave. N, Minneapolis, MN 55427

S. C. MURPHY
Department of Food Science, Stocking Hall, Cornell University, Ithaca, NY 14853

R. NICKELSON II
Applied Microbiological Services, Inc., 4402 Center Gate, San Antonio, TX 78217

S. NOTERMANS
National Institute of Public Health and Environmental Protection, P.O. Box 1 3720 BA, Bilthoven, The Netherlands

KARL E. OLSON
National Food Processors Association, 6363 Clark Ave., Dublin, CA 94568

SAMUEL PALUMBO
USDA-ERRC, 600 E Mermaid Lane, Philadelphia, PA 19118

CHONG E. PARK
Microbial Research Division, Bureau of Microbial Hazards, Health & Welfare Canada, Ottawa, Canada K1A OL2

M. E. PARRISH
University of Florida, Lake Alfred, FL 33850

CHARLOTTE M. PATTON
Enteric Bacteriology Section, Center for Infections Diseases, Centers for Disease Control, Atlanta, GA 30333

JAMES T. PEELER
Division of Microbiology, Food and Drug Administration, Washington, DC 20204

EUGENE H. PETERSON
U.S. Department of HHS-FDA, 240 Hennepin, Minneapolis, MN 55401

J. I. PITT
CSIRO Division of Food Processing, P.O. Box 52, North Ryde, N.S.W. 2113, Australia

DONALD J. PUSCH
Department of Food Science and Nutrition, University of Minnesota, St. Paul, MN 55108

MOSHE RACCACH
Division of Agriculture, Arizona State University, Tempe, AZ 85281

ALVIN P. RAINOSEK
Department of Mathematics & Statistics, University of South Alabama, Mobile, AL 36688

D. P. RANSOM
Ore-Ida Foods, P.O. Box 10, Ontario, OR 97914

BIBEK RAY
Department of Animal Science, University of Wyoming, P.O. Box 3354, Univ. Sta., Laramie, WY 82071

M. S. REDDY
American Dairy and Food Consulting Laboratories, Inc., 2460 S Broadway, Denver, CO 80210

JAMES REDMAN (Retired)
Bureau of Shellfisheries, N.Y. State Department of Environmental Conservation, Bldg. 40, SUNY, Stoney Brook, NY 11794

E. R. RICHTER
Silliker Laboratories of Ohio, 1224 Kinnaer Rd. Suite 114, Columbus, OH 43212

R. L. RICHTER
Department of Animal Science, Texas A&M University, College Station, TX 77843

GREG RILEY
Henningsen Foods, Inc., 14334 Industrial Road, Omaha, NE 68144

RICHARD A. RUDE
Minneapolis Center for Microbiological Investigations, Food and Drug Administration, 240 Hennepin Ave., Minneapolis, MN 55401

A. SALINGER (Deceased)
Maryland Department of Health and Mental Hygiene, Laboratory Administration, Division of Microbiology, 201 W Preston St., Baltimore, MD 21203

DONALD A. SCHIEMANN
Department of Microbiology, Montana State University, Bozeman, MT 59719

V. N. Scott
   National Food Processors Association, 1401 New York Ave., NW, Washington, DC 20005

James L. Segmiller
   Heinz USA, P.O. Box 57, Pittsburgh, PA 15230

Eugene W. Seitz
   International Flavors and Fragrances, 1515 Highway 36, Union Beach, NJ 07735

Wayne P. Segner
   Crown Cork and Seal, 711 Jorie Blvd., Oak Brook, IL 60521

Anthony N. Sharpe
   Bureau of Microbial Hazards, Health Protection Branch, Health and Welfare Canada, Ottawa, Ontario, Canada K1A OL2

Patrica A. Shields
   Lofstrand Labs., 7961 Cessna Ave., Gaithersburg, MD 20879

Linda M. Sieverding
   Department of Microbiology, Iowa State University, Ames, IA 50011

James L. Smith
   Microbial Food Safety Unit, Eastern Regional Research Center, U.S. Department of Agriculture, 600 E Mermaid Lane, Philadelphia, PA 19118

R. B. Smittle
   Silliker Laboratories of Pennsylvania, 749 Commerce St., Sinking Spring, PA 19608

Mark O. Sobsey
   Department of Environmental Sciences & Engineering, CB 7400, Rosenau Hall, School of Public Health, University of North Carolina at Chapel Hill, Chapel Hill, NC 27599

H. M. Solomon
   Division of Microbiology, Center for Food Safety & Applied Nutrition, Food and Drug Administration, Washington, DC 20204

Kent M. Sorrells
   Alta-Dena Certified Dairy, 17637 Valley Blvd., City of Industry, CA 91747

Don F. Splittstoesser
   Department of Food Science & Technology, Cornell University, NYS Agricultural Experiment Station, Geneva, NY 14456

GERALD STELMA JR.
EMSL—Cincinnati, 26 W Martin Luther King, Cincinnati, OH 45268

NORMAN J. STERN
R.B. Russell Agricultural Research Center, USDA-ARS, P.O. Box 5677, Athens, GA 30613

K. E. STEVENSON
National Food Processors Association, 6363 Clark Ave., Dublin, CA 94568

WILLIAM H. SVEUM
Oscar Mayer, 910 Mayer Ave., Madison, WI 53704

B. SWAMINATHAN
Centers for Disease Control, Building 1, Room 2243, Mail Stop D11, Atlanta, GA 30333

KATHERINE M. J. SWANSON
The Pillsbury Company, 330 University Ave. S.E., Minneapolis, MN 55414

RICHARD C. SWANSON
Division of Emergency & Epidemiology Operations, Food and Drug Administration, 5600 Fischers Lane, Rockville, MD 20857

MARK L. TAMPLIN
Food and Drug Administration, Fishery Research Branch, P.O. Box 158, Dauphin Island, AL 36528

S. R. TATINI
Department of Food Science & Nutrition, University of Minnesota, 1334 Eckles Ave., St. Paul, MN 55108

EWEN C. D. TODD
Health Protection Branch, Bureau of Microbiological Hazards, Health & Welfare Canada, Tunney's Pasture, Ottawa, Ontario, Canada K1A OL2

R. BRUCE TOMPKIN
Swift-Eckrich Inc., 2001 Butterfield Rd., Downers Grove, IL 60515

JOHN A. TROLLER
Procter & Gamble Co., 6071 Center Hill Rd., Cincinnati, OH 45224

R. M. TWEDT
Division of Microbiology, Center for Food Safety & Applied Nutrition, Food and Drug Administration, Washington, DC 20204

P. C. VASAVADA
Animal and Food Science Department, University of Wisconsin, River Falls, WI 54022

E. R. VEDAMUTHU
Microlife Technics, 1833 57th St., Sarasota, FL 33580

MARILYN E. VEEK
Division of Congressional and Public Affairs, Center for Biological Evaluation & Research, Food and Drug Administration, 5600 Fischers Lane, Rockville, MD 20857

GEORGE WAUTERS
Microbiology Unit, University of Louvain, Avenue Hippocrate 54, UCL 54.90, Brussels, Belgium B-1200

CHENG-I, L. WEI
Department of Food Science and Human Nutrition, University of Florida, Gainesville, FL 32611

J. L. WEIHE
Coca Cola Co., Box 2079, Houston, TX 77252

IRVING WEITZMAN
Division of Emergency & Epidemiology Operations, Office of Regulatory Affairs, Food and Drug Administration, 5600 Fischers Lane, Rockville, MD 20857

REVIEWERS

The editorial committee gratefully acknowledges the assistance of the following colleagues who reviewed one or more chapters of this book.

W. H. Andrews, Jr.
Division of Microbiology, Center for Food Safety & Applied Nutrition, Food & Drug Administration, Washington, DC 20204

D. H. Ashton
Beatrice/Hunt Wesson, Inc., 1645 West Valencia Drive, Fullerton, CA 92633-3899

A. C. Baird-Parker
Unilever Ltd., Colworth House-Sharnbrook, Bedford MK44 1LQ, United Kingdom

H. Beckers
Nestlé Nederland, Nunspeet, The Netherlands

M. S. Bergdoll
Food Research Institute, University of Wisconsin, 1925 Willow Drive, Madison, WI 53706

L. C. Blankenship
USDA ARS, Richard B. Russell Agricultural Research Center, P.O. Box 5677, Athens, GA 30613

C. V. Broome
Centers for Disease Control, Atlanta, GA 30333

L. A. Brown
VCS Samoa Packing Co., P.O. Box 957, Pago Pago, American Samoa 96799

V. K. Bunning
Division of Microbiology, Center for Food Safety & Applied Nutrition, Food and Drug Administration, Washington, DC 20204

F. F. Busta
Department of Food Science & Nutrition, University of Minnesota, 1334 Eckles Ave., St. Paul, MN 55108

J. Chirife
Universidad de Buenos Aires, Facultad de Ciencias Exactas Y Naturales, Ciudad Universitaria-Nunez, 1428 Buenos Aires, Argentina

M. A. Cousin
Department of Food Science, Purdue University, West Lafayette, IN 47907

P. A. D'ALESANDRO
    Dept. of Tropical Medicine, School of Public Health, Columbia University, 630 W 168th St., New York, NY 10032

CLEVE DENNY
    National Food Processors Association, 1401 New York Ave., N.W., Washington, DC 20005

M. EKLUND
    U.S. National Marine Fisheries Service, 2725 Montlake Blvd. E, Seattle, WA 98112

R. R. FACKLAM
    Centers for Disease Control, Atlanta, GA 30333

P. M. FOEGEDING
    Department of Food Science, North Carolina State University, Raleigh, NC 27695

J. F. FRANK
    Dept. of Food Science & Technology, University of Georgia, Athens, GA 30602

R. J. GILBERT
    Food Hygiene Laboratory, UK Public Health Laboratory Service, 61 Colindale Avenue, London NW9 5HT, England, UK

D. E. GOMBAS
    National Food Processors Association, 6363 Clark Ave., Dublin, CA 94568

R. R. GRAVES
    American National Can Co., 433 N Northwest Hwy., Barrington, IL 60010

J. H. HANLIN
    Campbell Soup Company, Campbell Institute, Research & Technology, Campbell Place, Camden, NJ 08101

T. L. Heyliger
    FMC Corporation, Food Proc. Machinery Division, 317 Brokaw Rd., #A, Santa Clara, CA 95050

A. D. HOCKING
    CSIRO, Division of Food Research, North Ryde NSW 2113, Australia

C. HUHTANEN
    Eastern Regional Laboratories, U.S. Department of Agriculture, 600 E Mermaid Lane, Philadelphia, PA 19118

J. Y. HUMBER
    Kraft USA, 801 Waukegan Road, Glenview, IL 60025

J. M. Jay
Department of Biological Science, Wayne State University, Detroit, MI 48202

A. Katsuyama
National Food Processors Association, 6363 Clark Avenue, Dublin, CA 94568

C. A. Kaysner
Food and Drug Administration, Seattle District Office, 22201 23rd Drive, S.E., Bothell, WA 98041-3012

C. W. Kim
Infectious Diseases Division, Dept. of Medicine, Health Sciences Center, State University of New York, Stony Brook, NY 11794

A. D. King, Jr.
USDA Western Regional Res. Lab., 800 Buchanan St., Berkeley, CA 94710

P. J. Konkel
Carnation Company, 132 S. Concord Road, Oconomowoc, WI 53066

J. W. Kvenberg
Office of Compliance, Center for Food Safety & Applied Nutrition, Food & Drug Administration, Washington, DC 20204

V. F. Lachica
U.S. Army Natick Research, Development and Engineering Center, SSD, Natick, MA 01760

G. Lancette
Food & Drug Administration, 60 8th St., NE, Atlanta, GA 30309

E. P. Larkin
400 Stanton Ave., Terrace Park, OH 45174

R. F. Legenhausen
Microbics Corporation, 716 Hawthorne Ave., Bound Brook, NJ 08805

F. D. McClure
Division of Mathematics, Food and Drug Administration, Washington, DC 20204

R. C. McKellar
Research Branch, Agriculture Canada, Research Centre, Ottawa, Canada K1A 0C6

P. B. Mislivec
Division of Microbiology, Food & Drug Administration, Washington, DC 20204

L. J. Moberg
General Mills, Inc., Box 1113, Minneapolis, MN 55440

S. Notermans
Rijksinstituut Voor Volksgezondheid en Milieuhygiene, P.O. Box 1, 3720 BA Bilthoven, The Netherlands

W. S. Otwell
Food Science and Human Nutrition Dept., University of Florida, Gainesville, FL 32611

N. G. Parkinson
National Food Processors Association, 6363 Clark Ave., Dublin, CA 94568

D. J. Pusch
Dept. of Food Science & Nutrition, University of Minnesota, 1334 Eckles Ave., St. Paul, MN 55108

T. J. Ragusa
American National Can Co., 433 N Northwest Hwy., Barrington, IL 60010

E. R. Richter
Silliker Laboratories of Ohio, Inc., 1224 Kinnear Rd., Suite 114, Columbus, OH 43212

G. P. Richards
U.S. National Marine Fisheries Service, P.O. Box 12607, Charleston, SC 29412

V. N. Scott
National Food Processors Association, 1401 New York Ave., N.W., Washington, DC 20005

W. P. Segner
Crown Cork and Seal, 711 Jorie Blvd., Oak Brook, IL 60521

D. B. Shah
Division of Microbiology, Center for Food Safety & Applied Nutrition, Food & Drug Administration, Washington, DC 20204

N. J. Stern
USDA-ARS, R.B. Russell Ag. Res. Ctr., P.O. Box 5677, Athens, GA 30613

W. H. Sveum
Oscar Mayer Food Corporation, P.O. Box 7188, Madison, WI 53707

K. M. J. Swanson
The Pillsbury Company, Technology Center, 330 University Ave. S.E., Minneapolis, MN 55414

R. B. Tompkin
Swift-Eckrich, Inc., Research Center, 2001 Butterfield Rd., Downers Grove, IL 60515-5429

S. D. WEAGANT
Food and Drug Administration, Seattle District Office, 22201 23rd Drive, S.E., Bothell, WA 98041-3012

M. M. WEKELL
Seafood Products Research Center, Food & Drug Administration, 22201 23rd Drive SE, Bothell, WA 98041

CONTENTS

MICROORGANISMS INVOLVED IN PROCESSING AND SPOILAGE OF FOODS

RAPID METHODS

FOOD SAFETY: FOODBORNE ILLNESS

FOODS AND THEIR SAFETY AND QUALITY

PREFACE TO THE THIRD EDITION

Food microbiology continues to be a dynamic discipline: New foodborne pathogenic microorganisms are being recognized; great strides are being made in the development of improved methods for detecting and enumerating the foodborne microorganisms; new formulations and new methods of processing and distribution are presenting challenges to the microbiologist who is responsible for maintaining the quality and safety of our foods.

New chapters in the third edition describe *Aeromonas hydrophila*, *Plesiomonas shigelloides*, *Listeria*, organisms that were just emerging as recognized foodborne pathogens at the time of the second edition. Other chapters, such as that devoted to *Vibrio*, have been expanded to include newly recognized species within the different groups. One or more new contributors were involved in the revision of 53 of the 62 chapters in this edition. Thus, in addition to containing new information, many chapters show significant changes in organization and emphasis.

Chapter 39 *Rapid Methods and Automation*, as well as sections within other chapters, describe many of the newer procedures that are being developed for the detection of pathogens and spoilage microorganisms. Included are various immunoassays, DNA probes, impediometry, luminescence, and a variety of minikits. This is a fast growing area of food microbiology, and undoubtedly future editions of the compendium will describe many new techniques. Perhaps there soon will be need for an edition devoted exclusively to rapid methods and instrumentation.

Previous editions of the compendium did not contain a chapter devoted to milk and milk products, because this is thoroughly covered in *Standard Methods for the Examination of Dairy Products* (SMEDP), also published by the American Public Health Association. A chapter on milk and milk products has been added to the third edition to improve the section on "Foods and the Microorganisms Involved in their Safety and Quality." For details of individual procedures on the analysis of milk and milk products, the reader is usually referred to SMEDP.

Many of the chapters have increased in length because of the vast amount of new literature relating to methods and specific microorganisms. As a means of reducing the number of pages, formulas for media are given for only those that are not commercially available (Chapter 62). More drastic measures undoubtedly will be required for the fourth edition.

Dr. H. L. Bodily again helped to administer the project. Jackie Alexander and Cheryl N. Jackson of APHA carried out the editing and other production activities. Last, but certainly not least, 152 scientists from government, academia, the food industry, and private laboratories contributed to one or more of the 62 chapters.

Don F. Splittstoesser and Carl Vanderzant, Editors

Chapter 1

LABORATORY QUALITY ASSURANCE

Russell S. Flowers, John S. Gecan, and Donald J. Pusch

1.1 INTRODUCTION

For a compendium of microbiological methods to begin with a chapter on laboratory quality assurance appropriately reflects that subject's importance.

The objective of laboratory quality assurance is to verify the accuracy and precision of information obtained from analyses and to ensure that data obtained from analyses are suitable for use in decision making. The accuracy and precision required may vary, depending on the use to be made of the information, and however strong the effort for precision may be, some variation in results from biological analyses is to be expected.

Generally, food microbiology laboratories—governmental, industrial, academic, or commercial—are active in one or more of the following areas:

1. Basic research determines the characteristics of microorganisms important in foods and the factors that affect their growth and survival.
2. Applied research uses basic information to develop and test new food products and microbiological methods.
3. Quality control monitors food production to detect deviations from good manufacturing practices, to assure conformance to criteria, and to detect contaminants.
4. Investigative activities seek to determine the causes of foodborne illness and spoilage problems.

Although the principal objective of a laboratory quality assurance program is to ensure the correctness of data, the systems and procedures required for an effective program of this sort provide additional benefits. For example, using good microbiological techniques not only prevents cross-contamination of the samples being examined, but also protects personnel against infection and their working environment against contamination. Monitoring and maintaining equipment to ensure proper functioning decreases the risk of electrical and fire hazards. Another indirect benefit of a laboratory quality assurance system is the standardization of analytical methods, resulting in decreased intra- and inter-laboratory variation. Finally, the record keeping activities required for laboratory quality assurance provide information that helps management and individual benchworkers evaluate proficiency. The ability of management and workers to monitor the quality of work promotes confidence and pride in the laboratory.

This chapter introduces the principal concepts in quality assurance for the food microbiology laboratory. It is not possible to present here specific quality assurance programs to meet the needs of all food microbiology laboratories. Rather, this chapter is concerned with the particular laboratory functions that must be controlled and the probable sources of laboratory error. The selection of appropriate methods for quality assurance will be addressed, but specific methods will be referenced rather than discussed in detail. Thus, the reader should be mindful that this chapter is intended to serve as a guide for the design and implementation of laboratory quality assurance programs, not as a detailed statement of the system itself.

1.2   MANAGEMENT'S ROLE IN LABORATORY QUALITY ASSURANCE

Direct responsibility for the design and implementation of a laboratory quality assurance program lies within the management of the laboratory. Management must evaluate the risks associated with laboratory error and the costs and benefits of reducing error through systematic quality assurance. Measurement of the cost of these activities requires a system to account for material, labor, and overhead costs. The likelihood and significance of errors arising from each particular activity of the laboratory and the costs associated with controlling and monitoring a particular activity must be considered in the development and operation of a quality assurance program. The principles of Hazard Analysis Critical Control Points (HACCP)[17] are useful for the development of concepts for a laboratory quality assurance system.

The following steps describe a general approach that should be followed in establishing a laboratory quality assurance program:[29]

1. Formalize objectives and policies that specify the accuracy of work required, including the selection of appropriate methods and sample handling procedures.
2. Select appropriate personnel to perform laboratory functions to maintain the desired level of quality.
3. Provide facilities and equipment necessary for the performance of laboratory functions.
4. Establish monitoring methods and record keeping protocols to verify the accuracy and consistency of the laboratory work.

5. Establish procedures for the initiation of corrective measures when unacceptable quality is discovered.

1.3 GENERAL LABORATORY OPERATIONS

The first step in implementing a quality assurance program for the laboratory is to make a formal statement of the objectives and scope of activities for the laboratory, after which general operating procedures are developed to meet the objectives. Specific standard operating procedures are installed to ensure that approved sample preparation and analytical methods are chosen and followed. Within any analytical method, procedural steps may be subject to interpretation that can result in minor modifications having a pronounced influence on the outcome of an analysis. Standard operating procedures should be sufficiently described to prevent minor modifications or deviations that could arise from misinterpretation of a method and to provide an accurate record of each stage of a procedure. For research laboratories, general standard operating procedures may be established for development of a research proposal, approval of the project, and periodic evaluation of the progress made on the project. Specific operating procedures, such as method validation and execution, may need to be modified during a project as new data are obtained and interpreted.

1.31 Sample Management

Chapter 2 offers specific information on the collection, shipment, and preparation of samples for microbiological analysis. This section discusses the criteria used to determine the acceptability of samples received by the laboratory and the proper handling of samples accepted for analysis.

1. Criteria for acceptance of a sample

   a. Adequate documentation and identification must accompany samples, including a description of the place of collection, manufacturer, date and time of collection (especially for perishable samples), reason for collection (such as, compliance with legal standards or routine surveillance), sampling plan followed, analysis requested, and storage conditions.

   b. The original condition of samples and the integrity of sample containers must be maintained from collection until receipt at the laboratory. The manner of shipment must be appropriate for the type of sample.

   c. Other considerations for acceptance of samples are (1) the samples must be representative of the lot of product and processes sampled, and (2) the laboratory must have the capability to do the requested analyses.

2. Handling of samples in the laboratory

    a. After receipt, samples must be stored to maintain their original condition until analyzed. Samples should be tested as soon as possible after receipt. Facilities should be available for both short-term storage before and during analyses and, when required for forensic reasons, long-term storage after analyses have been completed.

    b. It may be necessary for an individual in the laboratory to have the responsibility as sample custodian to maintain accountability records for samples in the laboratory. This individual may (1) receive samples, (2) record the date and time received, (3) initially verify the identity of samples, (4) store according to instructions accompanying samples, (5) record the date and time when samples are delivered to analyst(s) for examination and the date and time when they are returned to storage following analyses, (6) maintain a long-term sample storage system, and (7) dispose of samples as necessary.

1.32 Analytical Methods

The need for standardized methods to promote consistency of results nationwide by reducing inter- and intra-laboratory variation was recognized early by a committee of the American Public Health Association, whose report in 1910[3] was the beginning of "Standard Methods for the Examination of Dairy Products" (SMEDP), which is now in its 15th edition.[8] SMEDP contains methods assembled by a committee of experts who have selected the analytical procedures most appropriate to examine samples for groups of microorganisms and for specific pathogens.

The Association of Official Agricultural Chemists was organized in 1884 to provide to governmental regulatory and research agencies methods that perform with the required accuracy and precision under usual laboratory conditions.[1] Since its founding, the Association, now known as the Association of Official Analytical Chemists (AOAC), has provided a mechanism to select methods of analysis from published literature or to develop, approve, and publish new methods.[2]

Other organizations have published useful collections of microbiological methods. The American Public Health Association published methods for the microbiological analysis of foods in 1958,[4] and it published the first edition of this book in 1976.[5] The United States Food and Drug Administration (FDA) has published the procedures it uses to examine foods for regulatory compliance.[14] The International Commission on Microbiological Specifications for Foods (ICMSF)[16] has been active since 1962. ICMSF efforts have been directed to the selection and recommendation of suitable methods for microbiological evaluation of foods moving in international commerce. ICMSF has published a number of collaborative studies and books.

Less laborious and more rapid methods are always needed, but many adequate methods are available for analytical food microbiologists. Unfortunately, the methods available to be used for specific analyses vary considerably both internationally and nationally. To reduce variation, laboratory management should try to select standard or approved methods. Modifications of standard methods should not be used unless collaborative or comparative studies have shown that the modified methods are at least as reliable as the reference methods.

1.33 Laboratory Standard Operating Procedures

Each laboratory should have a standard operations manual that describes (1) procedures for the acceptance or rejection of samples, (2) methodology to be followed for specific analyses, (3) appropriate control procedures, (4) all quality assurance procedures, (5) procedures for cleaning and sterilizing equipment, (6) procedures for preparing media and reagents, and (7) procedures for handling and disposing of contaminated materials.

The manual should provide instructions to cover most of the normal situations that the laboratory will encounter. It will inform personnel about appropriate methodology, ensure uniformity of sample analysis, and promote quality assurance programs.

The selection of methods to be included in the manual will depend to a certain extent on the type of laboratory, i.e., governmental, commercial, or industrial. The description of each method in the manual should be complete and detailed enough that reference to other publications is unnecessary. Included should be all the necessary controls and checks on materials, media, reagents, positive and negative controls, the desired response from each control, and corrective measures that should be taken if a control is not correct.

Limitations of each test should be included, where known, as well as a list of precautions to be taken. Possible interferences should be described, such as natural inhibitory substances in foods that must be diluted out for growth of any organism to occur.

The manual should fully describe the quality assurance program in use. Included should be each quality assurance procedure, the frequency of use, specific analytical methods that may be required in each procedure, applicable tolerances for each procedure and, if possible, remedial steps to correct out-of-control procedures, and the names or titles of personnel to be notified if out-of-control procedures are found.

1.4 PERSONNEL

Quality results require quality personnel. The personnel selected must have the education, experience, and motivation necessary to perform their jobs and to carry out the requirements of the quality assurance program.[29] The number of persons and their technical training may vary considerably from laboratory to laboratory, depending on the types and numbers of analyses to be performed. However, general guidelines for selection of laboratory personnel are available. The U.S. Environmental Protection Agency (EPA) has published guidelines for the selection of personnel for water bacteriology laboratories,[12] and some states have specified personnel requirements for certification of analytical laboratories.[18] These guidelines should help develop personnel requirements, but they may be too tightly framed to fit the needs of food microbiology laboratories.

Successful management of laboratory personnel through motivation, training, supervision, and workload direction is as important as selection of the personnel. Workers must be properly trained to perform their duties, and the first step in training is to specify as completely as possible the duties of the position and the importance of these duties to the quality of results generated by the whole laboratory. The goals of training are that the workers know the exact duties they are to perform, with sufficient instruction and time to learn how to perform these duties so as to obtain results of the highest quality. Employees must be made fully aware of their quality assurance responsibilities and especially of the adverse consequences that will arise from failure to carry out their duties carefully.

Motivation of laboratory personnel to do high-quality work is essential for a successful quality assurance program. To achieve this requires a safe, efficiently designed facility, sufficient supplies and equipment, workloads that are not excessive, and suitable compensation.

1.41   Evaluation of Personnel

Uniform application of laboratory procedures by all analysts is very important for consistent results. The routine evaluation of the accuracy of each analyst's performance is necessary for such consistency. The supervisor is the best person to evaluate worker performance on a day-to-day basis. An appropriate outside agency or individual may occasionally check on-site worker performance. However, experience has shown that on-site evaluations alone are not enough to minimize variation among analysts.[25]

The proficiency of each analyst should be rated by having the laboratory participate in split/check sample programs in which the performance of each analyst can be compared to the performance of other analysts in the same laboratory or other laboratories. Split or check samples to verify analyst performance can be generated internally or supplied by external sources. Comparison of results obtained from laboratories participating in an external split/check sample program provides a valid evaluation of the proficiency of the laboratory as a whole. Statistically acceptable performances by individual analysts and the laboratory as a whole give the best indication that all elements associated with diagnostic procedures (personnel, media, reagents, and equipment) are satisfactory. Critics have asserted that split/check sample proficiency testing programs in clinical laboratories do not truly measure day-to-day capabilities because the laboratory staff usually is aware of the source of these samples and tends to be more careful than usual.[23] A more realistic measure of performance is the introduction of internal "blind" unknown samples.[30]

Split samples can be naturally or artificially contaminated. Naturally contaminated samples have the advantage that they represent the kinds of samples routinely received and examined by analysts. However, their microbiological character may not be known, and it may be difficult to obtain large enough quantities of such samples to distribute to several analysts or laboratories. A discussion of the preparation and distribution of split samples and the statistical procedures for evaluation of split sample results have been presented by Olson et al.[22] and Donnelly et al.[11]

Studies of clinical laboratories suggest that continuous participation in proficiency surveys results in improved analyst performance.[26] Participation in the national milk laboratory proficiency testing program has resulted in marked improvement in analyst performance. Although ongoing proficiency studies have not been conducted in food microbiology laboratories, it is likely that improvement in analyst and laboratory performance can be obtained.

1.5   FACILITIES

The safety of workers is of utmost importance in design and construction of laboratory facilities. The food microbiology laboratory should be designed and built to meet this priority and also to provide for the convenience of the workers and operations. It should be adequately equipped to carry out the stated objectives of the laboratory. The following points should be considered when designing a laboratory.[22, 12]

1.51   Laboratory Design

1. Ventilation, temperature, and humidity

    Laboratories should be well ventilated, preferably by use of central air-conditioning, to reduce the amount of particulates in the air and minimize temperature variation. Temperature and relative humidity should be comfortable for workers and suitable to the requirements of the laboratory equipment. Normally, an ambient temperature of 21° to 23°C and a relative humidity of 45% to 50% are recommended.

2. Lighting

    Laboratory lighting should be maintained at an average intensity of at least 50, and preferably 100, footcandles. Dependence upon natural sunlight during the day should be discouraged because of high variability in its intensity. Because direct sunlight is known to have deleterious effects on media, reagents, and specimens, preparation or storage of these items in direct sunlight should be avoided.

3. Laboratory space and bench areas

    Laboratory space should be organized to maximize usefulness. Where possible, media preparation and glassware cleaning areas should be separated from the analytical areas. Equipment and materials should be positioned to make the maximum amount of bench space available. For most routine work, 6 linear feet is the recommended minimum work area for each analyst. The ideal bench top height is 36 to 38 in with a depth of 28 to 30 in. The walls and ceiling of the laboratory should be covered with good-grade enamel or epoxy paint, or other material that provides a smooth, impervious surface that is easily disinfected. Floors should be covered with high-quality tile or other impenetrable material. Cracks and crevices should be minimized, as they provide an opportunity for the buildup of debris that may contribute to cross-contamination of samples. Unnecessary traffic through the laboratory should be prohibited. Eating or smoking should never be permitted in a microbiology laboratory.

4. Storage areas

Storage space for equipment, materials, and samples should be sufficient for needed media, reagents, glassware, and plasticware. The use of cabinets with doors and drawers will minimize dust buildup and allow easier cleaning and disinfection of laboratory surfaces. Test samples must be stored under conditions outlined in the particular analytical procedure being followed. Samples stored at room temperature should be placed in sealed containers to prevent the proliferation of pests. A written standard policy should outline the conditions and length of storage time for samples. Storage areas should be routinely inventoried, and superfluous samples, and outdated media and reagents should be disposed of according to an established, documented policy.

5. Other utilities

Every laboratory should be equipped with enough electrical outlets of the appropriate voltage and amperage, enough natural gas jets for bunsen burners, a waste disposal system, and laboratory-grade water. The laboratory also should have an adequate number of sinks with hot and cold tap water and, preferably, lines for deionized or distilled water. Sinks with foot-operated handwashing taps are recommended.

6. Laboratory-grade water

Laboratory-grade water, which should be available in the food microbiology laboratory, is defined as water that has been treated to free it from nutritive and toxic materials. Laboratory-grade water may be produced by distillation, reverse osmosis, ion exchange, filtration, or a combination of these. Viable microorganisms have been shown to accumulate in laboratory water systems such as ion exchange systems, and they should be monitored routinely for microbial growth according to a written standard operating procedure. In addition to this microbiological monitoring, the following physical-chemical elements should be measured monthly and documented to have met the indicated parameters:

a. Trace metals, a single metal not greater than 0.05 mg/L

b. Total metals, equal to or less than 1.0 mg/L
c. Specific conductance greater than 0.2 megaohm resistivity or less than 5.0 microohms per cm
d. pH 5.5 to 7.5
e. Residual chlorine less than 0.1 mg/L

"Standard Methods for the Examination of Water and Wastewater," 16th ed., describes a test for the bacteriological suitability of laboratory water.[7] This is a sensitive test for the determination of toxic or stimulatory substances in laboratory water. "Standard Methods for the Examination of Dairy Products," 14th ed., describes a procedure for the toxicity testing of phosphate-buffered dilution water.[8] Both of these tests should be performed annually to validate the quality of laboratory water.

7. Personnel safety

To ensure the safety of personnel, all facilities should be designed according to established federal, state, and local building and safety codes. All laboratories should be equipped with fire extinguishers and alarms, sprinkler systems, eyewash stations, and safety showers. Approved safety glasses should be available to laboratory workers and visitors. A comprehensive safety program, including worker training, should be a vital part of laboratory procedures.

8. Animal facilities

Some food microbiology procedures, such as botulinal toxin screening, require the use of laboratory animals. Laboratory animals should be maintained in separate areas other than those where routine analytical tests are performed. Animal rooms should have all air discharged to the outside without recirculation. A minimum of 15 air changes per hour is recommended. A specific written operating procedure should be designed outlining the details of animal maintenance.

Those who contemplate the use of animals for laboratory work should refer to the Public Health Service Policy of Humane Care and Use of Animals, Public Law 99-158, November 20, 1985, "Animals in Research," which can be obtained from the Office for Protection from Research Risks, National Institutes of Health (NIH).

1.52 Housekeeping

A routine cleaning and disinfection schedule for the entire laboratory should be established, documented, and monitored for effectiveness. Disinfectants such as iodophor, quaternary ammonium compounds, or phenolic disinfectants should be employed. All laboratory benches and equipment should be disinfected before and after each use.

Laboratory materials should be stored after use in order to maintain a clutter-free work area. Unneeded and outdated materials should be discharged according to a written procedure that includes a description of the methods of disposal, safety precautions, and frequency of inventory measurement.

Dust and soil should not be allowed to build up in a microbiology laboratory. Close attention should be paid to corners and hard-to-clean areas. Floors should be wet-mopped, preferably with a suitable disinfectant-detergent solution, not dry-mopped or swept with a broom because these practices will contribute to airborne contamination.

1.53   Environmental Monitoring

To assess the efficacy of the established laboratory disinfection schedule and to determine the microbial profile of the laboratory, a written operating procedure on environmental monitoring should be followed. This operating procedure should contain a description of the environmental sampling procedure and statements of locations to be sampled, tolerance limits, and frequency of monitoring. Chapter 3 of this book describes procedures for environmental sampling of food plant environments, including equipment, containers, air, and water. These same procedures are appropriate for sampling of the laboratory environment.

1.6   EQUIPMENT AND INSTRUMENTATION

The reliability of an analytical procedure is only as good as the reliability of the equipment and instruments used for the procedure. A protocol should be established to verify the reliability of the equipment and instruments. Equipment should be used only by properly trained personnel. All equipment (balances, pH meters, etc.) should be cleaned before and after use.

1. Thermometers and temperature recorders

   Thermometers should meet the minimum specifications outlined in "Standard Methods for the Examination of Dairy Products." [8] Their accuracy should be checked at least annually with a thermometer certified by the National Bureau of Standards (NBS). Mechanical windup temperature-recording devices are preferred for incubators and water baths that are used continuously. Such mechanically driven temperature recorders are recommended over electrical plug-in recorders in order to measure temperature fluctuations during power failures. This is especially important during nonworking hours. The recorders should be validated annually against a certified NBS thermometer and after any repair work. Chapter 2 describes a procedure for validating thermometer and temperature recorders. Written specifications should be established for these recorders, and at least daily, if not continuously, temperatures should be monitored in all active incubators, water baths, refrigerators, freezers, and ambient laboratory environments. Results of such monitoring should be placed in the permanent quality assurance records.

2. Balances

   Laboratory balances should be sensitive to 0.1 g with a 200 g load. An analytical balance having a sensitivity of 1 mg with a 10 g load should be used for weighing small quantities. Single pan balances are preferred. The accuracy of laboratory balances should be checked routinely, preferably daily, by standard reference weights that are calibrated annually against a certified NBS set of weights. Generally, the balance should be checked with several different weights. Written documentation should be maintained on the calibration of the standard reference set of weights as well as on routine accuracy checks of balances.

3. pH meters

pH meters should be standardized with a minimum of two standard buffers (pH 4.0, pH 7.0, or pH 10.0) before use. Aliquots of buffer solution should be used once and discarded. Standard buffer solutions should be dated upon receipt and an expiration date established after opening the container. The pH meter should be accurate within 0.1 pH unit. The life of pH electrodes will vary by type, brand, and frequency of use. Manufacturers' directions should be followed for servicing pH electrodes. Each standardization of the pH meter should be written in the permanent record. See Chapter 8 for further details on pH.

4. Autoclaves

Autoclaves should be equipped with accurate pressure and temperature gauges. They should be equipped with a calibrated thermometer located properly on the exhaust line to register the minimum temperature within the sterilizing chamber. It is preferable that the autoclave be equipped with a temperature recorder in order to provide a permanent record for each sterilization cycle. A permanent record keeping system should be established to document each sterilization cycle. This consists of a daily chart listing for each cycle such items as (1) temperature and time settings, (2) materials in the chambers, (3) pressure and temperature readings once the autoclave has reached the sterilizing region of the cycle, and (4) date and time that the sterilizing cycle is started and finished, followed by the signature or initials of the operator.

Ensuring the proper functioning of autoclaves is essential. This can be done through the use of biological indicators and through physical measurements. Biological indicators, such as *Bacillus stearothermophilus* spore ampules or strips, are available from several commercial sources. Physical measurements can be made with thermocouples and maximum registering thermometers. A combination of both biological indicators and physical measurements should be used to validate sterilization processes. Physical validations employing thermocouples located in various areas of the autoclave chamber should be performed annually. Biological indicators and maximum registry thermometers should be employed with each use.[12]

5. Hot air sterilizing ovens

Each sterilizing oven should be equipped with a thermometer and, preferably, a temperature recorder, both calibrated against an NBS thermometer. A time and temperature record should be maintained for each sterilization cycle. In addition, periodic physical and biological validations are suggested.

6. Other equipment

Equipment such as water baths, incubators, and refrigerators should be equipped with thermometers or temperature recorders, or both, calibrated against an NBS thermometer. Temperature specifications for these items are listed in specific chapters on analytical methods. Operating procedures should be established so that proper written records are maintained for each piece of equipment.

Laminar flow hoods should be checked with a particle counter on a routine basis by the dioctyphthalate test.[10] Specifications should be established on the filtering efficiency of the hoods. They should be routinely disinfected and monitored through the use of RODAC plates. Air flow rates should be monitored periodically with a certified flow meter.

Anaerobic chamber and glove boxes should contain appropriate anaerobiosis indicators. Indicator strips, which are commercially available, should be changed daily. Written records should be maintained to daily document the existence of anaerobic conditions in the chamber.

1.61   Preventive Maintenance of Equipment

It is important that the food microbiology laboratory have a formal, written preventive maintenance program. If the laboratory is small and does not have a maintenance department, preventive maintenance agreements with the manufacturers or dealers from whom the equipment was purchased should be arranged. Reputable independent maintenance firms also can provide preventive maintenance services. Regardless of laboratory size, the following points, as outlined in "Quality Assurance Practices for Health Laboratories," should be considered when establishing a preventive maintenance program:[6]

1. Inventory

Each piece of equipment, with its location, complete name, age, and description, and the appropriate supervisor or person responsible for the item, should be listed in the inventory. The pertinent information should be outlined on a separate page or card for each item of equipment. This record constitutes a portion of the inventory control.

2. Definition of service tasks

For each item of equipment, the tasks needed to keep the equipment calibrated, operating, and clean must be defined. Supportive information may be obtained from manufacturers' brochures, product guides, and journal reprints. These specific tasks should be included in the laboratory's written statement of standard operating procedures.

3. Interval establishment

The frequency with which the defined tasks should be performed must be determined. This will vary with the item of equipment, the type of installation, and the workload of the particular item of equipment. However, even equipment used infrequently must have minimum standards of preventive maintenance.

4. Personnel

Those individuals should be listed who are immediately available, or may be ultimately available, for function verification tasks, cleaning, preventive maintenance, troubleshooting, and repair. This assignment should be customized to the laboratory's own situation. In general, it is preferable to depend upon in-house personnel who can perform maintenance activities economically and efficiently. However, for some instruments, one must depend on a manufacturer's services or on an independent service company.

5. Job assignments

If the program is to succeed, responsibilities for the tasks outlined above must be assigned so that each person will know the responsibilities. Job assignments should be matched with training, experience, and aptitude.

6. Training

Laboratories having a large number of well-trained personnel who are familiar with laboratory equipment are indeed fortunate. Most laboratories must carry out some in-service training to teach personnel the use of special monitoring devices and the performance of some of the more difficult service tasks.

7. Special instruments

The monitoring devices, techniques, materials, and types of special equipment used to check each type of instrument in the laboratory should be listed. If the laboratory does not have the necessary monitoring equipment, it must be acquired.

8. Setting up the system

Once the effort has been made to inventory the equipment, define the tasks, and train the personnel on special instruments, the program should continue year after year. A record for each item of equipment should be established in which all entries are made. In addition, it may be necessary to develop a reminder system so that appropriate personnel are notified when certain tasks are to be performed.

9. Records and documentation

Documentation is needed to record that the appropriate service tasks have been accomplished. This may be the appropriate place to incorporate a system of reminders to ensure that the tasks are performed on time. Index card systems are good for this purpose and are inexpensive. Some laboratories use a computer to remind technologists of these tasks. The documentation scheme must be tailored to the laboratory's specific needs.

10. Surveillance

After setting up a program, periodic surveillance should be carried out to ensure that the records are legible and complete.

1.7   LABORATORY GLASSWARE AND PLASTICWARE

Specifications of laboratory glassware and plasticware should be established and followed. For example, the calibration of newly purchased glass or plastic pipettes should be checked upon receipt in the laboratory. The calibration marks on dilution bottles should be checked with NBS-certified volumetric glassware.[8]

Glassware should be made of high-quality, low-alkali borosilicate glass. Glassware composed of soft glass presents problems because of leaching of components and the presence of surface alkali, which may interfere with some analytical procedures. Etched or chipped glassware should be discarded. Plasticware should be free of defects and toxic residues.

Procedures must be established to sterilize and wash microbiologically contaminated reusable glass- or plasticware. Microbiologically contaminated reusable labware must be sterilized by autoclaving or other suitable means prior to being washed.

Reusable glassware and plasticware should be washed manually or mechanically with hot water containing a suitable detergent. Stubborn residues may be removed by soaking in a potassium dichromate cleaning solution on glassware before washing. Screw caps, test tube caps, and other reusable closures also should be washed in a detergent solution and rinsed thoroughly. Many detergents have a high affinity for glassware and plasticware and some are highly bacteriostatic; it is imperative to ensure their removal after washing. Glassware and plasticware should be checked routinely for alkaline or acidic residues by applying a few drops of bromthymol blue pH indicator. This indicator is useful because it displays color changes from yellow to blue-green to blue in a pH range of 6.5 to 7.3. Since most cleaning solutions are either acidic or alkaline, this simple test assures proper rinsing.

1.71   Toxicity Testing

Disposable glassware and plasticware may be sterilized by ethylene oxide gas. If these items, pipettes, petri dishes, etc., are not properly rinsed after the sterilization treatment, toxic residues may remain. Therefore, it is important to check these items periodically for toxic residues and to request certification from the supplier that no toxic residues are present. Similarly, glass items washed and sterilized in the laboratory may contain toxic detergent residues not detected by the bromthymol blue pH test. These items should be checked periodically for toxic detergent residues. Procedures for toxicity testing are detailed in several publications.[7, 8, 12] The washing procedures should be checked at least annually by performing toxicity tests and should be modified if necessary.

1.72   Sterility Testing as a Quality Assurance Tool

The sterility of sterilized supplies and equipment must be ensured. A sterility test may be performed on a portion of the sterilized items. Sterility control tests on petri dishes may be performed by simply pouring a nonselective medium such as Standard Methods Agar into several randomly selected plates from a case. Upon solidification, the plates are then incubated aerobically or anaerobically and examined for growth. Sterility controls on sampling containers, utensils, and dilution bottles may be performed by the rinse filtration technique. According to this technique, the items are aseptically rinsed with sterile phosphate buffer that is filtered through a membrane filter. The filter is placed on the surface of a nonselective agar and incubated under prescribed conditions.

Test tubes may be checked for sterility by adding a broth such as fluid thioglycollate to the tubes and observing for turbidity after incubation. Also, microbial growth controls should be performed for each plating group by placing 1 to 2 ml of dilution fluid from bottles into the agar medium being used. This procedure is a sterility check for the agar medium, diluent, petri dishes, and pipettes. However, this sterility monitoring method has limited reliability. A statistically valid sterility testing system is available that permits determination of the probability that n negative samples will occur at a specified concentration of organisms per test unit (dish, pipette, etc.).[22]

1.8   MEDIA AND REAGENTS

Food microbiology laboratories use many different media and reagents to detect and enumerate microorganisms, and most of them are purchased already prepared or in dehydrated form. Reagents and media should be tested before using to validate their efficacy.[24] Those media and reagents formulated in the laboratory also should be prepared carefully and validated for performance.

Common errors that occur in preparation of media and reagents are listed here:

1. Incorrect weighing of dry material.
2. Use of dry material that has deteriorated as a result of exposure to heat, moisture, oxidation, or other environmental factors.
3. Incorrect measurement of water volume, or use of tap water or water from a malfunctioning still or deionizing resin column. Water must meet the requirements for laboratory pure water and be proven to be microbiologically suitable.
4. Use of containers and glassware that are contaminated with detergent or other chemicals.
5. Incomplete mixing or solubilization of ingredients during preparation of media or solutions. This may result in excessive or insufficient gel strength of the medium and uneven concentrations of constituents among aliquots.

6. Overheating during preparation and sterilization, or holding too long in the molten state before dispensing into plates, tubes, or bottles. Overheating can result in loss of a medium's productivity through hydrolysis of the agar, caramelization of carbohydrates, lowering of pH, increase or decrease in inhibitory action because of the loss of dye content in selective or differential media, and the formation of inhibitory precipitates.
7. Improper determination of pH, resulting in the addition of too much acid or alkali.
8. Improper addition or incorporation of unsatisfactory supplements or enrichments, or addition of supplements at the wrong temperature, possibly causing chemical changes in the supplements if the temperature is too high, or solidification of media before proper mixing if too cold.
9. Failure of the laboratory to subject samples of finished media to quality control procedures before the media are used.
10. Failure of the laboratory to test samples of dehydrated media purchased from suppliers to ensure that the media are productive.

1.81   Receipt of Media, Reagents, and Ingredients

Containers of media and reagents should be dated upon receipt. The laboratory should maintain a media/reagent control file where the following information is recorded for each shipment of media or reagents received:

1. Manufacturer and manufacturer's code.
2. Quantity received, i.e., size and number of containers.
3. Date received.
4. Date opened.
5. Location where medium/reagent is to be stored.
6. Initials of person receiving and placing the item into stock.
7. Results of productivity and selectivity testing, if performed (see Section 1.83).

Each lot of medium/reagent should be inspected before use for volume, tightness of closure, clarity, color, consistency, and completeness of label.

1.82   Storage of Dehydrated Media, Reagents, and Ingredients

Directions for the storage of most media and ingredients are generally listed by the supplier on the label of each container. In addition, the supplier will often indicate an expiration date after which the item should not be used. When available, the supplier's directions should be followed. Some general guidelines are listed below.

1. Store dehydrated media in tightly capped bottles or tightly closed plastic liners in a cool, dry place protected from light. If specified, keep under refrigeration and in the dark.

2. Keep no more than 6 months' to a year's supply on hand, being sure to use older stocks first. Do not exceed supplier's expiration date.
3. Dehydrated media and reagents should be free-flowing powders or crystals. If a change is noted in this property or in the color, the item in question should be discarded.
4. Media containing dyes should be protected from light by storage in a dark room or a dark glass bottle or by wrapping the container with foil or brown paper.

1.83 Productivity/Selectivity Testing of Media and Reagents

Historically, clinical microbiologists have been concerned with performance testing of media and reagents. "Cumitech 3" recommends the verification of media and reagents performance for each new lot number or shipment received.[9] This publication provides a detailed outline of performance tests on various media, recommended control organisms, and expected results. No guidelines exist for performance testing of media and reagents employed specifically in food microbiology. Studies of commercially available media and reagents for use in clinical laboratories have suggested that these items generally perform as expected.[21] However, the studies provide several examples of media and reagent failure.[20] Considering the consequences of such failure, i.e., the generation of faulty data, it is appropriate that each new lot of medium or reagent be subjected to performance testing.

1. Media

"Standard Methods for Examination of Dairy Products"[8] gives a procedure for evaluating the performance of new lots of standard methods agar by comparing them to a standard control lot. This procedure can be used for testing any nonselective general purpose agar medium. Liquid nonselective media can be tested similarly using dilution-to-extinction techniques to compare new lots of media to standard lots. Careful consideration must be given to the selection of samples and cultures to be evaluated in these tests. If test cultures are to be employed in the evaluation of nonselective media, organisms should be chosen that are at least as fastidious as those for which the medium will be used routinely. Furthermore, it is suggested that more than one culture be used to evaluate a given medium.

In the examination of selective or differential media, cultures must be chosen that test both the productivity and selective/differential characteristics of the medium. Liquid media can be evaluated by inoculation with cultures expected to grow in the medium and with cultures expected to be suppressed. Following suitable incubation, titers on each culture must be determined. An acceptable medium should show high titers of organisms to be detected and low titers of organisms to be suppressed.[19] Performance of new lots should be similar to control or standard lots. The evaluation of solid media is performed in a similar manner. Organisms of the group for which the medium was designed should be recovered almost quantitatively compared to nonselective media. Organisms that should be suppressed by the medium should not develop or should be greatly reduced when compared to enumeration on nonselective media. Furthermore, the differential characteristics of the medium should be the same as expected for the known cultures.

Unfortunately, the variety of media employed in most food microbiology laboratories, and the number of control cultures and lengthy procedures required for the evaluation of these media, make the routine evaluation of each new lot a burden.

Mossel and coworkers[20] developed a relatively simple "ecometric" technique to evaluate liquid and solid selective media. In this method, cultures of test strains of the groups of cultures to be detected and those that are to be suppressed are streaked in parallel lines onto a solid medium or a liquid medium that has been solidified by the addition of about 15 g of agar/L and poured into each section of a quadrant petri plate. Organisms for which the medium was designed should develop in all quadrants, whereas "background" flora should develop in only the first or second quadrants streaked. Based upon the pattern of growth, an Absolute Growth Index (AGI)[20] is calculated for each test organism. The AGIs for new lots of media should be similar to those of standard or control lots.[20]

2. Reagents

A committee, part of a Centers for Disease Control (CDC) task force, was created to develop standards and create product classes for diagnostic reagents.[27] This committee divided diagnostic reagents into three general classes: immunodiagnostic reagents, microbiological media, and miscellaneous reagents. The miscellaneous reagents class consists of stains and chemical reagents, most of which are available from commercial sources. Although the manufacturer is charged with ensuring that the reagents meet minimum product standards, the committee suggested that quality control tests be performed by the recipient as well. Reagents routinely employed should be checked at least weekly with positive and negative control cultures. Less frequently used reagents should be checked by including positive and negative controls with each use. In addition, some commercial systems are available for evaluation of reagents (Analytab Products, Plainview, N.Y.), and recently a simple technique for testing a variety of reagents has been described.[15]

Salmonella antisera are the only serological reagents commonly used in most food microbiology laboratories. A survey of *Salmonella* antisera from five commercial suppliers indicated that 65% performed satisfactorily according to CDC specifications.[27] Most of the unsatisfactory *Salmonella* antisera were somatic polyvalent and grouping sera that failed to meet specifications because they did not react, or reacted weakly, with antigens containing homologous factors. In addition, several problems occurred with the labeling of *Salmonella* antisera. Often containers and brochures did not adequately identify agglutinins contained in the sera. Based upon the results of this survey, it appears essential that both positive and negative controls be run on all antisera received.

Such tests should be performed before initial use and monthly thereafter, depending on the frequency of use. Recommendations of the manufacturer for preparation, storage, and use of antisera should be followed closely.

The maintenance of stock cultures for productivity/selectivity testing of media and reagents is important. The stock culture collection must consist of strains of microorganisms that will reflect the productive, selective, and differential characteristics of each medium and reagent employed in the laboratory. Stock cultures may be maintained in the laboratory, usually by one of three methods: (1) lyophilization, (2) ultrafreezing, and (3) maintenance in appropriate media with frequent transferring.[26] Microorganisms used for quality control also may be obtained from several commercial sources.

1.84   Performance and Sterility Testing of Prepared Media and Reagents

The tests described above have been designed to test the performance of new lots of media and reagents. However, if desired, they can be applied to each batch of medium or reagents prepared in the laboratory. The decision of whether to test only new lots or to test each batch of medium or reagent must be made by the laboratory management based upon the cost of such tests and confidence in the quality of the laboratory personnel, equipment, and facilities to prepare each batch properly.

Each batch of media and reagents, whether prepared in the laboratory from dehydrated ingredients or purchased in prepared form, should be checked for sterility. Selected plates or tubed media, representative of the batch, should be incubated prior to use or along with inoculated media. Generally, incubation of sterility controls at the temperature normally used for these media is an adequate check of sterility. Selective media may present some problems, having been designed to inhibit a variety of microorganisms. Gross contamination may not be evident visually in the form of turbidity or colony formation. This problem can be overcome by transferring a portion of liquid selective media to a nonselective medium or by swabbing the surface of an agar plate and then incubating the swabs in a nonselective medium.

Procedures for sterility testing of reagents are presented in "The United States Pharmacopeia XX." [28]

1.9   RECORD KEEPING

It is essential for a food microbiology laboratory to maintain accurate and permanent records of sample analyses and quality assurance programs. The nature of the records can vary from individual worksheets and data books to entire electronic data processing systems. The length of time and the manner in which records are retained will depend on the laboratory's objectives, the nature of the records, the scope of the work performed, and the space available for storage.

1.91   Sample Analytical Data

1. Records should be kept documenting the care and disposition of samples during their time in the laboratory. These should show the storage conditions, the personnel with custody of samples, and the final disposition of samples when no longer required.
2. Records of all aspects of sample analyses, including sample descriptions, storage conditions and reverse sample retention, descriptions of analytical methods, all raw data, and observations, calculations, and conclusions, are required. The analyst(s) responsible for each segment of the procedure should be identified in the record.

   These records may be in the form of worksheets that become a part of the entire record for each sample or a notebook that can be referred to in the sample records and correspondence.
3. Analytical records should be reviewed for completeness and accuracy before the results are reported. This review should be at least a two-step operation, with the first review done by another analyst in the laboratory and a second by the supervisor.

1.92   Research Data

Analytical laboratories are occasionally faced with the need to develop a new method of analysis or to modify an existing method. The details of these research activities must be properly documented. One should also consider adopting applicable elements of the following recommendations to other types of record keeping in the laboratory.

The standard, bound laboratory notebook is the preferred medium for the recording of research data. At times, however, other media may replace or be used in conjunction with the laboratory notebook. Record maintenance procedures are as follows:

1. Each research project should have its own set of notebooks.
2. The first pages should be reserved for a brief table of contents that should include dates, type of information, and page numbers.
3. Notebook entries are to be made only in black or blue-black ink, with a fountain pen or ballpoint pen. Pencil or pen with water-soluble ink are not to be used. All entries must be dark and clear enough to be photocopied.

4. Illustrations such as charts, graphs, photographs, etc., may be pasted securely in the notebooks if they approximate the size of the page. Voluminous printouts, photographs, charts, etc., may be maintained in supplemental files and referenced in the notebook.
5. All entries made by someone other than the notebook owner should be initialed.
6. Entries are to be neat and legible. No erasures are to be made; errors will be marked through with a single line, initialed, and dated.
7. Experimental results will be summarized.
8. All unused notebook pages will be cancelled with diagonal lines.
9. Once a study has been completed, the researcher will maintain the related notebook(s) and other research records. The first-line supervisor is responsible for assuring access and will maintain a log of all such materials under his or her responsibility.
10. A notebook assigned to an employee who is separating from an organization will be returned to the first-line supervisor, who will be responsible for maintaining the notebook and all related information.

1.93 Quality Assurance Data

Records should be kept of all quality assurance and control testing. These records can be kept on analytical worksheets as a part of the analytical routine or on separate log sheets. The analysts responsible for each check should be indicated, and the steps taken to bring back into control any procedures or functions out of tolerance should be recorded. Quality assurance records should be maintained for the following:

1. Analytical split or check sample results.
2. Purity and authenticity data on biological standards such as bacterial or fungal stock strains.
3. Calibration records on non-precalibrated volumetric implements.
4. Calibration/standardization records on analytical instruments such as gas chromatographs, spectrophotometers, pH meters, etc.
5. Annual calibration data and daily use check weighings on analytical balances.
6. Temperature records for freezers, refrigerators, incubators, water-baths, etc.
7. Moisture level test results in incubators.
8. Time-temperature-pressure records for autoclaves.[13]
9. Thermometer calibration results.
10. Animal room hygrothermograph records.

Periodic review of these records should be carried out by supervisory personnel to assess the effectiveness of the quality assurance program. This review can be valuable in revealing potential problem areas and making corrections before serious problems occur.

1.94   Storage and Retrieval of Data

A system that provides storage and ready retrieval of all the data generated in the laboratory is necessary. The type of system will depend on the type of laboratory and the analyses performed. The length of time that these records should be kept can vary greatly. In the case of regulatory agency laboratories, they may need to be available for several years.

1.10   REFERENCES

1. AOAC. 1920. "Official Methods of Analysis," 1st ed. Assn. Offic. Anal. Chem., Washington, D.C.
2. AOAC. 1984. "Official Methods of Analysis," 14th ed. Assn. Offic. Anal. Chem., Arlington, Va.
3. APHA. 1910. Report of the committee on standard methods of bacterial milk analysis. Am. Pub. Health Assn. Am. J. Pub. Hyg. **6**: 315.
4. APHA. 1958. "Recommended Methods for the Microbiological Examination of Foods," 1st ed. Am. Pub. Health Assn., Washington, D.C.
5. APHA. 1976. "Compendium of Methods for the Microbiological Examination of Foods," 1st ed., ed. M. L. Speck. Am. Pub. Health Assn., Washington, D.C.
6. APHA. 1978. "Quality Assurance Practices for Health Laboratories." Am. Pub. Health Assn., Washington, D.C.
7. APHA. 1985a. "Standard Methods for the Examination of Water and Wastewater," 16th ed. Am. Pub. Health Assn., Washington, D.C.
8. APHA. 1985b. "Standard Methods for the Examination of Dairy Products," 15th ed. Am. Pub. Health Assn., Washington, D.C.
9. Blazevic, D. J., Hall, C. T., and Wilson, M. E. 1976. "Cumitech 3. Practical Quality Control Procedures for the Clinical Microbiology Laboratory." Am. Soc. for Microbiol., Washington, D.C.
10. Chatigny, M. A. 1986. Primary barriers. In "Laboratory Safety: Principles and Practices," ed. B. M. Miller. Am. Soc. for Microbiol., Washington, D.C.
11. Donnelly, D. B., Harris, E. K., Black, L. A., and Lewis, K. H. 1960. Statistical analysis of standard plate counts of milk samples split with state laboratories. J. Milk Food Technol. **21**: 315.
12. EPA. 1975. "Handbook for Evaluating Water Bacteriological Laboratories," 2nd ed. EPA-070/9-75-006. U.S. Environ. Protec. Agency, Cincinnati, Ohio.
13. FDA. 1982. "Bureau of Foods Laboratory Quality Assurance Manual." Food and Drug Admin., Washington, D.C.
14. FDA. 1984. "Bacteriological Analytical Manual," 6th ed. Food and Drug Admin. Assn. Offic. Anal. Chem., Arlington, Va.
15. Hicock, P. I. and Marshall, K. E. 1981. Reagent quality control in bacteriology: cost-effectiveness, easy-to-use methodology. J. Clin. Microbiol. **14**: 119.
16. ICMSF. 1980. Appendix I. In "Microbial Ecology of Foods," Vol. II, p. 945. Intern. Comm. on Microbiol. Spec. for Foods. Academic Press, New York.
17. ICMSF. 1988. "Microorganisms in Foods 4: Application of the Hazard Analysis Critical Control Point (HACCP) System to Ensure Microbiological Safety and Quality." Intern. Comm. on Microbiol. Spec. for Foods. Blackwell Scientific Pub. Boston, Mass.
18. IDPH and IEPA. 1980. "Certification and Operation of Environmental Laboratories." Ill. Dept. Pub. Health and Ill. Environ. Protec. Agency, Springfield, Ill.
19. Mossel, D. A. A. 1980. Food microbiology, how it used to be in the 1950s and what it may become in the 1980s. Culture 1:1. Oxoid Ltd., Hampshire, England.

20. Mossel, D. A. A., Van Rossem, F., Koopmans, M., Hendricks, M., Verdouden, M., and Eelderink, I. 1980. A comparison of the classic and the so-called ecometric technique. J. Appl. Bacterial. **49**: 439.

21. Nagel, J. G. and Kunz, L. J. 1973. Needless retesting of quality assured commercially prepared culture media. Appl. Microbiol. **26**: 31.

22. Olson, J. C., Belknap, R. A., Brazis, A. R., Peeler, J. T., and Pusch, D. J. 1978. Food microbiology. In "Quality Assurance Practices for Health Laboratories." Am. Pub. Health Assn., Washington, D.C.

23. Peddecord, K. M. and Cada, R. L. 1980. Clinical laboratory proficiency test performance. Its relationship to structural, process, and environmental variables. Am. J. Clin. Pathol. **73**: 380.

24. Power, D. A. 1975. Quality control of commercially prepared bacteriological media. In "Quality Control in Microbiology," ed. J. E. Prier, J. T. Bartola, and H. Friedman, Univ. Park Press, Baltimore, Md.

25. Prier, J. E., Bartola, J. T., and Friedman, H. 1975. "Quality Control in Microbiology." Univ. Park Press, Baltimore, Md.

26. Snyder, J. W. 1981. Quality control in clinical microbiology. API Spores **5**: 13. Analytab Products, Plainview, N.Y.

27. Suggs, M. T. 1975. Product class standards (specifications) and evaluation of microbiological in vitro diagnostic reagents. In "Quality Control in Microbiology," ed. J. E. Prier, J. T. Bartola, and H. Friedman, p. 87. Univ. Park Press, Baltimore, Md.

28. US Pharmacopeial Convention, Inc., 1980. "The United States Pharmacopeia XX." Rockville, Md.

29. Wilcox, K. R., Baynes T. E. Jr., Crable, J. V., Duckworth, J. K., Huffaker, R. H., Martin, R. E., Scott, W. L., Stevens, M. V., and Winstead, M. 1978. Laboratory management. In "Quality Assurance Practices for Health Laboratories," ed., S. L. Inhorn, p. 3. Am. Pub. Health Assn., Washington, D.C.

30. Wilson, M. E. 1975. Microbiological proficiency: what basis for confidence. In "Quality Control in Microbiology," ed. J. E. Prier, J. T. Bartola, and H. Friedman, p. 119. Univ. Park Press, Baltimore, Md.

SAMPLING PLANS, SAMPLE COLLECTION, SHIPMENT, AND PREPARATION FOR ANALYSIS

James W. Messer, Thaddeus F. Midura, and James T. Peeler

2.1 INTRODUCTION

The objective of this chapter is to enable the user to obtain representative samples of a food lot, submit the samples to the laboratory in a condition that is microbially unchanged from the time of sampling, and prepare the samples for analysis.

The person who collects the samples should be able to apply an appropriate sampling plan and sample correctly to prevent contamination of the samples and to minimize microbial changes within the samples during transport, storage, and handling.

The procedures described in this chapter apply generally to collecting, labeling, transporting, storing, and preparing samples for analysis.

For specific information and discussion about sampling and analytical procedures for canned foods, see Chapters 60 and 61. Other foods also may require special sampling and preparation procedures depending upon the specific microorganisms involved. For such procedures, see the chapters covering the relevant food types and specific microorganisms.

2.2 GENERAL CONSIDERATIONS

A proper sample—its collection, transportation to the laboratory, and preparation for examination—is the first priority in the microbiological examination of any food product. Laboratory results and their interpretation are valid only when appropriate samples are examined. Every effort must be made to ensure that samples are representative of the entire lot of material under evaluation, are the proper type for the determination to be made, and are protected against extraneous contamination and improper handling, especially at temperatures that may significantly alter the microflora. Refrigeration often must be provided to prevent destruction or growth of organisms in a sample. Perishable samples collected in the nonfrozen state must be refrigerated, preferably at 0° to 4.4°C, from the time of collection until receipt at the laboratory. To avoid melting ice, a sealed eutectic coolant is preferable for use in the shipment container. Samples collected while frozen should be kept solidly frozen. When dry ice is used, the containers should have tight closures to prevent pH changes in the sample caused by the absorption of carbon dioxide. As a general rule, samples should be examined within 36 hr after sampling. Perishable items that cannot be analyzed within 36 hr should be frozen or retained under refrigeration, depending upon the type of product, reason for analysis, and type of microorganisms sought. Nonfrozen samples of shellfish should be examined within 6 hr after collection; they cannot be frozen.[4]

Samples must be clearly and completely identified. The following information is considered necessary: sample description, collector's name, name and address of the manufacturer, lot number, dealer or distributor, and date, place, and time of collection. Frequently the temperature at the time of collection is also useful to the laboratory for the interpretation of results. Further, it is often desirable that the reason for testing be given, e.g., samples may be collected as part of a quality control or surveillance program, as official samples to determine conformity to regulatory standards, or as part of a foodborne disease investigation.

2.3 EQUIPMENT, MATERIALS, AND REAGENTS

1. Instruments for opening containers
Sterile scissors, knives, scalpels, can openers, or other hand tools as required.
2. Sample transfer instruments
Sterile multiple- or single-use spatulas, scoops, spoons, triers, forceps, knives, scissors, tongue depressors, drills and auger bits, corers, dippers, metal tubes, and swabs as required.
3. Sample containers
Sterile multiple-use containers, either large- or smallmouthed designs, nontoxic, leakproof, and presterilized polyethylene bags or other suitable sterile, nontoxic containers as required.
Nonsterile, nontoxic, single-service vials, polyethylene bags, or bottles that are clean and dry and do not have a viable bacterial count in rinse tests in excess of one organism per ml of capacity may be used. Sterile, evacuated sampling equipment also can be used. Sterile glass containers usually are not

desirable because of possible breakage and consequential glass contamination of the sampling environment.

4. Thermometers

Thermometers that measure $-20°$ to $100°C$ with graduation intervals not exceeding $1°C$. A metal dial type is preferred since glass thermometers may break and contaminate the food. Thermometers should be sanitized in hypochlorite solution or other equivalent microbicide. They should be dipped in a solution not less than 100 mg/L for at least 30 sec before being inserted into foods.

5. Microbicide

Medium strength (100 mg/L) hypochlorite solution or other approved disinfectant.

6. Labeling supplies

Pressure-sensitive tapes and labels, tags of adequate size to hold sample information, indelible marking pens.

7. Sample shipping containers

For frozen or refrigerated samples, rigid metal or plastic containers that are insulated and equipped with a tight cover. Each container should have ample space for the refrigerant so that samples will remain at the desired temperature until arrival at the laboratory.

Containers for nonperishable samples should be made of sturdy corrugated cardboard or other material capable of withstanding abusive shipping conditions.

Refrigerant or dry ice is to be added as needed for perishable samples.

8. Balance

Balance width 2000 g capacity having a sensitivity of 0.1 g with a 200 g load.

9. Blenders and mixers

Mechanical blender with several operating speeds or rheostat speed control, and sterile glass or metal blending jars with covers. Stomacher (The Tekmar Company, Cincinnati, Ohio).

10. Diluents

Sterile Butterfield's phosphate buffer (Chapter 62). Sterile 0.1% peptone water (Chapter 62). Sterile sodium chloride solutions (Chapter 62). Special diluents required for specific microorganisms and special analytical conditions (specific chapters).

2.4   PRECAUTIONS

Adequate precautions should be taken to prevent microbial contamination of samples from external sources, including the air, sample containers, sampling devices, and the shipping vehicle. When foods are packaged in small, sealed containers, collect the unopened containers rather than portions from each container.

The sampling operation should be organized in advance with all the needed equipment and containers on hand and presterilized. For collecting samples, use an instrument appropriate to the physical state of the food.

Protect sampling instruments from exposure and contamination before and during use. When removing sampling instruments from the food container to the sample container, do not pass them over the remaining presterilized instruments. When opening the sterile sampling container, open it sufficiently to admit the sample, then close and seal it immediately. Do not touch the inside of the sterile container lip or lid. Do not allow the open lid to become contaminated. Do not hold or fill a sampling container over the top of a bulk food container when transferring a sample. Fill the sample container not more than ¾ full to prevent overflow and to allow proper mixing of sample in the laboratory. Do not expel air when folding or whirling plastic sample bags. Submit an empty sterile sampling container similarly opened and closed as a control.

The sample collector should keep his or her hands away from the mouth, nose, eyes, and face. Hands should be washed immediately before beginning the sampling and during sampling when the hands may become contaminated. Sterile plastic gloves may be useful to enhance aseptic conditions for sampling.

Contaminated sampling equipment should be placed into proper containers for ultimate disposal and/or sterilization. Labels should never be moistened with the tongue. Use pressure-sensitive labels.

Chapter 1 gives additional safety precautions to ensure proper handling and preparation of samples for microbiological analysis. Food samples may contain infectious microorganisms or toxic materials that may be potentially hazardous. The best protection against hazards is the use of common sense in the practice of good sampling techniques and treating each sample as if it were contaminated.

2.5 PROCEDURES

2.51 Sampling Plans

Sampling plans were first developed in 1923 by engineers at the Western Electric Company, but were not widely used.[23] After World War II the Department of Defense developed Military Standards for attribute and variables sampling plans[16, 17, 18, 23] (definitions in Section 2.511). These plans considered single and multiple sampling based on the history of the producer performance. Levels of sampling (i.e., tightened, normal, and reduced) that reflected prior producer performance were established for these plans. Special categories of sampling plans have been adapted to agricultural products.[5, 6, 8, 15, 21, 22]

The use of sampling plans in food microbiology has been limited. A comprehensive set of single sampling attribute plans has been published for food microbiology.[7, 13] Typical points of sampling where sampling plans may be applied are shown in the following diagram:

Points of Sampling
raw materials
↓
production line
↓
producer's warehouse
↓
retail storage or sales outlet
↓
international port—export or import

This discussion of sampling plans will be clearer if certain basic concepts are stated at the outset. First, the lot to be sampled must be defined. When a given quantity of product is surveyed and units or portions of this lot are taken for examination, the procedure is called sampling. The removal of a portion of a sample unit from its container for microbiological analyses is referred to as sampling. This use of the word "sampling" should not be confused with the term "sampling" as it applies to a statistical sampling plan. A simple random sampling implies that in a selection of samples taken from a lot, each sample has the same chance of being chosen. For example, assume that a lot defined as "1000 packages in a warehouse" is to be sampled. Each package is assigned a number. If the 1000 items are stacked equally in 10 rows, then 1 to 100 would be assigned to the units in the first row, 101 to 200 to the second, and so on until all packages are numbered. A random number table is used to choose the required numbered containers for sampling.[13, 20] In this example, we will select five as the required number of packages. Then five typical random numbers (lot size being 1000) would be 586, 973, 99, 838, and 737. The appropriate numbered unit would be taken from rows 6, 10, 1, 9, and 8. The instructions that specify the number of packages to be taken and the basis for accepting or rejecting the lot is called the sampling plan.

A sampling plan as employed in this context states the number of units required to be randomly collected from a lot and lists the acceptance and rejection criteria.

Before using a sampling plan, it is usually prudent to consult a professional statistician to ascertain that the lot of food to be sampled meets the criteria required by that particular sampling plan.

2.511   Definitions used in sampling plans

Many statistical terms are common English words redefined for a specific use. The following terms are frequently used in the sampling literature.[8, 10, 13, 14, 18]

1. **Acceptance number(s)**—The maximum number(s) of defectives in an attribute sampling plan for which a lot will be accepted.

2. **Acceptance quality level (AQL)**—The maximum percent defective (or the maximum number of defects per 100 units) that for purposes of sampling inspection can be considered satisfactory as a process average.[17]

3. **Attribute**—A qualitative characteristic of a sample unit, e.g., the results of an analysis are positive or negative for *Salmonella*.

4. **Average outgoing quality limit (AOQL)**—The maximum possible percent defective that will result from employment of a given sampling plan provided that rejected lots are screened 100% to remove defective items and that such screening is 100% effective.[18]

5. **Consumer protection**—The ability of a sampling plan to reject unacceptable samples. This is measured as the complement of the probability of acceptance for Limiting Quality (LQ) lots.[8] The consumer protection is often set at 90%.

6. **Consumer's risk**—The risk a consumer takes that a lot will be accepted by a sampling plan even though the lot does not conform to requirements.[8] In many standards[8, 9, 17, 23] this risk is nominally set at 10%.

7. **Continuous distribution**—A distribution of a population of measures that take on a continuum of values. A variables sampling (Section 2.515) plan may be applicable.

8. **Control chart**—A graphic device that can be used to monitor repeated sampling from a manufacturing or measurement process.

9. **Destructive testing**—A testing process that results in destruction of the unit or sample under test.

10. **Discrete variate**—A random variable consisting of isolated points that can have a finite or infinite number of countable values. These values can be used in an attribute sampling plan. (Sections 2.512, 2.513, 2.514).

11. **Estimate**—Any value computed from sample data and used to infer a corresponding population (lot) value, e.g., the sample mean (average).

12. **Estimated process average**—The average percent defective or average number of defects per 100 units of product found at the time of original inspection.[18]

13. **Frequency distribution**—The mathematical description of the way the frequency of members of a population is distributed. The information about the distribution is used to calculate the probability of lot acceptance or rejection. The discrete random variable takes on a countable number of values, and the probability distribution is defined by a probability mass function. A continuous random variable is defined by a density function.

14. **Homogeneity of variances**—The equality of variances among populations, which must sometimes be tested.

15. **Homogeneous**—A product having a uniform texture or content.

16. **Limiting Quality (LQ)**—Percent defective or defects per 100 units.[8] A lot having a 10% probability of acceptance is referred to under many common standards[8, 9, 17, 23] as a lot having a quality level equal to LQ.

17. **Lot**—The number of sample units in one batch or produced in some specified period of time such that the units will be about the same quality. Each lot or batch should consist of units of product of a single type, grade, class, size, and composition. The lot should be manufactured under the same conditions and at essentially the same time.

18. **Lot inspection by attributes**—Inspection whereby either the sample unit is classified as defective or nondefective with respect to a requirement or set of requirements (when on a "defective" basis), or inspection whereby defects in each sample unit are counted with respect to a requirement or set of requirements (when on a "defect" basis).[8]

19. **Lot quality**—A measure of the characteristic being controlled. The results of lot inspection are often expressed as percent defective units (e.g., a unit containing salmonellae is defective). Less frequently, the quality will be expressed in terms of the variable measured (weight/unit, coliform/g).

20. **Operating characteristic (OC) curve**—A graphical representation of the relation of the probability of lot acceptance to lot quality (usually expressed as percent defective units). This curve will depend on the number of units required in the sampling plan and the acceptance number. The curve also shows the lot quality associated with the consumer's risk and the producer's risk. It thus describes the consequences of the sampling plan (decision rule) for accepting lots of different quality.

21. **Population**—Any finite or infinite collection of individuals (samples or units) on which decisions are to be made.

22. **Probability**—An estimate of the frequency of occurrence of an event, e.g., probability of *n* sample units out of a population being positive for *Salmonella*, expressed as a value from 0 to 1. For a sampling plan, assumption of a particular probability distribution (i.e., binomial or Poisson) allows the estimation of the computation of the probability of lot acceptance versus lot quality in an operating characteristic curve.

23. **Producer's risk**—The risk that a producer takes that a lot will be rejected by a sampling plan even though the lot conforms to requirements.[8] In many standards[8, 9, 17, 23] this risk is set at 5%.

24. **Proportion defective units (P)**—The number of defective units divided by total units in a lot. Proportion defectives P or percent defectives (100P) are often plotted as the abscissa on an OC curve.

25. **Random sample**—A sample that was chosen in such a way that every sample or unit in the lot had equal chance of being selected. This is often achieved with the aid of a random number table.

26. **Representative sample**—In the widest sense, a sample which is representative of a population. Some confusion arises if "representative" is regarded as meaning "selected by some process that gives all samples an equal chance of appearing to represent the population," or, alternatively, if it means "typical in respect of certain characteristics, however chosen."

27. **Sample unit**—The smallest definable part of a lot, also called a unit. This may mean a can or a package. When lots are bulk packaged in bins,

barrels, bags, etc., then the sample unit is arbitrary and may depend on the sampling device. The use of the word in this context should be differentiated from the analytical sample unit specified by the analytical method.

28. **Sampling plan**—A design that indicates the number of units to be collected from each lot and the criteria to be applied in accepting or rejecting the lot. This decision rule may require the lot to be judged on the basis of one set of sample units; this is a single sampling plan (Section 2.512). A double sampling plan (Section 2.513) is a sampling inspection in which the inspection of the first sample leads to a decision to accept, to reject, or to take a second sample. The inspection of a second sample, when required, then leads to a decision to accept or reject. Two or more such collections would mean that a multiple sampling plan was being used. Another procedure where units are drawn one by one (or in groups) and drawing at any stage determines whether to accept, reject, or continue sampling is called a sequential sampling plan.

29. **Stratified random sampling**—A procedure for sampling where the lot is divided into parts or strata that differ with respect to the characteristics under study. In some cases, this is a way of improving the estimate of lot quality.

30. **Zero defective tolerance**—An evaluation system implying that a lot must be free of the undesirable characteristic or defect. All units in the lot must be tested in order to ensure zero defectives. This can be performed only where the test is nondestructive. The requirement of zero defects is definitely not possible in microbiological sampling plans.

2.512   Single sampling (two-class) attribute plans

Single sampling procedures are useful in food inspection since, for a variety of reasons, the lot can be sampled and tested only once. In addition, the results of microbiological tests are often easy to define as attributes. For example, an attribute such as the presence or absence of a microorganism, say *Salmonella*, is frequently reported. In other instances, a certain level of organisms may be acceptable. For example, a unit may be acceptable if it has less than three *E. coli*/g.

Single sampling attribute plans also have the advantage that the true distribution of the variable in question (e.g., *E. coli*/g) does not have to be determined. Single sample plans and the multiple sample plans in the next section (2.513) can be evaluated by using the hypergeometric, binomial, or Poisson distributions. The choice of distributions used to compute the probability relationships[9, 10] depends on the number of units (**N**) in a lot. When **N** is large relative to the sample size (**n**), (**n/N**) <0.1) or estimated proportion defectives <0.1 (see tables p. 60[9]), or then the only parameters that need to be considered are the number of samples or units to be tested, **n**, and the acceptance number, **c**. The lots defined for this discussion are assumed to be of homogeneous quality, to be from large lots, and to satisfy the conditions above.

Steps for choosing and applying an attribute sampling plan are as follows:

- Select the measurements of interest.
- Define the sampling units that constitute a lot.
- Determine a value of consumer's and/or producer's risk to ensure the lot quality (LQ or AQL) desired.
- Obtain an estimate of process average.
- Compute or select a plan that meets the risk and lot quality requirements.
- Calculate the OC curve.
- Apply the plan on a group of randomly selected units from a lot.
- Maintain records on the process average (if you are a producer) and make changes in the plan as necessary.

Figure 1 presents the operating characteristics (OC) curves for seven single sampling plans. These OC curves for the sampling plans will be used to help illustrate the process of choosing a plan. The reader should refer to Dodge and Romig,[9] Duncan,[10] and International Commission on Microbiological Specifications for Foods[13] for presentations of complete sets of plans where OC curves for additional values of **n** or **c** are given. Figure 1 has an acceptance number (**c**) of zero, which means that any positive results on a test lot will result in the rejection of that specific lot.

As an example, consider that a lot **N** > 1000 units is to be analyzed for coliform MPN/g and a unit is to be called defective if it has MPN $\geq$ 100/g and to be called acceptable or nondefective if it has an MPN < 100/g. A sampling plan is wanted to define the number of units (**n**) to sample where the number of defectives (**c**) equals zero and the chance (consumer's risk) of accepting lots with 8% or more defective units is 10%. Using these criteria, the sampling plan to be chosen (Figure 1) is **n** = 30 and **c** = 0.

Since microbiological tests are destructive (the sample unit cannot be used after testing), cost of sampling may be balanced with the cost of the risk. For example, a plan may be designed to inspect incoming raw materials and, on the other hand, may be designed to sample consumer products before releasing lots for sale. The measurement (i.e., coliform MPN/g) may be the same, but the choice of plan will be affected by other factors such as (a) processing conditions, (b) potential health hazard of the products, (c) persistence of organisms under different storage conditions, and (d) type of plan used by regulatory agencies to inspect the same lots. The **n** = 15, 30, and 60 with **c** = 0 plans in Figure 1 are in common use[12, 13] to test for *Salmonella*. The **n** = 3, **c** = 0 plans could be used for screening raw materials.

Some analytical procedures are sufficiently sensitive to measure the presence of a single organism when the sampling units are pooled. A positive test indicates that one or more of the units was positive from **n** pooled units. This produces the same decision for a plan (i.e., **n** = 5, **c** = 0) as if the units had

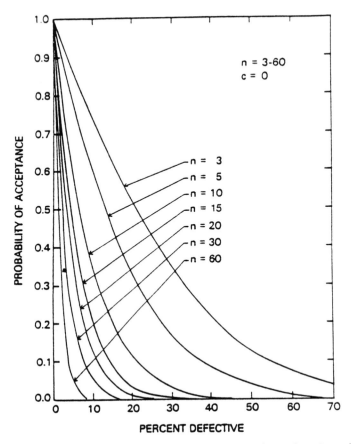

Figure 1—Single Sampling (Two-class) Attribute Plans for Sample Sizes **n** = 3, 5, 10, 15, 20, 30, 60 and **c** = 0.

been analyzed separately. Pooling of sampling units cannot be done when **c** > 0 or when a positive sample is defined as ≥ x organisms per gram. Calculations with OC curves are found in the references.[9, 10]

2.513   Multiple sampling attribute plans

Sampling plans of this type are designed to inspect lots based on multiple samplings. The lot is accepted or rejected based on a sequential decision. As an example, consider a double sampling plan (Figure 2) of $n_1 = 10$, $c_1 = 0$ and $n_2 = 6$, $c_2 = 1$. This plan requires that 10 units be analyzed (i.e., coliform MPN/g) and the lot be rejected if 2 or more units are observed to have ≥ 10 coliform/g. If all values are less than 10/g, the lot is accepted, then 6 additional units from the same lot are analyzed if 1 defective is observed in the first 10 units tested. If one or more of the six units are positive (≥ 10 coliform/g) the lot is rejected; otherwise it is accepted. The operating characteristic curve for this plan is given in Figure 2. If there were 24% defectives in the lot, the plan would accept 10 of 100 lots. The average outgoing quality would be 5% defectives.

Figure 2 shows the operating characteristic curve for the double sampling plan and one for a single sampling plan ($n = 7$, $c = 0$) that have the same average 5% outgoing quality limit (AOQL). Although the AOQLs are equal to the two plans, it can be seen that the degree of protection is not equal for

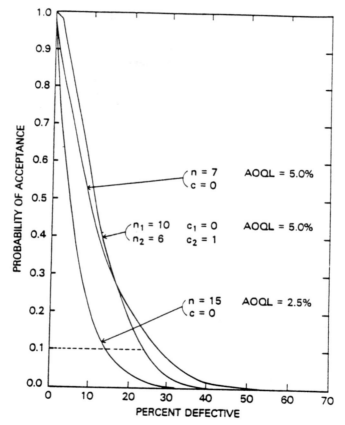

Figure 2—Operating Characteristic Curves for Two Single and One Double Sampling Plan with Average Outgoing Lot Quality Limit 2.5 and 5.0%. The $c = 0$ for a single sampling plan indicates that a lot will be rejected if a single unit of the sample is positive. Rejection of the lot will occur if two or more units of the first or second sample are positive for the double sampling plan.

all qualities. The choice of taking 15 units ($c = 0$) for a single sampling is presented for an AOQL equal to 2.5%. This illustrates some of the decisions that must be made in choosing sampling plans.

A double or other multiple sampling plan requires that the lot of units be available if extended sampling is necessary. This is not practical in many instances with foods. However, the advantage of multiple sampling plans is that lots of good quality (i.e., low coliform count) will on average require fewer samples to be tested than if tested by a single sample plan giving equal protection. For example, a two-stage or double sample plan of $n_1 = 10$, $n_2 = 6$ might require that just the first 10 units be analyzed. Thus, the average sample number tested would be decreased.

Further information on the design of multiple sampling plans can be found in Dodge and Romig[9] and Duncan.[10] An administrator with mathematical ability can calculate a plan if the desired average quality limit (LQ), consumer (AQL) and/or producer's risk has been selected. Dodge and Romig[9] present the operating characteristic curves for double sampling plans and several outgoing quality limits (0.1 to 10%, p. 112). The figures allow a quick assessment of risks for each plan. Their[9] diagram shown in Figure 3 is an interpretation of double sampling plans.

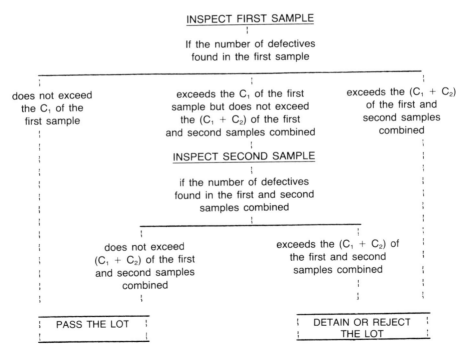

2.514   Three-class attribute plans

Three-class attribute plans were developed by Bray et al.[7] in conjunction with the ICMSF.[13] It was hoped that these sampling techniques could be used with methods recommended by Thatcher and Clark,[20] who stated[13] that the "test is concerned primarily with plans that may be applied to lots presented for acceptance at ports or similar points of entry." It was assumed that very little, if any, information would be known about lots and, thus, attribute plans, two-class plans (Section 2.513), and three-class plans would be applicable. These plans are also useful for inspecting lots within a country or corporation where more information is known about a lot.

Three-class attribute plans differ from those described in Section 2.513 by having two microbiological limits that create three classes of product. Bray et al.[7] noted that the choice of limits (e.g., for coliform MPN, a quality or sanitation indicator) is difficult. Nonetheless they state that "most scientists can provide two numbers: one below which they have little or no concern and a higher value above which they clearly begin to have critical concern. If we denote the lower level by m and the larger one by M, then the set of values in the range $[m, M]$ can be considered safe." Observations falling in the regions defined by the two limits are called acceptable, marginal, and unacceptable. The acceptable results have values equal to or less than m ($\leq m$). Marginal observations fall between greater than m and equal to or less than M (e.g., $[m, M]$). Unacceptable results are greater than M. Three-class attribute plans can be specified by a sample size n, the number of units allowed (c_1) between limits $\geq m$ and $\leq M$, and the number of units allowed (c_2) equal to or above M. It is assumed that all units $\leq m$ are acceptable. However, as stated above, the value of M is the decision point for this type of sampling plan. The value of $c_2 = 0$ was set in all plans discussed in "Microorganisms in Foods 2"[13] and in the discussion below. Thus, the sampling plans are noted as n, c where c is the number of marginal samples allowed. The three-class attribute sampling plans found in "Microorganisms in Foods 2"[13] present a detailed description of the type of microbiological methods to be recommended, potential risk of contamination, and subsequent hazard for a wide group of products and the choice of limits m, M for these products. Suggestions are presented for fish, fishery products, vegetables, dried foods, frozen foods, milk, milk products, raw meats, processed meats, shelf-stable canned foods, and fresh or frozen raw shellfish. Different measurements are of interest for each product and include aerobic plate count, coliform, *B. cereus*, *C. perfringens*, *C. botulinum*, fecal coliforms, *Salmonella*, *Staphylococcus aureus*, and *V. parahaemolyticus*. Limits $[m, M]$ were chosen for product-measurement combination and plans were established based on risk.

The ICMSF[13] categorized the types of microbiological hazards and conditions to which a lot of food would be exposed. This categorization is an aid to the microbiologist when considering a choice of sampling plan. These hazards were defined as follows:

1. No direct health hazard, utility (e.g., general contamination, reduced shelf life, and spoilage).
2. Health hazard low, indirect (indicator).
3. Health hazard moderate, direct, limited spread.
4. Health hazard moderate, direct, potentially extensive spread.
5. Health hazard severe, direct.

These hazards are linked with three conditions of risk (reduction, no change, or increase) that reflect how a food was expected to be handled and consumed after sampling. The combination of the types of hazards and conditions of risk yields 15 cases where suggestions of sampling plans and limits could be presented for products, although only a few cases would be realistically applicable for a given product and measurement.

Sampling plans for hazards 1, 2, and 3 are three-class plans. They are $n = 10$, $c = 1$; $n = 5$, $c = 3$; $n = 5$, $c = 2$; and $n = 5$, $c = 1$. In these cases limits [m, M] are set to define marginal quality. When the hazards are more severe (i.e., 4 and 5) the two-class plans $n = 60$, $c = 0$; $n = 30$, $c = 0$; $n = 20$, $c = 0$; $n = 15$, $c = 0$; $n = 10$, $c = 0$; and $n = 5$, $c = 0$ are suggested. As noted in Section 2.513, the two-class plans above mean that n units are analyzed and the lot is accepted only if all units are negative for some characteristic (e.g., *Salmonella*). The operating characteristic curves are given for the two-class plans above in Figure 1.

The approach of the ICMSF[13] on three-class plans was to define risks, suggest limits for a wide variety of specific cases, and suggest particular plans to be employed. This differs from other texts on sampling plans in that the mathematical tools for computing and comparing plans are presented, and the reader must make a choice of various conditions. Those desiring to compute their own three-class plan should consult Bray et al.[7]

Operating characteristic contours presented as two-way tables are used rather than operating characteristic curves for three-class attribute plans. These contours reflect the fact that the true marginal percent can vary from 0 to 100% at the same time the proportion of bad (value $\geq M$) varies from 0 to 100% with the obvious restriction that percent good units + percent marginal units + percent bad units = 100%.

The choice of an ICMSF sampling plan is straightforward. First, specify the food and measurement (e.g., freshwater fish and fecal coliforms). Second, specify the risk. ICMSF[13] suggests case 4, which reflects low indirect health hazard at reduced risk. The sampling plan is $n = 5$, $c = 3$. The last step is to choose limits m and M for the product to be sampled. ICMSF[13] recommends $m = 4$ and $M = 400$ for freshwater fish. The complete plan is listed (e.g., $n = 5$, $c = 3$; $m = 4$, $M = 400$), once the product and measurement are specified.

A microbiologist who wishes to derive his own three-class plan must consider (a) the assignment of risk to the product, (b) the choice of sampling plan based on a comparison of probability of acceptance versus percent marginal units (assuming we will not accept any bad units), and (c) the values of **m** and **M** for the product. A choice of risk and the setting of **m** and **M** may differ depending on the purpose of the sampling. One set of U.S. FDA sampling plans for *Salmonella* has values of $n = 15$, $c = 0$; $n = 30$, $c = 0$; $n = 60$, $c = 0$.[12]

2.515   Variables sample plans

A variables plan can be used when the probability density function of a measurement is known, and a majority of published plans are computed when the distribution of the variable or its transformation is normal (Gaussian). An advantage of the variables plans over single sampling plans is that fewer samples are required, resulting in a lower cost to achieve the same protection as a single attribute plan. Disadvantages include the calculations involved in judging a lot, the fact that different plans are required for each variable (coliform, *E. coli*, etc.), and the requirement that the probability distribution must be known or assumed for each measurement. The last two requirements may prove to be the most inconvenient. A series of three or four variable (e.g., aerobic plate count, coliform, *E. coli*, and *S. aureus*) measurements may be required on a product. The transformation that ensures a normal distribution may not be known, and the estimates of variance are often different for each measurement. For these reasons, variables sampling plans are not widely used in the food industry for microbiological measurements. For further information about derivation of variables sampling plans, refer to Duncan,[10] Kramer,[15] and MIL-STD 414.[16]

2.516   Sampling procedures for low contamination levels

The microbiologist often encounters a situation where production lots of a product with low levels of a pathogen must be sampled (e.g., 1 positive sample unit in 100). How many sample units should be taken to have a high probability of detecting the pathogen? Suppose 200 sample units have been analyzed and all are negative. What can be reported about the lot? Clearly, the whole lot may not be free of the pathogen. The same cases also arise in sterility testing. In both of these situations, it is assumed that the pathogen or contaminant can be detected if present in an analytical sample (e.g., 25 g) and the results will be reported as positive or negative. Other necessary assumptions are given in the discussion of single sampling attribute plans (Section 2.512).

Table 1 lists the number of sample units (**n**) needed to detect a positive result at a given level of fraction positive analytical units in a lot. This table can be used to determine how many units should be analyzed in order to detect a positive at a given fraction positive level. Suppose a regulator knows that the fraction positive of a certain pathogen is 0.04. How many sample

Table 1—Number of Samples Needed to Detect a Fraction Positive[a] with Probability 0.90, 0.95, and 0.99 Where at Least One Positive Result Occurs

Fraction positive[b] samples (P)	Number of analytical units to be tested (n)		
	Probability (1-Pr) 0.90	0.95	0.99
1.0	3	4	4
0.9	3	4	5
0.8	3	4	6
0.7	4	5	7
0.6	4	5	8
0.5	5	6	9
0.4	6	8	12
0.3	10	10	16
0.2	12	15	23
0.1	23	30	46
0.09	26	34	51
0.08	29	38	58
0.07	33	43	66
0.06	39	50	77
0.05	46	60	92
0.04	58	75	115
0.03	77	100	154
0.02	115	150	230
0.01	230	299	461
0.001	2,303	2,996	4,605
0.0001	23,026	29,963	46,052

[a]Can be computed from Thorndike Table, p. 35 of Dodge and Romig.[9]
[b]The fraction of positive units (e.g., 90 positives in 100 analytical units).

units should he or she obtain in order to find a positive unit with probability 0.95? In Table 1, we go down the left hand column (fraction positive samples) to 0.04 and over two columns to (1-Pr) = 0.95. Pr is the probability that all **n** units are negative. The required sample size is 75.

Let us examine the situation from another point of view. Suppose a producer knows that pathogens can be found in his product with a frequency of 6 in 1,000 units. The regulator takes 30 sample units per lot. What is the probability (Pr) that all 30 samples will be negative? The answer is $Pr = e^{-(30)} (0.006) = 0.84$. Thus, the regulator has a 0.16 chance of detecting a positive. The fact that 30 is a relatively small sample does not eliminate the chance of detecting a concentration of 6 in 1000.

Another situation arises when a sample of **n** units is examined and all are negative for the pathogen in question. What can be said about the lot fraction positives? Table 2 shows one way of expressing the result. The fraction positive per lot can be related to the probability, Pr, when all **n** sample units examined are negative. If 100 sample units were negative, then there is only 1 chance

Table 2—Fraction Positive Samples When the Probability[a] Is That All n Samples Are Negative

Number of negative analytical units (n)	P — Fraction positive samples		
	Probability (Pr) 0.10	0.05	0.01
3	0.77[b]	1.00	1.50
5	0.46	0.60	0.92
10	0.23	0.30	0.46
15	0.15	0.20	0.31
20	0.12	0.15	0.23
25	0.092	0.12	0.18
30	0.077	0.10	0.15
35	0.066	0.086	0.13
40	0.058	0.075	0.12
45	0.051	0.067	0.10
50	0.046	0.060	0.092
100	0.023	0.030	0.046
200	0.012	0.015	0.023
300	0.0077	0.012	0.015
400	0.0058	0.0075	0.012
500	0.0046	0.0060	0.0092
1000	0.0023	0.0030	0.0046

[a]Can be computed from Thorndike Table, p. 35 of Dodge and Romig.[9]
[b]Rounded to two significant digits.

in 10 that the fraction positive exceeds 0.023 per lot with $Pr = 0.10$. The probability is 0.90 that the fraction positive is 0.023 or lower. Stated yet another way, there is a probability of 0.10 or less that 230 sample units in 10,000 have a pathogen. So even a lot size of 10,000 gives some chance that a positive unit will reach a consumer. And there is, of course, an additional, though small, probability that the consumers will receive the unit because the distribution of the lot is not uniform.

If the samples are homogeneous and the organisms can be assumed to be randomly distributed throughout the lot, then an estimate of concentration can be obtained (Chapter 6). For example, assuming that one *Listeria monocytogenes* organism occurs in each 10 ml of milk, if **n** samples of milk are taken from a well-agitated bulk milk tank, then the concentration of pathogen could be estimated. If the analytical sample is 1 ml, how many sample units are required to obtain at least one positive sample with probability 0.95? From Table 1 we see that 30 samples should be examined.

Let us further suppose that upon examination 2 of the 30 results are positive. What is the estimate of concentration? Based on the results of a single dilution, the concentration of *L. monocytogenes*/ml = $\ln(n/\# \text{ negatives})$ = $\ln(30/28)$ = 0.069. Thus, sampling plans are useful not only for lot inspection but in determining risk and in detecting a specified level of organisms associated with a given probability. In addition, the concentration can also be estimated in some restricted cases.

2.517   Summary

The discussion of sampling plans in this section has been modified for application to microbiological measurements. A general survey of plans is presented, but some of these procedures do not lend themselves directly to microbiological sampling in foods. The brief discussion of multiple sampling plans does not mean that these procedures may not be found useful. The sampling for microorganisms is destructive, the results may be delayed for several days because of incubation requirements, and the foods may be perishable. Thus, single sampling plans are generally best suited to most situations.

Variables sampling plans are subject to additional disadvantages beyond those stated in Section 2.515. The general level of statistical knowledge in the typical food facility may prevent the use of these plans. Calculations needed to choose and apply the variables plans may prove burdensome. The two- and three-class attribute plans are easy to apply and thus should aid in the spread of statistics in microbiological sampling of foods. Additionally, the ICMSF[13] has presented extensive suggestions of specific plans and microbial criteria to be used on a wide variety of products. This reduces the amount of work necessary in calculations and time spent in plan selection. Thus, the single sampling two-class and three-class attribute plans have the most utility in sampling of foods for microbiological analysis. Individuals who wish to derive their own sampling plans are advised to use Dodge and Romig,[9] Duncan,[10] and MIL-STD 105.[17]

2.52   Sampling Procedures

It is necessary to consider the physical state of the product to be sampled (e.g., dry, semisolid, viscous) and the nature of the foodborne illness outbreak before sampling so that the number of units will be representative and/or statistically significant for the intended use.[13] The sampling procedures described in this section are those that generally apply. Unusual sampling procedures that may be required for specific foods are given in the chapters dealing with particular microorganisms or commodities.

2.521   Finished products

Consumer packages of foods should be sampled from original unopened containers of the same processing lot. Record processing information and product code of samples on forms submitted with samples. The practice of submitting unopened containers prevents contamination that might be introduced by opening at the sampling location. In addition, it allows laboratory examinations to be performed on products and packages or containers as they are offered to the public.

2.522   Bulk liquid material

If the products are in bulk form or in containers of a size impractical for submission, aseptically transfer a representative sample portion to a sterile, leakproof container. Before drawing a sample, aseptically mix the food mass so as to ensure that the sample is as homogeneous as possible. If adequate mixing or agitation of the bulk product is not possible, multiple samples should be drawn from the bulk container. Do not fill sample containers over bulk containers of food. Care must be taken to select sample containers with enough capacity to accommodate the needed sample volume when the container is ¾ full. Avoid the use of glass sample containers. Thermometers used in bulk food containers should be sanitized before use.[3] Cool perishable samples to 0° to 4.4°C quickly if they are not already refrigerated. Metal thermometers are preferred since breakage of a mercury thermometer would contaminate the product.

Where appropriate, a temperature control sample should be labeled as such and submitted with the samples to be tested. In addition, an empty sterile sample container should be submitted as a container control.

If a temperature control sample is needed for frozen samples, use a container of ethylene glycol.

The sample should be sealed in its container so that the container will not break or leak and introduce extraneous contamination. If the sample is to be examined for a regulatory purpose, the sample container must be sealed so that it cannot be opened without breaking the seal.

2.523   Bulk solids or semisolids

Sampling of dry or semisolid foods should be done with sterile triers, spoons, or spatulas. Sterile tongue depressors may be substituted for spatulas. Aliquots from several areas of the food under examination should be taken to ensure a representative sample. Care should be taken to protect this type of sample from excess humidity.

2.524   Frozen bulk materials

Frozen bulk foods may be sampled with sterile corers, auger bits, and other sharp sampling instruments. A presterilized auger bit or hollow tube may be used to obtain enough material for analysis. Frozen samples should be kept frozen until arrival at the laboratory. Thawing and freezing of samples must be avoided.

A suitable procedure for obtaining test portions of frozen foods (particularly from larger samples) is to use an electric drill combined with a funnel.[1] The sterile auger bit is inserted through a sterile plastic funnel (which has been cut off so the hole is just slightly larger than the bit) held against the frozen sample (Figure 4). The frozen shavings are conveyed to the surface and collected in the funnel. The shavings then can be placed in a sterile sample container. For larger solid food samples—frozen or unfrozen, test portions

Figure 4—Funnel Collection Apparatus[1]

should be taken aseptically from several areas using sterile knives and forceps. These portions should be mixed as a composite to provide a sample representative of the food to be evaluated.

2.525   Line samples (in-process samples)

1. Liquids
Sterile metal tubes or dippers may be suitable sampling instruments at certain plant locations. A special line sampling technique involves the use of a disposable sterile hypodermic needle and syringe. The needle is inserted into a rubber closure of a stainless steel nipple. The nipple can be clamped on or permanently located at any desired spot.[11]
Sampling cocks on holding tanks and product pipelines may be used, but disinfection and material flow-through of the sampling cock must be assured before collecting the sample.

2. Solids
Sampling of solid line samples may be accomplished using the same equipment and procedures as would be used for bulk solid or semisolid products. Automatic sampling devices are available for powdered products and other solid products not requiring refrigeration. When automatic samplers are used, the manufacturer's directions must be strictly followed.

2.526   Special purpose samples (food poisoning outbreaks, consumer
           complaints)

In some instances samples are tested as part of a foodborne disease outbreak investigation or on the basis of a consumer complaint. Such situations may be the subject of legal proceedings, and laboratory personnel may be required to testify concerning the results of their examinations. If the record of the sample is incomplete, or if samples are received in a partially decomposed state or having been temperature abused, the laboratory results may be of little or no value.

It is important to use common sense in outbreak investigations, and to collect all perishable leftover foods served at the suspect meal(s) as soon as possible. If there are no leftover foods, try to get samples of items prepared in a similar manner subsequent to the suspected food. Collect ingredients or raw items used in the suspect food, if available. All of these foods should be held under suitable conditions until an analysis of the attack rate data and other facts can define more accurately the suspect food(s).[13] The original containers in which the foods were found also should be collected, identified, and submitted for examination. Other specimens as well as foods from outbreak investigations should be considered. Human specimens may include stools, vomitus, and serum. These specimens should be collected in sterile leakproof containers and should be properly identified as to the patient's name, type of specimen, and date of collection.

Aseptic techniques always should be used to obtain samples even if the foods have been mishandled grossly.

2.53   Storage and Shipment of Samples

When it is necessary to store samples prior to shipment, a storage area for frozen ($-20°C$) and for refrigerated (0° to 4.4°C) samples should be available. Waterproof labels should be used on sample containers to prevent loss of labels.

Whenever possible, samples should be submitted to the laboratory in original unopened containers.

Samples should be delivered to the laboratory as rapidly as possible. The condition, time, and date of arrival at the laboratory should be recorded. The samples should be packed to prevent breakage, spillage, or change in temperature. Since laboratory examination of food samples requires preparatory work, the laboratory should be given advance notice, if possible, of the number and types of samples being submitted. If the product is in a dry condition or is canned (flat or normal), it need not be refrigerated for shipment. Swollen containers should be refrigerated during shipment. The product label should indicate whether refrigeration is required. Samples not requiring refrigeration or freezing may be packed in a cardboard box using appropriate packing material to prevent breakage.

Refrigerated products must be transported in an insulated shipping container with sufficient refrigerant to maintain the samples at 0° to 4.4°C until arrival at the laboratory. Water frozen in plastic containers or cold packs serves well for 0° to 4.4°C shipping and should last 48 hr under most conditions. Do not use free ice as this may cause product contamination if the container breaks or leaks. Dry ice may be used for longer transit times if the sample is separated from the dry ice packing material to avoid freezing. Refrigerated products should not be frozen, as destruction of certain microorganisms will occur. Frozen samples can be kept frozen by ensuring that the samples are in contact with dry ice. Frozen samples collected in plastic bags, however, must not come in direct contact with dry ice as the plastic bag will become brittle and subject to rupture from the extreme temperature. Use paper or another suitable material to protect the sample. Such samples should be transported to the laboratory by the fastest possible means. Mark the shipment of samples as "Perishable," "Packed in Dry Ice," "Refrigerated Biologic Material," or "Fragile," as appropriate. Label the shipment according to Federal Postal Regulations and Department of Transportation Regulations, which are stated in Title 49, Code of Federal Regulations.

2.54 Preparation of Homogenates

Use aseptic technique. Prior to opening, swab the exterior area of the container with 70% ethanol to destroy microorganisms that might contaminate the sample.

Samples should be examined promptly. When initiation of analysis must be postponed, store frozen samples at $-20°C$ until they are to be examined. Refrigerate unfrozen perishable samples at 0° to 4.4°C for not more than 36 hr.

Store nonperishable, canned (normal, flat), or low-moisture foods at room temperature until ready for analysis. Frozen samples should be thawed at refrigeration temperatures ($\lesssim4.4°C$) for no longer than 18 hr in the original container in which received.[3] If the sample must be removed from the original container, it should be done aseptically. Alternatively, higher temperatures may be used for a short period of time, but the temperature must remain low to prevent destruction of microorganisms ($<40°C$ for ≤15 min). Frequent shaking of samples is necessary when samples are thawed by the alternate procedure. A thermostatically controlled water bath with agitator is recommended for the rapid thawing of samples.

Liquid or semiliquid samples in containers that have an airspace can be mixed by rapidly inverting the sample container 25 times. Sample containers that are ⅔ to ¾ full should be shaken 25 times in 7 sec over a 30 cm arc. The interval between mixing and removing the test portion should not exceed 3 min. To ensure a homogeneous sample when no airspace is present, aseptically open the container and pour the product from the filled container back and forth into a sterile container three times.

Dry samples should be aseptically stirred with a sterile spoon, spatula, or other utensil to ensure a homogeneous sample.

Test portions of nonviscous liquid products (i.e., viscosity not greater than milk) may be measured volumetrically using a sterile pipette (11 ml into 99 ml, or 10 ml into 90 ml, or 50 ml into 450 ml). If the pipette becomes contaminated before completing the transfer, replace it with a sterile pipette.

Do not insert the pipette more than 2.5 cm below the surface of the sample. The pipette should be emptied into the diluent by letting the column drain from the graduation mark to the rest point of the liquid in the tip of the pipette within 2 to 4 sec with the lower edge of the tip touching the inside of the neck of the dilution container. Promptly and gently blow out the last drop. Do not rinse the pipette in the dilution fluid.[3] For viscous liquid products, the test portion for the initial dilution should be aseptically weighed (11 ± 0.1 g) into a sterile 99 ml dilution blank (or 10 ± 0.1 g into 90 ml, or 50 ± 0.1 g into 450 ml). This provides a 1:10 dilution.

Test portions of solid or semisolid foods should be 50 ± 0.1 g. The 50 ± 0.1 g test portion should be weighed aseptically (using sterile forceps or spatulas) into a sterile tared blender cup;[12, 13] then add 450 ml of sterile diluent. A variety of diluents may be used depending upon the nature of the product. Those most commonly used are Butterfield's phosphate buffer and 0.1% peptone water. When analyzing for specific organisms, other diluents may be appropriate, e.g., 3% NaCl for *Vibrio parahaemolyticus*. (Refer to the chapters on specific groups of organisms for other diluents.) When analyzing fatty foods or lump-forming powder, wetting agents such as Tergitol Anionic-7 (1% weight/volume) may be included in the diluent to promote emulsification. Blend for 2 min at low speed (approximately 8000 rpm) to disperse the material.[12] The blending time may vary depending on the type of food.[13] Some blenders may operate at speeds lower than 8000 rpm.

It is preferable to use a higher speed for a few sec initially. No more than 15 min should elapse from the time the sample is blended until all dilutions are in appropriate media.

Optionally, if the entire food sample is less than 50 g, weigh to the nearest 0.1 g portion approximately one-half of the sample into a sterile tared blender cup. Add sufficient sterile diluent to make a 1:10 dilution (i.e., add an amount of diluent equal to nine times the weight of the test portion in the blender cup). The total volume in the blender cup must cover the blades completely. Blend as described above.

If the sample is not homogeneous, weight 50 g from a representative portion of the package into a sterile, tared blender cup or analyze each portion of food separately. Proceed as described above. Caution should be exercised in the blending step to prevent excessive heating. The amount of heating may vary with foods of different consistencies and may be expected to increase if blending times greater than 2 min are required. Chilled diluent (i.e., tempered in an ice-water bath) may be employed to decrease the chances of excessive heating.

Stomaching has been recommended as an alternative to blending in preparing the food sample homogenate.[19] In this procedure, the food sample with diluent is placed in a clean, preferably sterile plastic bag. The plastic bag is positioned within the stomacher and agitated for 30 to 60 sec. Because the sample is contained in a plastic bag, the developers recommend that samples with bones or other sharp or protruding objects not be prepared by stomaching. Thirty foods were evaluated using this procedure to determine the usefulness in a regulatory agency's laboratory. Results indicated that only certain food homogenates should be prepared using this procedure.[2]

In some solid food products, the microbial flora is restricted primarily to the surface area. More accurate enumeration of these microorganisms may be obtained by rinsing the sample with sterile diluent rather than by blending. This can be accomplished by placing the sample in a suitable sterile container (plastic bag or sealable bottle) and adding a volume of sterile diluent equal to the weight of the sample. The container is then shaken in a manner similar to that used for preparing an initial dilution of a liquid food sample. Each ml of "rinse" thus prepared represents 1 g of sample.

See Chapter 4 for preparation of further dilutions and plate count procedures. Use media recommended in the specific chapter for the organisms of interest.

2.6   REFERENCES

1. Adams, D. M. and Busta, F. F. 1970. Simple method for collection of samples from a frozen food. Appl. Microbiol. **19**: 878.
2. Andrews, W. H., Wilson, C. R., Poelma, P. L., Romero, A., Duran, A. P., Rude, R., McClure, F. D., and Gentile, D. E. 1978. Usefulness of the stomacher in a microbiological regulatory laboratory. Appl. Environ. Microbiol. **35**: 89.
3. APHA. 1985a. "Standard Methods for the Examination of Dairy Products," 15th ed. Am. Pub. Health Assn., Washington, D.C.
4. APHA. 1985b. "Standard Methods for the Examination of Seawater and Shellfish," 5th ed. Am. Pub. Health Assn., Washington, D.C.
5. Bartlett, R. P. and Weatherspoon, H. H. 1964. USDA variables control chart plan applied to fill weights. Food Technol. **18**: 40.
6. Bartlett, R. P. and Wegener, J. B. 1957. Sampling plans developed by U.S. Dept. Agriculture for inspection of processed fruits and vegetables. Food Technol. **11**: 526.
7. Bray, D. F., Lyon, D. A., and Burr, I. W. 1973. Three-class attributes plans in acceptance sampling. Technometrics. **85**: 575.
8. CFR. 1988. Title 7, Part 43. p. 320. Code of Fed. Reg. U.S. Govt. Print. Office, Washington, D.C.
9. Dodge, H. F. and Romig, H. G. 1959. "Sampling Inspection Tables," 2nd ed. John Wiley and Sons, Inc. New York.
10. Duncan, A. J. 1959. "Quality Control and Industrial Statistics," revised ed. Richard D. Irwin, Inc., Homewood, Ill.
11. Elliker, P. R., Sing, E. L., Christensen, L. J., and Sandine, W. E. 1964. Psychrophilic bacteria and keeping quality of pasteurized milk. J. Milk Food Technol. **27**: 69.
12. FDA. 1984. "Bacteriological Analytical Manual," 6th ed., Assn. Offic. Anal. Chem., Arlington, Va.
13. ICMSF. 1984. Sampling for microbiological analysis: principles and specific applications. In "Microorganisms in Foods 2," 2nd ed. Intern. Comm. on Microbiol. Spec for Foods. Univ. Toronto Press, Toronto, Can.
14. Kendall, M. G. and Buckland, W. R. 1960. "A Dictionary of Statistical Terms," 2nd ed. Hafner Publishing Co., New York.
15. Kramer, A. and Twigg, B. A. 1966. "Fundamentals of Quality Control for the Food Industry," 2nd ed., The AVI Publishing Company, Inc., Westport, Conn.
16. MIL-STD 414. 1957. "Military Standard, Sampling Procedures, and Tables for Inspection by Variables for Percent Defective." U.S. DoD. U.S. Govt. Print. Office. Washington, D.C.

17. MIL-STD 105D. 1963. "Military Standard, Sampling Procedures, and Tables for Inspection by Attributes." U.S. DoD. U.S. Govt. Print. Office. Washington, D.C.
18. MIL-STD 109B. 1969. "Military Standard Quality Assurance Terms and Definitions." U.S. DoD. U.S. Govt. Print. Office. Washington, D.C.
19. Sharpe, A. N. and Jackson, A. K. 1972. Stomaching: A new concept in bacteriological sample preparation. Appl. Microbiol. **24**: 175.
20. Thatcher, F. S. and Clark, D. S. eds. 1968. "Microorganisms in Foods. Their Significance and Methods of Enumeration," Univ. of Toronto Press, Toronto, Can.
21. USDA. 1964. "United States Standards for Sampling Plans for Inspection by Attributes— Single and Double Sampling Plans." U.S. Dept. of Agri., Agric. Market. Serv. Washington, D.C.
22. USDA. 1966. "Accuracy of Attribute Sampling: A Guide for Inspection Personnel." U.S. Dept. of Agri., Consumer and Market. Serv. Washington, D.C.
23. USDoD. 1954. "Administration of Sampling Procedures for Acceptance Inspection (H-105)." U.S. Govt. Print. Office, Washington, D.C.

Chapter 3

MICROBIOLOGICAL MONITORING OF THE FOOD PROCESSING ENVIRONMENT

William H. Sveum, Lloyd J. Moberg, Richard A. Rude, and Joseph F. Frank

3.1 INTRODUCTION

The survival and growth of microorganisms in a food processing environment may lead to contamination of the finished product that may, in turn, result in a reduction of microbiological safety and quality. Sources of environmental microbial contamination include raw materials, processing equipment, manufacturing activities, sanitation and maintenance practices, workers, waste, animal and insect pests, and microbial growth niches embedded in equipment and in structural components of the building.

Most food plants have locations that can promote the growth of pathogens and spoilage microorganisms that may be transferred directly onto product or carried into additional niches. The origins of these growth habitats are mainly unhygienic design, construction, and maintenance and repair activities that prevent easy cleaning and disinfection. The presence of water and nutrients (food product) is required to form a microbial growth niche, and the chemical composition of the food and conditions of water activity, pH, temperature, etc., will select the "normal" organisms that can grow there.

The pathogen *Listeria monocytogenes* has been isolated from the environments of dairy plants[11] and ready-to-eat meat plants.[4] In a potato processing plant, listerias were isolated from floors and drains, condensed and stagnant water, process equipment, conveyor belts, and wiping cloths.[16] In addition, *Listeria* spp. have been isolated from dehumidifiers, air handling systems, wet insulation, cracks and crevices of floors, milk case conveyor belts, and crevices of many types of processing equipment in dairy[24] and meat processing plants.[4] Examples have been found of *Salmonella* contamination of dry foods, such as milk-based products, eggs, soybean meal, chocolate, and peanut butter, which resulted from environmental contamination (Gabis, personal communication).

Microbial growth niches may be established when water is used to clean dry processing environments not designed for wet cleaning and not all points in the equipment are promptly and completely dried.

Microbial growth on equipment for processing perishable foods is governed mainly by the ecology of the food, the process, packaging room temperature, presence of food residue on the equipment, and efficacy of cleaning and disinfection. Recontamination of a biocidally treated food may increase the risk of foodborne illness if the food is not heated to destroy pathogens before consumption. Perishable foods that do not receive a biocidal treatment in the final container may be recontaminated by spoilage microorganisms before packaging.

Adherence to good manufacturing practices, such as hygienic design, construction, and maintenance of the factory; hygienic operation and maintenance of the processes and equipment; and application of appropriate (e.g., dry vs. wet) cleaning and disinfection procedures constitute the principal effective approach for control of microbial contamination and growth. In order to suppress the establishment of niches, the environment must be designed and fabricated to resist microbial growth or be made easily cleanable.

3.2   ENVIRONMENTAL SAMPLING STRATEGIES

Microbiological monitoring and verification programs for the environment may be designed and carried out to meet one or more of these objectives: (1) verification of the effectiveness of cleaning and disinfection cycles; (2) determination of the frequency required for cleaning and disinfection; (3) determination of the presence of foodborne pathogens in the environment; (4) discovery of environmental sources of spoilage organisms; (5) determination of the frequency required for special maintenance procedures, e.g., changing of air filters to reduce airborne mold contamination; (6) evaluation of hygienic design and fabrication of food processing equipment and facilities.

A sampling program may be established to verify control of environmental critical control points within the context of a Hazard Analysis Critical Control Points (HACCP) system,[35] after the microbiological hazards and risks have been determined and appropriate critical control points have been put into place. However, the time required to obtain microbiological results is usually too long to make sampling and testing an effective tool for day-to-day monitoring. To be effective, monitoring systems must provide information promptly, if a critical point is to be controlled. Cleaning and disinfecting procedures for processing, conveying, and packaging equipment may be critical control points for prevention of post-processing recontamination, and monitoring can be best accomplished through sensory inspection (the plant and equipment look, smell, and feel clean) and chemical (measurement of sanitizer concentration and pH) and physical (measurement of temperature) tests of the equipment and environment. Microbial criteria for acceptance of cleanliness of equipment and the environment can be developed using a data base derived from repeated, routine sampling and testing of specific sites.[35]

Four approaches may be used to verify microbiological acceptability of food processing equipment and environments: (1) sampling and testing equipment; (2) measuring microbial loads in food products after all processing, packaging, and handling are completed; (3) collecting and testing process flow sheet samples; (4) collecting and testing samples from the food processing environment.[35]

Environmental sampling and testing can be an early warning system to detect and eliminate niches of undesirable microorganisms before the risk of product contamination increases significantly. Collection of microbiological samples should not be limited to sites that are easily cleaned and sanitized, because the results from only these points may not reveal critical hazards and risks. If cleaning and sanitizing is effective, such easily disinfected sites should yield satisfactory results. The verification procedures should include collections of food or other organic residue samples from inaccessible or neglected niches.

To avoid errors of judgment and interpretation in quantitating microbial hazards and risks associated with the equipment and environment, and to help establish which microorganisms should be sought in a monitoring or verification program, it is important to understand the microbial ecology of the specific food and its process. The ecological pressures of extrinsic and intrinsic factors, including heat processing steps, ambient or storage temperatures, packaging atmospheres, acidity, and water activity, should determine which organisms are important in a particular environment. In plants that process dry foods not intended to be cooked before consumption, e.g., nonfat dry milk, chocolate, and peanut butter, *Salmonella* may be a significant hazard, especially when high-moisture-containing niches are present.

The environmental monitoring program should be designed to measure the occurrence and numbers of the normal spoilage flora and the pathogens that present the greatest risk to the product.

If a food is processed to be an ingredient for another product, it is prudent to monitor the ingredient's production environment for those organisms that will be a hazard to the ultimate finished product. To cite one example, dried milk products are used to make chocolate and confectionary products and are a potential source of salmonellae; therefore, the milk processing environment should be monitored for salmonellae in order to reduce risks further up the processing chain.

An environmental monitoring or verification program that includes tests for indicators, such as the aerobic plate count, family *Enterobacteriaceae*, and fungi, as well as tests for the plant's unique microflora and foodborne pathogens, will permit a more accurate assessment of microbial contamination of equipment and the plant than pathogen testing alone will. Negative pathogen test results may be misinterpreted as meaning that the site is microbiologically inert. Such pathogen test results merely indicate that the pathogen of interest was not detected in that site at the time of sampling; they do not provide useful information about the general microbiological risks associated with that site.[27]

3.3 SAMPLING OF SURFACES—EQUIPMENT AND PHYSICAL PLANT

Sampling sites on equipment should be selected to include all points that are liable to harbor microorganisms that may directly or indirectly contaminate the product. Sampling sites should not necessarily be limited to direct contact zones because microbial contamination can also be transferred indirectly into product from condensation, aerosols, lubricants, packaging materials, line workers' garments, and so on.

The distinction between what is and is not a product contact zone is not always easy to make, especially in open systems where the product is exposed to the processing environment and not continuously protected by enclosure in a pipeline or vessel.[35]

Direct product contact surfaces include pipeline interiors, conveyors, product storage vessels, fillers, utensils, work tables, mixers, grinders, and so forth. Nonproduct contact sites include structural components of machinery; exteriors of equipment, pipelines, and vessels; walls; motors; bearings; floors and floor drains of buildings; heating, ventilation, and air-conditioning equipment; forklifts; workers' garments and footwear; mechanics' tools; and cleaning tools. Microbiological sampling of gloves, aprons, clothing, and boots can be achieved using appropriate swab procedures.

Microorganisms can be transferred from nonproduct contact surfaces to direct product contact surfaces during production and between cleaning and sanitation cycles. Failure to clean and disinfect all sites that harbor microbial growth will increase the risks of contamination of finished product. Verification that sites are microbiologically acceptable is best accomplished by sampling and testing. Sensory evaluation is useful to detect environmental conditions that may lead to microbial growth and survival, but visually clean sites may still harbor microorganisms. Therefore verification of microbiological acceptability requires sampling and testing. Sampling and testing merely provide a rough estimate of the microbial populations on equipment, but accumulation of data from repeated tests will permit development of criteria by which to judge the hygienic condition of specific pieces of equipment.[21]

Preoperative sampling and testing of equipment is not instantly useful because of the time required after sampling to obtain microbiological results. Generally, production will begin before sites with unacceptable numbers or types of microorganisms are identified. However, preoperative sampling of equipment is a useful technique to verify historically the efficacy of the cleaning and sanitizing procedures in order to evaluate the performance of the cleaning and sanitizing crew or the cleanability of a particular piece of equipment.

3.4   RINSE SOLUTION METHOD FOR SAMPLING PROCESSING EQUIPMENT SYSTEMS[6]

3.41   Equipment, Supplies, and Solutions

1. Buffered rinse solution (Chapter 62)
2. MF endo broth
3. Neutralizing buffer
4. Nutrient broth (May be used as a substitute for buffered rinse solution since it effectively neutralizes chlorine and quaternary ammonium compound.)
5. Plate count agar
6. Sterile petri dishes
7. Sterile pipettes
8. Stock phosphate buffer solution
9. Violet red bile agar

3.42   Packaging Containers

Remove containers from the conveyor line or container cartons.

Add 20 ml of sterile buffered rinse solution to each container and aseptically recap the container. For containers larger than 1 gal, use 100 ml of rinse solution.

Shake each container vigorously 10 times through a 20-cm arc. Turn the container 90 degrees and repeat the horizontal shaking treatment. Turn the containers 90 degrees twice more and repeat the horizontal shaking.

Swirl the container vigorously 20 times in a small circle with the long axis in the vertical position, then invert and repeat.

Analyze the rinse solutions from the container samples by distributing a total of 10 ml of the rinse among three sterile petri dishes. In addition, seed two other petri dishes with 1-ml portions of the rinse.

Pour the plates with 15 to 18 ml of the desired medium, e.g., plate count agar or violet red bile agar, using the appropriate incubation conditions for each. Yeasts and molds, proteolytic bacteria, and other specific microorganisms may be determined by the use of appropriate differential media and incubation temperatures and times as described in their respective chapters.

When using 100 ml or greater portions of rinse solutions, follow membrane filtration procedures for analysis, particularly if low levels of contamination are expected. Membrane filtration may also be used for analysis of the 20-ml rinse samples.

After incubation, count the colonies. If 20 ml of rinse solution was used, then the total number of colonies on the three plates that received 10 ml of rinse should be multiplied by 2, or the total number of colonies on the two plates that received 1 ml each should be multiplied by 10 to obtain the number of colonies per container. When the plates that received 1 ml each show more than 250 colonies, report the counts as more than 5,000 per container.

Interpretation of results from container rinse samples should take into consideration both numbers and types of microorganisms. The types of microorganisms may be important in terms of their potential to cause spoilage. Normally, the number of microorganisms should be very low. In most cases, the number of organisms added to the product from the container will be much lower than that indigenous to the product. However, under certain circumstances, such as with aseptic packaging, the microbiological condition of containers is a critical control point. Application of microbiological guidelines and standards for the myriad of containers in use today is not common. Nevertheless, bacterial standards for multiuse and single-service containers for packaging pasteurized milk and milk products[60] and bottled water[10] have been published. These standards require that such containers have a residual bacteria count of one colony or less per ml of capacity or not over one colony per square cm of product contact surface. No coliform organisms may be present. For pasteurized dairy product containers, four containers from any given day are sampled, and three out of four samples must meet this standard. The standard for bottled drinking water containers states that at least once each 3 months, bacteriological swab or rinse samples are to be taken from at least four containers and closures selected just prior to filling and sealing.

3.43   Processing Equipment Systems (Tanks, Pipelines, Fillers, Etc.)[6]

Water for large-volume rinse-sampling of equipment should be heat sterilized or may be treated by chlorinating to a residual concentration of 25 mg per L, holding for 10 min, and then neutralizing by adding an excess of sterile 10% sodium thiosulfate solution. Tap water may be used after sterilizing by membrane filtration followed by the addition of sterile 10% weight per volume (wt/vol) sodium thiosulfate to inactivate residual disinfectant.

A sufficient volume of treated rinse water is added to the system at the upstream end of the assembly, then pumped or allowed to flow by gravity through the assembly. A control sample (about 1 L) of the treated rinse water is taken before using the water for rinsing.

Samples of rinse water are collected from the discharge end of the assembly from the first, middle, and final portions of the rinse water. Samples may also be collected at various points throughout the assembly.

The membrane filtration procedure (Chapter 4) may be used to analyze large volumes of rinse water. Analyses of rinse solutions from CIP processing assemblies and control samples require use of membrane filtration procedures. Average the number of colonies obtained from rinse samples taken at the beginning, middle, and end of drainage, and subtract the number of colonies (if any) obtained from the control samples. Calculate the ratio of sample volume to rinse volume, and multiply by the corrected yield to obtain an indication of numbers of organisms present in the entire system. The presence of specific types of organisms may be determined by employing appropriate differential media and incubation temperatures. Refer to the specific chapters covering these organisms.

3.5 SURFACE CONTACT METHODS

Meaningful microbiological examination of surfaces requires selection of an appropriate method. Swab procedures and replicate organism direct agar contact (RODAC) plates are the usual methods of choice for sampling of surfaces. Swab techniques should be used for areas on equipment such as cracks, corners, or crevices, i.e., areas of such dimensions that the swab will be more effective in recovering organisms from them. Swab procedures should also be used for sampling utensils, tableware, and kitchenware. Sponge swab procedures are useful for sampling large areas of food processing equipment and environmental surfaces. The RODAC procedure should be used only on flat, impervious surfaces that are relatively easy to clean and disinfect. Selection of the proper technique is essential to obtain meaningful results.

3.51   Swab Contact Method A[8, 57]

3.511   Equipment and supplies

Sterile nonabsorbent cotton swabs with the head firmly twisted to approximately 0.5 cm in diameter by 2 cm long on an applicator stick 12 to 15 cm long may be used. Swabs should be packaged in individual or multiple convenient protective containers with the swab heads away from the closure. Calcium alginate, dacron, and rayon swabs may also be used. Presterilized swabs may be purchased, or the swabs may be sterilized in the laboratory. A commercially available test system that includes a swab sampler and various agar recovery media (Millipore Corp., Bedford, Mass.) has been shown to be comparable to conventional swab sampling procedures.[19, 54]

Swabs made of calcium alginate fibers are soluble in aqueous solutions (rinse, culture media, etc.) containing 1% of sodium hexametaphosphate (or sodium glycerophosphate, or sodium citrate, or 1% of any mixture of these). All organisms captured on the swab will be liberated from the calcium alginate swab.

Presterilized calcium alginate swabs contained in various transport media are commercially available. The transport medium maintains microbial viability while inhibiting multiplication.

Vials, small, screw-capped, 7 to 10 cm long, are to be prepared to contain 5 ml or 4.5 ml of buffered rinse solution after autoclaving.

When sampling is to be carried out on surfaces previously subjected to chemical disinfection, appropriate neutralizers should be incorporated into the rinse solution. A commonly used neutralizer is 0.5% polysorbate (Tween 80) plus 0.07% soy lecithin. Dehydrated media for preparing neutralizing solutions are commercially available. Polysorbate 80 neutralizes some substituted phenolic disinfectants, and soy lecithin neutralizes quaternary ammonium compounds. The efficacy of any disinfectant neutralizer should be validated under actual use conditions.

3.512   Sampling procedure

To sample equipment surfaces, open the sterile swab container, grasp the end of a stick, being careful not to touch any portion that might be inserted into the vial, and remove the swab aseptically.

Open a vial of buffered rinse solution, moisten the swab head, and press out the excess solution against the interior wall of the vial with a rotating motion.

Hold the swab handle to make a 30°-angle contact with the surface. Rub the swab head slowly and thoroughly over approximately 50 cm² of surface three times, reversing direction between strokes. Move the swab on a path 2 cm wide by 25 cm long or other dimensions to cover an equivalent area. Return the swab head to the solution vial, rinse briefly in the solution, then press out the excess. Swab four more 50-cm² areas of the surface being sampled, as above, rinsing the swab in the solution after each swabbing, and removing the excess.

After the areas have been swabbed, position the swab head in the vial, and break or cut it with sterile scissors or other device,[9] leaving the swab head in the vial. Replace the screw cap, put the vial in a waterproof container packed in cracked ice or other suitable refrigerant, and deliver to the laboratory. Analyze the sample within 24 hr after collection.

When sampling utensils such as knives and ladles, moisten the swab with dilution fluid and then run the swab slowly and firmly three times over the significant surfaces of the utensil, reversing the direction each time. After the utensil has been swabbed, return the swab to the buffered rinse solution using the procedure described above.

When unmeasured surface areas such as pump impellers, gaskets, rings, valve seats, and filler nozzles have been swabbed, the results may be reported on the basis of the entire sampling site instead of a measured area.

3.513   Plating swab rinse solutions

At the laboratory, remove the vial from refrigerated storage. Shake vigorously, making 50 complete cycles of 15 cm in 10 sec, striking the palm of the other hand at the end of each cycle. Groups of vials may be shaken together to save time.

Plate 1- and 0.1-ml portions of rinse solution plus additional dilutions if deemed necessary. Pour plates with plate count agar or other appropriate media, depending on the organisms of interest. Incubate plates, count colonies, and then calculate the number of colonies recovered from 50 cm² (equivalent to 1 ml of rinse). When groups of microorganisms other than the aerobic plate count are sought, plate with appropriate selective/differential media and incubate as required.

3.514   Interpretation

As a guide, the U.S. Public Health Service recommends that adequately cleaned and sanitized food service equipment have not more than 100 colonies per utensil or surface area of equipment sampled.[59] Interpretation of results obtained from unmeasured surface areas such as utensils, gaskets, and pump impellers should be based on knowledge of historical data obtained when it was known that the surfaces had been carefully and thoroughly cleaned and sanitized. Generally, the levels of microorganisms should not exceed more than a few colonies per sampling site. *In many cases, the types of microorganisms may be more significant than the numbers alone.* For example, the presence of even very low numbers of *Saccharomyces bailii* and/or *Lactobacillus fructivorans* on salad dressing processing equipment may be highly significant with respect to potential spoilage of the finished product. Thus, with spoilage organisms for specific foods, the standards for evaluating sanitation may be much more stringent than when only the total numbers are considered. When swabbing is done for purposes other than evaluation of sanitation procedures, interpretation of results must be based on knowledge of the product, process, and equipment in order to determine the significance of data. In addition, the objectives of sampling may govern the interpretation of results.

3.52   Sponge Contact Method[53]

3.521   Equipment and supplies

Cellulose or polyurethane[41] sponges free of antimicrobial preservatives should be cut into approximately 5-cm × 5-cm pieces, placed in individual kraft paper bags, and autoclaved. Alternatively, commercially available, sterile cotton gauze surgical swabs (ca. 10.2 cm × 10.2 cm) may be used. Sterile plastic bags are suitable to contain the sponges after sampling.

Sterile buffered rinse solution, nutrient broth, or 0.1% peptone water may be used as the rinse solution. If the surface to be sampled contains fatty materials, 0.5 to 1.0% Tween-80 or other noninhibitory surfactant solution may be used. For sampling equipment that may contain residual disinfectants, the use of neutralizers in the buffered rinse solution is recommended (see Section 3.511). It is prudent to incorporate neutralizers in all fluids used to collect samples from equipment and the plant. Neutralizing buffers and transport media are commercially available.

Sterile crucible tongs, sterile gloves, or another means may be used to hold the sponge aseptically during sampling.

3.522   Sampling procedure

Moisten the sponge with approximately 10 ml of the chosen sampling fluid.

While holding the sponge aseptically with tongs or sterile gloves, swab the surface to be sampled by vigorously rubbing the sponge over the designated area. If the surface is flat, the rinse solution may be applied directly to the surface and then taken up into the sponge by the rubbing action. An area of several square meters may be effectively swabbed.

After sampling, place the sponge aseptically in a sterile plastic bag and transport it to the laboratory under refrigeration.

3.523   Plating and analysis

Because large areas may be sampled with the cellulose sponge, this technique is particularly useful for detecting pathogens (e.g., *Salmonella* or *Listeria*) or spoilage microorganisms in the food plant environment. For *Salmonella* or *Listeria* analyses, the sponge is introduced directly into an enrichment broth, incubated, and then tested by approved methods for *Salmonella* (Chapter 25), and *Listeria* (Chapter 38).

The sponge sample may be subjected to a variety of microbiological analyses in the same fashion as fabric-tipped swabs. For quantitative analyses, 50 to 100 ml of diluent is added to the bag containing the sponge. The sponge is then vigorously massaged with diluent for 1 min or more to release the microorganisms. Aliquots of the diluent are removed from the bag, further diluted if required, and plated into the desired media for the microorganism(s) in question.

Numbers of microorganisms per unit surface can be calculated on the basis of the area swabbed, the amount of diluent used, and the size of aliquot plated. For example, if 50 colonies are obtained from a 1-ml aliquot derived from a sponge in 100 ml of diluent that swabbed 1 m^2, the count per m^2 will be 5,000.

3.524   Interpretation

Interpretation of results from sponge samples taken from cleaned and sanitized equipment is essentially the same as for results obtained from fabric-tipped swabs.

Historically, the sponge technique has been useful in sampling the environment for *Salmonella*. Recent experience shows it also to be useful for *Listeria*.[28] This technique can be used to evaluate the efficacy of cleaning and sanitizing programs for the environment, particularly for foodborne pathogens. Obviously, results should always be negative after the application of appropriate cleaning and sanitizing procedures. Sponge swabs can be taken to identify areas that harbor pathogens, and the results can be used to develop a program to control the organisms. Evaluation of results from samples taken of cleaned and sanitized floors and other areas where relatively high residual microbial levels are expected depends on the history and experience relating to those particular sites in a given plant. As a rule of thumb, a 4- to 5-log cycle reduction in the residual microbial level should be obtained on most floor surfaces after cleaning and sanitizing.

3.53 RODAC Plate (Agar Contact) Method[5, 33, 61]

The RODAC plate method (agar contact) provides a simple, valuable agar contact technique for estimating the sanitary quality of surfaces. The method is recommended particularly when quantitative data are sought from flat, impervious surfaces. It is not intended to be used for crevices or irregular surfaces, although the RODAC plate may be useful even if its only purpose is to demonstrate the presence or absence of a specific microorganism. Ideally, the RODAC plate method should be used on previously cleaned and sanitized surfaces. Samples taken from heavily contaminated areas will result in overgrowth on the plates. If accurate colony counts are desired, the plates should have fewer than 200 colonies. A sufficient number of sites should be sampled to yield representative data. Randomization of site selection may permit additional comparisons and inferences.

3.531   Equipment and supplies

Disposable plastic RODAC plates may be purchased prefilled with test medium, or they may be filled in the laboratory. When prepared in the laboratory, the plates should be filled with 15.5 to 16.5 ml of the appropriate medium. The meniscus of the agar should rise above the rim of the plate to give a slightly convex surface. This is necessary so that the agar makes proper contact with the surface to be sampled.

Normally, plate count agar is used for aerobic plate counts. However, if qualitative data for specific microorganisms are desired, selective or differential media may be used, e.g., LBS agar for lactic acid bacteria, violet red bile agar for coliforms, or Baird-Parker agar for *Staphylococcus aureus*.

Dey-Engley neutralizing medium may be used in place of plate count agar. This medium incorporates a variety of ingredients capable of neutralizing any of the germicidal chemicals likely to be encountered on surfaces.[22] Following preparation, the plates should be incubated at 32°C for 18 to 24 hr as a sterility check. They should be used within 12 hr after preparation unless wrapped and refrigerated.

In lieu of RODAC plates, two commercially available systems, Petri Film (3M Medical-Surgical Division, St. Paul, Minn.)[46] or Con-Tact-It (Birko Chemical Corp., Denver, Colo.),[54] can be used as a medium contact method. Another method is to use mylar adhesive tape (Dynatech Laboratory, Inc., Alexandria, Va.), which is transferred to the surface of an appropriate agar plate after being pressed to the surface of the sample site.[14]

3.532   Sampling procedure

Remove the cover from the RODAC plate and carefully press the agar surface to the surface being sampled. Make certain that the entire agar meniscus contacts the surface, using a rolling uniform pressure on the back of the plate to effect contact.

3.533   Incubation and colony-counting procedure

Replace the cover and incubate in an inverted position under the appropriate time and temperature conditions for the microorganism(s) in question.

Colonies should be counted using a Bactronic or Quebec colony counter and recorded as the number of colonies per RODAC plate or number of colonies per cm^2.

3.6   MICROBIOLOGICAL AIR-SAMPLING STRATEGIES

With many nonperishable foods, the quality of the air in a food plant does not directly affect the microbiological safety or keeping quality. On the other hand, some perishable products, such as dairy products and baked goods, are particularly sensitive to airborne contaminants. Environmental air quality, especially in the packaging areas, is a critical control point for these foods. Aseptically packaged foods may require that the air supplies in packaging rooms have very low microbial loads such as that supplied by air filtered through laminar flow systems. Measurement of the microbial quality of air is useful for assessing the effectiveness of disinfection procedures for air-handling equipment.

Microorganisms occur in air as aerosols consisting of single unattached cells or cells in clumps. They can become airborne from environmental sources such as worker activity, sink and floor drains, water spraying, air-conditioning systems, dust generated from raw material, and specific food-processing systems. Microorganisms may adhere to a dust particle or may exist as a free-floating particle surrounded by a film of dried organic or inorganic material. Particulates in microbial aerosols may range in size from <1 μm to 50 μm. Particle size is the major factor influencing aerodynamic behavior. Vegetative bacteria may be present in lesser numbers in air than bacterial and mold spores. Many vegetative bacterial cells ordinarily will not survive for long in air unless the relative humidity and other factors are favorable or unless the organism is enclosed in some protective matrix. As a rule of thumb, microbial aerosols generated from the environment will be primarily bacterial spores, molds, and yeasts. When personnel are the source of microbial contamination, the primary types are vegetative bacteria, especially staphylococci, streptococci, micrococci, and other organisms associated with the human respiratory tract, hair, and skin.

Quantitative and qualitative guidelines should be established that relate numbers and types of microorganisms per volume of air to critical levels of product contamination. These guidelines must be established for each plant or process so that data collected in an air-sampling program can be used to make decisions relating possible sources, such as air flow patterns, filtration systems, or personnel density and activity, to product contamination. Significant increases above an established guideline may indicate a breakdown of standard contamination control barriers. National Aeronautics and Space Administration (NASA) air cleanliness standards[47] (Table 1) may be used as a reference point, but their suitability for application in a particular processing environment will have to be determined experimentally.

3.7   AIR-SAMPLING METHODS[1,17,20,30,34,45]

Viable airborne microorganisms can be determined quantitatively by a variety of methods, including sedimentation,[32, 42] impaction on solid surfaces,[29, 39, 43] filtration,[25] centrifugation,[48] electrostatic precipitation, impingement in liquids,[40] and thermal precipitation. Of these, sedimentation and impaction on solid surfaces are most frequently used. Aerosol-sampling methods have been reviewed recently by Kang and Frank.[36, 37, 38]

Many collecting and culturing media are available for biological aerosol sampling. The selection of nutrient medium will depend on the nutritional requirements of the organism(s) under study, the type of information desired from the study, the sampling method, and the sampling conditions. When initial collection is in a liquid medium, the microorganisms must remain viable without growth until aliquots are taken for culture. Some of the more common liquid media used are tryptose saline, buffered gelatin, peptone water, buffered gelatin enriched with brain-heart infusion, buffered saline, and buffered water. These media are used also as diluting fluids to obtain suspensions suitable for plating. Buffered saline and buffered water are used only for collecting spores and other resistant microbial forms.

Table 1—NASA Air Cleanliness Classes[a]

Test	Class, English (Metric) System		
	100 (3.5)	10,000 (350)	100,000 (3500)
Max. no. of .5 μm and larger particles per ft³ (per L)	100 (3.5)	10,000 (350)	100,000 (3500)
Max. no. of .5 μm and larger particles per ft³ (per L)	[b]	65 (2.3)	700 (25)
Max. no. of viable particles per ft³ (per L)	0.1 (0.0035)	0.5 (0.0176)	2.5 (0.0884)
Avg. no. of viable particles per ft² (per M²) per week	1,200 (12,900)	6,000 (64,600)	30,000 (323,000)

[a]NASA standards for clean rooms and work stations for the microbially controlled environment.[47]
[b]Statistically unreliable except when a large number of samplings is taken.

When collection is made directly on solid nutrient medium, a sufficient concentration of agar (1.5% to 2.0%) to produce a stable medium capable of withstanding the action from a rapidly flowing airstream should be used. Some of the more common solid nutrient media employed for general bacterial air sampling are blood agar, tryptose agar, trypticase soy agar, proteose extract agar, and nutrient agar. These media are also employed for culturing the liquid collecting media by surface-plating methods, the pour-plate method, and the membrane filter method.

Under certain sampling conditions, incorporation of selective agents into the medium to inhibit interfering contaminants is desirable. Some commonly used inhibitory agents are crystal violet, brilliant green, potassium tellurite, and cyclohexamide. Chemicals should not be used unless preliminary screening has demonstrated that they do inhibit the target organism.

Air samplers should be sanitized or sterilized prior to use. Sieve samplers and filtration-type samplers that have been wrapped in kraft paper, as well as liquid impingers with cotton plugs inserted in the intake and exhaust ports, can be conveniently autoclaved. In actual use, it will be found that swabbing the sampler with disinfectant prior to each sampling period is adequate and convenient. Gaseous sterilization techniques can be used to sterilize all of the samplers.

The following air sampling methods are commonly used in environmental microbiology, and six types of commercially available aerosol samplers are listed in Table 2. It is important that the manufacturer's directions be followed for each sampler and that the limitations of each be understood. The methods listed below for air sampling are by no means comprehensive. The laboratory worker should review Public Health Monograph 60 for a detailed discussion of air-sampling principles.[58]

3.71   Sedimentation Methods

Sedimentation methods are easy to use, inexpensive, and collect particles in their original state. The exposure agar plate and microscopic slide exposure methods rely on the force of gravity and air currents to deposit airborne particles on a nonselective or selective agar surface. Results are obtained as colony forming units (CFU) or particles per min. Particle size distribution may be obtained by direct microscopic observation. The 15th edition of "Standard Methods for the Examination of Dairy Products"[6] recommends 15-min exposure of standard size (90-mm diam) petri plates containing standard methods agar or a selective medium. After exposure, plates are incubated according to the appropriate procedure. In addition, microscope slides coated with agar can be exposed and particles counted using a microscope. This technique is only used for total particulate counts.

Sedimentation methods have several disadvantages, including their measure of airborne microorganisms quantitatively, i.e., the number of viable particles per cubic unit of air, and their weak correlation with counts obtained by other

Table 2—Commercial Sources of Aerosol Samplers

Impingers

All-Glass Impinger 30 and Pre-Impinger; Ace Glass, Inc., P.O. Box 688, Vineland, NJ 08360.

Midget Impinger with Personal Air Sampler; Supelco Inc., Supelco Park, Bellefonte, PA 16823-0048.

May 3-stage Glass Impinger; A.W. Dixon Co., 30 Anerly Station Road, London S.E.20, England.

Impactors (slit type)

Casella Single-slit and Four-slit Sampler; BGI Incorporated, Air Sampling Instruments, 58 Guinan Street, Waltham, MA 02154.

Mattson-Garvin Air Sampler; Mattson-Garvin Company, 130 Atlantic Drive, Maitland, FL 32751.

New Brunswick STA Air Sampler; New Brunswick Scientific Company, Inc., P.O. Box 986, 44 Talmadge Road, Edison, NJ 08817.

Impactors (sieve type)

Andersen 6-stage, and 2-stage Samplers; Andersen Samplers, Inc., 4215-C Wendell Drive, Atlanta, GA 30336.

Ross-Microban Sieve Air Sampler; Ross Industries, Midland, VA 22728.

Personal Particulate, Dust, Aerosol Collector; SKC Inc., 334 Valley View Road, Eighty Four, PA 15330.

Filtration samplers

Millipore Membrane Filterfield Monitor; Millipore Corporation, Bedford, MA 01730.

Gelman Membrane Filter Air Sampler; Gelman Sciences Inc., 600 S. Wagner Road, Ann Arbor, MI 48106.

MSF 37 Monitor; Micro Filtration Systems, 6800 Sierra Court, Dublin, CA 94568.

Satorius MD8 Air Sampler; Satorius Filters Inc., 30940 San Clemente St., Bldg. D, Hayward, CA 94544.

Centrifugal samplers

RCS Centrifugal Sampler; Folex-Biotest-Schluessner, Inc., 6 Daniel Road East, Fairfield, NJ 07006.

Electrostatic precipitation samplers

LVS Sampler; Sci-Med Environmental Systems Inc., 8050 Wallace Road, Eden Prairie, MN 55344.

General Electric Electrostatic Air Sampler; General Electric Co., Lamp Components & Technical Products Div., 21800 Tungsten Road, Cleveland, OH 44117.

quantitative methods.[50] They are useful only when fallout onto a particular surface is of interest, and they require a relatively long sampling time. Air movement will influence the deposition of the particles. Thus, these methods are heavily biased toward large particles, which would settle more rapidly than smaller particles.

Samples may be taken at (a) openings in equipment subject to potential contamination from organisms transported by air currents, (b) selected points for testing general room air, (c) areas of employee concentration, and (d) process air passages where air is incorporated into products. Because of air turbulence during operating hours, sampling by volumetric methods will be more effective and dependable than sedimentation samples.[6]

3.72   Impaction Methods

Impaction usually involves collecting microbial aerosols on an agar surface, but dry or coated surfaces may be used for special purposes such as particle size determination. An impactor consists of an air jet that is directed over the impaction plate so that the particles collide with and stick to the surface. Impaction methods give higher particle recovery than other methods.[26, 55, 56] Impaction results in low sampling stresses after collection, and sample manipulation is not required. Impactors are of two types: slit samplers (e.g., Casella slit sampler) and sieve samplers (e.g., Andersen multistage sieve sampler).

3.721   Slit sampler

Slit samplers are usually cylindrical and have a slit tube that produces a jet stream when the air is sampled by vacuum. Beneath the slit is a platform that accepts a culture plate and that is rotated by a clock mechanism. The rate of the plate rotation may be varied. These samplers require a vacuum source sufficient to draw a constant flow of air through the sampler—usually 28.3 L per min, although the air flow may be changed by altering the dimensions of the slit. Some of the common characteristics of slit samplers are relatively high collection efficiency, fabrication from metal, ruggedness, portability, simplicity of operation, and relatively high sampling volume. Some slit samplers cannot be sterilized by autoclaving. While gaseous sterilization is desirable, swabbing with disinfectant is often sufficient. Samplers employing agar are limited to use in temperatures above 0°C unless some method of heating is provided to avoid freezing the medium. Slit samplers do not discriminate for size of airborne particles, and can be used to detect bursts of contamination associated with specific activities at certain times.

3.722   Sieve samplers

Sieve samplers are operated by drawing air through a large number of small, evenly spaced holes drilled in a metal plate (sieve). The suspended particles impact on an agar surface located a few millimeters below the perforated plate. There are single stage (e.g., Ross Microban) and multistage (e.g., Andersen) sieve samplers. A multistage sieve sampler consists of a series of two, six, or eight stacked sieves and plates, each with successively smaller holes. This arrangement causes increased particle velocity as air flows through the apparatus. Large particles impact at the initial stage, and small particles follow the air flow until accelerated sufficiently to impact at a later stage. The commonly used Andersen six-stage sampler consists of sieves with holes ranging from 1.81 mm to 0.25 mm. The distance of the agar collecting surface from the sieve, which is critical, is controlled by utilizing a special petri dish containing 27 ml of medium. However, with newer designs, conventional prefilled disposable petri plates can be used. Air is drawn successively through each of the sieves at increasing velocities so that larger airborne particles (>7 mm) impact in the first stage and smaller particles, depending on their sizes and inertia, impact on the later stages. The optimum flow rate is 28.3 L per min. After sampling, the plates are removed and incubated. Some models have only two stages, which are designed to differentiate non-respirable particles (> 5μm) from respirable particles (< 5μm). Some units have a single stage, which does not differentiate particle size. The multistage sieve samplers are used not only to detect the number of viable particles per unit volume of air during a prescribed sampling time but also to yield a size profile of the particulates in the microbial aerosol. This information is usually much more important in health care settings than in food processing environments. As with the slit sampler, no diluting or plating procedures are required. Final assay results are expressed as particles per unit volume.

Associated with sieve samplers are the following limitations: multistage sieve samplers are cumbersome to handle and are expensive; the exact volume of agar must be poured into all plates so that the gap between the sieve and the agar surface meets the manufacturer's specifications; and the inside of the sampler and the outside of the pre-poured agar plates should be maintained sterile until sampling, as they can contribute to contamination.

3.73 Centrifugal Samplers

Centrifugal force can be used to propel aerosol particles onto a collection surface. When the aerosol is spun in a circular path at high velocity, the suspended particles impact on the collecting surface with a force proportional to the particle's velocity and mass. Centrifugal samplers do not generate high-velocity jet flow during sampling, so less stress is imposed on airborne microbes as compared to impingement and impaction methods. Centrifugal samplers are simple and easy to operate and may be less expensive than impactor types. Generally, centrifugal samplers can rapidly sample a high volume of air, resulting in a more representative sampling. Assay results are expressed as particles per unit volume of air, e.g., CFU per L.

Limitations of some centrifugal samplers are associated with failure to generate sufficient centrifugal force to propel small particles onto the collection surface. The recovery efficiency of these samplers depends on the particle size being sampled and the amount of centrifugal force generated.

The Reuter centrifugal air sampler (RCS sampler, Biotest Diagnostics Co.) is battery operated, portable, lightweight (2.5 lb), and convenient to use. A plastic strip containing a culture medium lines the impeller drum. Air from a distance of at least 40 cm is sucked into the sampler by an impeller. Air enters the impeller drum concentrically from a conical sampling area. The impeller is set in rotation and the aerosol is impacted by centrifugal force onto the agar surface. Air then leaves the sampling drum in a spiral outside the cone of entering air. After the sample has been taken, the agar strips are incubated and the colonies counted. The sampler has a self-timer for sampling from 30 sec to 88 min. The actual sampling rate is 280 L per min. However, the manufacturer has published an effective sampling rate or separation volume of 40 L per min for 4 μm particles, a value derived from an attempt to reconcile the actual number of viable particles collected from an air sample with measurements involving airflow direction, air velocity, and available collecting surface area. Clark and Lidwell indicated that the effective sampling volume of the RCS sampler will vary widely depending on the aerosol particle size.[13] Consequently, the results obtained by using this sampler must be interpreted with considerable caution. Macher and First measured the collection efficiency with increasing particle size.[44] Particles larger than 15 μm are almost 100% collected, those in the 4 to 6 μm range are collected at 55% to 75% efficiency, and particles smaller than 1 μm pass through the sampler without significant retention. Although the RCS sampler does not accurately estimate total viable particle concentration, Placencia and Oxborrow recommended this sampler for good manufacturing practices investigations.[48] These investigators found that the RCS sampler will collect more viable particles than a slit sampler, and it could detect the difference in the environmental quality of each medical device manufacturing facility tested. In addition, the RCS sampler effectively detects various types of microorganisms.[48]

3.74   Filtration Methods

Filters are widely used for aerosol sampling because of their low cost and simplicity of operation. The air filtration apparatus consists of cellulose fiber, sodium alginate, glass fiber, gelatin membrane filter (GMF) (pore size 3 μm) or synthetic membrane filters (pore size 0.45 μm or 0.22 μm) mounted in an appropriate holder and connected to a vacuum source through a flow rate controller (e.g., critical orifice). After a fiber filter is used, the whole filter or a section of it is agitated in a suitable liquid until the particles are uniformly dispersed.

Aliquots of the suspension are then assayed by appropriate microbiological techniques. Membrane filters can either be treated similarly to fiber filters or placed directly on an agar surface and incubated.

The gelatin membrane is water soluble so that it can easily be diluted for plating or be solubilized on top of a nutrient medium, resulting in microbial colonies that are easily counted. The hygroscopicity of the gelatin membranes causes difficulty in sampling because of swelling of the membrane when the relative humidity exceeds 90%.[51] The large number of pores in these membranes allows a large volume of air to be sampled during a short time (2.7 L of air per min per cm^2 per 500-mm water column).

The technique has been shown to be effective in certain types of environments,[26] although some investigators have cautioned against drying of vegetative bacteria on the membrane filter and the consequent difficulty of recovery. Fields and co-workers have shown that recovery rates between membrane filter techniques and slit samplers are comparable for naturally occurring airborne microorganisms that have already survived drying.[25, 26]

Filtration methods are good for enumerating mold or bacterial spores, but they may not be effective for counting vegetative cells because of the stress of dehydration produced during sampling.[23] The shorter sampling times used in gelatin membrane filtration may reduce this stress. Filtration methods do not discriminate particle size.

3.75 Impingement Methods

Impingement methods use a liquid to collect microorganisms from air. When air is dispersed through the liquid, particles in the air are trapped. Quantitation of airborne microorganisms is accomplished by plating the collection fluid or by using a membrane filtration plating technique when the expected microbial load is low.

Liquid impingers can be either low-velocity or high-velocity samplers. Low-velocity samplers utilize the air washing principle: airborne particles entering the sampler at low velocity through a large jet, fitted glass dish, or perforated tube are bubbled through and trapped in the liquid collecting medium. Small particles (<5 μm) are not efficiently trapped in low-velocity samplers, remaining in air bubbles and being carried out with discharged air.

High-velocity samplers draw air through a small jet, directing it against a liquid surface. While these samplers efficiently collect all particle sizes greater than 1 μm diameter, the high velocity tends to destroy some vegetative cells. High-velocity collection disperses clumps of cells, producing counts that may be higher than those of gentler collection methods.

A suitable collecting medium for liquid impingement samplers must preserve the viability of the microorganism while inhibiting its multiplication. The more common collecting media include buffered gelatin, tryptose saline, peptone water, and nutrient broth. Use of an antifoam agent in the collecting medium is suggested if excessive foaming occurs. Acceptable agents are Dow Corning Anti-Foam A and B, General Electric Anti-Foam 60, and olive oil.

With extended sampling, air impact has a cooling effect on the liquid. If the ambient temperature is 40°F, the collecting liquid is likely to freeze. Use of a low-freezing-point diluent such as glycerol or some means of temperature control is necessary in such a situation.

After sampling, an aliquot of the collecting liquid is plated and incubated in a growth medium to obtain a viable count. In quantitative studies, the total air flow must be measured to calculate microorganisms per volume of air. The volume of collecting fluid must also be measured to determine the number of cells collected. This method is not suited to low concentrations of airborne microorganisms.

The All Glass Impinger (AGI-30, Ace Glass, Inc.) sampler is a high-velocity impinger widely used for air sample collection. The jet is held 30 mm above the impinger base and consists of a short piece of capillary tube designed to reduce cell injury. The AGI-30 sampler operates by drawing aerosols through an inlet tube curved to simulate the nasal passage.[15] This makes it especially useful for studying the respiratory infection potential of airborne microorganisms. The usual sampling rate is 12.5 L per min. When it is used for recovering total airborne microorganisms from the environment, the curved inlet tube should be washed with a known amount of collecting fluid after sampling since larger particles (i.e., over 15 μm in diameter) are collected on the tube wall by inertial force.

The glass impinger is relatively inexpensive and simple to operate, but viability loss may result from the amount of shear force involved in the collection. The air stream approaches sonic velocity when particulates impinge on the collection fluid, resulting in almost complete collection of suspended particles; however, this condition tends to cause the destruction of vegetative cells[3] or may result in overestimation because of the dispersion of dust particles and the breaking up of clumps of bacteria.[50] Another constraint is that the glassware should be sterilized before each sampling. Also, the apparatus is easily broken.

3.76 Electrostatic Precipitation

Electrostatic precipitation samplers impart a uniform electrostatic charge to incoming airborne particles, which are then collected on an oppositely charged rotating disc. A known volume of air at a given rate is sampled. Electrostatic precipitators may employ a variety of solid collecting surfaces, such as glass or agar. A liquid collecting medium with added wetting agent, to aid in uniform distribution, can also be used to wash the collected particles centrifugally into a collecting vessel. Although these precipitators can sample at a relatively high rate (up to 1,000 L per min) with high collection efficiency and low resistance to air flow, they are complex and must be handled carefully. Furthermore, little is known about the effect on viability and clumping of electrostatically charged particles. During ionization of the air sample, oxides of nitrogen and ozone are produced that may be toxic to microorganisms. Although several electrostatic precipitators are manufactured specifically for sampling microbial aerosols, they are not widely used for this purpose.[52]

3.77 Comparison Studies on Aerosol Samplers

Comparison studies of air-sampling devices indicate that the choice of the correct sampler to use is seldom obvious. A multistage sieve sampler such as the Andersen may be most efficient at viable particle recovery, but it may not be suitable for routine sampling, and it requires a vacuum source. Filter samplers work well for quality control monitoring of molds[52] and bacterial spores, but bacterial recovery efficiency may be less, depending on the extent of dehydration that occurs during sampling.[12] In addition, a vacuum source is required. The RCS sampler is convenient to use, creates its own air flow, and recovers bacteria as well as molds. Even though the RCS sampler does not recover the smallest viable particles, it is useful for determining relative air quality on a routine basis.[18, 48, 49] Slit samplers may not be as convenient to use as the RCS sampler, especially if a vacuum source is required. However, slit samplers are more efficient at recovering small particles.

3.8   AEROSOL SAMPLING AND MEASUREMENT GUIDELINES

3.81   Standard Methods for Examining Dairy Products

The 15th edition of the "Standard Methods for the Examination of Dairy Products"[6] lists no Class A standard method for testing the microbiological quality of air and dairy environments, though there are methods designated as Class D and B. Favero et al. introduced air-sampling strategies and various air-sampling methods in the previous edition of this compendium.[23] They pointed out that the first and most important decision is whether air sampling at any level is required. If it is, then quantitative and qualitative guidelines should be established that relate numbers and types of microorganisms per volume of air to critical levels of product contamination.

3.82   NASA Air Cleanliness Standards

Favero et al. also suggested that the NASA air cleanliness standards be used as a reference point after experiments to determine suitability.[23] The "NASA Standards for Clean Rooms and Work Stations for the Microbially Controlled Environment"[47] defines three air cleanliness classes (Table 1). According to the standards, the collection methods must conform to "Standard Procedures for the Microbiological Examination of Space Hardware (NHB 5340.1 or revisions thereof)," which specifies use of a slit sampler.

3.83   Federal Standard 209C[31]

Federal standard 209C for "Clean Rooms and Work Station Requirements, Controlled Environment" establishes standard classes of air cleanliness for airborne particulate levels in clean rooms and clean zones. These classes are based only on particle enumeration and place more emphasis on small particles that are not necessarily viable.[31] Consequently, this standard is not useful for food plant applications.

3.84   Standard Reference Samplers

Brachman et al. recommended the AGI-30 sampler as a standard reference sampler because of historical use, economics, availability, and simple design.[7] On the other hand, the American Conference of Governmental Industrial Hygienists Committee on Bioaerosols used the Andersen multistage air sampler as the reference sampler for its committee activities and reports.[2] In the pharmaceutical industry, the slit sampler is the most widely used device for monitoring sterile manufacturing and quality control environments.[3]

3.9   REFERENCES

1. ACGIH. 1978. "Air sampling instruments for evaluation of atmospheric contaminants," 5th ed. Amer. Conf. of Govern. Indust. Hygienists, Cincinnati, OH.
2. ACGIH. 1986. Committee on Bioaerosols. Amer. Conf. of Govern. Indust. Hygienists committee activities and reports. Appl. Ind. Hyg. 1: R19.
3. Akers, M. J. 1985. Sterility testing. In "Parenteral Quality Control," p. 1. Marcel Dekker, New York, Basel.
4. AMI. 1988. Interim Guideline: Microbial Control During Production of Ready-to-eat Meat Products, 2 ed. Amer. Meat Institute, Washington, D.C. 20007.
5. Angelotti, R. J., Wilson, L., Litsky, W. and Walter, W. G. 1964. Comparative evaluation of the cotton swab and RODAC methods for the recovery of Bacillus subtilis spore contamination from stainless steel surfaces. Health Lab. Sci. 1: 289.
6. APHA. 1985. "Standard Methods for the Examination of Dairy Products," 15th ed., ed. G. H. Richardson. Am. Pub. Health Assoc., Washington, D.C.
7. Brachman, P. S., Ehrlich, S. R., Eichenwald, H. F., Gabelli, V. J., Kehtley, T. W., Maltman, J. R., Middlebrook, G., Morton, J. D., Silver, I. H. and Wolfe, E. K. 1964. Standard sampler for assay of airborne microorganisms. Science 144: 1295.
8. Buchbinder, L., Buck, T. C. Jr., Phelps, P. M., Stone, R. V. and Tiedman, W. D. 1947. Investigation of the swab rinse technic for examining eating and drinking utensils. Amer. J. Pub. Health 37: 373.
9. Buck, T. C. Jr. and Kaplan, E. 1944. A sterile cutting device for swab vial outfits utilizing wood applicators. J. Milk Technol. 7: 141.
10. CFR. 1983. Code of Fed. Regs., Title 21, Food and Drugs. Part 129, Processing and Bottling of Bottled Drinking Water. U.S. Govt. Print. Office, Washington, D.C.
11. Charlton, B. R., Kinde, H. and Jensen, L. H. 1990. Environmental survey for *Listeria* species in California milk processing plants. J. Food Prot. 53: 198.
12. Chatigny, M. A. 1978. Sampling airborne microorganisms. In "Air Sampling Instruments for Evaluation of Atmospheric Contaminants, 5th ed., p. E1. Amer. Conf. of Govern. Indust. Hygienists, Cincinnati, Ohio.
13. Clark, S. and Lidwell, O. M. 1981. The performance of the Biotest RCS centrifugal air sampler. J. Hosp. Infect. 2: 181.
14. Cordray, J. C. and Huffman, D. L. 1985. Comparison of three methods for estimating surface bacteria on pork carcasses. J. Food Prot. 48: 582.
15. Cox, C. S. 1987. The Aerobiological Pathway of Microorganisms. John Wiley, Chichester, U.K.
16. Cox, L. J., Kleiss, T., Cordler, J. L., Cordellana, C., Konkel, P., Pedrazzini, C., Beumer, R. and Slebenga, A. 1989. *Listeria* spp. in food processing, non-food, and domestic environments. Food Microbiol. 6: 49.
17. Curtis, S. E., Balsbaugh, R. K. and Drummond, J. G. 1978. Comparison of Andersen eight-stage and two-stage viable air samplers. Appl. Environ. Microbiol. 35: 208.
18. Delmore, R. P. and Thompson, W. N. 1981. A comparison of air-sampler efficiencies. Med. Device Diagn. Ind. 3: 45.
19. Devenish, J. A., Ciebin, B. W. and Brodsky, M. H. 1985. Evaluation of Millipore swab-membrane filter kits. J. Food Prot. 48: 870.
20. Dimmick, R. L. and Akers, A. B. 1969. "An Introduction to Experimental Aero-biology." Wiley Interscience, New York.
21. Elliott, R. P. 1980. The microbiology of sanitation. In "Principles of Food Processing Sanitation," ed. A. M. Katsuyama and J. P. Strachan, p. 39. The Food Processors Institute, Washington, D.C.

22. Engley, F. B. and Dey, B. P. 1970. A universal neutralizing medium for antimicrobial chemicals. Chem. Specialties Manuf. Assn. Proc. of the 56th Meeting, New York.
23. Favero, M. S., Gabis, D. A. and Vesley, D. 1984. Environmental monitoring procedures. In "Compendium of Methods for the Microbiological Examination of Foods," 2nd ed., ed., M. L. Speck, p. 47. Amer. Pub. Health Assn., Washington, D.C.
24. FDA and Milk Ind. Foundation/Intern. Ice Cream Assn. 1988. Recommended guidelines for controlling environmental contamination in dairy plants. Food and Drug Admin. Dairy Food Sanit. 8: 52.
25. Fields, N. D., Oxborrow, G. S., Herring, C. M. and Puleo, J. R. 1973. An evaluation of two microbiological air samplers. Abs. Ann. Meeting A.S.M. E11. p. 2 (Abstr.).
26. Fields, N. D., Oxborrow, G. S., Puleo, J. R. and Herring, C. M. 1974. Evaluation of membrane filter field monitors for microbiological air sampling. Appl. Microbiol. 27: 517.
27. Gabis, D. and Faust, R. E. 1988. Controlling microbial growth in food processing environments. Food Technol. 42: 81.
28. Gabis, D., Flowers, R. S., Evanson, D. and Faust, R. E. 1989. A survey of 18 dry dairy product processing plant environments for *Salmonella* and *Listeria*. J. Food Prot. 52: 122.
29. Greene, V. W., Vesley, D., Bond, R. G. and Michaelsen, G. S. 1962. Microbiological contamination of hospital air. I. Quantitative studies. Appl. Microbiol. 10: 561.
30. Gregory, P. H. 1973. Air sampling technique. In "The Microbiology of the Atmosphere," 2nd ed., p. 126. John Wiley, New York.
31. GSA. 1987. Federal standard 209C. "Clean Room and Work Station Requirements, Controlled Environment." Gen. Serv. Admin., Federal Supply Service, U.S. Govt. Print. Office: 1988-181-251/73222, Washington, D.C.
32. Hall, L. B. and Decker, H. M. 1960. IV. Procedures applicable to sampling of the environment for hospital use. Amer. J. Pub. Health 50: 491.
33. Hall, L. B. and Hatnett, M. J. 1964. Measurement of bacterial contamination of surfaces in hospitals. Pub. Health Rep. 79: 1021.
34. Heldman, D. R. and Hedrick, T. I. 1971. Airborne contamination control in food processing plants. Res. Bull. 33. Mich. State Univ. Agr. Expt. Sta., East Lansing, Mich.
35. ICMSF. 1988. "Microorganisms in Foods 4: Application of the Hazard Analysis Critical Control Point (HACCP) System to Ensure Microbiological Safety and Quality," p. 93. Intern. Comm. on Microbiolog. Spec. for Foods. Blackwell Scient. Publs., Palo Alto, Calif.
36. Kang, Y-J. and Frank, J. F. 1989. Biological aerosols: a review of airborne contamination and its measurement in dairy processing plants. J. Food Prot. 52: 512.
37. Kang, Y-J. and Frank, J. F. 1989. Evaluation of air samplers for recovery of biological aerosols in dairy processing plants. J. Food Prot. 52: 665.
38. Kang, Y-J. and Frank, J. F. 1989. Comparison of airborne microflora collected by the Andersen sieve sampler and the RCS sampler in a dairy processing plant. J. Food Prot. 52: 877.
39. Kraidman, G. 1975. The microbiology of airborne contamination and air sampling. Drug Cosmet. Ind. 116: 40.
40. Lembke, L. L., Kniseley, R. N., Van Nostrand, R. C. and Hale, M. D. 1981. Precision of the all-glass impinger and the Andersen microbial impactor for air sampling in solid waste handling facilities. Appl. Environ. Microbiol. 42: 222.
41. Llabres, C. M. and Rose, B. E. 1989. Antibacterial properties of retail sponges. J. Food Prot. 52: 49.
42. Loughhead, H. O. and Moffett, J. A. 1971. Air-sampling techniques for monitoring microbiological contamination. Bull. Parenter. Drug Assn. 25: 261.
43. Lundholm, M. 1982. Comparison of methods for quantitative determinations of airborne bacteria and evaluation of total viable counts. Appl. Environ. Microbiol. 44: 179.
44. Macher, J. M. and First, M. W. 1983. Reuter Centrifugal Air Sampler: Measurement of effective air flow rate and collection efficiency. Appl. Environ. Microbiol. 45: 1960.

45. May, K. R. 1967. Physical aspects of sampling airborne microbes. In "Airborne Microbes, 17th Symposium of the Society for General Microbiology," p. 60. Cambridge Univ. Press, London, U.K.

46. McGoldrick, K. F., Fox, T. H. and McAllister, J. S. 1986. Evaluation of a dry medium for detecting contamination on surfaces. Food Technol. 40: 77.

47. NASA. 1967. NASA standards for clean rooms and work stations for the microbially controlled environment. NHB 5340.2. Natl. Aeronautics and Space Admin. U.S. Govt. Print. Office, Washington, D.C.

48. Placencia, A. M. and Oxborrow, G. S. 1984. Technical Report. Use of the Reuter centrifugal air sampler in good manufacturing practices investigations. U.S. Food and Drug Admin., Sterility Res. Center, Minneapolis Center for Microbiol. Invest. Minneapolis, Minn.

49. Placencia, A. M., Peeler, J. T., Oxborrow, G. S. and Danielson, J. W. 1982. Comparison of bacterial recovery by Reuter centrifugal air sampler and slit-to-agar sampler. Appl. Environ. Microbiol. 44: 512.

50. Radmore, K. and Luck, H. 1984. Microbial contamination of dairy factory air. S. Afr. J. Dairy Technol. 16: 119.

51. Scheurrman, E. A. 1972. The gelatin membrane filter method for the determination of airborne bacteria. Pharm. Ind. 34: 756.

52. Silas, J. C., Harrison, M. A., Carpenter, J. A. and Floyd, J. B. 1986. Comparison of particulate air samplers for detection of airborne *Aspergillus flavus* spores. J. Food Prot. 49: 236.

53. Silliker, J. H. and Gabis, D. A. 1975. A cellulose sponge sampling technic for surfaces. J. Milk Food Technol. 38: 504.

54. Stinson, C. G. and Tiwari, N. P. 1978. Evaluation of quick bacterial count methods for assessment of food plant sanitation. J. Food Prot. 41: 269.

55. Sullivan, J. J. 1979. Air microbiology and dairy processing. Aust. J. Dairy Technol. 34: 133.

56. Sunga, Fe C. A., Heldman, D. R. and Hedrick, T. I. 1966. Characteristics of airborne microorganism populations in packaging areas of a dairy plant. Mich. State Univ. Agr. Expt. Sta. Quart. Bull. 49: 155.

57. Tiedman, W. D., chairman. 1948. Technic for the bacteriological examination of food utensils. Committee report. Amer. J. Pub. Health Yearbook 1947–48. Part 2, p. 68.

58. U.S. HEW. 1959. Sampling Microbiological Aerosols. Publ. Health Monogr. 60, Pub. Health Serv. Publ. No. 686. Dept. Health Ed., Welfare. U.S. Govt. Print. Office, Washington, D.C.

59. U.S. HEW. 1967. Procedure for the Bacteriological Examination of Food Utensils and/or Food Equipment Surfaces. Pub. Health Serv. Publ. No. 1631, Tech. Info. Bull. No. 1. Dept. Health, Ed., Welfare. Food and Drug Admin., Washington, D.C.

60. U.S. HHS, Pub. Health Serv., Food and Drug Admin. 1985. Grade A Pasteurized Milk Ordinance—Recommendations of the Pub. Health Serv. Transmittal No. 87-3 IMS-a-25. Pub. Health Serv. Publ. No. 229. Dept. Health, Human Serv. U.S. Govt. Print. Office, Washington, D.C.

61. Walter, W. G. and Potter, J. 1963. Bacteriological field studies on eating utensils and flat surfaces. J. Environ. Health 26: 187.

Chapter 4

COLONY COUNT METHODS

K. M. J. Swanson, F. F. Busta, E. H. Peterson, and
M. G. Johnson

4.1 INTRODUCTION

The introduction of agar media in the late 1800s allowed the development of methods to enumerate microorganisms by colony count. Such methods have been used extensively for determining approximate viable microbial populations in foods. These procedures are based on the assumption that each microbial cell in a sample will form a visible, separate colony when mixed with an agar or other solid medium and permitted to grow. Since microorganisms in foods often represent a number of populations with many different growth requirements, some organisms may not be capable of growth under conditions employed in colony count methods. Consequently, the counts are, at best, an estimate and should not be reported as absolute.

The aerobic plate count (APC) is considered the major, but not the only, application of the colony count method. A more descriptive evaluation of the microorganisms present in the food sample may be obtained by using several nonselective media and incubating under more than one set of conditions, i.e., temperature, atmosphere, etc. Also, specific microorganisms can be enumerated using selective media or conditions or both. Consequently, this chapter is titled "Colony Count Methods" to reflect the broader utilization of this procedure.

The optimum medium and conditions for determining the colony count may vary from one food to another. However, once a procedure for a given food is determined, it can be very useful for routine microbial analysis of the food. Since minor variations in procedures can alter the results obtained with the colony count,[11] the competency and accuracy of the analysts are very important.

Methods described in this chapter will focus on the aerobic colony count, although dilution techniques, counting guidelines, and other details may be applicable to enumeration of other organisms described in subsequent chapters.

4.2   GENERAL CONSIDERATIONS

4.21   Other Tests on Same Sample

If additional tests are to be performed on the sample, first aseptically remove the portions for microbiological analysis.

4.22   Preparation

Equipment and supplies should meet the specifications described in "Standard Methods for the Examinations of Dairy Products"[25] unless otherwise specified in this book. All material to be sterilized by hot air should be heated or treated so that materials at the coldest part of the load are heated to at least 170°C for not less than one hr. (Usually this requires exposure in the oven for about two hr at 170°C.) To ensure sterility, do not crowd the oven. When the oven is loaded to capacity with apparatus, preferably use longer periods or slightly higher temperatures as determined by the quality assurance program for your laboratory and equipment. Recording devices with thermocouples distributed in several locations in the load are desirable.

All media and materials to be sterilized in the autoclave should be sterilized as described by the author, by the manufacturer, or for the specific method employed.

4.23   Controls

Sterility tests of media, plates, and diluents should be conducted for each lot of media.

Quality assurance laboratory procedures should include periodic checks of old vs. new lots of media with known cell numbers to verify that recovery of cell numbers is optimum and about 100%.

4.3   EQUIPMENT, MATERIALS, AND REAGENTS

4.31   General

Oven
Autoclave
Balance
Manual colony counter (Quebec or equivalent)
Dilution bottles and tubes
    Bottles—approximately 150-ml capacity
    Tubes—between 20-ml and 50-ml capacity

Incubator

Mechanical shaker—optional

Petri plates—at least 85 mm inside diameter and 12 mm deep, glass or plastic

Petri plate containers—stainless steel or aluminum, with covers

Pipettes—glass or plastic

Pipette aids, assists, or automatic pipetters

Pipette containers—stainless or aluminum

Refrigerator—0 to 4.4°C

Storage space—clean, dust-free

Thermometers— −1.1° to 55°C, 1°C gradations

Tally

Work area—clean, level bench or table

Waterbath

Media—e.g., plate count agar or equivalent, Trypticase soy agar, APT agar, deMan, Rogosa, Sharpe (MRS) agar

Diluents—e.g., Butterfields phosphate buffer, 0.1% peptone water

Bent glass rods

4.32   Additional Equipment for Special Tests—Petrifilm℠ Plating Method

Petrifilm aerobic count plates, including plastic spreader (available from Medical-Surgical Division/3M, 3M Center, St. Paul, Minn 55144)

Membrane Filter Method

Membrane filters—hydrosol analysis (Type HA 0.45 μm pores) filters 47 mm diameter with grid (Millipore number HAWG 047AG or HAWG 047SO or equivalent)

Nutrient pads—cellulosic pads, 45 mm diameter

Filter holders—Pyrex glass, stainless steel, or plastic

Filtering flask (1 L)

Vacuum tubing—6 mm inside diameter; 75 cm length

Vacuum source—vacuum pump

Forceps—smooth-tipped

Petri plates—47 mm inside diameter

Volumetric measuring devices, pipettes—10 ml

Stereoscopic microscope and illuminator

Media—selective or nonselective broths

Hydrophobic Grid-Membrane Filter Method

Hydrophobic grid-membrane filter (HGMF)—ISO-GRID (QA Laboratories, Ltd., 135 The West Mall, Toronto, Canada M9C 1C2)

Filtration units—equipped with 5 μm mesh prefilter to remove food particles during filtration, one unit per sample (QA Laboratories, Ltd.)
Vacuum source—pump or water aspirator
Manifold or vacuum flask
Sterile distilled water
Peptone/Tween 80 (PT) diluent
Tryptic soy-fast green agar
Tris buffer 1.0 M
Diastase stock solution
Trypsin stock solution

Spiral Plate Count

Spiral plater (Spiral Systems Instruments, Inc., 4853 Cordell Avenue, Bethesda, Md. 20814)
Spiral colony counter (Spiral Systems Instruments, Inc.) with special grid for relating deposited sample volumes to specific portions of petri dishes
Vacuum trap for disposal of liquids and vacuum source of 50–60 cm Hg
Disposable micro beakers—5 ml
Electronic hand calculator
Commercial sodium hypochlorite solution—about 5% NaOCl (bleach)

Anaerobic Conditions

Anaerobic culture jar with gases or gaspack
Anaerobic roll tubes and/or bottles (Bellco Glass, Inc., Vineland, N.J.)
Anaerobic media—e.g., Andersen's pork pea agar, blood agar, thioglycollate agar
Anaerobic incubator—optional

4.4   PRECAUTIONS AND LIMITATIONS

Colony count methods provide an estimate of the number of viable microorganisms in food according to the medium employed and the time and temperature of incubation. Microbial cells often occur as clumps or groups in foods. Whereas shaking samples and dilutions may uniformly distribute the clumps of bacteria, this may not completely disrupt the clumps themselves. Mixing the initial dilution in a mechanical blender may provide better breakdown of the clumps. However, this does not ensure that the microorganisms will be distributed as single cells. Consequently, each colony that appears on the agar plates can arise from a clump of cells or from a single cell and should be referred to as a colony forming unit (CFU).

Precision is defined as the likelihood of obtaining similar results when repetitive counts are made by the same person or other analysts. Accuracy is the minimizing of the difference between the count obtained and a "true" count. When considering the entire procedure and the results obtained, both are important.

The accuracy of a colony count method may be limited by the failure of some microorganisms to form visible colonies on the agar medium. This failure can result from nutritional deficiencies of the medium, unfavorable oxygen tension, unfavorable incubation temperature, or cell injury. Incubation time and temperature also may be factors. The presence of inhibitory substances on glassware or in diluents or produced by competitive microorganisms in the agar may adversely affect some microbial cells and limit their ability to form colonies.

Another factor that affects apparent counts is the analyst's ability to see colonies distinctly. This depends on colony separation and morphology. Procedures that enhance colony growth and improve size, shape, contrast, and distribution should be used. The analyst's eyesight and fatigue may reduce the reliability of the count.

Other factors that may influence the accuracy of the colony count include improper sterilization and protection of sterilized diluents, media, and equipment; inaccurate measurement of sample and dilutions; improper distribution of the sample in or on the agar medium; unsatisfactory working areas that permit contamination; erratic mixing or shaking of sample or dilution; inaccurate determination of colonies because of the presence of artifacts such as food particles in low dilutions and scratches on plates; improper evaluation of spreaders or pinpoint colonies; and other errors in counting and in computing counts.

Although there are some inherent limitations in enumerating microorganisms by the colony count method, many of the errors can be minimized if the analyst follows directions carefully and exercises extreme care in making all measurements.[5] Consistently accurate and meaningful results can be obtained from the routine examination of a food only if the same procedures are used to analyze each sample of that food. This includes sampling procedures, sample preparation, preparation of dilutions, plating medium, incubation conditions, and counting procedures.

4.5   PROCEDURES

Historically, colony count methods are based on the pour plate technique. Procedures have been identified as "standard plate count," "aerobic plate count," "total plate count," "viable plate count," "mesophilic count," etc. The aerobic mesophilic colony count will be the example for which the pour plate technique is described. This method is adapted from the aerobic plate count method as specified in the AOAC "Official Methods of Analysis," 14th edition,[30] and the standard plate count method as specified in the APHA "Standard Methods for the Examination of Dairy Products, 15th edition."[25] With the exception of the conditions specified for the incubation of plates in the various chapters, the aerobic mesophilic colony count method is in substantive agreement with the methods described in the AOAC and APHA publications.

4.51 Pour Plate

1. Sample preparation. Refer to Chapter 2 for complete details on sample preparation. For viscous or solid foods an initial 1:10 dilution is usually prepared. High-fat foods such as butter may require use of warm (40°C) diluent to facilitate mixing.[25]

2. Labeling. Label all petri plates, and tubes and bottles where necessary, with the sample number, dilution, date, and any other desired information. The bench area should be cleaned and sanitized, and all possible sources of contamination removed or reduced to a minimal level.

3. Dilutions. Dilutions should be selected to yield plates containing 25 to 250 colonies.[28] If the count is expected to be in the range of 2500 to 250,000 per ml or g, prepare plates containing 1:100 and 1:1000 dilutions. Figure 1 shows a schematic drawing of examples for preparing dilutions using a single plate for each dilution. For increased accuracy, two or more plates per dilution should be employed.

   Different ranges for the appropriate number of colonies on plates may be applicable for certain procedures because of the crowding of colonies and other factors. Dilutions should be selected to insure that plates containing the appropriate number of colonies will be produced.

4. Melting and tempering media. Melt agar media in flowing steam or boiling water, avoiding prolonged exposure to high temperatures. Temper melted media promptly and maintain between 44°C and 46°C until used. Set a thermometer into water or medium in a separate container similar to that used for the test medium; this temperature control medium must have been exposed to the same heating and cooling as the test medium. Do not depend upon the sense of touch to indicate the proper temperature of the medium when pouring agar. Cold gelling agents may be substituted for agar if previously shown to be equivalent.

5. Plating. Test portions of nonviscous (i.e., viscosity not greater than milk) liquid products or homogenates may be measured volumetrically using a sterile pipette. Do not insert the pipette more than 2.5 cm below the surface of the sample. The pipette should be emptied into the diluent (phosphate buffered water or 0.1% peptone water) by letting the column drain from the graduation mark to the rest point of the liquid in the tip of the pipette within 2 to 4 sec. Promptly and gently blow out the last drop when pipetting the undiluted sample,[25] or when using a pipette designed to be blown out. Do not rinse the pipette in the dilution water.

   For viscous liquid products or food homogenates, the test portion for the initial dilution should be aseptically weighed (11 ± 0.1 g) into a sterile 99 ml dilution blank (or 10 ± 0.1 g into 90 ml or 50 ± 0.1 g

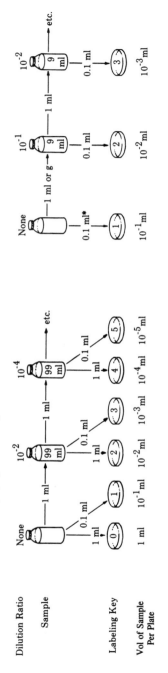

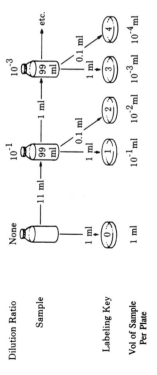

Figure 1—Preparation of Dilutions from a Nonviscous Liquid Food Sample.

into 450 ml). This provides a 1:10 dilution. Vigorously shake all dilutions 25 times in a 30-cm arc in 7 sec.[14] Optionally, a mechanical shaker may be used to shake the dilution blanks for 15 sec.[25]

If the pipette becomes contaminated before completing transfers, replace it with a sterile pipette. Use a separate sterile pipette for transfers from each dilution. Dilution blanks should be at room temperature (15°C to 25°C) when used. Caution: Do not prepare or dispense dilutions, or pour plates, in direct sunlight. When removing sterile pipettes from the container, do not drag tips over the exposed exteriors of the pipettes remaining in the case because exposed ends of such pipettes are subject to contamination. Do not wipe or drag the pipette across the lips and necks of dilution bottles. Draw test portions above the pipette graduation, then raise the pipette tip above the liquid level, and adjust to the mark by allowing the pipette tip to contact the inside of the container in such a manner that drainage is complete and excess liquid does not adhere when pipettes are removed from sample or dilution bottles.[5] Do not flame pipettes.

When measuring diluted samples of a food into petri plates, lift the cover of the petri plate just high enough to insert the pipette. Hold the pipette at about a 45-degree angle with the tip touching the inside bottom of the petri plate. Deposit the sample away from the center of the plate to aid in mixing. Allow 2 to 4 sec for the sample to drain from the 1 ml graduation mark to the rest point in the tip of the pipette (if a 1.0 or 1.1 ml pipette is used); then, holding the pipette in a vertical position, touch the tip once against a dry spot on the plate. Do not blow out. When 0.1 ml quantities are measured, hold the pipette as directed and let the diluted sample drain from one 0.1 ml graduation point down to the next 0.1 ml mark. Do not retouch the pipette to the plate when only 0.1 ml is delivered.[25] Replicate plates may be prepared for each dilution plated.

Roll tubes, screw-cap tubes, bottles, or other containers may be used as alternatives to petri plates if all appropriate standardizations are made and precautions are considered to assure equivalency.

Pipetter aids, assists, or automatic pipetters that are accurately calibrated and comply with pipette standards can be used in lieu of traditional pipetters. Apply all precautions identified for routine pipetting when using automatic pipetters or pipetting devices.

6. Pouring agar. After removing tempered agar medium from waterbath, blot bottle dry with clean towels to prevent water from contaminating the plates. Pour 12 to 15 ml of liquified medium at 44°C to 46°C into each plate by lifting the cover of the petri plate just high enough to pour the medium. Avoid spilling the medium on the outside of the container or on the inside of the plate lid when pouring. This may require holding the bottle in a near horizontal position or refraining from setting down the bottle between pouring steps. As each plate is

poured, thoroughly mix the medium with the test portions in the petri plate, taking care not to splash the mixture over the edge, by rotating the plate first in one direction and then in the opposite direction, by tilting and rotating the plate, or by using mechanical rotators. Allow agar to solidify (no longer than 10 min) on a level surface.

Select the number of samples to be plated in any one series so that not more than 20 min (and preferably 10 min) elapse between diluting the first sample and pouring the last plate in the series.[3, 15] Should a continuous plating operation be conducted by a team, plan the work so that the time between the initial measurement of a test portion into the diluent or directly into a dish and the pouring of the last plate for that sample is not more than 20 min. Stack pouring should be avoided unless the plates are distributed singly on a cooling surface immediately after mixing.[17]

Note: To obtain countable plates for foods having low colony counts, low dilutions must be used. For some foods this results in the presence of many food particles in the plate, which makes it difficult to distinguish the colonies easily for accurate counting. This problem often can be overcome by adding 1 ml of 0.5% (wt/vol) 2, 3, 5-triphenyltetrazolium chloride (TTC) per 100 ml of melted agar medium just prior to pouring the plates. Most bacteria form red colonies on an agar medium containing TTC. Counts should be made initially with and without TTC to determine if the TTC has any deleterious effect on the count. The TTC should be prepared as an aqueous solution and sterilized by passage through a sterilizing filter. To avoid decomposition, the solution must be protected from light and must not be exposed to excessive heat.

Sterility controls of medium, diluents, and equipment are recommended. Pour control plates for each lot of dilution blanks, medium, petri plates, and pipettes.

7. Incubation. After solidification, invert the plates to prevent spreaders, and promptly place them in the incubator.

Procedures for the mesophilic aerobic colony count, including conditions of plate incubation for various foods, differ depending on the nature of the food and the type of microbial flora to be enumerated.[2, 22, 16, 29] In the AOAC method,[30] plates are incubated at 35°C for 48 ± 3 hr; for dairy products,[25] plates are incubated at 32° ± 1°C for 48 ± 3 hr. Adaptations for specific commodities are presented in appropriate chapters. Agar within the plates should equilibrate to incubation temperature within 2 hr. Slower equilibration caused by excessive height of stacked plates or crowded incubators must be avoided.

Avoid excessive humidity in the incubator to reduce the tendency for spreader formation, but prevent excessive drying of the medium by controlling ventilation and air circulation. Agar in plates should not lose weight by more than 15% during 48 hr of incubation. Under some conditions, humidity control may become essential.

8. Counting colonies. Count colonies with the aid of magnification under uniform and properly controlled artificial illumination, using a tally. Routinely use a colony counter[24] equipped with a guide plate ruled in square centimeters. Examine plates in subdued light. Try to avoid mistaking particles of undissolved medium, sample, oil droplets, or precipitated matter in plates for pinpoint colonies. Examine doubtful objects carefully, using higher magnification, if necessary, to distinguish colonies from foreign matter. A stereo microscope or magnifying glass may be useful for this examination. Carelessness, impaired vision, or failure to recognize colonies can lead to erroneous results. It is generally suggested that laboratory workers who cannot duplicate their own counts on the same plate within 5%, and the counts of other analysts within 10%, should discover the cause(s) and correct such factors.[6] However, others indicate that these percentages should be 7.7% and 18.2%, respectively.[7] Schedules of the laboratory analyst should be arranged to prevent eye fatigue and the inaccuracies that inevitably result from this.

Count all colonies on selected plates containing 25 to 250 colonies promptly after the incubation period.[28] Refer to Item 9, Computing and reporting, for guidelines on selecting plates and computing counts. If impossible to count at once, the plates may be stored, after the required incubation, at approximately 0° to 4.4°C for under 24 hr.[7] This should not be a routine practice.

9. Computing and reporting.[25] To compute colony counts, multiply the total number of colonies (or the averge number if replicate plates of the same dilution are used) per plate by the reciprocal of the dilution used. Record the dilution used and the number of colonies counted or estimated on each plate. To avoid giving false ideas of precision and accuracy when computing colony counts, record only the first two left-hand digits. Raise the second digit to the next highest number only when the third digit from the left is 5, 6, 7, 8, or 9; use zeros for each successive digit to the right of the second digit (Table 1). Report counts (or estimates thereof) as CFU per g or ml, as applicable.

When counts on duplicate plates or consecutive dilutions are averaged, round off counts to two significant figures only at the time of conversion to the CFU per g. (Table 1, Sample No. 1117.)

The following guidelines should be used for selecting plates and calculating the CFU per g or ml, as applicable:

a. One plate with 25 to 250 colonies
Select a plate with 25 to 250 colonies unless excluded by spreaders or lab accidents (see Item h). Count all colonies, including those of pinpoint size, and record the dilution used and the total number of colonies counted. (Table 1, Sample Nos. 1001, 1004, 1011, and 1012.)

Table 1—Examples for Computing Colony Count per Gram or Milliliter

Sample no.	Colonies counted Dilution 1:100	Colonies counted Dilution 1:1000	Count ratio[a]	Colony count[b] (CFU/g or ml)	Rule
Common application, one plate from each of two dilutions					
1001	234[c]	23	—	23,000	*a*
1002	243	34	1.4	29,000	*c*
1003	140	32	2.3	14,000	*c*
1004	Spr[d]	31	—	31,000	*a, h*
1005	0	0	—	<100 Est	*f*
1006	TNTC	7150	—	>5,600,000 Est	*g*
1007	18	2	—	1800 Est	*e*
1008	Spr	Spr	—	Spr	*h*
1009	325	20	—	33,000 Est	*d, g*
1010	27	215	—	LA[e]	*h*
1011	305	42	—	42,000	*a*
1012	243	LA	—	24,000	*a, h*
1013	TNTC	840	—	840,000 Est	*g*
Procedure where two plates per dilution are poured					
1111	228 240	28 26	1.2	25,000	*b, c*
1112	175 208	16 17	—	19,000	*b*
1113	239 328	16 19	—	28,000	*b*
1114	275 280	24 35	—	30,000	*b*
1115	138 162	42 30	2.4	15,000	*b, c*
1116	228 240	28 23	1.1	24,000	*b, c*
1117	224 180	28 Spr	1.4	24,000	*b, c*
1118	287 263	23 19	—	28,000 Est	*d, g*
1119	18 16	2 0	—	1700 Est	*e*
1120	0 0	0 0	—	<100 Est	*f*

[a] Count ratio is the ratio of the greater to the lesser plate count, as applied to plates from consecutive dilutions having between 25 and 250 colonies.

[b] All counts should be made in accordance with instructions in Section 4.51, No. 8, as well as any other rules listed or given in the text.

[c] Underlined figures used to calculate count.

[d] Spreader and adjoining area of repressed growth covering more than one-half of the plate.

[e] LA = Laboratory accident.

b. Duplicate plates

Count plates with 25 to 250 colonies and average the counts to obtain the colony count. (Table 1, Sample No. 1112.) If only one plate of a duplicate pair yields 25 to 250 colonies, count both plates, unless excluded by spreaders, and average the counts. (Table 1, Sample Nos. 1113 and 1114.) When counting duplicate plates from consecutive decimal dilutions, compute the count per g for each dilution and proceed as in Item c. (Table 1, Sample Nos. 1111, 1115, 1116, and 1117.)

c. Consecutive dilutions with 25 to 250 colonies

If plates from two consecutive decimal dilutions yield 25 to 250 colonies each, compute the count per g for each dilution and report the arithmetic average as the CFU per g, unless the higher computed count is more than twice the lower one. In that case, report the lower computed count as the CFU per g. (Table 1, Sample Nos. 1002, 1003, 1111, 1115, 1116, and 1117.)

d. No plate with 25 to 250 colonies

If there is no plate with 25 to 250 colonies and one or more plates have more than 250 colonies, select plate(s) having nearest to 250 colonies and count as in Item g for crowded plates. Report count as the estimated (est.) CFU per g. (Table 1, Sample Nos. 1009 and 1118.)

e. All plates have fewer than 25 colonies

If plates from all dilutions yield fewer than 25 colonies, record the actual number of colonies on the lowest dilution (unless excluded by spreaders) and report count as est. CFU per g. (Table 1, Sample Nos. 1007 and 1119.)

f. Plates with no colonies

If plates from all dilutions have no colonies and inhibitory substances have not been detected, report the estimated count as less than ($<$) one times the corresponding lowest dilution. (Table 1, Sample Nos. 1005 and 1120.)

g. Crowded plates (more than 250 colonies)

If the number of colonies per plate exceeds 250, count colonies in portions of the plate that are representative of colony distribution to estimate the aerobic colony count. If there are fewer than 10 colonies per cm^2 count the colonies in 12 cm^2, selecting six consecutive squares horizontally across the plate and six consecutive squares at right angles, being careful not to count a square more than once. When there are more than 10 colonies per cm^2, count the colonies in four representative squares. In both instances, multiply the average number of colonies per cm^2 by the area of the plate to determine the estimated number of colonies per plate. Individual laboratories should determine the area of the plate and the proper factor for multiplication; however, the area of a standard 15 $\times$ 100 mm plastic petri plate is approximately 56 cm^2 and therefore, the appropriate factor is 56. For an example using an average count of 15 colonies per cm^2 on a 56-cm^2 plate, see Table 1, Sample No. 1013.

Do not report counts on crowded plates from the highest dilution as "too numerous to count" (TNTC). Where bacterial counts on crowded plates are greater than 100 colonies per cm^2, report as greater than (>) the plate area multiplied by 100, multiplied by the highest dilution plated. For example, for a 56-cm^2 plate, the count would be 5600 times the highest dilution plated. Report as est. CFU per g. (Table 1, Sample No. 1006.)

When all colonies on a plate are accurately counted and the number exceeds 250, report as est. CFU per g. (Table 1, Sample Nos. 1009 and 1118.)

h. Spreaders

There are three distinct types of spreaders. The first type is a chain of colonies, not too distinctly separated, that appears to be caused by disintegration of a bacterial clump when the inoculum is dispersed in or on the plating medium. If one or more chains appear to originate from separate sources, count each as one colony. Do not count each individual colony in such chain(s) as separate colonies.

The second type of spreading colony develops in a film of water between the agar and the bottom of the plate.[6] The third type forms in a film of water at the edge or over the surface of the agar. These two types develop mainly because of an accumulation of moisture at the point from which the spreader originates, and these spreaders may repress the growth of individual colonies. When dilution water is uniformly distributed throughout the medium, bacteria rarely develop into spreading colonies. Steps to eliminate spreaders of this type should be taken if 5% of a laboratory's plates have spreaders covering 25% of the plate.

If spreaders occur on the plate(s) selected, count colonies on representative portions thereof only when colonies are well distributed in spreader-free areas and the area covered by spreader(s), including the total repressed growth area if any, does not exceed 50% of the plate area. Calculate the estimated count by multiplying the average count per cm^2 by the area of the plate. Where the repressed growth area alone exceeds 25% of the total area, report as "spreaders" (spr) or "laboratory accident" (LA). (Table 1, Sample Nos. 1008 and 1010.) Inhibitory substances in a sample may be responsible for the lack of colony formation. The analyst may suspect the presence of inhibitory substances in the sample under examination when plates show no growth or show proportionately less growth in lower dilutions. Such developments cannot, however, always be interpreted as evidence of inhibition, and unless inhibition is demonstrated, should be reported as LA.

4.52 Surface or Spread Plate Method

Methods of plating designed to produce all surface colonies on agar plates have certain advantages over the pour plate method.[16] The use of translucent media is not essential with a surface or spread plate but is necessary with the pour plate to facilitate location of colonies. The colonial morphology of surface colonies is easily observed, improving the analyst's ability to distinguish between different types of colonies.[21] Organisms are not exposed to the heat of the melted agar medium, so higher counts may be observed in some situations.[4, 6, 23, 29] On the other hand, since relatively small volumes (0.1 to 0.5 ml) of the sample must be used, the method may lack precision for samples containing few microorganisms.

1. Prepare sample (see Chapter 2).
2. Pour approximately 15 ml of the agar into sterile petri plates. To facilitate uniform spreading, the surface of the solidified agar should be dried by holding the plates at 50°C for 1.5 to 2 hr.[16] Plates may also be dried at a lower temperature (25° to 35°C) for longer peiods (18 to 24 hr), or in a laminar flow hood, with covers ajar, for 0.5 to 1 hr.
3. Label all petri plates as in pour plate method.
4. Prepare tenfold serial dilutions following general procedures in pour plate method.
5. Measure 0.1 ml of diluted sample onto agar surface using a sterile pipette (graduated into 0.1 ml divisions). Larger volumes of sample may be appropriate under certain situations, but precautions should be taken that the liquid does not remain on the agar surface to promote spreaders. For example, 0.2 ml of a 1:10 dilution can be delivered to each of five plates to get the equivalent of 1 g of food for CFU determinations.
6. Spread the 0.1 ml sample on the surface of the agar medium with a sterile bent glass rod (hockey stick) as quickly and carefully as possible. Use a separate glass rod for each plate[16] or spread the plates for a given sample starting with the most dilute plate and proceed to the least dilute plate in series with aseptic technique throughout. Allow the plates to dry at least 15 min prior to inversion.
7. Incubate plates.
8. Compute and record colony counts as in pour plate method.

4.53   Petrifilm™ Plate Method[9]

A new approach to plating is the Petrifilm plate method (3M). The Petrifilm aerobic count plate consists of standard methods (SM) nutrients and a cold water-soluble gelling agent. The bottom film is coated with SM nutrients and the gelling agent; the top film is coated with the gelling agent and TTC indicator dye. The indicator stains the colonies red and facilitates counting.

1. Prepare sample (see Chapter 2).
2. Place the labeled Petrifilm aerobic count plate on a flat surface.
3. Prepare tenfold decimal dilutions following general procedures in pour plate method.
4. Lift the top film and inoculate 1 ml of sample onto the center of the bottom film with a pipette.

5. Release the top film down onto the inoculum. Place the plastic spreader (recessed side down) on the top film over the inoculum. Distribute the sample with a downward pressure on the center of the plastic spreader.
6. Remove spreader and leave the plate undisturbed for 1 min to permit the gel to solidify.
7. Incubate plates at 32° ± 1°C (or 35° ± 1°C) for 48 ± 3 hr with clear side up in stacks not exceeding 20 plates.
8. Colonies stain in various shades of red because of their interaction with the TTC indicator. Count colonies and report results as described for pour plating.

4.54   Calibrated Loop Methods

The plate loop method[27] and the oval tube (or bottle culture) method[12, 19] use volumetrically calibrated loops (0.01 or 0.001 ml) for transferring samples in lieu of decimal dilutions. These methods appear to be useful only for nonviscous liquids having greater than 2500 CFU/ml or for viscous and solid foods having greater than 25,000 CFU/ml. The oval tube method[12, 19] transfers a calibrated loopful of sample, or diluted sample, directly to agar in a tube. After solidification, tubes are incubated as desired. For the plate loop method,[27] a calibrated loop is fitted at the end of a Cornwall continuous pipetting device. After dipping the loop into the sample, the measured volume in the charged loop is rinsed into a petri plate by depressing the Cornwall plunger. See the literature for detailed procedures.[12, 19, 27]

4.55   Drop Plate Method[16]

This method of enumerating microorganisms is similar in principle to the spread plate method except that glass hockey sticks are not used to spread the diluted sample on the agar surface. The diluted samples are measured onto the surface of prepoured plates by adding a predetermined number of drops from a specially calibrated pipette.[16] The drops are allowed to spread and dry over an area, usually 1.5 to 3 cm in diameter, of the agar surface. The plates are incubated at the desired temperature and time. The colonies are counted and the computation of the colony count is based on the number of drops per plate, the number of drops per ml, and the dilution factor. The method is not recommended for food samples having counts of less than 3000 per g. For details, see the literature.[16]

4.56   Membrane Filter Method

For certain foods or food ingredients the ability to test relatively large samples will improve the accuracy of quantitative microbiological analyses. Large volumes of liquid foods or solutions of dry foods that can be dissolved and passed through a bacteriological membrane filter, pore size 0.45 μm, may be analyzed for microbial content by the membrane filter method. The method is especially useful for samples that contain low numbers of bacteria.

1. Aseptically assemble the membrane filter apparatus (following the manufacturer's directions) and connect to the vacuum system.
2. Prepare sample (Chapter 2).
3. Introduce appropriate amount of sample into funnel with a sterile pipette or graduated cylinder. For sample volumes of less than 10 ml, aseptically pour approximately 20 ml of sterile diluent in the funnel prior to adding the sample. If a graduated cylinder is used, rinse the cylinder with approximately 50 ml of sterile diluent and add the rinse to the funnel.
4. Apply vacuum to the filtering apparatus and allow the liquid to pass completely through the filter into the flask. Do not turn off vacuum.
5. Rinse inside of funnel with sterile diluent using an amount at least equal to the volume of liquid just filtered. After rinse has passed completely through the filter, turn off the vacuum.
6. Carefully and aseptically disassemble the part of the apparatus containing the filter. Using sterile smooth-tipped forceps, remove the filter and carefully place it, avoiding air bubbles, onto the surface of the chosen saturated nutrient pad or agar medium.
7. Incubate the culture.
8. Count the colonies. Colonies should be counted with the aid of low power magnification; an acceptable range of colonies per filter is 20 to 200.
9. Compute counts and report as membrane filter colony count per ml or per g based on the amount of sample filtered.

Examples of the filtration apparatus and supplies listed in this section are those manufactured by Millipore Corporation, Bedford, Mass. 01730. Comparable equipment manufactured by other companies may be used.

4.57   Hydrophobic Grid-Membrane Filter (HGMF) Method

The HGMF method represents another use of membrane filtration. This technique may be used to enumerate a variety of organisms including total mesophiles, coliforms, *E. coli* and others. Although colonies form, enumeration by this technique is based upon most probable number (MPN) determinations discussed in subsequent chapters.

The aerobic count HGMF method uses a tryptic soy agar medium (TSFA) containing the stain Fast Green FCF, which eliminates the need for post-incubation staining of the growth. Colonies develop varying degrees of intensity of green stain. At the recommended concentration the stain produces no evidence of toxicity.[26] The method has Official First Action status accorded by the Association of Official Analytical Chemists.[1]

Refer to HGMF General Procedures in Chapter 39 on Rapid Methods for general information on carrying out HGMF counts.

1. Prepare food sample, filtration apparatus, and TSFA plates as indicated. (Sample preparation may be significantly different from that used for other methods.[1])
2. Filter 1.0 ml or other volume of inoculum through the HGMF.
3. With forceps, aseptically transfer the HGMF from the filtration apparatus to the surface of a predried TSFA plate. Incubate raw milk, pasteurized milks and creams, and egg powders for 48 hr at 32°C. Incubate liquid egg for 72 hr at 32°C. Incubate all other foods for 48 hr at 35°C.
4. When counting manually, count those grid-cells containing green growth, calculate the HGMF score and the MPN per g of food (see Chapter 39, Rapid Methods). Food debris, e.g., tuna and corn, sometimes stains heavily. Do not mistake the resulting uniform green over the HGMF for positive grid-cells.
5. If optional automated counting is used, a red filter under the camera in this equipment will probably provide best contrast.

4.58 Spiral Plate Method

The spiral plate method[18, 25, 30] for determining the level of microorganisms has been collaboratively tested with milk and milk products,[20] foods,[8] and cosmetics[8] and was found equivalent to the standard pour plating procedure. A known volume of sample is dispensed onto a rotating agar plate in an Archimedes spiral. The amount of sample decreases as the spiral moves out toward the edge of the plate. A modified counting grid, which relates the area of the plate to sample volume, is used to count the colonies on an appropriate area of the plate. With this information the colony count for the sample can be computed. Detailed procedures are described elsewhere.[18]

1. Prepare sample (Chapter 2). If necessary, let diluted solid samples settle a few minutes before removing test portions since particles may clog tubing.
2. Check stylus tip angle daily by using the vacuum to hold a coverslip against the face of the stylus. The coverslip should be parallel with and 1 mm from the surface of the agar. Adjust, if necessary.
3. Decontaminate stylus tip and tubing by pulling household bleach and then sterile water through the system before pulling the liquid sample into the stylus.
4. Place a prepoured agar petri plate on turntable, and lower stylus. The sample is differentially dispersed as the stylus tip rides on the surface of the rotating agar plate. Remove the inoculated plate while returning the stylus to the starting position. Decontaminate the stylus and load for the inoculation of another sample.
5. Incubate plates.
6. Use the counting rule of 20 for determining counts. After incubation, center the spiral plate over the spiral plate counting grid. Choose any wedge and begin counting colonies from outer edge of first segment

toward center until 20 colonies have been counted. Complete by counting remaining colonies in segment where 20th colony occurs. Count a like area on the opposite side of the plate and divide the colonies counted from both sides by the sample volume deposited in those two areas. The volumes of sample associated with each portion of the counting grid are given in the operation manual that accompanies each spiral plater. An example of spirally inoculated plate (Figure 2) demonstrates the method for determining microbial count. Two segments of each wedge were counted on opposite sides of plate with 44 and 63 colonies, respectively. The sample volume contained in the darkened segments is .0018 ml. To estimate the number of microorganisms, divide count by volume contained in all segments counted. (See example under Figure 2.) When fewer than 20 colonies are counted on the total plate, report results as "less than 500 est. spiral plate count (SPLC) per ml." If colony count exceeds 75 in first segment of wedge, report results as "greater than 500,000 est. SPLC per ml."

The density pattern of colonies on each spiral plate is a check that the inoculation was correctly done. Any deviation from this pattern indicates some problem that should be corrected. If an irregular pattern of colonies is found on a sample plate, report the plate as not countable. If colonies overgrow or become confluent such that 20 recognizable colonies are not countable within a known area, report results as not countable or estimated, dependent on their position and your ability to estimate the colonies. Large spreaders may likewise cause a plate to be not countable or an estimated count, dependent on the size and coverage of the spreaders.

Round off the calculated concentration and report the concentration to two significant figures.

4.59   Enumeration Under Anaerobic or Other Atmospheres

Methods for determining total anaerobic colony counts are similar to those outlined in Chapter 19 for anaerobic sporeformers except that steps to eliminate vegetative cells are omitted. If the analyst is concerned with enumerating strict or sensitive anaerobes, the methodology developed at the Anaerobe Laboratory,[13] Virginia Polytechnic Institute and State University, may be of help. The Hungate method with prereduced, anaerobically sterilized media in tubes with butyl rubber stoppers is suggested for analysis of food samples for obligatory anaerobic bacteria.[10]

The specific procedure can follow individual steps of the pour plate or spread plate techniques (4.51, 4.52). The media may include plate count agar, Andersen's pork pea agar, blood agar, or similar complex media, and may be overlaid with thioglycollate agar. Incubation is under anaerobic conditions in an anaerobic culture jar, an anaerobic incubator, or some similar container that can contain an atmosphere free of oxygen and maintain an appropriate

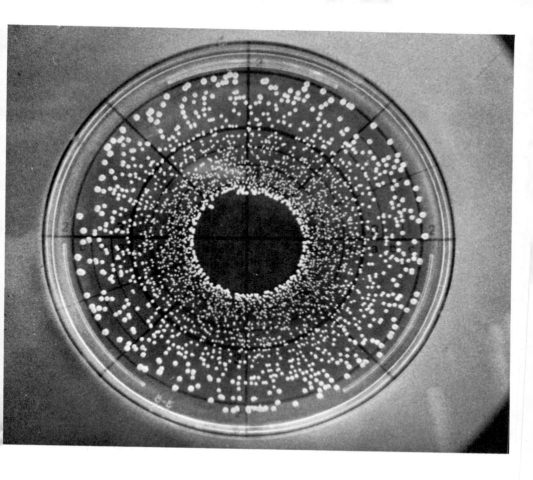

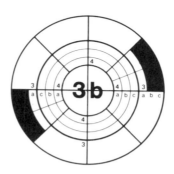

Figure 2—Spiral Plater Calculations for 10-cm Plate, Area (3b).

$$\frac{44\ +\ 63\ \text{colonies}}{0.0018\ \text{ml}} = 5.9\ \times\ 10^4\ \text{bacteria/ml}$$

temperature for incubation. Other gaseous atmospheres may be employed where required.

4.6 INTERPRETATION

The interpretion of microbial colony counts is beyond the scope of this book. Consult appropriate microbiological criteria regarding standards or limits.

When colony counts are used to compare the microbial quality of several samples of food, it is important that counts be made by the same procedure. Furthermore, extreme care must be exercised in following the procedures if the results are to be meaningful.

4.7 REFERENCES

1. AOAC. 1986. Aerobic plate count in foods hydrophobic grid-membrane filter method first action. J. Assn. Off. Anal. Chem. 69: 376.
2. Babel, F. J., Collins, E. B., Olson, J. C., Peters, I. I., Watrous, G. H., and Speck, M. L. 1955. The standard plate count of milk as affected by the temperature of incubation. J. Dairy Sci. 38: 499.
3. Berry, J. M., McNeill, D. A., and Witter, L. D. 1969. Effect of delays in pour plating on bacterial counts. J. Dairy Sci. 52: 1456.
4. Clark, D. S. 1967. Comparison of pour and surface plate methods for determination of bacterial counts. Can. J. Microbiol. 13: 1409.
5. Courtney, J. L. 1956. The relationship of average standard plate count ratios to employee proficiency in plating dairy products. J. Milk Food Technol. 19: 336.
6. Donnelly, C. B., Harris, E. K., Black, L. A., and Lewis, K. H. 1960. Statistical analysis of standard plate counts of milk samples split with state laboratories. J. Milk Food Technol. 23: 315.
7. Fowler, J. L., Clark, W. S. Jr., Foster, J. F., and Hopkins, A. 1978. Analyst variation in doing the standard plate count as described in *Standard Methods for the Examination of Dairy Products*. J. Food Prot. 41: 4.
8. Gilchrist, J. E., Donnelly, C. B., Peeler, J. T., and Campbell, J. E. 1977. Collaborative study comparing the spiral plate and aerobic plate count methods. J. Assn. Off. Anal. Chem. 60: 807.
9. Ginn, R. E., Packard, V. S., and Fox, T. L. 1986. Enumeration of total bacteria and coliforms in milk by dry rehydratable film methods: Collaborative study. J. Assn. Off. Anal. Chem. 69: 527.
10. Gray, W. M. and Johnson, M. G. 1976. Characteristics of bacteria isolated by the anaerobic roll-tube method from cheeses and ground beef. Appl. Environ. Microbiol. 31: 268.
11. Hartman, P. A. and Huntsberger, D. V. 1961. Influence of subtle differences in plating procedure on bacterial counts of prepared foods. Appl. Microbiol. 9: 32.
12. Heinemann, B. and Rohr, M. R. 1953. A bottle agar method for bacterial estimates. J. Milk Food Technol. 16: 133.
13. Holdeman, L. V. and Moore, W. E. C. 1977. "Anaerobe Laboratory Manual," 4th ed. VPI Anaerobe Laboratory, Va. Polytech. Inst. and State Univ., Blacksburg, Va.
14. Huhtanen, C. N., Brazis, A. R., Arledge, W.L., Cook, E. W., Donnelly, C. B., Ginn, R. E., Murphy, J. N., Randolph, H. E., Sing, E. L., and Thompson, D. I. 1970. Effect of dilution bottle mixing methods on plate counts of raw-milk bacteria. J. Milk Food Technol. 33: 269.

15. Huhtanen, C. N., Brazis, A. R., Arledge, W. L., Cook, E. W., Donnelly, C. B., Ginn, R. E., Jezeski, J. J., Pusch, D., Randolph, H. E., and Sing, E. L. 1972. Effects of time and holding dilutions on counts of bacteria from raw milk. J. Milk Food Technol. 35: 126.

16. ICMSF. 1978. "Microorganisms in Foods: Their Significance and Methods of Enumeration," 2nd ed. Intern. Comm. on Microb. Spec. Foods. Univ. Toronto Press, Toronto, Can.

17. Koburger, J. A. 1980. Stack-pouring of petri plates: A potential source of error. J. Food Prot. 43: 561.

18. Messer, J. W., Peeler, J. T., and Gilchrist, J. E. 1984. Aerobic plate count. In "Bacteriological Analytical Manual," 6th ed., p.4.01 U.S. Food and Drug Admin., Assn. of Off. Anal. Chem., Washington, D.C.

19. Myers, R. P. and Pence, J. A. 1941. A simplified procedure for the laboratory examination of raw milk supplies. J. Milk Technol. 4: 18.

20. Peeler, J. T., Gilchrist, J. E., Donnelly, C. B., and Campbell, J. E. 1977. A collaborative study of the spiral plate method for examining milk samples. J. Food Prot. 40: 462.

21. Punch, J. D. and Olson, J. C. Jr. 1964. Comparison between standard methods procedure and a surface plate method for estimating psychrophilic bacteria in milk. J. Milk Food Technol. 27: 43.

22. Randolph, H. E., Chakraborty, B. K., Hampton, O., and Bogar, D. L. 1973. Effect of plate incubation temperature on bacterial counts of grade A raw milk. J. Milk Food Technol. 36: 152.

23. Ray, B. and Speck, M. L. 1973. Discrepancies in the enumeration of *Escherichia coli*. Appl. Microbiol. 25: 494.

24. Richards, O. W. and Heijn, P. C. 1945. An improved darkfield Quebec colony counter. J. Milk Technol. 8: 253.

25. Richardson, G. H., ed. 1985. "Standard Methods for the Examination of Dairy Products," 15th ed. Am. Pub. Health Assn., Washington, D.C.

26. Sharpe, A. N. and Peterkin, P. I. 1988. "Membrane filter food microbiology." John Wiley & Sons, Inc., New York.

27. Thompson, D. I., Donnelly, C. B., and Black, L. A. 1960. A plate loop method for determining viable counts of raw milk. J. Milk Food Technol. 23: 167.

28. Tomasiewicz, D. M., Hotchkiss, D. K., Reinbold, G. W., Read, R. B. Jr., and Hartman, P. A. 1980. The most suitable number of colonies on plates for counting. J. Food Prot. 43: 282.

29. Vanderzant, C. and Matthys, A. W. 1965. Effect of temperature of the plating medium on the viable count of psychrophilic bacteria. J. Milk Food Technol. 28: 383.

30. Williams, S., ed. 1984. "Official Methods of Analysis," 14th ed. Assn. of Off. Anal. Chem., Washington, D.C.

Chapter 5

DIRECT MICROSCOPIC COUNT

D. F. Splittstoesser

5.1 INTRODUCTION

Various microscopic methods involving counting chambers, dried films on slides, and the use of membrane filters have been developed for the enumeration of microorganisms in foods. The advantages of such direct microscopic counts are that the results are rapid and that information can be obtained as to the nature of the organisms, e.g., morphological and gram stain types. Some of the disadvantages are that most procedures do not permit differentiation between live and dead cells, that food particulates may mask organisms, and that some techniques are useful only with high populations of microorganisms.

5.2 COUNTING CHAMBERS FOR BACTERIA

5.21 Principles

Numerous counting chambers are available, including the Helber,[5] the Hawksley,[8] the Petroff-Hausser, and the haemocytometer. All are similar: each consists of a grid of etched squares of a given area and is covered with a glass slip that is positioned a fixed distance from the etched surface. Counts are usually made at about $400 \times$ magnification, although some chambers such as the Hawksley permit the use of an oil immersion lens.

The volume of liquid within the etched square equals the area of the square times the depth of the film. The average cell count per square multiplied by the reciprocal of the volume in ml (the chamber factor) will equal the concentration of microorganisms in the diluent. Chamber factors commonly range from 4×10^6 to 2×10^7; thus the procedure is most applicable to foods that contain large microbial populations.

Major sources of error are the difficulty of accurate filling of chambers and the adsorption of cells to glassware surfaces.[8] When using a microscope in which the focus dial reads directly in micrometers, the exact chamber thickness can be measured by focusing on cells attached to the cover slip and to the bottom of the slide. Adsorption can be reduced by using high ionic diluents and plastic-tipped pipettes.

5.22   Equipment, Materials, Reagents

- Compound microscope with high dry and oil immersion objectives
- Counting chamber with cover glass
- Plastic tipped pipettes
- Platinum alloy loop
- 0.1% peptone water containing 0.1% lauryl sulfate

5.23   Procedure

1. Dilute the sample so that the concentration of bacteria will equal 5 to 15 cells per small square in the grid of the counting chamber.
2. Add the suspension to the counting chamber using a pipette or loop.
3. Allow the cells to settle for about 5 min.
4. Count a sufficient number of squares to give a total count of about 600 cells (for greatest accuracy).
5. Multiply the average count per small square × the chamber factor × the dilution to calculate the population per g or ml of food.

5.3   HOWARD MOLD COUNT[1]

5.31   Principles

The Howard mold count was established about 90 years ago[7] to insure that catsup would be made from tomatoes that were relatively free of visible rots. Although most widely applied to tomato products (catsup, juice, paste, sauce, canned tomatoes, soup, pizza sauce, etc.) the Howard mold count has also been used to assure the quality of other foods such as frozen berries, cranberry sauce, citrus and pineapple juices, fruit nectars and purees, and pureed infant food.

The mold count is a standardized procedure to determine the percentage of microscopic fields containing mold filaments whose combined lengths exceed one-sixth the diameter of the field. These are positive fields.

Defect action levels (DALs) based on mold counts of positive fields have been established by the U.S. Food and Drug Administration (FDA) for different products. These DALs are subject to modification with changes in processing methods. Homogenization and milling of tomato products, for example, have been recognized to result in an increase in the percentage of positive fields[10] and defect action levels have been adjusted accordingly.

5.32   Equipment, Materials, Reagents (Tomato Products)

- Compound microscope standardized to give a 1.382 mm diameter field at $100\times$ and equipped with $10\times$ and $20\times$ objective lenses
- Howard micrometer disc (optional) for placement within the ocular lens
- Howard mold counting slide with calibration circle or lines
- Cover glasses
- Refractometer, temperature controlled
- Scalpel and dissecting needle

5.33   Procedure[1]

The analyst must be familiar with the microscopic appearance of sound food tissue and with the morphology of the more common molds in order to distinguish mold filaments from other fibers.

1. Tomato juice and sauce are analyzed without modification; purees and pastes are diluted with water to give a refractive index at 20°C of 1.3448–1.3454; catsup is diluted 1:1 with a stabilizer solution (Section 5.42).
2. The Howard slide and cover slip must be clean. The resultant proper contact is confirmed by the appearance of the colored bands known as Newton's rings when the cover slip is placed on the slide.
3. With a scalpel, place a well-mixed sample on the center of a Howard slide and spread evenly.
4. Lower the cover glass rapidly so that the material is distributed evenly over the center of the slide but not drawn across the moat.
5. Count 25 representative fields from two or more mounts. Positive fields are those in which (a) a single filament exceeds one-sixth of the field diameter, (b) a filament plus the length of its branches exceeds one-sixth of the field diameter, or (c) an aggregate of not more than three filaments exceeds one-sixth of the field.
6. Calculate the results as percentage of positive fields.

"Official Methods of Analysis"[1] should be consulted for the methodology to be applied to specific products.

5.4   *GEOTRICHUM* COUNT[1]

5.41   Principles

Establishing the incidence of filaments of the mold *Geotrichum candidum* in canned and frozen fruit and vegetable products has been used as a method to assess the hygienic condition of food processing equipment. *Geotrichum* grows on the surfaces of processing equipment,[16] and thus has been termed machinery mold.[6] The detection method involves the counting of typical filaments using a rot fragment slide and a 30 to 45X stereoscopic microscope.[4] Low filament counts, under 1 per g, often do not correlate well with the aerobic plate counts obtained on frozen vegetables.[14]

5.42   Equipment, Materials, Reagents

- Stereoscopic microscope, 30 to 45X magnification, with transmitted (bottom) light
- Rot fragment slide with cover
- Sieves: 8″ No. 8, 5″ No. 16, 5″ No. 230
- Centrifuge (for fruit nectars and purees)
- Pipettes, 1 ml with tips cut off
- Stabilizer solution: 2.5 g Na carboxymethylcellulose and 10 ml formaldehyde in 500 ml water
- Crystal violet, 10 g in 100 ml 95% ethanol

5.43   Procedure

See "Official Methods of Analysis"[1] for details of methods as applied to specific foods.

1. Determine the weight of the food.
2. Drain the container contents on a No. 8 sieve positioned over a pan. (Thaw first if food is frozen.)
3. Remove the food. Wash the container with sieve with about 300 ml water.
4. Transfer the liquid portion and washings to a 5″ No. 16 sieve that rests on a 2 L beaker. Wash the residue with 50 ml water.
5. Transfer the liquid to a 5″ No. 230 sieve, tilted at 30° angle.
6. Flush residue (solids) to the sieve edge with a wash bottle, then transfer to a 50 ml graduated centrifuge tube with a spatula.
7. Dilute to 10 ml, stain with 1 drop crystal violet, then add an equal volume of stabilizer solution. The residue fraction will require concentration by centrifugation when the initial volume exceeds 10 ml.
8. After thorough mixing of the stained residue in the stabilizer solution, transfer duplicate 0.5 ml volumes to rot fragment count slides.
9. With a stereoscopic microscope at 30 to 45X, examine the entire surface of the slide using transmitted light.
10. Count typical *Geotrichum* filaments, those that contain three or more hyphal branches at 45° angles from the main filament.
11. *Geotrichum* count/500 g =
$$S(V/0.5)(500/W)$$
where S = average number of fragments/slide; V = volume of stabilized suspension; W = weight of food.

5.5   DRIED FILMS

5.51   Principles

Although a dried film process was originally developed and widely used for milk,[2, 3] similar methods have application for liquid and frozen eggs[1] as well as numerous other foods. The general principle is that a known quantity of food is spread over a prescribed area of a microscope slide. After drying and staining the film, the user determines the average number of organisms per microscope field. This count can be converted into numbers per g or ml of food based on the area of the microscope field. Advantages of the method are that it is rapid and that the slides may be retained for later reference; a disadvantage is that it is applicable only to foods containing large populations of microorganisms.

5.52   Equipment, Materials, Reagents

- Compound microscope
- Microscope slides with a circular area of 1 or 2 cm, delineated by an etched or painted ring
- Calibrated syringe, pipette, or platinum loop for the accurate transfer of 0.01 ml of sample
- Bent-point needle
- Ocular disc divided into quarters
- Stage micrometer slide
- Slide drying box or plate, 40 to 45°C
- Stains: Modified Levowitz-Weber (Chapter 62)
  North's aniline oil methylene blue (Chapter 62)

5.53   Procedure

Determine the microscopic factor (MF) by measuring the diameter of the oil immersion field to the third decimal place in millimeters using the stage micrometer. Convert to mm^2 by radius squared $\times$ pi.[1] Divide by 100 to convert the field area to cm^2. Divide the field area into 1 cm^2, the usual area of the slide, to determine the total number of fields. MF = this value $\times$ 100 (because 0.01 ml was spread over the slide surface).

1. Transfer 0.01 ml of well-mixed sample to a clean slide using a pipette, syringe, or loop. Spread uniformly over 1 cm^2 with the bent needle.
2. Dry at 40 to 45°C.
3. Fix in 95% ethanol. If necessary, first defat by immersing in xylene.
4. Treat with an appropriate stain: modified Levowitz-Weber for cow's milk;[2] North's aniline oil methylene blue for eggs.[1]
5. Count 10 to 100 fields under oil immersion using the ocular disc as a guide. Increase the number of fields when greater precision is desired.[15]

6. Calculate the direct microscopic count (DMC) by multiplying the average count per field × MF × the reciprocal of the sample dilution. Counts should be rounded off to two significant figures.

5.6   FLUORESCENCE MICROSCOPY

5.61   Principles

Procedures have been developed in which the microorganisms in beverages and diluted food homogenates are collected on membrane filters, stained with fluorescent dyes (acridine orange or aniline blue), and then counted with a microscope equipped with an epifluorescent illuminator. Direct epifluorescence filter technique (DEFT) is the name for one method. Although fluorescence microscopy has been used primarily for the enumeration of single cells and cell clumps, the transfer of membranes to agar media following filtration also permits the counting of microcolonies.[13] Advantages of the DEFT method are that it is rapid, may permit the differentiation of live from dead cells, and permits the detection of low numbers of organisms, especially in readily filterable beverages.

5.62   Equipment, Materials, and Reagents

- Compound microscope equipped with epifluorescent illuminator
- Stage micrometer
- Membranes, 25 mm diameter: Nucleopore polycarbonate, 0.6 μm;[11] Millipore AABG, 0.8 μm[9]
- Filter assemblies
- Stains: 0.025% acridine orange in 0.1 M Na-citrate, pH 6.6; 1% aniline blue in 15 M K_2HPO_4 adjusted to pH 8.9 with K_3PO_4

5.63   Procedures

The methods differ depending upon the food type, the microorganisms of interest, and whether cells or microcolonies are to be enumerated. Some food suspensions, for example, require prefiltration or digestion with hydrolytic enzymes before they will pass through the membrane filter. A number of publications provide specific details.[9, 11, 12]

Procedure for raw milk:[11]

1. Lyse somatic cells by adding to a 2 ml milk sample 0.5 ml rehydrated trypsin (Difco) and 2 ml 0.5% Triton X-100. Incubate 10 min at 50°C.
2. Add the sample to a previously warmed filter assembly (Millipore) holding a Nucleopore polycarbonate membrane, 25 mm diameter, 0.6 μm pore size. (Filtration of 5 ml of 50°C Triton X-100 is the method used to warm the assembly prior to addition of the sample.)
3. Turn on vacuum, 100 KPa.

4. Rinse the assembly with 5 ml 0.1% Triton X-100 at 50°C.
5. Overlay the membrane with 2 ml of stain for 2 min before applying vacuum. Stain: 0.025% acridine orange and 0.025% Tinopal AN in 0.1 M citrate-NaOH buffer, pH 6.6.
6. Rinse under vacuum with 2.5 ml 0.1 M pH 3 citrate-NaOH buffer, and 2.5 ml 95% ethanol.
7. Air dry and then mount on a slide for examination under a fluorescent microscope using nonfluorescent immersion oil.
8. Count orange fluorescent cell clumps and single cells that are present in a number of random fields. (A clump is defined as any cell or group of cells separated by a distance equal to or greater than twice the smallest distance of the two cells nearest each other.)
9. Calculate the count in the original sample by multiplying the average count per field by the number of fields in a 25 mm membrane and then dividing by the ml of sample that were filtered.

Rapid viable counts on selective media:[13]

1. Homogenize 10 g food in 90 ml 0.1% peptone water.
2. Prefilter through 5.0 μm nylon mesh in Swinnex filter holders (Millipore).
3. Filter through 0.4 μm Nucleopore polycarbonate membranes.
4. Transfer the membrane, top side up, to the desired agar media.
5. Incubate nonselective media and media for gram-negative bacteria 3 hr at 30°C; incubate media selective for gram-positive bacteria 6 hr at 30°C.
6. Stain as described above.
7. Count the microcolonies that contain more than four bright orange cells.
8. Calculate the viable count based on the microscope factor and volume of sample that was filtered, as described previously.

5.7 REFERENCES

1. AOAC. 1984. "Official Methods of Analysis," 14th ed. Assn. Offic. Anal. Chem. Arlington, Va.
2. APHA. 1985. "Standard Methods for the Examination of Dairy Products," 15th ed. Amer. Pub. Health Assoc., Washington, D.C.
3. Breed, R. S. 1911. The determination of bacteria in milk by direct microscopic examination. Zentralbl. Bakteriol. II. Abt. 30: 337.
4. Cichowicz, S. M. and Eisenberg, W. V. 1974. Collaborative study of the determination of Geotrichum mold in selected canned fruits and vegetables. J. Assn. Offic. Anal. Chem. 57: 957.
5. Collins, C. H. and Lyne, P. M. 1984. "Microbiological Methods," 5th ed. Butterworths, London, England.
6. Eisenberg, W. V. and Cichowicz, S. M. 1977. Machinery mold—Indicator organism in food. Food Technol. 31: 52.
7. Howard, B. J. 1911. Tomato catsup under the microscope with practical suggestions to insure a cleanly product. U.S. Dept. of Agric. Bureau of Chemistry. Circular No. 68.
8. Koch, A. L. 1981. Growth measurement. In "Manual of Methods for General Bacteriology." ed. P. Gerhardt, Amer. Soc. for Microbiol., Washington, D.C.

9. Koch, H. A., Bandler, R., and Gibson, R. R. 1986. Fluorescence microscopy procedure for quantitation of yeasts in beverages. Appl. Environ. Microbiol. 52: 599.
10. Olson, N. A. 1980. The effect of milling on mold counts in tomato products. Food Technol. 34: 50.
11. Pettepher, G. L., Mansell, R., McKinnon, C. H., and Cousins, C. M. 1980. Rapid membrane filtration-epifluorescent microscopy technique for direct enumeration of bacteria in raw milk. Appl. Environ. Microbiol. 39: 423.
12. Rodrigues, U. M. and Kroll, R. G. 1985. The direct epifluorescent filter technique (DEFT): Increased selectivity, sensitivity, and rapidity. J. Appl. Bacteriol. 59: 493.
13. Rodrigues, U. M. and Kroll, R. G. 1988. Rapid selective enumeration of bacteria in foods using a microcolony epifluorescence microscopy technique. J. Appl. Bacteriol. 64: 65.
14. Splittstoesser, D. F., Groll, M., Downing, D. L., and Kaminski, J. 1977. Viable counts versus the incidence of machinery mold (*Geotrichum*) on processed fruits and vegetables. J. Food Prot. 40: 402.
15. Wang, S. H. 1941. A direct smear method for counting microscopic particles in fluid suspension. J. Bacteriol. 42: 297.
16. Wildman, J. D. and Clark, P. B. 1947. Some examples of the occurrence of machinery slime in canning factories. J. Assn. Offic. Agr. Chem. 30: 582.

Chapter 6

THE MOST PROBABLE NUMBER TECHNIQUE

James T. Peeler, Gary A. Houghtby, and Alvin P. Rainosek

6.1 INTRODUCTION

The most probable number (MPN) dilution technique for estimating the number of microorganisms in a sample was originally based on Bayes's Theorem[28, 33] as derived by McCrady[23] and independently by Greenwood and Yule.[12] The MPN, however, can be derived under different assumptions,[10, 11] yielding a maximum likelihood estimate. Although the approaches are different, both statistical estimation procedures give the same result. Halvorson and Ziegler,[14–16] Ziegler and Halvorson,[35] and Halvorson and Moeglein[17] used maximum likelihood estimation in their classic papers on the MPN. A discussion of the early history of dilution techniques is given by Eisenhart and Wilson[10] and Oblinger and Koburger.[25] The latter article is useful for training students in understanding the test. More information on the source and history of the tables used to determine actual MPN estimates is given in Section 6.51.

An MPN is estimated from responses where results are reported as positive or negative in one or more decimal dilutions of the sample. For example, five tubes of medium for each of three dilutions are inoculated and incubated, and gas production is observed for each tube. Thus, unlike the aerobic plate count, the MPN does not provide a direct measure of the bacterial count. In addition, the MPN is more variable than the plate count[22, 35] and tends to yield a higher result.[22]

Although the MPN is not a precise measure, a specific value can be computed for a single dilution[15] or for multiple dilutions,[16] provided the tubes are not all positive or negative for all dilutions used, and assuming[7] that the organisms to be measured are distributed randomly throughout the liquid (or blended food) and that growth will occur when one or more organisms are present in a tube. Halvorson and Ziegler[16] have shown that for a multiple tube MPN, precision depends only on the number of tubes per dilution; for single dilution tests,[15] it depends on bacterial numbers and number of tubes. Swaroop[30] examined the design of MPN tests based on the coefficient of variation [(standard deviation/MPN) × 100], showing that the number of tubes must be greater than 500 for the coefficient of variation to be less than 10%. However, for practical reasons most microbiology methods books publish MPN tables for only three and five tubes per dilution.

As in any enumeration procedure, including direct plating, direct counting, or membrane filtration, the MPN presents certain problems to the analyst and is subject to several sources of error (see Section 6.31).[25] Although the MPN method is much maligned, it produces estimates of bacterial concentrations that are below the detectability of most current direct measurement microbiological methods.

6.2 GENERAL CONSIDERATIONS

6.21 Applications

The composition of many food products and ingredients makes it difficult to use standard plating procedures, particularly when the microbial concentration of the sample is less than 10 organisms or colony forming units (CFU) per gram. Work by Ziegler and Halvorson[35] showed that in these low-count situations, the MPN technique gave higher values for bacterial populations than did the plate count method; the direct microscopic count gave the same value as the plating and MPN method only when it was used on cultures that had not entered the death phase. McCarthy et al.[22] also demonstrated a considerable positive mathematical bias in MPN values relative to plate counts. The bias of 10 replicate MPN values was 1.29 times that of 10 replicate plate counts over 15 trials.

Depending upon the sampling and information sought, the sample may be mixed or macerated to bring about the homogeneous distribution of microorganisms. As this homogeneous sample is divided by serial dilution into subsamples and distributed, some of the aliquots eventually contain such small amounts of sample that they will contain none of the microorganisms. The MPN method is based on this subdividing of the sample, and therefore may be described as the "multiple tube dilution to extinction method." The most satisfactory information is obtained when all of the tubes with the larger sample portions show growth and the tubes with the smaller portions show no growth.

Applications of the MPN method are numerous. Use of the method is particularly important in the standard coliform procedure associated with water and wastewater testing and in testing foods in general. The method is also used in the isolation and enumeration of staphylococci, streptococci,

Vibrio parahaemolyticus, and salmonellae when quantitation rather than qualitative analysis is necessary.

The method also can be applied when a single sample dilution is used in several tubes, e.g., five 0.1-g samples for enumeration of very low numbers of organisms. A theoretical discussion of this particular application[15] showed that maximum accuracy was obtained with a bacterial population of 1.2 to 1.5 organisms per cubic centimeter. For this type of application, special tables are required.[4, 25]

Because the method uses liquid media, it offers the user considerable flexibility as to sample size. If allowances for appropriate dilutions of sample and ratios of medium to sample are made, sample volumes can be quite large. As indicated previously, precision is improved by increasing the number of tubes within each effective dilution, and at low population levels sensitivity is greater with the MPN than with the plate count.[6] Recovery of organisms may be enhanced by using a liquid technique because of the "bathing" aspect of nutrient availability. Later transfer of samples to a more inhibitory environment is possible after a period of resuscitation. If the appropriate media are available, numbers of a variety of different groups of microorganisms may be estimated. Finally, with the MPN process, materials can be prepared in advance and readily used under field conditions.

6.22   Treatment of Samples

Procurement, transport, and examination of samples should be done in accordance with procedures in Chapter 2 or chapters dealing with specific microorganisms or commodities.

6.3   PRECAUTIONS

6.31   Sources of Error

Variation among replicate aliquots is by far the most important source of error.[32] Extreme care is needed in preparing dilutions and transferring aliquots within the same dilutions. Other important factors that contribute to spurious results include difficulty in obtaining truly representative samples from a given lot and the possibility of an uneven distribution of microorganisms within the sample units selected.[29]

If the sample contains inhibitory substances, or the product itself is inhibitory (e.g., sodium chloride), growth in the tubes with high concentrations of sample may be inhibited. The possibility of injured cells that cannot grow out should not be overlooked. Nutrient in the sample may also interfere with the selectivity of the medium. For example, sucrose in a food will lead to a false indication of the presence of coliforms.

6.32   Special Considerations or Special Methods

The MPN method of enumeration is frequently used to determine the number of specific types of microorganisms in a sample. However, media for specific types of microorganisms must be selected carefully. For more specific information, refer to the section relating to specific microorganisms of interest or to specific commodities.

6.33   Sterility Controls on Media

One set of tubes from each batch of medium prepared should be used as an uninoculated control. If, for example, the five-tube MPN method is being used, a set of five tubes should be incubated as uninoculated controls to ensure that the medium was properly sterilized.

6.34   Other Controls

The temperature of incubators should be checked daily and must be controlled carefully. Outside control dials should be calibrated or checked monthly.

6.35   Underlying Assumptions

The analyst must take steps to ensure a random distribution of organisms being sought in the homogenate and subsequent dilutions. Sample homogenates are prepared by blending, stomaching, or exhaustive shaking as described elsewhere (Chapter 4). Consideration should be given to potentially injured organisms and appropriate resuscitation techniques (Chapter 7).

6.4   PROCEDURES

6.41   Preparation of Samples and Dilutions

The manipulation and dilution of samples for the MPN method is essentially identical to the procedure used in colony counts (Chapter 4). Usually, three, five, or even ten tubes are planted for each dilution used. The generally accepted time allowable from preparing sample homogenate to planting in the last tube is 20 min. Unless previous experience with a sample indicates the appropriate number of dilutions needed, a minimum of five dilutions should be prepared.

The ratio of sample volume to medium volume must be considered. Basically, one part of sample to ten parts of medium should be maintained. Thus, 0.1-g sample should be dispersed in 1 mL of medium. Similarly, 1-mL aliquots are dispersed into 10 mL of broth. When the microorganisms in liquids or diluted samples are enumerated, the strength of the medium can be adjusted so that the concentration of medium after the sample is added equals single strength medium. For example, in water analysis, one frequently uses double strength broth with an equal sample volume to avoid excessive nutrient and inhibitor dilution.

6.42   Incubation

1. General
   See appropriate chapter for each analysis.
   Depending on the objective, any temperature that is appropriate to the organisms may be used. An air incubator or a water bath may be used.
2. Special
   When using the MPN method, very specific and critically controlled incubation temperatures may be required. Refer to chapters on specific microorganisms to be enumerated or specific commodities to be evaluated.

6.43   Detection of Positive Tubes

1. Turbidity
   When using samples that do not cloud the medium in the tubes, the development of turbidity after incubation indicates growth (positive tubes). When the sample causes turbidity, other methods must be used to determine positive tubes.
2. Metabolic end products
   a. Detection of gas production
      Gases produced by developing microorganisms can be captured and observed with gas traps or inverted vials that are placed in the medium in the growth vessels before sterilization. A positive reaction is recorded when gas bubbles are observed in traps or inverted vials at the end of the incubation period. Other methods used to capture and observe the gases produced include overlay with vaspar or agar. Obviously these are useful only when the microorganisms to be enumerated are known to produce gases under the conditions of the test. In the event that tubed media have been stored for a period of time at low temperature, the analyst should note whether or not small bubbles have accumulated in the inverted fermentation tubes. This phenomenon is the result of air dissolving in the medium during cold storage and then being released as the medium warms. These bubbles can be removed by steaming or boiling the tubed media before use; however, one must consider the possibility of denaturation of sensitive medium components (depending on the medium being used).
   b. Detection of acid or base
      Acid or base production can be determined after incubation by measuring the pH or titratable acidity in each tube or by using a medium containing a pH-indicating dye. Detecting positive tubes by this method requires that the microorganisms being enumerated produce a pH change from a defined substrate.

   c. Detection with reduction methods

Electron acceptors such as resazurin, methylene blue, or 2,3,5-triphenyltetrazolium chloride, which change color upon reduction, can be incorporated into the medium. Reduction of any of these compounds by microbial action also indicates growth.

   d. Other

Specific media can be developed to assay for certain metabolic activities, e.g., NO_3 reduction, indole production, starch hydrolysis, and H_2S production, depending on the information desired.

6.44   Inconclusive Tests

1. Direct microscopic examination

Microscopic examination of stained smears of the tube contents is done by placing a loopful of the medium from the tube on a slide, drying, heat-fixing, and staining. The slide is examined for the specific microorganism, using oil immersion at $\sim 1000 \times$ magnification. This method is not applicable if the original sample contains high numbers of killed or inactivated microorganisms because there is no way to distinguish live from dead cells.

2. Subculturing

To confirm growth in questionable tubes, a loopful of the medium from the tube is transferred to a nonselective medium and incubated for an appropriate additional period of time. Growth in this medium confirms the presence of viable microorganisms in the tube. To confirm a questionable growth reaction (such as acid) in tubes of selective medium with heavy food turbidity, a loopful of medium from the incubated tube is transferred to a tube of the identical medium and similarly incubated. Growth reactions in such subcultures can be readily observed since they are free of the color and turbidity contributed by the sample being analyzed.

Although the process is time-consuming, another method to ascertain appropriate growth is available: aliquots may be streaked from MPN tubes onto either selective or nonselective media to ascertain appropriate growth.

6.5   INTERPRETATIONS

6.51   History and Source of MPN Tables and Confidence Limits

Confidence limits, which can be obtained from measures of the precision of MPN estimates, first appeared in the 11th edition of *Dairy Products Standard Methods*[5] and the 11th edition of *Water and Wastewater Standard Methods*[2] and were based on the paper by Woodward.[34] The confidence limits currently in the 16th edition of *Water and Wastewater Standard Methods*[4] and the 15th edition of Dairy Products Standard Methods[6] are based on papers by deMan.[8, 9] These limits are computed by assuming that the ln (MPN) is normally distributed. The estimate of precision is that of Haldane[13] as modified by Parnow.[26] Parnow[27] has written his calculation as a computer program that could be used on a mainframe or microcomputer. More recently, Hurley and Roscoe[19] have given Basic Language Program Listings and a concise explanation of the calculations. The difficulty in computations prevents most workers from computing their own estimates. A program has been published for a Hewlett-Packard Model W41C hand-held calculator;[20] however, the program does not compute confidence limits. An exact mathematical solution to confidence limits is given by Matuszewski et al.,[21] who provide formulae to obtain limits as end-points of confidence intervals based on the sum of positive tubes observed in the dilution procedure (i.e., an interval for each of the sums 0, 1, 2 . . . in r dilutions of n tubes per dilution).

End-points of confidence intervals represent the limits used to indicate the precision of the MPN estimates. If we are considering a 95% confidence interval, then the true, but unknown, number of organisms in the sampled population lies within the limits 95% of the time. This assumes repeated measurement of the sample source. All tabulated estimates of MPN[1-6, 9, 34] values are the same except for the number of significant digits reported. However, the confidence limits differ.

The Bacteriological Analytical Manual (BAM)[32] has two tables of confidence limits, one taken from the Water and Wastewater Standard Methods[3] and the other from deMan.[8, 9] Tables in this book follow the Dairy Products Standard Methods.[6] The tables[2-6, 8, 9, 34] present the combinations of positive tubes per dilution that occur most frequently (95% and 99% of the time). Halvorson and Ziegler[16] presented the formulae for computing the probability of a combination (i.e., 3,2,0) for given dilutions and organism concentrations. Woodward[34] and others[8, 9, 16, 25] have discussed the need to reduce the size of MPN tables to include only the most likely test results.

The Nordic Committee on Food Analysis[24] has different estimates of the MPN and confidence limits from the sources cited above. An estimate of the MPN is obtained by the Thomas formulae.[31] The $\log_{10}$ MPN is assumed to be normally distributed, and Cochran's[7] estimate of precision is used to compute the limits. These results represent approximations for both the MPN and corresponding confidence limits.

6.52   Use of MPN Tables

Tables 1 and 2 provide combinations of positive results that occur frequently enough to be statistically significant; combinations that occur less than 1% of the time have been omitted. When compared to other references,[3, 32] reported confidence limits are slightly different, a situation that can be attributed to assumptions made and computational methods used to derive the values. If further insight into these tabular differences or the methods used to compute the values is needed, the original work should be reviewed.[8, 9] If the appropriate combination of positive results is not found within the newer "abbreviated" tables given by deMan,[9] the analysis should be repeated, or

Table 1—Selected MPN Estimates and 95% Confidence Limits⁹ of Estimates for Fermentation Tube Tests When Three Tubes with 0.1-g, 0.01-g, and 0.001-g Volumes Are Used[a]

No. of positive tubes/3 tubes			MPN/g[b]	95% confidence limits	
0.1 g	0.01 g	0.001 g		Lower	Upper
0	0	0	<3	–	–
0	1	0	3+	<1	17
1	0	0	4	<1	21
1	0	1	7+	2	27
1	1	0	7	2	28
1	2	0	11+	4	35
2	0	0	9	2	38
2	0	1	14+	5	48
2	1	0	15	5	50
2	1	1	20+	7	60
2	2	0	21	8	62
3	0	0	23	9	130
3	0	1	39	10	180
3	1	0	43	10	210
3	1	1	75	20	280
3	2	0	93	30	380
3	2	1	150	50	500
3	2	2	210+	80	640
3	3	0	240	90	1400
3	3	1	460	100	2400
3	3	2	1100	300	4800
3	3	3	>1100	–	–

[a]Normal results, obtained in 95% of tests, are *not* followed by a plus. Less likely results, obtained in only 4% of tests, are followed by a plus. Combinations of positive tubes not shown occur in less than 1% of tests, and their frequent occurrence indicates that technique is faulty or that assumptions underlying the MPN estimate are not being fulfilled. MPN estimates for combinations that are not shown may be obtained by extrapolation (or by Thomas's formulae, Section 6.6) to the next highest combination that is shown in the table. For example, a result of 2, 0, 2 would have an MPN of approximately 20, which is the MPN for a more likely result of 2, 1, 1.

[b]All figures under "MPN/g" in this table may be multiplied by 100 for reporting "MPN/100 g."

more complete tables should be consulted.[1, 18, 25] DeMan gives an expanded table of likely MPN results, assuming the number of repeated tests are 1, 2, 3, 5, and 10. He states that combinations of tubes with a low probability of occurring for one MPN test can be accepted if they occur in the course of a sequence of tests. An alternative procedure for estimating the MPN is presented in Section 6.6.

When the multiple tube method is used, results are usually reported as "the most probable number of microorganisms per gram (or mL)." When specific groups of microorganisms have been estimated, results can be reported as a "presumptive MPN estimate" for that specific group until appropriate confirmatory tests have been completed. Tables 1 and 2 show the most probable numbers of microorganisms corresponding to the frequency of positive tubes obtained from three 1 to 10 dilution series beginning with 0.1-g test portions. Results for both three tubes and five tubes per dilution are given along with the 95% confidence limits.

Tables 3 and 4 give examples (explained in Section 6.53 below) for determining MPN estimates for three-tube and five-tube MPN series, respectively, when 1-g sample aliquots from serial dilutions are planted. Note that the tabular values are treated in terms of the actual sample volumes planted in these dilutions.

6.53   MPN Estimations

When more than three dilutions of a sample are prepared, the results from only three consecutive dilutions are used in determining the MPN. First, for all dilutions having all tubes positive, select the highest dilution (smallest sample volume). Second, use the next two higher dilutions (smaller sample volumes), as shown in examples a and b of Tables 3 and 4. When none of the tested dilutions yield all tubes positive (and if possible), select the first three consecutive dilutions (sample volumes) for which the middle dilution (volume) contains the positive result, as in example c of Tables 3 and 4. If a positive result occurs in a higher dilution (smaller sample volume) than the three selected, add the number of positive tubes in this dilution to the highest dilution (smallest sample volume) of the three selected, as in example d of Tables 3 and 4. When all dilutions tested have all tubes positive, select the three highest dilutions (smallest sample volumes), as in example e of Tables 3 and 4.

Often it is necessary to calculate the MPN from initial sample volumes other than those listed in Tables 1 and 2. If the largest (greatest) sample volume used for the table reference is 0.01 g, multiply the MPN index listed in the table by 10. Thus, results of a five-tube MPN determination showing 3 positive 0.01-g portions, 2 positive 0.001-g portions, and 1 positive 0.0001-g portion (3-2-1) are read from Table 2 as 17, and multiplied by 10 to arrive at 170 as the actual MPN/g for the sample. Similarly, if the greatest portion used for the table reference is 1 g rather than 0.1 g, divide the MPN derived

Table 2—Selected MPN Estimates and 95% Confidence Limits[9] of Estimates for Fermentation Tube Tests When Five Tubes with 0.1-g, 0.01-g, and 0.001-g Volumes Are Used[a]

| No. of positive tubes/5 tubes | | | MPN/g[b] | 95% confidence limits | |
0.1 g	0.01 g	0.001 g		Lower	Upper
0	0	0	<2	—	—
0	0	1	2+	<1	10
0	1	0	2	<1	10
1	0	0	2	<1	11
1	0	1	4+	1	15
1	1	0	4	1	15
1	2	0	6+	2	18
2	0	0	4	1	17
2	0	1	7+	2	20
2	1	0	7	2	21
2	1	1	9+	3	25
2	2	0	9	3	25
3	0	0	8	3	24
3	0	1	11	4	29
3	1	0	11	4	30
3	1	1	14+	6	35
3	2	0	14	6	35
3	2	1	17+	7	40
3	3	1	17+	7	41
4	0	0	13	5	38
4	0	1	17	7	45
4	1	0	17	7	46
4	1	1	21	9	55
4	2	0	22	9	56
4	2	1	26+	12	65

Table 2 Selected MPN Estimates and 95% Confidence Limits of Estimates for Fermentation Tube Tests When Three Tubes with 0.1-g, 0.01-g, and 0.001-g Volumes Are Used[a] (Continued)

0.1-g	0.01-g	0.001-g	MPN	Lower	Upper
4	3	0	27	12	67
4	3	1	33+	15	77
4	4	0	34+	16	80
5	0	0	23	9	68
5	0	1	31	13	110
5	1	0	33	14	120
5	1	1	46	20	150
5	1	2	63+	22	180
5	2	0	49	21	170
5	2	1	70	30	210
5	2	2	94+	40	250
5	3	0	79	30	250
5	3	1	110	40	300
5	3	2	140	60	360
5	4	0	130	50	390
5	4	1	170	70	480
5	4	2	220	100	580
5	4	3	280+	120	690
5	4	4	350+	160	820
5	5	0	240	100	940
5	5	1	350	100	1300
5	5	2	540	220	2000
5	5	3	920	300	2900
5	5	4	1600	600	5300
5	5	5	>1600		

[a]Normal results, obtained in 95% of tests, are *not* followed by a plus. Less likely results, obtained in only 4% of tests, are followed by a plus. Combinations of positive tubes not shown occur in less than 1% of tests, and their frequent occurrence indicates that technique is faulty or that assumptions underlying the MPN estimate are not being fulfilled. MPN estimates for combinations that are not shown may be obtained by extrapolation (or by Thomas's formulae, Section 6.6) to the next highest combination that is shown in the table. For example, a result of 4/0/2 would have an MPN of approximately 21, which is the MPN for a more likely result of 4/1/1.

[b]All figures under "MPN/g" in this table may be multiplied by 100 for reporting "MPN/100 g."

Table 3—Examples of Determining MPN Estimates: Three-tube Series
(1-g sample aliquot per tube)

Example	Sample volume (g)					Reported positive values	MPN estimate/g
	0.1	0.01	0.001	0.0001	0.00001		
a	3/3[a]	3/3	2/3	0/3	0/3	3-2-0	930
b	3/3	3/3	3/3	2/3	0/3	3-2-0	9300
c	0/3	0/3	1/3	0/3	0/3	0-1-0	30
d	3/3	3/3	2/3	1/3	1/3	3-2-2	2100
e	3/3	3/3	3/3	3/3	3/3	3-3-3	>110,000

[a] $\dfrac{\text{Numerator}}{\text{Denominator}} = \dfrac{\text{No. positive tubes}}{\text{No. tubes inoculated}}$

Table 4—Examples of Determining MPN Estimates: Five-tube Series
(1-g sample aliquot per tube)

Example	Sample volume (g)					Reported positive values	MPN estimate/g
	0.1	0.01	0.001	0.0001	0.00001		
a	5/5[a]	5/5	2/5	0/5	0/5	5-2-0	490
b	5/5	5/5	5/5	2/5	0/5	5-2-0	4900
c	0/5	0/5	1/5	0/5	0/5	0-1-0	20
d	5/5	5/5	3/5	1/5	1/5	5-3-2	1400
e	5/5	5/5	5/5	5/5	5/5	5-5-5	>160,000

[a] $\dfrac{\text{Numerator}}{\text{Denominator}} = \dfrac{\text{No. positive tubes}}{\text{No. tubes inoculated}}$

from the table by 10. Thus, the result of a three-tube MPN determination for salmonellae showing three positive 1-g portions, one positive 0.1-g portion, and no positive 0.01-g portions (3-1-0), is read from Table 1 as 43 and divided by 10, or 4.3 as the presumptive MPN/g for the sample.

An alternative approach to obtain the MPN per gram uses the following formula:[29]

[(MPN/g from Table/100)] × dilution factor of the middle tube = MPN/g. To obtain an MPN/100 g, multiply by 100.

6.54   Statistical Interpretation

Most available MPN tables[4, 6, 9, 32] include 95%, and sometimes 99%, confidence limits for the tabular MPN estimates. If the analyst assumes that the true number of organisms lies between these limits, then the assumption will be correct 95% of the time (or 99% of the time if 99% confidence limits are used). One must be able to read each table properly and understand the significance of the results. Given that the tabulated numbers are correctly computed, the next consideration should be an appreciation of the "confidence limit" surrounding a given value in each table. That is, the tabular MPN estimate represents a range and not an absolute value. It should be remembered that MPN estimates are often credited with unfounded precision. Woodward[34] published tables of confidence limits for three-tube and five-tube multiple dilution assays and pointed out that for a three-tube test the 95% confidence limits cover a 33-fold range from approximately 14% to 458% of the actual tabular MPN estimate. For a five-tube multiple dilution test, the 95% confidence limits cover a 13-fold range from approximately 24% to 324% of the MPN.

6.55   Reporting and Interpreting Counts

Results should be recorded as "Number of microorganisms per quantity (g or mL) of sample by the MPN method," e.g., coliform MPN/g = 11. With the report of microbiological counts by the MPN method, the number of tubes used in each dilution is included, i.e., five-tube MPN or three-tube MPN, and the particular method used.

6.6   APPROXIMATE MPN AND 95% CONFIDENCE LIMITS

The inherent complexity of actually computing MPNs and confidence limits means that most laboratory workers must use published tables to determine the MPN. Usually, these tables restrict the worker to n = 3, 5, or 10 tubes per dilution. Even with the standard design, a worker may be faced with irregular data or a laboratory accident where one or more results are missing from a dilution. The latter case might result in a dilution series of 5, 4, 4 tubes being observed, yielding a positive code of 5, 2, 0.

Three algorithms have been suggested in Section 6.51 for persons interested in programming a hand-held calculator[20] or a microcomputer.[19, 26] However, an approximation of the MPN can be computed without programming skills.

Thomas[31] published a simple formula that does not require iteration. MPNs approximated by this formula may not exactly agree with those obtained from theory; however, deviations are usually slight and of no practical consequence. (The approximation may not be acceptable for use in regulatory actions.) Additionally, the formula is not restricted to the number of tubes and dilutions used and may be applied to all types of tests. Thomas's approximation is given by the following:

$$MPN/g = P/\sqrt{NT}$$

    P = the number of positive tubes
    N = the total quantity of sample (g) in all negative tubes
    T = the total quantity of sample (g) in all tubes.

For example, consider the twofold dilution series given below:

g of sample	number of tubes	number of positive tubes
8	5	5
4	5	4
2	5	2
1	5	0
0.5	5	1
0.25	5	0

$P = (5 + 4 + 2 + 1) = 12$

$N = [(8 \times 0) + (4 \times 1) + (2 \times 3) + (1 \times 5) + (0.5 \times 4) + (0.25 \times 5)]$
$= 18.25$

$T = 5(8 + 4 + 2 + 1 + 0.5 + 0.25) = 78.75$

$MPN/g = 12/\sqrt{(18.25)(78.75)} = 0.32/g$ or 32/100 g

Estimates of the 95% confidence limits[7] can be obtained from the antilogs base 10 of the following:

$$\log (MPN/g) \pm (1.96)(0.55)\sqrt{(\log a)/n}$$

    a = the dilution ratio
    n = the number of tubes per dilution

This expression assumes that the dilution series is other than 1 to 10 (e.g., 1 to 2). For the 1 to 10 ratio, the $\pm$ quantity should be $(1.96)(0.58/\sqrt{n})$ for the best estimation. If the number of tubes per dilution are unequal (e.g., lab accident at a dilution), replace n in the above expression by the harmonic mean (n_H) of n_1 (the number of tubes per dilution). The harmonic mean is defined as $n_H = k/\sum_{i=1}^{k}(1/n_1)$ and k = number of dilutions. For example, suppose three dilutions resulted in n_i of 5, 4, 4; then $n_H = 3/(1/5 + 1/4 + 1/4) = 3/0.70 = 4.3$.

For the above MPN example, the approximate 95% confidence limits are

$$\log 0.32 \pm (1.96)(0.55)\sqrt{(\log 2)/5}$$
$$-0.495 \pm 0.265$$

then the lower limit is antilog $(-0.76) = 0.17/g$ or $17/100$ g and the upper limit is antilog $(-0.23) = 0.59/g$ or $59/100$ g. By comparison, the MPN and confidence limits computed using the deMan[9] procedure would be MPN = $0.31/g$ and limits $0.16/g$ and $0.57/g$.

6.7 REFERENCES

1. APHA. 1955. "Standard Methods for the Examination of Water, Sewage, and Industrial Wastes," 10th ed. Am. Pub. Health Assn., Washington, D.C.
2. APHA. 1961. "Standard Methods for the Examination of Water, Sewage, and Industrial Wastes," 11th ed. Am. Pub. Health Assn., Washington, D.C.
3. APHA. 1980. "Standard Methods for the Examination of Water and Wastewater," 15th ed. Am. Pub. Health Assn., Washington, D.C.
4. APHA. 1985. "Standard Methods for the Examination of Water and Wastewater," 16th ed. Am. Pub. Health Assn., Washington, D.C.
5. APHA. 1960. "Standard Methods for the Examination of Dairy Products," 11th ed. Am. Pub. Health Assn., Washington, D.C.
6. APHA. 1985. "Standard Methods for the Examination of Dairy Products," 15th ed. Am. Pub. Health Assn., Washington, D.C.
7. Cochran, W. G. 1950. Estimation of bacterial densities by means of the "Most Probable Number." Biometrics 6: 105.
8. deMan, J. C. 1975. The probability of most probable numbers. Eur. J. Appl. Microbiol. 1: 67.
9. deMan, J. C. 1977. MPN tables for more than one test. Eur. J. Appl. Microbiol. 4: 307.
10. Eisenhart, C. and Wilson, P. W. 1943. Statistical methods and control in bacteriology. Bacteriol. Rev. 7: 57.
11. Fisher, R. A. 1922. On the mathematical foundations of theoretical statistics. Philos. Trans. R. Soc. A. 222: 309.
12. Greenwood, M. and Yule, G. U. 1917. On the statistical interpretation of some bacteriological methods employed in water analysis. J. Hyg. 16: 36.
13. Haldane, J. B. S. 1941. Sampling errors in the determination of bacterial or virus density by the dilution method. J. Hyg. 39: 289.
14. Halvorson, H. O. and Ziegler, N. R. 1933a. Application of statistics to problems in bacteriology. I. A means of determining bacterial populations by the dilution method. J. Bacteriol. 25: 101.
15. Halvorson, H. O. and Ziegler, N. R. 1933b. Application of statistics to problems in bacteriology. II. A consideration of the accuracy of dilution data obtained by using a single dilution. J. Bacteriol. 26: 331.
16. Halvorson, H. O. and Ziegler, N. R. 1933c. Application of statistics to problems in bacteriology. III. A consideration of the accuracy of dilution data obtained by using several dilutions. J. Bacteriol. 26: 559.

17. Halvorson, H. O. and Moeglein, A. 1940. Application of statistics to problems in bacteriology. V. The probability of occurrence of various experimental results. Growth 4: 157.
18. Hoskins, J. K. 1933. The most probable number of *B. coli* in water analysis. J. Am. Water Works Assoc. 25: 867.
19. Hurley, M. A. and Roscoe, M. E. 1983. Automated statistical analysis of microbial enumeration by dilution series. J. Appl. Bacteriol. 55: 159.
20. Koch, A. L. 1982. Estimation of the most probable number with a programmable pocket calculator. Appl. Environ. Microbiol. 43: 488–490.
21. Matuszewski, T., J. Neyman, and J. Supinska. 1935. Statistical studies in questions of bacteriology. Part I. The accuracy of the "Dilution Method". Royal Stat. Society Supp. 2: 63–82.
22. McCarthy, J. A., H. A. Thomas, Jr., and J. D. Delaney. 1958. Evaluation of the reliability of coliform density tests. Amer. J. Pub. Health 48: 1628–1635.
23. McCrady, M. H. 1915. The numerical interpretation of fermentation tube results. J. Infect. Dis. 17: 183–212.
24. Niemela, S. 1983. Statistical evaluation of results from quantitative microbiological examinations. Nordic Committee on Food Analysis. Uppsala.
25. Oblinger, J. L., and J. A. Koburger. 1975. Understanding and teaching the most probable number technique. J. Milk Food Technol. 38: 540–545.
26. Parnow, R. J. 1972. Computer program estimates, bacterial densities by means of the most probable numbers. Food Technol. 26: (No.7):56,58,60,62.
27. Parnow, R. J. 1972. A computer program to estimate bacterial densities by means of the most probable number. RR 72–2. The Pillsbury Co., Minneapolis, MN 55414.
28. Pearson, E. S. 1978. The history of statistics in the 17th and 18th centuries. MacMillian Publishing Co. New York. pp. 361–378.
29. Silliker, J. H., D. A. Gabis, and A. May. 1979. ICMSF methods studies XI. Collaborative/comparative studies on determination of coliforms using the most probable number procedure. J. Food Prot. 42: 638–644.
30. Swaroop, S. 1940. Error in the estimation of the most probable number of organisms by the dilution method. Ind. J. Med. Res. 27: 1129–1147.
31. Thomas, H. A. 1942. Bacterial densities from fermentation tube tests. J. Am. Water Works Assoc. 34: 572–576.
32. U.S. Dept. Health, Education & Welfare. Bacteriological Analytical Manual. 1984. 6th ed. U.S. Food and Drug Administration. U.S. Dept. Health, Education and Welfare, Washington, D.C.
33. von Mises, R. 1942. On the correct use of Bayes' formula. Ann. Math. Stat. 13: 156–165.
34. Woodward, R. L. 1957. How probable is the most probable number? J. Amer. Water Works Assn. 49: 1060–1068.
35. Ziegler, N. R. and H. O. Halvorson. 1935. Application of statistics to problems in bacteriology. IV. Experimental comparison of the dilution method, the plate count, and the direct count for the determination of bacterial populations. J. Bact. 29: 609–634.

Chapter 7

REPAIR AND DETECTION OF INJURED MICROORGANISMS

P. M. Foegeding and Bibek Ray

7.1 INTRODUCTION

Microorganisms that are subjected to environmental stresses may become structurally or metabolically damaged or injured. Injured organisms are manifested by their inability to replicate in selective environments that undamaged organisms tolerate. Injured organisms may be resuscitated or permitted to repair the damage if incubated in an appropriate, nonselective environment.

Food and food ingredients usually contain viable microorganisms that are physiologically deficient or injured because of the environmental stresses to which the cells have been subjected. Injury may result from many food processing and handling methods, including thermal treatment, refrigeration, freezing, drying, and irradiation, or from exposure to preservatives, acidity, or low water activity. Equipment surfaces that have been sanitized, as well as water used in processing of foods or cleaning of equipment, may contain injured microorganisms. Available data indicate that both gram-negative and gram-positive bacterial cells, bacterial endospores, yeasts, and molds may be injured by stresses.[2, 8, 31, 43]

Ideally, a method used to detect microorganisms in a food or environmental sample should detect both the normal and the injured microorganisms. However, until recently, many of the accepted methods used for isolation and enumeration of microorganisms in foods did not allow for the injured state of some microorganisms and thus failed to detect them. Injured organisms are potentially as important as their normal counterparts[7, 36] since, in a favorable environment, injured vegetative microorganisms can resuscitate and become functionally normal while injured spores may bypass the injured systems (a germination or outgrowth system, for example) and form a functionally normal vegetative cell.[9, 17, 40]

Selective compounds such as surface-active agents, salts, antibiotics, sulfanilamides, acids, and dyes are added to media for the selective and differential detection of indicator, pathogenic, spoilage, or other microorganisms from foods. Some of these agents are inhibitory to the process of repair while others are toxic and cause death of the injured organisms. This suggests that when such media must be used, the injured microorganisms in the samples must be permitted to resuscitate in a suitable environment prior to their exposure to selective media.[14, 22, 31] The use of selective media without appropriate precautions to permit regular repair of injury results in failure to detect the injured, but viable and potentially normal microorganisms. Hence, selective media may underestimate the microbial content of a particular food product.

Injured bacterial spores, like injured vegetative cells, exhibit unique properties as a result of cellular damage induced during exposure to environmental stresses.[2, 8] Because of their greater resistance to these stresses, reports of injury to spores have been limited to heat, irradiation, and chemicals (ethylene oxide, hydrogen peroxide, sodium hydroxide, hypochlorite).[8, 15] With respect to foods, the most important of these stresses at the present time is heat. However, with the changing attitudes of regulatory agencies toward irradiation as well as the trend towards aseptic packaging of foods, which often involves the use of chemicals such as hydrogen peroxide for sterilizing packaging materials, spore injury induced by irradiation and chemicals will assume added importance.

Research has indicated that, for injured vegetative cells, regardless of the nature of stress imposed on a microbial population, (a) the injury is repaired when the injured organisms are held in an appropriate environment, (b) the optimum temperature and time required for repair may vary with the nature of stress, (c) the completely repaired cells regain their normal resistance to the selective agents in the media, and (d) the process of repair must precede cell multiplication.[14, 22, 31] Therefore, it is desirable to allow stressed cells to repair any damage before they are isolated or enumerated by customary procedures on selective media. The procedure that promotes maximum repair must be evaluated to eliminate or minimize multiplication of competing organisms. Unlike vegetative cells, bacterial spores must complete both germination and outgrowth before vegetative cell growth can begin. Both of these systems have been involved in spore injury.[2, 8] Repair of damaged germination and outgrowth systems may not occur. Hence, recovery would depend upon providing an environment suitable for the function of an alternative, non-damaged germination or outgrowth system.

The value of a repair period before selectively isolating salmonellae from dried egg products was recognized by North.[29] He used lactose broth as a nonselective pre-enrichment medium prior to selective enrichment in either selenite cystine or tetrathionate broth. The success of this method was attributed to resuscitation of cells injured by the egg drying process. However, incubation for 24 hr in lactose broth could allow overgrowth by competing microorganisms, which are present in far greater numbers than salmonellae in the products. Recognizing this, other workers suggested a shorter pre-enrichment period (2 to 7 hr).[11] Currently recommended procedures for the isolation of salmonellae from processed foods call for pre-enrichment of the sample in a suitable broth for 24 hr at 30° to 37°C before proceeding with the selective enrichment.

Vibrio parahaemolyticus injured by processing and storage of seafoods requires a nonselective low salt pre-enrichment for effective detection.[31] Pre-enrichment of injured *Yersinia enterocolitica* at 25°C for 2 to 3 hr may be favorable for resuscitation and subsequent recovery at 4°C.[37] In developing a method to detect pathogenic *Campylobacter* strains from processed food, a repair step may be needed.[12, 32, 33] *Listeria monocytogenes* may be injured by heat, and the current procedures in common use, which include enrichment steps, may not recover injured cells.[10]

High levels of NaCl and potassium-tellurite used in the agar and broth media for selective enumeration of pathogenic staphylococci from processed foods may be inhibitory to the growth of injured cells. Several procedures that include a pre-enrichment step to facilitate repair of stressed *Staphylococcus aureus* have been proposed. Addition of catalase, pyruvate, or other chemicals that will react with and remove H_2O_2 in the selective media has been found to increase the detection of stressed staphylococci in foods.[14] A membrane filter technique was described by Goff et al.,[19] but this method has limited application in foods.

Several methods to enumerate injured coliforms from foods either by plating or by a most probable number (MPN) technique have been developed. Warseck et al.[45] found that injured coliforms repair rapidly and without multiplying when incubated in trypticase soy broth (TSB) for 1 hr at 25°C prior to selective enumeration by plating. Others[31, 42] have reported that repair of injured coliforms could be obtained either by surface or pour plating the sample with trypticase soy agar (TSA) or plate count agar (PCA) and incubating the plates at 25° to 37°C for 1 to 2 hr, followed by overlaying with violet red bile agar (VRBA). The pour-plating procedure also could be used for selective enumeration of injured fecal coliforms by incubating the plates (TSA with VRBA) at 45 ± 0.5°C for 18 to 24 hr.[21, 30, 31] By changing the selective medium and the time and temperature of incubation, this overlay procedure could be used for the enumeration of injured enterococi (KF Streptococcus agar as selective medium), yeasts and molds, *Lactobacillus acidophilus*, etc. from processed foods.[21, 25, 31] Hartman[22] described a direct-plating method for enumeration of injured coliforms in which the sample was first surface-plated on VRBA without bile salts and dyes; this was followed by overlaying the surface with double strength VRBA for selective environment and enumeration.

Several methods have been developed using the membrane filtration technique for direct enumeration of injured coliforms and fecal coliforms from water and environmental samples.[20] After filtration of the sample, the membrane is first placed over a pad containing a nonselective medium and incubated at 35°C for 2 hr to facilitate repair. The filter is then transferred onto the surface of a selective medium and incubated for 24 hr at 35°C for coliforms or at 44.5°C for fecal coliforms. A variation of these methods to enumerate selectively *Escherichia coli* type I from foods was described by Holbrook et al.[23] and Sharpe et al.[39] Addition of catalase or other exogenous peroxide decomposers to the selective agar media has been found to increase the recovery of injured coliforms from samples.[28] These H_2O_2 decomposers also were reported to increase counts of total microorganisms on nonselective agar media.[14, 28]

Various modifications of the current MPN methods have been proposed to enumerate injured coliforms from foods. In one such method the sample is blended and diluted serially in 0.1% peptone, transferred in 1 ml portions to 4 ml TSB and incubated 1 to 4 hr at 25° to 37°C. After 1 to 4 hr, 5 ml double strength selective broth is added to each tube and the recommended procedure is followed.[31] Hartman[22] developed a method in which samples from decimal dilutions were transferred to tubes containing a nonselective broth and a "time-release" capsule containing brilliant green and bile salts; the injured cells were repaired before the selective agents were released to provide the selective environment necessary for coliform enumeration.

Modifications of the radiometric and impedance measurements to accommodate enumeration of injured coliforms and fecal coliforms from processed foods have been described by Rowley et al.[38] In these methods, the samples are incubated first in a nonselective broth before addition of selective media and further incubation. In this study, addition of catalase or sodium pyruvate to the selective broth did not aid in repair.

Recovery of stressed spores has been accomplished by the use of lysozyme in the recovery medium to germinate *Clostridium perfringens* and *Clostridium botulinum* spores.[1, 2, 3, 4, 7] Alternatively, a germination agent may be included in the recovery medium to stimulate an undamaged secondary germination system.[2, 16] Injured spores may have new optium temperatures for recovery.[2, 7, 18] The choice of medium can be very important. Wheaton and Pratt[46] reported that the recovery of heated *Clostridium sporogenes* PA 3679 spores was best with meat infusion medium and poorest with dehydrated media. Later, Augustin and Pflug[5] also reported the greatest recovery of PA 3679 spores with beef and pea infusion media and the lowest with a defined medium. Foegeding and Busta[15] reported that *C. botulinum* spores injured by hypochlorite treatment could be recovered by a colony count procedure using modified peptone yeast extract agar but not by an MPN-procedure using modified peptone colloid medium.

Ashton[4] identified starch as the agent in pea extract that improved the recovery of heat-injured PA 59-123 spores. Starch has been recognized for some time as an important medium adjunct for increasing the recovery of heated spores.[2, 5, 7]

7.2   GENERAL CONSIDERATIONS

Not only processing, but storage and subsequent handling of foods exert stress on microorganisms. Also, certain techniques used during analysis may inflict injury on the organisms present in a sample. In the pour-plating procedure, microorganisms present may be subject to the heat stress caused by the molten agar medium, and the presence of selective agents in a medium can accentuate the effect of this stress.[34] Even nonselective media used to determine aerobic plate counts (APC) and psychrotrophic plate counts yield fewer colonies when pour plating is done at 45°C or higher temperatures.[44] The effects of certain food ingredients,[41] rate and temperature of rehydration of dried foods,[35] rate of thawing of frozen foods,[31] duration of time the organisms are left in the diluent, especially in phosphate buffer or water,[24] temperature of the diluent and volume and temperature of the plating medium,[44] all exert stresses on microorganisms present in a sample and affect their detection, especially by selective procedures.

The degree of injury incurred by the organisms during processing, storage, and handling of foods affects their ability to repair under a given set of conditions. This can result in differences in the nutritional requirements as well as in the time and temperature required for repair. Synergistic effects of more than one stress on injury and repair also should be considered.

The inhibitory or lethal effects of many food ingredients and additives (lysozyme, lauryl sulfate, acids, etc.), components of recovery media, and conditions of repair should be taken into consideration in the development of methods. Increases in counts in nonselective plating media such as PCA or TSA with added catalase or pyruvate suggest that even these media contain materials that are toxic to the cells and prevent colony formation by some viable cells.

Various aspects of the handling of the samples, such as the rehydration rate of dried or semidried products (slower is usually better), the thawing rate of frozen products, the effect of blending, the composition and temperature of diluents, the temperature of the plating media, etc., could have profound effects on the injury and repair process. These need to be standardized for uniform results.

During prolonged repair-incubation, the uninjured fraction of the population can multiply and, depending upon the method used, increase the count. Care must be taken to distinguish between repair of injury and multiplication under a given set of repair conditions. This can be accomplished by separately monitoring populations recovered on selective and nonselective media. Multiplication would result in increases in numbers recovered on both media while repair would result in increases on selective media only.

To some degree, the importance of injured spores in heat-processed foods is not entirely clear. For inoculated packs, detection of injured spores able to germinate and grow in the product, albeit very slowly, is of paramount importance. Thus, the time and temperature used for incubation of the product and subcultures and the type of subculture medium are important. However, it is debatable whether a spore should be considered viable if it requires detection conditions never encountered outside the laboratory.

Lysozyme can be valuable for detecting spores with damaged germination systems or for shortening incubation times. However, lysozyme should be used with caution and only after its efficacy has been determined. Not all spores, even within a given spore suspension, may be sensitive to lysozyme, and for some sporeformers, lysozyme prevents vegetative cell formation.

7.3 PROCEDURES, PROBLEMS, AND PRECAUTIONS

Detailed methods for the detection of various groups of injured microorganisms from foods are given in the chapters in this book on specific microorganisms. This discussion outlines the general methods studied in different laboratories, their specificity, possible problems of the methods and precautions for their use, and their suitability for detecting injured microbial cells from processed foods. In general, the repair methods could be grouped as either liquid or solid media repair methods.

7.31 Liquid Media Repair of Vegetative Bacteria[11, 14, 22, 31, 33]

In this method the mixed or blended sample is incubated in a nonselective and preferably nutritionally complex liquid medium to facilitate repair of injury by the stressed organisms. Various incubation temperatures ($4°$ to $37°C$—with temperatures nearer $37°C$ being more effective for most mesophilic organisms) and times of 1 to 5 hr—longer time is necessary especially for heat-stressed cells—have been used for optimal repair. This method could be used as the initial step in selective isolation or for enumeration either by direct plating or by an MPN technique for a specific group of organisms from foods.[11, 14, 22, 31, 33]

1. Selective isolation methods

   a. Selective isolation procedures are suitable for isolation of *Listeria monocytogenes* (although injured cells may be inefficiently recovered[10]), enteropathogenic *E. coli*, *Salmonella*, *Shigella*, *Yersinia*, *Vibrio*, and *Campylobacter* (Chapters 24–29).

   b. For *V. parahaemolyticus* add extra NaCl to obtain 3% final concentration after 2 hr incubation at $35°C$. (Chapter 28).

   c. For *Yersinia* incubate at $25°C$ for 4 hr before incubating at $4°C$ (Chapter 27).

   d. For *Campylobacter jejuni* first incubate in brucella broth supplemented with Na-succinate (0.3%) + cystine-HCl (0.01%) and antibiotics (as in CAMPY-BAP and CAMPY THIO media), other than Polymyxin B, at 37°C for 6 hr. Then add Polymyxin B and shift incubation to 42°C. Microaerophilic incubation conditions are used (Chapter 29).

   e. Incubation periods over 4 to 6 hr may permit overgrowth of associated organisms that, in general, are present in larger proportions.

   f. Incubation for 24 or more hr may produce stress from nutrient depletion and toxic metabolites, causing reduced recovery upon subsequent exposure to selective enrichment media.

   g. Lysozyme, lauryl sulfate, salt, acid, etc., could cause further damage of injured cells and reduce their chances of isolation.

2. Enumeration by MPN method

   a. These procedures are suitable for MPN determination of coliforms and fecal coliforms, V. parahaemolyticus, fecal streptococci, and S. aureus.

   b. Distribute three 1-ml portions of 3 successive decimal dilutions of the sample each to 4 ml TSB, and incubate 4 to 6 hr at 35° to 37°C. Add 5 ml double-strength selective broth to each tube and proceed according to the recommended procedures.

3. Enumeration by direct-plating method

   a. These procedures are suitable for enumeration of coliforms and fecal coliforms (by incubating plates at 44.5°C), V. parahaemolyticus, fecal streptococci, and S. aureus.

   b. An aliquot of blended sample, after incubation in a nutritionally rich nonselective broth, is surface- or pour-plated with selective agar medium and incubated for colony formation.

   c. Higher counts partially result from the multiplication of the uninjured fraction of the population, especially during long repair-incubation at higher temperatures.

   d. Cells injured by different stresses require different times and temperatures for optimal repair.

   e. Cell multiplication, but not cell repair, can be prevented by adding inhibitors such as penicillin during repair incubation; but penicillinase should be added prior to plating (however, the uninjured population could be killed by penicillin in their attempt to multiply).

   f. Food ingredients that interfere with repair and survival of the injured cells may affect the result.

7.32 Solid Media Repair of Vegetative Bacteria[21, 30, 31, 42]

In these methods the sample aliquot is either surface-plated or pour-plated with a nonselective nutritionally rich medium and incubated for a suitable time (generally 1 to 4 hr) at 25° to 37°C to facilitate repair. After the repair period, the plates are overlaid with 10 to 12 ml of a selective agar medium, specific for the type of organism, and incubated. During incubation, the selective ingredients diffuse through the nonselective agar and produce the necessary selective environment because of the agar overlay. These procedures are not suitable for organisms that are enumerated by surface plating, e.g., *S. aureus* and *Vibrio*. Carryover of inhibitors and lethal components of food may affect repair and recovery.

1. Surface-plating methods

   a. Surface-overlay-plating methods are suitable for enumeration of coliforms, fecal coliforms (plates incubated at 44.5° to 45°C), fecal streptococci, *L. acidophilus*, and yeasts and molds.
   b. These procedures are effective only when small inocula of 0.1 to 0.5 ml of sample/plate are used. Thus, they are unsuitable for samples with low numbers of the specific organisms.
   c. During overlaying, microcolonies may break apart and give higher counts.

2. Pour-plating methods

   a. These procedures are suitable for enumeration of coliforms, fecal coliforms (plates incubated at 44.5° to 45°C), fecal streptococci, *L. acidophilus*, yeasts and molds, and other organisms that can be enumerated by pour-plating methodology.
   b. Up to 3.3 ml of sample can be used per plate; thus these procedures can be used for samples with low or high counts of the specific type of organisms.
   c. Other problems of the surface-overlay method are eliminated.

7.33   Other Repair Methods for Vegetative Bacteria

Several modifications of the liquid and solid media repair method have been developed for the enumeration of a specific group of injured organisms from processed foods.

1. Radiometric and impedance techniques[38]

   a. These are modifications of liquid media repair in combination with MPN methodology.
   b. The techniques have been tested to enumerate injured coliforms and fecal coliforms (at 44.5°C) from processed foods.
   c. Disadvantages associated with MPN methods are present.
   d. The rate of $^{14}CO_2$ production or change in impedance differs with strains and the incubation environment. Thus, counts calculated from the standard curves are estimates.

2. Membrane filtration method[19]

   a. The diluted sample is filtered through a sterile membrane filter (450 nm) and the filter is incubated first on a nonselective medium and then on a selective agar medium.

b. This technique has been tested to enumerate injured *S. aureus* in foods, but theoretically can be used for any organism that is enumerated by surface or pour plating methods, except spreaders.

c. The technique can be used for samples with low or high numbers of a specific type of organism.

d. The deleterious effects of inhibitory and toxic materials during repair can be avoided.

e. The major drawback of the method is that food materials may clog the pores during filtration, especially with lower dilutions.

f. Prefiltration to reduce suspended materials also removes organisms associated with food particles.

g. Improper drying of the filter surface, especially with large particles and fatty foods, encourages development of spreaders.

3. Membrane filter-plating method[23, 39]

a. A 1 ml portion of the blended sample is spread over a 450 nm pore membrane filter (85 mm diameter filter is useful for standard-size petri plates) placed on a nonselective agar medium, and incubated at 37°C for 4 hr to facilitate repair. The filter is transferred to a selective agar medium and incubated at 44°C for 18 hr for *E. coli* type I.

b. The method has been tested for *E. coli* type I along with the indole test, but theoretically can be used for any type of organism except spreaders.

c. The major advantage of this method is enumeration of *E. coli* type I, and presumably other organisms, within a short period of time.

d. Inhibitors and toxic materials present in foods affect repair.

e. Volume limits the use of the method to samples with numbers of *E. coli* type I detectable in ≤ 0.1 g.

f. Food particles and fatty materials may interfere with the drying of the membrane and encourage growth of spreaders.

g. The membrane filter may not adequately contact the selective agar. Indole positive non-*E. coli* type I may form colonies, or other organisms can interfere with the growth of *E. coli* type I in areas lacking good contact with selective components.

4. Catalase and other peroxide decomposers in selective media[14, 27, 28]

a. In these methods, catalase, pyruvate, or other agents to degrade H_2O_2 are added directly to the selective liquid or solid medium along with the sample.

b. The methods have been tested for enumeration of injured *S. aureus*, by MPN and direct-plating methods and for coliforms by a direct-plating method.

c. These methods may eliminate the need for repair incubation steps.

d. Addition of these compounds to media, including nonselective media such as PCA or TSA, increases total viable cell counts, coliforms and *S. aureus*. These results suggest that, even in a nonselective agar medium, many viable organisms fail to multiply and form colonies.

5. Supplemented agar method[28]

   a. This is similar to the pour-overlay method. However, the PCA to be used as a nonselective medium is supplemented with either 0.66% Na-pyruvate or 1% 3,3'-thiodipropionic acid (TDPA). Supplements, adjusted to pH 7.3, are added to the medium before sterilization.
   b. This method has been used to recover injured coliforms with VRBA as the selective overlaying medium.
   c. The supplements, through neutralization of the toxic effect of H_2O_2, allow better enumeration of injured bacteria.

6. Fluorogenic assay of *E. coli*[13]

   a. The sample is pour-plated with 10 ml TSA, incubated for 2 hr at 35°C, then overlaid with VRB-2 agar (VRBA with $2\times$ concentrations of bile salts, crystal violet, and neutral red) that has 200 μg/ml of 4-methylumbelliferone glucuronide (MUG).
   b. The plates are examined after 12 to 20 hr incubation at 35°C for *E. coli* colonies that give fluorescent halos.
   c. Some other, non-*E. coli*, *Enterobacteriaceae* can produce colonies with fluorescent halos. Thus, confirmatory testing is required.
   d. The plates need to be examined early, otherwise the fluorogenic compounds will diffuse in the medium.
   e. A microtitration assay system that could be used for MPN of *E. coli* by using MUG has been developed. Wells of a microtitration plate are filled with TSA containing 100 μg MUG/ml. Five wells are inoculated with 0.05 ml of sample/well for each of three or more successive dilutions. Plates are incubated at 35°C for 24 hr and checked for fluorescence. The MPN is estimated from the numbers of positive wells in three successive dilutions.
   f. Some foods (oysters, for example) contain glucuronidase, which may cause false positive fluorescence with MUG.[26]

7. Hydrophobic grid membrane (HGM) filtration method[6]

   a. This method has been tested for injured coliforms, *E. coli* biotype I and enterococci.
   b. An aliquot of a homogenized food is filtered through a HGM-filter, which is then placed on the surface of a prepoured plate of TSA supplemented with 0.15% $MgSO_4$. Filters are incubated for 2 hr at 35°C.
   c. The filter is then transferred to the surface of a prepoured selective agar medium, specific for the species or groups of organisms, and incubated.
   d. The selective media and incubation conditions are as follows: for *E. coli* biotype I, tryptone bile agar and 44.5°C for 24 hr; for coliforms,

m-FC agar without rosolic acid and 35°C for 24 hr; for enterococci, m-Enterococcus agar and 35°C for 48 hr.

e. For coliforms and enterococci the number of squares occupied by the characteristic colonies are determined. For *E. coli* biotype I, the filter is treated with an indole reagent and examined for the number of squares occupied by indole-positive colonies. The MPN is calculated from the number of squares occupied by specific types of colonies of interest.

7.34   Detection of Injured Bacterial Spores[1, 2, 8]

Only two modifications of standard spore enumeration or detection procedures have been adopted widely for the detection of injured spores. First, starch generally is included in the recovery medium to bind inhibitors that may be present. Second, for the detection of survivors in the inoculated packs or for measuring spore heat resistance by the end-point methods, the incubation period may be extended to as long as 12 months. This is necessary because heat-stressed spores germinate much more slowly than unstressed spores, and the development of a positive culture has a dramatic effect on the calculated heat resistance of the spores when using these methods.

Additional steps may be taken such as the inclusion of lysozyme in the recovery medium to germinate injured spores, incubation of the recovery cultures at temperatures 5° to 10°C lower than would be used for unstressed spores, and enumerating survivors on more than one medium. Sources and lots of recovery media may vary and affect spore recovery rates. Thus, batches of media should be evaluated and standardized for recovery of spores injured by heat or other treatments. In any case, the enumeration conditions should be those yielding the highest recovery of survivors; these will not necessarily be those yielding the highest recovery of heat-activated spores.

7.4   INTERPRETATION

Injured organisms can be present in foods. Their proportion will differ with the microbial type and the nature of the stress to which the organisms are exposed during processing, with the storage and handling of foods, and with the method used for their detection. Injured cells are viable and potentially as important as normal cells. Thus, inability to detect the injured population by a selective procedure results in inaccurate information and errors in the interpretation of data.[7] As media for detecting microorganisms differ, the use of different media by separate laboratories can give variable results. Furthermore, because many injured cells of a species can repair very fast even in a relatively simple environment, a slight difference in the time of transferring the sample with the injured cells into nonselective media can provide a chance for some cells to repair and thus subsequently be detected by the selective method. This may lead to differences in results obtained by different laboratories or technicians.

To monitor the microbiological quality of food products, standardized procedures should be used to obtain uniform results. Because of the presence of injured organisms in foods, many currently recommended methods, especially the selective methods, have an inherent deficiency of not detecting injured cells. Their suitability is questionable, especially for regulatory purposes. This problem can be solved by adding a repair step to the selective detection methods.

For a method to be useful, especially for regulatory purposes,[36] its applicability and suitability should be judged and its effectiveness should be evaluated through collaborative studies. Finally, because improved methods are expected to detect more microorganisms, present standards and guidelines should be reevaluated to see whether they need to be changed.

7.5   REFERENCES

1. Adams, D. M. 1974. Requirement for and sensitivity to lysozyme by *Clostridium perfringens* spores heated at ultra-high temperatures. Appl. Microbiol. **27**: 797.
2. Adams, D. M. 1978. Heat injury of bacterial spores. Adv. Appl. Microbiol. **23**: 246.
3. Alderton, G., Chen, J. K., and Ito, K. A. 1974. Effect of lysozyme on the recovery of heated *Clostridium botulinum* spores. Appl. Microbiol. **27**: 613.
4. Ashton, D. H. 1971. Identification of a pea component stimulatory for heat-stressed putrefactive anaerobe 59-123 spores. Appl. Microbiol. **21**: 38.
5. Augustin, J. and Pflug, I. J. 1967. Recovery patterns of spores of putrefactive anaerobe 3679 in various subculture media after heat treatment. Appl. Microbiol. **15**: 266.
6. Brodsky, M. H., Boleszczuk, P., and Entis, P. 1982. Effect of stress and resuscitation on recovery of indicator bacteria from foods using hydrophobic grid-membrane filtration. J. Food Prot. **45**: 1326.
7. Busta, F. F. 1976. Practical implications of injured microorganisms in foods. J. Milk Food Technol. **39**: 138.
8. Busta, F. F., Foegeding, P. M., and Adams, D. M. 1981. Injury and resuscitation of germination and outgrowth of bacterial spores. In "Sporulation and Germination, ed. H. S. Levinson, A. L. Sonenshein, and D. J. Tipper, p. 261. Amer. Soc. for Microbiol., Washington, D.C.
9. Collins-Thomson, D. L., Hurst, A., and Kruse, H. 1973. Synthesis of entertoxin B by *Staphylococcus aureus* S-6 after recovery from heat injury. Can. J. Microbiol. **19**: 1463.
10. Crawford, R. G., Beliveau, C. M., Peeler, J. T., Donnelly, C. W., and Bunning, V. K. 1989. Comparative recovery of uninjured and heat-injured *Listeria monocytogenes* cells from bovine milk. Appl. Environ. Microbiol. **55**: 1490.
11. D'Aoust, J. 1981. Update on pre-enrichment and selective enrichment conditions for detection of *Salmonella* in foods. J. Food Prot. **44**: 369.
12. Doyle, M. P. 1981. *Campylobacter fetus* subsp. *jejuni*: An old pathogen of new concern. J. Food Prot. **44**: 480.
13. Feng, P. C. S. and Hartman, P. A. 1982. Fluorogenic assay for immediate confirmation of *Escherichia coli*. Appl. Environ. Microbiol. **43**: 1320.
14. Flowers, R. S. and Ordal, Z. J. 1979. Current methods to detect stressed staphyloccocci. J. Food Prot. **42**: 362.
15. Foegeding, P. M. and Busta, F. F. 1983. Hypochlorite injury of *Clostridium botulinum* spores alters germination responses. Appl. Environ. Microbiol. **45**: 1360.
16. Foegeding, P. M. and Busta, F. F. 1983. Proposed role of lactate in germination of hypochlorite-treated *Clostridium botulinum* spores. Appl. Environ. Microbiol. **45**: 1369.

17. Fung, D. Y. C. and Vanden Bosch, L. L. 1975. Repair, growth, and enterotoxigenesis of *Staphylococcus aureus* S-6 injured by freeze-drying. J. Milk Food Technol. **38:** 212.
18. Futter, B. V. and Richardson, G. 1970. Viability of clostridial spores and the requirements of damaged organisms. I. Method of colony count, period and temperature of incubation, and pH value of the medium. J. Appl. Bacteriol. **33:** 331.
19. Goff, J. H., Claydon, T. J., and Iandola, J. J. 1972. Revival and subsequent isolation of heat-injured bacteria by a membrane filter technique. Appl. Microbiol. **23:** 857.
20. Green, B. L., Clausen, E. M., and Litsky, W. 1977. Two temperature membrane filter method for enumeration of fecal coliform bacteria from chlorinated effluents. Appl. Environ. Microbiol. **33:** 1259.
21. Hackney, C. R., Ray, B. R., and Speck, M. L. 1979. Repair detection procedure for enumeration of fecal coliforms and enterococci from seafoods and marine environments. Appl. Environ. Microbiol. **37:** 947.
22. Hartman, P. A. 1979. Modification of conventional methods for recovery of injured coliforms and salmonellae. J. Food Prot. **42:** 356.
23. Holbrook, R., Anderson, J. M., and Baird-Parker, A. C. 1980. Modified direct plate method for counting *Escherichia coli* in foods. Food Technol. Australia **32:** 78.
24. Jensen, J. P. and Hausler, W. J. Jr. 1976. Contribution of KH_2PO_4 to toxicity in phosphate buffered dilution water systems. J. Milk Food Technol. **39:** 852.
25. Johnson, M., Ray, B., and Speck, M. L. 1984. Freeze-injury in cell wall and its repair in *Lactobacillus acidophilus*. Cryo Letters **5:** 171.
26. Koburger, J. A. and Miller, M. L. 1985. Evaluation of a fluorogenic MPN procedure for determining *Escherichia coli* in oysters. J. Food Prot. **48:** 244.
27. Martin, S. E., Flowers, R. S., and Ordal, J. J. 1976. Catalase: The effect on microbial enumeration. Appl. Environ. Microbiol. **32:** 731.
28. McDonald, L., Hackney, C. R., and Ray, B. 1981. Enhanced recovery of injured *Escherichia coli* by compounds that degrade hydrogen peroxide or block its formation. Appl. Environ. Microbiol. **45:** 360.
29. North, W. R. 1961. Lactose pre-enrichment method for isolation of salmonellae from dried egg albumen. Appl. Microbiol. **9:** 188.
30. Powers, E. M. and Latt, T. G. 1979. Rapid enumeration and identification of stressed fecal coliforms. Appl. Environ. Microbiol. **42:** 342.
31. Ray, B. 1979. Detection of stressed microorganisms. J. Food Prot. **42:** 346.
32. Ray, B. and Johnson, C. 1984a. Sensitivity of cold-stressed *Campylobacter jejuni* to solid and liquid selective environments. Food Microbiol. **1:** 173.
33. Ray, B. and Johnson, C. 1984b. Survival and growth of freeze-stressed *Campylobacter jejuni* cells in selective media. J. Food Safety **6:** 183.
34. Ray, B. and Speck, M. L. 1973. Discrepancies in the enumeration of *Escherichia coli*. Appl. Microbiol. **25:** 494.
35. Ray, B., Jezeski, J. J., and Busta, F. F. 1972. Isolation of salmonellae from naturally contaminated dried milk products: Influence of preenrichment conditions. J. Milk Food Technol. **35:** 607.
36. Read, R. B. Jr. 1979. Detection of stressed microorganisms—implications for regulatory monitoring. J. Food. Prot. **42:** 368.
37. Restaino, L., Jeter, W. S., and Hill, W. M. 1980. Thermal injury of *Yersinia enterocolitica*. Appl. Environ. Microbiol. **40:** 939.
38. Rowley, D. B., VandeMark, P., Johnson, D., and Shattuck, E. 1979. Resuscitation of stressed fecal coliforms and their subsequent detection by radiometric and impedence techniques. J. Food Prot. **42:** 335.
39. Sharpe, A. N., Peterkin, P. I., and Rayman, M. K. 1981. Detection of *Escherichia coli* in foods: Indole staining methods for cellulosic and polysulfonate membrane filters. Appl. Environ. Microbiol. **41:** 1310.
40. Sorrells, K. M., Speck, M. L., and Warren, J. W. 1970. Pathogenicity of *Salmonella gallinarum* after metabolic injury by freezing. Appl. Microbiol. **19:** 39.

41. Speck, M. L. and Ray, B. 1977. Effects of freezing and storage on microorganisms in frozen foods: A review. J. Food Prot. **40:** 333.
42. Speck, M. L., Ray, B., and Read R. B. Jr. 1975. Repair and enumeration of injured coliforms by plating procedure. Appl. Microbiol. **29:** 549.
43. Traci, P. A. and Duncan, C. L. 1974. Cold shock lethality and injury in *Clostridium perfringens*. Appl. Microbiol. **28:** 815.
44. Vanderzant, C. and Matthys, A. W. 1965. Effect of temperature of the plating medium on the viable counts of psychrotrophic bacteria. J. Milk Food Technol. **28:** 383.
45. Warseck, M., Ray, B., and Speck, M. L., 1973. Repair and enumeration of injured coliforms in frozen foods. Appl. Microbiol. **26:** 919.
46. Wheaton, E. and Pratt, G. B. 1961. Comparative studies on media for counting anaerobic bacterial spores. II. J. Food Sci. **26:** 261.

Chapter 8

MEASUREMENT OF WATER ACTIVITY (A_w) AND ACIDITY

J. A. Troller and V. N. Scott

8.1 MEASUREMENT OF A_w

Water activity or a_w has been defined as the ratio of the vapor pressure of a solution to that of pure water at a specified temperature. This can be expressed mathematically as a function of Raoult's law, which states

$$a_w = \frac{P}{P_o} = \frac{n_1}{n_1 + n_2},$$ (1)

where P is the vapor pressure of a solution, P_o is the vapor pressure of pure water, n_1 is the number of moles of solvent, and n_2 is the number of moles of solute. This term is related to equilibrium relative humidity, ERH, as follows:

$$a_w = \frac{ERH}{100}$$ (2)

Relative humidity (RH) usually is reserved to characterize ambient atmospheric conditions such as might occur in a food warehouse or processing plant.

The a_w of a food significantly affects many of its attributes and characteristics. Texture, non-enzymatic browning reactions, enzymatic activity, lipid oxidation, and other aspects of foods may be influenced by manipulation of a_w levels. Microbial growth, and in some cases the production of microbial metabolites, may be particularly sensitive to alterations in a_w. Microorganisms generally have optimum and minimum levels of a_w for growth depending on other growth factors in their environments. Minimum levels permitting growth of a number of microorganisms are shown in Table 1. These and other aspects of the influence of a_w on microorganisms have been reviewed.[4, 19, 23]

The amount of water removed from or added to a food depends on the nature and amount of its water-soluble substances (its water binding capacity); the amount or percent of water present often does not adequately characterize the capacity to bind water or to limit its escaping tendency. A more useful parameter is the weight of water desorbed from the food into the vapor phase,

Table 1—Approximate Minimum Levels of A$_w$ Permitting Growth of Microorganisms at Temperatures near Optimal

Molds	a_w
Alternaria citri	0.84
Aspergillus candidus	0.75
A. conicus	0.70
A. flavus	0.78
A. fumigatus	0.82
A. niger	0.77
A. ochraceous	0.77
A. restrictus	0.75
A. sydowii	0.78
A. tamarii	0.78
A. terreus	0.78
A. versicolor	0.78
A. wentii	0.84
Botrytis cinerea	0.93
Chrysosporium fastidium	0.69
C. xerophilum	0.71
Emericella (Aspergillus) nidulans	0.78
Eremascus albus	0.70
E. fertilus	0.77
Eurotium (Aspergillus) amstelodami	0.70
E. carnoyi	0.74
E. chevalieri	0.71
E. echinulatum	0.62
E. herbariorum	0.74
E. repens	0.71
E. rubrum	0.70
Monascus (Xeromyces) bisporus	0.61
Mucor plumbeus	0.93
Paecilomyces variotii	0.84
Penicillium brevicompactum	0.81
P. chrysogenum	0.79
P. citrinum	0.80
P. cyclopium	0.81
P. expansum	0.83
P. fellutanum	0.80
P. frequentans	0.81

Table 1—(*continued*)

Molds	a_w
P. islandicum	0.83
P. martensii	0.79
P. palitans	0.83
P. patulum	0.81
P. puberulum	0.81
P. spinulosum	0.80
P. viridicatum	0.81
Rhizopus nigricans	0.93
Rhizoctonia solani	0.96
Stachybotrus atra	0.94
Wallemia sebi (Sporendonema epizoum)	0.75

Yeasts	
Debaryomyces hansenii	0.83
Saccharomyces bailii	0.80
S. cerevisiae	0.90
S. rouxii	0.62

Bacteria	a_w adjusted with salts
Enterobacter aerogenes	0.94
Bacillus cereus	0.95
B. megaterium	0.95
B. stearothermophilus	0.93
B. subtilis	0.90
Campylobacter jejuni	0.97
Clostridium botulinum type A	0.95
C. botulinum type B (proteolytic)	0.94
C. botulinum type E	0.97
C. perfringens	0.95
Escherichia coli	0.95
Halobacterium halobium	0.75
Lactobacillus viridescens	0.95
Listeria monocytogenes	0.93
Microbacterium spp.	0.94
Micrococcus halodenitrificans	0.86
M. lysodeikticus	0.93
Pseudomonas fluorescens	0.97
Salmonella spp.	0.95
Staphylococcus aureus	0.86
Vibrio costicolus	0.86
V. parahaemolyticus	0.94

which also can be defined as the partial pressure of water vapor (P in Equation (1)) at equilibrium in the food. Hence P is considered to be the concentration of desorbable water that is present,[11] and its ratio to the vapor pressure of pure water at the same temperature thus becomes its escaping "tendency" or fugacity ratio. The a_w level of a food actually is a measure or characterization of that water that is available to participate in the various chemical and physical reactions noted above. The approximate a_w levels of a number of foods are shown in Table 2.

Because of the strong influence of a_w on the wholesomeness and safety of many foods, regulations specifying a_w levels have appeared. An example is the exclusion of any food with an a_w of 0.85 or less from the Acidified and Low-Acid Canned Food Regulations (21CFR Parts 113 and 114). Another

Table 2—Approximate A$_w$ Values of Some Foods and Sodium Chloride and Sucrose Solutions

a_w	NaCl (%)	Sucrose (%)	Foods
1.00 to 0.95	0 to 8	0 to 44	Fresh meat, fruit, vegetables, canned fruit in syrup, canned vegetables in brine, frankfurters, liver sausage, margarine, butter, low-salt bacon
0.95 to 0.90	8 to 14	44 to 59	Processed cheese, bakery goods, high-moisture prunes, raw ham, dry sausage, high-salt bacon, orange juice concentrate
0.90 to 0.80	14 to 19	59 to saturation (0.86 a_w)	Aged chedder cheese, sweetened condensed milk, Hungarian salami, jams, candied peel, margarine
0.80 to 0.70	19 to saturation (0.75 a_w)	—	Molasses, soft dried figs, heavily salted fish
0.70 to 0.60	—	—	Parmesan cheese, dried fruit, corn syrup, licorice
0.60 to 0.50	—	—	Chocolate, confectionery, honey, noodles
0.40	—	—	Dried egg, cocoa
0.30	—	—	Dried potato flakes, potato crisps, crackers, cake mixes, pecan halves, peanut butter
0.20	—	—	Dried milk, dried vegetables, chopped walnuts

By permission of Academic Press.[23]

regulation (9CFR Part 319) specifies a brine salt content of 10% or an a_w level of 0.92 or less in hams not preserved with nitrates, nitrites, or a combination of these two. Other a_w-related standards have been proposed.

A number of methods have been described for the measurement of a_w. Some involve direct measurement of vapor pressure, which is then converted to a_w by reference to appropriate tables and applying Eq. (1). A vapor pressure manometer was described originally by Makower and Meyers;[14] however, subsequent articles[13, 22] have defined a number of improvements in this instrument. Other instruments, such as electric hygrometers, measure a_w indirectly through the measurement of crystal hydration, capacitance changes, etc. A psychrometric method for measuring a_w ranges above 0.5 has been described[16] as well as isopiestic equilibration techniques,[7, 15] bi-thermal equilibration procedures,[20] hair hygrometers, and dew point instruments.[1]

These and other methods have been summarized in Troller and Christian,[23] Prior,[17] and Guilbert and Morin.[10] Comparisons of the various techniques for measuring a_w levels have been conducted in several collaborative studies.[11, 12, 21]

Because of their ease of use, electric hygrometers and, more recently, dew point instruments are the instruments most frequently employed for the measurement of a_w by the U.S. food industry. For this reason, methods relating to these two types of instruments only will be included in this chapter. This, however, should not imply that these are the only acceptable methods. We recognize that the range of instrumentation in this field is expanding, and a single chapter containing operational procedures for each and every instrument is not feasible. We have chosen to approach this problem through specific recommendations concerning performance criteria for water activity measurement while leaving most of the specific operational procedures to the individual equipment manufacturer. The level of precision required in a_w measurement is dictated by how close the a_w of a specific product is to a specified critical value. It is felt generally that a laboratory routinely engaged in a_w determinations should be capable of measuring the a_w of a food with a precision of ± 0.01 a_w unit regardless of the method used. Since most commercial instruments, when properly calibrated and operated, are capable of achieving a standard deviation of ± 0.005 or less, this level of precision should not be difficult to attain. The sensitivity of these methods should be within 1% to 3% of solutions of known a_w values.

8.2   EQUIPMENT

8.21   Electric Hygrometers

Electric hygrometers consist of a potentiometer, a sample/sensor holder, and a sensor. Recorders, either built-in or added-on, are useful for determining the attainment of equilibrium, which is essential to all measurements. Indicators or panel lights designed to indicate an equilibrium condition within the sample holder are, in our opinion, unreliable and probably should best be ignored by the analyst.

Beckman/Sina, Novasina, and Rotronic Hygroskop are the brands of hygrometers most commonly in use at present. All of these instruments operate on the same basic principle; however, they vary with regard to certain features, for example, the integration of recorders and thermal control devices. Readout on recorder charts or liquid crystal digital displays appear as percent equilibrium relative humidity. This is easily converted to a_w by means of Equation (2). Range-specific potentiometers also may be built into these instruments or supplied as individual plug-in units. If these potentiometers are the adjustable type, they can be used for the calibration of the sensor around a specific set point or points. This will be covered in detail in Section 8.3.

1. Sample holders

Sample holders should be vapor-tight and of sufficient size to provide space for a representative sample, yet sufficiently small to permit equilibration of the sample within a reasonable amount of time. Samples can be stored in covered cups; however, some loss of moisture and consequent change in a_w level may occur. It is recommended that cups used for storage, for example, those containing calibration solutions, be sealed with a strip of electrical tape. Most instruments can be ordered with a sample holder and a supply of spare sample cups.

2. Sensors

Although the exact details of sensor composition are proprietary, these devices usually contain an immobilized electrolyte. Changes in the ERH within the closed sample chamber (sample and airspace are at equilibrium) are reflected in changes in the conductance of an electrical current through the sensor and across the electrolyte. This is detected electrically and read as described in Section 8.21.

8.22 Dew Point Instruments

Dew point instruments such as the Decagon CX-1 use a cooled mirror as the condensing surface. Cooling is usually achieved by a Peltier system that is electronically linked to a photo cell into which light is reflected from the condensing mirror. An air stream, in equilibrium with the sample, is directed at the mirror, which cools until condensation occurs on it. The temperature at which condensation begins is the dew point. The ERH can then be obtained by referring to a psychrometric chart. Because these instruments use a primary measurement of a_w, a calibration procedure is not necessary, although many users prefer to check readings of saturated salts occasionally.

Equilibration of these instruments is signaled by both sound and visual indicators and, according to the manufacturer's data, normally requires about 5 min. Sequential measurement of a wet and a dry sample may require intervening use of a desiccant, and only samples with an a_w of ≥ 0.30 can be measured with this device. As with many of these instruments, the Decagon dew point instrument can be interfaced with a computer and/or printer.

8.23   Constant Temperature Requirement for Hygrometers

Reference to standard tables relating temperature to the vapor pressure of water clearly shows that very small changes in temperature can produce disproportionate changes in vapor pressure. For this reason very precise control of temperature is essential when measuring a_w levels. There are several methods of achieving this.

The temperature employed should be the same as that used for calibration of the instrument. A temperature of 30°C is recommended because of its relative ease of temperature maintenance; however, most workers continue to use 25°C as their working temperature. Depending on the a_w range to be measured and the precision required, the temperature of the sensor should not fluctuate more than ± 0.2°C. Most commercially available hygrometers, in addition to relative humidity capability, also are able to measure and, in some cases, record temperatures within the sample headspace.

1. Integral thermal control

Some instruments, for example, those manufactured by Novasina, have temperature control systems that are basically integral with the instrument. Usually temperature maintenance is achieved with a heating and cooling Peltier element, and temperature fluctuations are minimized by use of large masses of metal surrounding the sample holder that serve as heat sinks, thus assuring greater accuracy and minimal temperature fluctuations.

2. Circulating water sample holders

One manufacturer, Rotronic, offers an optional sample holder that permits the circulation of water or other fluid within it. The fluid is obtained from a constant temperature bath, adjusted to the required temperature.

3. Other devices

Many hygrometers such as the Beckman/Sina and Rotronic units have no provision for controlling sample temperatures. Such control is most often attempted by placing the sensors and sample holders in a commercially available constant temperature box or incubator capable of holding a sample at 25°C. In our experience, few such units achieve the level of temperature control required unless modified with sensitive thermo-controllers and other electronic devices.

Uniform temperatures can be obtained within the cabinet by a forced draft fan, such as a small duct fan, placed within the chamber. It is advisable to operate this fan continuously to avoid temperature changes associated with heat from the fan motor should it be operated intermittently. Placing the sensor and sample holder in a styrofoam box or cooler chest also helps prevent temperature fluctuations. Immersion of sample holders within a waterbath is an alternative; however, care must be exercised to assure that water or water vapor does not contact the sensors.

8.3   CALIBRATION

For a variety of reasons, we recommend that saturated salts be used to calibrate instruments used for the measurement of a_w. The exception to this relates to measurements in the range of 0.92 to 0.97 and above. In this range, Flom et al.[8] found that solutions of varying NaCl content were superior to calibrating with saturated solutions. Here, care must be exercised to be sure that calibration errors do not occur as a result of moisture absorption from the environment.[5]

8.31   Preparation of Saturated Salts

A list of a_w values of a number of saturated salts suitable for the calibration of electric hygrometers is shown in Table 3. Reagent grade salts and deionized distilled water should be used for the preparation of solutions.[6] The salt is added to a sealable container and water is added in small increments, followed by stirring, until free liquid is observed. The volume of undissolved salt (slush) should be at least 25% of the total volume in the container. Slushes should be permitted to equilibrate to the measurement temperature prior to use and should be stored in the measurement cabinet or other site that approximates the measurement temperature. Slush containers must be sealed tightly. Some slushes such as NaBr may solidify gradually by crystal coalescence. This has no effect on a_w.

Some compounds are not suitable for calibration. Salts that decompose, hydrolyze, or undergo reactions with the components of air do not always give reliable, reproducible results and should not be used for this purpose. Compounds such as KOH, KI, chromates and dichromates, and ammonium compounds such as NH_4Cl are special problems in this regard.

8.32   Calibration Procedure

Depending on the type of instrument used, calibration procedures may involve either the establishment of a standard curve or the adjustment of a series of set point potentiometers, each one corresponding to a specific a_w standard. Generally, an instrument with three or fewer set points should be calibrated by means of a standard curve that has been obtained as recommended in the instructions accompanying the instrument.

1. Standard curve

If the equipment does not read out directly as ERH or a_w or has three or fewer set point potentiometers, a calibration curve can be constructed that relates instrument readout to standard a_w values for particular salts. This standard curve is constructed using at least five salts covering the range to

Table 3—Equilibrium Relative Humidity (ERH) of Some Saturated Salts[a]

Salt	20° C	25° C	30° C
LiBr	6.61 ± 0.58	6.37 ± 0.52	6.16 ± 0.47
LiCl	11.31 ± 0.31	11.30 ± 0.27	11.28 ± 0.24
KAc	23.11 ± 0.25	22.51 ± 0.32	21.61 ± 0.53
$MgCl_2$	33.07 ± 0.18	32.78 ± 0.16	32.44 ± 0.14
K_2CO_3	43.16 ± 0.33	43.16 ± 0.39	43.17 ± 0.50
$Mg(NO_3)_2$	54.38 ± 0.23	52.89 ± 0.22	51.40 ± 0.24
NaBr	59.14 ± 0.44	57.57 ± 0.40	56.03 ± 0.38
$NaNO_3$	75.36 ± 0.35	74.25 ± 0.32	73.14 ± 0.31
NaCl	75.47 ± 0.14	75.29 ± 0.12	75.09 ± 0.11
KBr	81.67 ± 0.21	80.89 ± 0.21	80.27 ± 0.21
KCl	85.11 ± 0.29	84.34 ± 0.26	83.62 ± 0.25
KNO_3	94.62 ± 0.66	93.58 ± 0.55[b]	92.31 ± 0.60
K_2SO_4	97.59 ± 0.53	97.30 ± 0.45	97.00 ± 0.40

[a]See reference 9.
[b]The value of 92.7 is considered to be more correct.[18]

be measured. It is recommended that calibration be conducted from highest to lowest a_w values. Readings are obtained after equilibrium has been obtained and plotted against values presented in Table 3, and a line is drawn through the points. This calibration plot will then be used for referral during the measurement of unknowns. All measurements must be within the range of calibration points; plots may not be extrapolated.

Where available, the use of a computer may be helpful in referring readout values to actual a_w levels. Usually a regression line of five or more points is plotted, and a_w levels along this plot can be programmed. In some cases, the a_w instrument may be connected directly to the computer.

2. Adjustable potentiometers

Some instruments are equipped with built-in or plug-in potentiometers that can be adjusted to a specific set point. The measurement of standard salt solutions is used to calibrate the potentiometers to specific a_w values according to the manufacturer's instructions. A few manufacturers provide an optional source of fixed or adjustable resistances that, for purposes of calibration, replace the sensor head with a known resistance. The potentiometer then is adjusted to the matching a_w level without the need to equilibrate the sensor. When used, this device circumvents the sensor, which usually is the most critical and sensitive portion of the instrument.

3. Combination

If the instrument to be used has a single set point potentiometer, or the set points supplied are not adequate to cover the desired measurement range, a combination of calibration procedures may be used. The set point is first calibrated and set according to the manufacturer's instructions. A calibration plot covering the range to be measured is then prepared as described above.

8.33   Equilibration

During calibration, care must be exercised to assure that equilibrium has been achieved within the sensor holder. Equilibration time increases directly with a_w. When plotted by a recorder, the tracing will be flat (unchanging) with time when equilibrium is reached. With analog or digital read-out devices, two consecutive readings differing by less than 0.01 a_w unit and obtained 10 min apart will usually indicate adequate equilibration when dealing with standard salts. Alternatively, successive dial readings can be plotted on a scale of a_w versus time.

8.34   Frequency of Calibration

The frequency with which instruments must be calibrated depends on the number of samples measured, desired precision of the instruments, type of foods measured, and age of the sensor. A standard salt with an a_w value close to that of the sample should be used to check calibration with sufficient frequency to ensure the degree of precision desired. This will permit mathematical compensation for a small amount of drift. If drift greater than 2% to 3% has occurred, the instrument should be recalibrated. It is advisable to recalibrate at least monthly; experience with each instrument usually will dictate calibration frequencies. Failure to maintain calibration for more than 1 or 2 days or the inability to bring the sensor within calibration limits usually indicates that it should be returned to the manufacturer for repair. These problems also may be the result of contamination (see Section 8.52). The instruction manual should be consulted in such cases.

8.4   MEASUREMENT OF SAMPLES

The sample to be measured must be uniform if possible, although care should be exercised in grinding a material to prevent excessive heat buildup with consequent reduction in a_w. Similarly, emulsions, especially water-in-oil emulsions, may be difficult to measure accurately, primarily because occlusion by the lipid portion prevents the "display" of water vapor pressure. In these cases, the emulsion may be broken through centrifugation or repeated freeze-thaw cycles and the resulting water phase measured. However, the water phase alone may not be representative of the a_w in emulsified water droplets, especially if the emulsifier itself has some capacity to bind water. Processed meat products can be especially troublesome in this respect.

To obtain measurements of unknown materials, the sample is placed in the sample dish, which is then placed in the holder and sealed. Following equilibration, which may require as many as 24 hr in rare cases, the a_w is determined from the digital readout, recorder plot, or calibration curve. The a_w should be determined for duplicate samples and averaged. Greater accuracy and precision may be possible with further replication.

As noted in Section 8.33, equilibration is generally considered to be achieved when two consecutive readings, obtained 10 min apart, differ by less than 0.01 a_w or when a plateau tracing is obtained on recording equipment. It should be cautioned that some samples, particularly those of relatively high a_w, may equilibrate slowly and these criteria may not always be sufficient. Conversely, some instruments may equilibrate faster, and experience with specific equipment and test samples may be the best guide to equilibration time.

8.5 PRECAUTIONS AND LIMITATIONS

8.51 Sample Considerations

The material to be sampled should be placed in the sample container quickly to minimize moisture exchange with ambient air. In the case of hygrometers, the sample volume should be as large as possible to reduce the amount of time required for equilibration. Dew point devices normally require that the sample cup be partially filled to prevent spilling and to avoid pickup of powdery materials by the circulating air stream.

Sample chambers must have properly fitted gaskets to prevent vapor exchanges with the atmosphere. Should leakage occur, it will manifest itself as erratic or continuously drifting readings or as excessively long equilibration periods. Sample holders should not absorb or contribute moisture to the sample void space.

8.52 Sensor Contamination

Mists, condensate, splashing, and all other forms of moisture must not contact the sensor. Mechanical filters and splash guards are integral with the sensor head in most instruments and should prevent this type of contamination.

A list of potential chemical contaminants is shown in Table 4. Should contamination occur, the sensor, in some cases, can be restored to normal functioning following a period of nonuse plus recalibration. Storage of the sensor at approximately 30°C under a slight vacuum may also be useful in this regard. In some situations, however, the damage is permanent, and the sensor must be discarded or returned to the manufacturer for repair. Some manufacturers provide a chemical filter, which is usually a fiber disc impregnated with charcoal. It should be used whenever the sensor is exposed to the substances listed in Table 4. Equilibration time will be significantly increased when the filter is used.

8.53 Sensor Care and Storage

Sensors are very sensitive to shock and vibrations and should be treated with care. When not in use, they should be stored in a dust- and odor-free

Table 4—Potential Chemical Contaminants of Hygrometric Sensors

Compound	Type of Contamination
Ammonia	T
Amines	T
Alcohols	T
Glycols	T
Mercury vapor	P
Ketones	P
Esters	P
Halogen gases	P
Hydrogen sulfide	P
Sulfur dioxide	P
Volatile acids (e.g., acetic)	T

T = Temporary
P = Permanent

environment at a relative humidity of less than 70% and a temperature between 20° and 50°C.

8.54   Other

The error inherent in measuring a_w by electric hygrometers is such that reporting results to three decimal places may give a false impression of the precision and accuracy of the method. It is suggested, therefore, that a_w readings be reported to only two decimal places.

8.6   MEASUREMENT OF ACIDITY

The term pH is defined as the hydrogen ion exponent.[24] The value of pH, the logarithm of the reciprocal of the hydrogen ion concentration in solution, is determined by measuring the difference in potential between two electrodes immersed in a sample solution. A suitable system consists of a potentiometer, a glass electrode, and a reference electrode. A precise pH determination can be made by making an electromotive force (emf) measurement of a standard buffer solution of known pH and then comparing that measurement with an emf measurement of a sample of the solution to be tested.

Although other methods, such as colorimetric, are available and occasionally used, potentiometric procedures probably represent the bulk of pH determinations in the examination of food.[3] Similarly, in-line and process determinations require somewhat different equipment and calibration procedures specific to the applications required. These are usually unique to the use intended and are beyond the scope of this chapter.

8.7   pH MEASUREMENTS

8.71   pH Meter

The primary instrument for pH determination is the pH meter or potentiometer. For most work, an instrument with a direct-reading pH scale is necessary. Batteries should be checked frequently to assure proper operation of battery-operated instruments. An instrument using an expanded unit scale or a digital read-out system is preferred since it allows more precise measurements.

The accuracy of most pH meters is stated to be approximately 0.1 pH unit, and reproducibility is usually ±0.05 pH unit or less. Some meters permit the expansion of any pH unit range to cover the entire scale and have an accuracy of approximately 0.01 pH unit and reproducibility of ±0.005 pH units.

8.72   Electrodes

The typical pH meter is equipped with a glass membrane electrode. The most commonly used reference electrode is the calomel electrode, which incorporates a salt bridge filled with saturated potassium chloride solution. Glass and reference electrodes may both be housed in a single combination electrode.

1. Care and use of electrodes
Calomel electrodes should be kept filled with saturated potassium chloride solution or other solution specified by the manufacturer because they may become damaged if they are allowed to dry out. For best results, electrodes should be soaked in buffer solution, distilled or deionized water, or other liquid specified by the manufacturer for several hours before using and should be kept ready by storing with tips immersed in distilled water or in buffer solution used for standardization. Electrodes should be rinsed with water before being immersed in the standard buffers and between sample determinations should be rinsed with water or the solution to be measured next.

2. Temperature
To obtain accurate results, the same temperature should be used for the electrodes, the standard buffer solution, and the samples for the standardization of the meter and pH determinations. Tests should be made at a temperature in the range from 20° to 30°C (68° to 86°F).

8.73   Standardization

When operating an instrument, the manufacturer's instructions should be followed and these techniques for pH determinations used:

1. Switch the instrument on and allow the electronic components to warm up and stabilize before proceeding.
2. Standardize the instrument and electrodes with standardization buffers

as close to the sample pH value as practical. For best accuracy, this should be within 0.15 pH units. Note the temperature of the buffer solution and set the temperature compensator control at the observed temperature.

3. Immerse the electrode tips in the buffer solution and take the pH reading, allowing 1 min for the meter to stabilize. Adjust the standardization control so that the meter reading corresponds to the pH of the known buffer (for example, 4.0) for the temperature observed. Rinse the electrodes with water and blot (do not wipe) with soft tissue. Repeat procedure with fresh portions of buffer solution until the instrument remains in balance on two successive trials. To check the operation of the pH meter, check the pH reading using another standard buffer.

Indicating electrodes may be checked for proper operation by using first an acid buffer, then a base buffer. First, standardize the electrodes using a pH 4.0 buffer at or near 25°C. Standardization control should be adjusted so that the meter reads exactly 4.0. Electrodes should be rinsed with water, then blotted and immersed in a pH 9.18 borax buffer. The pH reading should be within ± 0.3 units of the 9.18 value.

8.74   Measurement of Samples

The following procedures should be used to determine the pH of samples:

1. Adjust the temperature of the sample to the approximate room temperature, and set the temperature compensator control to the observed temperature. With some expanded-scale instruments, the sample temperature must be the same as the temperature of the buffer solution used for the standardization.

2. Rinse and blot the electrodes. Immerse the electrodes in the sample and take the pH reading, allowing 1 min for the meter to stabilize. Rinse and blot the electrodes and repeat on a fresh portion of sample. The two readings should be in agreement with one another to indicate that the sample is homogeneous. Report values to the nearest 0.05 pH unit. Oil and grease from the samples may coat the electrodes; therefore, it is advisable to clean and standardize the instrument frequently. When oily samples cause fouling problems, it may become necessary to rinse the electrode with ethyl ether.

8.75   Preparation of Samples

Some food products may consist of a mixture of liquid and solid components that differ in acidity. Other food products may be semisolid in character. The following are examples of preparation procedures for pH testing for each of these categories:

Liquid and solid component mixtures. Drain the contents of the container for 2 min on a U.S. standard No. 8 sieve (preferably stainless steel) or equivalent inclined at a 17° to 20° angle.

1. If the liquid contains sufficient oil to cause electrode fouling, separate the layers with a separatory funnel and retain the aqueous layer. Adjust the temperature of the aqueous layer to 25°C and determine its pH.

2. Remove the drained solids from the sieve. Blend to a uniform paste, adjust the temperature of the paste to 25°C and determine its pH.

3. Mix aliquots of solid and liquid fractions in the same ratio as found in the original container and blend to a uniform consistency. Adjust the temperature of the blend to 25° C and determine the equilibrated pH. Alternatively, blend the entire contents of the container to a uniform paste, adjust the temperature of the paste to 25°C and determine the equilibrated pH.

Marinated oil products. Separate the oil from the solid product. Blend the solid in a blender to a paste consistency; it may become necessary to add a small amount of distilled water to some samples to facilitate the blending. A small amount of added water will not alter the pH of most food products, but caution must be exercised concerning poorly buffered foods. No more than 20 ml of distilled water should be added to each 100 g of product. Determine the pH by immersing electrodes in the prepared paste after adjusting the temperature to 25°C.

Semisolid products. Food products of semisolid consistency such as puddings, potato salad, etc., may be blended to a paste consistency, and the pH may be determined on the prepared paste. Where more fluidity is required, 10 to 20 ml of distilled water may be added to 100 g of product. Adjust the temperature of the prepared paste to 25°C and determine its pH. Large amounts of water may alter pH levels; consequently, the amount of water addition should be minimized.

Large solid components. Internal pH level should be checked with spear electrodes as near as possible to the geometric center.

Emulsions. The pH of emulsions, such as margarine, peanut butter, meat products, etc., may be particularly difficult to obtain as a result of electrode contamination by lipids. In these situations, the water phase should be separated from the lipid phase and the pH of the former should be taken. This separation is most easily accomplished by centrifugation or alternating freeze-thaw cycles.

8.76   Precautions and Limitations

Temperature. Temperature can affect both the electrode potential and the hydrogen ion activity of a sample. Automatic temperature compensation adjusts for the effect of temperature change on the response of pH electrodes; however, it cannot compensate for pH changes in the sample that are the result of alterations in temperature. Thus, to obtain accurate results, standardization and pH determination should always be done at the same temperature and within the range of 20° to 30°C (68° to 86°F).

Buffers. Standard buffers may be commercially prepared or may be freshly prepared as outlined in "Official Methods of Analysis" of the Association of Official Analytical Chemists (AOAC).[2] Do not use buffers after their expiration date or if there is precipitation or microbial growth; CO_2 absorption and microbial growth or other contamination cause changes in the buffer pH. Do not pour used buffer back into the bottle. Buffers should be tightly capped during storage to reduce CO_2 absorption. Since pH buffer values change with temperature, the temperature of the buffer should be determined and the pH meter standardized accordingly.

8.8   pH PAPER MEASUREMENTS

Although not used in application requiring a high level of sensitivity, pH determinations using pH paper continue to be useful in some circumstances.

The normal procedure is to tear off a 3-in strip of pH paper from a roll specified for the expected pH range. The strip should be held only at one end and should not come in contact with other materials before use. The untouched end of the strip should be dipped in the sample to be measured and the color compared with that of various pH levels on the pH paper container label. As noted above, this method should not be considered in situations requiring sensitivity.

8.9   TITRATABLE ACIDITY

Measurement of the amount of acid present may be accomplished by titration of a suitable quantity of the sample with 0.1 N NaOH to pH 8.3 using a pH meter with constant stirring or to a phenolphthalein end-point. The percent of acid present is calculated as follows:

$$\% \text{ acid} = \frac{(\text{ml NaOH})(\text{N NaOH})(\text{millequivalent weight of acid})(100)}{\text{weight of sample in grams}}$$

8.10   REFERENCES

1. Anagnostopoulos, G. D. 1973. Water activity in biological systems: A dew-point method for its determination. Y. Gen. Microbiol 77: 233.

2. AOAC. 1990. Buffer solutions for calibration of pH equipment. "Official Methods of Analysis," 15th ed., p. 1214. Assn. of Off. Anal. Chem., Washington, D.C.

3. APHA. 1984. Canned foods-tests for cause of spoilage. 1984. In "Compendium of Methods for the Microbiological Examination of Foods," 2nd ed., ed. M. L. Speck, p. 774. Am. Pub. Health Assn., New York.

4. Beuchat, L. R. 1983. Influence of water activity on growth, metabolic activities, and survival of yeasts and molds. J. Food Prot. 46: 135.

5. Chirife, J. and Resnik, S. 1984. Unsaturated solutions of sodium chloride as reference sources of water activity at various temperatures. J. Food Sci. 49: 1486.

6. Chirife, J., Favetto, G., Ferro Fontan, C., and Resnik, S. 1983. The water activity of standard saturated salt solutions in the range of intermediate moisture foods. Lebensm. Wiss. Technol. 16: 36.

7. Fett, H. 1973. Water activity determination of foods in the range 0.80 to 0.99. J. Food Sci. 38: 1097.

8. Flom, W. D., Tanaka, N., Kayots, S. K., and Finn, L. M. 1986. Improved procedure for determining water activity in a high range. J. Assn. Off. Anal. Chem. 69: 952.

9. Greenspan, L. 1977. Humidity fixed points of binary saturated aqueous solutions. J. Res. Nat. Bur. Stand. -A, Phys. & Chem. 81A: 89.

10. Guilbert, S. and Morin, Ph. 1986. Definition and measurement of the activity of water: Review of usual methods and theoretical critiques. Lebensm. Wiss. Technol. 19: 395.

11. Hardman, T. M. 1976. Measurement of water activity. A critical appraisal of methods. In "Intermediate Moisture Foods," ed. R. Davies, G. G. Birch, and K. V. Parker. Appl. Sciences Publ., London.

12. Labuza, T. P., Acott, K., Tatini, S. R., and Lee, R. Y. 1976. Water activity determination: A collaborative study of different methods. J. Food Sci. 41: 910.

13. Lewicki, P. P., Busk, G. C., Peterson, P. L., and Labuza, T. P. 1978. Determination of factors controlling accurate measurement of a_w by the vapor pressure manometer. J. Food Sci. 43: 244.

14. Makower, B. and Meyers, S. 1943. A new method for the determination of moisture in dehydrated vegetables. Proc. Institute of Food Technologists. p. 156.

15. McCune, T. D., Lang, K. W., and Steinberg, M. P. 1987. Water activity determination with the proximity equilibration cell. J. Food Sci. 52: 37.

16. Prior, B. A. 1977. Psychrometric determination of water activity in the high a_w range. J. Food Prot. 40: 537.

17. Prior, B. A. 1979. Measurement of water activity in foods: A review. J. Food Prot. 42: 668.

18. Resnik, S. L., Favetto, G., Chirife, J., and Ferro Fontan, C. 1984. A world survey of water activity of selected saturated salt solutions used as standards at 25°C. J. Food Sci. 49: 510.

19. Rockland, L. B. and Beuchat, L. R. 1987. "Water Activity: Theory and Applications to Food." IFT Basic Symposium Series. Marcel Dekker, Inc., New York.

20. Stokes, R. H. 1947. The measurement of vapor pressures of aqueous solutions by bi-thermal equilibration through the vapor phase. J. Am. Chem. Soc. 69: 1291.

21. Stoloff, L. 1978. Calibration of water activity measuring instruments: Collaborative study. J. Assn. Off. Anal. Chem. 61: 1166.

22. Troller, J. A. 1983. Water activity measurements with a capacitance manometer. J. Food Sci. 48: 739.

23. Troller, J. A. and Christian, J. H. B. 1978. "Water Activity and Food." Academic Press, New York.

24. Wescott, C. C. 1978. "pH Measurements." Academic Press, New York.

Chapter 9

PSYCHROTROPHIC MICROORGANISMS

M. A. Cousin, J. M. Jay, and P. C. Vasavada

9.1 INTRODUCTION

9.11 History and Definition of Terms

In 1887 Forster observed microbial growth at 0°C, but not until 1902 was the term "psychrophile" used.[42] Psychrophiles have been defined by growth at low temperature, optimum temperature of growth, temperature of enumeration, and other criteria not related to temperature.[110] Mossel and Zwart[68] and Eddy[19] proposed the term "psychrotrophs" for microorganisms that grow at low temperatures but have higher temperature optima. Morita[66] suggested that the mesophilic microorganisms that grow at 0°C be called either psychrotolerant or psychrotrophic to contrast with psychrophilic microorganisms, which have a temperature optimum of 15°C, a maximum of 20°C, and a minimum of 0°C or below.

Microorganisms that grow in foods at refrigerated temperatures but have temperature optima above 20°C are now called psychrotrophs. Psychrotrophs can be defined as those microorganisms that produce visible growth at 7° ± 1°C within 7 to 10 days, regardless of their optimum growth temperatures. These definitions honor the long-standing practice of classifying microorganisms into three temperature groups—thermophiles, mesophiles, and psychrophiles—with psychrotrophs being a subgroup of the mesophiles. From a practical standpoint, the microorganisms that are most commonly associated with refrigerated foods and cause food spoilage are psychrotrophs and not psychrophiles.

9.12 Growth of Psychrophiles and Psychrotrophs

If a microorganism is to grow at low temperatures, then the substrate uptake, cell permeability, enzyme systems, and synthetic pathways must all function at low temperatures. Some of the theories concerning the mechanism of growth of psychrophiles and psychrotrophs focus upon the generation of low activation energy, presence of unsaturated fatty acids in the cell membranes,

153

conformational changes in the ribosomal proteins and regulatory enzymes, alterations in substrate uptake, and cell permeability.[14, 30, 35, 36, 66, 80, 82, 94]

9.13   Psychrophiles Involved in Food Spoilage

Psychrophilic bacteria are mainly gram-negative and are found in environments where temperatures are constantly below 15° to 20°C.[36] Most psychrophiles found in foods are among certain species of *Aeromonas, Alcaligenes, Cytophaga, Flavobacterium, Pseudomonas, Serratia,* and *Vibrio*. The gram-positive genera that have been isolated from arctic waters and soils include *Arthrobacter, Bacillus, Clostridium,* and *Micrococcus*. Psychrophilic yeasts, molds, and algae have also been identified. Among the psychrophilic genera of yeasts are *Cryptococcus, Leucosporidium,* and *Torulopsis*. Psychrophiles may be important in fish harvested from cold waters.

9.14   Psychrotrophs Involved in Food Spoilage

Psychrotrophs, which are widely distributed in nature, include bacteria, yeasts, and molds. Psychrotrophic bacteria have been studied more than either yeasts or molds. These bacteria include rods, cocci, and vibrios; sporeformers and non-sporeformers; gram-negative and gram-positive bacteria; and aerobes, facultative anaerobes, and anaerobes. The major psychrotrophic bacteria found in milk and dairy products,[12, 14, 44, 63] meats and poultry,[44, 51, 63, 64] and fish and seafood[39, 40, 44, 63, 103] include species of *Acinetobacter, Aeromonas, Alcaligenes, Arthrobacter, Bacillus, Chromobacterium, Citrobacter, Clostridium, Corynebacterium, Enterobacter, Escherichia, Flavobacterium, Klebsiella, Lactobacillus, Microbacterium, Micrococcus, Moraxella, Pseudomonas, Serratia, Staphylococcus,* and *Streptococcus*. In addition, species of *Alteromonas* (formerly *Pseudomonas putrefaciens*), *Photobacterium,* and *Vibrio* are also important in fish spoilage.[39, 103] Species of *Bacillus, Clostridium, Enterobacter, Erwinia, Flavobacterium, Pseudomonas,* and *Yersinia* cause soft-rotting of refrigerated vegetables.[9, 10, 58]

Psychrotrophic fungi have been isolated from refrigerated fresh animal and marine products and from fruits and vegetables. Among the yeast genera involved are *Candida, Cryptococcus, Debaryomyces, Hansenula, Kluveromyces, Pichia, Saccharomyces, Rhodotorula, Torulopsis,* and *Trichosporon*.[9, 14, 15, 41, 45] Mold genera that have psychrotrophic species include *Alternaria, Aspergillus, Botrytis, Cladosporium, Colletotrichum, Fusarium, Geotrichum, Monascus, Mucor, Penicillium, Rhizopus, Sporotrichum, Thamnidium,* and *Trichothecium*.[14, 41, 45, 51, 91] Fungi predominate in refrigerated food spoilage when water activity, acidity, processing, or packaging conditions select for their growth over bacteria.

The use of vacuum or modified atmospheric packaging of raw and processed meat, fish, and other foods favors the growth of both facultative anaerobes and true anaerobes in the oxygen-reduced environment. The major bacterial genera found in vacuum or modified atmospheric packaged foods include

Brochothrix, Lactobacillus, Leuconostoc, Pediococcus, and members of the *Enterobacteriaceae.*[55, 83] Makarios-Laham and Levin[59, 60] isolated psychrophilic *Vibrio* species from haddock, but their significance in fish spoilage is unknown.

9.15   Psychrotrophic Pathogens

The emergence of psychrotrophic foodborne pathogens in recent years has raised new concerns about the safety of refrigerated foods. The pathogenic psychrotrophs that grow at or below 5°C include *Aeromonas hydrophila, Clostridium botulinum* type E and nonproteolytic types B and F, *Listeria monocytogenes, Vibrio cholera, Yersinia enterocolitica,* and some strains of enteropathogenic *Escherichia coli.*[56, 74, 105] *A. hydrophila* is only a suspect foodborne pathogen at this time. Further information on these pathogenic psychrotrophs can be obtained in their respective chapters. Several recent reviews examined the role of psychrotrophic pathogens in vacuum or modified atmospheric packaged foods.[13, 26, 38, 50, 85, 104]

Foodborne pathogens such as *Bacillus cereus, Clostridium perfringens,* the proteolytic strains of *Clostridium botulinum, Salmonella* species, and *Staphylococcus aureus*[26, 74] have minimal growth temperatures between 5° and 15°C. The growth of these bacteria depends upon the ecology of the food, the competitive microflora, storage temperature and time, and other conditions. Nonpsychrotrophic mesophilic pathogens can survive at 5°C or less, but time and temperature abuse of the food may allow them to resume growth.

9.16   Significance of the Presence and Growth of Psychrotrophs in Foods

Psychrotrophs metabolize carbohydrates, proteins, and lipids across the range of temperatures at which foods are stored, but reaction rates are slower at temperatures at and below 7°C. Minor biochemical changes may occur early during the growth phase of some psychrotrophs, but several weeks of refrigeration may be necessary for the changes to become organoleptically apparent.

Information about the spoilage of specific food commodities can be found in their respective chapters. Some general reviews are available for the spoilage of milk and dairy products,[14, 20, 63] meat and poultry,[51, 63, 64] fish and seafoods,[39, 40, 63] and fruits and vegetables.[9, 41, 58, 91]

There is currently a trend in the United States, Europe, and Japan to market "minimally processed" refrigerated foods that range from deli-type salads to complete dinners.[10, 50, 56] Minimal processing calls for procedures such as low heat instead of sterilization or peeling and cutting fresh produce instead of leaving whole. Minimal processing includes various heat treatments, vacuum or modified atmospheric packaging, conventional or microwave heating after product-package assembly, and strict refrigerated distribution systems.[56] Two methods, "sous-vide," in which the food is placed in an oxygen impermeable bag, and "nouvelle carte," in which the food is packaged on a plate and placed in a vacuum pouch, involve minimal heat processing in the vacuum package and refrigerated distribution at 2° to 4°C. These processes for refrigerated foods create new microbiological concerns for both safety and expected shelf life. Packaging in vacuum and modified gaseous atmospheres selects for facultative anaerobes and anaerobes. The minimal heating kills vegetative cells, but not sporeformers. Since these processing and packaging methods are intended only to extend the shelf life, surviving psychrotrophic spoilage and pathogenic microorganisms can grow and dominate the microflora of these products. To avoid this situation, proper processing, packaging, storage, and distribution conditions must be maintained.

9.2 REVIEW OF METHODS USED TO ENUMERATE PSYCHROTROPHS IN FOODS

9.21 Cultural and Microscopic Methods

General reviews of the methods used to enumerate psychrotrophs have been published for dairy products,[14] fish,[40] and meats.[51] The traditional methods for enumerating psychrotrophs have involved either a manipulation of time and temperature and use of various media for plate counting methods or microscopy.[27, 28] Examples of the time and temperatures of incubation for psychrotrophic plate counts are 10 days at 7°C for pour plates or 7 to 8 days at 7°C for spread plates and 16 hr at 17°C followed by 3 days at 7°C. Incubation conditions using shorter times and higher temperatures have included 25 hr at 21°C for milk and cream,[33, 72, 81, 90, 97] 45 hr at 18°C for milk,[70] and 24 hr at 25°C for meat.[32]

Several variations of the plate count procedure provide equivalent accuracy for the enumeration of psychrotrophs. These methods (Chapters 4 and 39) include spiral plating,[33, 43, 81] dry film culture methods like Petrifilm™,[2, 29, 62] and hydrophobic grid-membrane filter (HGMF).[11, 88]

The composition of some selective media used for psychrotrophs is based on the assumption that most psychrotrophs are gram-negative bacteria. In the last two editions of this book,[27, 28] a selective medium was recommended that contains crystal violet and triphenyl tetrazolium chloride (CVT) and is incubated for either 48 hr at 30°C or 5 days at 22°C. Jay and Bue[47] found that the use of CVT agar with incubation for 48 hr at 30°C was not suitable for the enumeration of gram-negative psychrotrophs since many nonpsychrotrophic mesophiles grew well under these conditions. While crystal violet does inhibit gram-positive bacteria, CVT does not at the recommended usage of 50 ppm in CVT agar.[89] Although some investigators have found media containing these inhibitors to be suitable for assessing gram-negative psychrotrophs at temperatures that permit the growth of many nonpsychrotrophic mesophiles, this is a reflection of the relatively large numbers of psychrotrophs in the products examined. Most nonpsychrotrophic mesophiles will proliferate at temperatures between 22° and 40°C when incubated for 48 hr or more.

The direct microscopic count (DMC) and the microscopic colony count (MCC) have been used to enumerate psychrotrophs. Zall et al.[111] used a preincubation of 5 hr at 30°C before doing a DMC and noted that this method could be used since the psychrotrophic value was about 1% of the DMC. Juffs and Babel[48] did not find very good correlation between the MCC and the standard psychrotrophic count; however, they suggested that a slide incubated at 7°C for 48 hr may be useful for enumerating psychrotrophs.

9.22 Rapid and Automated Methods

Rapid methods have been developed for enumeration of psychrotrophs to overcome the disadvantage of the 7- to 10-day incubation time. Because many psychrotrophic bacteria are aerobic and possess the enzyme catalase, an increase in the concentration of this enzyme has been used to estimate the number of psychrotrophic bacteria in foods. The disk flotation method using the Catalasemeter correlated well with the psychrotrophic plate count for raw poultry.[108] Dodds et al.[16] concluded that the Catalasemeter was not reliable at determining the quality of vacuum-packaged cooked turkey ham when the counts were less than 10^4 cfu/g. The feasibility of using a catalase-based method for rapid evaluation of raw and pasteurized milk quality has been studied.[24, 37, 79, 106] Phillips and Griffiths[79] found no correlation between the catalase activity and the total count of milk; however, after a preincubation at 21°C for 25 hr in plate count agar with penicillin, crystal violet, and nisin, the detection limit was 10^5 to 10^6 cfu/ml. From these results, the catalase test would have little value for foods that have low psychrotrophic numbers or that have undergone conditions that select for a psychrotrophic spoilage microflora that is catalase-negative, e.g., lactobacilli.

Cytochrome c oxidase has been used to estimate the numbers of psychrotrophs in milk in order to predict its keeping quality.[52, 53, 54] Kroll[52] found that more than 10^4 microbes/ml of milk were needed to detect cytochrome c oxidase. For pasteurized milk, a preincubation for 18 hr at 20°C in the presence of benzalkonium chloride to inhibit gram-positive bacteria was needed for the population to reach 10^4 microbes/ml.[53] The standard plate count was a better predictor of keeping quality than the cytochrome c oxidase test; however, this method may be useful as an initial screening for the presence of $> 10^4$ psychrotrophs/ml or g of food.[54]

The impedance[17] method has been used to estimate the number of bacteria in fresh fish,[71, 102] raw meat,[22] raw milk,[23, 96] and pasteurized milk and cottage cheese.[4, 5, 6, 49] The rapid estimation of psychrotrophs in cod fillets, using brain heart infusion (BHI) broth at 20°C and impedance measurements for 5 to 16 hr, correlated well with the standard psychrotrophic plate count.[102] The estimation for raw milk showed good correlation with the plate count for psychrotrophs if the samples were analyzed after 16 to 21 hr at 20°C.[23, 96] Shelf life testing of milk and cottage cheese requires a preincubation of 18 hr at 18° to 21°C before impedance is measured at 21°C.[6, 49] The impedance method required only 1 to 2 days, compared to 7 to 9 days needed by the Moseley Keeping Quality Test, predicted the length of shelf life better, and required less labor. When Bishop and White[4, 5] compared plate counts to rapid methods for estimating the microbial shelf life of pasteurized milk and cottage cheese, both impedance and endotoxin detection were significantly correlated to shelf life. However, the impedance method produced a better predictive equation than endotoxin determination. Impedance has also been used to detect the growth of yeasts and molds in laboratory media.[87]

Gram-negative bacteria produce lipopolysaccharides (LPS) as part of their cell envelopes. A lysate produced from amoebocytes of the horseshoe crab (*Limulus polyphemus*) reacts with LPS, and the reaction can be measured by one of three methods—gelation, turbidity, or chromogenesis. Test results can be obtained in 1 hr by tube gelation, or in about 30 min by the other methods. The *Limulus* amoebocyte lysate (LAL) test can be used to detect gram-negative bacteria in foods. The LAL test has been used to estimate the number of gram-negative psychrotrophs in such refrigerated foods as meats, milk, fish, and salads.[3, 4, 5, 16, 21, 34, 46, 61, 65, 95, 98] Dodds et al.[16] reported that LAL values correlated with the number of *Enterobacteriaceae* in vacuum-packaged cooked turkey with a sensitivity less than 100 cells/g. A sensitivity of 15 bacteria per test was reported for analysis of milk.[95] LAL correlated well with the bacterial count for determining the shelf life of non-acidified vegetable salads stored at refrigeration and abuse temperatures.[61] In a study of lean fish, Sullivan et al.[98] found that LAL values agreed with aerobic plate counts and total volatile bases. Using a microtiter plate method for LAL, Fallowfield and Patterson[21] were able to detect 10^2 to 10^3 *Pseudomonas* spp/g in beef and pork stored at 4°C. If LAL is to be used to estimate psychrotrophs in refrigerated foods, then correlation factors for the accept-reject levels need to be established.[5, 25, 34, 95]

Other rapid methods that have been studied may not always distinguish psychrotrophs from nonpsychrotrophic mesophiles. These methods include HGMF,[11, 88] direct epifluorescent filter technique (DEFT),[18, 53, 69, 76, 77, 78, 84] (Chapter 5) estimation of adenosine triphosphate (ATP) by bioluminescence,[1, 7, 8, 57, 73, 92, 93, 107, 109] (Chapter 39) and calorimetry.[31] Methods that are based on detection of amines[86] and aminopeptidase activity[75] still need more research before their significance in enumerating psychrotrophs can be assessed.

9.3   GENERAL RECOMMENDATIONS

9.31   Method Selection

The choice of a method will depend on the reason for enumerating psychrotrophs, time and equipment available, accuracy needed, intended use of the results, type of refrigerated food, and degree of processing. When an accurate number of psychrotrophs is needed, plate count methods must be used. It may be necessary to choose time and temperature conditions that simulate either the storage conditions of the food or the possible abuse conditions. Selection of the method for enumerating psychrotrophs must involve consideration of sublethally injured or stressed cells. Absolute conditions cannot be given for every food or every situation.

9.32   Media Selection

The selection of media for enumeration will depend on the food, types of psychrotrophs expected, recommendations of equipment manufacturers, length of incubation, reactions expected, and other relevant factors. Media other than those listed below may prove valuable.

9.4   SAMPLE PREPARATION

9.41   Sample Collection

Samples must be collected aseptically (Chapter 2) and anlayzed promptly. Refrigerated storage could allow psychrotrophs to increase. Refrigerated samples should not be frozen because many psychrotrophs are sensitive to freezing and can be injured or killed. If samples must be frozen for shipment, then the possibility of some death must be considered.

9.42   Sample Homogenization

Samples should be homogenized with diluent in a blender for 2 min or in a stomacher. Because psychrotrophs are sensitive to heat, blending for more than 2 min is discouraged to prevent the generation of heat that can result in cell injury or death. Also, excessive blending of molds can cause fragmentation of the mycelia, depending on blade sharpness, volume, speed, and time (Chapter 16). The use of a stomacher in preference to the blender lessens the likelihood of these problems.

9.5   EQUIPMENT, MEDIA, MATERIALS, AND REAGENTS

Refer to the specific section in recommended methods for equipment that is needed for each method. Incubators that can be maintained at 7° to 25° ± 1°C are necessary.

9.51   Media

1. Nonselective agars: standard methods (plate count) agar or trypticase soy agar for bacteria; and potato dextrose agar, malt extract agar, or plate count agar plus antibiotics for yeasts and molds (Chapter 16).
2. Media and reagents for the rapid methods can be obtained from the manufacturers (Chapter 39).

9.6   PRECAUTIONS

9.61   Incubation Temperatures

Different types of refrigerated foods are normally processed and held at temperatures of refrigeration that are specific for the food commodity. The incubation temperature used for the enumeration may not lead to adequate assessment of the psychrotrophic population that will grow in the food because microorganisms may grow in laboratory media but not in the food, and vice versa. Therefore, caution must be used when interpreting results of the enumeration of psychrotrophic populations in foods.

Sublethally injured psychrotrophs may not be detected analytically but may cause food spoilage or foodborne illness. Therefore, steps to recover sublethally injured cells should be included in enumeration and detection methods. (Chapter 7.)[67]

9.62   Pour Plate Versus Spread Plate Techniques

Psychrotrophs are especially susceptible to injury or death when agar that is held above 45°C is used for the pour plate.[101] Hence, a spread/surface plate or spiral plater technique (Chapter 4) should be used whenever possible. Plates can be pre-poured and stored at 5°C for several days or weeks before use. Dry film such as Petrifilm℠ may also be used in place of the traditional plating technique.

9.7   RAPID DETECTION

Obtaining results sooner than 10 days is pragmatically desirable, and efforts must continue to find more rapid methods for the enumeration of psychrotrophs in foods. Rapid detection of psychrotrophs in raw ingredients, on-line quality control samples, and shelf life samples is important. Three useful rapid methods are impedance, LAL assays, and enzymatic assays.

9.71   Impedance Determination

Samples of solid foods (meats, poultry, fish, vegetables, etc.) are blended for 1 min in 0.1% peptone water to make a 1:10 dilution. A 1.0 ml aliquot of the 1:10 dilution is added to 1.0 ml of BHI broth in the sterile well of the inpedance detection instrument. Samples are incubated at 21°C and continuously monitored for up to 24 hr depending on the sample and the degree of contamination. Preliminary incubation for 15 to 24 hr at 18° to 21°C in BHI broth may be used to obtain early detection and shelf life predictions because foods that have undergone processing normally will have lower counts than raw foods. After preincubation, 1 ml of the mixed sample is placed in the well of the impedance detection instrument and incubated at 21°C; thereafter, measurements are recorded for up to 24 hr. The impedance detection time is recorded and used to estimate the number of psychrotrophs in the sample.

Liquid foods such as milk and juice can be added directly to either broth or agar in the wells of the impedance detection instrument. Modified plate count agar has been used for milk, and potato dextrose agar can be used to detect yeasts and molds in juices. A 0.5 ml sample of the liquid food is added to the agar in the well and incubated at 21°C for up to 24 hr for bacteria and 25° to 28°C for 1 to 2 days for yeasts and molds. Preincubation in plate count broth at 18°C for 18 hr can be done to assess the keeping quality of heat-processed milk and dairy products. The impedance detection time is recorded and the estimation of microbial numbers made.

The equipment manufacturers recommend media and incubation conditions, which should be followed for the specific foods being analyzed.

9.72   *Limulus* Amoebocyte Lysate (LAL) Assay

The tube gelation method has been used more extensively than either the turbidity or the chromogenic substrate methods, and its use is described below. However, the chromogenic substrate is the newer of the three basic methods, provides results in about 30 min, is more sensitive (LPS detected from 1 to < 5pg/ml), and is becoming popular. The basic operation and automation of the chromogenic substrate has been described by Tsuji et al.[100] and reviewed by Jay.[46]

The most important considerations in the use of the tube gelation method are (a) source and sensitivity of LAL reagent, (b) whether single- or multi-test vials or reagent are to be used, and (c) the choice of endotoxin or LPS standard. Suppliers of freeze-dried LAL reagents, such as Association of Cape Cod (Woods Hole, Mass.), Difco Laboratories with Pyrotest (Detroit, Mich.), and Sigma Chemical Co. with E-Toxate (St. Louis, Mo.), generally provide complete instructions for the proper use of their reagents, and these should be followed carefully. LAL reagents can be obtained with different levels of sensitivity, usually expressed in endotoxin units (EU).

Since LPS from different gram-negative bacteria varies in its reactivity to the LAL reagent, it is essential that a standard reference endotoxin preparation be used. These are available with complete instructions for use from LAL reagent suppliers. The two reference endotoxins of choice are those prepared from *Escherichia coli* 0113:H10 (EC-2) or *E. coli* 055:B5.

The tube gelation method described below is taken from the review by Jay.[46] LAL assay methods require that all utensils and glassware be pyrogen free. Glassware can be depyrogenated by heating in a dry-air oven at temperatures above 180°C for about 3 hr. Sterile pipettes and disposable tubes are generally free of pyrogens before use, and pyrogen-free water is best purchased from a firm that supplies parenteral products. Specific instructions for conducting a tube gelation test are usually provided by the LAL reagent manufacturer.

LAL reagent is supplied either in ready-to-use or single-test vials, or in multi-use vials. Follow the preparation and storage directions that come with the reagents. It is generally a good idea to cover the tubes with aluminum foil until used. The tubes should be used the same day although some manufacturers indicate that the tubes may be frozen and thawed once. Quality control procedures and both negative and positive controls are supplied by the manufacturers.

Food samples should be serially diluted, using pyrogen-free water or suitable buffer, so as to provide dilutions that will produce negative results. Tenfold dilutions provide results comparable to twofold dilutions with great savings of both reagents and labor. Beginning with the highest dilution (lowest endotoxin concentration), one may use the same pipette tip to transfer either 0.1 or 0.2 ml of diluted sample to separate LAL reagent tubes. The tubes are vortexed gently, incubated in a waterbath at 37°C for 1 hr, and read by inverting 180° and noting gelation. Simultaneously, an endotoxin standard should be included using an appropriate reference endotoxin. The two-fold diluted endotoxin standard should be treated in the same way as the diluted test preparation; the sensitivity of the LAL preparation to LPS is determined by using this standard to define the lowest quantity that produces a gel.

The quantity of endotoxin or LPS in test samples is determined by multiplying the reciprocal of the highest sample dilution by the LAL-determined sensitivity value. For example, if the highest dilution of endotoxin standard that produces a firm gel in the LAL reagent is 0.1 ng, the sensitivity of the LAL reagent is, thus, 0.1 ng. If using the above LAL reagent and the highest dilution of food that produces a firm gel is 10^3, then the total endotoxin or LPS in food is 0.1 ng $\times$ 1000 = 100 ng/ml.

9.73   Enzymatic Methods—Catalase and Cytochrome Oxidase

Enzymatic methods are not sensitive enough to detect microbial populations below 10^4 cells/ml or g; therefore, use is restricted to foods with high microbial loads. A preincubation of 4 to 6 hr that may or may not involve selective enrichment media can improve both the selectivity and the sensitivity of these methods. Use of these methods for solid foods needs further refinement for the extraction of the enzymes from foods.

The catalase test can be done by using instruments such as the Catalase-meter (Bioengineering Group, Ltd., New Haven, Conn.). The Catalasemeter operates on the principle of disc flotation. A paper disc is saturated with liquid foods and the disc is then dropped into a tube containing 5 ml of stabilized peroxide reagent (3% H_2O with 10^{-6} M EDTA). The disc flotation time (time elapsed between the disc's sinking and then floating up in the reagent) as measured by the instrument is inversely proportional to the concentration of catalase in the solution that was absorbed by the disc. Consult the instrument manufacturer's manual for more information.

The cytochrome c oxidase test can be done by treating 4 ml of sample with 1 ml of a freshly prepared 1% N,N,N',N'-tetramethyl-p-phenylene-diamine dihydrochloride followed by incubation at 25°C for 5 min. Blue color can be evaluated either visually against reference color standards or spectrophotometrically. The intensity of the blue color is proportional to the concentration of microorganisms in the food.

9.8 PROCEDURES FOR ENUMERATION OF PSYCHROTROPHS

9.81 Plate Count Method

An agar plate-count method using plate count or trypticase soy agar, or dry film such as Petrifilm℠, is recommended for general enumeration of bacteria. Details and procedures are described in Chapter 4. Enumeration procedures for yeasts and molds can be found in Chapter 16. Incubate plates for 10 days at 7° ± 1°C since this is the reference definition for psychrotrophs. Alternatively, incubation for 16 hr at 17°C followed by incubation for 3 days at 7°C can be used when results are needed in less than 10 days[99].

Count the colonies as described in Chapter 4. Record all counts as psychrotrophs per milliliter, gram, or square centimeter depending upon the method of sampling.

9.9 INTERPRETATION

The enumeration of psychrotrophs in refrigerated foods gives an indication of the potential spoilage, keeping quality, or safety of the food. However, caution should be exercised when trying to make absolute predictions about a food based on these results. Some temperatures of refrigeration may be close to the minimal growth temperature, and the enumeration temperature may be closer to the optimum. The temperatures used for food storage and for detection should be closely comparable to achieve meaningful results. Also, the nature of the food is important. If the food has been refrigerated for some time, the numbers can represent a normal increase in psychrotrophs rather than a poor quality product.

Processing can kill or injure psychrotrophs, and analyzing foods immediately after processing may not allow time for injured cells to recover. If processed foods are stored in the refrigerator for extended periods, even a few cells can grow to large enough numbers to cause eventual spoilage in a few days or weeks. Also, psychrotrophic pathogens can grow and cause outbreaks of foodborne disease if growth is not controlled during processing, packaging, storage, and distribution.

9.10   REFERENCES

1. Anderson, R. and Labell, F. 1988. Rapid microbial tests safeguard fresh deli foods. Food Proc. 49 (12): 90.
2. Bailey, J. S. and Cox, N. A. 1987. Evaluation of the Petrifilm™ SM and VRB dry media culture plates for determining microbial quality of poultry. J. Food Prot. 50: 643.
3. Bishop, J. R. and Bodine, A. B. 1986. Quality assessment of pasteurized fluid milk as related to lipopolysaccharide content. J. Dairy Sci. 69: 3002.
4. Bishop, J. R. and White, C. H. 1985a. Estimation of potential shelf life of pasteurized fluid milk utilizing bacterial numbers and metabolites. J. Food Prot. 48: 663.
5. Bishop, J. R. and White, C. H. 1985b. Estimation of potential shelf life of cottage cheese utilizing bacterial numbers and metabolites. J. Food Prot. 48: 1054.
6. Bishop, J. R., White, C. H., and Firstenberg-Eden, R. 1984. Rapid impedimetric method for determining the potential shelf life of pasteurized whole milk. J. Food Prot. 47: 471.
7. Bossuyt, R. 1981. Determination of bacteriological quality of raw milk by an ATP assay technique. Milchwissenschaft 36: 257.
8. Bossuyt, R. 1982. A 5 minute ATP platform test for judging the bacteriological quality of raw milk. Neth. Milk Dairy J. 36: 355.
9. Brackett, R. E. 1987. Microbiological consequences of minimally processed fruits and vegetables. J. Food Qual. 10: 195.
10. Brocklehurst, T. F., Zaman-Wong, C. M., and Lund, B. M. 1987. A note on the microbiology of retail packs of prepared salad vegetables. J. Appl. Bacteriol. 63: 409.
11. Brodsky, M. H., Entis, P., Entis, M. P., Sharpe, A. N., and Jarvis, G. A. 1982. Determination of aerobic plate and yeast and mold counts in foods using an automated hydrophobic grid-membrane filter technique. J. Food Prot. 45: 301.
12. Collins, E. B. 1981. Heat resistant psychrotrophic microorganisms. J. Dairy Sci. 64: 157.
13. Corlett, D. A. 1989. Refrigerated foods and use of hazard analysis and critical control point principles. Food Technol. 43(2): 91.
14. Cousin, M. A. 1982. Presence and activity of psychrotrophic microorganisms in milk and dairy products: A review. J. Food Prot. 45: 172.
15. Davenport, R. R. 1980. Cold-tolerant yeasts and yeast-like organisms. In "Biology and Activities of Yeasts," ed. F. A. Skinner, S. M. Passmore, and R. R. Davenport, p. 215. Academic Press, New York.
16. Dodds, K. L., Holley, R. A., and Kempton, A. G. 1983. Evaluation of the catalase and *Limulus* amoebocyte lysate tests for rapid determination of the microbial quality of vacuum-packed cooked turkey. Can Inst. Food Sci. Technol. J. 16: 167.
17. Easter, M. C. and Gibson, D. C. 1989. Detection of microorganisms by electrical measurements. Prog. Indus. Microbiol. 26: 57.
18. Easter, M. C., Kroll, R. G., Farr, L., and Hunter, A. C. 1987. Observations on the introduction of the DEFT for the routine assessment of bacteriological quality. J. Soc. Dairy Technol. 40: 100.
19. Eddy, B. P. 1960. The use and meaning of the term "psychrotrophic." J. Appl. Bacteriol. 23: 189.
20. Fairbairn, D. J. and Law, B. A. 1986. Proteinases of psychrotrophic bacteria: Their production, properties, effects, and control. J. Dairy Sci. 53: 139.
21. Fallowfield, H. J. and Patterson, J. T. 1985. Potential value of the *Limulus* lysate assay for the measurement of meat spoilage. J. Food Technol. 20: 467.
22. Firstenberg-Eden, R. 1983. Rapid estimation of the number of microorganisms in raw meat by impedance measurement. Food Technol. 37: 64.
23. Firstenberg-Eden, R. and Ticarico, M. K. 1983. Impedimetric determination of total, mesophilic, and psychrotrophic counts in raw milk. J. Food Sci. 48: 1750.
24. Fischer, J. and Vasavada, P. C. 1987. Rapid detection of abnormal milk by the catalase test. J. Dairy Sci. 70(Suppl. 1): 75.

25. Forster, M. A. 1985. Factors affecting the use of the Limulus amoebocyte lysate test in the food industry. N. Z. J. Dairy Sci. Technol. 20: 163.
26. Genigeorgis, C. A. 1985. Microbial and safety implications of the use of modified atmospheres to extend the storage life of fresh meat and fish. Int. J. Food Microbiol. 1: 237.
27. Gilliland, S. E., Michener, H. D., and Kraft, A. A. 1976. Psychrotrophic microorganisms. In "Compendium of Methods for the Microbiological Examination of Foods," 1st ed., ed. M. L. Speck, p. 173. Am. Pub. Health Assn., Washington, D.C.
28. Gilliland, S. E., Michener, H. D., and Kraft, A. A. 1984. Psychrotrophic microorganisms. In "Compendium of Methods for the Microbiological Examination of Foods," 2nd ed., ed. M. L. Speck, p. 135. Am. Pub. Health Assn., Washington, D.C.
29. Ginn, R. E., Packard, V. S., and Fox, T. L. 1984. Evaluation of the 3M dry medium culture plate (Petrifilm® SM) method for determining numbers of bacteria in raw milk. J. Food Prot. 47: 753.
30. Gounot, A.-M. 1986. Psychrophilic and psychrotrophic microorganisms. Experientia 42: 1192.
31. Gram, L. and Sogaard, H. 1985. Microcalorimetry as a rapid method for estimation of bacterial levels in ground beef. J. Food Prot. 48: 341.
32. Greer, G. G. 1981. Rapid detection of psychrotrophic bacteria in relation to retail beef quality. J. Food Sci. 46: 1669.
33. Griffiths, M. W., Phillips, J. D., and Muir, D. D. 1980. Rapid plate counting techniques for enumeration of psychrotrophic bacteria in pasteurized double cream. J. Soc. Dairy Technol. 33: 8.
34. Hansen, K., Mikkelsen, T., and Moller-Madsen,A. 1982. Use of the Limulus test to determine the hygienic status of milk products as characterized by levels of Gram-negative bacterial lipopolysaccharide present. J. Dairy Res. 49: 323.
35. Herbert, R. A. 1981. A comparative study of the physiology of psychrotrophic and psychrophilic bacteria. In "Psychrotrophic Microorganisms in Spoilage and Pathogenicity," ed. T. A. Roberts, G. Hobbs, J. H. B. Christian, and N. Skovgaard, p. 3. Academic Press, New York.
36. Herbert, R. A. 1986. The ecology and physiology of psychrophilic microorganisms. In "Microbes in Extreme Environments," ed. R. A. Herbert and G. A. Codd, p. 1. Academic Press, New York.
37. Hill, S. D., Richter, R. L., and Dill, C. W. 1988. Evaluation of a catalase-based method to predict the shelf life of pasteurized milk. J. Dairy Sci. 71(Suppl. 1): 112.
38. Hintlian, C. B. and Hotchkiss, J. H. 1986. The safety of modified atmosphere packaging: A review. Food Technol. 39(12): 70.
39. Hobbs, G. 1983. Microbial spoilage of fish. In "Food Microbiology: Advances and Prospects," ed. T. A. Roberts and F. A. Skinner, p. 217. Academic Press, New York.
40. Hobbs, G. and Hodgkiss, W. 1982. The bacteriology of fish handling and processing. In "Developments in Food Microbiology—1," ed. R. Davies, p. 71. Applied Science Publishers, Englewood, N. J.
41. Hsu, E. J. and Beuchat, L. R. 1986. Factors affecting microflora in processed fruits. In "Commercial Fruit Processing," 2nd ed. ed. J. G. Woodroof and B. S. Luh, p. 129. AVI Publ. Co., Westport, CT.
42. Ingraham, J. L. and Stokes, J. L. 1959. Psychrophilic bacteria. Bacteriol. Rev. 23: 97.
43. Jarvis, B., Lach, V. H., and Wood, J. M. 1977. Evaluation of the spiral plate maker for the enumeration of microorganisms in food. J. Appl. Bacteriol. 43: 149.
44. Jay, J. M. 1986. "Modern Food Microbiology," 3rd ed. Van Nostrand Reinhold Co., New York.
45. Jay, J. M. 1987. Meats, poultry, and seafoods. In "Food and Beverage Mycology," 2nd ed., ed. L. R. Beuchat, p. 155. Van Nostrand Reinhold Co., New York.
46. Jay, J. M. 1989. The Limulus amoebocyte lysate (LAL) test. Prog. Indus. Microbiol. 26: 101.

47. Jay, J. M. and Bue, M. B. 1987. Ineffectiveness of crystal violet tetrazolium agar for determining psychrotrophic gram-negative bacteria. J. Food Prot. 50: 147.

48. Juffs, H. S. and Babel, F. J. 1975. Rapid enumeration of psychrotrophic bacteria in raw milk by the microscopic colony count. J Milk Food Technol. 38: 333

49. Kahn, P. and Firstenberg-Eden, R. 1987. Prediction of shelf life of pasteurized milk and other fluid dairy products in 48 hours. J Dairy Sci. 70: 1544.

50. King, A. D. and Bolin, H. R. 1989. Physiological and microbiological storage stability of minimally processed fruits and vegetables. Food Technol. 43(2): 132.

51. Kraft, A. A. 1986. Psychrotrophic organisms. In "Advances in Meat Research." Volume 2. "Meat and Poultry Microbiology," ed. A. M. Pearson and T. R. Dutson, p. 191. AVI Publishing Co., Westport, CT.

52. Kroll, R. G. 1985. The cytochrome c oxidase test for the rapid detection of psychrotrophic bacteria in milk. J. Appl. Bacteriol. 59: 137.

53. Kroll, R. G. and Rodrigues, U. M. 1986. The direct epifluorescent filter technique, cytochrome c oxidase test, and plate count method for predicting the keeping quality of pasteurized cream. Food Microbiol. 3: 185.

54. Kroll, R. G. and Rodrigues, U. M. 1986. Prediction of the keeping quality of pasteurized milk by the detection of cytochrome c oxidase. J. Appl. Bacteriol. 60: 21.

55. Lannelongue, M., Finne, G., Hanna, M. O., Nickelson, R., and Vanderzant, C. 1982. Microbial and chemical changes during storage of swordfish (*Xiphias glasius*) steaks in retail packages containing CO_2-enriched atmospheres. J. Food Prot. 45: 1197.

56. Lechowich, R. V. 1988. Microbiological challenges of refrigerated foods. Food Technol. 42(12): 84.

57. Littel, K. J., Pikelis, S., and Spurgash, A. 1986. Bioluminescent ATP assay for rapid estimation of microbial numbers in fresh meat. J. Food Prot. 49: 18.

58. Lund, B. M. 1983. Bacterial spoilage. In "Post-Harvest Pathology of Fruits and Vegetables," ed. C. Dennis, p. 219. Academic Press, New York.

59. Makarios-Laham, I. and Levin, R. E. 1984. Isolation from haddock tissue of psychrophilic bacteria with maximum growth temperature below 20°C. Appl. Environ. Microbiol. 48: 439.

60. Makarios-Laham, I. and Levin, R. E. 1985. Autolysis of psychrophilic bacteria from marine fish. Appl. Environ. Microbiol. 49: 997.

61. Manvell, P. M. and Ackland, M. R., 1986. Rapid detection of microbial growth in vegetable salads at chill and abuse temperatures. Food Microbiol. 3: 59.

62. McGoldrick, K. F., Fox, T. L., and McAllister, J. S. 1986. Evaluation of a dry medium for detecting contamination on surfaces. Food Technol. 40(4): 77.

63. McKellar, R. C., ed. 1989. "Enzymes of Psychrotrophs in Raw Food." CRC Press, Boca Raton, Fla.

64. McMeekin, T. A. 1982. Microbial spoilage of meats. In "Developments in Food Microbiology—1," ed. R. Davies, p. 1. Applied Science Publishers, Englewood, N.J.

65. Mikolajcik, E. M. and Brucker, R. B. 1983. Limulus amoebocyte lysate assay—A rapid test for the assessment of raw and pasteurized milk quality. Dairy Food Sanit. 3: 129.

66. Morita, R. Y. 1975. Psychrophilic bacteria. Bacteriol. Rev. 39: 144.

67. Mossel, D. A. A. 1987. The microbiological examination of food and drinking water in the framework of health protection. In "Royal Society of Medicine Congress and Symposium Series No. 113," ed. A. J. Balows, p. 45. Royal Society of Medicine Series Ltd., London.

68. Mossel, D. A. A. and Zwart, H. 1960. The rapid tentative recognition of psychrotrophic types among *Enterobacteriaceae* isolated from foods. J. Appl. Bacteriol. 23: 185.

69. Neaves, P., Jervis, D. I, and Prentice, G. A. 1987. A comparison of DEFT clump counts obtained in eight dairy laboratories receiving replicate samples of preserved raw milk. J. Soc. Dairy Technol. 40: 53.

70. Oehlrich, H. K. and McKellar, R. C. 1983. Evaluation of an 18°C/45-hour plate count

technique for the enumeration of psychrotrophic bacteria in raw and pasteurized milk. J. Food Prot. 46: 528.

71. Ogden, I. D. 1986. Use of conductance methods to predict bacterial counts in fish. J. Appl. Bacteriol. 61: 263.

72. Oliveria, J. S. and Parmelee, C. E. 1976. Rapid enumeration of psychrotrophic bacteria in raw and pasteurized milk. J. Milk Food Technol. 39: 369.

73. Patel, P. D. and Williams, A. P. 1985. A note on estimation of food spoilage yeasts by measurement of adenosine triphosphate (ATP) after growth at various temperatures. J. Appl. Bacteriol. 59: 133.

74. Palumbo, S. A. 1986. Is refrigeration enough to restrain foodborne pathogens? J. Food Prot. 49: 1003.

75. Perez De Castro, B., Asensio, M. A., Sanz, B., and Ordonez, J. A. 1988. A method to assess the bacterial count of refrigerated meat. Appl. Environ. Microbiol. 54: 1462.

76. Pettipher, G. L. 1981. Rapid methods for assessing bacterial numbers in milk. Dairy Ind. Int. 46(11): 15.

77. Pettipher, G. L. 1989. The direct epifluorescent filter technique. Prog. Indus. Microbiol. 26: 19.

78. Pettipher, G. L., Mansell, R., McKinnon, C. H., and Cousins, C. M. 1980. Rapid membrane filtration-epifluorescent microscopy technique for direct enumeration of bacteria in raw milk. Appl. Environ. Microbiol. 39: 423.

79. Phillips, J. D. and Griffiths, M. W. 1987. A note on the use of the Catalasemeter in assessing the quality of milk. J. Appl. Bacteriol. 62: 223.

80. Phillips, J. D. and Griffiths, M. W. 1987. The relation between temperature and growth of bacteria in dairy products. Food Microbiol. 4: 173.

81. Philips, J. D., Griffiths, M. W., and Muir, D. D. 1983. Accelerated detection of post-heat-treatment contamination in pasteurized double cream. J. Soc. Dairy Technol. 36: 41.

82. Reichardt, W. and Morita. R. Y. 1982. Temperature characteristics of psychrotrophic and psychrophilic bacteria. J. Gen. Microbiol. 128: 565.

83. Reuter, G. 1981. Psychrotrophic lactobacilli in meat products. In "Psychrotrophic Microorganisms in Spoilage and Pathogenicity," ed. T. A. Roberts, G. Hobbs, J. H. B. Christian, and N. Skovgaard, p. 253. Academic Press, New York.

84. Rodrigues, U. M. and Kroll, R. J. 1985. The direct epifluorescent filter technique: Increased selectivity, sensitivity, and rapidity. J. Appl. Bacteriol. 64: 67.

85. Ronk, R. J., Carson, K. L., and Thompson, P. 1989. Processing, packaging, and regulation of minimally processed fruits and vegetables. Food Technol. 43(2): 136.

86. Sayem El Daher, N. and Simard, R. E. 1985. Putrefactive amine changes in relation to microbial counts of ground beef during storage. J. Food Prot. 48: 54.

87. Schaertel, B. J., Tsang, N., and Firstenberg-Eden, R. 1987. Impedimetric detection of yeast and mold. Food Microbiol. 4: 155.

88. Sharpe, A. N. 1989. The hydrophobic grid-membrane filter. Prog. Indus. Microbiol. 26: 169.

89. Smith, T. L. and Witter, L. D. 1979. Evaluation of inhibitors for rapid enumeration of psychrotrophic bacteria. J. Food Prot. 42: 158.

90. Sogaard, H. and Lund, R. 1981. A comparison of three methods for the enumeration of psychrotrophic bacteria in raw milk. In "Psychrotrophic Microorganisms in Spoilage and Pathogenecity," ed. T. A. Roberts, G. Hobbs, J. H. B. Christian, and N. Skovgaard, p. 109. Academic Press, New York.

91. Sommer, N. F. 1985. Strategies for control of postharvest diseases of selected commodities. In "Postharvest Technology of Horticultural Crops," ed. A. A. Kader, R. F. Kasmire, F. G. Mitchell, M. S. Reid, N. F. Sommer, and J. F. Thompson, p. 83. Cooperative Extension, U. of California, Davis, CA.

92. Stannard, C. J. 1989. ATP estimation. Prog. Indus. Microbiol. 26: 1.

93. Stannard, C. J. and Wood, J. M. 1983. The rapid estimation of microbial contamination

of raw meat by measurement of adenosine triphosphate (ATP). J. Appl. Bacteriol. 55: 429.

94. Stannard, C. J., Williams, A. P., and Gibbs, P. A. 1985. Temperature/growth relationships for psychrotrophic food-spoilage bacteria. Food Microbiol. 2: 115.

95. Sudi, J., Suhren, G., Heeschen, W., and Tolle, A. 1981. Entwicklung eines miniaturisierten Limulus-Tests im Mikrotiter-System zum quantitativen Nachweis gram-negativer Bakterien in Milch and Milchprodukten. Milchwissenschaft 36: 193.

96. Suhren, G. and Heeschen, W. 1987. Impedance assays and the bacteriological testing of milk and milk products. Milchwissenschaft 42: 619.

97. Suhren, G., Heeschen, W., and Tolle, A. 1982. Quantitative Bestimmung psychrotropher Mikroorganismen in Roh- und pasteurisierter Milch—ein Methodenvergleich. Milchwissenschaft 37: 594.

98. Sullivan, J. D. Jr., Ellis, P. C., Lee, R. G. Combs, W. S. Jr., and Watson, S. W. 1983. Comparison of the Limulus amoebocyte lysate test with plate counts and chemical analyses for assessment of the quality of lean fish. Appl. Environ. Microbiol. 45: 720.

99. Thomas, S. B. 1969. Methods of assessing the psychrotrophic bacterial content of milk. J. Appl. Bacteriol. 32: 269.

100. Tsuji, K., Martin, P. A., and Bussey, D. M. 1984. Automation of chromogenic substrate Limulus amoebocyte lysate assay method endotoxin by robotic system. Appl. Environ. Microbiol. 48: 550.

101. Vanderzant, C. and Matthys, A. W. 1965. Effect of temperature of the plating medium on the viable count of psychrophilic bacteria. J. Milk Food Technol. 28: 383.

102. Van Spreekens, K. J. A. and Stekelenburg, F. K. 1986. Rapid estimation of the bacteriological quality of fresh fish by impedance measurements. Appl. Microbiol. Biotechnol. 24: 95.

103. Van Spreekens, K. J. A. and Toepoel, L. 1981. Quality of fishery products in connection with the psychrophilic and psychrotrophic bacterial flora. In "Psychrotrophic Microorganisms in Spoilage and Pathogenicity," ed. T. A. Roberts, G. Hobbs, J. H. B. Christian, and N. Skovgaard, p. 283. Academic Press, New York.

104. Vasavada, P. C. 1988. Low acid foods defy liabilities. Prep. Foods 157(6): 122.

105. Vasavada, P. C. 1988. Pathogenic bacteria in milk—A review. J. Dairy Sci. 71: 2809.

106. Vasavada, P. C., Bon, T. C., and Bauman, L. 1988. The use of Catalasemeter in assessing abnormality in raw milk. J. Dairy Sci. 71(Suppl. 1): 113.

107. Waes, G. M. and Bossuyt, R. G. 1982. Usefulness of the benzalkonium-crystal violet-ATP method for predicting the keeping quality of pasteurized milk. J. Food Prot. 45: 928.

108. Wang, G. I. J. and Fung, D. Y. C. 1986. Feasibility of using catalase activity as an index of microbial loads on chicken surfaces. J. Food Sci. 51: 1442.

109. Ward, D. R., LaRocco, K. A., and Hopson, D. J. 1986. Adenosine triphosphate bioluminescent assay to enumerate bacterial numbers on fresh fish. J. Food Prot. 49: 647.

110. Witter, L. D. 1981. Psychrophilic bacteria. A review. J. Dairy Sci. 44: 983.

111. Zall, R. R., Chen, J. H., and Murphy, S. C. 1982. Estimating the number of psychrotrophs in milk using the direct microscopic method. Cult. Dairy Prod. J. 17(2): 24.

Chapter 10

THERMODURIC MICROORGANISMS AND HEAT RESISTANCE MEASUREMENTS

David L. Collins-Thompson and V. Kelly Bunning

10.1 INTRODUCTION

This chapter deals primarily with thermal resistance exhibited by some non-sporeforming bacteria, although some reference will be made to *Bacillus* because of its importance in the spoilage of pasteurized milk and egg products. Thermoduric organisms have the property of thermotolerance and hence have the capacity to survive some form of pasteurization or other minimal heat process.[27] Such organisms usually survive heating in a food substrate at temperature ranges of 60° to 80°C. Thermoduric organisms normally grow at temperatures in the mesophilic range (15° to 37°C), but several examples are known of growth at refrigerated temperatures.[28, 57] Organisms described as thermoduric are listed in Table 1. Although not included in this table, *Listeria* and select strains of *Salmonella* should also receive considerations.

Our knowledge about the thermoduric group of bacteria has been largely influenced by studies with milk, milk products, and liquid eggs. From these studies and others it can be noted that the capacity for heat resistance is not solely dependent upon the properties of microorganisms, but is also influenced by the factor of initial numbers, ingredients of the food, and method of heat treatment. Sometimes, survival of some microorganisms after heat treatment may be simply the result of high initial numbers.

The nature of the organism, however, is the first factor. A large group of thermoduric microorganisms is associated with milk, whereas their growth especially results from low-temperature/long-time (LTLT) treatments (Table 1). Some of these organisms appear to be environmental contaminants that result from improper handling and cleaning of milk processing equipment.[26, 41] The types of organisms surviving the pasteurization of liquid egg, as demonstrated by Shafi et al.,[46] were predominantly *Bacillus*, *Micrococcus*, and *Staphylococcus*. Furthermore, these genera appeared to survive regardless of type of egg product or heat treatment. Payne et al.[43] found that many of the organisms that survived pasteurization of whole egg were of the coryneform group of *Microbacterium lacticum*. Two strains of coryneform bacteria survived 20 and 38 min at 80°C in phosphate buffer at pH 7.1. None of the

Table 1—Thermoduric Microorganisms Associated with Foods.

Organism	Source	Reference
Arthrobacter	Milk	52, 57
Bacillus	Milk/eggs	21, 28, 48
Clostridium	Milk	35
Corynebacterium	Eggs	43
Lactobacillus	Juices/meats/milk	23, 26, 29
Microbacterium	Milk/eggs	26
Micrococcus	Eggs/milk	26
Pseudomonas	Eggs	21, 46
Staphylococcus	Eggs	26
Streptococcus	Eggs/meat/milk	21, 26, 34

isolates studied grew at 5°C, but each was capable of growing at 10°C. Freezing the coryneform bacteria in liquid whole egg at −18°C had little effect on heat resistance or viability. Foegeding and Stanley[21] examined microorganisms that survived ultrapasteurization of liquid whole egg and subsequently grew at 4° or 10°C in this product. The most heat-resistant isolates found were *Enterococcus faecalis* (formerly *Streptococcus*) and *Bacillus circulans*.

In meat products, some lactobacilli and streptococci may be recovered after the pasteurization process. This survival is particularly true of the fecal streptococci in such products as canned hams. These organisms are considered part of the normal flora of pasteurized canned meats.[26]

The nature of the food has also been reported to influence the heat resistance of spoilage organisms. Ingredients such as pectins have been linked to the survival of *Lactobacillus fermentum* in tomato juice after heat treatment (55° to 60°C).[29] Other factors such as pH and water activity (a_w) can influence survival of microorganisms.

Raw milk also contains proteinases from both indigenous and bacterial sources. Apparently, proteinases are involved in gelation or proteolysis of ultra-high temperature (UHT) pasteurized milk. Many of these proteinases are heat resistant or may regenerate activty during storage.[1] Spoilage resulting from heat-resistant enzymes may be misinterpreted as being caused by surviving thermoduric organisms.

In addition to commonly known thermoduric non-pathogenic bacteria, several thermal resistance studies,[4, 14, 17] epidemiological reports of milkborne disease outbreaks,[20, 51] and pasteurized milk surveys[18, 56] have indicated the potential for certain milkborne pathogens to survive recommended pasteurization treatments,[16] especially high-temperature/short-time (HTST) parameters. The criterion for survival is the presence in the raw product of unusually high numbers of these bacteria, resulting either from milk obtained from a mastitic herd or from storage temperature abuse. Survival might also come about by an increase in a particular bacterium's heat resistance brought on either by heating at rising temperatures or by exposure to sublethal heat shock, as shown for *Salmonella typhimurium* and *S. thompson*.[32, 33, 34] A proposed protective effect of intracellular location within bovine leuko-cytes[14, 20] for certain milkborne facultative intracellular pathogens, such as *L. monocytogenes*, might also permit survival after heating.

The presence of high numbers ($\geq 10^6$ organisms/ml) of a pathogen, *L. monocytogenes* being the best example, in a raw product is mimicked in typical laboratory thermal inactivation experiments that attempt to accurately determine the kinetics of death. A qualifier in these situations is that the low numbers of a particular pathogen surviving HTST are found only by using special detection procedures (cold enrichment; preincubation in non-selective enrichment broth media before selective enrichment),[7, 14, 17] where heat-stressed bacteria are given time and proper physiological conditions to recover.[2, 7, 9, 10, 17, 24, 25, 42, 44, 47]

The induction of thermotolerance by heat-shock[39, 40, 55] may be important in commercial vat pasteurization of large milk volumes that require relatively lengthy heating lags (come-up times), potentially permitting the development of enhanced resistance, as observed during the heating of *Salmonella*.[33] The available evidence, however, suggests that the recommended HTST pasteur-ization procedures, when properly carried out, can easily overcome the limited protective effect (temperature range) of the global stress response or heat-shock response.[25, 36, 39, 40, 55]

Survival of bacteria within leukocytes during pasteurization has been attrib-uted either to heat-shielding or to an acquired heat-resistant physiological state (thermotolerance).[6, 7, 14] Thermal inactivation studies with *L. mono-cytogenes*, which used intracellular bacteria generated from an in vitro phag-ocytosis reaction compared to freely suspended bacteria, disproved the heat-shielding mechanism.[6, 7] Testing of the acquired thermotolerance theory using artificially or naturally infected bovine milk, however, has given conflicting results, with the majority of studies failing to support listeria survival of HTST pasteurization.[11, 14, 15, 30, 54] The critical factor in these latter studies may simply be the low numbers of *L. monocytogenes* in milk shed by infected cows (10^2–10^4/ml). In addition, reported somatic cell (SC) infectivities (<1% of usually about 10^6 SC/ml at 1 to 10 bacteria/infected cell)[14, 15, 54] were not high enough to determine accurately any intracellular protective effect.

Clearly, then, the potential for milkborne pathogens to survive mini-mum HTST pasteurization treatment is very small. When proper handling at all junctures of milk processing is considered in a risk analysis model,[37] the possibility of survival of true thermoduric milk flora appears minimal.[6, 7, 54, 58]

10.2   GENERAL CONSIDERATIONS FOR ANALYTICAL SAMPLING, HEATING, AND DETECTION

Detailed examination of the fate of either true thermodurics or a particular pathogen in products such as milk after commercial HTST pasteurization requires strategic samples from (1) the raw milk bulk tank, (2) the end of the holding tube, (3) the exit of the pasteurizer regenerator, (4) the exit of the cooler before the vacuum breaker, (5) the pasteurized discharge after the vacuum breaker, (6) the finished product, (7) the air usually continuously monitored during processing, and (8) the cleaned pasteurized equipment. Samples in pipelines can be taken with a large-volume syringe (18-gauge needle) through appropriate sampling ports (e.g., TRU-TEST samplers, Food and Dairy Quality Management, Inc., St. Paul, Minn.). Similar sampling plans that involve monitoring raw products before, during, and after commercial vat or LTLT pasteurization (holding method) also apply. The sample taken at the end of the holding tube (HTST) or from the vat after processing (LTLT) should be rapidly cooled by placing it into a flask filled with glass beads that were held at −20°C. All analytical samples should be taken and handled aseptically,[54] as outlined in Chapter 2. Less detailed examination of pasteurization products for thermodurics and pathogens may simply involve the analysis of finished products from the processing plant. The detailed sampling measures, however, will allow a more definitive determination of true thermodurics in raw products by providing the necessary control samples to exclude any in-process and post-pasteurization contaminants.

The laboratory (in vitro) determination of thermoduric milk flora in raw milk should be determined for a producer's milk sample by both LTLT- and HTST-simulated methods. Techniques for the latter are not widely used, as most sets of appropriate apparatus are complex and difficult to operate and maintain.[22] Moreover, a vast difference in the inactivation process at 71.7°C for 15 sec (HTST) and at 62.8°C for 30 min (LTLT) should be expected for milk flora since, in historical development of pasteurization guidelines, the two sets of parameters were never deemed synonymous.[6, 58] Similar reasoning applies to the UHT pasteurization guidelines.[49, 58] The presence of true thermodurics in products such as raw milk is easily demonstrated by nonselective microbiological culture techniques after the sample is heated.[22] In contrast, the recovery of low numbers of certain pathogens that are probably heat injured and their distinction from the pasteurized product background flora can be difficult and often requires specialized selective enrichment protocols.[2, 7, 9, 10, 24, 25, 42, 44] Most selective culture media contain inhibitors, such as high salt concentrations, antibiotics, and dyes, however, that are detrimental to the recovery of injured bacterial cells. Cold enrichment (4°C for 7 to 28 days) of heated foods or of an aliquot of heated product inoculated into a nonselective enrichment broth has been shown to detect certain pathogens (psychrotrophs),[14, 17] but these methods are tedious and time consuming, and they produce erratic results.[9]

The limitations of detectability described above have necessitated that the thermal resistance of known milkborne bacterial pathogens be determined in sterile whole milk, autoclaved at 121°C for 10 to 15 min, followed by immediate cooling to 4°C to prevent caramelization.[4, 5, 7, 9, 13, 12] Large numbers (≤ 10^6 organisms/ml) of a particular pathogen are inoculated into the sterile menstruum, which is then heated at various optimal time intervals for either

LTLT or HTST pasteurization temperature parameters. A typical bacterial survivor curve showing the logarithmic or exponential rate of destruction—heating time intervals on the abscissa vs. $\log_{10}$ number of survivors on the ordinate—can be plotted from these data, and the D-value—the time required at a constant temperature to destroy 90% of the organisms present—can be calculated from the slope of the line. The rate of death from wet heat under given conditions is constant at any given temperature and independent of the initial number of cells.[38, 44, 50] The use of sterile milk as the heating menstruum along with nonselective media as the detection system, previously tested for optimal time-temperature incubation parameters, has indicated a higher thermal resistance for such organisms as *L. monocytogenes*.[5, 7] With raw milk as the heating menstruum coupled with selective or nonselective recovery media, lower D-values may result because of competition from the milk's surviving microflora[5, 6], or because of inhibition of injured survivors by the selective media.[2, 7, 9, 24, 25, 47] These observations have suggested a potential for certain milkborne bacterial pathogens to survive minimal HTST pasteurization when high numbers (> 10^4 organisms/ml) are initially present.[7, 9, 14, 17, 22] This phenomenon, however, is clearly dissimilar to the heat resistance of true thermodurics that survive pasteurization of raw milk that has an initial standard plate count of $\leq 10^4$ organism/ml.[22]

10.3   EQUIPMENT, MATERIALS, AND PROCEDURES

10.31   Low-Temperature/Long-Time (LTLT) Pasteurization

The thermal death time (TDT) tube technique for LTLT pasteurization has been recommended in "Standard Methods for the Examination of Dairy Products."[22]

1. Equipment: Test tubes, sterile, screw-capped 20 × 125 mm, cap with rubber or plastic liner. Pipettes, sterile, graduated, 5 ml, 10 ml, or 11 ml delivery.
2. Thermometers: The thermometers used in the waterbath and in the pilot tube with sample should cover the critical range of temperature during heat treatment, should have divisions of 0.1°C (0.2°F), and should be checked at least biennially with a National Bureau of Standards-certified thermometer.
3. Waterbath, electrically heated, thermostatically controlled (at 62.8° ± 0.5°C; 145° ± 0.9°F for milk work), equipped with stirrer and thermometer. The water volume must be enough to absorb the cooling effect of tubes placed in the bath without a drop in temperature of more than 0.5°C (0.9°F).
4. Metal or wire rack for holding test tubes.

A 5-ml quantity of the initial liquid sample or of the 1:10 dilution is transferred aseptically to a sterile test tube, using precautions to avoid contamination of the tube above the level filled by the sample. Material deposited on the upper portions of the tube may lead to false results, as it may not be subjected to the same degree of heat as the bulk of the material. It also may dry somewhat, and dry heat is considerably less microbiocidal than is moist heat. While a group of tubes is being prepared for heating, all should be held in an ice bath to retard microbial growth and to have all tubes at a uniform temperature for standardization of the subsequent heating rate. A pilot tube containing sample, with thermometer inserted therein, is used to monitor temperatures at all stages. A rack of tubes is placed in the bath after the bath temperature has stabilized. The tubes may be immersed completely, tightly closed, or they may be immersed so that the water line is 4 cm or more above the sample level. Timing begins when the pilot material is within 0.5°C (0.9°F) of the treatment temperature. At the end of the holding period, samples are cooled below 10°C (50°F) by immersion in an ice water bath. Determine the thermoduric count by the plate count method (Chapter 4) or, for nonregulatory purposes, by one of the simplified viable count procedures (Chapter 4). The results are reported as thermoduric count per unit of sample (ml, g, cm^2, etc.).

The above protocol, however, suggests using relatively large (20 × 125 mm) screw cap tubes as heating vessels without specifying the need to limit the airspace remaining after distributing the sample volume. The test tube heating method has been criticized by many scientists because of the open space that exists in the tubes, potentially allowing organisms to adhere to the sides and caps of the vessels. Adhering bacteria would not receive adequate heat, and their subsequent detection would produce "tailing" and nonlinearity in thermal death curves.[13, 53] Similar criticism applies to the use of Erlenmeyer flasks and, in commercial practice, improperly operated vat pasteurizers, where airspace heaters are mandated by the Pasteurized Milk Ordinance.[13, 21, 50, 53]

The immersed sealed tube (IST) method is the preferred and optimal method for measuring either the thermal resistance of bacteria or determining the thermoduric count at the longer heating times required for low-temperature pasteurization.[5, 7, 12, 50]

10.32   Immersed Sealed Tube (IST) Method

1. Equipment: Either test tubes, sterile, 7 to 10 mm diameter, or glass vials, sterile, 2 ml that are crimp sealable with metal caps containing teflon-lined seals. Pipettes, sterile, graduated 1 ml, 5 ml, 10 or 11 ml.
2. Thermometers (see Section 10.31).
3. Waterbath (see Section 10.31).

In the TDT-IST method, either a producer's milk sample (raw milk) or an inoculated sterile or raw milk food sample is distributed in small-diameter (7 to 10 mm) test tubes that are subsequently sealed near the mouth in the flame of a blast burner.[43, 39] Capillary tubes have also been used in this procedure.[32, 33, 44] Alternatively, menstruum may be pipetted into glass reaction vials that are then crimp-sealed with metal caps containing teflon-lined seals.[12, 14] The volume of product per vessel usually is from 1 to 4 ml, and the remaining airspace should be as small as possible. The sealed tubes of product are then heated at 62.8°C ± 0.5°C in a thermostatically controlled waterbath equipped with a stirrer and thermometer. The volume of water should be sufficient to absorb the cooling effect of the tubes immersed in the bath without a drop in temperature of more tha 0.5°C. Heating can be 30 min to determine the thermoduric count in raw milk or for optimal time intervals. These intervals are based on preliminary heat inactivation runs with standardized suspensions of a particular test bacterium, to determine a $D_{62.8°C}$-value.

Correction factors for the heating and cooling lags of immersed sealed tubes heated in a waterbath at 62.8°C should be determined under the same conditions as those used for the test. A pilot tube containing the sample volume of product is sealed instead with a rubber stopper through which a thermometer has been inserted to the geometric center of the sample. The time required for the pilot tube to reach the selected heating temperature from the initial temperature—usually 0.4° to 4°C—is determined after total submersion into the waterbath. The timing of the pasteurization treatment may begin either when the selected temperature is reached which should be within 5 min when determining the thermoduric count in raw milk at a single holding time of 30 min,[22] or at a initiation of submersion, with the come-up and come-down times recorded during the process. The latter method is most often used when determining a D-value from a thermal inactivation run. The statistical method for calculating correction factors from the data obtained above is complex and has been adequately described by Anellis et al.[3] The larger the mass and thermal capacity of the product being heated in a thermal resistance experiment, the longer will be the heating and cooling lags, with correspondingly larger corrections.[38, 44, 50] When a relatively small volume, 1 to 4 ml, of product is sealed in a glass tube with a limited remaining airspace and is then immersed in a 62.8°C waterbath for up to 30 min, the TDT-IST method is accurate for determining the thermal resistance of the bacterial population present.[22, 44, 50, 54] This approach is adaptable to other liquid food products that are heat processed at relatively low temperatures and for lengthy times, e.g., liquid egg.[3, 34]

10.33   High-Temperature/Short-Time (HTST) Pasteurization

HTST pasteurization can be simulated in a laboratory setting with certain highly specialized devices.[6, 7, 22, 44, 51] The two-phase slug-low tubular heat exchanger (SFHE)[50] is used by the U.S. Food and Drug Administration (FDA) to evaluate the thermal resistance of milkborne pathogens at HTST parameters (Figure 1). The SFHE method is used to study the shorter heating times required at the higher heating temperatures used in HTST processing.[7, 9] The TDT-IST method is valid for examining the thermal resistance of milk-

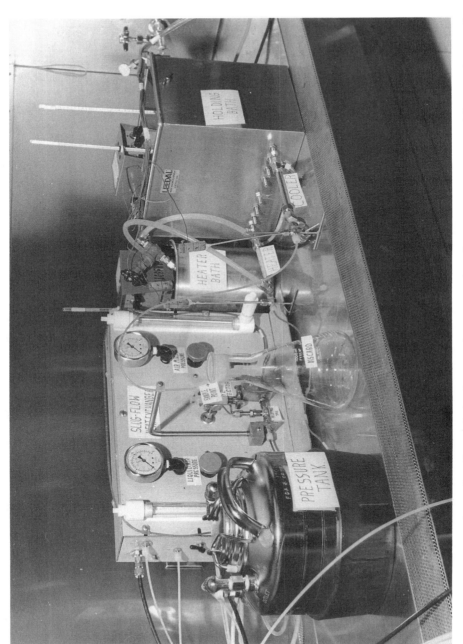

Figure 1—The two-phase slug-flow tubular heat exchanger or "bench top pasteurizer" used for simulation of HTST pasteurization by the U.S. Food and Drug Administration. A schematic flow diagram of this apparatus can be found in the original descriptive publication.[48]

borne flora at or near LTLT parameters,[22, 50] but extrapolation outside the experimental range instead of actual measurement is scientifically inappropriate.[7, 49, 50, 53] Therefore, direct methods were developed to determine inactivation within the HTST pasteurization range in a laboratory setting.[22, 49, 58] Because the total come-up and come-down (heating and cooling lags) times are essentially instantaneous (1.3 sec) in the SFHE systems, inactivation data obtained are minimally affected by correction factors. The detection of potentially low levels of certain milkborne pathogens may require complex selective enrichment protocols, as previously mentioned.

The setup and operation of the SFHE apparatus is complex and expensive, as are other methods for simulating HTST processing. The method is aptly described in the original publication,[49] and further details can be obtained from the FDA.

10.34   Determination of D-Values

When performing a thermal inactivation experiment with a standardized suspension of a known thermoduric or milkborne pathogen, the presence of microorganisms can be reported quantitatively as plate counts or qualitatively as positive or negative from enrichment broths. The straightforward calculation of D-values from plate count data has been described by Stumbo[50] and Pflug.[44] Estimates of D-values cannot be obtained directly from methods that measure presence or absence of bacteria, i.e., enrichments. If there is evidence that a linear relation exists between $\log_{10}$ count and time of heating, then the D-value can be estimated from the holding-time point between all positive and all negative results (the end-point).

One way to obtain a consistent estimate of the end-point is to determine the time of heating at a constant temperature where 50% of samples tested are positive. The experiment is optimally designed so that the holding times bracket the end-point and yield from all-positive to all-negative results. The number of tests performed at each holding time—at least three—are chosen based on the precision desired for the estimate. The Spearman-Karber procedure for computing the 50% end-point has been detailed by Finney.[19]

Lewis[31] and Pflug and Holcomb[44] have shown how a D-value can be computed using a 50% end-point (t_m). It is assumed that the detection method recovers a viable microorganism when present. Correcting for the bias in the procedure, D can be computed as follows:

$$D = \frac{t_m}{\log_{10}N_0 + 0.251} \qquad (1)$$

where

t_m = the 50% time estimated from the Spearman-Karber procedure, i.e., the time when 50% of the analytical units are positive.

N_0 = the concentration of bacteria measured by plate count at heating time zero.

10.35   Media

Media used for thermoduric/heat resistance studies should be nonselective, e.g., standard methods agar. Detection of fastidious organisms such as *Lactobacillus* might require APT agar or other rich media (Chapter 15). Food-borne pathogens that are heat-stressed will require special enrichment protocols (see Chapter 7 and specific pathogens). Incubation times and temperatures depend on the particular application or organism. When using the standard plate count procedure (Chapter 4), an incubation temperature of 32°C for 48 hr is recommended.

10.4   INTERPRETATION

The significance of thermoduric microorganisms in foods is open to various interpretations. In some foods, such as milk and milk products, a link has been established between thermoduric counts and sanitary practices.[28] In particular, the occurrence and numbers of thermoduric microorganisms can be related to poor cleaning of equipment and utensils in milk plants.[26] These microorganisms can also be responsible for flavor defects (fruity or bitter) and spoilage problems (bitter cream and sweet curdling).[8] Thermoduric psychrotrophs in milk have been reported to invalidate the methylene blue reduction test, causing the rejection of pasteurized milk with good bacterial quality.[28] Levels of thermoduric microorganisms in producer's milk will vary in different situations. For example, higher levels of thermoduric organisms in milk have been associated with winter housing of cattle.[28] Counts of less than 1000/ml in producer's milk are considered possible, and levels above 1000/ml indicate that an investigation into the problem is needed.

A similar situation exists with pasteurized liquid egg products. Shafi et al.[46] reported bacterial levels in pasteurized frozen whole egg samples that ranged from 6×10^1 to 6×10^2/ml. Bacterial levels of >1000/ml in pasteurized whole egg have been reported as unacceptable.[42]

Thermoduric organisms associated with meat and meat products have caused several problems. Studies have shown that greening of meats resulted from the survival of heat-resistant lactobacilli such as *L. viridescens*.[23] In canned hams, the survival of thermoduric streptococci and lactobacilli gave rise to problems of souring, color loss, and swollen cans. In selected dried foods, low levels of thermoduric streptococci (< 100/g) have been reported.[45]

In general, thermodurics grow poorly at 5°C, but there are some psychrotrophic thermoduric microorganisms that, if present in large enough numbers, can lead to spoilage within 10 to 15 days of refrigerated storage.[26]

10.5   REFERENCES

1. Adams, D. M., Barach, J. T., and Speck, M. L. 1976. Effect of psychrotrophic bacteria from raw milk on milk proteins and stability of milk proteins to ultrahigh temperature treatment. J. Dairy Sci. 59: 823.

2. Allwood, M. C. and Russell, A. D. 1970. Mechanisms of thermal injury in non-sporulating bacteria. In "Advances in Applied Microbiology," ed. D. Perlman, Vol. 12, p. 89. Academic Press, New York.
3. Anellis, A., Lubas, J., and Rayman, M. M. 1954. Heat resistance in liquid eggs of some strains of the genus *Salmonella*. Food Res. 19: 377.
4. Bradshaw, J. G., Peeler, J. T., Corwin, J. J., Barnett, J. E., and Twedt, R. M. 1987a. Thermal resistance of disease-associated *Salmonella typhimurium* in milk. J. Food Prot. 50: 95.
5. Bradshaw, J. G., Peeler, J. T., Corwin, J. J., Hunt, J. M., and Twedt, R. M. 1987b. Thermal resistance of *Listeria monocytogenes* in dairy products. J. Food Prot. 50: 543.
6. Bunning, V. K., Crawford, R. G., Bradshaw, J. G., Peeler, J. T., Tierney, J. T., and Twedt, R. M. 1986. Thermal resistance of intracellular *Listeria monocytogenes* cells suspended in raw bovine milk. Appl. Environ. Microbiol. 52: 1398.
7. Bunning, V. K., Donnelly, C. W., Peeler, J. T., Briggs, E. H., Bradshaw, J. G., Crawford, R. G., Beliveau, C. M., and Tierney, J. T. 1988. Thermal inactivation of *Listeria monocytogenes* within bovine milk phagocytes. Appl. Environ. Microbiol. 54: 364.
8. Collins, E. B. 1981. Heat resistant psychrotrophic microorganisms. J. Dairy Sci. **64**: 157.
9. Crawford, R. G., Beliveau, C. M., Donnelly, C. W., Peeler, J. T., and Bunning, V. K. 1988. Recovery of heat-stressed *Listeria monocytogenes* cells from pasteurized bovine milk. Abstr. Ann. Mtg. Am. Soc. Microbiol., #P46, p. 281.
10. Dominguez-Rodriguez, L., Suarez-Fernandez, G., Fernandez-Garayzabal, J. F., and Rodriguez-Ferri, J. A. E. 1984. New methodology for the isolation of *Listeria* microorganisms from heavily contaminated environments. Appl. Environ. Microbiol. 47: 1188.
11. Donker-Voet, J. 1962. My view of the epidemiology of *Listeria* infections. In "Second Symposium on Listeric Infection," ed. M. L. Gray, p. 133. Montana State College, Bozeman, Mont.
12. Donnelly, C. W. and Briggs, E. H. 1986. Psychrotrophic growth and thermal inactivation of *Listeria monocytogenes* as a function of milk composition. J. Food Prot. 49: 994.
13. Donnelly, C. W., Briggs, E. H., and Donnelly, L. S. 1987. Comparison of heat resistance of *Listeria monocytogenes* in milk as determined by two methods. J. Food Prot. 50: 14.
14. Doyle, M. P., Glass, K. A., Beery, J. T., Garcia, G. A., Pollard, D. J., and Schultz, R. D. 1987. Survival of *Listeria monocytogenes* in milk during high-temperature/short-time pasteurization. Appl. Environ. Microbiol. 53: 1433.
15. Farber, J. M., Sanders, G. W., Emmons, D. B., and McKellar, R. C. Heat resistance of *Listeria monocytogenes* in artificially-inoculated and naturally-contaminated raw milk. J. Food Prot. 50: 893 (Abstr.).
16. FDA. 1978. Grade A Pasteurized Milk Ordinance. 1978 Recommendations. Pub. Health Serv. Public. No. 229 (revised 1983). U.S. Food and Drug Admin. Gov. Print. Off., Washington, D.C.
17. Fernandez-Garayzabel, J. F., Dominguez-Rodriguez, L., Vasquez-Boland, J. A., Rodriguez-Ferri, E. F., Briones Dieste, V., Blanco Cancelo, J. L., and Suarez-Fernandez, G. S. 1981. Survival of *Listeria monocytogenes* in raw milk treated in a pilot plant size pasteurizer. J. Appl. Bacteriol. 63: 533.
18. Fernandez-Garayzabel, J. F., Dominguez-Rodriguez, L., Vasquez-Boland, J. A., Blanco Cancelo, J. L., and Suarez-Fernandez, G. S. 1986. *Listeria monocytogenes* dans le lait pasteurise. Can. J. Microbiol. 32: 149.
19. Finney, D. J. 1978. "Statistical Methods in Biological Assay," 3rd ed. MacMillan Publ. Co., Inc., New York. p. 394.
20. Fleming, D. W., Colchi, S. L., MacDonald, K. L., Brondum, J., Hayes, P. S., Plikaytis, B. D., Holmes, M. B., Audurier, A., Broome, C. V., and Reingold, A. L. 1985. Pasteurized milk as a vehicle of infection in an outbreak of listeriosis. N. Engl. J. Med. 312: 404.
21. Foegeding, P. M. and Stanley, N. W. 1987. Growth and inactivation of microorganisms isolated from ultrapasteurized egg. J. Food Sci. 52: 1219.

22. Frank, J. F., Hankin, L., Koburger, J. A., and Marth, E. H. 1985. Tests for groups of microorganisms. In "Standard Methods for the Examination of Dairy Products," 15th ed., ed. G. H. Richardson, p. 189. Am. Pub. Health Assn., Washington, D.C.

23. Grant, G. F., McCurdy, A. R., and Osborne, A. D. 1988. Bacterial greening in cured meats. A review. Can. Inst. Food Sci. Technol. J. 21: 50.

24. Hansen, N. H. and Riemann, H. 1963. Factors affecting the heat resistance of non-sporing organisms. J. Appl. Bacteriol. 26: 314.

25. Hurst, A. 1977. Bacterial injury: A review. Can. J. Microbiol. 23: 935.

26. ICMSF. 1980. Chapter 15. Meat and Meat Products. In "Microbial Ecology of Foods," Vol. 2, "Food Commodities," p. 333. Internatl. Comm. Microbiol. Spec. for Foods. Academic Press, New York.

27. Jay, J. M. 1986. "Modern Food Microbiology," 3rd ed. Van Nostrand Reinhold Co., New York.

28. Johnston, D. W. and Bruce, J. 1982. Incidence of thermoduric psychrotrophs in milk produced in the west of Scotland. J. Appl. Bacteriol. 52: 333.

29. Juven, B. J., Ben-Shalom, N., and Weisslowicz, H. 1983. Identification of chemical constituents of tomato juice which affect the heat resistance of *Lactobacillus fermentum*. J. Appl. Bacteriol. 54: 335.

30. Kovincic, I., Vujicic, I., Stajner, B., Galic, M., and Vulic, M. 1986. Multiplication and thermal resistance of *Listeria monocytogenes* in inoculated milk. In "Listeriose, Listeria, Listeriosis 1985–1986: Proceedings of the 9th International Symposium of the Problems of Listeriosis," ed. A. L. Courtieu, p. 356. Universite de Nantes, Nantes, France.

31. Lewis, J. C. 1956. The estimation of decimal reduction times. Appl. Microbiol. 4: 211.

32. Mackey, B. M. and Derrick, C. M. 1986. Elevation of the heat resistance of *Salmonella typhimurium* by sublethal heat shock. J. Appl. Bacteriol. 61: 389.

33. Mackey, B. M. and Derrick, C. M. 1987a. Changes in the heat resistance of *Salmonella typhimurium* during heating at rising temperatures. Lett. Appl. Bacteriol. 4: 13.

34. Mackey, B. M. and Derrick, C. M. 1987b. The effect of prior heat shock on the thermoresistance of *Salmonella thompson* in foods. Lett. Appl. Bacteriol. 5: 115.

35. Martin, J. H. 1974. Significance of bacterial spores in milk. J. Milk Food Technol. 37: 94.

36. Morgan, R. W., Christman, M. F., Jacobson, F. S., Storz, G., and Ames, B. N. 1986. Hydrogen peroxide-inducible proteins in *Salmonella typhimurium* overlap with heat shock and other stress proteins. Proc. Natl. Acad. Sci. 83: 8059.

37. Mossel, D. A. A. 1987. An approach to the evaluation of the risk of transmission of *Listeria monocytogenes* by foods and its management. In "Listeriosis: Joint WHO/ROI Consultation on Prevention and Control," ed. A. Schonberg, p. 146. Institut fur Veterinarmedizin des Bundes-gesundheitsamets, Berlin.

38. NCA Research Laboratories. 1968. Thermal death times. In "Laboratory Manual for Food Canners and Processors," Vol. 1, "Microbiology and Processing," p. 166. Natl. Canners Assn. AVI Publishing Co., Westport, Conn.

39. Neidhardt, F. C. and Van Bogelen, R. A. 1987. Heat shock response. In *"Escherichia coli and Salmonella typhimurium*: Cellular and Molecular Biology," ed. J. L. Ingraham et al., p. 1334. Am. Soc. for Microbiol., Washington, D.C.

40. Neidhardt, F. C., Van Bogelen, R. A., and Vaughn, V. 1984. The genetics and regulation of heat-shock proteins. Ann. Rev. Genet. 18: 295.

41. NRC. 1985. "An Evaluation of the Role of Microbiological Criteria for Foods and Food Ingredients." Natl. Research Council. Natl. Acad. Press, Washington, D.C.

42. Olson, J. C. Jr. and Nottingham, P. M. 1980. Temperature. In "Microbiological Ecology of Foods," Vol. 1: "Affecting Life and Death of Microorganisms," ed. J. H. Siliker and R. P. Elliot, p. 1. Academic Press, New York.

43. Payne, J., Gooch, J. E. T., and Barnes, E. M. 1979. Heat resistant bacteria in pasteurized whole egg. J. Appl. Bacteriol. 46: 601.

44. Pflug, I. J. and Holcomb, R. G. 1983. Principles of thermal destruction of microorganisms. In "Disinfection, Sterilization and Preservation," ed. S. S. Block, p. 751. Lea and Febiger, Philadelphia, Penn.

45. Powers, E. M., Ay, C., El-Bisi, H., and Rowley, D. B. 1971. Bacteriology of dehydrated space foods. Appl. Microbiol. 22: 441.

46. Shafi, R., Cotterill, O. J., and Nichols, M. L. 1970. Microbial flora of commercially pasteurized egg products. Poultry Sci. 49: 578.

47. Smith, J. L. and Archer, D. L. 1988. Heat induced injury in *Listeria monocytogenes*. J. Indust. Micro. 3: 105.

48. Stewart, D. B. 1975. Factors influencing the incidence of *B. cereus* spores in milk. Soc. Dairy Technol. J. 28: 80.

49. Stroup, W. H., Dickerson, R. W. Jr., and Read, R. B. Jr. 1969. Two-phase slug flow heat exchanger for microbial thermal inactivation research. Appl. Microbiol. 18: 889.

50. Stumbo, C. R. 1965. Thermal resistance of bacteria. In "Thermobacteriology in Food Processing: Food Science and Technology—A Series of Monographs," ed. M. L. Anson et al., p. 79. Academic Press, London.

51. Tacket, C. O., Narain, J. P., Sattin, R., Lofgren, J. P., Konigsberg, C., Rendtorff, R. C., Rausa, A., Davis, B. R., and Cohen, M. S. 1984. A multistate outbreak of infections caused by *Yersinia enterocolitica* transmitted by pasteurized milk. J. Am. Med. Assn. 251: 483.

52. Thomas, S. B., Druce, R. G., Peters, G. J., and Griffiths, D. G. 1967. Incidence and significance of thermoduric bacteria in farm milk supplies: A reappraisal and review. J. Appl. Bacteriol. 30: 265.

53. Tierney, J. T. and Larkin, E. P. 1978. Potential sources of error during virus thermal inactivation. Appl. Environ. Microbiol. 36: 432.

54. Tierney, J. T., Stroup, W. H., Lovett, J., and Dickerson, R. W. 1988. Personal communication. Food and Drug Admin., Cincinnati, OH.

55. Van Bogelen, R. A., Acton, M. A., and Neidhardt, F. C. 1987. Induction of the heat shock regulon does not produce thermo-tolerance in *Escherichia coli*. Genes Develop. 1: 525.

56. Walker, S. J. and Gilmour, A. 1986. The incidence of *Yersinia enterocolitica* and *Yersinia enterocolitica*-like organisms in raw and pasteurized milk in Northern Ireland. J. Appl. Bacteriol. 61: 133.

57. Washam, C. J., Olson, H. C., and Vedamuthu, E. R. 1977. Heat-resistant psychrotrophic bacteria isolated from pasteurized milk. J. Food Prot. 40: 101.

58. Westhoff, D. C. 1978. Heating milk for microbial destruction: A historical outline and update. J. Food Prot. 41: 122.

Chapter 11

LIPOLYTIC MICROORGANISMS

James L. Smith and Michael J. Haas

11.1 INTRODUCTION

11.11 Hydrolytic and Oxidative Lipolysis

Many foods contain significant amounts of fats that may be susceptible to hydrolysis. The free fatty acids (FFAs) liberated by hydrolysis can be responsible for unpleasant flavors, or they may oxidize to compounds with undesirable flavor notes. Only FFAs of low molecular weight are sufficiently volatile to contribute directly to flavor changes; however, FFAs released by hydrolysis are more susceptible to oxidation with resultant changes in flavor than those esterified in a triglyceride. Many of the problems of fat breakdown in foods are nonmicrobial in origin, but numerous bacteria, yeasts, and molds produce lipolytic enzymes that are capable of causing both hydrolytic and oxidative deterioration of fats when present in food products. In addition to lipases, which act on triglycerides, microorganisms can produce other lipid hydrolyzing enzymes such as phospholipase C.[13] Phospholipase C isolated from *Bacillus cereus* or *Pseudomonas fluorescens* was shown to enhance the lipolytic activity of milk lipoprotein lipase and that of a commercial *Rhizopus* lipase, but not the lipolytic action of *P. fluorescens* lipase.[10, 15] The extracellular phospholipase C enzymes produced by a number of gram-negative psychrotrophic species are stable to high temperature-short time (HTST) and ultra-high temperature (UHT) pasteurization temperatures[15] and thus are similar in heat resistance to the thermostable lipases produced by psychrotrophic microorganisms (Section 11.14).

Microorganisms that produce glycosidic enzymes can, in conjunction with bacterial proteases, degrade milk membranes and thereby expose lipids to action by lipases and phospholipases.[20, 21] Thus, the glycosidases can contribute indirectly to lipolytic activity. The glycosidases of *P. fluorescens*, in contrast to phospholipase C and lipase produced by that organism, are completely inactivated by milk pasteurization temperatures.[19]

Microbial oxidation of lipids has been investigated,[26] but little is known about oxidative changes or their importance.

By the use of special plating media, microorganisms that produce lipase can be enumerated; however, enumeration of lipolytic microorganisms is not usually performed on a routine basis. Food manufacturers and processors analyze for lipolytic microorganisms only when a problem arises. Determination of the number of lipolytic microorganisms present in a food sample can tell the food processor whether the particular lipid-related problem is microbial or nonmicrobial in origin.

11.12 Foods Involved

Fat-containing foods may spoil because of oxidative rancidity that is nonmicrobial in origin, but microbial lipolysis can contribute to the loss of quality or spoilage of fat-containing foods such as milk, cream, butter, and high-moisture cheeses, such as cottage cheese,[27] as well as margarine.[9] In fact, any fat-containing food is susceptible to spoilage caused by microbial lipolysis. On the other hand, lipolytic changes in foods are not necessarily bad. Desirable changes in foods such as cheese and sausages are brought about by microbial lipolysis; for example, cheese ripening is strongly dependent on microbial lipases,[27] and some desirable flavors in fermented sausage are due to microbial lipolysis.[24]

11.13 Microorganisms

The genera *Pseudomonas*, *Alcaligenes*, *Moraxella*, and *Staphylococcus* among the bacteria; *Rhizopus*, *Geotrichum*, *Aspergillus*, *Mucor*, and *Penicillium* among the molds; and *Candida*, *Rhodotorula*, and *Hansenula* among the yeasts contain some lipolytic species.[9, 18] Microorganisms producing lipase are widespread in nature and not limited to those listed above.

11.14 Lipase Stability

The failure to detect lipase-producing microorganisms in a spoiled fatty food may indicate that the defect is nonmicrobial in origin. However, since microbial lipases are generally exocellular, they can be found in the absence of viable microorganisms, which may have been killed by the food processing conditions. Moreover, microbial lipases are often heat resistant,[1, 27] even though the cells themselves are not. Lipases from some psychrotrophic *Pseudomonas* species have D values measured at 150° or 160°C ranging from 4.8 to 0.7 min,[1, 2, 8, 11, 28] and lipases from *P. fluorescens* or *Moraxella* spp. when heated for 30 sec at 100°C lost 2 to 60% of their activity.[12] Thus, selected sterilization temperatures may confer microbial sterility, but not inactivate a considerable portion of the microbial lipase, leading to a later loss of product quality under appropriate conditions. Milk and milk products sterilized by UHT processing at temperatures of 138° to 150°C for 2 to 6 sec are a case in point. Raw milk held under refrigerated conditions for extended periods prior to UHT processing may show growth of psychrotrophic *Pseudomonas* species with concomitant production of UHT-resistant lipases.

Lipases may retain activity in foods for long periods even at low temperatures. In cell-free cultures of *Pseudomonas fragi*, *Staphylococcus aureus*, *Geotrichum candidum*, *Candida lipolytica* and *Penicillium roqueforti*, significant amounts of free fatty acids were liberated from fats in 2 to 4 days at −7°C and within one week at −18°C.[3] Some of the cell-free cultures showed significant lipase action after 3 weeks at −29°C.

Reduced metabolic activity of microorganisms in the frozen state can be partly explained by lowered water activity (a_w) caused by ice formation. Microbial lipases, however, were found to be effective in the frozen state,[3] which means that they are active at reduced a_w. Andersson[7] studied the activity of *Pseudomonas fluorescens* lipase in full-fat milk powder as a function of a_w. Enzyme activity remained high but constant over an a_w range of 0.00 to 0.54; however, at an a_w of 0.85, the lipase action was three times that at 0.54. The results obtained by Alford and Pierce[3] and by Andersson[7] indicate that microbial lipases can cause drastic changes in fatty substrates during frozen or dehydrated storage even though the metabolic activities of the lipase-producing species are dormant.

11.15   Detection of Lipase

Determination of the numbers and types of microorganisms that can hydrolyze fats is not always enough, especially if the microorganisms do not survive the processing conditions. Therefore, measurement of lipase activity will give a more realistic evaluation of the spoilage potential of a food in which lipolytic microorganisms have grown. However, determination of lipase activity does not appear to be a routine test in food microbiology laboratories.

The activity of free lipase in a food can be determined by the use of a diffusion assay employing a fatty substrate such as tributyrin or triolein incorporated into agar plates. Wells are cut into the agar and lipase solutions (milk or food extract) are added to the wells. Lipase activity is indicated by a clearing of the opaque triglyceride; the area of the zone of clearing is proportional to the concentration of the lipase.[27] Lipase activity can also be estimated by measuring the release of FFA from triglycerides.[27] Kouker and Jaeger[17] developed a plate assay for bacterial lipase consisting of an agar medium containing triolein and the fluorescent dye, rhodamine B. Lipase solutions are pipetted into wells cut into the agar; fluorescent halos appear upon ultraviolet (UV) irradiation if the triglyceride has been hydrolyzed. The logarithm of lipase activity is linearly correlated with the diameter of the halos. The procedure of Kouker and Jaeger[17] also can be used to detect lipolytic microorganisms if a nutrient medium is incorporated. Immunological procedures such as enzyme-linked immunosorbent assay (ELISA) would appear to be a logical choice for detecting the presence of lipase in food products, but seem to have received little study.[27] Various enzyme parameters, assay procedures, and the food spoilage potential of lipases produced by psychrotrophic bacteria have been reviewed recently.[27]

11.2   GENERAL CONSIDERATIONS

Samples are prepared and dilutions are made as outlined in Chapters 1 and 4.

11.3   EQUIPMENT, MATERIALS, AND REAGENTS

11.31   Reagents

Victoria blue B; (Color Index 44045; Sigma Chemical Co., St. Louis, Mo.). If Victoria blue B is not available, Victoria blue without a subdesignation may be used, although a deep blue zone of lipolysis may not result.[4]

Petroleum ether. ACS specifications. bp 30° to 60°C.

Activated alumina (commercially available). Glass columns 2 to 3 cm in diameter × 10 to 15 cm in length are packed with 25 g activated alumina that has been prewashed with petroleum ether. A column of this size will remove the FFA from 50 g of fat containing 2% to 3% FFA.

11.32   Fat Substrates

Tributyrin. Reagent grade, from which the FFAs have been removed as follows: Dissolve tributyrin in petroleum ether (5 to 10 g per 100 ml) and pass through a column of activated alumina. Remove the petroleum ether from the purified triglyceride by evaporating it on a steam table under a stream of nitrogen. Note: If the tributyrin is known to contain only negligible amounts of FFA, the purification step may be omitted.

Corn oil, soybean oil, olive oil, or other liquid oil can be used as the fat substrate. Any fresh, commercially available cooking oil also is suitable, provided it does not contain antioxidants or other materials at concentrations inhibitory to microbial growth. FFAs should be removed as described for tributyrin.

Solid fats such as lard, tallow, butter, or a solid vegetable shortening such as Crisco™ also may be used, particularly for examinations of foods in which only solid fats are present. FFAs should be removed as described above and the fat melted before emulsification.

Other triglycerides such as triolein may be used, if cognizance is taken of the problems of emulsification and mono- and diglyceride contamination.

11.33   Media

Base layer agar
Nutrient agar
Single layer agar
Standard methods agar
Trypticase soy agar

11.4   PROCEDURES

11.41   Double Layer Method

Pour the base agar layer as described in Chapter 62. Prepare dilutions of the food product and plate in the manner described for colony counts (Chapter 4), except that dilutions are spread plated on the surface of the base layer and allowed to dry, and this is followed by the addition of 10 to 12 ml of nutrient overlay agar.

11.42   Single Layer Method

Double layered agar plates give the best detection of weakly lipolytic bacteria and should be used, particularly when added carbohydrate is necessary for good growth.[4, 9, 14, 30] However, in many cases, regular single layer plating procedures with a fat-containing medium will give satisfactory counts.

Prepare dilutions of the food product and pour plates as described under agar plate count method (Chapter 4) except pour the plates with 12 to 15 ml of the single layer medium containing the fat substrate (Chapter 62).

11.43   Incubation

Incubate plates at 20° to 30°C for 3 days if tributyrin is the fat substrate and 4 to 7 days for other fats.

11.44   Counting and Reporting Colonies

Lipolytic microorganisms on tributyrin agar without Victoria blue B are detected by a transparent zone surrounding the colony on an opaque background. On media containing Victoria blue B, a dark zone surrounds the lipolytic colonies on an opaque, light blue background. The dye acts as an acid indicator, and when fats are hydrolyzed, the nonsoluble long chain fatty acids give an intense dark blue color. Short chain soluble fatty acids diffuse through the agar and give a weak blue color.[4] Indistinct zones sometimes occur because of weak lipolysis or acid production that is due to utilization of sugar (see Section 11.54). Use of a stereoscopic microscope to detect these weak zones may be helpful. However, careful substrate preparation will help minimize the appearance of weak indistinct zones of hydrolysis. Count only the colonies surrounded by a lipolytic zone and report as numbers of lipolytic microorganisms per ml (or g) of food sample.

11.45   Recommended Controls

Control plates should be run for each batch of fat substrate and dye. Streak separate plates with *Geotrichum candidum*, *Pseudomonas fragi*, and a non-lipolytic organism such as *Escherichia coli*. Incubate plates for 3 to 7 days at 20° to 25°C for *G. candidum* and *P. fragi* and at 30°C for *E. coli*. Interpretation: Tributyrin will be hydrolyzed very slowly, if at all, by *G. candidum*. Inhibitory substances present in the fats or oils are indicated by weak zones of hydrolysis (not dark blue of typical Victoria blue B reaction) by one or both of the lipolytic organisms. No zones of hydrolysis should be seen with *E. coli*.

11.5   PRECAUTIONS

11.51   Temperature

The temperature of incubation is important, since lipase production is sometimes inhibited in cultures at the upper limits of their growth range.[6, 18] Incubation should be at least 5°C below maximum growth temperature of the culture. When the samples to be plated represent unknown microorganisms such as might be present in foods, multiple plates should be prepared and incubated at 10°, 25°, and 30°C to make certain that all potential lipase-producing colonies are detected.

11.52   Substrate

True lipases attack only insoluble substrates, whereas esterases attack only soluble substrates. Therefore, avoid soluble substrates such as simple esters, monoglycerides, and Tweens, which may make substrate preparation easier and the zone of hydrolysis sharper. Hydrolysis of these compounds indicates esterase activity, not true lipase activity. Tributyrin is the simplest triglyceride occurring in natural fats and oils. Although a true fat, it is hydrolyzed by some microorganisms that will not hydrolyze other triglycerides or fats containing longer chain fatty acids. However, for screening purposes to enumerate lipolytic microorganisms of potential importance in foods, it is the substrate of choice[4, 14, 23, 25] unless *Geotrichum* species are present (Section 11.45). As noted in Section 11.32, other substrates may give more meaningful information concerning a specific product (e.g., lard as a substrate for lipolytic microorganisms from pork); for a discussion of the comparison of the use of tributyrin with other fats such as butterfat, see Lawrence[18] and Thomas and Thomas.[29]

11.53   Lipase Specificity

Most lipases, including microbial lipases, appear to be rather nonspecific with respect to the natural fats or oils that they can hydrolyze. Alford et al.[5] found that a number of lipases elaborated by bacteria and fungi exhibited a preference for the 1-position of synthetic triglycerides. Purified lipase from *P. fragi* attacked preferentially the 1-position of synthetic triglycerides and also hydrolyzed diglycerides and monoglycerides.[22] The lipase produced by *G. candidum* liberated large amounts of oleic and linoleic acids from corn oil and lard[16] suggesting that the lipase attacked positions on the triglycerides occupied by unsaturated fatty acids. When the *Geotrichum* lipase was tested against synthetic triglycerides containing oleic, palmitic, and stearic acids, a preferential liberation of oleic acid occurred, regardless of its position in the triglyceride.[5, 16] Other lipases such as those of *Aspergillus flavus* and *Staphylococcus aureus* attack synthetic triglycerides at either 1-, 2-, or 3-positions, thereby showing no position preference at all.[5, 18] Additional research is needed to determine if other microbial lipases have positional and/or fatty acid preferences during hydrolysis of lipids.

11.54   Growth Medium

Lipase production by some microorganisms is limited by the presence of a readily fermentable carbohydrate[6, 18] while other microorganisms require it for growth.[9, 30] The amount of carbohydrate included in a medium should be limited to that required for reasonable growth. If the microorganism will grow on nutrient agar, it is the medium of choice; if not, media such as standard methods agar or tryptic soy agar, both of which contain limited amounts of carbohydrate, may be used.

11.55   Emulsification

Good emulsification of the substrate is essential, since lipase activity occurs at the fat-water interface. Although vigorous shaking often will give a satisfactory medium, the most consistent results are obtained by blending or homogenizing the fat to produce small globules. Stabilizing gums such as gum acacia may be used, but emulsifiers such as Tweens, monoglycerides, and diglycerides should not be employed because of their possible use as a substrate by the microorganisms being evaluated. Alford and Steinle[4] and Fryer et al.[14] did not add emulsifying agents in preparations of tributyrin agar plates. However, polyvinyl alcohol[23] and polyoxyethylene-(20)-hydrogenated castor oil[25] have been recommended as emulsifiers for the preparation of tributyrin agar.

11.56   Multiple Plating

Tributyrin is the most widely used substrate because of its ease of handling and of hydrolysis. However, as indicated above, it may lead to false positives and false negatives. Use of two substrates, at least for spot checks, is desirable.

11.57   Indicator Dyes

Victoria blue B, spirit blue, Nile blue sulfate, night blue, and other dyes have been used as indicators of fat hydrolysis. However, toxicity to one or more microorganisms has been reported for all of them.[4, 9, 18] Victoria blue B has little toxicity, and it is the dye of choice if a dye indicator is considered necessary.

11.6   REFERENCES

1. Adams, D. M. 1979. The role of heat resistant bacterial enzymes in UHT processing. In "Proc. International Conference on UHT Processing and Aseptic Packaging of Milk and Milk Products, November 27–29, 1979, at N. C. State Univ.," p. 89. Dept of Food Science, N.C. State Univ., Raleigh, N.C.
2. Adams, D. M. and Brawley, T. G. 1981. Heat resistant bacterial lipases and ultra-high temperature sterilization of dairy products. J. Dairy Sci. 64: 1951.
3. Alford, J. A. and Pierce, D. A. 1961. Lipolytic activity of microorganisms at low and intermediate temperatures. III. Activity of microbial lipases at temperatures below 0 C. J. Food Sci. 26: 518.
4. Alford, J. A. and Steinle, E. E. 1967. A double layered plate method for the detection of microbial lipolysis. J. Appl. Bacteriol. 30: 488.
5. Alford, J. A., Pierce, D. A., and Suggs, F. G. 1964. Activity of microbial lipases on natural fats and synthetic triglycerides. J. Lipid Res. 5: 390.
6. Alford, J. A., Smith, J. L., and Lilly, H. D. 1971. Relationship of microbial activity to changes in lipids of foods. J. Appl. Bacteriol. 34: 133.
7. Andersson, R. E. 1980. Microbial lipolysis at low temperatures. Appl. Environ. Microbiol. 39: 36.
8. Andersson, R. E., Hedlund, C. B., and Jonsson, U. 1979. Thermal inactivation of a heat-resistant lipase produced by the psychrotrophic bacterium, *Pseudomonas fluorescens*. J. Dairy Sci. 62: 361.
9. Bours, J. and Mossel, D. A. A. 1973. A comparison of methods for the determination of lipolytic properties of yeasts mainly isolated from margarine, moulds, and bacteria. Arch. Lebensmittelhyg. 24: 197.
10. Chrisope, G. L. and Marshall, R. T. 1976. Combined action of lipase and microbial phospholipase C on a model fat globule emulsion and raw milk. J. Dairy Sci. 59: 2024.
11. Driessen, F. M. and Stadhouders, J. 1974. Thermal activation and inactivation of exocellular lipases of some gram-negative bacteria common in milk. Neth. Milk Dairy J. 28: 10.
12. Fitz-Gerald, C. H. and Deeth, H. C. 1983. Factors influencing lipolysis by skim milk cultures of some psychrotrophic microorganisms. Austral. J. Dairy Technol. 38: 97.
13. Fox, C. W., Chrisope, G. L., and Marshall, R. T. 1976. Incidence and identification of phospholipase C-producing bacteria in fresh and spoiled homogenized milk. J. Dairy Sci. 59: 1857.
14. Fryer, T. T., Lawrence, R. C., and Reiter, B. 1967. Methods for isolation and enumeration of lipolytic organisms. J. Dairy Sci. 50: 477.
15. Griffiths, M. W. 1983. Synergistic effects of various lipases and phospholipase C on milk fat. J. Fd. Technol. 18: 495.
16. Jensen, R. G., Sampugna, J., Quinn, J. G., Carpenter, D. L., Marks, T. A., and Alford, J. A. 1965. Specificity of a lipase from *Geotrichium candidum* for *cis*-octadecenoic acid. J. Am. Oil Chem. Soc. 42: 1029.
17. Kouker, G. and Jaeger, K.-E. 1987. Specific and sensitive plate assay for bacterial lipases. Appl. Environ. Microbiol. 53: 211.
18. Lawrence, R. C. 1967. Microbial lipases and related esterases. Dairy Sci. Abst. 29: 1.

19. Marin, A. and Marshall, R. T. 1983a. Characterization of glycosidases produced by *Pseudomonas fluorescens* 26. J. Food Prot. 46: 676.
20. Marin, A. and Marshall, R. T. 1983b. Production of glycosidases by psychrotrophic bacteria. J. Food Sci. 48: 570.
21. Marin, A., Mawhinney, T. P., and Marshall, R. T. 1984. Glycosidic activities of *Pseudomonas fluorescens* on fat-extracted skim milk, buttermilk, and milk fat globule membranes. J. Dairy Sci. 67: 52.
22. Mencher, J. R. and Alford, J. A. 1967. Purification and characterization of the lipase of *Pseudomonas fragi*. J. Gen. Microbiol. 48: 317.
23. Mourey, A. and Kilbertus, G. 1976. Simple media containing stabilized tributyrin for demonstrating lipolytic bacteria in foods and soils. J. Appl. Bacteriol. 40: 47.
24. Palumbo, S. A. and Smith, J. L. 1977. Chemical and microbiological changes during sausage fermentation and ripening. In "Enzymes in Food and Beverage Processing, ACS Symposium Series, #47," ed. R. J. Ory and A. J. St. Angelo, p. 279. Am. Chem. Soc., Washington, D.C.
25. Rapp, M. 1978. Elektive Nahrmedien zum Nachweis von Lipolyten. Milchwissenschaft 33: 493.
26. Smith, J. L. and Alford, J. A. 1969. Action of microorganisms on the peroxides and carbonyls of fresh lard. J. Food Sci. 34: 75.
27. Stead, D. 1986. Microbial lipases: Their characteristics, role in food spoilage and industrial uses. J. Dairy Res. 53: 481.
28. Stepaniak, L., Birkeland, S.-E., Sorhaug, T., and Vagias, G. 1987. Isolation and partial characterization of heat-stable proteinase, lipase and phospholipase C from Pseudomonas fluorescens P1.16. Milchwissenschaft 42: 75.
29. Thomas, S. B. and Thomas, B. F. 1975. The bacteriological grading of bulk collected milk. Part 8. Differential and selective agar media. Dairy Industries 40: 397.
30. Umemoto, Y. 1969. A method for the detection of weak lipolysis of dairy lactic acid bacteria on double layered agar plates. Agr. Biol. Chem. (Japan) 33: 1651.

Chapter 12

PROTEOLYTIC MICROORGANISMS

J. S. Lee and A. A. Kraft

12.1 INTRODUCTION

12.11 Protein Hydrolysis

Protein hydrolysis by microorganisms in foods may produce a variety of odor and flavor defects. Some of the common psychrotrophic spoilage bacteria are strongly proteolytic and cause undesirable changes in dairy, meat, poultry, and seafood products, particularly when high populations are reached after extended refrigerated storage.

On the other hand, microbial proteolytic activity may be desirable in certain foods, such as in the ripening of cheese, where it contributes to the development of flavor, body, and texture. Opinions differ about the usefulness of proteolytic counts to evaluate quality losses of refrigerated dairy, meat, poultry, and fishery products.[6, 8, 9]

In some foods the level of proteolytic microorganisms may be of value to predict refrigerated storage life and to assess processing methods.[8, 9]

Psychrotrophic bacteria that produce heat-stable proteases in milk were reviewed by Speck and Adams.[17] They indicated that most raw milk supplies may contain proteolytic enzymes that remain active after ultra-high temperature (UHT) sterilization. Psychrotrophs, mainly *Pseudomonas* species, produce the proteases. Mayerhofer et al.[10] characterized a strain of *Pseudomonas fluorescens* that formed a protease of much greater heat resistance than the organism itself. While proteolysis may be favored at higher temperatures (about 40°C), activity still may be pronounced at refrigeration temperatures.[5] Activity of psychrotrophs in producing heat stable proteases may be expected to occur with longer term storage of raw milk at low temperature before processing. Heat-stable proteases also may adversely affect the flavor of other foods that contain dairy products.

12.12 Microorganisms

Proteolytic species are common among the genera *Bacillus*, *Clostridium*, *Pseudomonas*, and *Proteus*; there are also proteolytic yeasts and molds (Chapter 16). Microorganisms that carry out protein hydrolysis and acid fermentation are called acid-proteolytic, e.g., *Streptococcus faecalis var. liquefaciens* and *Micrococcus caseolyticus*.[3]

12.13   Milk Agar Medium

The hydrolysis of casein in an opaque skim milk agar is often used to determine proteolysis by microorganisms on or in agar plates.[4] Colonies of proteolytic bacteria will be surrounded by a clear zone as a result of the conversion of casein into soluble nitrogenous compounds. However, clear zones on milk agar can be produced by bacteria that produce acid from fermentable carbohydrates in the medium.[4] The clear zone on common milk agar medium reflects only the more complete breakdown of casein, since the early stages of proteolysis cannot be detected against the opaque background.

An improved skim milk agar medium has been developed[9] by adding sodium caseinate, trisodium citrate, and calcium chloride to standard methods agar. Its greater sensitivity is related to the detection of the early stages of casein breakdown, the formation of a zone of precipitation (insoluble paracaseins) in a transparent medium. This medium is well buffered, and this reduces the occurrence of false positive zones caused by acid production. No significant differences were found between total counts of raw milk on standard methods medium and the caseinate standard methods medium. This latter medium then can be used for the simultaneous determination of total and proteolytic counts.

12.14   Gelatin Agar Medium

Numerous methods have been used to detect gelatin hydrolysis by microorganisms, among them gelatin liquefaction (gelatin stab), and the detection of hydrolyzed gelatin in agar media with or without chemical protein precipitants. Pitt and Dey[12] developed a gelatin agar medium for the detection of gelatinase without the use of a protein precipitant.

A double-layer gelatin medium with a soft agar gelatin overlay is available that detects both weak and strong gelatinolytic bacteria in a direct plating procedure.[8] Advantages claimed for the medium are (1) rapid diffusion of proteolytic enzymes through the soft overlay, creating large zones of clearing; (2) reduction in swarming; and (3) more rapid colony development than with pour plates. If enumeration of proteolytic bacteria is desired from dairy or seafoods, incorporation of skim milk or fish juice in the overlay will detect proteolysis without the application of a chemical precipitant. This will be advantageous if further purification or identification of colonies is needed.

A double-layer plating technique can also be applied when one or more components of the growth medium are not compatible with the protein used to check hydrolysis. A two-layer plate has been developed[16] with a base indicator layer of milk agar and an upper layer of marine agar to detect proteolytic marine bacteria. Samples are placed on the upper layer by the spread plate method. No chemical precipitant is required to detect proteolysis.

12.2 GENERAL CONSIDERATIONS

Prepare samples and appropriate dilutions as described for the agar plate count (Chapter 4) and for the hide powder azure (HPA) method (Section 12.45).

12.3 EQUIPMENT, MATERIALS, AND REAGENTS

12.31 Media

Skim milk agar[1]
Standard methods caseinate agar[9]
Soft agar gelatin overlay medium[8]
Thin-layer enzyme assay (TEA) plate[19]

12.32 Reagents

HCl, 1%
Acetic acid, 10%
NaOH 1.0, 0.5 and 0.1 M
Diethyl ether
Trichloroacetic acid
Hide powder azure
Trypsin, 10 μg/ml
Tris buffer, 0.05 M
Ethanol
Bovine serum albumin

12.4 PROCEDURES

12.41 Skim Milk Agar Method

Incubate streak or pour plates at 21°C for 72 hr (or use the incubation conditions recommended for the food under study). Flood the plates with 1% HCl or 10% acetic acid solution for 1 min.[1] Pour off excess acid solution, then count colonies that are surrounded by clear zones produced by proteolysis.

12.42 Standard Methods Caseinate Agar Method[9]

Place appropriate dilutions of sample in 0.1 ml quantities on the surface of plates and distribute evenly by spreading with a sterile bent glass rod.

Allow the plates to dry for 15 min. Incubate plates for 24 to 72 hr at 30°C. To enumerate proteolytic psychrotrophic bacteria, incubate plates at 7°C for 10 days. Count colonies that form white or off-white precipitate around the colony. (Organisms that are strongly proteolytic can further break down the precipitate to soluble components with the formation of an inner transparent zone.)

12.43   Soft Agar Gelatin Overlay Method[8]

Place appropriate dilutions of sample in 0.1 ml quantities on the surface of the basal medium and distribute uniformly by spreading with a sterile bent glass rod. Pour 2.5 ml of melted gelatin overlay medium and distribute evenly over surface of agar. Incubate plates at 20°C for 3 days. Flood surface of plate with 10 ml of 5% acetic acid for 15 min. Count colonies with clear zones.

The standard methods caseinate agar method and the soft agar gelatin overlay method have not yet received collaborative evaluation.

12.44   Thin-Layer Enzyme Assay (TEA)[19]

Pour an agar medium that will support optimal growth of the test microorganism into a protein-coated polystyrene petri dish. Spot inoculate with the microorganism or add culture supernatant and enzyme solution controls to 3 mm-diameter wells that have been aseptically drilled into the agar. After incubation at an optimal time and temperature, remove the agar, wash the bottom of the petri dish with distilled water, and blow dry with compressed air. Expose the protein-coated surface to water vapor at 50°C for 1 min; then measure the area of water vapor condensation (proteolysis) with a ruler.

12.45   Hide Powder Azure (HPA) Assay[2]

Proteinases in milk can be assayed directly using HPA[13, 15] (Calbiochem or Sigma Chemical Co.) as a substrate. Adjust the pH of suspected milk to 8.3 with 1.0, 0.5, or 0.1 M NaOH. Add 100 mg of HPA to 5 ml of milk in a screw-capped tube. Incubate the tube at 37°C for 5 hr. Shake occasionally to keep the HPA in suspension. Terminate the reaction by cooling in ice water. Centrifuge the tube at $800 \times g$ for 5 min, add 1 ml of diethyl ether, and shake vigorously for 1 min. Centrifuge at $800 \times g$ for 15 min and remove the ether layer carefully with a Pasteur pipette. Repeat the ether extraction two more times. Finally, centrifuge the aqueous phase at $150,000 \times g$ for 60 min to remove casein. Instead of centrifugation, the casein may be precipitated with 2% trichloroacetic acid (TCA).[11] Measure the blue dye released from HPA by reading the absorbance at 595 nm.

If this assay is performed in 0.05 M Tris or similar buffer, the insoluble HPA may be removed by centrifugation or filtration.

12.5 PRECAUTIONS

The most serious disadvantage of the milk agar method is that the early stage of casein hydrolysis is not apparent until the medium is flooded with a protein precipitant to confirm proteolysis rather than clearing because of acids formed by the fermentation of carbohydrates.

Treatment with the protein precipitant prevents the isolation of colonies for further study. If this is an objective, replicate plating procedures can be used.

Simultaneous determination of total and proteolytic counts on the same plate is difficult if the ratio of the two counts varies widely. The zones of clearing may not be distinct unless the colonies are well separated. In this case the plates that contain fewer colonies must be counted, with resulting loss of accuracy. In addition, weakly proteolytic bacteria may not be detectable unless the plate incubation period is extended, sometimes beyond the optimum length for the total count. This difficulty may be further compounded if a mixture of bacteria with widely varying proteolytic activities is present on the same plate.

TEA is extremely sensitive because of the thinness of the protein layer. Enzyme activity would quickly remove the hydrophilic film and would restore the hydrophobic polystyrene surface.

TEA can be used to study enzyme kinetics as well as to screen the proteolytic activity of microorganism.[18] Concentration of protein that can be absorbed on the polystyrene surface is self limiting, thus requiring low concentrations of the substrate.

Agar concentration recommended is 2%. Beyond this level the rate of diffusion is affected. Some media, such as Rogosa agar, decrease the wettability of protein-coated surface, so they cannot be used with TEA.

Besides simplicity and convenience, the HPA assay is said to detect protease produced by as few as 1.5×10^6 bacteria per ml.[5]

12.6 INTERPRETATION

Ideally the proteolytic activity of a microorganism should be measured against the specific protein(s) of the food being examined. The temperature of plate incubation should reflect that of the food during the time that microbial proteolytic activity is expected or has taken place. Convenience and the need for standardization have limited the media mainly to those containing gelatin or casein (skim milk). Gelatin is an incompletely hydrolysed protein, and the ability to liquefy gelatin, or the lack of that ability, may not be correlated to the specific proteolytic potential being measured.[14] Ability to hydrolyze casein, on the other hand, is more closely related to the ability to hydrolyze animal protein.[7] The measurement of the level of proteolytic bacteria and the ratio of proteolytic organisms to the total microbial flora can be useful in some foods to predict their refrigerated shelf life.[8, 9]

12.7   REFERENCES

1. APHA. 1972. "Standard Methods for the Examination of Dairy Products," 13th ed. Am. Publ. Health Assn., New York.

2. Cliffe, A. J. and Law, B. A. 1982. A new method for the detection of microbial proteolytic enzymes in milk. J. Dairy Res. 49: 209.

3. Frazier, W. C. 1967. "Food Microbiology," 2nd ed. McGraw-Hill, New York.

4. Frazier, W. C. and Rupp, P. 1928. Studies on the proteolytic bacteria of milk. 1. A medium for the direct isolation of caseolytic milk bacteria. J. Bacteriol. 16: 57.

5. Gebre-Egziabher, A., Humbert, E. S., and Blankenagel, G. 1980. Heat-stable proteases from psychrotrophs in milk. J. Food Prot. 43: 197.

6. Jay, J. M. 1972. Mechanism and detection of microbial spoilage in meats at low temperatures: A status report. J. Milk Food Technol. 35: 467.

7. Kazanas, N. 1968. Proteolytic activity of microorganisms isolated from fresh water fish. Appl. Microbiol. 16: 128.

8. Levin, R. E. 1968. Detection and incidence of specific species of spoilage bacteria on fish. 1. Methodology. Appl. Microbiol. 16: 1734.

9. Martley, F. G., Jayashankar, S. R., and Lawrence, R. C. 1970. An improved agar medium for the detection of proteolytic organisms in total bacterial counts. J. Appl. Bacteriol. 33: 363.

10. Mayerhofer, H. J., Marshall, R. T., White, C. H., and Lu, M. 1973. Characterization of a heat-stable protease of *Pseudomonas fluorescens* P 26. Appl. Microbiol. 25: 44.

11. McKellar, R. C. 1984. Comparison of the hide powder azure and casein-trinitrobenzene sulfonic acid methods for determining proteolysis in skim milk. J. Food Prot. 47: 476.

12. Pitt, T. L. and Dey, D. 1970. A method for the detection of gelatinase production by bacteria. J. Appl. Bacteriol. 33: 687.

13. Rinderknecht, H., Geokas, M. C., Silverman, P., and Haverback, B. J. 1968. A new ultrasensitive method for the determination of proteolytic activity. Clin. Chim. Acta. 21: 197.

14. SAB. 1957. "Manual for Microbiological Methods." Soc. Am. Bacteriol., McGraw-Hill, New York.

15. Sanjose, C. L., Fernandez, L., and Palacios, P. 1987. Compositional changes in cold raw milk supporting growth of *Pseudomonas fluorescens* NCDO 2085 before production of extracellular proteinase. J. Food Prot. 50: 1004.

16. Sizemore, R. K. and Stevenson, L. H. 1970. Method for the isolation of proteolytic marine bacteria. Appl. Microbiol. 20: 991.

17. Speck, M. L. and Adams, D. M. 1976. Symposium: Impact of Heat Stable Microbial Enzymes in Food Processing. Heat resistant proteolytic enzymes from bacterial sources. J. Dairy Sci. 59: 786.

18. Wikstrom, M. B. 1983. Detection of microbial proteolytic activity by a cultivation plate assay in which different proteins adsorbed to a hydrophobic surface are used as substrates. Appl. Environ. Microbiol. 45: 393.

19. Wikstrom, M., Elwing, H., and Linde, A. 1981. Determination of proteolytic activity: A sensitive and simple assay utilizing substrate adsorbed to a plastic surface and radial diffusion in gel. Analyt. Biochem. 118: 240.

Chapter 13

HALOPHILIC AND OSMOPHILIC MICROORGANISMS

John A. Baross and Lawrence M. Lenovich

13.1 INTRODUCTION

Microorganisms can grow over a wide range of solute concentrations. Only a few species can grow at the high osmotic pressures characteristic of environments having supersaturated brine and sugar concentrations (i.e., reduced water activity). Inconsistency in terminology exists in the literature describing this group of microorganisms. However, for practical reasons, microorganisms that require minimum concentrations of salt (NaCl and other cations and anions) are called halophiles, whereas organisms that can grow in high concentrations of organic solute, particularly sugars, have been called osmophiles. See Tilbury[49] for a discussion of "osmophiles." The terms "osmo- and xero-tolerant" have been used in place of "osmophilic" because these organisms do not have an absolute requirement for reduced water activity (a_w) or high osmotic pressure, but merely tolerate drier environments better than non-osmotolerant species.[1] To minimize confusion, the name "osmophile," coined by von Richter[52] in 1912, will be adopted for discussion purposes.

In general, the requirement for salt by halophilic microorganisms is not an exclusive need for NaCl since many species require low levels of K^+, Mg^{++}, and other cations and anions in addition to NaCl.[26,27,31,39] Furthermore, for some bacteria, the apparent requirement for NaCl is not specific but strictly osmotic, and other salts and sugars can be substituted. See Rodriquez-Valera[43] for the characteristics and microbial ecology of bacteria in hypersaline environments. The level of salt required by microorganisms varies greatly. Therefore, the microbial types associated with a particular salted food depend on the concentration and type of salt and the type of food. The most practical classification of halophilic microorganisms is based on the level of salt required.[15,26] *Slight halophiles* grow optimally in media containing 0.5% to 3% salt; *moderate halophiles* grow optimally in media containing 3% to 15% salt, and *extreme halophiles* in media containing 15% to 30% salt. Additionally, many halotolerant microorganisms grow without added salt as well as in salt concentrations exceeding 12%. Some halotolerant microorganisms are involved in the spoilage of foods with low a_w values, including salted foods. See Reed[39] for a discussion of a_w limitations of different microbial species. Non-halophilic bacteria grow best in media containing less than 0.5% NaCl.

Among salted foods, low-salted foods (1% to 7% salt by weight) are more susceptible to microbiological spoilage and are also more likely to contain viable human pathogens. This is particularly true of untreated fresh seafoods. Heavily brined foods do not spoil easily unless maintained at elevated temperatures. A compilation of the types of halophilic, spoilage, and pathogenic microorganisms associated with various salted foods is shown in Table 1.

Yeasts are the most common osmophilic microorganisms encountered in nonionic environments of high osmolarity, such as foods containing high concentrations of sugar. Osmophilic yeasts are usually the cause of spoilage of high-sugar foods, including jams, honey, concentrated fruit juices, chocolate candy with soft centers, etc.[53] Osmophilic yeasts are of no public health significance, but are of economic importance to the food industry. For a discussion on xerophilic molds and their significance in foods, see Pitt.[36]

13.2 HALOPHILIC MICROORGANISMS

13.21 Equipment, Materials, and Reagents

13.211 Diluents

1. Phosphate buffer with salt.
Prior to sterilization, add the required amount of NaCl to pH 7, 0.1 M potassium phosphate solution. The addition of 3% NaCl in the buffer has been shown to be useful in protecting *Vibrio parahaemolyticus* against cold and heat inactivation.[3] Under circumstances where a phosphate buffer is not desirable, diluents made with 0.5% peptone supplemented with the appropriate concentrations of NaCl will also give satisfactory results.
2. Synthetic sea water (SW)[8] (Chapter 62).
Synthetic sea water is used as a diluent and as a salt base in the preparation of sea water agar (SWA).

13.212 Media

1. Trypticase soy agar with added salt (TSA-NaCl)
Add the required amount of NaCl to TSA prior to sterilization.
2. Sea water agar[29,32] (Chapter 62)

3. Halophilic agar (HA)[15] (Chapter 62)

4. Halophilic broth (HB) (Chapter 62)

Halophilic broth (HB) is used as a diluent and as an enrichment medium for the isolation of extremely halophilic bacteria. Sterilize medium by autoclaving at 121°C for 15 min.

13.22 Procedures

13.221 Slightly halophilic bacteria

1. General

Most of the slightly halophilic bacteria originate from marine environments. Marine psychrotrophic bacteria of the genera *Pseudomonas*, *Moraxella*, *Acinetobacter*, and *Flavobacterium* contribute to the spoilage of marine fish and shellfish. Gram-negative rods of terrestrial origin and other gram-negative and gram-positive psychrotrophic organisms are frequently involved.[19,45] Some of the organisms have complex ionic requirements and may require Mg^{++} and K^+ in addition to NaCl for growth and proteolytic activity, whereas the salt requirement for other slightly halophilic bacteria is osmotic. Growth of most of these marine bacteria is inhibited if the NaCl concentration of the growth medium is lower than 0.5% or higher than 5%. Dilution of seafood samples with distilled water may cause lysis of many representative spoilage bacteria. Holding marine foods for sustained periods at temperatures exceeding 25°C will reduce the numbers of psychrotrophic microorganisms significantly. To identify the degree of initial microbial contamination of marine origin, prechill diluent, reagents, and sampling equipment to 5°C. Avoid washing food sample with distilled water, and do not use diluents containing less than 3% NaCl.

The microbial flora associated with salted meats and vegetables are variable and dependent on many factors, including the type of food, the presence of other salts or organic preservatives, the concentration of salt, and the storage conditions of temperature and packaging.[15,16,42] In general, microorganisms involved in the spoilage of low salt meats and vegetables (1% to 7% brine) can be enumerated without the use of special media provided the diluents and plating media are supplemented with NaCl equivalent to the concentration in the food sample.

2. Sampling

Low-salted foods to be analyzed for psychrotrophic spoilage microorganisms should be tested without delay (within 24 hr); otherwise, growth will occur. Samples should be maintained at 0° to 5°C until tested.

3. Procedure

a. Fish (Teleosts). Remove skin samples with a sterile cork borer (1.6 cm diameter) by punching the cork borer through the skin and then removing the disc of skin with a sterile scalpel and forceps. Collect six pieces, three from the ventral side and three from the dorsal side of the fish. Take flesh

Table 1—Halophilic, Spoilage, and Pathogenic Microorganisms

Food type	Salt associated with food (%)	Halophilic types
I. Marine fish (Teleosts)	1% to 4% (similar to seawater)	Slight and halotolerant types: (*Listonella* and *Shewanella*) *Vibrio*, *Pseudomonas*, *Moraxella*, *Acinetobacter*, and other gram-negative bacteria
II. Molluscan shellfish	0.5% to 4% (similar to seawater)	Same as for fish—but greater percentage of *Vibrio*
III. Crustaceans	0.5% to 4% (similar to seawater)	Same as for fish—but greater percentage of *Vibrio*
IV. Brined meats (ham, bacon, corned beef, prepared meats, and sausage)	1% to 7% brine[b]	Halotolerant molds, yeasts, gram-positive bacteria (e.g., micrococci, enterococci, lactobacilli)
V. Salted vegetables	1% to 15%	Moderate and halotolerant molds, yeasts and gram-positive bacteria
VI. Salted fish (A) Light salt	1% to 10%	Slight and halotolerant types
(B) Heavy salt	20 to 25% NaCl wt/vol (10% to 15% salt in interior of fish)	Moderately and extremely halophilic types

[a]Refer to specific section for the isolation of specific pathogens.

[b]Brine concentration is $\dfrac{\text{g salt}}{\text{g salt } + \text{ g water}} \times 100$.

Spoilage microorganisms	Pathogens[a]	References
Proteolytic *Pseudomonas, Moraxella*, and *Acinetobacter*	*Vibrio parahaemolyticus, Vibrio cholerae, Vibrio vulnificus, Clostridium botulinum* E, *Clostridium perfringens, Staphylococcus aureus, Salmonella* and other pathogenic *Enterobacteriaceae, Erysipelothrix insidiosa*	6, 7, 17, 18, 19, 23, 24, 25, 29, 30, 41, 42, 44, 45
Same as for fish at early stages. Lactic acid bacteria and yeasts in later stages of spoilage	Same as for fish plus human enteric viruses and *Gonyaulax*	6, 7, 10, 12, 14, 17, 18, 23, 24, 25, 29
Same as for fish, also yeasts and chitinoclastic microorganisms	Same as for fish except increased likelihood of chitinoclastic pathogenic *Vibrio* spp.	6, 7, 10, 12, 14, 17, 18, 23, 24, 25, 29, 46, 49
Mixed flora in aerobic packaging. Predominantly gram-positive bacteria in refrigerated meats in anaerobic packaging	*C. botulinum, C. perfringens, S. aureus.* Pathogenic *Enterobacteriaceae* in meats containing low salts	9, 11, 13, 14, 15, 16, 18, 19, 21, 23, 25, 27, 39, 42
Lactic acid bacteria, yeasts and molds, *Bacillus, Enterobacteriaceae* in foods with low salt content. *Clostridium* in packaged foods	Dependent on level of salt in food. Pathogenic members of *Enterobacteriaceae* in low-salt foods. *S. aureus* in highly salted food	16, 19, 33, 41, 50
Pseudomonas in lightly salted fish. *Clostridium* in packaged fish. *Micrococcus* in fish containing 5% to 10% salt	Dependent on salt concentration, same as for salted vegetables. *V. parahaemolyticus* may occur when salt is 1% to 7%. *Salmonella* spp. capable of growing in 8% NaCl at high temperatures (22° to 37°C) and surviving for up to 70 days at 5°C in curing brines	17, 19, 21, 32, 33, 41, 42, 44, 45, 46
Halobacterium, Halococcus (cause condition called "pink" in fish). Also some members of the *Micrococcaceae*	*S. aureus.*	17, 19, 21, 41, 42, 44, 45

samples from just below the skin by peeling the skin with a sterile scalpel and forceps and dissecting the flesh. Add the discs of skin to 90 mL phosphate buffer-3% NaCl (Section 13.211.1) or synthetic sea water with either sterile sand or glass beads (10 g). Mix sample and diluent thoroughly by shaking vigorously for 1 min. Prepare dilutions (to 10^{-6}) in phosphate buffer-3% NaCl or sea water agar. Place 0.1-mL aliquots on either TSA plus 3% NaCl or sea water agar with the spread plate technique. Incubate plates at 7°C for 10 days for the enumeration of psychrotrophic spoilage bacteria.

For fish flesh samples, fillets, or small whole fish (less than 6 in), cut samples aseptically into slices (2.5 cm²) and weigh in a sterile container. Add 50 g of flesh (skin removed) to 450 mL of diluent (phosphate buffer-3% NaCl, Section 13.211.1) in a sterile blender jar and blend for 2 min. If the sample is not sufficiently homogenized, let it stand for 2 min before blending for an additional 2 min. Prepare serial dilutions and plates as described above.

Frozen fish or other seafood blocks are sampled using an electric drill and bit.

The detection and enumeration of the slightly halophilic pathogens *Vibrio parahaemolyticus*, *Vibrio cholerae*, and *Vibrio vulnificus* are described in detail in Chapter 28.

b. Molluscan shellfish. Collect and prepare samples for microbiological analysis as described by Hunt et al.[20] Prepare initial 1:1 dilution by blending 100 g of shellfish meat with 100 mL of sterile diluent (phosphate buffer-3% NaCl, Section 13.211.1). Plate samples as described in a above. It is advisable to prepare two sets of plates, one to be incubated at 7°C and the other at 25°C, since shellfish generally reside in near-shore environments that are subject to wide fluctuations in temperature and, therefore, harbor both psychrotrophic and mesophilic bacteria.

c. Crustaceans. Collect and prepare samples as described by Nickelson and Finne.[34] Prepare dilutions as for fish flesh. Plate samples as described in a above.

d. Low-salted meats and vegetables (1% to 7% brine). Prepare dilutions by blending 50-g samples with 450 mL diluent (phosphate buffer-3% NaCl, Section 13.211.1) plus NaCl equivalent to salt concentration of food sample. Plate samples on TSA supplemented with NaCl equivalent to NaCl concentration of food. If food sample usually is not refrigerated, use 1-mL aliquot for pour plates and incubate plates for 4 days at 25°C. For refrigerated foods such as bacon, plate 0.1-mL aliquots with the spread plate technique. Incubate plates for 10 days at 7°C.

4. Interpretation

In general, fish contaminated with greater than 10^8 psychrotrophic bacteria per cm² of skin or per g of muscle is considered spoiled.[19, 46] The most common seafood spoilage bacteria are *Pseudomonas* species, which are psychrotrophic (Chapter 9) and actively proteolytic (Chapter 12). Chemical and organoleptic tests (odor, particularly associated with gills) are used in conjunction with bacterial counts to assess the extent of spoilage. High total volatile nitrogen (TVN) and trimethylamine (TMA) values are used as an indication of bacterial activity.[51]

No microbiological standards have been established for low-salted meats and vegetables.

13.222   Moderately halophilic bacteria

1. General

Most of the moderately halophilic bacteria involved in the spoilage of salted foods (5% to 20% NaCl by weight) are gram-positive species of *Bacillaceae* and *Micrococcaceae*. *Paracoccus halodenitrificans* and other *Micrococcus* spp. have a specific requirement for NaCl.[26, 27] This is also true for moderately halophilic *Acinetobacter/Moraxella* species isolated from salted herring, *Vibrio costicola* isolated from bacon curing brines, and *Vibrio alginolyticus* isolated from seafoods.[13, 26] In contrast, the requirement for salt by many moderately halophilic *Bacillus* spp. is not specific for NaCl and many other Na^+ and K^+ salts can be substituted. *Pseudomonas* spp. isolated from sea salts and *Planococcus halophilus* can grow in the absence of added salt although they grow optimally in salt concentrations ranging from 4% to 9%.[26] Salted foods that can spoil because of moderately halophilic microorganisms commonly harbor high numbers of halotolerant gram-positive bacteria, yeasts, and molds. (Consult Table 1 for references on isolation and enumeration procedures of osmophilic and halotolerant pathogens.)

2. Procedure

Moderately salted foods are sampled for spoilage microorganisms as described in Section 13.221.2. Prepare 1:10 dilutions by mixing 50 g of food in 450 mL sterile phosphate buffer (Section 13.211.1) with added NaCl equivalent to the salt concentration of the food sample. Plating procedures with plating media and plate incubation temperatures and times are described in Section 13.221.3d. For the isolation and enumeration of specific bacterial types, consult Table 1 and related chapters.

3. Interpretation

No microbiological standards have been set for moderately salted foods. Use organoleptic tests (odor and visual evidence of spoilage such as slime or gas formation) in conjunction with total bacterial counts to determine the extent of spoilage. *Staphylococcus aureus* and *Clostridium perfringens* can grow in some moderately salted foods.

13.223   Extremely halophilic bacteria

1. General

The extreme halophiles are normally found in aquatic environments of unusually high salt concentrations and in solar evaporated sea salts. These grow optimally in media containing 15% to 30% wt/vol NaCl.[26, 27] They are principally species of the genera *Halobacterium* and *Halococcus* that produce bright red or pink pigments, grow very slowly even under optimal conditions, and are readily lysed when exposed to low salt concentrations (less than 10%). Halobacteria are grouped with the archaeobacteria based on features such as 5S and 16S ribosomal RNA sequences, ether-linked lipids, and their lack of a peptidoglycan wall.[54, 55] Extremely halophilic bacteria have been incriminated in the spoilage of fish, bacon, and hides preserved in sea salts. Severe contamination of foods with *Halobacterium* or *Halococcus* will generally result in a pink discoloration on the outer surface of the sample accompanied by decomposition and putrefaction.[46]

2. Procedure

For isolation, transfer surface slime from salted fish or bacon to an HA plate (Section 13.212.3) using a cotton or alginate swab. For the quantitative enumeration of *Halobacterium* and *Halococcus* from food samples, blend 50 g of sample with 450 mL HB. Place 0.1-mL aliquots of each dilution (to 10^{-6}) on HA plates with the spread plate technique. For the detection of extremely halophilic bacteria from solar sea salts or brine solutions (70% to 80%), prepare serial dilutions in HB up to 10^{-6}. Prepare plates on HA. Alternately, for samples with low numbers of halophilic bacteria, place 10-mL or 10-g sample into 90 mL of HB broth and incubate at 35°C for up to 12 days. Then streak from broth onto HA plates. Incubate plates at 33° to 35°C in a humid incubator for 5 to 12 days.

3. Interpretation

No microbiological criteria for heavily brined foods have been set, and usually only an organoleptic observation for presence of red or pink slime and putrefaction is performed to check for spoilage. Since *Halobacterium* and *Halococcus* are normally present in sea salts, food spoilage by these organisms can be prevented by dry heat sterilization of salt prior to use for curing. Extremely halophilic bacteria will not grow on foods stored at temperatures below 7°C.

Extreme halophiles are not pathogenic to humans, and any incidence of food poisoning associated with heavily salted foods is invariably caused by *S. aureus* (Chapter 33).

13.224   Halotolerant microorganisms

1. General

Microorganisms capable of growing in NaCl concentrations exceeding 5% as well as in media containing no NaCl are called halotolerant. Most halotolerant bacteria are gram-positive and belong to the *Micrococcaceae*, the *Bacillaceae*, and some *Corynebacterium* species. A few gram-negative species will also grow in foods cured with 10% salt. Many human pathogens, such as *S. aureus* and *C. perfringens* and some strains of *Clostridium botulinum*, are responsible for food poisoning outbreaks involving low and moderately salted foods.[41, 42]

Most halotolerant microorganisms are isolated when foods are tested for slight or moderate halophiles. Specific media, however, are required to isolate halotolerant molds and yeasts from food samples (see Section 13.3).

2. Procedure
Refer to Sections 13.221 and 13.222.

3. Interpretation
Refer to Sections 13.221 and 13.222.

13.3 OSMOPHILIC MICROORGANISMS

13.31 General Considerations

Osmophilic yeasts can cause spoilage of honey, chocolate candy with soft centers, jams, molasses, corn syrup, flavored syrups and toppings, concentrated fruit juices, and similar products.[49, 53] Many of the common spoilage yeasts in this group belong to the genus *Zygosaccharomyces*.[56]

Techniques for the enumeration of osmophilic microorganisms have been reported by numerous investigators. However, wide acceptance of standard methods has not been attained. Generally, the enumeration of osmophilic yeasts requires a consideration of both the a_w of the diluents and the plating media. Inaccurate results may be obtained if a high a_w diluent or agar medium is used or if the agar medium has a reduced a_w but the diluent does not.[44] The type of solute used to reduce the a_w may also play an important role in enumeration techniques.[28]

Because of the particulates in many food products, the pour plate technique is the method of choice for enumeration. With products having suspected low counts, products with low viscosity, and products that may require the isolation of contaminants, membrane filtration techniques have been suggested.[22, 57] A simple presence-absence test for detection of small numbers of osmotolerant yeasts in high-sugar foods may be useful for qualitative purposes.[22]

13.32 Equipment, Materials, and Reagents

13.321 Equipment

Stainless steel filter apparatus
Type HA filters with grid marks and absorbent pads
Vacuum pump
Filter flask, 1 L
Erlenmeyer flask, 500 ml screw cap
Stomacher or blender

Petri dishes, 15 × 100 mm
Incubator, 30°C
Colony counter

13.322   Diluents

Diluents with reduced a_w are needed to detect and enumerate osmophilic microorganisms.[4, 43, 47] When hypotonic diluents are used, osmophilic yeasts may be destroyed. Generally, the use of 40% to 50% wt/wt of hexose in diluents is recommended. Glucose or invert sugar is most suitable. Sucrose and corn syrup in the intermediate range of dextrose equivalents are unlikely to provide a sufficiently low a_w environment at reasonable concentrations. Additional research is needed in this area.

13.323   Media

No single medium is optimal for quantitation, though several have been suggested.[37, 48] It is best to evaluate several media depending on the food being analyzed. Tests to select the best medium for each product category may be appropriate. Pivnick and Gabis[38] suggested malt extract-yeast extract 40% wt/wt glucose agar (MY40G), among others, as a general-purpose medium for most osmotolerant microorganisms. Restaino et al.[40] found that recovery of *Saccharomyces rouxii* from chocolate syrup was significantly improved with the addition of 60% sucrose (wt/vol) and 2% glucose to potato dextrose agar ($a_w = 0.92$). Recently investigators have reported the use of filtration techniques in combination with fluorescent staining to detect low numbers of osmophilic yeasts in confectionery products.[2, 35]

13.33   Procedures

Several media may be used for enumeration. A more detailed discussion on appropriate media selection can be found in Pitt and Hocking.[37]

13.331   Sampling

Samples should be collected in sterile containers and stored in conditions that will not promote the growth of viable fungi. Analysis should be conducted the same day the samples are collected.

13.332   Plate count method

Stomach or blend samples. Prepare dilutions with sterile, phosphate-buffered water supplemented with glucose or other solute. Inoculate 1 mL of the desired dilution into petri dishes, then pour with 15 to 20 mL of the appropriate agar medium. Incubate at 30°C for 5 to 7 days. The use of a colony counter will facilitate enumeration because many yeasts grow slowly and thus their colonies are difficult to see with the unaided eye.

13.333   Membrane filter technique

Enumeration of low numbers of spoilage yeasts in viscous products of low a_w has been reported using standard filtration techniques.[57]

Weigh a 25-g sample aseptically into a sterile tared Erlenmeyer flask. Add approximately 1 to 2 volumes of sterile distilled water. Mount a presterilized stainless steel filter apparatus containing a sterile HA filter on a filter flask. Cover the filter holder with a sterile petri dish. Attach vacuum source to filter flask and filter sample. Rinse the walls of the sample flask and funnel with sterile water. Remove the filter from the filter base and place it, grid side up, on one of the previously discussed media. Incubate the dish for 5 days at 30°C and count the colonies.

13.34   Precautions

Analysis of products by the membrane filter technique requires that the sample be diluted with distilled water. Although dilution may facilitate sample analysis, it may cause osmotic stress to the mycoflora present by altering the a_w of the sample.

Sterilization of high-sugar media may result in compounds that are toxic to osmophiles. Steaming media containing high sugar at 100°C for 30 min will destroy all microorganisms except bacterial spores, which are unlikely to grow in media with more than 60% hexose.

Because of the high viscosity of many of these plating media, it is important to swirl the plates more than one would with standard plating media to ensure that the sample is uniformly distributed throughout the agar.

Incubation of plates with low a_w media in a forced-draft incubator will cause plates to dry and prevent colonies from developing fully. Placing a shallow pan of distilled water in the bottom of the incubator will prevent drying.

None of the above methods account for the possibility of injury that is due to environmental stress such as heat, osmotic, or freeze injury. It may be desirable to consider methodology for recovering injured cells. However, the literature does not provide a wealth of information on the injury phenomenon in yeasts and molds.[5] One may need to develop protocols for specific food types.

13.35   Interpretation

It is important to collect baseline data on different product types in order to interpret quantitative estimates of osmophiles. Acceptable levels of osmophiles are ultimately product-dependent and are based on each product's history and likelihood of spoilage. In certain circumstances, the presence of a particular osmophile at any level is unacceptable. Counts of 10 or fewer per g in products such as liquid sugars or syrups may prove to be highly significant if the yeast is a spoilage type such as *Zygosaccharomyces rouxii*. When one detects low level contamination by yeasts, identification of the species is often beneficial so that an effective course of action can be implemented.

Low counts (10 or fewer per g) may be indicative of inadequate processing that did not destroy vegetative cells originating from raw materials or post-processing contamination from equipment, air, or packaging materials.

13.4   REFERENCES

1. Anand, J. C. and Brown, A. D. 1968. Growth rate patterns of the so-called osmophilic and non-osmophilic yeasts in solutions of polyethylene glycol. J. Gen. Microbiol. 52: 205.
2. Baumgart, V. J. and Vieregge, B. 1984. Rapid detection of osmophilic yeasts in marzipan. Susswaren 28: 190.
3. Beuchat, L. R. 1977. Suitability of some enrichment broths and diluents for enumerating cold and heat-stressed *Vibrio parahaemolyticus*. Can. J. Microbiol. 23: 630.
4. Beuchat, L. R. 1983. Influence of water activity on growth, metabolic activities, and survival of yeasts and molds. J. Food Prot. 46: 135.
5. Beauchat, L. R. 1986. Consideration of media for enumerating injured fungi. In "Methods for the Mycological Examination of Food," ed. A. D. King, Jr., J. I. Pitt, L. R. Beuchat, and J. E. L. Corry, P. 168. Plenum Press, New York.
6. Blake, P. A., Merson, M. H. Weaver, R. E., Hollis, D. G., and Heublein, P. C., 1979. Disease caused by marine *Vibrio*. New Engl. J. Med. 300: 1.
7. Colwell, R. R., ed. 1984. "Vibrios in the Environment." John Wiley & Sons, New York.
8. Colwell, R. R. and Morita, R. Y. 1964. Reisolation and emendation of description of *Vibrio marinus* (Russell) Ford. J. Bacteriol. 88: 831.
9. Draughon, F. A., Melton, C. C., and Maxedon, D. 1981. Microbial profiles of country-cured hams aged in stockinettes, barrier bags, and paraffin wax. Appl. Environ. Microbiol. 41: 1078.
10. Eklund, M. W., Spinelli, J., Miyauchi, D., and Groninger, H. 1965. Characterization of yeasts isolated from Pacific crab meat. Appl. Microbiol. 13: 985.
11. Escher, F. E., Koehler, P. E., and Ayres, J. C. 1973. Production of ochratoxins A and B on country-cured hams. Appl. Microbiol. 26: 27.
12. Fieger, E. A. and Nokva, A. F. 1961. Microbiology of Shellfish Deterioration. In "Fish as Food," Vol. I, ed. G. Borgstrom, p. 561. Academic Press, New York.
13. Gardner, G. A. 1973. A selective medium for enumeratring salt requiring *Vibrio* spp. from Wiltshire Bacon and curing brines. J. Appl. Bacteriol. 36: 329.
14. Gardner, G. A. and Kitchell, A. G. 1973. The microbiological examination of cured meats. In "Sampling-Microbiological Monitoring of Environments," ed. R. R. Board and D. N. Lovelock, p. 11. Academic Press, New York.
15. Gibbons, N. E. 1969. Isolation, growth, and requirements of halophilic bacteria. In "Methods in Microbiology," ed J. R. Norris and D. W. Ribbons, p. 169. Academic Press, New York.
16. Harrigan, W. F. and McCance, M. E. 1966. "Laboratory Methods in Microbiology." Academic Press, London, England.
17. Hennessey, J. P. 1971. Salted and dried groundfish products. In "Fish Inspection and Quality Control," ed. R. Krueger, p. 114. Fishing News (Books) Limited, London, England.
18. Herbert, R. A., Hendrie, M. S., Gibson, D. M., and Shewan, J. M. 1971. Bacteria active in the spoilage of certain seafoods. J. Appl. Bacteriol. 34: 41.
19. Hobbs, G. 1983. Microbial spoilage of fish. In "Food Microbiology: Advances and Prospects," ed. F. A. Skinner, p. 217. Academic Press, London, England.
20. Hunt, D. A., Miescier, J., Redman, J., Salinger, A., and Lucas, J. P. 1984. Molluscan shellfish, fresh or fresh-frozen oysters, mussels, or clams. In "Compendium of Methods for the Microbiological Examination of Foods," 2nd ed., ed. M. L. Speck, p. 590. Am. Pub. Health Assn., Washington, D.C.

21. Ingram, M. and Dainty, R. H. 1971. Changes caused by microbes in spoilage of meats. J. Appl. Bacteriol. 34: 21.
22. Jermini, M. F. G., Geiges, O., and Schmidt-Lorenz, W. 1987. Detection, isolation, and identification of osmotolerant yeasts from high-sugar products. J. Food Protect. 50: 468.
23. Kaper, J., Lockman, H., Colwell, R. R., and Joseph, S. W. 1979. Ecology, serology, and enterotoxin production of *Vibrio cholerae* in Chesapeake Bay. Appl. Environ. Microbiol. 37: 91.
24. Kelly, M. T. and Avery, D. M. 1980. Lactose-positive *Vibrio* in seawater: A cause of pneumonia and septicemia in a drowning victim. J. Clin. Microbiol. 11: 278.
25. Koelensmid, W., Blanche, A. A. and van Rhee, R. 1964. *Salmonella* in meat products. Annales de L'Institut Pasteur de Lille. 15: 85.
26. Kushner, D. J. 1978. Life in high salt and solute concentrations: Halophilic bacteria. In "Microbial Life in Extreme Environments," ed. D. J. Kushner, p. 317. Academic Press, London, England.
27. Kushner, D. J. 1985. The Halobacteriaceae. In "The Bacteria," Vol. 8 "Archaeobacteria," ed C. R. Woese and R. S. Wolfe, p. 171. Academic Press. New York.
28. Lenovich, L. M., Buchanan, R. L., Worley, N. J., and Restaino, L. 1988. Effect of solute type on sorbate resistance in *Zygosaccharomyces rouxii*. J. Food Sci. 53: 914.
29. Liston, J., Matches, J. R., and Baross, J. 1971. Survival and growth of pathogenic bacteria in seafoods. In "Fish Inspection and Quality Control," ed. R. Kreuger, p. 246. Fishing News (Books) Limited, London, England.
30. MacDonell, M. T. and Colwell, R. R. 1985. Phylogeny of the *Vibrionaceae*, and recommendation for two new genera, *Listonella* and *Shewanella*. System. Appl. Micribiol. 6: 171.
31. MacLeod, R. A. 1965. The question of the existence of specific marine bacteria. Bacteriol. Rev. 29: 9.
32. MacLeod, R. A., Onofrey, E., and Norris, M. E. 1954. Nutrition and metabolism of marine bacteria. I. Survey of nutritional requirements. J. Bacteriol. 68: 680.
33. Matches, J. R. and Liston, J. 1972. Effects of incubation temperature on the tolerance of *Salmonella*. J. Milk Food. Technol. 35: 39.
34. Nickelson, R. II and Finne, G. 1984. Fish, crustaceans, and precooked seafoods. In "Compendium of Methods for the Microbiological Examination of Foods," 2nd ed., ed. M. L. Speck, p. 573. Amer. Pub. Health Assn., Washington, D.C.
35. Pettipher, G. L. 1987. Detection of low numbers of osmophilic yeasts in creme fondant within 25 h using a pre-incubated DEFT count. Letters Appl. Microbiol. 4: 95.
36. Pitt, J. I. 1975. Xerophilic fungi and the spoilage of foods of plant origin. In "Water Relations of Foods," ed. R. B. Duckworth, p. 273. Academic Press, London, England.
37. Pitt, J. I. and Hocking, A. D. 1985. Xerophiles. In "Fungi and Food Spoilage," p. 313. Academic Press, Australia.
38. Pivnick, H. and Gabis, D. A. 1984. Confectionery products. In "Compendium of Methods for the Microbiological Examination of Foods," 2nd ed., ed. M. L. Speck, p. 700. Am. Pub. Health Assn., Washington, D.C.
39. Reed, R. H. 1986. Halotolerant and halophilic microbes. In "Microbes in Extreme Environments," ed. R. A. Herbert and G. A. Codd, p. 55. Academic Press, London, England.
40. Restaino, L., Bills, S., and Lenovich, L. M. 1985. Growth response of an osmotolerant, sorbate-resistant *Saccharomyces rouxii* strain: Evaluation of plating medium. J. Food Prot. 48: 207.
41. Riemann, H. 1969. Food processing and preservation effects. In "Food Borne Infection and Intoxications," ed. H. Riemann, p. 489. Academic Press, New York.
42. Riemann, H., Lee, W. H., and Genigeorgis, C. 1972. Control of *Clostridium botulinum* and *Staphylococcus aureus* in semi-preserved meat products. J. Milk Food. Technol. 35: 514.
43. Rodriquez-Valera, F., ed. 1988. "Halophilic Bacteria," Vol. 1, "Characteristics and Microbial Ecology of Hypersaline Environments." CRC Press, Inc., Boca Raton, Fla.
44. Seiler, D. A. L. 1986. Effect of diluent and medium water activity on recovery of yeasts

from high sugar coatings and fillings. In "Methods for the Mycological Examination of Food," ed. A. D. King, Jr., J. I. Pitt, L. R. Beuchat, and J. E. L. Corry, p. 162. Plenum Press, New York.

45. Shaw, B. G. and Shewan, J. M. 1968. Psychrophilic spoilage bacteria in fish. J. Appl. Bacteriol. 31: 89.

46. Shewan, J. M. and Hobbs, G. 1967. The bacteriology of fish spoilage and preservation. In "Progress in Industrial Microbiology," Vol. 6. ed. D. J. D. Hockenhull, p. 169. Chemical Rubber Co. Press, Cleveland, Ohio.

47. Shipp, H. L. 1958. Enumeration of clostridia in brines. In "The Microbiology of Fish and Meat Curing Brines," ed. B. P. Eddy, p. 277. Proc. of the Second International Symposium on Food Microbiology. Her Majesty's Stationery Office, London, England.

48. Stecchini, M. and Beuchat, L. R. 1985. Effects of sugars in growth media, diluents and enumeration media on survival and recovery of *Saccharomyces cerevisiae*. Food Micribiol. 2: 85.

49. Tilbury, R. H. 1980. Xerotolerant (osmophilic) yeasts. In "Biology and Activities of Yeasts," ed. F. M. Skinner, S. M. Passmore, and R. R. Davenport. Academic Press, London, England.

50. van der Walt, J. P. and Yarrow, D. 1984. Methods for isolation, maintenance, classification, and identification of yeasts. In "The Yeasts—A Taxonomic Study," ed. N. J. W. Kreger-van Rij, p. 45. Elsevier Science Publ. B. V., Amsterdam.

51. Vanderzant, C., Cobb, B. F., and Thompson, C. A., Jr. 1973. Microbial flora, chemical characteristics and shelf life of four species of pond-reared shrimp. J. Milk Food Technol. 35: 443.

52. von Richter, A. A. 1912. Uber einem osmophilen Organisms den Hefepilz *Zygosaccharomyces mellis acidi* sp. n. Mykologisches Zentralblatt 1: 67.

53. Walker, H. W. and Ayres, J. C. 1970. Yeasts as spoilage organisms. In "The Yeasts," Vol. 3, ed. A. H. Rose and J. S. Harrison. Academic Press, New York.

54. Woese, C. R. 1987. Bacterial Evolution. Microbiol. Rev. 51: 221.

55. Woese, C. R. and Wolfe, R. S., ed. 1985. "The Bacteria," Vol. 8, "Archaeobacteria." Academic Press, New York.

56. Yarrow, D. 1984. *Zygosaccharomyces* Barker. Ch. III, Genus 33. In "The Yeasts, a Taxonomic Study," ed. N. J. W. Kreger-van Rij, p. 449. Elsevier Science Publ. B. V., Amsterdam.

57. Zottola, E. A. and Walker, H. W. 1984. Osmophilic microorganisms. In "Compendium of Methods for the Microbiological Examination of Foods," 2nd ed., ed. M. L. Speck, p. 170. Am. Pub. Health Assn., New York.

Chapter 14

PECTINOLYTIC AND PECTOLYTIC MICROORGANISMS

R. F. McFeeters, L. Hankin, and G. H. Lacy

14.1 INTRODUCTION

Pectic substances are important cell wall components of higher plants, particularly dicots. The specific functions that pectic materials perform in the cell wall are not understood. However, it appears that they are important in cementing plant cells together. BeMiller[6] has reviewed pectin structure. Pectic substances are polymers of D-galacturonic acid residues glycosidically linked alpha-1,4. Pectin molecules contain occasional rhamnose units with 1,2 linkages in the main chain. They also have side chains on both the galacturonic acid and rhamnose residues that contain mainly galactose and arabinose residues. The carboxyl groups of galacturonic acid residues are usually methylesterified to a substantial degree. This has major effects on physical properties of pectin, such as gelation. The degree of methylation in plants has been found to range from about 40% to 90% of the carboxyl groups.[2] Data on the distribution of carboxyl groups are limited, but it appears most often to be random in pectin isolated to minimize enzymatic or chemical modification.[2] In some plants, substantial numbers of the hydroxyl groups of galacturonic acid residues are acetylated. This modification inhibits pectin gelation.[6]

The nomenclature for pectic substances has been somewhat variable and confused over the years. For the purpose of this chapter, pectic substances is an inclusive term for galacturonic acid-containing polymers from plant cell walls. Pectin is used for pectic substances with a substantial fraction of the galacturonic acid carboxyl groups esterified. Pectic acid refers to polymers with a negligible amount of the carboxyl groups esterified. Polypectate or pectate refers to pectic acid with carboxyl groups in the salt form. Pectinolytic refers to the degradation of pectin and pectolytic to the degradation of pectic acid or pectate. Commercially available pectin of the type used for microbiological or enzymatic assays generally has >60% methylation. Pectic acid or polypectate is <5% esterified.

14.11 Sources of Pectinolytic and Pectolytic Enzymes

Most pectin-degrading organisms are associated with raw agricultural products and with soil. Up to 10% of the organisms in soil have been shown to be pectinolytic.[22] These include, but are not limited to, bacteria in the genera *Achromobacter, Aeromonas, Arthrobacter, Agrobacterium, Enterobacter, Bacillus, Clostridium, Erwinia, Flavobacterium, Pseudomonas, Xanthomonas*,[48, 53] and many yeasts, molds, protozoa, and nematodes.[3] Many of these organisms are plant pathogens.[3, 16] Recently, pectolytic activity was found in a strain of *Leuconostoc mesenteroides*.[29] This is the first report of pectolytic activity in lactic acid bacteria. Studies have reviewed the role of pectic enzymes, their regulation, and their molecular genetics in plant pathogenesis by plant pathogenic erwiniae.[11, 12, 33] The discussion that follows refers to aerobic procedures. However, the detection of anaerobic pectinolytic bacteria also has been described.[38, 43]

14.2 DETECTING PECTINOLYTIC AND PECTOLYTIC ORGANISMS

The basic method used to detect pectinolytic or pectolytic organisms has been to grow the organisms on a gel medium that contains pectin or pectate substrates, respectively. Production of enzymes by a culture is detected either by observing depressions in the gel around the colony where the substrate has been degraded or by flooding the plate with a precipitant solution. Around producer colonies a clear zone will appear where the substrate has degraded to the point that precipitation does not occur, while nonproducing colonies will be surrounded by opaque gel containing the nondegraded pectin or pectate substrate. Wieringa[54] reported the first medium of this type. Over the years, many variations of this theme have been developed to address particular problems of sample handling, enzyme specificity, sensitivity, or isolation of organisms from the plates. For example, a researcher can cut holes in agar gel plates with a cork borer in order to assay liquid samples, such as culture filtrates, for enzyme activity. This is the so-called well plate or cup plate technique for enzyme assays.

14.21 Pectate and Pectin Lyase Producers

Since publication of the previous edition of this book, considerable research has been conducted on techniques to detect pectate lyase-producing organisms. This is because these enzymes from *Erwinia* species have been cloned into *Escherichia coli*. Since lyases have alkaline pH optima, while polygalacturonases have acidic optima, a medium pH of 7.0 or above is the main parameter used to distinguish pectate or pectin lyase producers from polygalacturonase producers. Durrands and Cooper[17] provided a recent sample of this approach, in which media were designed to detect polygalacturonase and pectin lyase production by *Verticillium albo-atrum* mutants. Roberts et al.[46, 47] and Allen et al.[1] used the pH 8.5 PEC-YA medium of Starr et al.[51] to clone pectate lyase genes from *Erwinia carotovora*.

14.211 Bacterial pectate lyases

Several media have been developed for the detection of bacteria that produce pectate lyases. King and Vaughn[32] developed a pectate medium with a pH of 7.0 that contained crystal violet to make it selective for gram-negative bacteria. Adding cycloheximide further inhibits the growth of yeasts and molds. Detection of pectolytic colonies is based on formation of depressions in the pectate gel because of enzymatic degradation.

Hankin et al.[23] used a mineral medium with 0.1% yeast extract, pectin, and agar to detect pectolytic colonies of *Erwinia* and *Pseudomonas*. A 1% aqueous solution of hexadecyltrimethylammonium bromide[28] was used to precipitate nondegraded substrate so that pectolytic colonies showed a clear zone on a white background. The researchers emphasized that a high phosphate level in the medium was needed to observe pectolytic activity. Sands et al.[49] modified the medium of King and Vaughn[32] by using 2% pectin and 1.5% agar instead of 7% polypectate. They then added a mixture of novobiocin, penicillin G, and cycloheximide to make the medium selective for fluorescent pseudomonads. Hexadecyltrimethylammonium bromide solution was used to precipitate the pectin for visualization of clear zones around pectolytic colonies.

Cuppels and Kelman[15] did a detailed evaluation of the selectivity for and recovery of *Erwinia* from natural samples using another pectate medium containing crystal violet to prevent the growth of unwanted organisms. The medium gave an excellent recovery of pectolytic *Erwinia*, but did allow growth and enzyme production by some pseudomonads. This medium has also been used to isolate pectolytic strains of *Cytophaga johnsonae* from spoiled, fresh bell peppers and watermelon.[36] It has been shown that not all commercial polypectate samples will give a suitable gel in this medium, and a procedure has been described to produce polypectate from orange peel and apple pulp that will give a good gel.[13] Starr et al.[51] used a similar medium without crystal violet to demonstrate pectolytic activity in *Yersinia enterocolitica*, *Yersinia pseudotuberculosis*, and *Klebsiella pneumoniae*.

An essential element of work to identify and characterize pectin-degrading genes from *Erwinia chrysanthemi* was the development of plating techniques to make it possible to identify clones that contained the genes of interest. Keen et al.[30] described the isolation of *E. coli* clones that contain pectate lyase genes. They used a pectate agar at pH 8.0. After incubating samples, they detected lyase activity by flooding the plates with 1 M CaCl$_2$. A white halo formed around positive clones. Kotoujansky et al.[34] developed a technique to isolate clones of lambda-L47-1 phage to which pectate lyase genes had been transferred. They used a medium for *E. coli*, the phage host, in one layer, and a pectate medium in the bottom layer. The two gels were separated by a nylon membrane that allowed enzymes to diffuse into the pectate layer, but prevented transfer of the phage. Zones with pectate lyase activity were visualized by removing the nylon membrane and the upper gel and flooding the pectate medium with 1 M CaCl$_2$. The nylon membrane was then placed back on the plate so that phage clones could be isolated from the appropriate plaque.

14.212   Bacterial pectin lyases

Pectin lyases should give clearing zones on plates with pectin as the substrate. However, plates are not very sensitive for this group of pectic enzymes, and the zones produced can be indistinct.[50] Detection is accomplished by spectrophotometric assays at 235 nm on culture filtrate samples with high methyoxl pectin as substrate. Pectin lyases will give little or no measurable activity with polypectate as the substrate.

14.213   Fungal pectate lyases

Hankin and Anagnostakis[21] describe a plate technique with a medium that contains 1% pectin, 0.2% yeast extract, mineral salts, and 3% agar adjusted to pH 7.0. After a 3- to 5-day incubation period, plates are flooded with 1% aqueous hexadecyltrimethylammonium bromide to precipitate nondegraded pectin. Clear zones occur around colonies that produce pectate lyase. If the precipitant is not allowed to remain in contact with fungal cells for more than 5 min, viable colonies can be isolated from the flooded plates. For fungal samples from natural isolations that contain bacteria, a mixture of the antibiotics neomycin and chloramphenicol provides control of bacterial growth with the least inhibition of growth or enzyme production by fungi. However, the authors emphasize that fungi should be purified and enzyme production checked in the absence of the antibiotics.

14.22   Fungal Polygalacturonase Producers

The detection of polygalacturonases by plate assays has generally been done simply by lowering the pH of a medium designed for detection of pectate lyase to 6 or below, so that polygalacturonases will be active and pectate lyases will be inactive.[21, 52]

14.23   Detecting Pectic Enzymes During Germination of Fungal Spores

Hagerman et al.[20] described a plate procedure for detection of pectolytic enzymes, protease, and cellulase activity during germination of *Botrytis cinerea* spores. The method is very sensitive for the detection of lyases and pectin-esterase, but it is considerably less sensitive for polygalacturonase.

14.24   Evaluating Macerating Activity of Pectic Enzymes

Mussell and Morre[41] analyzed in detail factors affecting the maceration of cucumber tissue by commercial polygalacturonase from *Aspergillus niger*, basing their procedure on the measurement of weight loss of the cucumber tissue after enzyme treatment. They pointed out that tissue maceration assay for polygalacturonase activity was about 500 times more sensitive than viscosity assays. Ishii[27] developed a procedure to evaluate the maceration of potato, onion, and radish tissues by measuring the volume of separated cells released from tissue samples. A polygalacturonase and pectate lyase, separately and in combination with *Aspergillus japonicus*, were used. Both enzymes caused tissue maceration, but the relative activity of the enzymes varied with the plant tissue.

14.3   VISUALIZATION AND ASSAY OF PECTIC ENZYMES

14.31   Detecting Pectic Enzymes in Electrophoresis Gels

The visualization of pectic enzymes in gels following electrophoresis has been described. Cruickshank and Wade[14] incorporated citrus pectin into acrylamide slab gels. By using suitable incubation and staining procedures, they were able to differentiate pectate lyases, polygalacturonases, and pectin-esterases in the gels. Bertheau et al.[7] developed a sandwich technique in which suitable buffers and substrates could diffuse into acrylamide slab gels so that a variety of enzymes, including pectate lyases and polygalacturonases, could be detected in the gels.

14.32   Detecting Pectic Enzymes on Isoelectric Focusing Gels

A sensitive and rapid method for visualizing the isoelectric profiles of pectic enzymes using activity overlays has been devised.[45] Isoelectrically focused proteins in ultra-thin (0.35 mm) 5% acrylamide gels containing broad-range (pH 3.5 to 10) and high-pH (pH 9 to 11) ampholytes bonded to plastic support (Gel Bond PAG acrylamide support, FMC BioProducts, Rockland, ME 04841-2994) are overlaid with an ultra-thin (0.35 mm) layer of 1% agarose containing 0.1% polygalacturonic acid bonded on Gel Bond agarose support and also supported on plastic. After sufficient reaction time, the overlay film is stained with ruthenium red (0.05% wt/vol). The substrate gel stains a deep pink because of reaction of the ruthenium red with polygalacturonate, while the substrate in areas over the isoelectrically focused pectic enzymes has been degraded so that a clear band shows on the pink background.

14.33 Pectinesterase

Pectinesterase can be assayed based on the release of either free carboxyl groups or methanol from pectin. The most common technique is to measure the rate of release of free carboxyl groups from pectin using a pH stat.[35] A rapid, continuous spectrophotometric assay has been developed.[19] It is based on measuring the change in absorbance of a pH indicator as the pH decreases because of the formation of free carboxyl groups in pectin. Methanol may be measured colorimetrically[55] or by gas chromatography.[40] For colorimetric analysis, the modifications described by Hudson and Buescher[25] should be used because the incubation procedure of Wood and Siddiqui[55] results in nonlinear color development.

14.34 Pectate and Pectin Lyase

Pectate lyase activity can be assayed spectrophotometrically at 235 nm because of the formation of the 4,5-double bond in the nonreducing galacturonic acid residues.[51] For pectin lyase activity, pectin may be substituted for polypectate as the substrate. A pectin lyase should show little or no activity with polypectate as the substrate.

14.35 Polygalacturonase

The release of reducing groups because of hydrolysis of polypectate is the most common method for measurement of polygalacturonase activity. Lee and MacMillan[35] used 0.5% polypectate in 0.1 M sodium acetate buffer, pH 4.5 at a temperature of 30°C for tomato polygalacturonase. These are reasonable conditions for most microbial polygalacturonases, though 0.1% polypectate is usually a saturating substrate level. For measurement of reducing groups, the procedure of Nelson[42] has been used for many years. However, this method requires the addition of one reagent solution before heating and a second after heating for color development. Also, the samples must be centrifuged prior to measurement of the absorbance because of cloudiness caused by precipitated substrate. Gross[18] has demonstrated the use of 2-cyanoacetamide for the measurement of polygalacturonase activity. This reagent reacts with reducing groups to give a product that absorbs at 276 nm. Only a single addition of reagent is required, and samples do not become cloudy. Reagents are simple to prepare, and product formation is highly reproducible. The 2-cyanoacetamide reagent is preferable for most applications. However, if crude enzyme preparations have high ultraviolet (UV) absorption because of the presence of high protein concentrations, this can interfere with absorbance measurements at 276 nm. In that situation, the bicinchoninate reagent, which gives an absorption maximum at 560 nm after reaction with reducing sugars, also avoids the problems of the Nelson procedure.[39]

Decline in the viscosity of polypectate solutions has also been used to assay polygalacturonases.[10] Bell et al.[4] have described a specialized assay specifically to assess softening activity that is due to fungal enzymes in pickle fermentation brines.

Pectic enzymes are inhibited by phenolic compounds, indoleacetic acid, fatty acid, and endopolygalacturonase end-products.[3] Tannins from certain plants inhibit both pectic enzymes and cellulase.[5] Specific protein inhibitors of polygalacturonases have also been reported in various plants. Cervone et al.[9] purified an inhibitor protein from French bean hypocotyls and demonstrated that it inhibited polygalacturonases from *Colletotrichum lindemuthianum*, *Fusarium moniliforme*, and *Aspergillus niger*.

14.4   SOURCES OF PECTIC ENZYMES

No pectic enzymes commercially available are free of other classes of pectic enzymes. The ability to clone pectate lyase genes from *E. chrysanthemi* into *E. coli* makes available clones with sequenced genes that are good producers of individual *E. chrysanthemi* pectate lyases.[31] In addition, *E. coli* clones containing *E. carotovora* genes for endo- and exo-pectate lyases are available.[46, 47] Since *E. coli* does not produce pectic enzymes, these clones will not produce pectinesterase or polygalacturonase. Phaff[44] described a yeast, *Kluyveromyces fragilis*, that reliably secretes large amounts of polygalacturonase into the growth medium. The polygalacturonase was estimated to be about 95% pure in the culture filtrate. The organism does not produce either pectinesterase or pectate lyase. Recent papers have demonstrated that three or more polygalacturonases are present in the preparation.[8, 26, 37] All of the enzymes appear to be endo-splitting with similar tissue-macerating properties.[37] Despite the presence of multiple enzymes, this is a source for easily produced polygalacturonases that are free of other classes of pectic enzymes. The culture can be obtained from Dr. Phaff for a nominal handling free.

14.5   EQUIPMENT, MATERIALS, AND REAGENTS (Chapter 62)

Crystal violet pectate (CVP) medium
Medium to detect pectate lyase (MP-7 medium)
Medium to detect polygalacturonase (MP-5 medium)
Polypectate gel medium
Polysaccharide precipitant
Selective medium for fluorescent pectinolytic pseudomonads (FPA medium)

14.6   PROCEDURES

14.61   Sample Preparation

Prepare a homogenous suspension and appropriate dilutions of the food (Chapter 2). In food containing a large amount of glucose, sufficient dilution may be necessary to avoid possible catabolite repression of pectic enzyme synthesis.[24] Also, in high-sugar foods such as jams and jellies, exercise care in the dilution of the sample to prevent osmotic shock to the cells by the use of an appropriate buffer or isotonic solution.

14.62   Preparation and Incubation of Plates

Place not more than 0.25 mL quantities of appropriate dilutions (to obtain 20 to 30 colonies and to avoid a wet agar surface) on the surface of pre-poured plates. Distribute by a spread plate technique. Incubation of plates inoculated with a variety of plant materials has been carried out at 30°C for 48 hr. Incubation of plates inoculated with foods probably should be made at the temperature at which the food is stored. Some pectinolytic bacteria grow at 37°C, but do not produce pectate lyase until the temperature is 32°C or below. *E. carotovora* subsp. *atroseptica* often will not grow above 28°C.

14.63   Counting and Reporting

Colonies that cause depressions in polypectate gel medium or that are surrounded by a clear zone after flooding plates with a pectin precipitant are pectinolytic. Fluorescent bacteria are detected on FPA plates with long-wavelength UV light before adding pectin precipitant.

14.7   INTERPRETATION

The varieties of organisms that can degrade pectic substances are diverse. Thus, choice of the most suitable medium depends on the type of organism expected, as well as the type of food to be examined. Media and procedures are described for the detection, enumeration, and isolation of pectolytic and pectinolytic microorganisms. In addition, procedures are described for the detection of pectic enzymes. These techniques can be used to characterize degradation of fruits, vegetables, and processed foods, to screen for plant pathogens or soil organisms that degrade pectic substances, and to indicate the stability of raw plant products for storage and transport.

14.8   REFERENCES

1. Allen, C., George, H., Yang, Z., Lacy, G. H., and Mount, M. S. 1987. Molecular cloning of an *endo*-pectate lyase gene from *Erwinia carotovora* subsp. *atroseptica*. Physiol. Molec. Plant Pathol. 31: 325.
2. Anger, H. and Dongowski, G. 1985. Distribution of free carboxyl groups in native pectins from fruits and vegetables. Die Nahrung 29: 397.
3. Bateman, D. F. and Millar, R. L. 1966. Pectic enzymes in tissue degradation. Ann. Rev. Phytopathol. 4: 119.
4. Bell, T. A., Etchells, J. L., and Jones, I. D. 1955. A method for testing cucumber salt-stock brine for softening activity. USDA ARS-72-5.

5. Bell, T. A., Etchells, J. L., and Smart, W. W. G., Jr. 1965. Pectinase and cellulase enzyme inhibitor from sericea and certain other plants. Botan. Gaz. 126: 40.
6. BeMiller, J. N. 1986. An introduction to pectins: Structure and properties. In "Chemistry and Function of Pectins," eds. M. L. Fishman and J. J. Jen, p. 2. American Chemical Society, Washington, D.C.
7. Bertheau, Y., Madgidi-Hervan, E., Kotoujansky, A., Nguyen-The, C., Andro, T., and Coleno, A. 1984. Detection of depolymerase isoenzymes after electrophoresis or electrofocusing, or in titration curves. Anal. Biochem. 139: 383.
8. Call, H. P. and Emeis, C. C. 1983. Characterization of an "endopolygalacturonase" of the yeast *Kluyveromyces marxianus*. J. Food Biochem. 7: 59.
9. Cervone, F., De Lorenzo, G., Degra, L., Salvi, G., and Bergami, M. 1987. Purification and characterization of a polygalacturonase-inhibiting protein from *Phaseolus vulgaris* L. Plant Physiol. 85: 631.
10. Cervone, F., Scala, A., Foresti, M., Cacace, M. G., and Noviello, C. 1977. Endopolygalacturonase from *Rhizoctonia fragariae* purification and characterization of two isoenzymes. Biochem. Biophys. Acta 482: 379.
11. Collmer, A., Berman, P. M., and Mount, M. S. 1982. Pectate lyase regulation and bacterial soft-rot pathogenesis. In "Phytopathogenic Prokaryotes," ed. M. S. Mount and G. H. Lacy, Vol. 1, p. 395. Academic Press, Inc., New York, N.Y.
12. Collmer, A. and Keen, N. T. 1986. The role of pectic enzymes in plant pathogenesis. Ann. Rev. Phytopathol. 24: 383.
13. Cother, E. J., Blakeney, A. B., and Lamb, S. J. 1980. Laboratory-scale preparation of sodium polypectate for use in selective media for pectolytic *Erwinia* spp. Plant Disease 64: 1086.
14. Cruickshank, R. H. and Wade, G. C. 1980. Detection of pectic enzymes in pectin-acrylamide gels. Anal. Biochem. 107: 177.
15. Cuppels, D. and Kelman, A. 1974. Evaluation of selective media for isolation of soft-rot bacteria from soil and plant tissue. Phytopathol. 64: 468.
16. Dowson, W. J. 1957. "Plant Diseases Due to Bacteria," 2nd ed. Cambridge University Press, Cambridge, England.
17. Durrands, P. K. and Cooper, R. M. 1988. Development and analysis of pectic screening media for use in the detection of pectinase mutants. Appl. Microbiol. Biotechnol. 28: 463.
18. Gross, K. C. 1982. A rapid and sensitive spectrophotometric method for assaying polygalacturonase using 2-cyanoacetamide. HortScience 17: 933.
19. Hagerman, A. E. and Austin, P. J. 1986. Continuous spectrophotometric assay for plant pectin methyl esterase. J. Agric. Food Chem. 34: 440.
20. Hagerman, A. E., Blau, D. M., and McClure, A. L. 1985. Plate assay for determining the time of production of protease, cellulase, and pectinases by germinating fungal spores. Anal. Biochem. 151: 334.
21. Hankin, L. and Anagnostakis, S. L. 1975. The use of solid media for detection of enzyme production by fungi. Mycologia 67: 597.
22. Hankin, L., Sands, D. C., and Hill, D. E. 1974. Relation of land use to some degradative enzymatic activities of soil bacteria. Soil Sci. 118: 38.
23. Hankin, L., Zucker, M., and Sands, D. C. 1971. Improved solid medium for the detection and enumeration of pectolytic bacteria. Appl. Microbiol. 22: 205.
24. Hsu, E. J. and Vaughn, R. H. 1969. Production and catabolite repression of the constitutive polygalacturonic acid *trans*-eliminase of *Aeromonas liquefaciens*. J. Bacteriol. 98: 172.
25. Hudson, J. M. and Buescher, R. W. 1986. Relationship between degree of pectin methylation and tissue firmness of cucumber pickles. J. Food Sci. 51: 138.
26. Inoue, S., Nagamatsu, Y., and Hatanaka, C. 1984. Preparation of cross-linked pectate and its application to the purification of endopolygalacturonase of *Kluyveromyces fragilis*. Agric. Biol. Chem. 48: 633.

27. Ishii, S. 1976. Enzymatic maceration of plant tissues by endo-pectin lyase and endo-poly-galacturonase from *Aspergillus japonicus*. Phytopathol. 66: 281.

28. Jayasankar, N. P. and Graham, P. H. 1970. An agar plate method for screening and enumerating pectinolytic microorganisms. Can. J. Microbiol. 16: 1023.

29. Juven, B. J., Lindner, P., and Weisslowicz, H. 1985. Pectin degradation in plant material by *Leuconostoc mesenteroides*. J. Appl. Bacteriol. 58: 533.

30. Keen, N. T., Dahlbeck, D., Staskawicz, B., and Belser, W. 1984. Molecular cloning of pectate lyase genes from *Erwinia chrysanthemi* and their expression in *Escherichia coli*. J. Bacteriol. 159: 825.

31. Keen, N. T. and Tamaki, S. 1986. Structure of two pectate lyase genes from *Erwinia chrysanthemi* EC16 and their high-level expression in *Escherichia coli*. J. Bacteriol. 168: 595.

32. King, A. D. Jr., and Vaughn, R. H. 1961. Media for detecting pectolytic gram-negative bacteria associated with the softening of cucumbers, olives, and other plant tissues. J. Food Sci. 26: 635.

33. Kotoujansky, A. 1987. Molecular genetics of pathogenesis by soft-rot erwinias. Ann. Rev. Phytopathol. 25: 405.

34. Kotoujansky, A., Diolez, A., Boccara, M., Bertheau, Y., Andro, T., and Coleno, A. 1985. Molecular cloning of *Erwinia chrysanthemi* pectinase and cellulase structural genes. The EMBO J. 4: 781.

35. Lee, M. and MacMillan, J. D. 1968. Mode of action of pectic enzymes. I. Purification and certain properties of tomato pectinesterase. Biochem. 7: 4005.

36. Liao, C.-H. and Wells, J. M. 1986. Properties of *Cytophaga johnsonae* strains causing spoilage of fresh produce at food markets. Appl. Environ. Microbiol. 52: 1261.

37. Lim, J., Yamasaki, Y., Suzuki, Y., and Ozawa, J. 1980. Multiple forms of endo-polygalact-uronase from *Saccharomyces fragilis*. Agric. Biol. Chem. 44: 473.

38. Lund, B. M. 1972. Isolation of pectolytic clostridia from potatoes. J. Appl. Bacteriol. 35: 609.

39. McFeeters, R. F. 1980. A manual method for reducing sugar determinations with 2,2'-bicinchoninate reagent. Anal. Biochem. 103: 302.

40. McFeeters, R. F. and Armstrong, S. A. 1984. Measurement of pectin methylation in plant cell walls. Anal. Biochem. 139: 212.

41. Mussell, H. W. and Morre, D. J. 1969. A quantitative bioassay specific for polygalacturon-ases. Anal. Biochem. 28: 353.

42. Nelson, N. 1944. A photometric adaptation of the Somogyi method for the determination of glucose. J. Biol. Chem. 153: 375.

43. Ng, H. and Vaughn, R. H. 1963. *Clostridium rubrum* sp. N. and other pectinolytic clostridia from soil. J. Bacteriol. 85: 1104.

44. Phaff, H. J. 1966. Alpha-2,4-polygalacturonide glycanohydrolase (endo-polygalacturonase) from *Saccharomyces fragilis*. In "Methods in Enzymology, Complex Carbohydrates," ed. E. F. Neufeld and V. Ginsburg, Vol. 8, p. 636. Academic Press, New York, N.Y.

45. Reid, J. L. and Collmer, A. 1985. Activity stain for rapid characterization of pectic enzymes in isoelectric focusing and sodium dodecyl sulfate-polyacrylamide gels. Appl. Environ. Microbiol. 50: 615.

46. Roberts, D. P., Berman, P. M., Allen, C., Stromberg, V. K., Lacy, G. H., and Mount, M. S. 1986. *Erwinia carotovora*: Molecular cloning of a 3.4 kilobase DNA fragment mediating production of pectate lyases. Can. J. Plant Pathol. 8: 17.

47. Roberts, D. P., Berman, P. M., Allen, C., Stromberg, V. K., Lacy, G. H., and Mount, M. S. 1986. Requirement for two or more *Erwinia carotovora* subsp. *carotovora* pectolytic gene products for maceration of potato tuber tissue by *Escherichia coli*. J. Bacteriol. 167: 279.

48. Rombouts, F. M. 1972. Occurrence properties of bacterial pectate lyases. Agric. Res. Report (Versl. Landbouwk. Onderz.) 779. Centre for Agric. Pub. and Doc., Wageningen, The Netherlands.

49. Sands, D. C., Hankin, L., and Zucker, M. 1972. A selective medium for pectolytic fluorescent pseudomonads. Phytopathol. 62: 998.
50. Schlemmer, A. F., Ware, C. F., and Keen, N. T. 1987. Purification and characterization of a pectin lyase produced by *Pseudomonas fluorescens* W51. J. Bacteriol. 169: 4493.
51. Starr, M. P., Chatterjee, A. K., Starr, P. B., and Buchanan, G. E. 1977. Enzymatic degradation of polygalacturonic acid by *Yersinia* and *Klebsiella* species in relation to clinical laboratory procedures. J. Clin. Microbiol. 6: 379.
52. Vaughn, R. H., Balatsouras, G. D., York, G. K. II, and Nagel, C. W. 1957. Media for detection of pectinolytic microorganisms associated with softening of cucumbers, olives, and other plant tissues. Food Res. 22: 597.
53. Voragen, A. G. J. 1972. Characterization of pectin lyases on pectins and methyl oligogalacturonates. Agric. Res. Report (Versl. Landbouwk. Onderz.) 780. Centre for Agric. Pub. and Doc., Wageningen, The Netherlands.
54. Wieringa, K. T. 1949. A method for isolating and counting pectolytic microbes. 4th Intern. Cong. Microbiol. Proc., 1947, p. 482.
55. Wood, P. J. and Siddiqui, I. R. 1971. Determination of methanol and its application to measurement of pectin ester content and pectin methyl esterase activity. Anal. Biochem. 39: 418.

Chapter 15

ACID-PRODUCING MICROORGANISMS

E. R. Vedamuthu, M. Raccach, Bonita A. Glatz, E. W. Seitz, and M. S. Reddy

15.1 INTRODUCTION

A variety of acid-producing bacteria are found in nature, in the soil, on raw agricultural products, and in certain processed foods. One of the most important groups of acid-producing bacteria in the food industry is the lactic acid bacteria. Members of this group are gram-positive, nonsporulating cocci or rods, dividing in one plane only with the exception of the pediococci. They are catalase negative (with the exception of some pediococci, which either form a pseudocatalase or incorporate preformed hemin, supplied exogenously, into a catalase molecule). The organisms are usually nonmotile and are obligate fermenters, producing mainly lactic acid and sometimes also volatile acids and CO_2. They are subdivided into the genera *Streptococcus* (proposed change in genus nomenclature to *Lactococcus*[33]), *Leuconostoc*, *Pediococcus*, and *Lactobacillus*. The homofermentative species produce lactic acid from available sugars, while the heterofermentative types produce, in addition to lactic acid, mainly acetic acid, ethanol, CO_2, and other components in trace amounts. Lactic acid bacteria are widespread in nature and are best known for their activities in major foods such as dairy, meat, and vegetable products.

Many sporeforming species belonging to the genera *Bacillus* and *Clostridium* also are important acid producers. Their role in the deterioration of quality and subsequent spoilage of foods, particularly canned foods, is discussed in detail in Chapters 18 to 23.

Propionibacterium and *Acetobacter* species are other well-known acid-producing bacteria. These organisms play important roles in several industrial processes. For instance, several *Propionibacterium* species are important in the development of the characteristic flavor and eye production in Swiss-type cheeses. Members of the genus *Acetobacter* are best known for their use in the manufacture of vinegar.

Most enteric bacteria are able to carry out either a mixed acid or butylene glycol fermentation. The significance in foods of species of *Escherichia*, *Enterobacter*, *Salmonella*, and *Shigella*, as well as methods for their enumeration are presented in Chapters 24, 25, and 26.

15.2 GENERAL CONSIDERATIONS

15.21 Titration and pH

Titratable acidity expressed as lactic acid may be used as an indirect measure of bacterial growth in brines and liquid foods. Measurement of pH reduction is another indicator of growth.

15.22 Indicator Media

Complex media containing an indicator dye may be used to enumerate different acid-producing types of bacteria present in food products. The acid produced by the colonies will change the color of the surrounding medium and thus will facilitate their identification and enumeration. Bromcresol green or bromphenol blue may be used for high acid producers while phenol red may be used for those producing moderate amounts.

15.23 Special Media

Numerous complex media are available that support the growth of various acid-producing bacteria. A few can be employed for the qualitative and quantitative differentiation of certain species, e.g., the lactic streptococci and propionibacteria. However, most of these media are nonselective and other microorganisms may grow on them. Also, since acid-producing microorganisms with the exception of some pediococci are usually fermentative and lack a cytochrome system, they are resistant to azide. Hence, sodium azide can be incorporated into these media to render them more selective. Some of these media can be employed only in special situations where one or only a limited number of species is present. In other instances, a numerical estimation may depend on (a) recognition of colony characteristics such as size, shape, color, and biochemical reactions in the medium (e.g., acid production, arginine hydrolysis, and citrate utilization); or (b) identification by picking individual colonies from plates and placing them into different test media; and (c) use of selective media containing a specific antibiotic for which the specific bacterial group is naturally resistant, (e.g., *Leuconostoc* spp. are naturally resistant to relatively high concentrations of vancomycin[25]).

15.3   EQUIPMENT, MATERIALS, AND REAGENTS

15.31   Reagents

0.1 N NaOH
Phenolphthalein solution
   Unless otherwise specified, phenolphthalein used as an indicator is a 1% alcoholic solution.
Bromcresol purple solution
0.1% peptone water
Nessler's reagent
Bromcresol purple dye may be added directly to the medium (0.02 to 0.04 g/L) before autoclaving, or prepared as a stock solution. In the latter case, about 1 ml of a 1.6% ethanolic solution is added per liter of medium.[35] This indicator has a pH range of 5.4 (yellow) to 7.0 (purple). Stock solutions of bromcresol green (yellow 3.8 to 5.4 blue) or bromphenol blue (yellow 3.1 to 4.7 blue) may be similarly prepared and used at a final concentration of 0.002%. Caution: Some lots of indicator may be more inhibitory to bacterial growth than other. In addition, some indicators are more inhibitory to a particular bacterial species than to others.

Vancomycin hydrochloride, dissolved in distilled water and filter-sterilized, is added to sterile tempered media such as lactic agar or deMan, Rogosa, and Sharpe (MRS) agar before pouring plates to give a final concentration of 100 µg per ml. Suitable dilutions of samples are surface-spread on poured, dried agar plates.

GasPak Anaerobic systems (BBL) or equivalents may be used in the place of candle-oats jar or CO_2 incubator for enumeration of lactic acid bacteria and propionibacteria.

15.32   Media (Chapter 62)

Plate count agar (standard methods agar) containing bromcresol purple (PCA-BCP)
Lactic (Elliker) agar[7]
MRS broth and agar[5]
Rogosa, Mitchell, and Wiseman (RMW) agar[30]
M 16 agar[18] (a modification of Rogosa sodium lactate agar)
M 17 agar[37]
Eugon agar[39]
APT agar[8]
LBS agar[9]
Dextrose tryptone agar
LBS oxgall agar[9]
Differential broth for lactic streptococci[28]
Agar medium for differential enumeration of lactic streptococci[29]

Lactic streak agar[21]
Kempler, McKay (KM) agar[15]
Modified Nickels and Leesment medium in association with X-gal solution[40]
Lee's agar[17]
HYA agar[27]
ST agar[6] (for *S. thermophilus*)
LB agar[6] (for *L. bulgaricus*)
Modified lactic agar for yogurt bacteria[20] (15.433)
Sodium lactate agar[19]
Modified sodium lactate agar[12]
ASLA agar[26]
Chopped liver broth[4]
Acetobacter agar[2]

15.33   Equipment

To enumerate acid producers, materials commonly used in bacteriological analyses are required (Chapter 4 and 62). To determine titratable acidity of milk and milk products, consult "Standard Methods for the Examination of Dairy Products."[1]

15.4   PROCEDURES

15.41   Acid-Producing Bacteria

Various media are used to determine acid producers in foods (Chapter 62). Following is a description of methods and media frequently employed to determine the major types and activities of acid producers in foods.

15.411   Thermophilic flat sour sporeformers (Chapter 21)

15.412   Total acid producer count

Prepare pour plates (Chapter 4) of samples with PCA-BCP or dextrose tryptone agar (Chapter 62). For conditions of plate incubation, consult Chapter 4. After incubating the plates, count the colonies with a yellow halo and report as acid-forming organisms per gram of product.

15.413   Lactic acid-producing bacteria

The large number of media proposed for lactic acid bacteria, particularly for streptococci and lactobacilli, is indicative of the difficulties encountered in growing some strains of these organisms. The choice of medium is governed to some extent by the particular strains under study and, therefore, by product or habitat. The media listed below have merit in the support of colony development of lactic acid bacteria, but are not highly selective, and some, such as Eugon agar, are not selective at all. Hence, organisms other than lactic acid bacteria may develop on these media and produce acid.

While the lactic acid bacteria in general are tolerant of low pH, they can be very sensitive to other adverse conditions. Samples to be examined for numbers of viable lactic acid bacteria should not be frozen prior to analyses. Many of the lactic acid bacteria are easily killed or injured by freezing. If the product to be examined is normally frozen, it should not be thawed and refrozen prior to microbial analyses since this would tend to increase damage caused by freezing.

Dilution of products with phosphate-buffered diluent for plating can damage lactic acid bacteria in samples to the point that reduced counts are obtained. Thus, it is best to use sterile 0.1% peptone water (Chapter 4) as the diluent since it protects bacteria during the dilution process.[11, 14, 16]

Depending on the product, it may be advantageous to blend the initial dilution for the plate count to disrupt chains of lactic acid bacteria. This is especially true for many freshly prepared cultured food products. Blending the initial dilution can produce a more accurate count of the number of bacteria actually present. Chilled diluent and a chilled blender cup should be used.

These bacteria do not grow well aerobically, although most of them are considered to be facultative. Thus it is usually important to pour overlays of the appropriate agar medium onto the surface of the solidified agar in plates containing the lactic acid bacteria. An alternative is to incubate the plates in an environment containing little or no oxygen.

The fastidious nature of lactic acid bacteria restricts them in the environment to wherever carbohydrate, protein breakdown products, vitamins, and minerals occur in ample quantity and proportion. Therefore, the greatest natural reservoir for these bacteria is growing green plants. Enrichment culture of blended plant material added to skim milk supplemented with 0.05% glucose and 0.1% yeast extract, with subsequent plating on appropriate media is a common isolation procedure. Mundt[22], Mundt et al.,[24] Mundt and Hammer[23] and Sandine et al.[32] are often consulted for the isolation of streptococci and lactobacilli from plants, including vegetables.

15.42 Media

15.421 Lactic agar[7] (Chapter 62)

This medium was developed to support colony development of lactic streptococci and lactobacilli. Prepare pour plates of samples as described in Chapter 4 using lactic agar. After incubation of plates, prepare gram stains of individual colonies, examine these microscopically, and test for catalase reaction. Gram-positive, catalase-negative cocci or rods may be tentatively considered to be lactic acid bacteria. If further identification is needed, consult Sharpe.[36]

15.422   MRS media (Chapter 58)

MRS broth was developed by deMan, Rogosa, and Sharpe[5] to support the growth of various lactobacilli, particularly of dairy origin. Pediococci and leuconostocs grow luxuriously in this medium. MRS broth with added agar may be used to prepare pour plates of samples as described in Section 15.421 using MRS agar instead of lactic agar. Identification of individual colonies is described in Section 15.421.

15.423   RMW agar[30] (Rogosa SL agar) (Chapter 62)

This is a selective medium for the cultivation of oral and fecal lactobacilli. Pediococci can also be isolated using this medium. For the preparation of agar plates, proceed as in Section 15.421, but substitute RMW agar for lactic agar. Since some lactobacilli will not grow on this medium if incubated aerobically, plates should be incubated in a CO_2-enriched atmosphere. The plates can be placed in plastic bags, flushed 1 min with CO_2, sealed, and incubated at the desired temperature.

15.424   M 16 agar[18] (Chapter 62)

This medium was developed to support growth of lactic streptococci used in cheddar cheese manufacturing in New Zealand. Prepare agar plates as in Section 15.421, but substitute M 16 agar for lactic agar.

15.425   M 17 agar[37] (Chapter 62)

This medium was developed by Terzaghi and Sandine[37] to support the growth of lactic streptococci. It is buffered with β-disodium glycerolphosphate and also is useful for plaque assay of lactic bacteriophages. Prepare plates as in Section 15.421, but substitute M 17 agar for lactic agar.

15.426   Eugon agar[38] (Chapter 62)

This medium is reported to support the surface growth of lactic acid bacteria.[39] Prepare agar plates as in Section 15.421.

15.427   APT agar[8] (Chapter 62)

APT agar was developed for the cultivation and enumeration of heterofermentative lactic acid bacteria of discolored, cured meat products.[8] This medium is also commonly used for the propagation of pediococci. Prepare agar plates as in Section 15.421.

15.428   LBS oxgall agar[9] (Chapter 62)

LBS oxgall agar is made selective for bile-resistant lactobacilli[10] by incorporating 0.15% oxgall into its formulation. More consistent results often are obtained by preparing the LBS plus oxgall from individual ingredients rather than by using commercially available premixed media. Agar plates are prepared as in Section 15.421 using LBS agar plus oxgall in place of lactic agar. The plates should be placed in plastic bags, flushed with CO_2 for 1 min, sealed, and incubated at 37°C for 48 hr. Incubation for dried products should be increased to 72 hr.[9]

15.43   Differential Media for Lactic Acid Bacteria

This section presents methods for the qualitative and quantitative differentiation of some lactic acid bacteria employed in the dairy industry. The media are not selective and must be used only in pure culture studies or as recommended in this section. The broth and agar media for lactic streptococci can be used to identify members of the lactic group streptococci when commercial starter cultures or products are first plated on a general-purpose agar, or on media more efficient for the detection of lactic acid bacteria, such as lactic agar or eugon agar.

15.431   Separation of lactic streptococci—*Lactococcus lactis, Lactococcus lactis* subsp. *cremoris,* and *Lactococcus lactis* subsp. *diacetylactis*

The most common microorganisms in starter cultures used in dairy products are streptococci. *Lactococcus lactis* and its subspecies *cremoris* and *diacetylactis* belong to this group. Their separation can be made by biochemical tests, the major criteria being arginine hydrolysis and tests for diacetyl and acetoin. Reddy et al.[28] developed differential broth for lactic streptococci to separate these species. In addition to direct inoculation with a loopful of an active (pure) milk culture, the broth is suitable for the qualitative differentiation of individual colonies of lactic streptococci developing on agar plates containing dilutions of a commercial starter culture. After inoculation, close the test tube caps tightly to prevent escape of liberated NH_3 and CO_2. Incubate the tubes at 30°C for 24 to 72 hr and observe the indicator color reactions and CO_2 accumulation at 24 hr intervals. Subspecies *cremoris* produces a deep yellow color (acid) in the broth. *L. lactis* initially turns the broth yellow (acid), but later the violet hue returns because of the liberation of NH_3 from arginine. *L. lactis* subsp. *diacetylactis* yields a violet color and produces copious amounts of CO_2 (from citrate) in the fermentation tubes within 48 hr. *L. lactis* subsp. *diacetylactis* produces a more intense purple than *L. lactis. Leuconostoc* starter strains cause no appreciable color change in the violet differential broth, and only minute amounts of gas are observed with some *Leuconostoc dextranicum* strains. Arginine hydrolysis in the differential broth can be further checked by testing a portion of the broth with Nessler's reagent on a porcelain spot plate. A deep red precipitate indicates arginine hydrolysis.

15.432   Differential enumeration of lactic streptococci

Agar medium for differential enumeration of lactic streptococci (Reddy et al.[29]) can be used for the qualitative and quantitative differentiation of a mixture of *L. lactis* and its subspecies *cremoris* and *diacetylactis*. This medium contains arginine and calcium citrate as specific substrates, diffusible (K_2HPO_4) and undiffusible ($CaCO_3$) buffer systems, and bromcresol purple as the pH indicator. Milk is added to provide carbohydrate (lactose) and growth-stimulating factors. Production of acid from lactose causes yellow bacterial colonies. Subsequent arginine utilization by *L. lactis* and *L. lactis* subsp. *diacetylactis* liberates NH_3 and results in a localized pH change back to neutrality, with a return of the purple indicator hue. *L. lactis* subsp. *diacetylactis* utilizes suspended calcium citrate, and after 6 days of incubation, the citrate degrading colonies exhibit clear zones against a turbid background. The buffering capacity of $CaCO_3$ limits the effects of acid and NH_3 production around individual colonies. From a practical standpoint this medium can be used (a) to study associative growth relationships in starter mixtures of these species; (b) to verify the composition of mixed starter cultures; and (c) to screen single strains for compatibility in mixed cultures.

Prepare decimal dilutions of the culture with sterile 0.1% peptone solution (Chapter 62) and spread 0.1-ml quantities of the dilution evenly over the surface of agar plates (Section 15.32) with a sterile bent glass rod. Incubate the plates in a candle-oats jar (Section 15.442) at 32°C and examine plates after 36 to 40 hr and after day 6 of incubation.

After 36 to 40 hr, count all colonies and then count the yellow subspecies *cremoris* colonies separately. Return the plates to the candle-oats jar for an additional 4 days. After this period, expose the plates to the air for 1 hr. First determine the total count, and then count all colonies showing zones of clearing of the turbid suspension of calcium citrate (*L. lactis* subsp. *diacetylactis*). Subtract the subspecies *cremoris* (after 36 to 40 hr) and *diacetylactis* counts from the total count to obtain the *L. lactis* population in the mixture. Slow arginine hydrolyzing or nonhydrolyzing strains of *L. lactis* subsp. *diacetylactis* in cultural mixtures sometimes produce yellow colonies similar to subspecies *cremoris* after 36 to 40 hr. In such an instance, mark the yellow colonies (after 36 to 40 hr) with an indelible felt pen. When the final count is taken, count the marked colonies that show clearing as *L. lactis* subsp. *diacetylactis* and subtract their number from the original yellow colony count to obtain the accurate value for subspecies *cremoris*.

Maximum differential efficiency is obtained only when the counts on the individual plates do not exceed 250 colonies and when fresh medium is employed. This medium is not selective and must be used in pure culture studies only. Mullan and Walker[21] described lactic streak agar for the differentiation of lactic streptococci. The basic principles applied in this medium for differentiation are the same as those of Reddy et al.[29] Mullan and Walker[21] reported that results were available faster by their technique than by that of Reddy et al.[29] and that, with the use of their agar, there was no need for incubation of petri plates in a CO_2-enriched atmosphere. In addition to these two media, Kempler and McKay[15] described KM agar for the differentiation of citrate-fermenting lactic streptococci (*L. lactis* subsp. *diacetylactis*) from the nonci-trate-fermenting *L. lactis* and subspecies *cremoris*. Recently, Vogensen et al.[40] described another differential agar medium for separating lactic strep-tococci and *Leuconostoc cremoris* found in mixed cultures [Modified Nickels and Leesment agar in association with X-gal solution (5-Bromo-4-chloro-3-indoyl-β-D-galactopyranoside dissolved in dimethylsulfoxide at 1 mg/ml and filter-sterilized)]. Samples (0.5 to 1.0 ml of suitable dilutions) are mixed with 6 to 8 ml of modified Nickels and Leesment agar and allowed to solidify. An overlayer of 4 to 5 ml of the same medium is then poured. The plates are incubated at 25°C for 3 days. One-half ml of X-gal solution is added to the plate, evenly distributed over the entire agar surface, reincubated for another day at 25°C, and examined. Lactic streptococcal colonies appear white, while *Leuconostoc cremoris* colonies appear blue.

15.433   Ratio of *Streptococcus thermophilus* and *Lactobacillus bulgaricus* in yogurt

Yogurt is a fermented milk product in which *S. thermophilus* and *L. bul-garicus* are the essential microbial species and are active in a symbiotic rela-tionship. To obtain optimum consistency, flavor, and odor, many investigators claim that the two species should be present in about equal numbers in the culture. Dominance by either species can cause defects. Because of the empha-sis on maintaining a balance between coccus and rod, techniques are needed to determine the relative proportions of *S. thermophilus* and *L. bulgaricus* when grown together in milk cultures. A microscopic examination to deter-mine the ratio of coccus to rod is inadequate because dead cells cannot be distinguished from viable ones by this technique.

An agar medium (Lee's agar) for differential enumeration of yogurt starter bacteria has been described by Lee et al.[17] This medium contains sucrose, which most *L. bulgaricus* strains will not ferment, but *S. thermophilus*, will, and lactose, which both species utilize. With a suitable combination of sucrose and lactose, the rate of acid production by *S. thermophilus* is enhanced and that of *L. bulgaricus* restricted. Sufficient lactose is provided to obtain ade-quate colony formation of *L. bulgaricus* on the agar. Directions for the prep-aration of the agar plates should be followed very carefully.

Dilute culture in 0.1% peptone solution to 1×10^{-6} and spread 0.1 ml volumes of the dilutions over the agar surface with a sterile bent glass rod. Incubate plates for 48 hr at 37°C in a CO_2 incubator. *S. thermophilus* will form yellow and *L. bulgaricus* will form white colonies. For satisfactory dif-ferentiation, the total number of colonies on the plates should not exceed 250. A preponderance of either species in a mixture prevents the distinction of colony types on this medium. This is because differentiation on this medium is based on acid-producing activity, the restriction of acid diffusion within a small area, and its detection with a pH indicator. Obviously, this is not a selective medium, and many other microorganisms can be expected to grow on it. In addition, some strains of *L. bulgaricus* can form yellow colonies indistinguishable from those of *S. thermophilus*. This difficulty may be eliminated by the use of pretested strains in the culture mixtures.

Porubcan and Sellars[27] described a medium (HYA agar) on which *L. bulgaricus* grows as diffuse, low-mass colonies (2 to 10 mm in diameter) and *S. thermophilus* as discrete, high-mass colonies (1 to 3 mm in diameter). Differentiation is achieved in this medium by adding an appropriate sugar or sugar mixture to the melted agar base before plating. The limitation of this method, particularly when used by personnel with limited training, is that differentiation is based on colony morphology.

Shankar and Davies[34] found that β-glycerolphosphate, when incorporated into growth media generally, was inhibitory for *L. bulgaricus* strains, but did not affect *S. thermophilus* strains. They suggested that this principle could be used to get a differential count of rod-coccus cultures. A total count is obtained on lactic agar, and a differential *S. thermophilus* count on β-glycerolphosphate-containing medium such as M-17 agar.[37] The *L. bulgaricus* population is calculated by subtracting the *S. thermophilus* count from the total count. Driessen et al.[6] reported two separate media to count cocci and rods respectively in mixed cultures. The medium used for *S. thermophilus* is called ST agar, and that for *L. bulgaricus* is designated LB agar. Matalon and Sandine[20] described modifications of lactic agar that allowed good differentiation of *S. thermophilus* and *L. bulgaricus*. The media are easy to make and give good differentiation with various strains of the two species in mixtures. The basal medium is lactic agar with 0.1% Tween 80 added to it. One modification involved the addition of sufficient amount of filter-sterilized 1% aqueous solution of 2,3,5-triphenyltetrazolium chloride to give a final concentration of 50 μg per ml of the dye in the agar. On this agar, *L. bulgaricus* appeared as white, large, smooth colonies with entire edges, while *S. thermophilus* formed smaller red entire colonies. The second modification involved the addition of 7.0% (vol/vol) reconstituted nonfat dry milk (11% solids, sterilized by autoclaving at 121°C for 15 min). Plates are poured and surface dried. Suitable dilutions are surface-plated and incubated at 35 to 37°C for 48 to 72 hr. On this agar, *L. bulgaricus* appeared as large, white, smooth, slightly raised entire colonies surrounded by a distinctive cloudy halo. *S. thermophilus* formed small, white, smooth colonies with no halo.

15.44   Propionic Acid-Producing Bacteria

The propionibacteria can be difficult to isolate from foods and other natural sources. They grow slowly on solid media and prefer anaerobic or microaerophilic conditions. For samples in which different types of competing microorganisms are present in equal or higher concentrations, the propionibacteria may be the last colonies to appear on agar plates and may be difficult to pick out. Selective media designed for the propionibacteria have been based on their ability to metabolize lactic acid under anaerobic conditions. Complex media do not completely suppress the growth of competing organisms, especially those present on agricultural materials and plant surfaces. Defined media are more selective, but may not support the growth of all propionibacteria present in natural sources.

15.441 Media

Sodium lactate agar is a complex medium containing protein digests, yeast extract, various salts, and sodium lactate as carbon source. Various versions of this medium[12, 13, 26] have been used since it was described by Vedamuthu and Reinbold.[38] If trypticase soy broth is used as an ingredient (modified sodium lactate agar), dextrose is also present, and the medium loses some selectivity. Pour plates or spread plates may be prepared. These are incubated at 30° to 32°C for 5 to 7 days under anaerobic or microaerophilic conditions (see below). Colonies that appear within 2 days are probably not propionibacteria. Individual colonies may be confirmed as propionibacteria by microscopic examination for typical pleomorphic rod shape and by detection of propionic acid production by gas chromatography or HPLC.

A defined selective medium (sodium lactate agar) has been described by Peberdy and Fryer[26] for the isolation of propionibacteria from cheese. This medium contains several salts, four vitamins, cysteine, ammonium sulfate as nitrogen source, and sodium lactate as carbon source. Several known bacterial species commonly found in cheese did not grow on this medium; 16 of 22 *Propionibacterium* strains tested did grow. Incubation is at 30° to 32°C under anaerobic or microaerophilic conditions for 11 to 14 days. Colonies may be confirmed as propionibacteria as described above. Competing organisms are less likely to grow on this medium than on sodium lactate agar.

15.442 Anaerobic conditions

These methods to obtain anaerobic or microaerophilic conditions are listed in increasing order of convenience.

Vedamuthu and Reinbold[38] described the use of the candle-oats jar to obtain a CO_2-enriched atmosphere. Plates are incubated in a desiccator with moistened oats in the desiccant chamber. A candle is placed on the platform in the chamber and lit just before closing the lid. An atmosphere high in humidity and CO_2 is obtained.

Hettinga et al.[12] adapted the pouch method, first described by Bladel and Greenberg[3] for enumeration of clostridia, to the cultivation of propionibacteria. Pouches are prepared by sealing two sheets of plastic film together with a pouch-shaped sealing iron. A 1-ml aliquot of sample is pipetted into the pouch through the neck, and 30 ml of tempered growth medium (containing 2% agar) is added. The sample and medium are mixed by gently working the pouch between the fingers, and the pouch is placed in a holder until the medium solidifies. The agar seal in the neck of the pouch excludes oxygen sufficiently. Colonies can be easily seen and counted through the sides of the pouch.

Pour plates or spread plates prepared in standard petri plates can be incubated in an anaerobic or CO_2-enriched atmosphere by placing them in sealed plastic jars. The jars can be flushed repeatedly with CO_2 through a vent that can be closed, or GasPak (BBL) hydrogen + CO_2 generator envelopes can be used in the jars. Colonies appear sooner and grow better on a defined medium if the GasPak envelopes are used.

15.45   Spores of Butyric Acid-Producing Bacteria

If the food product is acidic, it should be neutralized with sterile calcium carbonate. Heat a 50- to 100-g sample in a waterbath at 80°C for 20 min to kill vegetative cells. Prepare decimal dilutions, and inoculate previously heated and cooled tubes of chopped liver broth.[4] Seal with a melted mixture of petroleum jelly, 50 g; agar, 2 g; Tween 80, 1 ml; and H_2O, 50 ml; and incubate 7 days at 32°C. Record positive tubes daily as evidenced by the production of gas and a strong butyric acid odor. Caution: Spores of *Clostridium botulinum* may germinate and grow in this medium.

15.46   Acetic Acid-Producing Bacteria

The biochemistry and taxonomy of acetic acid bacteria have been well described by Sakaguchi et al.[31] Unlike all the previously described acid-producing bacteria, these rod-like microorganisms are aerobic and gram-negative. Under acid conditions they oxidize ethanol to acetic acid. They have been used in making vinegar from the early days of the Roman civilization. These bacteria are found on fruits where the high carbohydrate concentration selects for yeasts that produce ethanol, which the acetic acid bacteria may then oxidize to acetic acid. They can spoil beers, wines, and ciders.

In discussing the nutritional requirements of acetic acid bacteria, Asai[2] lists several synthetic and maintenance media for *Acetobacter* cultures. A typical maintenance medium is acetobacter agar[2].

15.5   REFERENCES

1. APHA. 1978. "Standard Methods for the Examination of Dairy Products," 4th ed. Am. Pub. Health Assn., New York.
2. Asai. 1968. "Acetic Acid Bacteria Classification and Biochemical Activities." Univ. of Tokyo Press, Tokyo, Japan, and Univ. Park Press, Baltimore, Md.
3. Bladel, B. O. and Greenberg, R. A. 1965. Pouch method for the isolation and enumeration of clostridia. Appl. Microbiol. 13: 281.
4. Cameron, E. J. 1936. Report on culture media for non-acid products. J. Assn. Off. Agr. Chem. 19: 433.
5. deMan, J. C., Rogosa, M., and Sharpe, M. Elisabeth. 1960. A medium for the cultivation of lactobacilli. J. Appl. Bacteriol. 23: 130.

6. Driessen, F. M., Ubbels, J., and Stadhouders, J. 1977. Continuous manufacture of yogurt. I. Optimal conditions and kinetics of the prefermentation process. Biotechnol. Bioeng. 19: 821.

7. Elliker, P. R., Anderson, A. W., and Hannesson, G. 1956. An agar culture medium for lactic acid streptococci and lactobacilli. J. Dairy Sci. 39: 1611.

8. Evans, J. B. and Niven, C. F. Jr. 1951. Nutrition of the heterofermentative lactobacilli that cause greening of cured products. J. Bacteriol. 62: 599.

9. Gilliland, S. E. and Speck, M. L. 1977. Enumeration and identity of lactobacilli in dietary products. J. Food Prot. 40: 760.

10. Gilliland, S. E., Speck, M. L. and Morgan, C. G. 1975. Detection of *Lactobacillus acidophilus* in feces of humans, pigs, and chickens. Appl. Microbiol. 30: 541.

11. Hartman, P. A. and Huntsberger, D. V. 1961. Influence of subtle differences in plating procedure on bacterial counts of prepared frozen foods. Appl. Microbiol. 9: 32.

12. Hettinga, D. H., Vedamuthu, E. R., and Reinbold, G. W. 1968. Pouch method for isolating and enumerating propionibacteria. J. Dairy Sci. 51: 1707.

13. Hofherr, L. A., Glatz, B. A., and Hammond, E. G. 1983. Mutagenesis of strains of *Propionibacterium* to produce cold-sensitive mutants. J. Dairy Sci. 66: 2482.

14. Jayne-Williams, D. J. 1963. Report of a discussion on the effect of the diluent on the recovery of bacteria. J. Appl. Bacteriol. 26: 398.

15. Kempler, G. M. and McKay, L. L. 1980. Improved medium for detection of citrate-fermenting *Streptococcus lactis* subsp. *diacetylactis*. Appl. Environ. Microbiol. 39: 926.

16. King, W. L. and Hurst, A. 1963. A note on the survival of some bacteria in different diluents. J. Appl. Bacteriol. 26: 504.

17. Lee, S. Y., Vedamuthu, E. R., Washam, C. J., and Reinbold, G. W. 1974. An agar medium for the differential enumeration of yogurt starter bacteria. J. Milk Food Technol. 37: 272.

18. Lowrie, R. J. and Pearce, L. E. 1971. The plating efficiency of bacteriophages of lactic streptococci. New Zealand J. Dairy Sci. Technol. 6: 166.

19. Malik, A. C., Reinbold, G. W., and Vedamuthu, E. R. 1968. An evaluation of the taxonomy of *Propionibacterium*. Can. J. Microbiol. 14: 1185.

20. Metalon, M. E. and Sandine, W. E. 1986. Improved media for differentiation of rods and cocci in yogurt. J. Dairy Sci. 69: 2569.

21. Mullan, M. A. and Walker, A. L. 1979. An agar medium and simple streaking technique for the differentiation of lactic streptococci. Dairy Ind. Int. 44: 16.

22. Mundt, J. O. 1973. Litmus milk reaction as a distinguishig feature between *Streptococcus faecalis* of human and non-human origins. J. Milk Food Technol. 36: 364.

23. Mundt, J. O. and Hammer, J. L. 1968. Lactobacilli on plants. Appl. Microbiol. 16: 1326.

24. Mundt, J. O., Johnson, A. H., and Khatchikian, R. 1958. Incidence and nature of enterococci on plant materials. Food Res. 23: 186.

25. Orberg, P. K. and Sandine, W. E. 1984. Common occurrence of plasmid DNA and vancomycin resistance in *Leuconostoc* spp. Appl. Environ. Microbiol. 47: 677.

26. Peberdy, M. F. and Fryer, T. F. 1976. Improved selective media for the enumeration of propionibacteria from cheese. N. Z. J. Dairy Sci. Technol. 11: 10.

27. Porubcan, R. S. and Sellars, R. L. 1973. Agar medium for differentiation of *Lactobacillus bulgaricus* from *Streptococcus thermophilus*. J. Dairy Sci. 56: 634.

28. Reddy, M. S., Vedamuthu, E. R., and Reinbold, G. W. 1971. A differential broth for separating the lactic streptococci. J. Milk Food Technol. 34: 43.

29. Reddy, M. S., Vedamuthu, E. R., Washam, C. J., and Reinbold, G.W. 1972. Agar medium for differential enumeration of lactic streptococci. Appl. Microbiol. 24: 947.

30. Rogosa, M., Mitchell, J. A., and Wiseman, R. F. 1951. A selective medium for the isolation and enumeration of oral and fecal lactobacilli. J. Bacteriol. 62: 132.

31. Sakaguchi, K., Vemura, T., and Kinoshita, S. 1971. "Biochemical and Industrial Aspects of Fermentation." Kodansha Ltd., Tokyo, Japan.

32. Sandine, W. E., Radich, P. C., and Elliker, P. R. 1972. Ecology of lactic streptococci. A review. J. Milk Food Technol. 35: 176.

33. Schliefer, K. H. 1987. Recent changes in the taxonomy of lactic acid bacteria. FEMS Microbiol. Rev. 46: 201.

34. Shankar, P. A. and Davies, F. L. 1977. A note on the suppression of *Lactobacillus bulgaricus* in media containing beta-glycerolphosphate and application of such media to selective isolation of *Streptococcus thermophilus* from yogurt. J. Soc. Dairy Technol. 30: 28.

35. SAB. 1957. "Manual of Microbiological Methods." Soc. of Amer. Bacteriol. McGraw-Hill, New York.

36. Sharpe, M. E. 1979. Identification of the lactic acid bacteria. In "Identification Methods for Microbiologists," 2nd ed., eds. F.A. Skinner and D.W. Lovelock, Academic Press, New York.

37. Terzaghi, B. E. and Sandine, W. E. 1975. Improved medium for lactic streptococci and their bacteriophages. Appl. Microbiol. 29: 807.

38. Vedamuthu, E. R. and Reinbold, G. W. 1967. The use of candle-oats jar incubation for the enumeration, characterization, and taxonomic study of propionibacteria. Milchwissenschaft 22: 428.

39. Vera, H. D. 1947. The ability of peptones to support surface growth of lactobacilli. J. Bacteriol. 54: 14.

40. Vogensen, F. K., Karst, T., Larsen, J. J., Kringelum, B., Ellekjaer, D., and Nielsen, E. W. 1987. Improved direct differentiation between *Leuconostoc cremoris, Streptococcus lactis*, subsp. *diacetylactis*, and *Streptococcus cremoris/Streptococcus lactis* on agar. Milchwissenschaft 42: 646.

Chapter 16

YEASTS AND MOLDS

P. B. Mislivec, L. R. Beuchat, and M. A. Cousin

16.1 INTRODUCTION

Yeasts and molds constitute a large and divergent group of microorganisms consisting of several thousand species. Most can be readily detected in soil[22] and air. Because of their heterotrophic nature and their ability to adapt to a wide range of environmental conditions, these fungi are frequently encountered as actively growing contaminants in and on various commodities including foods, inadequately cleaned food processing equipment, and food storage facilities.

Unlike most bacteria, molds and, to a lesser extent, yeasts can initiate growth over a wide pH range, from below pH 2 to above pH 9. Once growth has been established, given time and the absence of strong buffering, many fungi can change the initial pH of the substrate to one more favorable to their growth, usually a pH of 4 to 6.5. The temperature range for growth of most yeasts and molds is likewise broad (5° to 35°C), with some species capable of growth above or below this range. Many foodborne yeasts and molds, e.g., *Zygosaccharomyces*, *Eurotium*, and *Xeromyces* species, can grow in foods having a water activity (a_w) of 0.85 or below.[17, 38] Most of the fungi of importance in foods are aerobes.

Yeasts and molds can cause various degrees of food decomposition. Invasion and growth may occur on virtually any type of food if environmental conditions are not limiting. Commodities such as corn, small grains, legumes, nuts, and fleshy fruits can be invaded prior to harvesting as well as during storage. Growth can also occur on processed foods and food ingredients. The detectability of fungal invasion of foods depends on the food type, the microorganisms involved, the degree of invasion, and the methods of analysis. Appearance of contaminated food may range from no blemish to severe blemish to complete decomposition. Growth of yeasts and molds may be manifested as rot spots, pustules or scabs, slime, white or variously colored mycelia, and spores. The absence of visual fungal growth does not mean that yeasts and molds are not present; their numbers may be low or their growth may be internal. Depending on the degree of invasion, substantial economic losses may be sustained by the producer, the processor, and the consumer.

Some foodborne yeasts and molds are undesirable because of potential hazards to human and animal health.[7] Numerous molds produce mycotoxins,[55] (Chapter 43) and some yeasts and molds are responsible for human and animal infections.[7] Although most infectious fungi are rarely associated with foods, and their infection site is normally not the gastrointestinal tract, some foodborne fungi can cause opportunistic infections in immunocompromised humans. Finally, certain foodborne yeasts and molds may be hazardous because of their ability to elicit allergic reactions.

16.2   GENERAL CONSIDERATIONS

Much of this chapter is concerned with cultural procedures for the enumeration of viable fungi. Chapter 5 describes several widely used microscopic methods.

Traditionally, acidified media have been used to enumerate yeasts and molds in foods. Such media are now recognized as inferior to antibiotic supplemented media[5, 8, 20, 37, 56, 57, 58] that have been formulated to suppress bacterial colony development,[39, 41] enhance resuscitation of injured fungi,[9, 59] and minimize precipitation of food particles.[67] Although acidified media may be appropriate for certain types of foods,[9, 39, 40] their use should first be carefully evaluated.

Depending on the nature of the food and the species of fungi likely to predominate, numerous media may be appropriate for viable counts.[16, 24, 26, 33, 38, 42, 43, 58] Antibiotic supplemented plate count agar[43] or dichloran rose bengal agar[37] are recommended as general-purpose media for enumerating yeasts and molds by the dilution plating procedure. Media supplemented with solutes such as glycerol, glucose, sucrose, or sodium chloride are most appropriate for enumerating xerophilic molds and osmotolerant yeasts.[27, 32, 34, 81] Certain media are formulated to detect specific genera and species of foodborne fungi.[1, 3, 21, 71]

Yeast and molds should usually be enumerated by a surface spread-plate technique rather than with pour plates. This technique provides maximal exposure of the cells to atmospheric oxygen and avoids heat stress from molten agar. Agar spread plates should be dried overnight before being inoculated.

Most probable number (MPN) techniques may be appropriate for some foods.[44] Membrane filter techniques are applicable for beverages and similar clear liquids[32] and for certain solid foods.[12] Sometimes, however, entrapment of mycelia and food particles in membrane pores limits applicability.

Phosphate buffer or 0.1% peptone water is a suitable diluent when culturing samples for yeasts and molds. An appropriate solute such as 20% sucrose should be added to the diluent when enumerating osmotrophs in foods such as syrups and fruit juice concentrates.[15] (Chapter 13)

The antibiotics most frequently employed in media of neutral pH are chlortetracycline (Aureomycin), chloramphenicol, oxytetracycline, gentamicin, streptomycin, and kanamycin (Sigma Chemical, St. Louis, Mo.). Chloramphenicol (100 μg/ml) or gentamicin (50 μg/ml) are recommended because of their heat stability and broad antibacterial spectra. Both antibiotics can be sterilized by autoclaving in complete media. Stock solutions of antibiotics can be stored at 5°C for up to 10 weeks without loss of activity.

Rose bengal may be added to media to restrict excessive mycelial growth by some molds.[4, 30] Care should be taken, however, not to expose these media to light since photodegradation of rose bengal yields compounds that are toxic to fungi.[6] Dichloran (2,6-dichloro-4-nitroaniline) at 2 μg/ml also restricts the spread of mold colonies.

Some degree of soaking may be beneficial for the recovery of yeasts and molds from died or intermediate moisture foods.[33] Soaking may enhance repair of sublethally damaged cells (resuscitation) and may also soften the food and thereby facilitate release of organisms from tissues. Because mold propagules may settle out within a few minutes, it is important to mix liquid samples and diluents immediately prior to transferring and culturing.

Inoculated plates should be incubated undisturbed in an upright position at 22° to 25°C for 5 days before colonies are counted. If an incubator is not available, use room temperature and report accordingly. Plates with 15 to 150 colonies are usually counted. If the mycoflora consists primarily of molds, the lower population range is selected; if primarily yeast colonies, the upper limit is counted.

Wet mounts and gram stains of cells from at least 10 colonies per sample should be examined to confirm that bacteria are not present. Yeast cells and asexual mold spores are generally gram-positive, whereas mold mycelia are gram-negative.

16.3 PRECAUTIONS

Some yeasts and molds can be infectious or can elicit allergic responses, sometimes even in healthy individuals. Thus it is important to be reasonably cautious when working with fungi. Ideally, plates should be held in incubators, not in an open room. Plate lids should be removed sparingly, normally only for critical purposes such as the preparation of a slide for microscopic examination. Flamed needles should be cooled before making transfers, to avoid dispersal of conidia and other cells. Under no circumstances should a culture be smelled. Before disposal, plates and other cultures should be autoclaved. Work benches and incubators should be disinfected routinely. An acceptable quality assurance program (Chapter 1) should be established and followed.

16.4   EQUIPMENT, MATERIALS, AND REAGENTS

Methods and equipment for dilution plating are the same as for the aerobic plate count (Chapter 4).

Plate count agar with chloramphenicol
Dichloran rose bengal chloramphenicol (DRBC) agar
Potato dextrose agar (PDA), pH 3.5

16.5   PROCEDURES

16.51   Antibiotic Method (Preferred)

1. Medium: Plate count agar or DRBC agar containing 100 μg/ml chloramphenicol is recommended. The chloramphenicol can be added to the medium prior to sterilization in the autoclave.
2. Petri plates, 9 cm diameter, are poured with 15 to 20 ml of the medium and then dried overnight at room temperature (21 to 25°C). Store DRBC plates in the dark to avoid photogeneration of inhibitors from the rose bengal dye.
3. Inoculate 0.1 ml of appropriate decimal dilutions in duplicate on the solidified agar and spread over the entire surface using a sterile bent glass rod.
4. Incubate upright plates 5 days at 22° to 25°C; do not disturb until colonies are to be counted. Count plates containing 15 to 150 colonies. Count from the underside of the plate when mold overgrowth has occurred (usually not a problem with DRBC).
5. Report the counts as cfu per g or ml of sample.

16.52   Acidified Media

The methods are identical to those described in Section 16.51 for the antibiotic procedure except that the medium is made selective for fungi by acidification, usually to a pH of 3.5. PDA acidified with sterile 10% tartaric acid is the medium of choice. Commercial PDA usually prescribes on the label the amount of tartaric acid that must be added. The medium is acidified after sterilization and tempering at 47° to 50°C. The accuracy of the adjusted pH can be determined by placing electrodes into poured media after solidification. Acidified agar cannot be remelted.

16.6   INTERPRETATION

The interpretation of viable yeast and mold counts often is difficult because background data on expected and excessive levels for many foods have not been established. Criteria for fungi should take into consideration the specific food, the manner of use, the primary age group and health of consumers, and the frequency and amount of food consumed. Although admittedly a difficult task, the determination of the predominant species also is important.

16.7   NEW METHODS UNDER DEVELOPMENT

Research in recent years has been concerned with methods alternative to plate counting for the enumeration of fungi in foods (see Chapter 39). The food industry needs more rapid, less laborious procedures that can assess levels of both viable and nonviable fungi.

Generally, the new methods have revolved around five major technical areas: (1) detection of a specific metabolite that is produced by fungi but is absent in the food; (2) microscopic analysis using fluorescent or selective dyes; (3) chemical analysis for specific cell wall or other components unique to fungi; (4) immunological detection after development of antibodies specific for a fungus or a group of fungi; and (5) refinement of methods based on impedimetric, spectrophotometric, or filtration techniques. The method chosen for each application will depend on how quickly or accurately the fungi must be estimated, what growth conditions exist in the environment, whether a specific fungus or group of fungi must be identified, and whether only viable fungi must be determined. It is anticipated that, through research, methods will be developed for fungi that will be similar to those currently being used to detect bacteria.

16.71   Stains

Several staining methods have been used to determine numbers of viable fungi in beverages and other foods.

The staining of yeast cells with methylene blue has application because viable yeasts usually convert the dye to the colorless form while dead cells take on the blue color.[35, 47] However, some viable cells may stain blue, and so other attempts for differential counts have used fluorescent dyes and optical brighteners such as analine blue,[45] viablue,[29] euchrysine 2GNX,[2] fluorescein-diacetate,[28, 35] acridine orange,[28] and other compounds.[28, 35]

Evaluation of the direct epifluorescent filter technique (DEFT) for foods[69, 74] showed that it cannot always distinguish between viable and dead cells (see Chapter 5). Chilver et al.[13] found that immunofluorescence combined with methylene blue staining had limited value for brewery samples when the yeast cells were stressed. Weaver et al.[82] used gel microdroplets and a pH-sensitive fluorescent indicator of fluorescein-isothiocyanate-dextran and luminol to detect *Saccharomyces cerevisiae*. Pettipher et al.[70] found that DEFT correlated well with plate counts for molds. Robertson et al.[73] extended DEFT by producing an antibody "cocktail" from *Alternaria alternata*, *Botrytis cinerea*, *Fusarium solani*, *Rhizopus stolonifer*, and *Mucor piriformis*. Samples of tomato paste were mixed with the antibodies plus fluorescent dye and were then examined by fluorescent microscopy. The fluorescent characteristic of mold-contaminated commodities has also been used to detect the presence of mold optically by measuring fluorescence at 442 and 607 nm.[10] Ruiz and Chen[75] used the first derivative of the spectral reflectance at 590 and 710 nm to detect mold in tomatoes. The near-infrared spectra changed as mold contamination increased in tomato puree.[19]

16.72 Metabolites and Components

The analyses for various cell components and metabolites have been used to estimate the incidence of fungi. The measurement of adenosine triphosphate (ATP) by the firefly luciferase bioluminescent technique has been used to enumerate yeasts in carbonated beverages.[46, 52, 53] The ATP readings did not always correlate well with plate counts, and thus traditional methods to confirm ATP-positive samples were recommended.[53]

DNA restriction patterns have been used to differentiate brewing yeasts from other strains of *S. cerevisiae*.[68] The use of gas chromatography to measure methyl esters of long-chain fatty acids has permitted the differentiation of brewing yeasts within 4 hr.[66]

Measurement of cell wall glucan has potential for detecting yeasts in different foods.[54] Chitin, a cell wall polysaccharide, has been evaluated for the detection of mold in foods.[11, 18, 31, 48] Although chitin could be determined with spectrophotometric and chromatographic methods, the procedures were too complex for routine quality control operations. Ergosterol, the major sterol of most fungi, has been evaluated for detecting mold in cereal grains and flour.[14, 77, 78, 79] Other fungal components are pectinesterase,[64, 65] carbonyl compounds,[23] and the anthroquinone pigment, pachybasin.[83]

Impedance-type instruments have been recommended for the monitoring of fungi.[25, 76, 80, 84, 85] Henschke and Thomas[25] suggested their use for wine because many samples could be analyzed at once. The addition of chloramphenicol to a yeast medium permitted the detection of yeasts in yogurt within 40 hr.[80] Zindulis[85] developed a medium containing yeast carbon base and ammonium sulfate for the detection of yeasts by polarization capacitance. Schaertel et al.[76] also found that capacitance was a better measure for yeasts than conductance with specially designed yeast agar.

16.73 Hydrophobic Filter

A comparison of the hydrophobic grid-membrane filter (HGMF) technique using the ISO-GRID automatic counting system with spread plate methods indicated no significant difference for the enumeration of yeasts and molds.[12, 50] Lin et al.[50] used a trypan blue agar to eliminate the need for staining colonies with safranin when using the ISO-GRID system.

16.74 Immunology

Recently, research efforts have shifted to the detection of molds in foods using immunological methods, especially the enzyme-linked immunosorbent assay (ELISA). This method is based on the production of antibodies to molds and the use of these antibodies to bind to mold antigens that are present in foods. Antibodies to *Alternaria, Aspergillus, Botrytis, Cladosporium, Fusarium, Geotrichum, Mucor, Penicillium,* and *Rhizopus* have been produced and used to detect these molds in bread, cereals, cottage cheese, fruits, nuts, spices, and other foods.[36, 49, 51, 60, 61, 62, 63, 72] ELISA could detect *Alternaria, Cladosporium, Fusarium,* and *Geotrichum* to the genus level. Molds in related families, such as *Aspergillus* and *Penicillium,* or *Mucor* and *Rhizopus,* cross-reacted since they share common antigens. When a mold mixture of *Alternaria alternata, Botrytis cinerea, Fusarium solani, Mucor piriformis,* and *Rhizopus stolonifer* was used to produce antibodies, about 50% or more cross-reactivity occurred between all genera.[72] There was no cross-reactivity with yeasts.[49] The mold antigens were heat stable and water soluble.[49, 60, 72] ELISA correlated well with the amount of mold added to food at detection levels as low as μg to ng/g of food. Notermans et al.[62] found that molds with high aflatoxin B, patulin, and penicillic acid contents had high levels of antigens to the *Penicillium/Aspergillus* ELISA. More research is needed to correlate mold antigen to mycotoxin levels. The immunodominant fraction of the mold antisera is now being determined so that rapid test kits can be developed. Kamphuis et al.[36] reported that a 10- to 20-min latex agglutination test for the detection of antigens to *Penicillium* and *Aspergillus* species was used to determine if these molds were in nuts and spices.

Research is continuing on the immunological detection of molds in foods since the method has promise for the development of rapid methods.

16.8 REFERENCES

1. Abildgren, M. P., Lund, F., Thrane, U., and Elmholt, S. 1987. Czapek-Dox agar containing iprodione and dichloran as a selective medium for the isolation of *Fusarium* species. Lett. Appl. Microbiol. 5: 83.
2. Andrews, D. W. 1982. A note on a microcolony method for the rapid detection of yeasts using Euchrysine 2GNX. J. Appl. Bacteriol. 52: 117.
3. Andrews, S. and Pitt, J. I. 1986. Selective medium for isolation of *Fusarium* species and dematiaceous hyphomycetes from cereals. Appl. Environ. Microbiol. 51: 1235.
4. Baggerman, W. I. 1981. A modified rose bengal medium for the enumeration of yeasts and molds from foods. European J. Appl. Microbiol. Biotechnol. 12: 242.
5. Banks, J. G. and Board, R. G. 1987. Some factors influencing the recovery of yeasts and molds from chilled foods. Intl. J. Food Microbiol. 4: 197.
6. Banks, J. G., Board, R. G., and Paton, J. 1985. Illuminated rose bengal causes adenosine triphosphate (ATP) depletion and microbial death. Lett. Appl. Microbiol. 1: 7.
7. Beneke, E. S. and Rogers, A. L. 1971. "Medical Mycology Manual," 3rd ed. Burgess Publishing Co., Minneapolis, Minn.
8. Beuchat, L. R. 1979. Comparison of acidified and antibiotic-supplemented potato dextrose agar from three manufacturers for its capacity to recover fungi from foods J. Food Prot. 42: 427.
9. Beuchat, L. R. 1984. Injury and repair of yeasts and moulds. In "Revival of Injured Microbes." eds. M. H. E. Andrew and A. D. Russell, p. 293. Academic Press, London.
10. Birth, G. S. and Johnson R. M. 1970. Detection of mold contamination in corn by optical measurements. J. Assn. Off. Analyt. Chem. 53: 931.

11. Bishop, R. H., Duncan, C. L., Evancho, G. M., and Young, H. 1982. Estimation of fungal contamination of tomato products by a chemical assay for chitin. J. Food Sci. 47: 437.
12. Brodsky, M. H., Entis, P., Entis, M. P., Sharpe, A. N., and Jarvis, G. A. 1982. Determination of aerobic plate and yeast and mold counts in foods using an automated Hydrophobic Grid-Membrane Filter technique. J. Food Prot. 45: 301.
13. Chilver, M. J., Harrison, J., and Webb, T. J. B., 1978. Use of immunofluorescence and viability stains in quality control. Amer. Soc. Brew. Chem. J. 36: 12.
14. Cooks, R. G., Daftary, R. D., and Pomeranz, Y. 1970. Changes in mold damaged wheat flours stored at various temperatures. J. Agr. Food Chem. 18: 620.
15. Corry, J. E. L. 1976. The effect of sugars and polyols on the heat resistance and microscopic morphology of osmophilic yeasts. J. Appl. Bacteriol. 40: 269.
16. Corry, J. E. L. 1982. Assessment of the selectivity and productivity of media used in analytical mycology. Arch. Lebensmittel hyg. 33: 137.
17. Corry, J. E. L. 1987. Relationships of water activity to fungal growth. In "Food and Beverage Mycology," ed. L. R. Beuchat, p. 51. Van Nostrand Reinhold, New York.
18. Cousin, M. A., Zeidler, C. S., and Nelson, P. E. 1984. Chemical detection of mold in processed foods. J. Food Sci. 49: 439.
19. Davies, A. M. C., Dennis, C., Grant, A., Hall, M. N., and Robertson, A. 1987. Screening of tomato pureé for excessive mould content by near infrared spectroscopy: A preliminary evaluation. J. Sci. Food Agric. 39: 349.
20. Flannigan, G. 1974. The use of acidified media for enumeration of yeasts and molds. Lab Practice 23: 633.
21. Frisvad, J. C. 1983. A selective and indicative medium for groups of *Penicillium viridicatum* producing different mycotoxins in cereals. J. Appl. Bacteriol. 54: 409.
22. Gilman, J. C. 1957. "A Manual of Soil Fungi," 2nd ed. Iowa State U. Press, Ames.
23. Hansen, A. P. and Keeney, P. G. 1970. Comparison of carbonyl compounds in moldy and non-moldy cocoa beans. J. Food Sci. 35: 37.
24. Hartog, B. T. 1984. The detection and quantification of fungi in food. In "Introduction to the Food-borne Fungi," ed. R. A. Samson, E. S. Hoekstra, and C. A. N. Van Vorschot, p. 206. Centraalbureau Voor *Schimmel*(cultures), Baarn, The Netherlands.
25. Henschke, P. A. and Thomas, D. S. 1988. Detection of wine-spoilage yeasts by electronic methods. J. Appl. Bacteriol. 64: 123.
26. Hocking, A. D. 1981. Improved media for enumeration of fungi from foods. CSIRO Food Res. Quarterly 41: 7.
27. Hocking, A. D. and Pitt, J. I. 1980. Dichloran-glycerol medium for enumeration of xerophilic fungi from low moisture foods. Appl. Environ. Microbiol. 39: 488.
28. Hope, C. F. A. and Tubb, R. S. 1985. Approaches to rapid microbial monitoring in brewing. J. Inst. Brew. 91: 12.
29. Hutcheson, T. C., McKay, T., Farr, L. and Seddon, B. 1988. Evaluation of the stain viablue for the rapid estimation of viable yeast cells. Lett. Appl. Microbiol. 6: 85.
30. Jarvis, B. 1973. Comparison of an improved rose bengal chlortetracycline agar with other media for the selective isolation and enumeration of molds and yeasts in foods. J. Appl. Bacteriol. 36: 723.
31. Jarvis, B. 1977. A chemical method for the estimation of mold in tomato products. J. Food Technol. 12: 581.
32. Jarvis, B. and Williams, A. P. 1987. Methods for detecting fungi in foods and beverages. In "Food and Beverage Mycology," ed. L. R. Beuchat, p. 599. Van Nostrand Reinhold, New York.
33. Jarvis, G, Seiler, D. A. L., Ould, A. J. L., and Williams, A. P. 1983. Observations on the enumeration of moulds in food and feedingstuffs. J. Appl. Bacteriol. 55: 325.
34. Jermini, M. F. G., Geiges, O., and Schmidt-Lorenz, W. 1987. Detection and identification of osmotolerant yeasts from high-sugar products. J. Food Prot. 50: 468.

35. Jones, R. P. 1987. Measures of yeast death and deactivation and their meaning: Part I. Proc. Biochem. 22: 118.
36. Kamphuis, H. J., Notermans, S., Veeneman, G. H., Van Boom, J. H., and Rombouts, F. M. 1989. A rapid and reliable method for the detection of molds in foods: Using the latex agglutination assay. J. Food Prot. 52: 244.
37. King, A. D., Hocking, A. D., and Pitt, J. I. 1979. Dichloran-glycerol medium for enumeration and isolation of molds from foods. Appl. Environ. Microbiol. 37: 959.
38. King, A. D., Pitt, J. I., Beuchat, L. R., and Corry, J. E. L. eds. 1986. "Methods for Mycological Examination of Food." Plenum Press, New York.
39. Koburger, J. A. 1970. Fungi in foods. I. Effects of inhibitor and incubation temperature on enumeration. J. Milk Food Technol. 33: 433.
40. Koburger, J. A. 1971. Fungi in foods. II. Some observations on acidulants used to adjust media pH for yeast and mold counts. J. Milk Food Technol. 34: 475.
41. Koburger, J. A. 1972. Fungi in foods. IV. Effect of plating medium pH on counts. J. Milk Food Technol. 35: 659.
42. Koburger, J. A. 1986. Effect of pyruvate on recovery of fungi from foods. J. Food Prot. 49: 231.
43. Koburger, J. A. and Farhat, B. Y. 1975. Fungi in foods. IV. A comparison of media to enumerate yeasts and molds. J. Milk Food Technol. 38: 466.
44. Koburger, J. A. and Norden, A. R. Fungi in foods. VII. A comparison of surface, pour plate, and most probable number methods for enumeration of yeasts and molds. J. Milk Food Technol. 38: 745.
45. Koch, H. A., Bandler, R., and Gibson, R. R. 1986. Fluorescence microscopy procedure for quantitation of yeasts in beverages. Appl. Environ. Microbiol. 52: 599.
46. LaRocco, K. A., Galligan, P., Littel, K. J., and Spurgash A. 1985. A rapid bioluminescent ATP method for determining yeast contamination in a carbonated beverage. Food Technol. 39: 49.
47. Lee, S. S., Robinson, F. M., and Wang, H. Y. 1981. Rapid determination of yeast viability. Biotechnol. Bioengineer. Symp. 11: 641.
48. Lin, H. H. and Cousin, M. A. 1985. Detection of mold in processed foods by high performance liquid chromatography. J. Food Prot. 48: 671.
49. Lin, H. H. and Cousin, M. A. 1987. Evaluation of enzyme-linked immunosorbent assay for detection of molds in foods. J. Food Sci. 52: 1089.
50. Lin, C. C. S., Fung, D. Y. C., and Entis, F. 1984. Growth of yeast and mold on trypan blue agar in conjunction with the ISO-GRID system. Can. J. Microbiol. 30: 1405.
51. Lin, H. H., Lister, R. M., and Cousin, M. A. 1986. Enzyme-linked immunosorbent assay for detection of mold in tomato puree. J. Food Sci. 51: 180.
52. Littel, K. J. and LaRocco, K. A. 1985. Bioluminescent standard curves for quantitative determination of yeast contaminants in carbonated beverages. J. Food Prot. 48: 1022.
53. Littel, K. J. and LaRocco, K. A. 1986. ATP screening method for presumptive detection of microbiologically contaminated carbonated beverages. J. Food Sci. 51: 474.
54. Meyer, M. T. and Phaff, H. J. 1981. An enzymatic method for the determination of yeast cell wall glucan in foods. J. Food Sci. 46: 1489.
55. Mislivec, P. B. 1981. Mycotoxin production by conidial fungi. In "Biology of Conidial Fungi," G. T. Cole and B. Kendrick, eds. p. 37. Vol. 2. Academic Press, New York.
56. Mislivec, P. B. and Bruce, V. R. 1976. Comparison of antibiotic-amended potato dextrose agar and acidified potato dextrose agar as growth substrate for fungi. J. Assn. Off. Anal. Chem. 59: 720.
57. Mossel, D. A. A., Visser M., and Mengerink, W. H. 1962. A comparison of media for the enumeration of moulds and yeasts in foods and beverages. Lab Practice 11: 109.
58. Mossel, D. A. A., Vega, C. L., and Put, H. M. 1975. Further studies on suitability of various media containing antibacterial antibiotics for the enumeration of molds in food and food environments. J. Appl. Bacteriol. 39: 15.

59. Nelson, F. E. 1972. Plating medium pH as a factor in apparent survival of sublethally stressed yeasts. Appl. Microbiol. 24: 236.
60. Notermans, S. and Heuvelman, C. J. 1985. Immunological detection of moulds in food by using the enzyme-linked immunosorbent assay (ELISA); preparation of antigens. Int. J. Food Microbiol. 2: 247.
61. Notermans, S., Heuvelman, C. J., Beumer, R. R., and Maas, R. 1986a. Immunological detection of moulds in food: Relation between antigen production and growth. Int. J. Food Microbiol. 3: 253.
62. Notermans, S., Heuvelman, C. J., van Egmond, H. P., Paulsch, W. E., and Besling, J. R. 1986b. Detection of mold in food by enzyme-linked immunosorbent assay. J. Food Prot. 49: 786.
63. Notermans, S., Defrenne, J., and Soentoro, P. S. 1988. Detection of molds in nuts and spices: The mold colony count versus the enzyme-linked immunosorbent assay (ELISA). J. Food Sci. 53: 1871.
64. Offem, J. O. and Dart, R. K. 1982. Rapid method of estimating viable spores of *Aspergillus*. J. Chromatogr. 249: 139.
65. Offem, J. O. and Dart, R. K. 1983. Rapid determination of spoilage fungi. J. Chromatogr. 260: 109.
66. Oosthuizen, A., Koch, J. L. F., Viljoen, B. C., Muller, H. B., and Lategan, P. M. 1987. The value of long-chain fatty acid composition in the identification of some brewery yeasts. J. Inst. Brew. 93: 174.
67. Overcast, W. W. and Weakley, D. J. 1969. An aureomycin-rose bengal agar for enumeration of yeast and mold in cottage cheese. J. Milk Food Technol. 32: 442.
68. Panchal, C. J., Bast, L., Dowhanick, T., and Stewart, G. S. 1987. A rapid, simple and reliable method of differentiating brewing yeast strains based on DNA restriction patterns. J. Inst. Brew. 93: 325.
69. Pettipher, G. L. 1987. Detection of low numbers of osmophilic yeasts in creme fondant within 25 h using a pre-incubated DEFT count. Lett. Appl. Microbiol. 4: 95.
70. Pettipher, G. L., Williams, R. A., and Gutteridge, C. S. 1985. An evaluation of possible alternative methods to the Howard Mould Count. Lett. Appl. Microbiol. 1: 49.
71. Pitt, J. I., Hocking, A. D., and Glenn, D. R. 1983. An improved medium for the detection of *Aspergillus flavus* and *A. parasiticus*. J. Appl. Bacteriol. 54: 109.
72. Robertson, A., Upadhyaya, D., Opie, S., and Sargeant, J. S. 1986. An immunochemical method for the measurement of mold contamination in tomato paste. In "Immunoassays for Veterinary and Food Analysis—1," eds. B. A. Morris, M. N. Clifford, and R. Jackman, p. 163. Elsevier Applied Science, London and New York.
73. Robertson, A., Patel, N., and Sargeant, J. S. 1988. Immunofluorescence detection of mould— an aid to the Howard mould counting technique. Food Microbiol. 5: 33.
74. Rodriques, U. M. and Kroll, R. G. 1986. Use of the direct epifluorescent filter technique for the enumeration of yeasts. J. Appl. Bacteriol. 61: 139.
75. Ruiz, M. and Chen, P. 1982. Use of the first derivative of spectral reflectance to detect mold on tomatoes. Trans. Am. Soc. Agric. Engr. 25: 759.
76. Schaertel, B. J., Tsang, N., and Fistenberg-Eden, R. 1987. Impedimetric detection of yeast and mold. Food Microbiol. 4: 155.
77. Seitz, L. M. and Paukstelis, J. V. 1977. Metabolites of *Aternaria alternata*: Ergosterol and ergosta-4, 6, 8(14), 2-tetraenone. J. Agric. Food Chem. 25: 838.
78. Seitz, L. M., Mohr, H. E., Burroughs, R., and Sauer, D. B. 1977. Ergosterol as an indicator of fungal invasion in grains. Cereal Chem. 54: 1207.
79. Seitz, L. M., Sauer, D. B., Burroughs, R., Mohr, H. E., and Hubbard, J. D. 1979. Ergosterol as a measure of fungal growth. Phytopathology. 69: 1202.
80. Shapton, N. and Cooper, P. J. 1984. Rapid determination of yeast numbers by impedance measurement using a Bactometer 32. J. Soc. Dairy Technol. 37: 60.

81. Snow, D. 1949. The germination of mould spores at controlled humidities. Ann. Appl. Biol. 36: 1.
82. Weaver, J. C., Williams, G. B., Klibanov, A., and Demain, A. L. 1988. Gel microdroplets: Rapid detection and enumeration of individual microorganisms by their metabolic activity. Bio/Technology 6: 1084.
83. Weijman, A. C. M., Van Eijk, G. W., Windig, W., and Samson, R. A. 1986. Modern detection methods for food spoilage fungi. In "Methods for the Mycological Examination of Food," eds. A. D. King, Jr., J. I. Pitt, L. R. Beuchat, and J. E. L. Corry, p. 238. Plenum Press, New York.
84. Williams, A. P. and Wood, J. M. 1986. Impedimetric estimation of molds. In "Methods for the Mycological Examination of Food," eds. A. D. King, Jr., J. I. Pitt, L. R. Beuchat, and J. E. L. Corry, p. 230. Plenum Press, New York.
85. Zindulis, J. 1984. A medium for the impedimetric detection of yeasts in foods. Food Microbiol. 1: 159.

Chapter 17

DETECTION AND ENUMERATION OF HEAT-RESISTANT MOLDS

L. R. Beuchat and J. I. Pitt

17.1 INTRODUCTION

Spoilage of thermally processed fruits and fruit products by heat-resistant molds has been recognized in several countries.[5, 8-10, 12, 15, 20, 22, 26] *Byssochlamys fulva, B. nivea, Neosartorya fischeri, Talaromyces flavus, T. bacillisporus,* and *Eupenicillium brefeldianum* have been most frequently encountered.[10] *Byssochlamys* species have been recognized as spoilage molds in canned fruit since the early 1930s[12, 13] and have been extensively studied.[2, 5, 14, 18, 25] Spoilage by other heat-resistant molds is a less serious problem recognized only in recent years. Consequently, less information is available concerning their behavior in thermally processed fruit products.

These molds are characterized by the production of ascospores that frequently show high heat resistance, in some instances comparable to bacterial spores. This enables them to survive the thermal processes given to some fruit products (Table 1). Germination of ascospores may result in visible growth of mycelia on fruits and fruit products. Production of pectic enzymes by *Byssochlamys* can result in complete breakdown of texture in fruits[26] and also can result in off-flavor development.

Some *Byssochlamys* species produce patulin, byssotoxin A, and byssochlamic acid, all having toxic effects on laboratory animals.[5, 19, 27] *Neosartorya fischeri* is known to produce fumitremorgin A, B, and C, terrein, and verruculogen.[11, 24] Heat-resistant molds, therefore, may constitute a public health hazard as well as a spoilage problem.

17.11 Distribution

Heat-resistant molds are widely distributed in the soil, particularly in vineyards, orchards, and fields in which fruits are grown.[8, 12, 13, 25, 31] Consequently,

Table 1—Tolerance of Heat-resistant Molds Isolated from Foods[a]

Mold	Heat-resistant structure	Heating medium	Heat resistance
Byssochlamys fulva	Ascospores	Glucose-tartaric acid, pH 3.6	90°C, 51 min, 1000-fold inactivation[2]
		Grape juice, 26° Brix	85°C, 150 min, 100-fold inactivation[18]
Byssochlamys nivea	Ascospores	Grape juice	88°C, survived 60 min[20]
		Apple juice	99°C, survived in juice containing 4.7% sucrose[1]
Eupenicillium lapidosum	Ascospores	Blueberry juice	81°C, 10 min, survival; 81°C, 15 min, death[35] z = 10.3°F
	Cleistothecia	Blueberry juice	93.3°C, 9 min, growth; 93.3°C, 10 min, death[35] z = 10.6°F
Eupenicillium brefeldianum	Ascopores	Apple juice	90°C, 1 min, death[34] z = 7.2°C
	Cleistothecia	Apple juice	90°C, 220 min, death[34] z = 11.7°C
Talaromyces flavus	Ascospores	Apple juice	90°C, 2 min, death[34] z = 7.8°C
	(3 isolates)	Fruit-based fillings	D91°C = 2.9 to 5.4 min[3] z = 9.4 to 23.3°F
		Apple juice	D90.6°C = 1.4 min[3] z = 9.5°F
		Apple juice	D90.6°C = 2.2 min[28] z = 5.2°C
	Cleistothecia	Apple juice	90°C, 80 min, death[34] z = 11.7°C
Monascus purpureus	Whole culture	Grape juice	Survival several min 100°C[9]
Humicola fuscoatra	Chlamydospores	Water	80°C, 101 min, 10-fold inactivation[21]
Phialophora sp	Chlamydospores	Apple juice	80°C, 2.3 min, 10-fold inactivation[14]
Neosartorya fischeri	Ascospores	Water	100°C, 60 min, survival[17]
	(3 isolates)	Fruit-based fillings	D91°C = <2.0 min; D88°C = 4.2–16.2 min[3] z = 5.4 = 11°F
		Apple juice	87.8°C, 1.4 min[28] z = 5.6°C
Neosartorya fischeri var. *glaber*	Ascospores	Water	90°C, 60 min, survival[22]
		Grape juice	85°C, 10 min, 10% survival[30]
Thermoascus auranthiacum	Whole culture	Grape juice	88°C, 60 min, survival[20]

[a]Adapted from Splittstoesser and King.[29]

these molds may become contaminants on fruit and other vegetation upon contact with soil, before delivery to the processing plant. The number of ascospores on fruits is generally low, less than 1 per g.[20, 31]

17.2   GENERAL CONSIDERATIONS

17.21   Samples

Because of their low incidence in fruit, ascospores are not likely to exceed 1 to 10 per 100 g or ml of processed product. Thus, for their effective detection, it is important that relatively large samples be analyzed. Centrifugation may be used to concentrate ascospores in liquid fruit products, the force and time necessary being influenced by volume, viscosity, and specific gravity of the sample.

Since the viability of ascospores is not appreciably affected by freezing and thawing, food samples can be stored frozen prior to analysis.

17.22   Enumeration Principles

A secondary but perhaps important point is that ascospores of heat-resistant molds may require heat activation before growth will occur.[3, 16, 19, 32] The composition of the heating menstruum can influence the rate and extent of activation.[4, 7, 33] Maximal activation of *B. fulva* and *N. fischeri* var. *glaber* ascospores was obtained by heating at 70°C for 30 min in grape juice; in distilled water, 120 min were required for *B. fulva* while only 1% of the *N. fischeri* ascospores were activated.[30] Different strains within the same species may require different treatment times and temperatures to achieve maximal activation.

Detection and enumeration of heat-resistant ascospores rely on a selective heat treatment that inactivates vegetative cells of fungi and bacteria as well as less heat-resistant spores.

Heat-resistant molds are not fastidious in their nutrient requirements, and therefore the media listed below as well as many fruit juice agars will support germination of ascospores and subsequent vegetative growth. Since ascospores may be stressed by the heating process, highly acidic media are not recommended. However, when culturing low-acid foods that are heavily contaminated with bacterial spores, acidification or the addition of chloramphenicol to the plating medium may be required to inhibit the bacteria.

17.3   EQUIPMENT, MATERIALS, AND REAGENTS

Potato dextrose agar (PDA)
Malt extract agar (MEA)
Orange serum agar (OSA)
Czapek yeast autolysate (CYA) agar

17.4   PROCEDURES

17.41   Petri Dish Method[23, 31]

Fruits and products containing pieces of fruits must be blended or homogenized before analysis can proceed. To a tared sterile blender jar, add 100 g of fruit or fruit product plus 100 ml of sterile water and blend 5 min or until mixture appears homogeneous. After blending, enclose the jar in a polyethylene bag to safeguard against leakage through the bottom bushing and place the jar in a closed 75°C to 80°C waterbath for 1.5 hr. This holding time ensures that the homogenate will be at 75°C for at least 30 min.

Alternatively, samples (100 g plus 100 ml of sterile water) may be homogenized in a stomacher for 2 to 4 min (see Chapter 2). Two 50-ml portions of homogenate are then transferred to sterile 200×30 mm test tubes and placed in a closed waterbath at 75°C to 80°C for 30 min. The surface of the sample in the jars or tubes should be well below the surface of the water in the bath throughout the heat treatment.

After heating, duplicate 50-ml samples of thoroughly mixed homogenate in blender jars or the entire contents (50 ml) of duplicate tubes of sample that had been homogenized in a stomacher are combined with PDA or MEA in 150-mm petri dishes. Each 50-ml sample is equally distributed in four dishes and thoroughly mixed with 10 ml of 1.5 strength agar. Petri dishes are loosely sealed in a plastic bag to prevent drying and incubated at 30°C for up to 30 days. Most viable ascospores will germinate and form visible colonies within 7 to 10 days; however, heat-injured and other debilitated ascospores may require additional time to form colonies. The 30-day incubation time also enables molds to mature and sporulate, thus aiding their identification.

Fruit juices (35° Brix or less) are analyzed in a manner identical to that described above. Fruit juice products (35° Brix or more) and fruit juice concentrates should be diluted (1:1) with sterile water and thoroughly mixed before heat treatment is applied to duplicate 50-ml samples. The general procedure is illustrated in Figure 1.

17.42   Direct Incubation Method[10, 23]

The petri dish method is subject to error from aerial contamination (see Section 17.51). An alternative method that avoids this problem is described in this section. It is suitable for fruit pulps and homogenates.

Homogenized 50-ml samples are heated in flat-sided bottles such as 100-ml medicine flats. Bottles are heated in an upright position in a waterbath at 80°C for 30 min and then incubated on their sides, allowing as large a surface area as possible, at 30°C for up to 30 days. This procedure avoids the risk of contamination from the air and minimizes loss of moisture. Colonies develop on the surface of the homogenate.

Larger samples, such as 100-ml quantities in 200-ml bottles, can also be

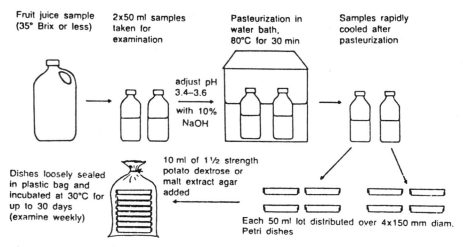

Figure 1 — Procedure for detection and enumeration of heat-resistant mold spores. (From Hocking and Pitt[10]).

handled by this method. One apparent disadvantage is that colonies developing in the bottles must be picked and grown on suitable media for identification. However, cultivation on identification media is also recommended with the petri dish method.

17.5   PRECAUTIONS

17.51   Air Contamination

With the petri dish method, aerial contamination during plating may be a problem. The appearance of green *Penicillium* colonies, or colonies of common *Aspergillus* species such as *A. flavus* and *A. niger* is a clear indication of contamination, as these fungi are not heat resistant. To minimize this problem, pour plates in clean, still air or use a laminar flow hood, if possible. Alternatively, use the direct incubation method.

17.6   INTERPRETATION

Heat-resistant mold ascospores are not uncommon on fruit when it is received at the processing plant.[31] The acceptable level of contamination will depend on whether the fruit is a major or minor ingredient, whether the final product will contain a preservative such as sorbate or benzoate, and the thermal process to which the fruit is to be subjected. A count of 5 ascospores per 100 g (ml) of product at a stage just prior to the retort or heat exchanger indicates a serious problem. For ultra-high temperature (UHT) processed fruit juice blends that do not contain a preservative, even a lower level of contamination is unacceptable. One manufacturer of pasteurized fruit juices has issued a specification that calls for the absence of *Byssochlamys* from a 100-ml sample taken from each 200-L drum of raw material.[6]

17.7   TAXONOMY OF IMPORTANT HEAT-RESISTANT FUNGI

The basis for high heat resistance in these fungi is the production of a teleomorphic state; that is, they form ascospores. Ascospores are produced, generally, in groups of eight, within a closed sac, the ascus (plural, asci); ascospores are the prime characteristic of the class of fungi called ascomycetes. In nearly all ascomycete genera, asci are in turn enclosed, in large numbers, within larger bodies. In genera of interest here, these bodies may have a solid, totally enclosed wall (a cleistothecium) or be composed of fine, interwoven hyphae (a gymnothecium). Only in *Byssochlamys* are asci borne singly and unenclosed.

As well as ascospores, ascomycetes generally produce an anamorphic state with asexual spores called conidia (singular, conidium). Conidia are not very heat resistant and are usually readily destroyed by pasteurizing heat processes or the screening techniques outlined above. The fungi of interest here produce conidial states characteristic of the genera *Aspergillus*, *Paecilomyces*, and *Penicillium*.

17.71   Identification of Isolates

To identify heat-resistant fungal isolates, proceed as follows. Inoculate each isolate onto media in four 90-mm diameter petri dishes, two each of CYA and MEA. Inoculate each plate at three equally spaced points. Incubate one plate each of MEA and CYA at 25°C, and the others at 30°C.

After incubation for 7 days, examine plates by eye, measuring colony diameters with a ruler, and make wet mounts to examine small pieces of mold under a compound microscope. The following key will assist in identification of common heat-resistant fungi. For less common species, see Hocking and Pitt.[10]

17.72   Key to Common Heat-resistant Fungi

1. Colonies on CYA and MEA predominately buff or brown—*Byssochlamys fulva*
   Colonies on CYA and MEA persistently white or cream—*Byssochlamys nivea*
2. Asci produced in discrete bodies with totally enclosed walls (cleistothecia)—*Neosartorya fischeri*

Asci produced in bodies with walls of woven hyphae (gymnothecia) or openly—2

3. Asci enclosed in gymnothecia—*Talaromyces flavus*
    Asci produced openly; fine hyphae may be present, but asci not enclosed—3

17.721   Genus *Byssochlamys* Westling

Byssochlamys has the distinction of being almost uniquely associated with food spoilage and in particular with the spoilage of heat-processed acid foods. Its natural habitat appears to be soils, but the genus is mentioned very seldom in lists of fungi from soils other than those used for the cultivation of fruits.

Byssochlamys is an ascomycete genus characterized by the absence of cleistothecia, gymnothecia, or other bodies that in most ascomycetes envelop asci during development. Asci in *Byssochlamys* are borne in open clusters, in association with, but not surrounded by, unstructured wefts of fine white hyphae.

In our experience, the temperature range for observation of *Byssochlamys* asci and ascospores in the laboratory is sometimes very narrow. Cultures need to be incubated at 30°C as some isolates do not produce asci at 25°C or 37°C. However, presumptive evidence of the presence of *Byssochlamys* or other heat-resistant molds can be made from plates at 25°C or 37°C if the isolate has come from heat-processed food or raw materials.

Byssochlamys fulva Olliver and G. Smith (Figure 2)
Anamorph: *Paecilomyces fulvus* Stolk and Samson

At 25°C, colonies on CYA and MEA are at least 60 mm diameter, often covering the whole petri dish, relatively sparse, low or somewhat floccose, with conidial production heavy, uniformly colored olive brown, and reverse in similar colors or pale. At 30°C, colonies on CYA and MEA usually cover the whole petri dish, and are low to moderately deep, sparse, with moderate conidial production, colored brown, overlaid by white hyphae from which asci are produced; reverse is olive brown to deep brown.

Teleomorphic-state, single asci are borne from, but not enveloped by, wefts of contorted white hyphae, best developed at 30°C, maturing in 7 to 12 days, occasionally formed at 25°C in fresh isolates but maturing slowly if at all, with asci spherical to subspheroidal, 9 to 12 μm diameter, and ascospores ellipsoidal, hyaline, or straw-colored, 5 to 7 μm long, and smooth-walled.

Anamorphic state is best observed at 25°C, consisting of penicilli borne from surface hyphae or long, trailing, aerial hyphae, stipes 10 to 30 μm long, with phialides of nonuniform appearance, flask-shaped or narrowing gradually to the apices, 12 to 20 μm long, and conidia mostly cylindrical or barrel-shaped, narrow and 7 to 10 μm long, but sometimes longer, wider, or ellipsoidal from particular phialides, smooth-walled.

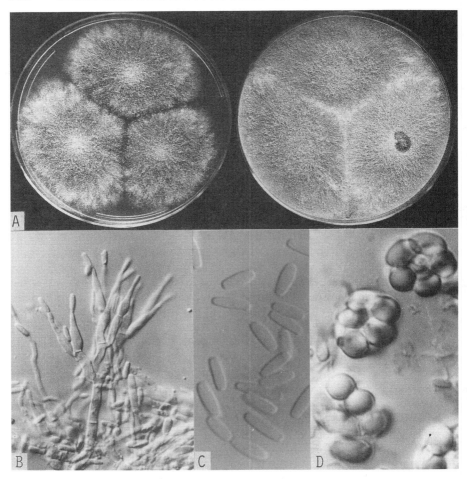

Figure 2—*Byssochlamys fulva*: (A) colonies on CYA and MEA, 7 days, 25°C; (B) penicillus, × 750; (C) conidia, × 1875; (D) asci and ascospores, × 1875.

Byssochlamys nivea Westling
Anamorph: *Paecilomyces niveus* Stolk and Samson

At 25°C, colonies on CYA are 40 to 50 mm diameter, low and quite sparse, white to slightly grey, with reverse pale to mid-brown. Colonies on MEA cover the whole petri dish, low and sparse, white to creamish, with small knots of dense hyphae, and reverse pale to brownish. At 30°C on CYA, colonies cover the whole petri dish, similar to those on MEA at 25°C, but often more dense, enveloping distinct knots of dense hyphae.

Teleomorphic state is similar to that of *B. fulva* except for slightly smaller asci (8 to 11 μm diam) and ascospores (4 to 6 μm diam), maturing in 10 to 14 days at 25°C and in 7 to 10 days at 30°C.

Anamorphs of two kinds are produced, aleurioconidia and penicilli; aleurioconidia borne singly, common at 30°C and 37°C, spherical to pear-shaped, 7 to 10 μm diameter, with irregular penicilli sparsely produced and phialides sometimes borne solitarily from hyphae as well, phialides 12 to 20 μm long, cylindrical then gradually tapering, and conidia ellipsoidal to pear-shaped, 3 to 6 μm long, smooth-walled.

17.722   Genus *Neosartorya* C. R. Benjamin

A genus of soil fungi, *Neosartorya* is of interest here because of its highly heat-resistant ascospores. It occurs from time to time in heat-processed foods and has occasionally been reported as a cause of spoilage. Although there are several species, only *N. fischeri* is common.

Neosartorya fischeri (Wehmer) Malloch and Cain (Figure 3)
Anamorph: *Aspergillus fischeri* Wehmer
On CYA and MEA at 25°C, colonies 50 to 65 mm or more diameter, low and sparse to moderately deep, and cottony white to cream mycelium, surround abundant white developing cleistothecia and are overlaid by scattered, usually inconspicuous blue to green conidial heads, with reverse pale to yellow. At 30°C, colonies cover the whole petri dish, similar to those at 25°C, but often are deeper and more luxuriant.

Cleistothecia white, 300 to 400 μm diameter, mature in 1 to 2 weeks at 25°C, with ascospores ellipsoidal, overall 6 to 7 × 4 to 5 μm, ornamented with two prominent, sinuous, longitudinal ridges and usually with other irregular ridges as well. Anamorph *Aspergillus*, with sparse conidiophores, 300 to 1000 μm long, terminate in small swellings, 12 to 18 μm diameter, with phialides crowded, 5 to 7 μm long, and conidia spheroidal, 2.0 to 2.5 μm diameter, with finely roughened walls.

17.723   Genus *Talaromyces* C. R. Benjamin

Talaromyces is characterized by the production of yellow or white gymnothecia in association with an anamorphic state characteristic of *Penicillium*, *Paecilomyces,* or *Geosmithia*. It is a genus of about 25 species, mostly soil inhabiting. By far the most commonly encountered species is *T. flavus*, which has a *Penicillium* anamorph.

Talaromyces flavus (Klöcker) Stolk and Samson (Figure 4)
Anamorph: *Penicillium dangeardii* Pitt
At 25°C, colonies on CYA are 18 to 30 mm diameter, plane, low and quite sparse to moderately deep and cottony, with mycelium bright yellow, less commonly buff or reddish brown, in most isolates concealing developing

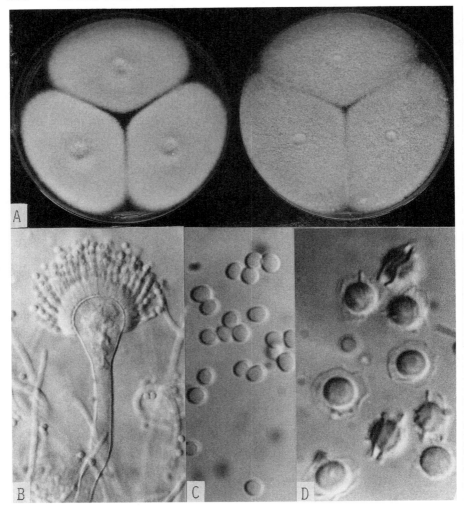

Figure 3—*Neosartorya fischeri*: (A) colonies on CYA and MEA, 7 days, 25°C; (B) conidiophore, × 750; (C) conidia, × 1875; (D) ascospores, × 1875.

gymnothecia, also clear to reddish exudate present occasionally, and reverse sometimes yellow, more usually orange, reddish or brown. Colonies on MEA are 30 to 50 mm diameter, generally similar to those on CYA, but gymnothecia are more abundant, with reverse usually dull orange or brown, but sometimes deep brown or deep red. At 30°C on CYA, colonies 30 to 45 mm diameter, are generally similar to those at 25°C, but sometimes with white or brown mycelium or overlaid with grey conidia or with conspicuous red soluble pigment and reverse color. At 30°C on MEA, similar to those at 25°C, usually produce abundant gymnothecia, and reverse sometimes also red or olive.

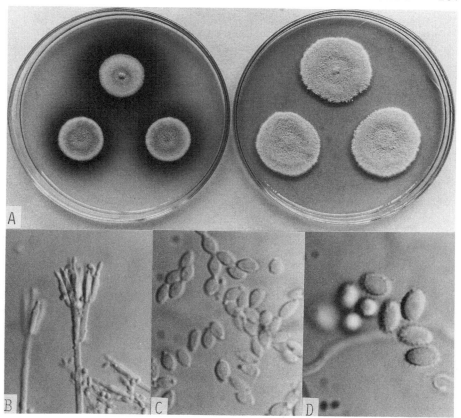

Figure 4—*Talaromyces flavus*: (A) colonies on CYA and MEA, 7 days, 25°C; (B) penicillus, × 750; (C) conidia, × 1875; (D) ascospores, × 1875.

Gymnothecia of tightly interwoven mycelium, bright yellow, about 200 to 500 μm diameter, closely packed, mature within 2 weeks, with ascospores yellow, ellipsoidal, 3.5 to 5.0 μm long, with spinose walls. Anamorph *Penicillium*, with conidiophores borne from aerial hyphae and stipes 20 to 80 μm long, bear terminal biverticillate or, less commonly, monoverticillate penicilli, and have phialides needle-shaped, 10 to 16 μm long, and conidia ellipsoidal, 2.5 to 4.0 μm long, with smooth to spinulose walls.

17.8   REFERENCES

1. Baumgart, J. and Stocksmeyer, G. 1976. Heat resistance of ascospores of the genus *Byssochlamys*. Alimenta 15: 67.
2. Bayne, H. G. and Michener, H. D. 1979. Heat resistance of *Byssochlamys* ascospores. Appl. Environ. Microbiol. 37: 449.

3. Beuchat, L. R. 1986. Extraordinary heat resistance of *Talaromyces flavus* and *Neosartorya fischeri* ascospores in fruit products. J. Food. Sci. 51: 1506.
4. Beuchat, L. R. 1987. Influence of organic acids on heat resistance characteristics of *Talaromyces flavus* ascospores. Intl. J. Food Microbiol.
5. Beuchat, L. R. and Rice, S. L. 1979. *Byssochlamys* spp. and their importance in processed fruits. Advan. Food Res. 25: 237.
6. Cartwright, P. and Hocking, A. D. 1984. *Byssochlamys* in fruit juices. Food Technol. Aust. 36: 210.
7. Conner, D. E. and Beuchat, L. R. 1987. Heat resistance of ascospores of *Neosartorya fischeri* as affected by sporulation and heating medium. Intl. J. Food Microbiol. 4: 303.
8. Fravel, D. R. and Adams, P. B. 1986. Estimation of United States and world distribution of *Talaromyces flavus*. Mycologia 78: 684.
9. Hellinger, E. 1960. The spoilage of bottled grape juice by *Monascus purpureus* Went. Ann. Inst. Pasteur., Lille 11: 183.
10. Hocking, A. D. and Pitt, J. I. 1984. Food spoilage fungi. Heat-resistant fungi. CSIRO Food Res. Quart. 44: 73.
11. Horie, Y. and Yamazaki, M. 1981. Productivity of tremorgenic mycotoxins, fumitremorgins A and B in *Aspergillus fumigatus*, and allied species. Trans. Mycol. Soc. Japan 22: 113.
12. Hull, R. 1933–34. Investigation of the control of spoilage of processed fruit by *Byssochlamys fluva*. In "Annual Report of the Fruit and Vegetable Preservation Research Station," p. 64. Univ. of Bristol Campden, England.
13. Hull, R. 1939. Study of *Byssochlamys fulva* and control measures in processed fruits. Ann. Appl. Biol. 26: 800.
14. Jensen, M. 1960. Experiments on the inhibition of some thermoresistant moulds in fruit juices. Ann. Inst. Pasteur., Lille 11: 179.
15. Jesenska, D., Havranekova, I. and Sajbidorova, I. 1984. On the problems of moulds on some products of canning industry. Cs. Hyg. 29: 102.
16. Katan, T. 1985. Heat activation of dormant ascospores of *Talaromyces flavus*. Trans. Br. Mycol. Soc. 84: 748.
17. Kavanagh, J., Larchet, N. and Stuart, M. 1963. Occurrence of a heat-resistant species of *Aspergillus* in canned strawberries. Nature 198: 1322.
18. King, A. D. Jr., Michener, H. D. and Ito, K. A. 1969. Control of *Byssochlamys* and related heat-resistant fungi in grape products. Appl. Microbiol. 18: 166.
19. King, A. D. Jr., Booth, A. N., Stafford, A. E. and Waiss, A. C. Jr. 1972. *Byssochlamys fulva*, metabolite toxicity in laboratory animals. J. Food Sci. 37: 86.
20. King, A. D. Jr., Bayne, H. G. and Alderton, G. 1979. Nonlogarithmic death rate calculations for *Byssochlamys fulva* and other microorganisms. Appl. Environ. Microbiol. 37: 596.
21. Lubieniecki-von Schelhorn, M. 1973. Influence of relative humidity conditions on the thermal resistance of several kinds of spores of molds. Acta Alimentaria 2: 163.
22. McEvoy, I. J. and Stuart, M. R. 1970. Temperature tolerance of *Aspergillus fischeri* var. *glaber* in canned strawberries. Irish J. Agric. Res. 9: 59.
23. Murdock, D. I. and Hatcher, W. S. Jr. 1978. A simple method to screen fruit juices and concentrates for heat-resistant mold. J. Food Prot. 41: 254.
24. Nielsen, P. V., Beuchat, L. R. and Frisvad, J. C. 1988. Growth and fumitremorgin production by *Neosartorya fischeri* as affected by temperature, light, and water activity. Appl. Environ. Microbiol. 54: 1504.
25. Put, H. M. C. 1964. A selective method for cultivating heat resistant moulds, particularly those of the genus *Byssochlamys*, and their presence in Dutch soil. J. Appl. Bacteriol. 27: 59.
26. Put, H. M. C. and Kruiswijk, J. T. 1964. Disintegration and organoleptic deterioration of processed strawberries caused by the mould *Byssochlamys nivea*. J. Appl. Bacteriol. 27: 53.
27. Rice, S. L., Beuchat, L. R. and Worthington, R. E. 1977. Patulin production by *Byssochlamys* spp. in fruit juices. Apl. Environ. Microbiol. 34: 791.

28. Scott, V.N. and Bernard, D. T. 1987. Heat resistance of *Talaromyces flavus* and *Neosartorya fischeri* isolated from commercial fruit juices. J. Food Prot. 50: 18.
29. Splittstoesser, D. F. and King, A. D. Jr. 1984. Chapter 18 In "Compendium of Methods for the Microbiological Examination of Foods," 2nd ed., ed. M. Speck, p. 203. Am. Pub. Health Assn., Washington, D.C.
30. Splittstoesser, D. F. and Splittstoesser, C. M. 1977. Ascospores of *Byssochlamys fulva* compared with those of a heat-resistant *Aspergillus*. J. Food Sci. 42: 685.
31. Splittstoesser, D. F., Kuss, F. R., Harrison, W. and Prest, D. B. 1971. Incidence of heat resistant molds in eastern orchards and vineyards. Appl. Microbiol. 21: 335.
32. Splittstoesser, D. F., Wilkison, M. and Harrison, W. 1972. Heat activation of *Byssochlamys fulva* ascospores. J. Milk Food Technol. 35: 399.
33. Splittstoesser, D. F., Einset, A., Wilkison, M. and Preziose, J. 1974. Effect of food ingredients on the heat resistance of *Byssochlamys fulva* ascospores. In Proc. 4th Intl Congress Food Sci. and Technol. III, p. 79, Madrid, Spain.
34. Van der Spuy, J. E., Matthee, F. N. and Crafford, D. J. A. 1975. The heat resistance of moulds *Pencillium vermiculatum* Dangeard and *Penicillium brefeldianum* Dodge in apple juice. Phytophylactica 7: 105.
35. Williams, C. C., Cameron, E. J. and Williams, O. B. 1941. A facultative anaerobic mold of unusual heat resistance. Food Res. 6: 69.

Chapter 18

MESOPHILIC AEROBIC SPOREFORMERS

Kenneth E. Stevenson and Wayne P. Segner

18.1 INTRODUCTION

18.11 Classification

Members of the mesophilic aerobic sporeformers of significance in the spoilage of food belong to the genera *Bacillus* and *Sporolactobacillus*. Of these genera, the genus *Bacillus* is, by far, the more important.

The genus *Sporolactobacillus* contains a single species, *S. inulinus*. The organism is mesophilic, microaerophilic, motile, catalase-negative, and a homofermentative endospore-forming rod. Except for its ability to produce endospores, the organism is closely aligned taxonomically with some species of the genus *Lactobacillus*. Since spores of *S. inulinus* possess a comparatively low order of heat resistance and they are apparently distributed in low numbers in food and the environment, this organism appears to have little importance in food spoilage.[6]

Mesophilic aerobic sporeformers classified in the genus *Bacillus* are aerobic to facultatively anaerobic rods that may appear as spindles, clubs, or wedges when bulged by endospores. However, swelling of the sporangium is not a prerequisite to membership in this genus.[8] While most mesophilic aerobic sporeformers are catalase-positive, catalase-negative strains culturally similar to *B. macerans* have been isolated from spoiled insufficiently acidified, commercially canned onions and from inadequately sterilized, commercially canned cream-style corn.[20] All of the *Bacillus* species have the ability to produce refractile endospores under aerobic conditions, provided that other require-

The authors are indebted to the late Paul J. Thompson for his work associated with chapters on mesophilic aerobic sproeformers in previous editions.

ments for sporulation are met. Growth temperature is not a criterion for distinguishing *Bacillus* species that are important in food spoilage, except for *B. stearothermophilus* and *B. coagulans*. These two organisms differ in that *B. stearothermophilus* is capable of growing at 65°C[8] and will not grow on Thermoacidurans agar (pH 5.0). Overlapping temperature ranges for growth of *Bacillus* strains necessitate an arbitrary distinction between mesophiles and thermophiles. The mesophilic aerobic sporeforming bacteria are considered here as all strains of *Bacillus* species that grow better at 35°C than at 55°C, a delimitation that is compatible, but not identical, with views of others.[3, 19]

The balance of this discussion is confined to the mesophilic aerobic sporeformers of the genus *Bacillus*. The facultative thermophile *B. coagulans* and the mesophile *B. cereus* are discussed separately in Chapters 20 and 35, respectively.

18.12   Sources and Growth Requirements

Bacillus species encountered in foods are generally widespread. Spores and also vegetative cells of mesophilic aerobic sporeformers are found in food, water, soil, and decomposing vegetation. Excepting the insectivorous strains, and those residing primarily in the alimentary tract of animals, the mesophilic *Bacillus* species appear to occupy no distinctive habitats.[5, 8] An incubation temperature of 30° to 35°C is favorable for culture and sporulation of mesophilic sporeformers important to food microbiologists. Most strains recovered from food spoilage sporulate well aerobically on nutrient agar slants containing manganese.[4] The catalase-positive strains commonly sporulate readily. The catalase-negative strains are somewhat more demanding in their nutritional requirements; growth and sporulation are favored by the presence of yeast extract in the sporulation medium and by incubation at 35°C rather than 30°C.[20]

18.13   Nature and Characteristics

The presence of spores of the mesophilic *Bacillus* species permits their survival in mixed populations such as those found in foods. Resistance to bacteriophage, lytic factors such as bacteriocins, antibiotics produced by other organisms, lethal radiations, extremes of temperature, germicidal chemicals, and autolytic principles generally is greater in spores than in vegetative cells. Therefore, it is not surprising that spores are detected readily in many foods and ingredients such as starches, dried fruits, vegetables, cereal grains, dried milk, and spices.

18.14   Significance in Foods

Food handling equipment properly designed to eliminate niches wherein bacteria may multiply prevents the problem of the buildup of sporeforming populations during processing. Equipment with pits, crevices, dead ends, open seams, and square corners produces opportunities for bacterial buildup that may lead to deterioration of food even as it is being processed (incipient spoilage), especially when a shutdown extends the dwell time. The terminal thermal processes for low-acid foods in hermetically sealed containers generally provide lethality sufficient to inactivate spores of mesophilic bacteria. However, products that receive a mild thermal process, such as canned, cured meats, may undergo spoilage that is due to *Bacillus* species.[12] Cooling water and equipment surfaces that contact seams or lids on jars immediately following the heat process should be kept clean and as free of organisms as possible.[9]

18.15   Spoilage

Spoilage in thermally processed low-acid foods (pH>4.6) by mesophilic aerobic sporeformers is often characterized by flat sour spoilage in normal-appearing containers. Occasionally, loss of container vacuum or bulging of the container ends occurs because of growth and gas production by strains of either *B. macerans* or *B. polymyxa*. In addition, some *B. licheniformis* strains produce small amounts of gas during spoilage of thermally processed foods, although gas production is not a characteristic reported for *B. licheniformis* in "Bergey's Manual."[5] Failure to carry out the prescribed thermal process, rather than a faulty thermal process design, is commonly responsible for spoilage of commercially processed low-acid foods, since the spores of mesophilic bacteria are usually only moderately resistant to moist heat. $D_{121°C}$ values are frequently of the order of 0.1 min or less. Spores of *B. macerans* or *B. polymyxa* strains commonly have $D_{100°C}$ values from 0.1 to 0.5 min.[21] In contrast, spores of the catalase-negative strains isolated from spoiled cream-style corn are quite resistant when heated in this product with a $D_{121°C}$ value similar to that found for spores of *Clostridium sporogenes* PA 3679.[20]

In some instances, *B. licheniformis*, *B. polymyxa*, *B. subtilis* and, of course, *B. coagulans* (see Chapter 20) have caused spoilage of acid and acidified foods (pH<4.7). Growth of *B. licheniformis*, *B. polymyxa* and *B. coagulans* in acid foods, such as tomatoes, tomato juice, and acidified onions and green peppers, is of concern, because some strains can raise the product pH into the range where growth of *Clostridium botulinum* is possible.[2, 7, 14, 15] Whether this rise in pH is due to the utilization of citric acid by *B. licheniformis* and some strains of *B. coagulans* or the deamination of certain amino acids by members of the *B. polymyxa-macerans* group is not definitely known.

On occasion, mesophilic aerobic sporeformers may be recovered from, or cause spoilage of, acidified foods and fruit drinks, since such products normally receive only a hot-fill-and-hold or pasteurization heat treatment. For example, at least one report has been published of growth of spoilage isolates of *B. polymyxa* and *B. macerans* at as low a pH as 3.8 to 4.0 in sucrose nutrient broth and in canned cling peaches with a sucrose syrup.[23] However, if a food or drink shows normal appearance and odor and no evidence of growth microscopically, the significance of finding viable mesophilic aerobic sporeformers upon culturing is nil since germination of spores and vegetative cell growth in the food is prevented by its acid content. The product is commercially sterile (Chapter 60). In any instance where there is a question, spores of the isolate should be inoculated back into the original product for incubation and confirmation of growth.

18.2   SPECIAL CONSIDERATIONS

18.21   Ropy Bread Spoilage

Food products that do not receive a sporicidal terminal process, such as bakery products (Chapter 55), dried foods, and frozen foods, are not usually susceptible to spoilage by mesophilic aerobic sporeformers unless abused. However, a case study[18] illustrates an exception, the problem of ropy bread, a troublesome defect that can occur in a clean, modern bakery. Breaking or cutting open the spoiled loaf releases a strong odor of decomposed or overripe watermelons.[17] The discolored, softened portions can be drawn out into long threads when teased with forceps or a glass rod.

Mucoid variants of *Bacillus subtilis*, formerly classified as *B. mesentericus* strains, are considered agents of ropy bread spoilage by virtue of endospore resistance to temperatures reached in the centers of loaves where the usual water activity (a_w) is about 0.95.[11] Almost any ingredient used in bread making may contribute "rope spores"; coarse and uncommon flours are reported likely sources.[22]

Good sanitation, modern bakery practices, and preservatives combine to keep rope spoilage under control so that incidents are rare.[11] However, the current trend toward elimination of preservatives in some bakery products increases the potential for this type of spoilage. Under any given conditions of bread production and storage, the higher the rope spore content of the ingredients, the greater the likelihood of the product's becoming ropy.[13] Flour and other ingredients have been tested by a number of methods, but none of the procedures are sufficiently selective or discriminative to enumerate spores of only those organisms that produce ropy bread. A bread-baking and incubation test[22] is most reliable, but is qualitative, not quantitative. A widely used method,[1] a modified version of which is given below (Section 18.62), may be employed to determine presumptive counts of rope spores in flour, yeast, or other ingredients.

18.3   SOURCES OF ERROR

18.31   Mesophilic Aerobic Spores

The dilutions of sample material selected for culture in the given procedure permit enumeration of mesophilic spores in foods that contain relatively few spores and also in materials such as raw spices or soil samples where dense spore populations may occur. However, spore crops prepared in the laboratory will require greater dilution prior to the heating step. Certain strains of *Bacillus* that are considered facultatively thermophilic because they grow at 55° to 65°C are also capable of growth at 35°C.[10] Such organisms should not be counted since sporangia and vegetative cells are killed by the heat shock, and the incubation temperature is below that required for germination of surviving spores. Separate enumeration of (facultatively thermophilic) aciduric flat-sour sporeformers and thermophilic flat-sour sporeformers may be conducted according to methods described in Chapters 20 and 21, respectively.

18.32   Rope Spores

The enumerative techniques for rope spores all detect spores that survive a heat treatment to form colonies or pellicles in media that are neither selective nor differential. Indeterminate error stems from the assumption that all spores thus counted can produce rope. Inoculation of cells from morphologically typical colonies or pellicles into a susceptible bakery product,[22] or stepwise identification of *B. subtilis*, as described below, may be used to confirm presumptive results as occasion demands.

18.4   EQUIPMENT, MATERIALS, AND MEDIA

18.41   Equipment

Thermostatically controlled waterbath, with stirrer, adjusted to 45°C.
Weighted rings that fit 250-ml and 500-ml Erlenmeyer flasks to prevent bobbing and possible upset in bath.
Waterbaths for 80 and 100°C operation.
Incubators rated for operation in the 30° to 35°C temperature range with uniformity of temperature of ±1°C at the extremes of the range.
Microscope, pH meter, blenders.

18.42   Media, Dilution Menstruum (Chapter 62)

18.421   Dilution menstruum

Peptone water diluent (0.1%)

18.422   Culture media

Dextrose tryptone agar
Tryptone glucose extract (TGE) agar

18.5   PROCEDURES

18.51   Mesophilic Aerobic Spores

18.511   Sampling

Sample collection, shipment, and preparation are conducted in conformance with procedures given in Chapter 2. Ingredients need not be sampled routinely except in special cases, e.g., spices or gelatin to be used in pasteurized canned ham or ham products that receive mild heat treatment. The commonly used aerobic colony count (Chapter 4), a portion of which is contributed by aerobic spores, indicates overall "bacteriological quality" of ingredients without resorting to a separate count on mesophilic spores. A similar index of good manufacturing procedures holds true for food processing lines and equipment, where swab or surface contact platings indicate the adequacy of cleaning and other sanitation practices.

A freshly produced, thermally processed product is not likely to contain mesophilic spores or vegetative cells in numbers detectable by usual plating procedures.[16] Consequently, about 24 containers of each code lot should be placed in incubators adjusted to 35°C, where they are held, usually for 14 days. If "flat sour" spoilage is detected, by lowered pH and/or liquefaction in a given sample set held at 35°C, the procedures listed in Chapter 61 should be followed.

18.512   Procedure

Fifty grams of ingredient or food material are weighed in a sterile, tared container and transferred to 450 ml of sterile 0.1% peptone water in a blender jar. Dispersion is accomplished by blending at high speed for 2 min. If a stomacher is used, dispersion requires 30 to 60 sec (Chapter 2).

TGE agar is prepared, 100 ml per 500-ml Erlenmeyer flask. One additional flask of medium is prepared to serve as a sterility control. Sterilization at 121°C moist heat for 15 min is followed by cooling to 45°C in a waterbath. Volumes of blended food are pipetted into a set of 3 flasks of TGE agar while they are held in the bath: 10 ml into the first, 1 ml into the second, and 0.1 ml into the third. Flasks are agitated gently to disperse the blended material throughout the medium.

Flasks are transferred without delay to a stirred water or oil bath adjusted to 80°C and held so that the liquid level is above the sample level in the flasks for 30 min. Flasks are occasionally agitated gently to assist heat distribution. Cooling is done in tepid tap water, taking care that the temperature does not fall to the point where agar congeals. Flasks are transferred to the 45°C bath following the rapid cooling step and held there for a period not to exceed 10 min. The 100-ml volume in each flask, representing test material and sterility control, is poured into a set of 5 sterile plates in approximately equal volumes, i.e., about 20 ml per plate. When the agar has solidified, plates are inverted in the 35°C incubator and allowed to incubate 48 hr.

Counts are made of surface and subsurface colonies. The sum of colonies on the set of 5 plates poured from TGE agar containing 10 ml of blended sample represents the number of aerobic mesophilic spores per gram. Similarly, the number of colonies in sets of plates receiving 1.0 and 0.1 ml of blended sample is equal to 0.1 and 0.01 of the number of spores per g and must be multiplied by 10 and 100, respectively, to calcuate the count per g.

The number of spores that can be enumerated by this method ranges from 1 to 150,000 spores per g.

18.52   Rope-producing spores

18.521   Sampling

Sampling, collection, shipment, and preparation are conducted as directed in Chapter 2.

18.522   Procedure

Fifty grams of flour or other ingredient are weighed in a tared, sterile container and transferred to 450 ml of sterile 0.1% peptone water in a blender jar. Dispersion is achieved by blending at high speed for 2 min. If a stomacher is used, mixing is done for 30 to 60 sec (Chapter 2).

Ten- and one-ml volumes of the peptone water suspension are pipetted into separate 100-ml portions of melted dextrose tryptone agar contained in 250-ml Erlenmeyer flasks and held at about 45°C. The flasks, and an additional uninoculated control flask, are submerged in a boiling waterbath so that bath water level is above the liquid level in the flasks. Contents are gently swirled from time to time as the internal temperature climbs to about 94°C at the end of 5 min heating. An additional 15 min in the boiling waterbath is required during which time the temperature should hold between 94° and 100°C.

After heating, cool the contents of the flask in tepid water to about 45°C, taking care that the agar does not lump, and pour contents of each flask into 5 sterile plates in approximately equal volumes. When the agar has solidified, invert the plates and incubate them at 35°C for 48 hr.

Count as rope-producing organisms the surface colonies that are grey-white, vesicle-like, becoming at first drier and finally wrinkled. Add to this count any subsurface colonies that display stringiness when tested. The total colonies on the set of 5 plates from the flask that received 10 ml suspension is considered as rope spores per g. The sum of colonies on plates representing the 1.0-ml volume of suspension is multiplied by 10 to get the number of rope spores per g of sample. The concentrations of spores enumerated by this method range from 1 to 15,000 per g.

When required, *B. subtilis* may be identified by conducting the following tests: catalase; acetoin production; nitrate reduction; utilization of citrate; growth in 7% NaCl; acid from glucose, arabinose, xylose, and mannitol; growth at pH 5.7; and hydrolysis of starch, casein, and gelatin (see USDA Handbook "The Genus *Bacillus*"[8] for media and procedures). Positive results should be obtained for each test. Additionally, the isolate should be examined microscopically for morphology, gram-stain reaction, and the presence of ellipsoidal or cylindrical spores that do not produce a distinct swelling of the sporangium.[5, 8]

18.6 MODIFICATIONS

18.61 Rope Spore Count

The method given is essentially that of the AACC,[1] modified as follows: (1) the analytical sample weight was increased from 20 g to 50 g; (2) the 24-hr examination of incubating plates and "drawing" subsurface colonies to the surface were deleted; (3) subsurface colonies displaying stringiness are added to the count of surface colonies displaying typical characteristics; and (4) peptone water diluent was substituted for Butterfield's buffered phosphate diluent.

18.62 Mesophilic Aerobic Spore Count

The method given is basically that of the National Food Processors Association (NFPA) for enumeration of thermophilic spores in starch.[16] Modifications consisted of (1) an increase in analytical sample weight from 20 g to 50 g; (2) a reduction in heat stimulation from 10 min at 108°C (autoclave) to 10 min at 80°C, excluding equilibration time (waterbath); (3) a reduction in incubation temperature to 35°C from 55°C; and (4) a change in dilution procedure to increase the enumeration limit to 150,000 spores per g.

The heating step was considered critical to reproducibility and efficiency of recovery because treatments stimulatory to some spores in a mixed, natural population are lethal to others. The method described above was used to test a variety of dry foods and soils. A family of curves reflecting the recovery of spores naturally occurring in mixed populations is presented in Figure 1. Results were similar at all temperatures in that no net stimulatory effect was observed. Heating at 90°C caused a reduction in spores recovered during the 19-min equilibration period. Somewhat greater spore inactivation was experienced during the 24-min temperature rise to 100°C.

The 80°C heat treatment was selected to provide minimum loss of endospore viability while ensuring death of vegetative cells. Fungal spores that may have been present in the samples examined did not produce colonies even after the 70°C heat treatment. While ascospores of *Byssochlamys fulva* (Chapter 17) and other molds that produce relatively heat-resistant spores are expected to survive the 80°C heat treatment, subsequent growth in TGE agar in competition with *Bacillus* species is unlikely.

18.7 INTERPRETATION

18.71 Rope Spore Count

The range in which rope-producing spores are estimated in the above procedure, assuming that 300 colonies per pour plate are countable, is 1 to 15,000 per g. Additional decimal dilutions prior to the boiling water step may be introduced to extend the upper limit of enumeration.

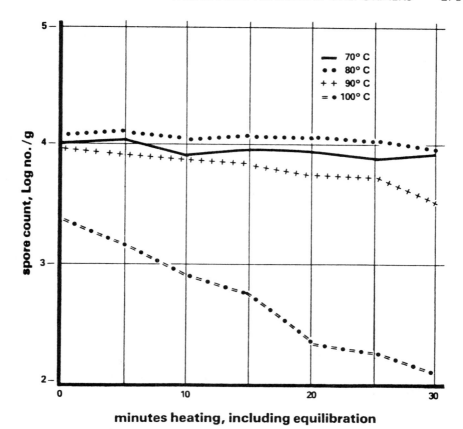

Figure 1—Survival of a mixed population of mesophilic aerobic spores occurring in Chili powder. Initial temperature = 47°C. Average equilibration time at 70°C = 18 min; 80°C = 18 min; 90°C = 19 min; 100°C = 24 min. Heating menstruum was tryptone glucose extract agar, which also served as recovery medium.

Negative results are significant if a suitable control plating established that the recovery medium supports growth of *B. subtilis.*

Positive results should be interpreted following confirmatory inoculation tests or stepwise identification of *B. subtilis.* Counts must be interpreted in accordance with the requirements of bakeries or other food processors, whose acceptance specifications vary.

18.72   Mesophilic Aerobic Spores

Elevated counts in ingredients to be used in low-acid products (pH>4.6) that undergo a mild heat process, such as canned pasteurized luncheon meats or canned cured hams, may result in spoilage if mishandling occurs in marketing channels or by consumers. Otherwise the mesophilic spore count is of little significance to the processor. A report of spoilage in commercially canned fruit and fruit products because of *B. macerans* or *B. polymyxa* left open the question of whether underprocessing or post-process recontamination was at fault.[23] The presence of mesophilic aerobic spores in frozen or dried foods is innocuous provided mishandling does not result in large populations of *Bacillus cereus* (Chapter 35).

18.8   REFERENCES

1. AACC. 1983. "Approved Methods of the American Association of Cereal Chemists," 8th ed. Am. Assn. Cereal Chem., St. Paul, Minn.
2. Anderson, R. E. 1984. Growth and corresponding elevation of tomato juice pH by *Bacillus coagulans*. J. Food Sci. 49: 647.
3. Cameron, E. J. and Esty, J. R. 1926. The examination of spoiled foods. II. Classification of flat sour spoilage organisms from nonacid foods. J. Infect. Dis. 39: 89.
4. Charney, J., Fisher, W. P., and Hegarty, C. P. 1951. Manganese as an essential element for sporulation in the genus *Bacillus*. J. Bacteriol. 62: 145.
5. Claus, D. and Berkeley, R. C. W. 1986. Genus *Bacillus* Cohn 1872. In "Bergey's Manual of Systematic Bacteriology," ed. P.H.A. Sneath, N.S. Mair, and M.E. Sharpe, Vol. 2, p. 1105. Williams and Wilkens, Baltimore, Md.
6. Doores, S. and Westhoff, D. 1981. Heat resistance of *Sporolactobacillus inulinus*. J. Food Sci. 46: 810.
7. Fields, M. L., Zamora, A. F., and Bradsher, M. 1977. Microbiological analysis of home-canned tomatoes and green beans. J. Food Sci. 42: 931.
8. Gordon, R. E., Haynes, W. C., and Pang, C. Hor-Nay. 1973. "The Genus *Bacillus*." USDA Agriculture Handbook No. 427. U.S. Dept. of Agric., Washington, D.C.
9. Graves, R. R., Lesniewski, R. S., and Lake, D. E. 1977. Bacteriological quality of cannery cooling water. J. Food Sci. 42: 1280.
10. Harris, O. and Fields, M. L. 1972. A study of thermophilic, aerobic, sporeforming bacteria isolated from soil and water. Can. J. Microbiol. 18: 917.
11. ICMSF. 1980. Microbial ecology of foods," Vol. 2, "Food Commodities." Interntl. Comm. Microbiol. Spec. for Foods. Academic Press, New York.
12. Jensen, L. B. 1954. "Microbiology of Meats," 3rd. ed. Garrard Press, Champaign, Ill.
13. Kent-Jones, D. W. and Amos, A. J. 1967. "Modern Cereal Chemistry," 6th ed. Food Trade Press, London, England.
14. Montville, T. J. 1982. Metabolic effect of *Bacillus licheniformis* on *Clostridium botulinum*: Implications for home-canned tomatoes. Appl. Environ. Microbiol. 44: 334.
15. Montville, T. J. and Sapers, G. M. 1981. Thermal resistance of spores from pH elevating strains of *Bacillus licheniformis*. J. Food Sci. 46: 1710.
16. NCA. 1968. "Laboratory manual for food canners and processors," Vol. 1, "Microbiology and Processing," 3rd ed. Natl. Canners Assn. AVI Publishing Co., Westport, Conn.
17. Pyler, E. J. 1973. "Baking Science and Technology." Siebel Press, Chicago, Ill.
18. Raffaele, F. 1981. Case histories in sanitation. Case no. 17: Rope in bread. Dairy Food San. 1: 302.
19. Richmond, B. and Fields, M. L. 1966. Distribution of thermophilic aerobic sporeforming bacteria in food ingredients. Appl. Microbiol. 14: 623.
20. Segner, W. P. 1979. Mesophilic aerobic sporeforming bacteria in the spoilage of low-acid canned foods. Food Technol. 33: 55.
21. Stumbo, C. R. 1973. "Thermobacteriology in Food Processing," 2nd ed. Academic Press, New York.
22. Tanner, F. W. 1944. "The Microbiology of Foods," 2nd ed. Garrard Press, Champaign, Ill.
23. Vaughn, R. H., Kruelevitch, I. H., and Mercer, W. A. 1952. Spoilage of canned foods caused by the *Bacillus macerans-polymyxa* group of bacteria. Food Res. 17: 560.

Chapter 19

MESOPHILIC ANAEROBIC SPOREFORMERS

Donald E. Lake, Dane T. Bernard, and Donald A. Kautter

19.1 INTRODUCTION

The mesophilic sporeforming anaerobes all belong to the genus *Clostridium*, and those of greatest interest in foods fall into two main groups. One group consists of (a) *C. sporogenes* and other relatively heat resistant putrefactive anaerobes, and (b) the proteolytic and the nonproteolytic strains of *C. botulinum*. The other group consists of *C. perfringens* and a variety of other similar clostridia, such as the butyric anaerobes, that are relatively nonresistant to heat. Only general methodology for the mesophilic sporeforming anaerobes will be considered here, since methods for detecting *C. botulinum* are treated in Chapter 36 and *C. perfringens* in Chapter 37.

Mesophilic sporeforming anaerobes are rather large, gram-positive rods measuring from 0.4 to 1.0 by 3.0 to 15.0 micrometers (μm). Motility is characteristic of most species. Although considered to be strict anaerobes, some strains are able to grow in the presence of relatively high levels of oxygen.[22, 28]

These anaerobes are distributed widely in nature. They are found in the soil, and therefore may be normal contaminants of vegetables at the time of harvest.[14, 30] Some species commonly are found in the intestinal tracts and excreta of animals, and hence may become contaminants of milk and meat.[14] Others are found in fish, shellfish, and aquatic environments.

The various species of clostridia are basically either proteolytic (putrefactive) or nonproteolytic, although a few may show strain differences. Since this property relates to their significance in food spoilage, they will be separated into these two groups for the purpose of further discussion.

19.11 Proteolytic (Putrefactive) Anaerobes

All mesophilic sporeforming anaerobes that digest proteins such as coagulated egg white, coagulated serum, or coagulated milk or blacken and digest brain or meat media with a putrid odor will be grouped together as proteolytic anaerobes and called by the more common term, putrefactive anaerobes.

These organisms are capable of decomposing proteins, peptides, or amino acids anaerobically with resulting foul-smelling sulfur-containing products such as hydrogen sulfide, methyl and ethyl sulfide, and mercaptans. Ammonia and amines, putrescine and cadaverine, usually are produced along with indole and skatole as well as carbon dioxide and hydrogen.[10, 14] They will grow within an approximate temperature range of 10° to 50°C, with the exception of *C. putrefaciens*, which will grow from 0° to 30°C. This growth range covers the normal storage temperature of canned and other processed foods, including the refrigerated storage of cured meats.

The spores of putrefactive anaerobes in general have high heat resistance and are the organisms most often associated with underprocessing spoilage of low-acid canned foods. A number of species have been isolated from canned food spoilage having an original pH above 4.8, but the cans had been underprocessed. These organisms include *C. sporogenes*, *C. bifermentans*, *C. putrefaciens*, *C. histolyticum*, *C. botulinum* types A and B, and the closely related nontoxic organism identified as PA 3679.[10, 13, 14, 32]

Since putrefactive anaerobes will not grow in foods with a pH of less than 4.6, testing such foods for the presence of these organisms is not necessary.

19.12 Nonproteolytic Anaerobes

Mesophilic sporeforming anaerobes that do not digest protein and therefore do not produce the putrid growth end-products typical of the putrefactive anaerobes will be grouped as nonproteolytic anaerobes. These anaerobes have essentially the same characteristics as the putrefactive anaerobes with a few notable exceptions. Some nonproteolytic anaerobes such as strains of *C. botulinum* (Chapter 36) can germinate and grow at refrigeration temperatures. The spores of these anaerobes have low heat resistance compared to the putrefactive anaerobes, and generally will not survive even minimal retort processing. Therefore, they usually are not encountered in underprocessing spoilage of low-acid canned foods. The isolation of nonproteolytic anaerobes from spoilage in these foods is more likely to be an indication of postprocessing contamination as the cause of spoilage rather than underprocessing. This situation, however, is seldom encountered. When this does occur, poor sanitation of the post-processing can-handling lines is suspected since the primary cause of this type of spoilage is physical abuse of wet containers following processing.[6, 29] The quality of the can cooling water also should be questioned; however, spores of anaerobes are found infrequently in cooling water, and if found, generally are present in very low numbers.[12, 27]

The butyric anaerobes are exemplified by *C. butyricum* and *C. pasteurianum*. Because of their unique characteristics as well as their ability to cause large economic losses in certain canned foods, they will be discussed separately. The butyric anaerobes are capable of sporulation and growth at a pH of 4.35 and above,[1, 35] and consequently are of spoilage significance in non-pressure processed acid foods such as tomatoes and certain fruits, particularly if the pH is above 4.3. The pH of these products normally is below 4.35, and under these circumstances spoilage by butyric anaerobes is seldom a problem. However, because of a number of factors such as fruit variety, growing conditions, etc., the pH of the product may exceed 4.3 and be subject to this type of spoilage. In those cases where the acidity of these products is too low, spoilage by butyric anaerobes may be controlled by acidification of the product, or increasing the thermal process. Growth of these organisms in such products is characterized by a butyric acid odor and the production of hydrogen. These organisms are also of spoilage significance in underprocessing of these foods, and occasionally in low-acid foods as well. Although not considered to be toxigenic, a strain of *C. butyricum* that produces a toxin that can be neutralized by *C. botulinum* type E antitoxin has been isolated.[21] This strain has not been associated with any food products.

19.13   Spoilage in Food

Because of the high heat resistance of many strains of mesophilic sporeforming anaerobes plus their ability to grow in the absence of oxygen and a growth range that covers the temperature of the normal storage of canned and other processed foods, including the refrigerated storage of cured meats, these anaerobes are of primary importance in the spoilage of low-acid foods packed in hermetically sealed containers.

The spores of mesophilic anaerobes germinate and grow readily in low-acid foods having pH values of 6.0 or higher, with irregular spoilage patterns occurring in inoculated packs of low-acid foods having a pH value as low as 5.5.[31] Cameron and Esty[7] noted that putrefactive anaerobes may show abnormal development resulting in nongaseous spoilage in low-acid products in the range of pH 4.6 to 5.0. Mesophilic anaerobes may cause spoilage in any canned food having a pH of 4.8 or above (the lowest pH at which *C. botulinum* spores have been observed to germinate and grow in commercial food products) if the spores are not destroyed by the thermal process to which the canned foods have been subjected, or if they gain access through container leakage after processing.

Because of the public health significance of their toxins, all types of *C. botulinum* (Chapter 36) are the most important anaerobes to control in food processing. However, the spores of many of the nontoxic species are much more heat resistant than those of *C. botulinum*, and although these nontoxic strains are not a hazard to health, they can result in severe economic losses through spoilage if not controlled by adequate thermal processing. As an illustration of their relative heat resistance, the $D_{121}°C$ of proteolytic *C. botulinum* spores of Types A and B ranges from 0.10 to 0.20 min, while that of PA 3679 ranges from 0.50 to 1.50 min.[32] Thus, adequate thermal processing to control the greatest economic hazard to the canning industry also would control the greatest health hazard.

Because of the lack of anaerobic conditions in most equipment in food processing plants, except for the dead ends of pipes, porous surfaces, etc., conditions are not conducive to the growth and sporulation of anaerobes, and thus areas of heavy buildup seldom occur.

However, when this does occur, understerilization spoilage can result because of the very heavy load of spores in the product. The spoilage pattern within the affected lots is often spotty and scattered, more typical of post-processing spoilage that is due to container leakage than of the pattern expected from sporeformers that survive a thermal process. Thermal processing records and other canning parameters usually give no indications of any irregularities. In most cases the problem can be identified only by investigation at the cannery, including a bacteriological survey, plus the absence of demonstrable leakage and can defects in the spoiled containers.

The recovery in pure culture of mesophilic anaerobic sporeformers from putrid swelled cans is the classic condition encountered in underprocessing spoilage of low-acid canned foods. In rare instances spoilage of canned foods by these organisms may be the result of post-processing contamination, and the microflora observed can be a mixed culture, mesophilic anaerobic sporeformers in pure culture, or a combination of both.[19] Therefore, it is critical in the diagnosis of canned food spoilage that cannery thermal processing data, results of can leakage tests using recommended laboratory test procedures,[36] and any other information relative to the spoilage outbreak be a part of the decision-making process.[24]

It is not possible with our present knowledge to make an unqualified statement of the significance of numbers or presence of mesophilic anaerobe spores in ingredients or at any step in a food processing operation. It must be remembered also that heat processes for low-acid commercially canned foods are designed to destroy an average load of putrefactive anaerobe spores. Thus, to be significant, the spore count would have to be extremely large or consist of a population of extremely resistant spores.

Underprocessing spoilage is of primary concern because it presents the danger of toxin production by *C. botulinum*. However, three outbreaks of botulism from food canned in the United States have occurred in which defective cans resulted in post-processing contamination of fish products with Type E *C. botulinum*.[4, 15, 26, 34]

Although spoilage by mesophilic sporeforming anaerobes usually occurs in low-acid foods packed in hermetically sealed and thermally processed containers, these organisms must be considered a potential problem in spoilage of any low-acid food that fulfills the necessary growth requirements for these organisms, particularly anaerobiosis. As an example, such conditions can be present in fresh produce marketed with plastic film overwrap or plastic bags. The oxygen present in such packages is usually insufficient to inhibit the growth of some of the clostridia since certain strains are relatively oxygen tolerant.[23, 28] Under mesophilic storage temperatures, growth of these organisms is possible in nonventilated packages. It has been shown that *C. botu-*

linum is capable of reproducing and forming toxin in mushrooms wrapped in nonventilated polyvinylchloride film.[18, 33] The use of perforated film prevents the growth of these organisms.

Other food products, which may or may not be thermally processed, rely on artificial acidification or reduced water activity to prevent spoilage. These products are covered by the Food and Drug Administration's Good Manufacturing Practices regulations (foods with a_w of less than 0.85 are exempted).[8] Properly prepared, these foods will not support the growth of mesophilic sporeforming anaerobes. If bacteriological examination of these foods is made, caution should be exercised in interpreting the results of anaerobic cultures if the usual culture media are employed. These cultures may show positive growth of mesophilic sporeforming anaerobes, but this is the result of removing the spores from an inhibitory environment into one favorable to germination and growth. Consequently, isolation of these bacteria in this situation is of no significance, unless they are present in large numbers. The same holds true for other foods such as cured meats that employ preservatives or other ingredients to retard spoilage.

Other potential sources of contamination with mesophilic sporeforming anaerobes include spices, cereals and cereal products, dried eggs, dried milk and milk products, dried vegetables (onions and garlic),[5] and rendered tallow. In general, no microbiological standards exist by which the suitability of these ingredients may be evaluated, but since they are often substantial contributors to the microbial flora and, at the same time, pose special problems in handling for analysis, specific procedures will be described for their preparation.

19.2 GENERAL CONSIDERATIONS

It is sometimes desirable to have an estimate of the total number of mesophilic sporeforming anaerobes in a food material or ingredient. However, there is probably no way in which such an estimate can completely represent the total number present. Methods in use inevitably favor one group of anaerobes or the other of the total possible flora. For example, if an estimate of the proteolytic clostridia is desired, it is usual to heat-shock for maximum germination of the spores, but such treatment is destructive of the spores of most nonproteolytic clostridia (such as those of *C. botulinum* Type E—Chapter 36). If, on the other hand, ethanol treatment[16] is used to destroy other contaminating nonsporulating organisms, a more accurate estimate of the nonproteolytic clostridia will be obtained, but this does not provide for maximal germination and outgrowth of proteolytic strains. Thus, in either case, the total count will be in error by the failure of some clostridia to grow. Furthermore, neither method will destroy the spores of aerobic bacilli (Chapter 18), many of which are facultative anaerobes and inevitably will be counted along with the strict anaerobes. The same, of course, is also true with respect to both clostridia and facultative aerobic sporeformers that are also facultative thermophiles,[2] so that aerobes and facultative thermophiles also may be counted by any method designed for the enumeration of mesophilic anaerobes. An additional complication arises if the total microflora capable of surviving either treatment contain bacteriocin or antibiotic-producing organisms and, at the same time, strains sensitive to these agents.[17]

Given these limitations, it is best to choose a procedure most likely to give a reasonable estimate of the groups expected to be present in a particular food, since it is likely that only when spore stocks of pure cultures are being counted can estimates be made with any degree of certainty.

Several methods are used for counting mesophilic anaerobes. Most probable number (MPN) methods (Chapter 6) seem to be the most widely used, and generally give more reproducible results with higher counts on pure cultures than other methods. Colony counts in prickett tubes and anaerobic petri dishes also have had considerable use. Methods that incorporate the inoculum into melted agar with the production of deep colonies, as in pour plates or prickett tubes, often have the handicap that gas production concomitant with the development of colonies splits the agar and renders accurate counting of well developed colonies impossible unless a very short incubation period is used. Such counts are subject to the possible further inaccuracy that slow growing colonies may not be counted at all. Counts made by spreading the inoculum over the surface of a solid agar medium may show too much variation between replicates to be reliable, although the use of pre-reduced agar may solve this problem. Details of these methods will be found in Section 19.5.

Although oxygen will not affect the viability of dormant spores of anaerobes, care must be taken, nevertheless, to exclude oxygen from culture media at the time of use. Vegetative cells of these organisms are especially sensitive to the lethal effects of oxygen, particularly at the stages of germination and outgrowth. The simplest procedure for oxygen removal is to boil or steam the medium for 10 to 20 min and quickly cool it just prior to use. Similarly, care must be taken when mixing the spore inoculum into molten agar or other liquid media to avoid the reincorporation of more oxygen.

Stress-damaged spores may also require special consideration. If, as a consequence of heat treatment or the use of other lethal agents, it is desired to know how many spores have survived, prolonged incubation may be necessary. The recovery of viable spores from the damage done them by the stressing agent may require weeks or months in a rich culture medium.

19.3   EQUIPMENT, MATERIALS, AND SOLUTIONS

19.31   Equipment

Culture tubes, either clip top or screw cap, for liquid media
Prickett tubes

Petri dishes
Veillon tubes
Serological pipettes
Quebec colony counter or similar device
Anaerobic jar (Gaspak, Case, or similar jar)
Incubator set at 30° to 35°C
Transfer loops
Sterile swabs
Sterile knives and spoons
10-ml water blanks in screw-cap tubes
Sterile water collection bottles—250-ml screw cap
Sterile plastic bags

19.32 Media

Andersen's pork pea agar
Trypticase peptone glucose yeast extract broth
Tryptose cycloserine dextrose agar
Orange serum agar
Thermoacidurans agar
PE-2 medium
Liver broth
Beef heart infusion broth
Thioglycollate agar

19.4   PRECAUTIONS

Whenever spoiled low-acid canned foods are examined to determine the cause of spoilage, the possibility exists that this spoilage may be due to the growth of mesophilic sporeforming anaerobes. One must assume that the causative organism could be *C. botulinum*. Therefore, extreme care should be taken in handling the spoiled food if it has a putrid odor or typical clostridial forms are observed in direct smears of the food prior to culturing. In such cases the food should be sufficiently heated in the container to destroy botulinal toxin before disposal. The amount of heat will vary according to the size of the container and the nature of the product. It is strongly recommended that all persons who handle spoiled canned food routinely in the laboratory be immunized with antibotulinal toxoid.

19.5   PROCEDURES

Chapter 61 describes the procedures to be used for the examination of canned foods for various types of bacteria, including mesophilic sporeforming anaerobes; therefore, this subject is not covered in detail here.

Sometimes it may be desirable to identify the source of the mesophilic sporeforming anaerobes if they have been implicated in canned food spoilage. This may be determined by a bacteriological survey of the cannery and by examination of ingredients that had been used in the preparation of the food.

19.51   Plant Survey

The survey can be accomplished best by collecting canned samples at the closing machine before the heat process and culturing for putrefactive anaerobes. If putrefactive anaerobic spores are found in relatively high numbers, it may be advantageous to collect product samples at key points along the canning line. Samples should be collected from the washed or blanched product, from the filler, and finally from closed, but unprocessed, containers. Formulated product samples should be collected from mixing tanks, from filler bowls, and from closed but unprocessed cans.

Equipment samples (swabs or scrapings) should be collected from apparent hard-to-clean areas and places that show visible buildup of food. Examples of typical problem areas are pumps, dead ends of pipes, frayed or worn conveyor belts, and wooden equipment.

All product samples should be examined immediately after collection at the cannery. However, if they must be transported to a laboratory for examination, the samples should be heated for 20 to 30 min at 100°C and cooled before being transported under refrigeration to the laboratory. These heated samples should be cultured the same day that they are collected.

Swab samples from equipment and scrapings or splinters from wooden or other porous materials that have been placed in 10-ml water blanks are heated for 20 to 30 min at 100°C and cooled.

The line samples collected in sealable plastic bags are weighed, and an equal weight of sterile water is added. This will approximate the product brine ratio of most canned vegetables. The samples are mixed thoroughly after sealing the bag securely. Half-fill 25 × 200-mm screw-cap tubes with the liquid. Heat in flowing steam for 20 to 30 min at 100°C. Samples of formulated products are diluted with an equal weight of sterile water to facilitate handling. After mixing, half-fill 25 × 200-mm screw-cap tubes with the diluted product and either heat at 100°C for 20 to 30 min or pipette portions of the unheated sample into anaerobic medium of choice and then heat as above.

The unprocessed cans collected at the closing machine are opened aseptically, and portions of brine are poured into sterile 25 × 200-mm screw-cap tubes, or portions of formulated product are pipetted into the medium of choice; these samples are heated for 20 to 30 min at 100°C.

If an autoclave is available at the cannery where the samples are collected, the samples may be heated for 10 min at 5 psi (108.4°C) rather than at 100°C.

When canned food spoilage has been determined to be caused by mesophilic anaerobic sporeformers that entered the container through leakage following thermal processing, a microbiological survey of the post-processing can-handling lines will be helpful in identifying the areas of contamination. Sterile cotton swabs moistened with diluent (sterile distilled water containing 60 ppm sodium thiosulfate to inactivate residual halogen) are used to swab 8 in² of sample area. The swab samples are placed in 10 ml of diluent in an 18 × 150-mm screw-cap tube. A 150-ml sample of can cooling water should also be obtained for examination. Collect the sample in a sterile bottle and add 1.1 ml of sterile 3% sodium thiosulfate. All samples may be held refrigerated for up to 30 hr prior to culturing.[11] They should be heat activated at 71°C for 10 min[20] when cultured.

19.52 Ingredient Examination

For the preparation of foods or ingredients other than those specifically mentioned in succeeding paragraphs, some judgment will have to be used. Samples should be collected in sterile plastic bags, and, if collection utensils are needed, these should be sterile also.

1. Sugar

Weigh 20 g of granulated sugar or 30 g of liquid sugar (approximately 67° Brix) into sterile 250 ml Erlenmeyer flasks and add sterile water to make 100 ml samples. Shake the flasks until the sugar is in solution. Heat the samples rapidly to boiling and hold at boiling for 5 min before chilling rapidly to room temperature.[25]

2. Starch, flour, and other cereal products

Weigh 11 g of the product into a sterile 250-ml Erlenmeyer flask and add 99 ml of sterile cool water. Shake until the sample is in suspension. Do not heat before culturing.[5] (Samples are heated after subculturing.)

3. Dehydrated vegetables

Weigh 10 g of dehydrated vegetable into a sterile 250 ml Erlenmeyer flask and add 190-ml of sterile water. Rehydrate for 30 min at refrigerator temperature. Then shake vigorously for 2 to 3 min. Heat the sample for 10 min at 5 psi (108°C) and cool to room temperature. Samples may be heated for 20 to 30 min at 100°C and then cooled.[5]

4. Rendered tallow

Place 11 g in a sterile 250-ml Erlenmeyer flask and add 99 ml of sterile water. Heat to boiling and hold for 5 min. Samples must be held at 45° to 50°C and shaken vigorously just prior to culturing.[1]

5. Spices

The weight of the spice sample to be examined will depend on the type of spice to be examined. Weigh 10 g of whole spice, 2 g of bulk spice, or 1 g of ground spice into a sterile 250-ml Erlenmeyer flask; add sterile water to make 100 ml. Shake vigorously and boil for 5 min. Allow coarse particles to settle out before culturing or making dilutions for culturing.[5]

6. Dried Eggs

Weigh 11 g of dried eggs into dilution bottles containing 99 ml of sterile water or saline and glass beads. Shake the samples vigorously until all lumps of dried eggs have been dispersed. Do not heat the sample before culturing.[1, 5]

19.53   Culture Methods

Samples obtained from the plant survey, which include swab or scraping samples and product samples, are placed in broth cultures freshly heated and quickly cooled to exclude dissolved oxyen. Usually, 1-ml and 0.1-ml portions of these samples are cultured.[1, 5, 25] These cultures are stratified with either sterile Vaseline or 2% agar, depending on the medium used, before incubation. If PE-2 medium[9] is used, stratification is not necessary. The prepared samples of heated sugar, dehydrated vegetables, rendered tallow, and spices are cultured by taking 20-ml portions of these heated ingredients and dividing equally among 6 tubes of freshly heated culture medium. These are handled in the same manner as the survey samples.

These cultures are incubated at 30° to 35°C for 72 hr. Although most of these organisms will show growth within 2 or 3 days in those tubes in which it can be expected, it is sometimes desirable to incubate for 7 days since some spores may be slow in germinating and growing out. The presence or absence of putrefactive anaerobic spores may be detected by this method.

Twenty milliliter portions of the unheated starch, flour, or cereal products and dried egg samples are distributed among 6 tubes of culture medium. These tubes are heated at 100°C for 20 min. The cultures must be agitated several times during this heating period. After heating, the infusion tubes must be stratified with sterile 2% agar. The cultures are incubated for 72 hr at 30° to 35°C and examined for the growth of putrefactive anaerobes.

19.54   Enumeration of Mesophilic Anaerobic Spores

If counts of mesophilic anaerobic spores are desired on a food product or ingredient, several methods are in current use.

19.541   Enumeration by the MPN method

For the general procedure, see Chapter 6. Serial dilutions may be made in distilled water, saline solution, or culture medium. Preparation of dilutions in the culture medium used for detecting growth has the advantage of minimizing any effect of the inoculum on the nutrients in the final culture. Generally, 3 culture tubes for each dilution will give sufficient accuracy, but if greater precision is needed, 5 or more tubes may be used. From each dilution inoculate 1.0 ml or 0.1 ml into the number of tubes chosen. Incubate the inoculated cultures at 30° to 35°C. Record the number of tubes of each dilution showing growth and refer to the appropriate MPN table for the number of tubes per dilution and the size of the inoculum (1.0 ml or 0.1 ml) to determine the count of viable spores per g or ml of the product. Although most mesophilic sporeforming anaerobes will show growth within 2 or 3 days in all cultures in which it can be expected, the final reading should be made in 1 to 3 weeks because of slow germination, particularly if coming out of an inhibitory environment.

19.542   Enumeration by the prickett tube method

Prickett tubes are deep, flattened oval tubes with a cylindrical neck.[23] The tubes are filled nearly to the neck with agar medium and autoclaved to sterilize. If tubes of sterile agar are stored between preparation and inoculation, melt the agar, and heat in flowing steam or boiling water 10 to 15 min to drive off dissolved oxygen just before use. Cool quickly to 42° to 45°C and inoculate with serial dilutions of the material being examined after preparing as described in Chapter 4. Distribute the inoculum uniformly throughout the medium by swirling the melted agar, taking care not to reincorporate oxyen. Cool and solidify the agar quickly by immersing in cold water, and stratify a layer of thioglycolate agar or sterile petroleum jelly over the surface to fill the neck of the tube partially to aid in maintaining anaerobic conditions during the incubation period. At the end of the incubation period, count the colonies and average the counts for replicate tubes. Calculate the number of viable spores per g from the count and dilution factor. Counts may be made with the aid of a Quebec colony counter or similar grid. Counts should be made before the gas generated by the growth of the colonies has caused splitting and blowing of the agar. Record the temperature and time of the incubation period, normally 48 to 72 hr at 30° to 35°C.

19.543   Isolation of colonies

If colonies are to be isolated from the tubes used for counts, veillon tubes[37] may be substituted for prickett tubes and the counts made in a similar manner. After colonies have been counted, the veillon tubes, which are made of cylindrical glass tubing plugged at one end with a rubber stopper and at the other with cotton, are aseptically opened at both ends, the agar pushed out onto a sterile surface, and material fished from isolated colonies with a loop.

19.544   Enumeration by the plate count method

Prepare samples and dilutions (Chapter 4) and inoculate duplicate plates of agar medium with 0.1 ml of each of the appropriate dilutions of the food material, using a sterile 1.0 ml serological pipette. Spread the inoculum uniformly over the surface of the agar with a sterile bent glass rod. It is important that the surface of the agar medium be relatively dry to prevent spreading growth, which frequently results from excessive moisture. Freshly poured plates, with their lids on, should be left at room temperature overnight before being inoculated. Older plates, after storage under refrigeration, should be allowed to temperature equilibrate at room temperature for at least 1 hr before inoculating.

Incubate the inoculated plates at 30 to 35°C for 2 days in an anaerobic atmosphere such as that produced by the BBL Gaspak system or a Case jar, evacuated and refilled with nitrogen. For the latter, the jar should be flushed three times with nitrogen by drawing a vacuum and flushing before finally refilling with nitrogen the fourth time.

Count all colonies, multiply by the dilution factor, and report as anaerobic sporeformers per g of food if the samples were heated or alcohol treated.

Pour plates can be prepared by placing the inoculum in the petri dish and pouring with Andersen's agar.[3] This is overlaid with a heavy layer of thioglycolate agar (Chapter 62) and the plates incubated at 32°C for 5 to 6 days.[5] Count and report as for surface inoculated plate.

Plating is the least reliable method of counting mesophilic sporeforming anaerobes. It is not uncommon to find wide variations in the numbers of colonies developing on replicate plates of the same dilution, and when pour plates are used, the production of gas bubbles by subsurface colonies frequently causes separation of the agar, thereby complicating their enumeration.

19.545   Media

For culturing sugar, starch, flour, and other cereal products, dehydrated vegetables, rendered tallow, spices, or dried eggs as described in 19.52, use liver broth, beef heart infusion broth, or PE-2 medium.[10] For other food samples, liver broth, PE-2, or trypticase peptone glucose yeast (TPGY) extract broth may be used. In order to insure anaerobic conditions during incubation, broth cultures should be stratified with sterile petroleum jelly. If tubed solid or semisolid media are used, sterile 2% agar may be substituted. Stratification is not necessary with PE-2. For enumerating mesophilic anaerobic spores, other media are recommended.

Although several media for enumerating mesophilic anaerobic spores are available, experience in a number of laboratories has shown that TPGY and Andersen's agar[3] are the media of choice for recovering spores that have received a high heat treatment such as in thermal death time (TDT) determinations. Therefore, they are suggested for use in pure culture work. The effectiveness of these media is enhanced by the addition of filter sterilized sodium bicarbonate (0.14%) and sterile sodium thioglycolate (0.1%) to the tempered media just prior to use. These media have the advantage of being clear so that growth may be readily detected visually. If the medium has not been freshly sterilized, it is important to steam it at 100°C for 10 to 15 min to drive off dissolved oxygen shortly before inoculating. It is also important to cool the tubes quickly by partial immersion in tempered water to avoid reabsorption of oxygen. Fifteen g of agar per L are used in the medium if it is to be used as a solid medium.

For enumerating and detecting butyric anaerobes, either tubed orange serum medium (broth or agar) or thermoacidurans agar should be used (see Chapter 62). Tryptose cycloserine dextrose agar has been effectively used as a selective medium for the isolation and enumeration of mesophilic anaerobic sporeformers from environmental samples collected from cannery plant surveys.[20]

19.6 INTERPRETATION OF RESULTS

The diagnosis of canned food spoilage when mesophilic sporeforming anaerobes are isolated is covered in Chapter 61 and will not be discussed here.

The data obtained from the plant survey will provide the information needed to implement a corrective sanitation program in the canning plant. Evidence of heavy buildup of mesophilic sporeforming anaerobes on the equipment indicates that corrective action must be taken immediately to prevent a possible outbreak of underprocessing spoilage or to control a current one. Also, the cultures of these samples should be tested for the presence of C. botulinum toxin.

No standards for mesophilic anaerobe spores in ingredients have been established as they have been for thermophilic spores in sugars.[25] Therefore, judgment must be exercised as to whether or not the contaminated ingredients should be used, taking into account the spore count level, how much of the ingredient is used in the product, the sterilizing value of the process used for the canned product, and any other criteria that may appear to be significant.

The interpretation given to positive growth in any anaerobic cultures should be made carefully, since the growth observed may be due totally or in part to facultative anaerobes (usually aerobic sporeformers) rather than clostridia. Therefore, before making a judgment, take certain other factors into account, such as sample preparation (e.g., degree of heat treatment, if any), the presence of a putrid odor, amount of gas produced in the cultures, colony morphology, cell morphology (particularly spore location), catalase production, etc. If these observations still leave some doubt, then the identification procedures outlined in Chapter 61 to determine whether growth is due to mesophilic sporeforming anaerobes or to facultative anaerobes should be followed.

19.7 REFERENCES

1. ACC. 1972. "Microbiology of Canned Foods." Amer. Can Co. Barrington, Ill.
2. Allen, M. B. 1953. The thermophilic aerobic sporeforming bacteria. Bact. Rev. 17: 125.
3. Andersen, A. A. 1951. A rapid plate method of counting spores of Clostridium botulinum. J. Bacteriol. 62: 425.
4. Anonymous. 1978. England bans import of U.S. canned salmon in botulism scare. Food Chem. News. 20(21): 45.
5. APHA. 1966. "Recommended Methods for the Microbiological Examination of Foods." AM. Pub. Health Assn. New York.
6. Bee, G. R. and Hontz, L. R. 1980. Detection and prevention of post processing container handling damage. J. of Food Prot. 43: 458.
7. Cameron, E. J. and Esty, J. R. 1940. Comments on the microbiology of spoilage in canned foods. Food Research 5: 549.
8. CFR. 1979. Code of Fed. Regs. Title 21 Sect. 108, 113, 114. Dept. Health & Human Serv., U.S. Govt. Print. Office, Washington, D.C.
9. Folinazzo, J. F. and Troy, V. S. 1954. A simple medium for the growth and isolation of spoilage organisms from canned foods. Food Technol. 8: 280.

10. Frazier, W. C. 1988. "Food Microbiology," 4th ed. McGraw-Hill Book Co., N.Y.
11. Goldreich, E. E., Nash, H. D., Reasoner, D. J., and Taylor, R. H. 1972. The necessity of controlling bacterial populations in potable waters: Community water supply. J. Am. Water Works Assn. 64: 596.
12. Graves, R. R., Lesniewski, R. S., and Lake, D. E. 1977. Bacteriological quality of cannery cooling water. J. Food Sci. 42: 1280.
13. Gross, C. E., Vinton, E., and Stumbo, C. R. 1946. Bacteriological studies relating to thermal processing of canned meat. V. Characteristics of putrefactive anaerobes used in thermal resistance studies. Food Research 11: 405.
14. Hersom, A. C. and Hulland, E. D. 1964. "Canned Foods, an Introduction to Their Microbiology," (Baumgartner), 5th ed. Chemical Publ. Co., Inc., N.Y.
15. Johnston, R. W., Feldman, J. and Sullivan, R. 1963. Botulism from canned tuna fish. Public Health Reports 78: 561.
16. Johnston, R., Harmon, S. M., and Kautter, D. A. 1964. Method to facilitate the isolation of *Clostridium botulinum* type E. J. Bacteriol. 88: 1521.
17. Kautter, D. A., Harmon, S. M., Lynt, R. K. Jr., and Lilly, T. Jr. 1966. Antagonistic effects on *Clostridium botulinum* type E by organisms resembling it. Appl. Microbiol. 14: 616.
18. Kautter, D. A., Lilly, T. Jr., and Lynt, R. K. Jr. 1978. Evaluation of the botulism hazard in fresh mushrooms wrapped in commercial polyvinylchloride film. J. of Food Protection 41: 120.
19. Lake, D. E., Graves, R. R., Lesniewski, R. S., and Anderson, J. E. 1985a. Post-processing spoilage of low acid canned foods by mesophilic anaerobic sporeformers. J. of Food Protection 48: 221.
20. Lake, D. E., Lesniewski, R. S., Anderson, J. E., Graves, R. R., and Bremser, J. F. 1985b. Enumeration and isolation of mesophilic anaerobic sporeformers from cannery post-processing equipment. J. of Food Protection 48: 794.
21. McCroskey, L. M., Hathaway, C. L., Fenicia, L., Pasolini, B., and Aureli, P. 1986. Characterization of an organism that produces type E toxin but which resembles *C. butyricum* from the feces of an infant with type E botulism. J. Clin. Microbiol. 23: 201.
22. Meyer, K. F. 1929. Maximum oxygen tolerance of *C. botulinum* A, B, and C, of *C. sporogenes*, and *C. welchii* J. Inf. Dis. 44: 408.
23. Miller, N. J., Garrett, O. W., and Prickett, P. S. 1939 Anaerobic technique—A modified deep agar shake. Food Research 4: 447.
24. NCA. 1962. Diagnosis of canned food spoilage. Research Information Bull. No. 62. Washington, D.C.
25. NCA. 1968. "Laboratory Manual for Food Canners and Processors," Vol. 1. "Microbiology and Processing." Natl. Canners Assn. Research Labs. The AVI Publishing Co., Inc., Westport, CT.
26. NFPA. 1978. Botulism Investigation. National Food Processors Assn. Research Labs. Annual Report.
27. Odlaug, T. E. and Pflug, I. J. 1978. Microbiological and sanitizer analysis of water used for cooling containers of food in commercial canning factories in Minnesota and Wisconsin. J. Food Sci. 43: 954.
28. Rolf, R. D., Huetger, D. J., Campbell, B. J., and Barret, J. T. 1978. Factors relating to the oxygen tolerance of anaerobic bacteria. Appl. and Environ. Microbiol. 36: 306.
29. Segner, W. P. 1979. Mesophilic aerobic sporeforming bacteria in the spoilage of low acid canned foods. Food Technology. 33: 55.
30. Sneath, P. H. A. 1986. Endospore-forming gram-positive rods and cocci. 1200. In "Bergey's Manual of Systematic Bacteriology." P. H. A. Sneath, N. S. Mair, M. E. Sharpe, and J. G. Holt, eds. Vol. 2, p. 1141. Williams and Wilkens, Baltimore, Md.
31. Sognefest, P., Hays, G. L., Wheaton, E., and Benjamin, H. A. 1948. Effect of pH on thermal process requirements of canned foods. Food Research 13: 400.

32. Stumbo, C. R. 1973. "Thermobacteriology in Food Processing," 2nd ed. Academic Press, New York and London, England.
33. Sugiyama H. and Rutledge, K. S. 1978. Failure of *Clostridium botulinum* to grow in fresh mushrooms packed in plastic film overwraps with holes. J. of Food Protection. 41: 348.
34. Thompson, R. C. 1982. The tin of salmon had but a tiny hole. FDA Consum. 16(5): 7.
35. Townsend, C. T. and Esty, J. R. 1939. The role of microorganisms in canning. Western Canner and Packer. 31(8): 21, 23, 25.
36. USHEW. 1978. Chapter 22. In "Bacteriological Analytical Manual," 5th ed. Food and Drug Admin. Bureau of Foods. U.S. Dept. of Health, Ed. & Welfare. Washington, D.C.
37. Veillon, R. 1922. Sur quelques microbes thermophiles strictement anaerobies. Ann. Inst. Pasteur. 36: 422.

Chapter 20

ACIDURIC FLAT SOUR SPOREFORMERS

James L. Segmiller and George M. Evancho

20.1 INTRODUCTION

The taste of spoiled tomato juice has been described as "medicinal," "phe-nolic," and "fruity," and this taste is usually accompanied by a reduction of from 0.3 to 0.5 in pH.[10] Ends of cans of spoiled tomatoes remain flat; hence the term "flat sour." In 1933, while investigating off-flavor in commercially canned tomato juice, R.N. Berry isolated and described a new type of spoilage organism.[4] He determined the organism to be a sporeforming bacterium of soil origin.

20.11 Classification

Berry[4] named the organism responsible for "flat sour" spoilage of tomato products *Bacillus thermoacidurans*.[4] From comparative cultural studies, Smith et al.[9] concluded that *B. thermoacidurans* was identical with *Bacillus coagulans* of Hammer.[7] From their careful studies of the two species, Becker and Pederson[3] stated: "There is no justification for considering *B. thermoacidurans* as a species distinct from *B. coagulans*, and the latter name has priority."

B. coagulans is a nonpathogenic, motile, sporeforming aerobe having as many as 10 flagella per cell. The gram-stain reaction is usually positive although a few variable strains have been observed. The species is identified stepwise by the following test results: catalase positive, Voges-Proskauer positive (this property may be variable), growth in anaerobic agar (without glucose or Eh indicator), growth at 50°C, and absence of growth in 7% NaCl.[5]

20.12 Occurrence

B. coagulans is a common soil organism. It has been isolated from canned tomato products, particularly tomato juice, and from cream, evaporated milk, cheese, and silage. Spoilage and subsequent curd formation of evaporated milk have been caused by this organism. Hammer's original studies on the coagulation of evaporated milk led to the naming of the organism.[7] Among tomato products, *B. coagulans* has been isolated from canned whole tomatoes, tomato juice, tomato puree, tomato soup, and tomato-vegetable juice mixes.

The organism has been found to multiply in tomato-washing equipment where the volume of cold water is insufficient and the water temperature may reach 27° to 32°C. Spores have been isolated from empty cans and empty can washers, tomato product lines, conveyor belts, and filled can runways. Spores of the organism have been isolated from chipboard separators frequently used in the packaging of empty cans. They have been found in the sweepings of railcars previously used to ship grain products.

20.2   GENERAL CONSIDERATIONS

20.21   Sampling

1. Ingredients

Since the adequacy of a canned food process is, among other things, related to the bacterial spore load of the product to be processed, it is often advantageous to determine the load of flat sour spores in the unprocessed product as well as in the product ingredients. Pinpointing the ingredient that is contributing most to the total spore load may prove very beneficial to a packer. Depending on the canned tomato product being manufactured, spore analysis on ingredients such as raw tomatoes, fresh tomato pulp, puree, concentrated or evaporated milk, cream, and nonfat dry milk may be undertaken. Sampling of dairy products is conducted in accordance with the procedures given in Sections 10.1 to 10.7 of "Standard Methods for the Examination of Dairy Products," 15th edition. Section 9.6, page 194, also gives details on the examination for *B. coagulans*.[2]

2. Equipment and systems

Periodic sampling of tomato wash water and material from conveyor belts, pipelines, and tanks may reveal potential problem areas. A preseasonal bacteriological survey of pipelines, valves and valve bonnets, storage tanks, heaters, and other equipment surfaces that normally contact a product may indicate where cleaning and sanitation need to be improved. Sampling of such equipment may be carried out using swabbing or membrane filter techniques.

3. Product in process

Canners of tomatoes and tomato products may find it advantageous to monitor flat sour spores in certain phases of manufacturing. On analysis, finished tomato products, such as juice, puree, samples of chopped tomatoes before and after the hot break, or extracted tomatoes, may indicate potential foci of spore buildup. In the canning of whole tomatoes, sampling should include juice accumulated during peeling and puree made from sound tomatoes, both of which are used frequently as the liquid portion of canned tomatoes. Aciduric flat sour spore counts of tomato products prior to processing may assist in preventing spoilage where the product is not presterilized.

4. Finished products

Since most processes for tomato products either completely eliminate flat sour spores or drastically reduce their number, the advantage of making spore counts of the finished product must be seriously questioned. Where spore numbers have been reduced substantially, the probability of recovering spores by subculturing 1 ml in replicates up to five or more is small. No attempt should be made to plate more than 1-ml quantities of tomato juice because of its inhibitory action. Experience has shown that incubation of the canned finished product is much more meaningful.

5. Special equipment and supplies

When analyzing sugar, starch, flour, nonfat dry milk, and cream, 250-ml Erlenmeyer flasks permanently marked for 100 ml should be used. The newer type of graduated flasks should be checked for accuracy.

20.22   Temperature and pH Requirements

Becker and Pederson[3] reported that *B. coagulans* was obligately thermophilic, yet they were successful in growing the organism at temperatures as low as 18°C. Optimum growth in an artificial medium occurred between 37° and 45°C. In 1949, Gordon and Smith reported that 53 of 73 cultures studied grew at 28°C; 73 at 33°, 37°, and 45°C; 72 at 50°C; 66 at 55°C; 23 at 60°C; and none at 65°C.[6] In a more recent article, Thompson states the organism is generally regarded as "facultatively thermophilic," growing in artificial media at 20° to 55°C (all strains) or 60°C (16 of 22 strains).[11] The latter view is accepted more readily.

Packers of tomato products have observed spoilage development at temperatures of 21° to 38°C. The organism will not grow in tomato products with normal pH at 55°C. Berry indicated that a temperature of 37°C appeared optimum for the production of off-flavor.[4] *B. coagulans* does not grow in tomato products at solids levels over 18%.[12]

B. coagulans grows well in artificial media at pH values between 5.0 and 7.0. Pederson and Becker[8] showed that many cultures in their vegetative form could grow at values as low as pH 4.02. In artificial media, heat-resistant spores were incapable of germinating and producing growth below pH 5.0. It has been shown that a low pH in tomato serum decreased the heat resistance of spores, and the combined effect of acidity and NaCl concentrations (1% to 3%) caused more damage to spores at the same temperature.[1]

20.3   EQUIPMENT, MATERIALS, AND REAGENTS

20.31   Culture Media, Reagents

Dextrose tryptone agar (with bromcresol purple)
Gum arabic

Gum tragacanth
Litmus milk
Sodium hydroxide (.02 N)
Thermoacidurans agar

20.32   Equipment

Autoclave
Blender and blender jars
Colander/sieve
Colony counter
Incubator 55°C ± 1°C
Water bath 88° to 90°C

20.33   Glassware

Blender jars and blender
Erlenmeyer flasks, 250 ml marked at 100 ml
Petri plates
Rubber stoppers
20 × 150-mm screw-cap tubes
25 × 150-mm screw-cap tubes
Thermometer (−20° to 110°C)

20.4   PROCEDURE

20.41   Raw Tomatoes, Fresh Tomato Pulp, Puree, Concentrated Milk, Tomato Washer Water

20.411   Sample preparation

Extract the juice from raw whole or chopped tomatoes by pressing the sample in a sterile colander or sieve. The sample also may be prepared using a sterile blender jar and suitable blender. Transfer 10 ml of the expressed juice to a sterile 20 × 150-mm screw-cap tube for heat shocking, and tighten the rubber-lined caps securely. Samples of tomato puree and products of similar consistency are handled more conveniently using 25 × 150-mm tubes.

Completely immerse the tubes containing the samples in a waterbath adjusted to 88° to 90°C. Using an extra tube fitted with a slotted rubber stopper, check the rising temperature of a similar sample of ingredient or product. After the temperature in the "control" tube reaches 88°C, the timing of the heat-shock treatment begins and should last 5 min. Normally 10 ml of water, or product of a similar consistency, in a 20 × 150-mm screw-cap tube requires approximately 3 min to reach 88°C. Cool the sample tubes in cold water immediately after the shock treatment, keeping the screw-cap tops well above the surface of the water. Samples of ingredient or product that, in their preparation or manufacture, have had a recent heat treatment of 82°C or higher need no further shock treatment and can be plated directly. Place a control tube containing sterile tomato juice inoculated with spores known to be *B. coagulans* in the waterbath with the tubes of samples to be shocked.

20.412   Cultural procedures

Transfer 1 ml of the shocked sample or decimal volume thereof into each of 4 petri dishes. Add 18 to 20 ml of dextrose tryptone agar to each of 2 plates and add 18 to 20 ml of thermoacidurans agar tempered to 44° to 46°C to each of 2 plates. After solidification, invert the plates and promptly incubate at 55°C ± 1°C for 48 hr ± 3 hr. Surface colonies on dextrose tryptone agar resulting from the germination and growth of spores of *B. coagulans* will appear slightly moist, usually slightly convex, and pale yellow. Subsurface colonies on this medium are compact with fluffy edges. They are slightly yellow to orange and usually 1 mm or greater in diameter. Both surface and subsurface colonies will be surrounded by a yellow zone caused by acid formation. In 48 hr, plates may turn completely yellow. *B. stearothermophilus* will also grow on dextrose tryptone agar giving pinhead-size colonies, usually brown, which are of no consequence since they do not spoil tomato juice. Suspicious colonies should be transferred to litmus milk, where they will produce coagulation if the organisms are *B. coagulans*; *B. stearothermophilus* will not grow on the thermoacidurans agar at pH 5.0, and therefore counts on the latter acid medium may have more significance. Typical colonies on the latter agar are large and white to cream in color.

20.42   Nonfat Dry Milk

20.421   Sample preparation

Weigh 10 g of the sample into a sterile 250-ml Erlenmeyer flask marked at 100 ml. Add .02 N sodium hydroxide to the mark and shake to dissolve the sample completely. Heat 10 min at 5 psi (108.4°C) steam pressure, then cool immediately. Bring volume back to mark with sterile .02 N sodium hydroxide.

20.422   Cultural procedures

Transfer 2 ml of the solution to each of 10 sterile petri plates. Add to each plate 18 to 20 ml of dextrose tryptone agar tempered to 44° to 46°C. After solidification, invert the plates and promptly incubate at 55°C ± 1°C for 48 hr ± 3 hr. Count the typical acid flat sour colonies previously described and report on the basis of number of colonies per 10 g of sample.

20.43   Cream

20.431   Sample preparation

Mix 2 g of gum tragacanth and 1 g of gum arabic in 100 ml of water in an Erlenmeyer flask. Sterilize in the autoclave for 20 min at 121°C. Transfer 20 ml of sample to a sterile 250-ml Erlenmeyer flask marked at 100 ml. Add the sterilized gum mixture to the 100-ml mark and carefully shake, using a sterile rubber stopper. Loosen stopper and autoclave for 5 min at 5 psi (108.4°C).

20.432   Cultural procedures

Because of the viscosity of the mixture, first pour 5 petri plates with dextrose tryptone agar, then immediately transfer 2 ml of the cream emulsion and swirl in the usual manner. After solidification, invert the plates and promptly incubate at 55° ± 1°C for 48 hr ± 3 hr. Count the typical acid flat sour colonies and report on the basis of 1 ml of sample.

20.5   PRECAUTIONS AND LIMITATIONS OF THE PROCEDURE

When plating samples of acid products such as tomato juice and tomato puree, the tempered medium should be poured directly on the sample in a petri plate. A minimum of 18 ml of medium per plate should be used per 1 ml of tomato product. Pouring should be followed immediately by gentle swirling to ensure adequate dispersion of the sample in the melted medium. In addition to providing a uniform distribution of any surviving spores, the precautions will also ensure a uniform color to the poured plate because of the acid product and the indicator in the medium. Precautions also must be taken to prevent drying out or splitting of agar in plates during incubation at 55°C. This can be accomplished by placing the plates in appropriate canisters or by providing additional moisture in the air within the incubator.

20.6   INTERPRETATION

True acid "flat sour" (*B. coagulans*) spores have significance in canned products in the pH range of 4.1 to 5.0. Surviving spores of *B. stearothermophilus* will not grow in this pH range, and, therefore, care must be used in distinguishing between the two organisms. The presence of *B. coagulans* can lead to serious spoilage while presence of *B. stearothermophilus* spores at this pH range is of no consequence.

Some representatives of industry show concern when counts in excess of five spores of *B. coagulans* per g are encountered in the ingredients used in canned foods in the pH range of 4.1 to 5.0.

20.7 REFERENCES

1. Alain, A. M., El-Shimi, N. M., Abd El-Magied, M. M., and Tawadrous, A. G. 1986. Heat Resistance of *Bacillus coagulans* Spores Isolated from Tomato Juice. Egypt. J. Food Sci. 14: 2: 323.
2. APHA. 1985. "Standard Methods for the Examination of Dairy Products," 15th ed., ed. Gary Richardson, Am. Pub. Health Assn., Washington, D.C.
3. Becker, M. E. and Pederson, C. S. 1950. The physiological characters of *Bacillus coagulans (Bacillus thermoacidurans)*. J. Bacteriol. 59: 717.
4. Berry, R. N. 1933. Some new heat resistant, acid tolerant organisms causing spoilage in tomato juice. J. Bacteriol. 25: 72.
5. Gordon, R. E., Haynes, W. C., Pang, C. H. 1973. "The genus *Bacillus*." USDA Handbook No. 427. Washington, D.C.
6. Gordon, R. E. and Smith, N. R. 1949. Aerobic spore forming bacteria capable of growth at high temperatures. J. Bacteriol. 58: 327.
7. Hammer, B. W. 1915. Bacteriological studies on the coagulation of evaporated milk. Iowa Ag. Expt. Sta., Res. Bull. 19. Iowa City, Iowa.
8. Pederson, C. S. and Becker, M. E. 1949. Flat sour spoilage of tomato juice. Tech. Bull. No. 287. N.Y. State Agricultural Experiment Station, Cornell Univ., Geneva, N.Y.
9. Smith, N. R., Gordon, R. E., and Clark, F. E. 1946. Aerobic mesophilic sporeforming bacteria. USDA Misc. Publ. No. 559. Washington, D.C.
10. Stern, R. M., Hagarty, C. P., and Williams, O. B. 1942. Detection of *Bacillus thermoacidurans* (Berry) in tomato juice, and successful cultivation of the organism in the laboratory. Food Res. 7: 186.
11. Thompson, P. J. 1981. Thermophilic organisms involved in food spoilage: Aciduric flat sour sporeforming aerobes. J. Food Prot. 44: 154.
12. Unpublished communication. 1985. H. J. Heinz Co., Microbiology Dept., Pittsburgh, PA.

Chapter 21

THERMOPHILIC FLAT SOUR SPOREFORMERS

Karl E. Olson and Kent M. Sorrells

21.1 INTRODUCTION

Typical thermophilic flat sour spoilage of low-acid canned foods is caused by the growth of sporeforming, thermophilic facultative aerobes. *Bacillus stearothermophilus* is the typical species responsible for this type of spoilage.[2,5,10] These organisms characteristically ferment carbohydrates with the production of short-chain fatty acids that "sour" the product. They do not produce enough, if any, gas to change the usual "flat" appearance of the ends of the container. Although the flat sour bacteria are considered obligate thermophiles, in fact, they may grow at temperatures as low as 30° to 45°C, especially if the incubated organisms are in the vegetative state and if proper environmental conditions are imposed. The group's upper temperature limit for growth is 65° to 75°C.

In canned low-acid foods, particularly those having a pH no lower than about 5.3, thermophilic flat sour spoilage seldom occurs if holding temperatures are maintained below approximately 43°C. If these foods are held at a temperature above about 43°C long enough and if the food contains viable spores capable of germinating and growing out in the product, then the product may undergo flat sour spoilage.[3]

Spores of *B. stearothermophilus* have exceptionally high thermal resistance. The $D_{121}°C$ ranges between 4.0 and 5.0 min, with a z-value (slope of the thermal death time curve) between 7.8° to 12.2°C.[9] Thus, their presence in some containers of any given lot of commercially sterile low-acid canned foods may be considered normal. Since flat sour spoilage does not develop unless the product is at temperatures above 43°C, proper cooling after thermal processing and avoiding high temperatures during warehouse storage or distribution are essential.

Bacterial spores enter canneries in soil, on raw foods, and in ingredients, e.g., spices, sugar, starch, flour.[6,7,9] Populations may increase at any point where a proper environment exists. For example, food handling equipment in a canning line that is operated within the thermophilic growth range (about 43° to 75°C) may serve as a focal point for the buildup of an excessive flat sour spore population.

Spores of flat sour bacteria show exceptional resistance to destruction by heat and chemicals; hence, they are difficult to destroy in a product or in the plant. Methods to minimize spore contamination include control of spore population in ingredients and products entering the plant, as well as the use of sound plant sanitation practices.

Inadequate cooling subsequent to thermal processing is a major contributor to the development of flat sour spoilage. Localized heating of sections of stacks of canned foods placed too close to heaters is another.

21.2 GENERAL CONSIDERATIONS

21.21 Sampling

1. Ingredients

Approximately half-pound samples from each of five bags, drums, or boxes of a shipment or lot of dry sugar, starch, flour, or similar ingredients should be collected and sealed in cans, jars, plastic bags, or other appropriate containers and taken to the laboratory.[6] Samples of ingredients used in lesser proportions in the finished product, e.g., spices, may be taken in appropriately smaller amounts. In any case, samples should be reasonably representative of the entire lot or shipment in question. For liquid sugar collect five separate 6- to 8-oz. (200- to 250-ml) samples from a tank or truck when it is being filled or emptied.[1]

2. Equipment and product in process

Only those units held at temperatures within the thermophilic growth range are of direct concern. Scrapings or swab samples of food contacting surfaces or of wet surfaces positioned directly over food materials, from which drippage may gain access to the food materials, may be cultured. Collect the samples in sterile tubes or sampling bags. Examination of food samples taken before and after passage through a particular piece of equipment, e.g., a blancher or a filler, will reveal whether a significant buildup of flat sour spores is occurring in that item of equipment. Multiple samples of a volume equivalent to the volume of the container being packed generally are taken. Unused clean metal cans and covers are convenient sample containers. (Do not use glass containers to collect samples because of the danger of breakage or of being dropped into the equipment.) Solid materials in the presence of excess liquid may be collected in a sieve or similar device; this permits draining excess liquid. Chill the samples thoroughly without delay to prevent the activity of thermophilic bacteria prior to the laboratory examination. Immersion of the sample container in cold tap water usually is adequate for this purpose.

3. Finished product

The method of sampling depends on the objective of the examination. When spore contamination levels during production are the concern, take processed containers representing conditions (a) at the start of operations when the shift begins, (b) before midshift shutdown, (c) at startup after midshift shutdown, and (d) at the end of the shift. Samples of each time period should consist of at least 10 containers. The probability of finding one positive can in 10 samples if 25% of the production contains viable flat sour spores is 0.95.[6] Incubate at 55°C for 5 to 7 days.

When known or suspected insufficient cooling or storage at temperatures above 43°C is a reason for concern, take containers at random from the production lot in question. Record the location from which each container was taken, i.e., its position on a pallet and the location of the pallet. The larger the number of samples examined, the greater will be the probability of detecting flat sour spoilage. The probability of detecting at least one spoiled container in the sample when the real spoilage level is 1% is about 95% with a 300-unit sample, 89% with a 200-unit sample, and 62% with a 100-unit sample.[6] Because growth of flat sour organisms may cause a slight loss of vacuum or a loss of consistency of a product, separation of these products sometimes is possible without destruction of normal product cans.[6]

21.22 Spore Recovery

Much of the work in the area of spore recovery deals with recovery from heat resistance tests, and these results may or may not apply in the recovery of the spores from ingredients and the recovery of vegetative cells from production equipment. Recovery of heated spores occurs best at 45° to 50°C and in neutral media. After spore heating, water is the best diluent for spore recovery,[3] and best recovery occurs if heating has been done in distilled water.

For optimum vegetative growth, the cell needs adequate oxygen supply and a culture medium at pH 7. No growth of *B. stearothermophilus* occurs at pH 5.

21.3 EQUIPMENT, MATERIALS, AND REAGENTS

Equipment and supplies are needed in accordance with specifications in Chapters 2 and 62. The following additional media and apparatus are recommended.

21.31 Culture Media

Dextrose tryptone agar
Dextrose broth
Nutrient broth or dextrose tryptone broth (if needed for nutrient supplementation; see Section 21.52)

21.32 Equipment

Autoclave—for heat shocking food samples in addition to normal laboratory sterilization purposes

Bacti-Disc Cutter (Figure 3 in Chapter 61)—for opening canned food samples aseptically. It may be purchased from Wilkens-Anderson Co., 4525 West Division Street, Chicago, Ill. 60651, No. 10810-01, or from Dixie Canner Equipment Co., P. O. Box 1348, Athens, Ga. 30601, No. D-173-A.

Flasks—250-ml and 300-ml Erlenmeyer flasks (for analysis of thermophilic spores ingredients)

Glassware—dilution bottles: 6 to 8 oz. for dilution blanks containing distilled water

Incubator—temperature controlled to about 55°C

Microscope

Petri dishes—sterile: either glass or plastic may be used

pH Meter, Electrometric—pH Color Comparator with bromcresol purple and methyl red reagents and standards may be substituted

Pipettes, sterile—1-ml and 10-ml Mohr pipettes; sample pipettes made from either straight wall borosilicate tubing (7 to 8 mm in diameter × 35 to 40 cm). Disposable pipettes may also be used.

Special waterbath (starch)[4]

Swabs—sterile 6-in cotton or alginate swabs

21.33 Reagent

Crystal violet solution

21.4 PRECAUTIONS

Samples other than finished products must be handled so that there will be no opportunities for spore germination or spore production between the collection of the samples and the start of examination procedures.

Before making a positive judgment on a sample based on pH or microscopic examination of direct smears, be sure that these characteristics are known for "normal" control products. Controls should be from the same production code as the suspect samples; if such controls are not available, use a product from the same manufacturer and bearing the next closest production code. This is particularly important where formulated products are concerned, although it is not necessarily confined to such products. Incubated agar plates should not be allowed to dehydrate during incubation. Placement in oxygen-permeable bags will minimize dehydration.

21.5 PROCEDURE

Thermophilic flat sour spores possess greater heat resistance than most other organisms encountered in foods. This characteristic is advantageous to the examination of foods and ingredients because, by controlled heat treatment of samples (heat shock), it is possible to eliminate all organisms except the spores with which we are concerned. Further, heat shock, or activation, is necessary to induce germination of the maximum number of spores in a population of many species, including the flat sours.[3, 9] Because the most heat-resistant spores are generally the ones of concern in food canning operations, a heat shock favoring recovery of such spores is preferable. Unless otherwise specified, i.e., in a standard procedure, 30 min at 100°C or 10 min at 110°C, followed by rapid cooling, should be used.

21.51   Sample Preparation and Examination

Sugar and starch: The National Food Processors Association (NFPA) (formerly National Canners Association) has suggested a method and standard for determining thermophilic flat sour spore contamination of sugar and starch to be used in low-acid canned foods.[4, 6, 9]

1. Sugar (AOAC)[1]

Place 20 g of dry sugar in a sterile 250-ml Erlenmeyer flask marked at 100 ml. Add sterile water to the 100-ml mark. Agitate thoroughly to dissolve the sugar. (Liquid sugar is examined by the same procedure, with this difference: a volume of liquid sugar calculated to be equivalent, based on degree Brix, to 20 g of dry sugar is added to the 250-ml flask and diluted with water to 100 ml.)

Bring the prepared sample rapidly to a boil and continue boiling for 5 min, then water cool immediately. Pipette 2 ml of the heated sugar solution into each of 5 petri plates. Add dextrose tryptone agar (Chapter 62), swirl gently to distribute the inoculum, and allow to solidify. Incubate the inverted plates at 50° to 55° for 48 to 72 hr.

2. Starch

Place 20 g of starch in a dry, sterile 250-ml Erlenmeyer flask and add sterile cold water to the 100-ml mark, with intermittent shaking. Shake well to obtain a uniform suspension of the starch in water. Pipette 10 ml of the suspension into a 300-ml flask containing 100 ml of sterile dextrose tryptone agar at a temperature of 55° to 60°C. Use large-bore pipettes; keep the starch suspension under constant agitation during the pipetting operation. After the starch has been added to the agar, shake the flask in boiling water for 3 min to thicken the starch. Then place the flask in the autoclave and heat at 5 lb pressure (108.4°C) for 10 min. After autoclaving, the flask should be gently agitated while cooling as rapidly as possible. Violent agitation will incorporate air bubbles into the medium, which subsequently may interfere with the reading of the plates. When the agar starch mixture is cooled to the proper point, distribute the entire mixture about equally into 5 plates and allow to harden. Then stratify with a thin layer of sterile plain 2% agar in water and allow to harden. This prevents possible "spreader" interference. Incubate the inverted plates at 50° to 55°C; count in 48 hr and in 72 hr.

3. Other ingredients

The NFPA procedures for sugar and starch may be applied to other ingredients used in low-acid canned foods.[6] Modifications may be necessary because of physical or chemical characteristics of a particular ingredient, e.g., use of smaller sample sizes or plating smaller volumes of suspension in more than 5 plates because of colony particle size interference during counting.

4. Calculating counts

Flat sour colonies are round, are 2 to 5 mm in diameter, show a dark, opaque center, and usually are surrounded by a yellow halo in a field of purple. The yellow color (acid) of the indicator may be missing when low-acid-producing strains are present, or where alkaline reversion has occurred. (Subsurface colonies are compact and biconvex to pinpoint in shape. If the analyst is unfamiliar with subsurface colonies of flat sour bacteria, it is advisable to streak subsurface colonies on dextrose tryptone agar to confirm surface colony morphology.)

The combined count of typical flat sour colonies from the 5 plates represents the number of flat sour spores in 2 g of the original sample (20-g sample diluted to 100 ml: 10 ml of this dilution plated). Multiply this count by 5 to express results in terms of number of spores per 10 g of sample.

The total thermophilic spore count is made by counting every colony on each of the 5 plates, then calculating in terms of number of spores per 10 g of sample.

21.52 Equipment and Product in Process

The source of excessive flat sour spores in a canning operation may best be determined by "line samples" (Section 21.21). Use quantities of sample equivalent to the amount of the material included in a container of finished product; prepare several replicates (5 to 20); after closing, warm the containers to the initial temperature of the commercial process, subject them to the normal commercial thermal process, incubate at 55°C for 5 to 7 days; open and determine growth of flat sour bacteria by pH measurement, supplemented by microscopic examination of a direct smear if necessary. Many line samples are nutritionally complete so that plain water may be added to fill the container; however, some formulated product components may lack essential nutrients, in which case nutrient broth or dextrose broth (Chapter 62), for example, should be added instead of water. If in doubt, inoculate a control sample with *B. stearothermophilus* spores, heat shock, and incubate at 55°C for 48 to 72 hr to determine whether the sample material will support spore germination and outgrowth.

Another procedure is to make agar plate counts on serial dilutions of each heat-shocked line sample. Use dextrose tryptone agar and incubate at 55°C for 48 to 72 hr.

Swabs or scrapings from equipment surfaces should be shaken in a known volume of diluent, and the suspension heat shocked and plated on dextrose tryptone agar and incubated at 55°C for 48 to 72 hr. Then calculate the numbers of microorganisms per unit area sampled.

21.53   Finished Product

Incubate containers of processed product at 55°C for 5 to 7 days, open, and examine for flat sour spoilage.[6] Comparison of pH of incubated samples and normal unincubated controls will usually be sufficient to show the presence of flat sour spoilage. If the results are not clear, confirm the presence or absence of spoilage flora by direct microscopic examination of smears of the product from both incubated and unincubated control containers. The bacteriological condition of products whose physical characteristics provide confusing artifacts when seen in a stained smear can be examined best in a wet mount using phase optics.

Samples collected from a warehouse where insufficient cooling or storing at elevated temperatures is known or suspected are examined as above, but without preliminary incubation at 55°C.

21.6   INTERPRETATION OF RESULTS

21.61   Ingredients

NFPA standards for thermophilic flat sour spores in sugar or starch for canners' use[6] state, "For the five samples examined there shall be a maximum of not more than 75 spores and an average of not more than 50 spores per 10 g of sugar (or starch)."

The total thermophilic spore count standard is, "For the five samples examined there shall be a maximum of not more than 150 spores and an average of not more than 125 spores per 10 g of sugar (or starch)."[6]

The sugar and starch standard may be used as a guide for evaluating other ingredients, keeping in mind the proportion of the other ingredients in the finished product relative to the quantity of sugar or starch used.[4, 6, 9]

The presence of thermophilic flat sour spores in ingredients for foods other than thermal-processed low-acid foods is probably of no significance provided those foods are not held within the thermophilic growth range for many hours. The flat sour bacteria have no public health significance.[8]

21.62   Equipment and Product in Process

Canned and processed line samples usually indicate a point or points at which a spore buildup has occurred. A high percentage of positive samples taken from one point in the line, when a low level or no positive samples were found prior to this point, shows a spore buildup in this piece of equipment. The time of day yielding positive samples may indicate whether the buildup is due to operating temperatures within the thermophilic growth range, or whether inadequate cleanup and sanitization procedures were used prior to sampling. The former condition is suggested when a majority of positive samples occurs in those taken after the line has been in operation for several hours. The latter condition is suggested when samples at the startup of the line are predominantly positive and those taken later are predominantly negative.

Plate count data for equipment line samples may be meaningful, especially when taken over a long period of time. They can show trends regarding buildups, inadequate cleanups, etc. Because counts are made in a laboratory medium that may be a better spore germination and growth medium than certain specific food products themselves, and because the sample does not receive the equivalent of the commercial thermal process, results may reflect greater than the actual potential surviving spore load in the finished product. They can, however, indicate buildup situations that are undesirable.

21.63   Finished Products

Dormant thermophilic spores are of no concern in commercially sterile canned foods destined for storage and distribution where temperatures will not exceed about 43°C. However, some canned foods are destined for exposure to temperatures above 43°C during part or most of their shelf life, i.e., those shipped to tropical locales and those intended for hot-vend service. To be considered commercially sterile, these specialized foods must not contain thermophilic spores capable of germination and outgrowth in the product.

Randomly selected warehouse samples of low-acid canned foods, some of which are found to have undergone flat sour spoilage, can reveal information about the condition contributing to the development of spoilage. Spoilage confined to product situated in the outer layers or rows of cases on a pallet suggests localized heating, e.g., from close proximity to a space heater or having been too close to the building roof during hot weather. Spoilage confined to inner cases on a pallet is indicative of insufficient cooling, i.e., palletizing cases while the product was still in the thermophilic growth temperature range. Inner cases are insulated by exterior cases and may retain heat for several days.

21.7   REFERENCES

1. AOAC. 1984. "Official Methods of Analysis of the Association of Official Analytical Chemists," 14th ed., ed. S. Williams, p. 954. J. Assn. Off. Anal. Chem., Arlington, Va.
2. Ayres, J. C., Mundt, J. O., and Sandine, W. E. 1980. "Microbiology of Foods." W. M. Freeman and Co., San Francisco, Calif.
3. Cook, A. M. and Gilbert, R. J. 1968. Factors affecting the heat resistance of *Bacillus stearothermophilus* spores. J. Food Technol. 3: 285.
4. DoD. 1981. "Military Standard. Bacterial Standards for Starches, Flours, Cereals, Alimentary Pastes, Dry Milks, and Sugars Used in the Preparation of Canned Foods for the Armed Forces." MIL-STD-900. U.S. Dept. of Defense, Washington, D.C.

5. Gordon, R. E., Haynes, W. C. and Pang, C. H-N. 1973. The genus *Bacillus*. Agriculture Handbook No. 427. U.S. Dept. of Agric., Washington, D.C.
6. NCA Research Laboratories, 1968. "Laboratory Manual for Food Canners and Processors," Vol. 1, p. 88, 102. Natl. Canners Assn. (now Natl. Food Processors Assn.) AVI Pub. Co. Inc., Westport, Conn.
7. Richmond, B. and Fields, M. L. 1966. Distribution of thermophilic aerobic sporeforming bacteria in food ingredients. Appl. Microbiol. 14: 623.
8. Schmitt, H. P. 1966. Commercial sterility in canned foods, its meaning and determination. Quart. Bull., Assn. Food and Drug Off. of the U.S. 30: 141.
9. Stumbo, C. R. 1973. "Thermobacteriology in Food Processing," 2nd ed. Academic Press, New York.
10. Walker, P. D. and Wolf, J. 1971. The Taxonomy of *Bacillus stearothermophilus*. In "England Spore Research," ed. A. N. Barber, G. W. Gould, and J. Wolf, p. 247. Academic Press, London, England.

Chapter 22

THERMOPHILIC ANAEROBIC SPOREFORMERS

David Ashton and Dane Bernard

22.1 INTRODUCTION

The thermophilic anaerobes that do not produce hydrogen sulfide have been responsible for the spoilage of canned products such as spaghetti with tomato sauce, sweet potatoes, pumpkin, green beans, and asparagus.[7] They have also caused spoilage of highly acid products such as mixtures of fruit and farinaceous ingredients. The nonhydrogen sulfide-producing thermophilic anaerobic sporeformers are classified in the family *Bacillaceae*, genus *Clostridium*.[8] The type species of this group is *Clostridium thermosaccharolyticum*.[9] These organisms are obligately anaerobic and are strongly saccharolytic, producing acid and abundant gas from glucose, lactose, sucrose, salicin, and starch. Proteins are not hydrolyzed, and nitrites are not produced from nitrates.[5] Vegetative cells are long, slender, straight or slightly curved, often weakly staining, gram-negative rods. Spores are terminal and swollen. Neither toxins nor infections are produced, and, therefore, the organisms are of spoilage, but not of public health, significance.

One of the noticeable characteristics of these organisms is the heat resistance exhibited by their spores. It is not unusual for the spores to have D-values at 121°C of 3 to 4 minutes or higher. Their z-value (slope of the thermal death time curve) is about 6 to 7°C. Thus, the organisms can have extreme resistance in the 105 to 113°C range.[1,10] Their survival in canned foods is therefore not unexpected, but thermophilic anaerobes are rarely found in foods processed above 121°C. Only when the finished product is improperly cooled or is held for extended periods at elevated temperatures do the thermophilic anaerobes express themselves.

The optimum growth temperature of these organisms is 55 to 60°C. They seldom grow at temperatures below 32°C but can produce spoilage in 14 days at 37°C if the spores are first germinated at a higher temperature. They have an optimum for growth of pH 6.2 to 7.2 but grow readily in products having a pH of 4.7 or higher. They have been responsible on occasion for spoilage in tomato products at pH values of 4.1 to 4.5.[7]

Ingredients such as sugar, dehydrated milk, starch, flour, cereals, and alimentary pastes have been found to be the predominant sources of thermophilic anaerobes. These organisms occur widely in the soil and therefore are found on raw materials, such as mushrooms and onion products, that have a history of contact with the soil. Excessive populations of thermophilic anaerobes can develop in ingredients such as chicken stock, beef extract, or yeast hydrolysate if an incubation period in the thermophilic temperature range is provided during concentration or hydrolysis steps. The thermophilic anaerobes do not multiply on equipment and handling systems unless an anaerobic environment containing nutrients and moisture at an elevated temperature is provided. The organism has also been observed to grow well in the cooling leg (55°C area) of hydrostatic cookers, if the water is contaminated with food. Accumulation of excessive numbers of organisms in this area, followed by improper cooling, has resulted in leaker-type spoilage of canned foods.

22.2 GENERAL CONSIDERATIONS

Methods outlined in this chapter are dictated by the fact that *C. thermosaccharolyticum* is a thermophilic obligately anaerobic sporeformer. The primary objective is to limit the number of spores in ingredients used in canned foods.

The recommended substrate for recovery and growth of nonhydrogen sulfide-producing thermophilic anaerobes is PE-2 medium.[4] The medium should be supplemented to contain 0.3% yeast extract for detection of severely heat-stressed spores.

The Association of Official Analytical Chemists (AOAC) detection procedure for thermophilic anaerobes not producing hydrogen sulfide specifies liver broth as the medium of choice,[2] but experience indicates that non-commercially prepared liver broth is difficult to make and is a potential source of metabolic inhibitors, including antibiotics, without offering any increased sensitivity of detection.

22.3 EQUIPMENT, MATERIALS, AND SOLUTIONS

22.31 Equipment

Blender
Incubator that will maintain a uniform temperature of 55°C ± 2°C

Microscope with 1000X oil immersion objective
Pipettes with 10-, 1.0-, and 0.1-ml capacity
18 × 150-mm tubes with venting caps

22.32 Media

Liver broth
PE-2
Vaspar

22.4   PRECAUTIONS

Every precaution should be taken to ensure that the ingredients of the detection medium are free from growth inhibitors. For example, try to obtain peas free of pesticides. As an added precaution, each new lot of ingredients should be incorporated into the medium and tested for growth inhibitors with a known suspension of a thermophilic anaerobe. These precautions will help to eliminate or minimize the occurrence of false negatives.

The detection procedures described in Section 22.5 are not truly quantitative. The objective in surveying ingredients is to detect spores in a known quantity of the ingredient rather than to achieve absolute quantitation.

It is important that in the preparation of PE-2 the dried peas be soaked in the peptone solution 1 hr before autoclaving to ensure the proper sterilizing effect. Repeated steaming of unused tubes of medium does not reduce its effectiveness as a substrate for the thermophilic anaerobes.

Spoiled canned food suspected of thermophilic growth should not be refrigerated because vegetative cells of thermophilic anaerobes usually die under refrigeration and spores are not generally produced in canned foods.

22.5   PROCEDURE

The following procedures apply for the detection of spores only rather than of spores and vegetative cells. If the heating step is omitted, vegetative cells can be propagated by these procedures.

22.51   Culture Medium

Unless freshly prepared medium is used, previously sterilized tubes should be subjected to flowing steam for 20 min to exhaust oxygen and cooled to 55°C before use. After inoculation, tubes are stratified with 3 ml of sterile 2% agar or Vaspar that is allowed to harden before tubes are tempered to 55°C and incubated. As a safety precaution, venting caps are recommended on tubes because of the abundant gas production by the organism of interest.

22.52 Sampling

22.521   Ingredients

Samples of dry ingredients should consist of 200 g taken aseptically from five different bags or barrels per shipment or lot for lot sizes of 50 or fewer containers, from 10% of the containers for lot sizes 50 to 100, and from a number of containers equal to the square root of the lot size for shipments with greater than 100 containers. Liquid sugar should be sampled by drawing five 200-g portions per tank during transfer or at the refinery during the tank-filling operation. Samples should be placed in sterile, sealed containers. If preliminary analyses indicate considerable variability in a lot, the number of samples should be increased.

22.522   Equipment and systems

The thermophilic anaerobes will not develop on equipment unless elevated temperatures are provided in a relatively anaerobic environment containing nutrients. Accumulated food materials in such locations should be sampled with a sterile spatula or similar device and placed in sterile, sealed containers, and the analysis should be conducted as soon as possible. Examination of food materials before and after exposure to processing equipment will help to reveal the contamination level of the equipment.

22.523   Product in process

A 200-g sample of product in process should be obtained periodically to monitor the system. Sample timing should be arranged to coincide with the introduction of a new batch of ingredients or a shutdown that may have permitted an incubation period. The samples should be cooled immediately but slowly to room temperature and the analysis conducted as soon as possible. Refrigeration is not recommended.

22.524   Finished product

Representative containers of finished product should be obtained to reflect the condition of the entire population of containers in a production period. The need for sampling will be dictated by considerations such as the previous record of the product with respect to thermophilic spoilage and the temperature stresses to which the product is expected to be subjected during transit and storage. The number of containers sampled should be of the order of one per thousand containers produced. If immediate post-processing cooling to 43°C is not achievable, monitoring of surviving thermophiles becomes extremely important. Incubate the finished product at 55°C for 5 to 7 days.

22.53 Enumerating

22.531 Dry sugar and powdered milk[2]

Place 20 g of sample in a sterile flask and add sterile distilled water to a final volume of 100 ml. Stir to dissolve the sample and bring the contents of the flask to a boil rapidly. Boil for 5 min, cool by placing the flask in cold water, and bring the volume back to 100 ml with sterile distilled water. Divide 20 ml of boiled solution equally among 6 freshly exhausted tubes of PE-2 medium. Stratify each tube with 3 ml of sterile 2% agar or Vaspar, allow the agar to solidify, preheat the tubes to 55°C, and incubate at 55°C for 72 hr.

22.532 Liquid sugar

Place a sample containing 20 g of dry sugar, determined on the basis of degree Brix (29.411 g of 68° Brix liquid sugar is equivalent to 20 g of dry sugar) in a sterile flask, and proceed as for dry sugar.

22.533 Fresh mushrooms

Place 200 g of mushrooms in a sterile blender jar and dice with a sterile knife. Blend the diced sample until the pieces are finely chopped. Frequent shaking of the jar is essential to ensure proper blending. Place 20 g of blended sample in a sterile flask, and proceed as for dry sugar.

22.534 Starches and flours[6]

Place 20 g of sample in a sterile flask containing a few glass beads and add sterile distilled water to a final volume of 100 ml. Shake well to obtain a uniform suspension. Divide 20 ml of the suspension equally among 6 freshly exhausted tubes of PE-2 medium. Spin 3 tubes at a time in the hands immediately after adding the sample. Place the tubes in a boiling waterbath and continue to spin the tubes for the first 5 min of heating. Continue heating for an additional 10 min; then remove the tubes and place them in cold water. Stratify the tubes with 3 ml of sterile 2% agar or Vaspar, allow to solidify, preheat the tubes to 55°C, and incubate at 55°C for 72 hr.

22.535 Cereals and alimentary pastes[6]

Place 50 g of well-mixed sample into a sterile blender jar, and add 200 ml of sterile distilled water. Blend for 3 min to obtain a uniform suspension. Proceed as for starches and flours. For calculations assume that 10 ml of the blended materials contain 2 g of the original sample.

22.536   Product in process

Place 100 g of product in a sterile blender jar and blend for 3 min. Distribute 20 ml or g of the blended sample equally among 6 freshly exhausted tubes of PE-2 medium, and proceed as for starches and flours.

22.537   Finished product

Representative samples of finished product should be incubated at 55°C for 5 to 7 days and observed daily for evidence of loss of vacuum or container distortion. Samples that show signs of spoilage such as gas formation, cloudy brine, etc., should be removed from incubation and opened aseptically. Three grams of the contents should be placed in each of 2 tubes of freshly exhausted PE-2 medium by means of a wide bore pipette. Smears of the product should be made for morphological confirmation. The conditions necessary for preventing laboratory contamination when subculturing cans of finished product are detailed in the literature.[3]

22.538   Spore suspensions

When spore suspensions are prepared for thermal inactivation studies, a greater degree of quantitation is desirable than is practiced for ingredients or finished product. In this case, 10 ml of the desired dilution of the spore suspension is placed in an 18 × 150-mm screw-cap tube and immersed in boiling water for 8 min, followed by rapid cooling in cold water. A conventional 5-tube most probable number (MPN) dilution series of the boiled suspension is prepared in freshly exhausted PE-2 medium. The inoculated tubes are treated as for dry sugar. The population of the original spore suspension is computed from MPN tables.

22.6   INTERPRETATION

Tubes of PE-2 medium positive for growth of nonhydrogen sulfide-producing thermophilic anaerobes show gas production with the peas rising to the top of the liquid medium. Thermophilic flat sour bacteria may change the color from purple to yellow without gas (see Chapter 21).

22.61   Ingredients

1. For canners' use

Spores of nonhydrogen sulfide-producing thermophilic anaerobes should not be found in more than 60% of the samples tested or in more than 66% of the tubes for any single sample.[5] Use of ingredients meeting this standard will minimize the possibility of spoilage in the finished product. Canned foods with a pH below 4.0 are not susceptible to spoilage by thermophilic anaerobes.

2. For other use

The presence of excessive numbers of spores of thermophilic anaerobes that do not produce hydrogen sulfide in ingredients for use other than in canned products is of little significance unless a thermophilic incubation period is provided during processing. In such a case, the number of vegetative cells present after a processing step is important and should be determined as outlined above, but omitting the boiling step.

22.62   Equipment and Systems

The presence of detectable levels of spores of nonhydrogen sulfide-producing thermophilic anaerobes on equipment and systems suggests that equipment is in need of thorough cleaning and sanitation, or growth is occurring, or both. If proper sanitation is practiced, and if the systems are properly designed, spore buildup should not occur. It is especially important to sample foams and their residues on equipment.

22.63   Product in Process

Excessive numbers of vegetative cells or spores in the product in process, prepared from ingredients meeting the requirements of ingredients for canners' use and for other use, suggest that multiplication is occurring during one or more of the manufacturing steps. The manufacturing sequence should be sampled and the point of increase in the microbial population determined. Remedial steps should be taken immediately. The presence of vegetative cells suggests that sporulation can and will occur.

22.64   Finished Products

The presence of low numbers of spores of the nonhydrogen sulfide-producing thermophilic anaerobes in processed canned foods is not unusual. The organisms possess extreme resistance to the center-can temperatures achieved in many commercial processes.[10] An attempt to eliminate the spores by increased thermal treatments may endanger the nutritional and functional integrity of many products.

If the cooling of processed cans to a center-can temperature of 43°C or less is effected immediately and the cans are stored at temperatures below 35°C, remote from heating ducts and other sources of heat, the presence of spores of thermophilic anaerobes is of no consequence. However, with such a presence the potential for spoilage exists if temperature abuse of the cans occurs, and therefore, this situation should be avoided through the use of meticulously selected ingredients that are carefully handled throughout the production sequence. If thermophilic anaerobes are present, the importance of efficient cooling followed by storage below 35°C cannot be overemphasized.

The presence of detectable thermophilic anaerobes in canned foods destined for hot-vend service or tropical distribution constitutes an unacceptable spoilage hazard. The situation must be overcome by the use of thermophile-free ingredients or by increasing the thermal process.

22.7 REFERENCES

1. Ashton, D. H. 1981. Thermophilic organisms involved in food spoilage: Thermophilic anaerobes not producing hydrogen sulfide. J. Food Prot. 44: 146.
2. AOAC. 1972. Detecting and estimating numbers of thermophilic bacterial spores in sugars. J. Assn. Off. Anal. Chem. 55: 445.
3. Evancho, G. M., Ashton, D. H., and Briskey, E. J. 1973. Conditions necessary for sterility testing of heat-processed canned foods. J. Food Sci. 38: 185.
4. Folinazzo, J. F. and Troy, V. S. 1954. A simple bacteriological medium for the growth and isolation of spoilage organisms from canned foods. Food Technol. 8: 280.
5. NCA Research Laboratories. 1968. "Laboratory Manual for Food Canners and Processors," Vol. I, p. 104. Natl. Canners Assn. (now Natl. Food Processors Assn.) Avi Pub. Co., Westport, Conn.
6. Powers, E. M. 1973. Microbiological requirements and methodology for food in military and federal specifications. Tech. Rep. 73-33-FL. U.S. Army Natick Labs., Natick, Mass.
7. Rhoads, A. T. and Denny, C. B. 1964. Spoilage potentialities of thermophilic anaerobes. Research report No. 3-64. Natl. Can. Assn. (now Natl. Food Processors Assn.) Washington, D.C.
8. Sneath, P. H. A. 1986. Endospore-forming gram-positive rods and cocci. In "Bergey's Manual of Systematic Bacteriology," ed. P. H. A. Sneath, N. S. Mair, M. E. Sharpe, and J. G. Holt, Vol. 2, p. 1141. Williams and Wilkins, Baltimore, Md.
9. Stumbo, D. R. 1973. "Thermobacteriology in Food Processing," 2nd ed. Academic Press, New York.
10. Xezones, H., Segmiller, J. L., and Hutchings, I. J. 1965. Processing requirements for a heat-tolerant anaerobe. Food Technol. 19: 1001.

Chapter 23

SULFIDE SPOILAGE SPOREFORMERS

L. Scott Donnelly and Richard R. Graves

23.1 INTRODUCTION

Early studies on "sulfide stinker" spoilage in canned sweet corn and other vegetables were reported by Werkman and Weaver[18] and Werkman.[17] The cans involved showed no evidence of swelling; however, upon opening, a decided odor of hydrogen sulfide was evident. The product had a blackened appearance caused by the reaction between the sulfide and the iron of the container.

Sulfide spoilage, the presently preferred designation for this type of spoilage, is not common. It is nonexistent in acid foods because of the pH requirements for the growth of the causative organism.

Products suffering this spoilage, although possessing a strong, disagreeable odor of hydrogen sulfide, exhibit no other putrefactive odor.

No evidence of pathogenicity for man or laboratory animal has been associated with *Desulfotomaculum nigrificans*, the causative organism, or with products spoiled by this organism. Evidence has indicated that *D. nigrificans* spores may possess heat resistance in excess of the $D_{120°C}$ value of 2.0 to 3.0 min.[11]

Cameron and Williams[3,4] and Cameron and Yesair[5,6] found sugar and starch to be important sources of these organisms in canneries. More recently, Donnelly and Busta[10] reported that soy isolates and carrageenan contain *D. nigrificans* spores.

23.11 Classification

The type species of the sulfide spoilage group was originally classified and named *Clostridium nigrificans* by Werkman and Weaver.[18] In 1938, Starkey isolated cultures from mud, soil, and sewage at both 30° and 55°C.[16] Those organisms growing at 55°C were large, slightly curved, sporeforming rods, while those isolated at 30°C were asporogenous, short vibrios. Cultures isolated at 30°C failed to grow when transferred directly to 55°C. Those isolated at 55°C and transferred to 30°C underwent morphological changes, eventually resulting in small vibrios resembling those originally isolated at this temperature. As a result, Starkey[16] proposed the new genus *Sporovibrio* for the anaerobic vibrio-shaped cells that produced endospores. The organism *Sporovibrio desulfuricans* was later shown by Campbell et al.[7] to be identical to *C. nigrificans*. Since the latter had taxonomic priority, the thermophilic sporeforming organism that reduced sulfate was considered properly to be named *C. nigrificans*. Campbell and Postgate later proposed the name *Desulfotomaculum nigrificans* for this organism.[8] This classification is followed by Sneath.[14]

23.12   Occurrence

Although relatively rare, sulfide spoilage may occur in canned sweet corn, peas, mushroom products, infant formulas, and other non-acid foods. Spoiled peas sometimes show no discoloration, but more frequently show blackening, with a dark-colored brine. In many instances, spangling of the enamel system of the can occurs as a result of the interaction of the dissolved hydrogen sulfide with the iron of the container. This is evident through the interior enamel because of the semitransparency of the coating.

The cause of sulfide spoilage is a combination of high spore numbers, the heat resistance of the spores, and the holding of finished product at elevated temperatures. This latter factor may be the result of inadequate cooling of processed product.

23.2   GENERAL CONSIDERATIONS

23.21   Sampling

Since there is little evidence to indicate a serious in-plant buildup potential with *D. nigrificans* in modern food processing plants, recommended sampling will be limited to frequently used ingredients.[13]

23.211   Ingredients

Half-pound samples of sugar, starch, or flour are taken from each of 5 100-pound bags of a shipment or lot. In the case of bulk shipments of such ingredients, sampling probably will have to be carried out through a loading port or hatch at the top of the car or tank. A suitable sampler should be used so that samples can be taken from various depths of the load. Samples of liquid sugar are obtained from tank trucks with the use of a sterile, long-handled dipper.

The adequacy of sampling will vary with the size of a shipment; however, when there is any significant variability in the shipment, individual tests on 5 samples are likely to make this evident in the majority of cases.

23.22 Temperature and pH requirements

Most isolates from sulfide spoilage achieve optimum growth at 55°C. Most of these stains will grow at 43°C but not 37°C. Therefore, using the Cameron and Esty definition,[2] these are considered to be obligate thermophiles. Organisms resembling *D. nigrificans* have been isolated from soil, mud, and sewage, as well as from certain food ingredients. Such isolates may be classified as mesophiles, facultative thermophiles, or obligate thermophiles, using again the Cameron and Esty guidelines.

According to Breed et al., the type species, isolated from canned corn showing "sulfur stinker" spoilage, will grow between 65° and 70°C, with optimum growth at 55°C.[1] Campbell and Postgate reported that the organism can be "trained" to grow slowly at 37° or 30°C.[8]

Optimum growth of *D. nigrificans* occurs between pH 6.8 and 7.3. Scanty growth occasionally occurs as low as pH 5.6; however, pH 6.2 is considered the lower limit. Maximum pH for growth has been reported as pH 7.8. The pH values of most vegetables fall below pH 5.8, corn and peas being the exceptions. This may be responsible for the limited and relatively uncommon occurrence of sulfide spoilage.

23.3 EQUIPMENT, MATERIALS, AND REAGENTS

23.31 Culture Media

Common 6-d nails or iron strips, or 5% ferric citrate
Gum arabic
Gum tragacanth
Hydrochloric acid
Sodium hydroxide (.02 N)
Sulfite agar
Vaspar (half mineral oil, half paraffin)

23.32 Equipment

Erlenmeyer flasks, 250 ml marked at 100 ml
Incubator 55°C ± 1°C
Petri dishes
Rubber stoppers
20 × 150-mm screw-cap tubes
Thermometer ($-10°$ to 110°C)
Waterbath[9,12]

23.4   PRECAUTIONS AND LIMITATIONS OF PROCEDURE

When analyzing ingredients, thorough dispersion of the sample solution or slurry in each tube of medium is essential. More difficulty will be encountered in the analysis of starch or flour because of the thickening effect during heating. Frequent swirling of the tubes during the first 10 min of heating will assure proper dispersion.

Since tubes containing colonies of *D. nigrificans* may become completely blackened after 48 hr of incubation, a preliminary count should be made after 20 to 24 hr ± 3 hr.

When preparing tubes of sulfite agar, nails or iron strips should be cleaned in hydrochloric acid and rinsed well to remove all traces of rust before adding to the tubes of medium. The clean nails will combine with any dissolved oxygen in the medium and provide an anaerobic environment. As an alternative to the iron nails, add 10 ml of a 5% solution of ferric citrate to the sulfite agar.

Since the organism is extremely sensitive to oxygen, the inoculum should be added below the surface of the medium in the tube to obtain maximum counts.

23.5   PROCEDURE

23.51   Sugar, Starch, Flour[13]

The following method for preparation of a sample of sugar is recommended by the Association of Official Analytical Chemists (AOAC). The similar method that follows is used for preparation of starch or flour samples.

23.511   Sample preparation

Place 20 g of dry sugar into a dry, sterile, 250-ml Erlenmeyer flask closed with a rubber stopper. Add sterile water to the 100-ml mark, and shake to dissolve. Replace the stopper with a sterile cotton plug, bring the solution rapidly to a boil, and continue boiling for 5 min. Replace the evaporated liquid with sterile water. Cool immediately in cold water.

Prepare samples of liquid sugar the same way, except the amount added to the sterile flask should be determined, depending upon the degree Brix, to be equivalent to 20 g of dry sugar.

Place 20 g of starch or flour in a dry, sterile, 250-ml Erlenmeyer flask, and add sterile cold water to the 100-ml mark, with intermittent swirling. Close the flask with the sterile rubber stopper and shake well to obtain a uniform, lump-free suspension of the sample in water. Sterile glass beads added to the sample mixture will facilitate thorough mixing during shaking.

23.512   Cultural methods

When examining sugar, divide 20 ml of the heated solution among 6 20 × 150-mm screw-cap tubes each containing approximately 10 ml of sulfite agar and a nail. Make the inoculations into freshly exhausted medium, and solidify rapidly by placing the tubes in cold water. Preheat the tubes to 50° to 55°C, and incubate at that temperature for 24 and 48 hr.

In the case of starch or flour, divide 20 ml of the cold suspension among 6 20 × 150-ml screw-cap tubes, each containing approximately 10 ml of sulfite agar and a nail. The tubes should be swirled manually several times before heating and during the 15-min heating period in a boiling waterbath to ensure even dispersion of the starch and flour in the tubes of medium. Following heating, cool the tubes immediately in cold water. Preheat the tubes to 50° to 55°C and incubate at that temperature for 24 to 48 hr. *D. nigrificans* will appear as jet-black spherical areas, the color due to the formation of iron sulfide. No gas is produced. Certain thermophilic anaerobes that do not produce H_2S give rise to relatively large amounts of hydrogen, which splits the agar and, in the case of sulfite agar, reduces the sulfate, thereby causing general blackening of the medium. Count the number of colonies in the 6 tubes. Calculate and report as number of spores per 10 g of ingredient.

A more sensitive method for the detection (not enumeration) of *D. nigrificans* was recommended by Speck.[15]

23.52   Nonfat Dry Milk

23.521   Sample preparation

Weigh 10 g of the sample into a sterile, 250-ml Erlenmeyer flask marked to 100 ml. Add .02 N sodium hydroxide to the 100-ml mark and shake to dissolve the sample completely. Heat 10 min at 5-lb steam pressure, then cool immediately.

23.522   Culturing methods

Transfer 2 ml of the heated solution to each of 2 20- × 150-mm screw-cap tubes of freshly exhausted sulfite agar and nail. Gently swirl several times and solidify rapidly by placing the tubes in cold water. Preheat the tubes to 50° to 55°C, and incubate at that temperature for 24 and 48 hr ± 3 hr. Count colonies of *D. nigrificans* described earlier, and report on the basis of 10 g of sample.

23.53   Cream

23.531   Sample preparation

Mix 2 g of gum tragacanth and 1 g of gum arabic in 100 ml of water in an Erlenmeyer flask. Sterilize in the autoclave for 20 min at 121°C. Transfer 20 ml of sample to a sterile, 250-ml Erlenmeyer flask marked for 100 ml. Add the sterilized gum mixture to the 100-ml mark and carefully shake, using a sterile rubber stopper. Loosen the stopper and autoclave for 5 min at 5-psi pressure.

23.54   Soy Protein Isolates

23.541   Sample preparation

Prepare a 10% suspension of soy protein isolate in sterile 0.1% peptone water in milk dilution bottles (or equivalent). Adjust the pH to 7.0 ± 0.1. Steam in an autoclave (approximately 5 lb steam) for 20 min.

23.542   Culturing methods

Following the steaming procedure, add 1.0 ml of the suspension to each of 10 tubes containing molten sulfite agar and a nail. Heat the tubes immediately before inoculation to eliminate oxygen. After inoculation, tubes are mixed, solidified in an ice waterbath, overlaid with Vaspar, and preheated to 55°C. Incubate the tubes for 14 days at 55°C. Count the jet-black spherical areas for the 10 tubes and report as the number of spores per gram of soy isolate. Preliminary counts should be made at 48 hr, 7 days, and 14 days in case tubes become completely blackened. Note that Donnelly and Busta[10] reported on an alternative medium to sulfite agar for use with soy protein isolates. Additional 10-tube sets can be used to examine a larger sample.

23.6   INTERPRETATION

A standard for sulfide spoilage applies only to ingredients (sugar, starch, flour, etc.) to be used in low-acid, heat-processed canned foods.

Sulfide spoilage spores should be present in not more than 2 (40%) of the 5 samples tested, and in any one sample to the extent of not more than 5 spores per 10 g.[12]

23.7   REFERENCES

1. Breed, R. S., Murray, E. G. D., and Smith, N. R. 1957. "Bergey's Manual of Determinative Bacteriology," 7th ed., p. 649. Williams and Wilkins, Baltimore, Md.
2. Cameron, E. J. and Esty, J. R. 1926. The examination of canned spoiled foods, 2. Classification of flat sour spoilage organisms from nonacid foods. J. Infect. Dis. 39: 89.
3. Cameron, E. J. and Williams, C. C. 1928a. The thermophilic flora of sugar in its relation to canning. Centbl. Bakt. 76: 28.
4. Cameron, E. J. and Williams, C. C. 1928b. Thermophilic flora of sugar in its relation to canning. J. Bacteriol. 15: 31.
5. Cameron, E. J. and Yesair, J. 1931a. About sugar contamination: Its effect in canning corn. Canning Age 12: 239.
6. Cameron, E. J. and Yesair, J. 1931b. Canning tests prove presence of thermophiles in sugar. Food Indus. 3: 265.
7. Campbell, L. L. Jr., Frank, H. A., and Hall, E. R. 1957. Studies on thermophilic sulfate-reducing bacteria. I. Identification of *Sporovibrio desulfuricans as Clostridium nigrificans*. J. Bacteriol. 73: 516.
8. Campbell, L. L. and Postgate, J. R. 1956. Classification of the sporeforming sulfate-reducing bacteria. Bact. Rev. 29: 359.

 9. DoD. 1981. "Military Standard. Bacterial Standards for Starches, Flours, Cereals, Alimentary Pastes, Dry Milks, and Sugars Used in Preparation of Canned Foods for the Armed Forces." MIL-STD-900. U.S. Dept. of Defense, Washington, D.C.
10. Donnelly, L. S. and Busta, F. F. 1981. Alternative procedures for the enumeration of *Desulfotomaculum nigrificans* spores in raw ingredients of soy protein-based products. J. Food Sci. 46: 1527.
11. Donnelly, L. S. and Busta, F. F. 1980. Heat resistance of *Desulfotomaculum nigrificans* spores in soy protein infant formula preparations. Appl. Environ. Microbiol. 40: 721.
12. NCA Research Laboratories. 1968. "Laboratory Manual for Food Canners and Processors," Vol. 1, p. 104. Natl. Canners Assn. (now Natl. Food Processors Assn.) AVI Publ. Co., Inc., Westport, Conn.
13. AOAC. 1972. Official First Action: Detecting and estimating numbers of thermophilic bacterial spores in sugars. J. Assn. Off. Anal. Chem. 55: 445.
14. Sneath, P. H. A. 1986. Endospore-forming gram-positive rods and cocci. In "Bergey's Manual of Systematic Bacteriology," ed. P. H. A. Sneath, N. S. Mair, M. E. Sharpe, and J. G. Holt, p. 1200. Vol. 2, Williams and Wilkins, Baltimore, Md.
15. Speck, R. V. 1981. Thermophilic organisms in food spoilage: Sulfide spoilage anaerobes. J. Food Prot. 44: 149.
16. Starkey, R. L. 1938. A study of spore formation and other morphological characteristics of *Vibrio desulfuricans*. Arch. Mikrobiol. 9: 268.
17. Werkman, C. H. 1929. Bacteriological studies on sulfide spoilage of canned vegetables. Iowa Agr. Exp. Sta. Res. Bul. 117: 163.
18. Werkman, C. H. and Weaver, H. J. 1927. Studies in the bacteriology of sulfur stinker spoilage of canned sweet corn. Iowa State College J. Sci. 2: 57.

Chapter 24

COLIFORMS—*ESCHERICHIA COLI* AND ITS TOXINS

A. D. Hitchins, P. A. Hartman, and E. C. D. Todd

24.1 INTRODUCTION

In 1887, Escherich observed the ubiquity of what we now designate *Escherichia coli* in human stools. Shardinger, in 1892, suggested that members of this species be used as an index of fecal pollution because they could be recovered more easily than *Salmonella* species. Thus, in the earliest methods of microbial water analysis, the emphasis was on the recovery of *E. coli*. However, in 1914 the U.S. Public Health Service standard was changed from *E. coli* to the coliform group. This change was based on the questionable assumption that all members of the coliform group possess equal sanitary significance. Recently, the indicator group has been limited to species capable of proliferation at elevated temperatures.

The fecal coliform group is restricted to organisms that grow in the gastrointestinal tract of humans and warm-blooded animals. It includes members of at least three genera: *Escherichia*, *Klebsiella*, and *Enterobacter*. Because evidence implicates some *E. coli* as enteric pathogens, and because klebsiellae are more ubiquitous than previously presumed, some workers are suggesting a return to the recovery and enumeration of *E. coli* as an index of fecal pollution. A countertrend has been to detect and enumerate all fermentative gram-negative organisms, i.e., the *Enterobacteriaceae* group concept.[39] This concept can be extended even further because some processed foods such as pasteurized milk or canned foods should contain no viable gram-negative bacteria whatsoever; in these instances culture media selective for all gram-negative bacteria might be appropriate.

Successful implementation of each approach has depended on development of technology for precise control of incubation temperature, formulation of satisfactory media with adequate standards of quality control, and understanding of the physiology, ecology, and taxonomy of these organisms.

24.2   DEFINITIONS

The definitions used are often only working concepts, and they do not always delineate classical taxa.

24.21   Coliform Group

The coliform group includes aerobic and facultatively anaerobic, gramnegative, nonsporeforming rods that ferment lactose, forming acid and gas within 48 hr at 35°C. For dairy products, some workers specify 32°C.[2, 32] Test media include a variety of lactose-containing liquid or solid media supplemented with antibiotics, dyes, and/or surface-active agents. Specification of the medium and temperature is critical in the interpretation of data. The coliform group may contain organisms not included, or only provisionally included, in the *Enterobacteriaceae*, e.g., *Aeromonas* species. On the basis of available evidence, representatives of 20 or more species may conform to criteria for the coliform group. If nitrophenyl-beta-D-galactoside, rather than lactose, is used as the substrate, the list becomes even more extensive because many *Enterobacteriaceae* that do not ferment lactose will hydrolyze the nitrophenyl galactoside; examples are *Citrobacter* spp., *Enterobacter agglomerans*, *Hafnia alvei*, and *Serratia marcescens*.

24.22   Fecal Coliform Group

Elevated temperature tests for the separation of coliform organisms into those of fecal and nonfecal origins have been used in many parts of the world with diverse modifications; however, none will absolutely differentiate the two groups. Practical methods have been developed to favor the selection and growth of fecal coliform organisms and eliminate many types that have little or no public health significance.

The following discussion indicates the variations in test procedures for the enumeration of fecal coliforms. In "Standard Methods for the Examination of Water and Wastewater," three approaches to fecal coliform determinations are described: (1) subculture from positive presumptive lauryl sulfate tryptose (LST) broth to *E. coli* (EC) broth with incubation at 44.5° ± 0.2°C for 24 ± 2 hr; (2) inoculation of tubes of A-1 broth and incubation for 3 hr at 35° ± 0.5°C, followed by incubation at 44.5° ± 0.2°C for an additional 21 ± 2 hr; and (3) a membrane filter procedure using modified fecal coliform (mFC) broth or agar with incubation at 44.5° ± 0.2°C for 24 ± 2 hr.[3, 51] Canadian authorities specify incubation of EC broth at 44.5° ± 0.2°C for 24 hr for fecal coliform counts of fish, fish products, and shellfish, but 45.0° ± 0.2°C for other foods. In the United States, the fecal coliform method used in the National Shellfish Sanitation Program also specifies incubation in EC broth at 44.5° ± 0.2°C for 24 ± 2 hr.[1] Recent evidence[51] indicates that an incubation temperature of 45.0° ± 0.2°C for all tests would be a logical compromise.

Like the term "coliform," the term "fecal coliform" has no taxonomic validity. Therefore, the meaning of a fecal coliform count becomes clear only when it is expressed in terms of the test procedure used and the specimen under examination.

24.23   *Enterobacteriaceae* Group[39]

In Europe, considerable use has been made of the total *Enterobacteriaceae* group concept. A brilliant green oxgall broth with glucose substituted for lactose is used for enrichment. Cultures are recovered from violet red bile agar (VRBA) fortified with 1% glucose. Although in theory all *Enterobacteriaceae* may be recovered, in practice members of other groups may also be enumerated unless suitable differential tests are subsequently applied.

24.24   *Escherichia coli*

In the identification and enumeration of *E. coli* of sanitary significance, isolates must conform to the coliform and fecal coliform group definitions. Traditionally, the isolates were identified by their IMViC pattern: + + − − (Type I) and − + − − (Type II). Recent data indicate that this profile is inadequate for identification of the species. According to information from the U.S. Centers for Disease Control, the aforementioned patterns may be found in most strains of all five species[21] (Table 1).

Methodology is also critical. The relatively high incidence of Type II "*E. coli*" in some specimens is at least partly explained by the fact that many cultures require 48 hr to produce a detectable amount of indole, and additional tests are essential for speciation. The success of the classical differential tests in previous years is attributed to the enhanced selectivity of enrichments and the stereotyped criteria for selection of colonies from Levine's eosin methylene blue (L-EMB) agar. With increased use of direct streak and less selective enrichments, the difficulty in identification undoubtedly will increase.

24.25   Enteropathogenic *Escherichia coli* (EEC)

Enteropathogenic *E. coli* cause gastroenteritis in humans and domestic animals. Recognition of these cultures requires a regimen of serological, pathological, and biochemical-physiological tests. Not all EEC strains may conform to the definitions of the coliform group, the fecal coliform group, and *E. coli*. Some cannot ferment lactose within 48 hr or do not produce gas.[36] Moreover, a positive reaction must be obtained in one or more tests

Table 1—Differentiating *Escherichia coli* from Other *Enterobacteriaceae* spp. and Related Bacteria[21, 30]

Culture	IMViC	Motility 37°C	Cytochrome oxidase	Glucose gas	KCN	Lactose	Mannitol	Sorbitol	Cellobiose acid	Malonate	Adonitol acid	Urease
Typical *E. coli*	+ + − −	±	−	+	−	+	+	±	−	−	−	−
Inactive *E. coli*[a]	+ + − −	−	−	−	−	±	+	−	−	−	−	−
Escherichia blattae	− + − ±	−	−	+	−	−	−	−	−	+	−	−
Escherichia fergusonii[a]	+ + − ±	+	−	+	−	−	+	−	+	±	+	−
Escherichia hermanii	+ + − −	+	−	+	±	±	+	−	+	−	−	−
Escherichia vulneris	− + − −	+	−	+	±	±	+	−	+	±	−	−
Plesiomonas shigelloides	+ + − −	+	+	−	−	±	−	−	−	−	−	−
Klebsiella pneumoniae	− ± + +	−	−	+	+	+	+	+	+	+	±	+
Klebsiella ozaenae	− + − ±	−	−	±	±	±	+	±	+	−	+	±
Klebsiella oxytoca	+ ± + +	−	−	+	+	+	+	+	+	+	+	+
Hafnia alvei	− ± ± −	+	−	+	+	−	+	−	±	±	−	−
Aeromonas hydrophila	+ + ± ±	+	+	+	±	−	+	±	±	−	−	−

+ = ≥90% positive; ± = 10% to 90% positive, − = <10% positive.
[a]Groups tentatively recognized at the Centers for Disease Control.

for attributes of enteropathogenicity, e.g., production of one or more entero-toxins, colonization of epithelial cells, invasiveness, or in the absence of positive data in the aforementioned tests, possession of somatic, capsular, and flagellar antigens found in the classical human, enteropathogenic, and infantile serotypes. Use of these tests is hindered by the absence of com-mercially available reagents and the relative nonspecificity of pathogenicity tests.

24.3   PRECAUTIONS

24.31   Cultures

Control cultures of *E. coli* (+ + − −) and *Enterobacter aerogenes* (− − + +) should be maintained for testing IMViC media and reagents and Gram stain reagents. Check the performance of all media. The control strain of *E. coli* should produce gas in EC medium at 45.5°C within 24 hr. Note that water and food bacteriologists use different temperatures for the coliform tests.[51] The control strain of *E. aerogenes* should produce a negative reaction. Monitor the temperature of the 45.5°C bath at least three times a day; keep readings at least 3 hr apart.

24.32   Dilutions

Prepare only as many test dilutions as can be inoculated and incubated within 15 min.

24.33   Media

Liquid media absorb air during cold storage and should be allowed to reach laboratory temperature gradually after removal from refrigeration. Include uninoculated medium as a control.

24.34   General Limitations of Liquid Enrichment Test

The most probable number (MPN) technique indicates the most likely number of organisms present. Further details in the use of this procedure are found in Chapter 6.

24.35   Minimal Number of Fecal Coliforms

The only easily recognizable organism of fecal habitat in the fecal coliform group is *E. coli*. Fecal types other than *E. coli* may be present, but are not conclusively identified by the IMViC tests, and are not referable to an original fecal habitat. Without speciation of all isolates, the minimum number of probable fecal coliforms in a food corresponds to the number of *E. coli* present. The upper limit is unknown.

24.36   General Limitations of EMB Agar

Physical and subjective limitations are encountered in the use of EMB agar. The ability to discern one distinctive colony among many, and specifically to recognize an *E. coli* colony among many coliform colonies, is critical to the success of the entire analytical procedure. Also, some biotypes of *E. coli* do not produce a typical colony with green sheen. Slow or nonlactose-fermenters produce colorless colonies.

24.37   Limitations of the Coliform, Fecal Coliform, and *E. coli* Tests

In the coliform and fecal coliform group tests, only the lactose fermentations of total bacterial populations are observed and quantitated by the MPN technique. Individual organisms are not isolated in pure culture, transferred to lactose broth, or Gram stained. Thus, conformity with the definitions for the coliform and fecal coliform group is not obtained. Uncertain identity is compensated by rapid results.

With the *E. coli* test, all requirements of the original definition are met. The organism is isolated in pure state, Gram stained, and examined for lactose fermentation and conformity with the IMViC tests. Nevertheless, some other *Escherichia* spp. can be misidentified as *E. coli* if only these tests are conducted (Table 1).

24.38   Interferences

The importance of false-negative reactions in recovering coliforms from water supplies has been emphasized.[20, 33] Part of the difficulty in recovering these organisms has been the damage introduced by low pH, refrigeration, and use of bactericidal or bacteriostatic agents.[40] Coliform counts can often be increased by resuscitation of the coliform microflora (see Chapter 7) in an unselective medium before addition of selective agents (see Section 24.54). Furthermore, turbid but not gassy lauryl sulfate broth tubes (see Section 24.52) might be streaked onto a solid medium to determine whether anaerogenic coliforms were present or gas production was inhibited by the indigenous food microflora.

An alternative procedure to identify *E. coli* is to incorporate 4-methylumbilliferyl-beta-D-glucuronic acid (MUG) into a culture medium selective for coliforms.[23] Generally, 50 μg/ml is used for liquid media (24.72) and 100 μg/ml for agar media (24.54) that contain lactose. After incubation, the tubes or plates are held under a long-wave (365 nm) ultraviolet lamp in a darkened area. The presence of a bluish fluorescence indicates the hydrolysis of MUG by glucuronidase enzymes. The test is about 94% specific for *E. coli*.[23]

24.4   EQUIPMENT, MATERIALS, AND REAGENTS

This section lists equipment, media, reagents and stains, and animals used. Chapter 62 discusses composition and preparation of media, reagents, and stains.

24.41   Equipment

Air incubators, 35°, 37°, 40°, 43°, and 50°C (all ± 0.5°C)

Bactometer™ microbial system or equivalent

Carbon dioxide gas analytical kit

Carbon dioxide incubator (95% air, 5% CO_2) moisture-saturated atmosphere, 35°C

Cell-counting chamber, Spencer Bright Line or Fuchs-Rosenthal

Cellulose acetate or nitrate membrane, 85 mm diameter, 0.45 μm pore size, sterile

Circulating, humidified air incubator, maintaining a temperature of 44° ± 0.5°C

CO_2, compressed

Coplin staining dishes or trays, 100 to 250 ml

Culture containers, glass prescription bottles, or plastic tissue culture flasks, sterile 2 oz (57 ml), 3 oz (85 ml), and 6 oz (171 ml); 75 sq cm

Darkroom

Epoxy-coated or stainless steel test tube racks, accommodating 75 × 8, 150 × 18, 150 × 16, and 175 × 22 mm tubes

Equipment for steaming petri dishes (steamer, autoclave, etc.)

Forceps

Freezer, −20° or −70°C

Glass cover slips, 2.5 × 5.1 cm

Glass rod spreader

Hydrophobic grid membrane filter (HGMF) replicator

McFarland nephelometer

Microscopes, standard 900× magnification, inverted stage, 100× magnification, and microscope illuminator

Microtiter tissue culture plates, 96 flat-bottom wells, sterile, plastic with lid

Microtitration plate washer

Multichannel pipetter, 8 channel, variable capacity 0.05 to 0.2 ml

Petri dishes, sterile, 15 × 150 or 20 × 150 mm (plastic and glass)

Petrifilm VRB and plastic spreader (Medical-Surgical Division/3M 255-55 3M Center, St. Paul, MN 55144)

pH test paper, range 5.0–8.0

Pipette filler

Pipettes, 0.1 and 0.2 mm serological; Pasteur; and 25 ml

Pipettes, continuous adjustment, 0.02 to 0.2 ml, 0.1 to 1.0 ml, and 0.5 to 5.0 ml

Plastic tube, 50 ml

Prefilters, disposable 100 μm, (Richard Brancker Research Ltd., 27 Monk St., Ottawa, Ontario K1S 3Y7, Canada)

Reciprocal and/or rotary shaker

Refrigerated centrifuge, with adaptor, to accommodate 13 × 100-mm tubes, and covered centrifuge cups to prevent aerosolization of pathogens

Replicator, toothpicks (sterile), or microbiological needle

Shaker incubator, 37°C

Single-edged razor blade

Spectrophotometer or microtitration plate reader

Spreadfilter, Model MF 10 (Richard Brancker Research Ltd.)

Sterile plastic plates containing 16-mm diameter wells

Swinnex™ filter holder, 25 mm, with sterile 0.45-μm pore diameter membrane filters

Syringes, 1.0 and 5.0 ml

Tissue culture chamber slides, 4 compartments per slide

Total immersion thermometer approximately 45 to 55 cm long, range 1° to 55°C, graduated in subdivisions of 0.1°C, and standardized against a National Institute of Standards and Technology-certified thermometer or equivalent

Ultraviolet lamp fitted with Woods' filter, 365 nm wavelength

Vacuum desiccator if filters are to be stored longer than 1 week

Vertical laminar flow biological hood equipped with HEPA™ filter

Water baths with plastic or metal gable covers and mechanical circulation systems capable of maintaining temperatures of 35° ± 1°, 44.0° ± 0.2°, 44.5° ± 0.2°, 49° ± 1°, and 55° ± 1°C

Whatman filter papers, assorted sizes and thicknesses, including Nos. 1 and 541

X-ray film holder cassettes with intensifying screens (Kodak regulator or DuPont Cronex lightening plus)

X-ray film (Kodak XAR-2, 8 × 10 in, is convenient)

24.42 Materials

A-1 medium

Antibiotics currently used in therapy, available on disks

Bile salts, No. 3, 0.5% in ES. Dissolve 5 g bile salts No. 3 formulation in 1 L ES. Sterilize by filtration.

Blood agar base

Brain heart infusion (BHI) broth

BHI broth for HeLa technique, 1.25% in ES. Dissolve 12.5 g BHI powder in 1 liter ES. Sterilize by filtration. Final pH, 7.2 ± 0.2.

Brilliant green bile (BGB) broth

Bromcresol purple carbohydrate broth base supplemented with carbohydrates

Buffered glucose broth (MR-VP medium)

Casamino acid-yeast extract (CAYE)-lincomycin medium

Casamino acid-yeast extract—salts (CAYE-S) broth

Cell growth medium

Coliform medium (CM)

Colonization medium

Eagle's minimal essential medium (MEME), containing glutamine and Earle's salts; store at 4°–10°C

Earle's balanced salts (ES) solution (phenol red-free)

E. coli (EC) broth

Fetal bovine serum (FBS), sterile, virus-screened, mycoplasma-free (Flow Laboratories, Rockville, MD 20852). To inactivate, heat 2 hr at 55° ± 1°C.

Gentamicin in Dulbecco's phosphate-buffered saline (DPBS) Dissolve 50 mg gentamicin (Schering Corp., Kenilworth, NJ 07033) in 100 ml DPBS to give solution containing 500 µg/ml. Sterilize by filtration.

Ham's F-10 medium with glutamine and $NaHCO_3$

Hemorrhagic coli (HC) agar

Infection medium (IM)

Intracellular growth phase (IGP) medium

KCN broth

Koser's citrate medium

L15 medium

Lauryl sulfate tryptose (LST) broth

Levine eosin methylene blue (L-EMB) agar

MacConkey agar (MAC)

Malonate broth with added glucose and yeast extract

MEME-FBS (Antibiotic-free medium for cultivating of HeLa cells before infection)

MEME-FBS-Pen-Strep solution (Routine HeLa mammalian cell growth medium)

Minerals modified glutamate agar

Minimal essential medium with Hank's salts

Modified coliform medium (mCM)

Modified fecal coliform (mFC) agar

Motility test medium

Methyl red-Voges Proskauer (MR-VP) broth

Nutrient agar

Penicillin G-streptomycin antibiotic concentrate (500 IU/ml, 500 µg/ml)

Plate count agar (PCA)

Proteose agar

Pure nitrocellulose membrane, 82 mm (Bio-Rad Labs, Cambridge, MA 02189 or Schleicher & Schuell, Keene, NH 03431)

Sorbitol-MacConkey agar (Difco Laboratories, Detroit, MI 48232)

Syncase broth

Tryptic soy agar (TSA)

Tryptic soy agar with $MgSO_4$ (TSAM)

Trypticase-novobiocin (TN) broth

Trypticase soy agar

Tryptone bile agar

Tryptone phosphate-brain heart infusion-yeast extract (TPBY) agar

Tryptone phosphate (TP) broth
Tryptone (trypticase) soy broth (TSB)
Tryptone (tryptophane) broth
Urea broth
Veal infusion broth agar and nutrient agar
Violet red bile agar (VRBA)
Y-1 cell medium

24.43   Reagents

Affinity purified goat antiserum (to rabbit IgG) conjugated to horseradish peroxidase (Bio-Rad Labs)

Butterfield's phosphate-buffered dilution water

Calf-thymus DNA (sonicated)

Chloroform

Cholera enterotoxin. Dilute 1:1000 in Y-1 phosphate saline solution; store at 5°C

Cytochrome oxidase reagent

Decolorizing and dehydrating reagents: acetone-xylene (50:50) and (33:67); pure xylene

Dulbecco's phosphate-buffered saline (DPBS), calcium- and magnesium-free

E. coli antisera, store at 5°C

Human infantile enteropathogenic polyvalents A, B, and C

Alkalescenes-Dispar polyvalent

Polyvalent M, comprising equal volumes of high titer monovalent sera toward the following somatic antigens of E. coli; 6, 8, 11, and 78. This polyvalent, which is unavailable commercially, can be prepared by mixing equal aliquots of high titer monovalent sera.

Monovalent O sera—6, 8, 11, 18, 20, 26, 28, 44, 55, 78, 86, 111, 112, 119, 124, 125, 126, 127, and 128

E. coli ST[49]

E. coli strains

H10407 (LT$^+$, ST$^+$)
H10407P (LT$^+$, ST$^-$)
O4100C$_1$ (LT$^-$, ST$^-$)

End-labeled radioactive DNA probe

Evans blue stain, 2%

Gelatin, ELISA grade

Giemsa stain

Goat antiserum

Gram stain reagents

H:7 antiserum (Difco)

Hanks' phosphate-buffered saline, calcium- and magnesium-free

Horseradish peroxide (HRP) color development solution

Human cervical epithelial cell culture

HeLa culture, American Type Culture Collection (ATCC). Other cultures, including Henle 407 human intestine and human laryngeal carcinoma, give comparable data; however, HeLa cell culture is more suitable with regard to growth characteristics.

Hybridization mixture B

Hydrogen peroxide, 30% aqueous solution, stabilized

Immersion oil, nondrying, type B (150 centistokes viscosity)

Indole oxidant accelerated reagent

Kovacs' indole reagent

Lincomycin

Lysis mixtures C and D

May-Grunwald stain

McFarland standards

Eagle's minimal essential medium and L15 medium mixed in equal proportions (MEME-L15)

Methanol, ACS reagent grade

Methyl red indicator

4-Methylumbilliferyl-beta-D-glucuronic acid (MUG)

Milk serum, 2%

Mounting medium. Dilute mounting medium with xylene to give easily dispensed colloidal suspension; 20 ml Permount™ (Fisher Scientific Co., Fairlawn, NJ 07410) diluted with 5 ml xylene is satisfactory.

Mouse adrenal cell (Y-1) culture, ATCC No. 75

NaCl, 0.5%, sterile

O157 monoclonal antibody solution

Pathogenic biotypes of *E. coli*

    Enteroinvasive

    Enterotoxigenic, producing heat-labile toxin (LT)

    Enterotoxigenic, producing heat-stable toxin (ST)

    Classical, infantile enteropathogenic

Penicillin G-streptomycin (gentamicin) solution

Peptone water

Peroxidase (ABTS) substrate

Phosphate buffered saline-merthiolate (PBS-M)

Phosphate buffered saline-merthiolate gelatin (PBS-M-GEL)

Phosphate buffered saline-merthiolate rabbit serum albumin (PBS-M-RSA)

Polymyxin B sulfate, 20 mg/ml water; store frozen

Positive and negative control cultures for gene probe methods. The specific strains used will depend upon the particular gene probe used.

Protein A labeled with horseradish peroxidase (HRP-PA)

Rabbit antiserum to *E. coli* LT

Rabbit antiserum to enterotoxin[28]

Saline Tween merthiolate (STM)

Salts-phosphate buffered saline solution (Salts-PBS)

Shigella antisera, store at 5°C

  S. boydii 8

  S. dysenteriae 10

Spicer-Edwards EN complex antibody solution

Standard invasive and noninvasive control strains of *E. coli*, based on the Sereny test, available from laboratories actively engaged in research on enteric illness.

Stopping reagent (ELISA)

Tris buffered saline (TBS) with or without Tween; or TBS with 1% or 3% gelatin

  Trypan blue, 0.01%. Dissolve 10 mg stain (Allied Chemical and Dye Corp., New York, NY 10006) in 100 ml 0.85% saline

  Trypsin, 0.25%. Suspend 2.5 g 1:250 trypsin powder (Difco) in 100 ml calcium- and magnesium-free Hanks' phosphate-buffered saline and let particles settle. Sterilize by filtration. Dilute 10 ml of this solution in 90 ml sterile calcium- and magnesium-free DPBS to prepare 0.25% trypsin. Store at 4°–10°C.

  Tween-20

  Vaseline-paraffin, 50:50 w/w. Heat gently to melt and to mix. Apply to slides mounted with cover slip to seal. Caution: Mixture is flammable.

  Verocytotoxin rabbit antibody

  Voges-Proskauer reagents

  Vracko-Sherris indole reagent

  X-ray film developer

  X-ray film fixer

  Y-1 phosphate saline solution

24.44   Animals

Guinea pigs, 300 to 500 g

Infant mice, Swiss albino, 3 to 5 days old

24.5   COLIFORM GROUP

24.51   Preparation of Food Test Samples

If the food is frozen and must be thawed, refrigerate at 2°–5°C for 18 hr before analysis. Weigh 25 g of regular or thawed food aseptically into a sterile blender jar. Add 225 ml of Butterfield's phosphate buffer diluent or 0.1% peptone to the blender jar and blend for 2 min. Prepare decimal dilutions of 1:10, 1:100, and 1:1000, or higher if necessary, by adding 10 ml of the previous dilution to 90 ml of the sterile diluent. Shake all dilutions 25 times in a 1-ft arc for 7 sec.

24.52   Presumptive Test for Coliform Group MPN[7] (Note: see Section 24.72 for simultaneous coliform/*E. coli* tests)

Inoculate 3 replicate tubes of lauryl sulfate tryptose (LST) broth per dilution with 1 ml of the previously prepared 1:10, 1:100, and 1:1000 dilutions. But note that in Recommended Procedures for the Examination of Sea Water and Shellfish,[1] the use of 5 tubes of LST broth for the presumptive test for coliforms is specified. Incubate tubes for 24 and 48 ± 2 hr at 35° ± 0.5°C. Observe all tubes for gas production either in the inverted vial or by effervescence produced when the tube is gently shaken. Read tubes for gas production at the end of 24 hr. Reincubate negative tubes for an additional 24 hr. Record all LST tubes showing gas within 48 ± 2 hr; refer to MPN tables for the 3-tube dilutions (Chapter 6) and report results as the presumptive MPN of coliform bacteria per g or ml (see Section 24.53).

If shellfish from certain sources are examined frequently on a routine basis and the frequency of false-positive presumptive tests is known to be low, it may not be necessary to confirm all positive presumptive tubes, especially the 24-hr tubes. An acceptable alternative procedure for plating 3 or more replicate portions of a series of 3 or more decimal dilutions is as follows:

Select the tubes of the highest dilution (smallest test volume) in which all the tubes show gas production in 24 hr. Perform the confirmed test on these tubes and on all gas-positive tubes in any higher dilutions. If no dilutions provide tubes without gas, perform the confirmed test on all gas-positive tubes of the highest and next-to-the-highest dilutions. Submit to the confirmed test all tubes of all dilutions in which gas is produced only at the end of 48 hr of incubation. If fewer than 3 portions of any dilution or volume or if fewer than 3 decimal dilutions of the original test portion are plated, submit all tubes producing gas during 24 or 48 hr of incubation to the confirmed test. Record all tubes producing gas as containing organisms of the coliform group.

24.53   Confirmed Test for Coliform Group (see Note in Section 24.52)

Subculture all positive LST tubes that show gas within 48 ± 2 hr (see Section 24.52) into brilliant green bile (BGB) broth by means of a 3-mm loop. Incubate all BGB tubes at 35° ± 0.5°C for 48 ± 2 hr. Record all BGB tubes showing gas and refer to MPN tables for 3- or 5-tube dilutions, whichever is applicable (Chapter 6), and report results as confirmed MPN of coliform bacteria per g (or ml).

24.54   Coliform Group: Solid Medium Method (VRBA)[2]

Prepare violet red bile agar (VRBA) and pasteurize it by boiling on the day of use. Note: Overheating may result in decreased productivity.[24] If an autoclave is used to sterilize VRBA, heat small aliquots of about 100 ml for no longer than 5 min at 121°C. Store sterile medium in the dark for no longer than 2 weeks before use, and remelt the agar in flowing steam, in boiling water, or in a microwave oven. Cool to 48°C before use. The pH of the VRBA should be 7.0 to 7.2. Weigh a 25-g test portion, and homogenize at high speed for 2 min in 225 ml Butterfield's phosphate-buffered dilution water or 0.1% peptone water. Prepare serial tenfold dilutions in Butterfield's diluent or 0.1% peptone water in accordance with the anticipated level of coliforms. Transfer two 1-ml aliquots of each dilution to petri dishes.

Use either of two plating methods.[2] For the conventional method, pour 10 ml of VRBA tempered to 48°C into the plates. Swirl plates to mix, and let solidify. Overlay with 5 ml VRBA and let solidify. If a resuscitation step is necessary, pour a basal layer of 8 to 10 ml of tryptic soy agar tempered to 48°C. Swirl plates to mix, and incubate at room temperature for 2.0 ± 0.5 h. Then overlay with 8 to 10 ml of melted, cooled VRBA and allow to solidify. To find *E. coli* among the coliforms, use 100 µg MUG/ml in the VRBA overlay and observe as stated in Section 24.72. Use aliquots of up to 4 ml of dilution when deeper plates and 15 ml VRBA are added.

After solidification, invert plates and incubate 18 to 24 hr at 35°C. For dairy products, incubate at 32°C.[2] Examine plates with illumination under a magnifying lens. Count purple-red colonies, 0.5 mm in diameter or larger, surrounded by a zone of precipitated bile acids. Optimally, plates should have 30 to 100 colonies.

For confirmation select colonies representing different types in accordance with their relative numbers and transfer each to a tube of BGB broth. Incubate tubes at 35°C. Examine at 24 to 48 hr. Colonies producing gas are confirmed as coliform organisms. Perform a Gram stain on a test portion from any tube showing a pellicle in order to exclude gram-positive, lactose-fermenting bacilli. Determine the number of coliforms per g by multiplying the percentage of tubes confirmed as positive by the original VRBA count, i.e., the number of suspicious coliform colonies multiplied by the dilution factor.

24.55   Petrifilm VRB (Violet Red Bile) Method[35]

This method is an alternative to the coliform plate count with VRBA. It uses the dry ingredients of VRB lactose agar with a cold-water soluble gelling agent (replacing the agar) coated onto plastic film. These reagents are hydrated when 1 ml of a diluted or undiluted test portion is added. Pressure applied to a plastic spreader placed on an overlay film distributes test portions over 20 sq cm. Colonies develop after incubation at $32° \pm 1°C$ for 24 ± 2 hr. Colonies with one or more gas bubbles within one colony diameter are counted as coliforms. Note that colonies will be red regardless of whether they are coliforms or not.

24.56   Coliform Group—Impedence Method for the Coliform Count in Ice Cream, Pasteurized Cream, Raw Milk, and Yogurt

These methods were designed for use in a system like the Bactometer™ microbial system (see Chapter 39).

24.561   Handling test samples

Keep test samples frozen (or refrigerated: yogurt, cream, milk). Avoid keeping thawed or refrigerated test samples at room temperatures for a prolonged period.

24.562   Procedure

Set instrument incubator to 35°C. Thaw ice cream in a 30°C water bath until it is thoroughly melted. Add 5.0 ml of the ice cream to 45 ml of coliform medium (CM). Other kinds of test samples are processed as follows: add 10 ml yogurt or 10 ml cream to 90 ml modified CM (mCM); add 2 ml raw milk to 18 ml CM. Shake cream dilutions 25 times before and after preincubation.

Preincubate test portion and medium for 3 hr at 35°C. Shake 25 times after preincubation. If cut-off level for raw milk is above 100 organisms per ml, omit the preincubation step. Remove caps from module wells after preincubation period, and add 1.5 ml of the dilution into a module well. Replace caps securely. Insert module into instrument and start test at 35°C.

24.563   Interpreting results

A detection time with a color change in the well from purple to yellow indicates coliform. Detection times shorter than the caution time without color change require the following confirmation:

Make a 1:10,000 dilution of the well in question. Add 0.1 ml of the dilution to BGB broth tubes containing fermentation tubes. Incubate at 32°C for 48 hr. Gas production within 48 hr indicates coliforms.

24.57   Coliform Group—Hydrophobic Grid Membrane Filter (HGMF) Method (see Chapter 39)[46]

The method uses mFC agar with no rosolic acid added and incubation for 18 to 24 hr at 35°C. After collaborative studies,[15-17] the method was accorded Official Final Action status for all foods by the Association of Official Analytical Chemists.[8] The HGMF method exhibited better recovery, repeatability, and reproducibility than the MPN reference method.[47]

Prepare food test sample, filtration apparatus, and mFC plates as indicated. Filter 1.0 ml or other volume of inoculum through the HGMF. With forceps, aseptically transfer the HGMF from the filtration apparatus to the surface of a dry mFC agar plate. Incubate plates in an inverted position for 18 to 24 hr at 35°C. When counting manually, count grid-cells containing dark blue or grey coliform growth, calculate the HGMF score and the MPNGU/g (ml) of food. Do not count any other color (e.g., creamy yellow) colonies. For automated counts, a red filter under the camera will probably provide the best contrast.

24.6   FECAL COLIFORM GROUP

24.61   EC Broth Method[1, 3, 7]

Subculture all positive LST tubes showing gas within 48 ± 2 hr (Section 24.52) to *E. coli* (EC) broth by means of a standard 3-mm loop. Incubate EC tubes 24 ± 2 hr at 44.5° ± 0.2°C for waters and shellfish[1, 7] or 45.5° ± 0.2°C for foods.[2] If a variety of food types are to be examined, a single incubation temperature of 45.0° ± 0.2°C should suffice.[51] Examine tubes for gas. Calculate MPN values by using the appropriate table. Report results as MPN of fecal coliforms per g or ml.

24.62   A-1 Fermentation Test for Shellfish-Growing Waters[1, 6, 7]

This rapid test may be used to enumerate fecal coliforms as a presumptive test for *E. coli* in shellfish-growing waters only.[29] Because geographical differences of various shellfish-growing waters may affect the efficiency of this test, analysts should demonstrate comparability with the conventional method before using the A-1 medium method exclusively.

Prepare test samples as in presumptive test for coliform bacteria (Section 24.51). Incubate A-1 medium tubes 3 hr at 35° ± 0.5°C in an air incubator. Transfer to a water bath and incubate 21 ± 2 hr at 44.5° ± 0.2°C. Maintain water level in bath above level of liquid in inoculated tubes. Presence of gas in the inverted vial or of dissolved gas that forms fine bubbles when slightly agitated constitutes a positive test. Report results as A-1 fecal coliform MPN/ 100 ml of test sample. Fecal coliform counts tend to be greater than *E. coli* counts because no effort is made to obtain pure cultures and to identify them. Interpretation of the data requires understanding of the microflora of the specimen.

24.63   Modified MacConkey Procedure for Shellfish and Shellfish Meats

The official Food and Drug Administration (FDA) procedure for the bacteriological analysis of domestic and imported shellfish is fully described elsewhere.[1] Methods are described for examining shellfish, fresh-shucked frozen shellfish, and shellfish frozen on the half shell. This procedure does not apply to the examination of crustaceans (crabs, lobsters, and shrimp) or to processed shellfish meats such as breaded, shucked, precooked, and heat-processed products.

24.64   HGMF Method[15-17] (see general discussion for coliforms in Section 24.57)

The method is based on incubation at 44.5°C and the use of mFC medium with no rosolic acid added and if necessary use of tryptic soy agar with $MgSO_4$ (TSAM) for a preliminary resuscitation of any stressed cells on the HGMF.

1. Proceed as described in Section 24.57. If the organisms have been stressed, aseptically transfer the inoculated HGMF with forceps from the filtration apparatus to the surface of a TSAM plate. Otherwise, proceed to step 3.
2. To resuscitate, incubate in an inverted position for 4 hr at 25°C for dry foods or 4 hr at 35°C for all other foods.
3. With forceps, transfer the HGMF to the surface of a dry mFC plate. Incubate plates in an inverted position for 18 to 24 hr at 44.5°C, preferably in a water-jacketed incubator.
4. Count manually or automatically as described in Section 24.57.

24.7 ESCHERICHIA COLI

24.71 Liquid Test for *E. coli* ("Completed" Test)[7]

Subculture all positive LST tubes showing gas within 48 ± 2 hr (Section 24.52) into EC broth by means of a 3-mm loop. Incubate EC tubes in a circulating water bath at 45.5° ± 0.2°C. Subculture all EC tubes that show gas within 48 ± 2 hr by streaking on L-EMB agar plates and incubate 24 ± 2 hr at 35°C. Examine plates for typical nucleated, dark-centered colonies with or without sheen.

If typical colonies are present, pick two from each EMB plate by touching needle to center of colony and transferring each to a plate count agar (PCA) slant. If typical colonies are not present, pick two or more colonies considered likely to be *E. coli* from every plate instead. Incubate slants at 35°C for 18 to 24 hr. Transfer growth from PCA slants into the following broths for identification by biochemical tests:

Tryptone broth. Incubate 24 ± 2 hr at 35°C and test for indole.

MR-VP medium. Incubate 48 ± 2 hr at 35°C and test 1 ml for acetylmethylcarbinol. Incubate remainder of MR-VP culture an additional 48 hr and test for methyl red reaction.

Koser's citrate broth. Incubate 96 hr at 35°C and record growth as + or −.

Lauryl sulfate tryptose (LST) broth. Incubate 48 ± 2 hr at 35°C. Examine tubes for gas formation from lactose.

Gram stain. Perform Gram stain on a smear prepared from 18 to 24 hr PCA slant. Coliform organisms stain red (negative); gram-positive organisms stain blue-black.

Compute MPN of *E. coli* per g (or ml), considering gram-negative, non-sporeforming rods producing gas in lactose and producing + + − − or − + − − IMViC patterns as *E. coli*. Note: This procedure will not enumerate anaerogenic strains.

24.72 LST-MUG Test for Coliforms and *E. coli*[22, 38] (accepted Official First Action by AOAC, September 1987)

MUG (4-methylumbelliferyl-beta-D-glucuronic acid) is a fluorogenic substrate. When nonfluorescent MUG is cleaved by the enzyme beta-glucuronidase (GUD), a fluorescent product, 4-methylumbelliferone, is generated. The 4-methylumbelliferone exhibits a bluish fluorescence when exposed to long-wave (365 nm) ultraviolet light. Thus, MUG can be used to determine the presence of GUD. More information about fluorogenic tests is given in Chapter 39. About 94% of *E. coli*, including many anaerogenic strains, produce GUD. About 6% of *E. coli* strains, including enterohemorrhagic strains, do not produce GUD.[23] Specific procedures are needed to identify enterohemorrhagic *E. coli*, which are present in about 2% of beef, pork, lamb, and poultry samples.[13] Some shigellae (44%) and salmonellae (29%) also produce GUD. GUD production by other *Enterobacteriaceae* is infrequent.[23] The procedure used for the simultaneous determination of coliforms and *E. coli* is the same as that outlined in 24.52, with two exceptions.[38] First, LST broth that contains 50 µg MUG/ml is used. Second, incubation is usually terminated after 24 hr, which will identify 83% to 95% of *E. coli*-positive tubes, depending on product. Incubation for 48 hr will identify 96% to 100% of *E. coli*-positive tubes.[38] To observe fluorescence, the LST-MUG tubes are held under a long-wave (365 nm) ultraviolet light in a darkened area. A 6-watt, hand-held UV lamp is satisfactory for this purpose and is entirely safe. When a more powerful UV source, such as a 15-watt fluorescent tube type of lamp, is used to view MPN tubes, protective glasses or goggles (available from laboratory supply houses) should be used if personal exposure exceeds a few minutes each day. All tubes for MUG tests should be examined before use because some manufacturers add cerium oxide to glass as a quality control measure; tubes that contain cerium oxide will fluoresce and interfere with the LST-MUG assay.

Some foods, such as shellfish, contain natural GUD activity.[42] In these instances, a tube of LST broth is inoculated and incubated for 24 hr in the usual manner, and then all growth-positive tubes are subjected to a confirmatory 24-hr EC test (Section 24.61) using EC-MUG broth (EC broth that contains 50 µg MUG/ml).

24.73 Plating Method for coliforms and *E. coli* (modified Baird-Parker Procedure)[26, 47] with provision for resuscitation of debilitated cells. This procedure applies only to foods with 500 or more *E. coli* cells/g.

Homogenize 25 g of test sample in 225 ml peptone water diluent. Prepare serial tenfold dilutions in peptone water in accordance with anticipated microbiological quality. Using forceps, aseptically transfer sterile cellulose acetate membranes to the surface of dried nutrient agar. Plates should be dried for 2 hr at 50°C in an incubator with the lids removed and the agar surface turned down or under a laminar flow hood for 30 min. The inoculated membrane of a suitable plate should appear free of excess moisture within 15 min after spreading. If Oxoid Nuflow™ membranes are used, place shiny surface on the agar. Gently flatten membrane on the surface to minimize air pockets.

Transfer duplicate 0.5- to 1.0-ml aliquots of each dilution to cellulose acetate membranes. Using a sterile glass spreader, distribute the fluid over entire membrane, except periphery.

Incubate plates right side up, in stacks of 3 or less, for 4 hr at 35°C to facilitate resuscitation. Transfer each membrane to a tryptone bile agar (TBA) plate. Incubate plates 18 hr at 44.5° ± 0.2°C.

Remove lids of plates. Pipette 2 ml of Vracko-Sherris indole reagent into each lid. Remove membrane from agar and immerse in reagent 5 min. Remove membrane and drain excess reagent. Dry membranes under a short-wave (germicidal) UV lamp or in sunlight (window glass does not interfere) for about 20 min. Count pink-stained colonies within 30 min because the color fades. Calculate number of type I *E. coli* by selecting the dilution that gives an average of 20 to 50 pink colonies on both membranes and multiply total by the dilution factor.

24.74   HGMF Method for Coliforms and *E. coli*.[2] (see also Section 24.57)[8, 16, 17]

The method is based on the demonstration of indole production on TBA at 44.5°C, preferably in a water-jacketed incubator. It is similar to the direct plate method of Anderson and Baird-Parker,[4] except for the use of filtration and oxidant-accelerated indole reagent.

1. Proceed as in Section 24.57, but note that one filter paper (50 to 80 mm diameter) is also required per HGMF for the indole reaction. If organisms have been stressed, aseptically transfer HGMF from filtration apparatus to surface of a tryptic soy agar with $MgSO_4$ (TSAM) plate. Otherwise, proceed to step 3.
2. To resuscitate stressed cells, incubate plate in an inverted position for 4 hr at 25°C for dry foods or at 35°C for all other foods.
3. With forceps, aseptically transfer HGMF from filtration apparatus or TSAM plate to surface of a dry TBA plate and incubate plate in an inverted position for 18 to 24 hr at 44.5° ± 0.5°C.
4. Just before use, prepare oxidant-accelerated indole reagent by mixing equal volumes of solution A and solution B.
5. Place a filter paper in each petri dish lid and add 1.5 ml of indole reagent to it.
6. Transfer HGMF to a filter paper, taking care to avoid trapping air bubbles, and leave on the bench for 15 min. Return HGMF to surface of TBA, and allow to destain for a further 15 min.
7. When counting manually, include as *E. coli* only those grid cells that contain pink to red growth. Calculate the HGMF scores and MPNGU/ g (ml) of food (see Chapter 39).
8. For automated counts (see Chapter 39), a green filter under the camera will probably provide best contrast.

24.8   INTERPRETATION

24.81   The Coliform Group

Recovery from foods of the coliform group, with its unidentified individual members, has less interpretive impact than the single indicator organism, *E. coli*, or the fecal coliform group because the coliform group may contain such nonenteric members as the genera *Serratia* and *Aeromonas*. The specificity of the coliform group as an indicator is diminished by the anonymity of its individual members. Although this may be considered a weakness in the coliform method, the presence of coliforms in processed foods is a useful indicator of post-sanitization and post-processing (pasteurization) contamination. Practices that permit their presence in such instances are not consistent with good sanitation standards required for food processing.

Coliform counts can differ significantly, depending on food tested, medium used, and other testing conditions. Various conditions in food processing may cause cell injury. A resuscitation period in or on a nonselective medium (see Chapter 7) is necessary for accurate enumeration of coliforms.[5, 40] The temperature of tempered medium, 48°C, used in a pour plate technique may impose additional stress on many coliform cells. The repair and subsequent formation of colonies are inhibited in selective media such as VRBA.

24.82   The Fecal Coliform Group

Because the fecal specificity of the coliform group is low, public health microbiologists have turned to the use of the more restrictive fecal coliform group, which gives greater fecal specificity because of the high *E. coli* incidence within the group. The presence of *E. coli* may be attributed to contamination from environmental sources and subsequent growth in the product. Thus, their number may not be explained by direct fecal contamination. Members other than *E. coli* have doubtful fecal associations; their presence within the fecal coliform group compromises the group's specificity and represents a deficiency in methodology.

The test incubation period for fecal coliforms in foods may be limited to 24 hr as in water and shellfish bacteriology, or it may be extended to 48 hr as required in the classical identification of the coliform group. Generally, it is used as a 48-hr test to recover *E. coli* isolates that develop after 24 hr. This extended 48-hr fecal coliform test for foods generally produces higher fecal coliform counts than do similar tests of only 24-hr duration.

24.83   *Escherichia coli*

The recovery of *E. coli* from foods implies that other organisms of fecal origin, including pathogens, may be present (see Section 24.82). The numbers and species, however, must be established by appropriate procedures. Failure to recover *E. coli* does not ensure the absence of *E. coli* and other enteric pathogens because *E. coli* is not a perfect indicator organism. Nevertheless, *E. coli* is the best-known fecal indicator at present.

24.9 ENTEROPATHOGENIC *E. COLI* (EEC)

Certain biotypes of *E. coli* are etiological agents of gastrointestinal illness in humans and several mammals.[34] These organisms exhibit specificity with regard to host, age, and target organ. With respect to mechanism of pathogenesis, at least four major groups of EEC are recognized. (1) Toxigenic biotypes produce heat-stable and/or heat-labile enterotoxins that cause the secretion of water and electrolytes in the small intestine. (2) Enteroinvasive strains invade the epithelial cells of the colon, producing lesions and symptoms of bacillary dysentery. (3) Infantile enteropathogenic biotypes tend to be neither toxigenic nor invasive by the aforementioned criteria. (4) Finally, there appears to be a group including the hemorrhagic colitis strains that produces diarrhea in rabbits and humans by means of a cytotoxin. Toxigenic, invasive, and infantile enteropathogenic biotypes have been implicated in food- and waterborne human illness.

The incidence of *E. coli* foodborne illness may be underestimated for several reasons: (1) Because of the empirical approach to their recovery, cultures possessing attributes of enteropathogenicity are only rarely encountered. In the absence of primate feeding studies, it is uncertain whether the cultures recovered are enteric pathogens for humans. (2) Recovery of pathogenic biotypes requires modification of the standard procedures. (3) Many laboratories lack the resources to identify potentially virulent strains. Because of the plasmid-associated basis for enteropathogenicity, every isolate of *E. coli* can be considered potentially virulent.

24.91 Serotyping Reagents

Commercially available serotyping reagents are listed in Table 2. Certain O serogroups are associated with the different pathogenic types of *E. coli* (Table 3). Unfortunately, as comparisons of the entries of Tables 2 and 3 show, sera for the pathogenic serotypes are not always commercially available.

24.92 Recommended Controls

To ascertain the productivity of tryptone phosphate (TP) enrichment broth, inoculate 100-ml aliquots with three strains of enteropathogenic *E. coli* for a final concentration of 100 cells/ml. Incubate for 20 hr at 44°C. Examine for growth. If poor growth or no growth occurs, examine individual components for toxicity and substitute with suitable lots.

To determine the accuracy of rapid test kits for identification, examine as prescribed with three strains of *E. coli* and three other species of *Enterobacteriaceae*.

Table 2—Serogroups Recognizable with Commercially Available Sera

Escherichia coli			Alkalescens-Dispar (A-D)	Entero-toxigenic	Entero-invasive	Entero-hemorrhagic
Group A	Group B	Group C				
O26:K60	O86:K61	O18:K77	O1	O6	O28:K73	O157:H7
O55:K59	O119:K69	O20:K61	O2	O8	O112:K66	
O111:K58	O124:K72	O20:K84	O3	O11	O124:K72	
O127:K63	O125:K70	O28:K73	O4	O78	O143:K (detected with *Shigella boydii* 8 antiserum)	
	O126:K71	O44:K74				
	O128:K67	O112:K66			O144:K (detected with *Shigella dysenteriae* 10 antiserum)	

Table 3—Serogroups and Serotypes of Pathogenic Types of *Escherichia coli* Isolated from Humans with Intestinal Infections

Pathogenic type	Serogroups and serotypes		
Enteropathogenic (EPEC)	O18a,18c:H7	O20a,20b:H26	O26:NM*
	O26:H11	O28a,28c:NM	O44:H34
	O55:NM	O55:H6	O55:H7
	O86a:NM	O86a:H34	O111a,111b:NM
	O111a,111b:H2	O111a,111b:H12	
	O114:H10	O114:H32	O119:NM
	O119:H6	O125a,125c:H21	O126:NM
	O126:H27	O127:NM	O127:H9
	O127:H21	O128a,128b:H2	O128a,128c:H12
	O142:H6	O158:H23	O159
Enterotoxigenic (ETEC)	O6:H16	O8:H9	O11:H27
	O15:H11	O20:NM	O25:H42
	O25:NM	O27:H7	O63
	O78:H11	O78:H12	O128:H7
	O148:H28	O149:H10	O159:H20
	O167		
Enteroinvasive (EIEC)	O28a,28c:NM	O112a,112c:NM	O124:NM
	O124:H30	O124:H32	O136:NM
	O143:NM	O144:NM	O152:NM
	O159:H2	O164	
	O167:H4	O167:5	
Enterohemorrhagic (EHEC)	157:H7 (and O26, O111, O113, and O145 serogroups of EPEC)		

*NM = nonmotile.

Examine batches of polyvalent OK, monovalent OK and monovalent O sera with the classical infantile enteropathogenic strains of *E. coli*. Procure the cultures from recognized sources.

Acquire strains of invasive and enterotoxigenic *E. coli* from centers engaged in this research. Simultaneously evaluate known positive and negative cultures with strains of unknown behavior in the recommended model systems for enteropathogenicity. Cholera enterotoxin preparations, both unheated and heated for 30 min at 60°C, serve as positive and negative controls for the recognition of heat-labile enterotoxin in the Y-1 adrenal cell test.

24.93   General Considerations

Direct procedures for recovery of specific groups of enteropathogenic *E. coli* are not available at present. However, screening methods have been described that selectively identify enterohemorrhagic *E. coli*.[31, 50] Standard enrichment and plating procedures for enumeration of *E. coli* of sanitary significance do not quantitatively recover pathogenic biotypes.[7] Pathogenic strains tend to lose plasmids, and therefore should be maintained at $-70°C$. Finally, suggested criteria for the establishment of human enteropathogenicity in lieu of controlled primate feeding studies have not been proved unequivocally. For infantile diarrheal types, with the possible exception of colonization potential and cytotoxicity, no attribute of pathogenicity has been recognized. The tentative empirical approach offers options for laboratories with limited resources.

24.94   Isolation and Serological Tests

Examine test samples as promptly as possible after receipt. Refrigerate perishable material less than 1 day to avoid damage to the bacteria. Aseptically weigh a 25-g test portion into 225 ml BHI, agitate gently, and incubate 2 hr at 35°C. Agitate gently, and streak on MacConkey agar and on L-EMB agar. Incubate agar plates 24 hr at 35°C. Pour supernatant into 250 ml double-strength TP broth. Incubate 20 ± 2 hr at 44°C. Streak a plate of L-EMB agar and a plate of MacConkey agar.

Examine plates from direct streak and elevated temperature enrichment tubes. If possible, select 10 suspicious *E. coli* colonies from the L-EMB plates of both the primary and secondary broth cultures. Many pathogenic biotypes of *E. coli* do not produce colonies with green sheen. Colonies may be mucoid and show an uneven margin. Select 10 colorless, shigella-like cultures from both L-EMB and MacConkey agar plates. Since some biotypes of *E. coli* grow poorly on L-EMB, selection may be confined to MacConkey agar. From each selected colony inoculate a veal infusion agar slant. Incubate 18 hr at 35°C. Use one of the recommended rapid test kits or systems (Chapter 39) to identify.

Examine each confirmed *E. coli* isolate, by using growth from veal infusion agar, in *E. coli* polyvalent antisera (A, B, C, A–D, M) or in *Shigella* species monovalent antisera (see Table 2). Sera for invasive serogroups O124:K72, O28:K73, and O112:K66 are found in *E. coli* polyvalents B, C, and D, respectively. Suspend growth in 5 ml 0.5% saline to a density corresponding to McFarland standard number 4. Discard rough cultures, i.e., those failing to yield homogeneous, stable suspensions. Add 1 drop each of growth suspension, 0.5% saline, and polyvalent serum to wax-marked rectangles on a glass surface. Mix drops and gently rock plates for about 3 min. Examine for agglutination against a dark background with overhead illumination. Reject cultures showing roughness, i.e., agglutination in several sera or in saline. If negative in all sera, heat bacterial suspension 15 min at 100°C to hydrolyze interfering surface factors. Reexamine in sera.

If positive in polyvalent serum, reexamine in constituent monovalent sera. If positive, perform a quantitative tube agglutination test. If negative and the food was involved in an outbreak, examine isolates regardless of serotype for attributes of pathogenicity described in Sections 24.101–24.1010. Note: Sera for all serotypes of *E. coli* involved in enteric illness are not commercially available. Consult World Health Organization (WHO) *E. coli* Reference Centers for identification of serotype, i.e., somatic, capsular, flagellar, and colonization antigens.

Perform test for O antigen by using colonies from veal infusion agar. Suspend growth in 0.5% saline to McFarland standard number 3. Heat 60 min at 100°C. Dilute 0.1 ml monovalent O serum in 0.9 ml 0.5% saline. Prepare a 1:20 to 1:1280 series twofold dilutions by successive transfers of 0.5-ml aliquots to 0.5 ml of 0.5% saline in 12 × 75-mm tubes. Add 0.5 ml heated suspension to each dilution of antiserum. This results in an additional twofold dilution. For a control on autoagglutination, add 0.5 ml heated suspension to 0.5 ml saline. Gently agitate tubes and incubate 16 hr at 49° ± 1°C. Chill tubes 1 hr at 4°C and examine for agglutination, i.e., a disc of cells at the bottom of the tube that does not resuspend after gentle agitation. If the culture agglutinates to the titer reported by the manufacturer or if the titer differs by only one dilution from this value, the culture may be considered to possess the homologous somatic antigen.

Because of complex interrelationships among somatic (O), capsular (K, mainly B type), and flagellar (H) antigens and the unknown specificity of sera available commercially, the serological analysis of *E. coli* is somewhat more difficult than that of other *Enterobacteriaceae*. It should not be attempted on a routine basis. Likewise, virulence cannot be completely correlated with the presence of somatic, capsular, and colonization antigens. If serological identification of an isolate seems advisable, contact specialized laboratories, such as the Centers for Disease Control.

24.95   Interpretation of Pathogenicity Test Results

Cultures giving positive responses in one or more of the tests described in Sections 24.9 and 24.101–24.1010 should be examined in the ileal loop system.[11] Those failing to react are probably not pathogenic for humans. However, not all cultures producing a positive ileal loop reaction may be pathogenic for humans. In addition to heat-labile toxin (LT), heat-stable toxin (ST), and invasiveness, other factors appear to be involved, e.g., presence of pili facilitating colonization of the gastrointestinal tract, colicins, cytotoxins, and endotoxins.[18, 19] However, procedures to determine these attributes have not been standardized, and the necessary reagents are not commercially available. The most meaningful test is a controlled primate feeding study.[14]

24.96   Biochemical-Physiological Characterization

It is essential to establish the identity of all isolates possessing attributes of pathogenicity by standard methods of examination. Enteropathogenic biotypes of *E. coli* frequently exhibit aberrant reactions with regard to fermentation of lactose, ability to grow at 45.5°C, and production of gas. These reactions may reflect added genetic potential encoded by one or more plasmids found in these strains. For this reason, additional tests are necessary to differentiate them from the other species recently proposed by Brenner et al.[9, 10] Members of the species *E. coli* frequently are difficult to identify in clinical and food microbiological laboratories.

24.100   PATHOGENICITY TESTS

Laboratories unable to perform the following tests should arrange for the examination in laboratories with this potential.

24.101   HeLa Cell Test for Colonization

Virulence prerequisites for enterotoxigenic strains of *E. coli* include the ability to attach to the jejunal lining, to proliferate in situ, and to elaborate one or more toxins. Host specificity is manifested by possession of unique colonization factors, including antigens and lectins. At least three factors have been elucidated in strains of human significance: CFA I, CFA II, and 8775. Because of the commercial nonavailability of sera for these factors, several types of mammalian cells have been proposed to show colonization: buccal, FLOW 11000, and HeLa. In the previous edition of this book, Mehlman proposed this test to demonstrate the attachment potential of many human strains as well as porcine strains.

24.1011   Preparation of bacteria

Inoculate proteose agar slant and incubate 16 hr at 35°C. Scrape cells from agar and suspend to 0.1 optical density in colonization medium.

24.1012   Preparation of HeLa monolayer

Prepare monolayers in MEME:FBS plus penicillin and streptomycin in 4-chamber slides as described in Section 24.102. Incubate at 35°C in 5% CO_2

incubator until monolayer is 50% confluent. Examine for purity and appearance of cells. Remove spent medium and wash monolayer once with colonization medium.

24.1013   Colonization test

Add 0.2 ml bacterial suspension in colonization medium to monolayer and incubate 2 hr at 35°C in CO_2 incubator. Wash monolayer three times with DPBS. Add 1 ml 90% MEME:10% FBS and incubate 2 hr at 35°C in CO_2 incubator. Wash monolayer 10 times with calcium- and magnesium-free DPBS. Stain and mount preparations as described in Section 24.102. Examine at $900 \times$ magnification. Count number of bacteria attached to 30 HeLa cells. An average value of 10 or more bacteria per HeLa cell indicates colonization.

24.102   HeLa Cell Test for Invasiveness[37]

To spare test animals, use this procedure to screen for *E. coli* strains with invasive potential.

1. Preparation of HeLa cell culture. Using standard cell culture techniques, grow host cell on inner surface of 3-oz glass prescription bottles or plastic flasks, using 5 ml MEME-FBS-Pen-Strep medium, for 7 days at 35°C in CO_2 incubator. Replace with fresh medium on fourth day to prevent accumulation of toxic metabolites. In preparing inoculum for pathogenicity testing, wash monolayer once with 5 ml DPBS prewarmed at 35°C. Add 5 ml prewarmed 0.25% trypsin and hold 2 min at room temperature. Aseptically remove and discard about 4.5 ml trypsin. Incubate flask at 35°C with occasional agitation. After monolayer has detached and cells are fairly uniformly distributed in residual trypsin, add 25 ml prewarmed Eagles minimal essential medium-fetal bovine serum (MEME-FBS) antibiotic-free medium. Estimate cell density using counting chamber. Add enough MEME-FBS to dilute suspension to density of 5×10^5 to 1×10^6 cells/ml. With occasional agitation, rapidly transfer 1-ml portions to each compartment of chamber slide. Place chamber slides in large petri dish or other suitable container. Incubate 20 to 24 hr at 35°C in CO_2 incubator. Before infection, aseptically remove medium from each chamber with Pasteur pipette and wash successively with 1-ml portions of prewarmed Earle's balanced salts (ES) and infection medium (IM).
2. Preparation of bacteria. With needle, inoculate 5 ml veal infusion broth, using growth from veal infusion agar slant. Incubate broth cultures 18 to 24 hr at 35°C. Invasive potential is critically temperature dependent in the range of 30° to 37°C, being maximal at the high end of this range and negligible at the low end. Centrifuge suspension 20 min at $1200 \times g$ at 18°C. Resuspend cells in 5 ml ES. Recentrifuge 20 min at $1200 \times g$. Resuspend in ES to McFarland standard density number 2. Dilute latter suspension 1:10 in prewarmed IM (see comment in 4, below, regarding antibiotics to use in the post-infection medium).

3. Infection. Transfer 0.2 ml bacterial suspension in IM to compartment of chamber slide. Use 0.2 ml uninoculated IM for negative control. Simultaneously examine known invasive and known noninvasive strain of *E. coli*, using identical conditions. Incubate 3 hr at 35°C in CO_2 incubator.

4. Intracellular growth stage. Remove contents of chamber slides aseptically, using individual Pasteur pipette for each compartment. Wash each compartment twice with 1-ml portions of prewarmed ES. Subsequently, wash each compartment with 1 ml intracellular growth phase (IGP) medium. Add 0.8 ml IGP medium to each chamber. Incubate 2.5 hr at 35°C in CO_2 incubator. Examine for change of phenol red indicator from red to yellow, indicating production of acid and extracellular growth of bacteria. If there is no change in color between inoculated chambers and negative control, incubate additional 2.5 hours. If color change has occurred, repeat washing procedure, and reincubate. Determine antibiotic sensitivity pattern of culture before pathogenicity testing to ensure optimal use of antibiotics for inhibiting extracellular growth.

5. Fixing and staining. Remove contents of chamber slides. Wash monolayers three times with 1-ml portions of DPBS. Add 1 ml absolute methanol. Hold 5 min at room temperature. Remove methanol and side walls of chamber slide. Insert razor blade between gasket and slide and gently pry gasket from slide. Do not let specimen dry before staining. If necessary, cautiously remove remnants of gasket from slide with razor blade. Immerse slides 10 min in May-Grunwald stain. Withdraw slides, remove excess stain, and immerse 20 min in Giemsa stain. Withdraw slides, remove excess stain, and immerse 10 to 20 sec in water. Rinse twice briefly in acetone. Immerse slides briefly in the following sequence of solvents: acetone-xylene (50:50), acetone-xylene (33:67), and xylene. Examine slide again for remnants of gasket and remove if present. Add drop of mounting medium to each monolayer. Place cover slip on preparation. Blot gently to remove excess mounting medium. Let specimens harden overnight. If necessary to examine preparation immediately, seal by applying melted Vaseline-paraffin mixture to edges of cover slip.

6. Microscopic examination and interpretation of data. Examine specimen with oil immersion objective (900×). Locate intracellular bacteria by using the parfocality of cytoplasmic ground substance and bacteria. If invasive, *E. coli* will be present in cytoplasm, but not in nucleus. On occasion, intracellular bacteria may be located along nuclear membrane. Intracellular bacteria tend to be more elongated than extracellular bacteria. In general, they appear encapsulated, possibly in remnants of the phagolysosome. At least one difference between invasive and noninvasive strains is minimal phagocytosis of the latter. In general, noninvasive strains tend to be found in less than 1% of mammalian cells, and the number per cell is less than 5. Invasive strains are phagocytized to

a greater extent and their number per cell is greater than 5. Frequently, the host cell may appear as a bag of bacteria. Two or more sites of infection may be observed. Initially test each culture twice on different slides. Confirm positive response in both compartments by the Sereny test. If both are negative, consider the culture noninvasive. If only one compartment is positive, perform a third trial, and if reaction is positive, submit culture to Sereny reaction.

24.103   Sereny Test for Invasiveness[44]

This examination should be limited to shigella-like strains of *E. coli* that exhibit one or more of the following characteristics: members of *E. coli* O28, O112, O124, O143, O144 serogroups (Table 2), delayed fermentation of lactose, and anaerogenesis. When only a small number of strains are under consideration, examine each in triplicate in guinea pigs. If a large number of strains must be examined, consult reference 21 for a preliminary screening test.

Performance of the test. Inoculate 5 ml veal infusion from a veal infusion agar slant. Incubate at 35°C for 21 ± 3 hr. Centrifuge at $1200 \times g$ for 20 min. Resuspend cells in 5 ml DPBS. Recentrifuge as previously described. Suspend cells to a density of 1×10^9 cells/ml in the same solution.

Using guinea pigs with no symptoms of eye irritation or infection, transfer a drop of suspension to the left eye of each of three animals. Apply a drop of sterile Dulbecco buffer to the right eye of each animal. Gently open and close lid to spread fluid evenly over the conjunctiva. Return animals to individual cages.

Examine animals daily for 5 days. A positive reaction is a keratoconjunctivitis, i.e., ulceration and opacity of the cornea. Confirmation by a veterinarian may be helpful in distinguishing keratoconjunctivitis from conjunctivitis. Invasiveness is determined by a positive reaction in at least two of the three animals.

Note: This is not a generalized test for invasive potential. Cultures producing dysentery and lesions of the colon give a positive reaction. Cultures capable of passing the intestinal barrier by translocation, such as some of the classical infantile diarrheal types, give a negative reaction.

24.104   Test for Heat-labile Toxin (LT)[43]

LT stimulates the enzyme adenylate cyclase with the production of cyclic adenosine monophosphate. The toxin is closely related structurally and physiologically to *Vibrio cholerae* enterotoxin. The cyclic monophosphate is active in many systems. In this system it promotes the conversion of elongated fibroblast-like cells to round, refractile cells.

Using standard cell culture procedures, grow mouse adrenal (Y-1) cells in 75 sq cm plastic cell flasks with 20 ml Y-1 cell medium for 7 days at 35°C in a CO_2 incubator. The monolayer should be confluent. Replace medium on fourth day. Examine flasks daily with regard to color of medium (pH) and appearance of cells. Cells should be elongated with no evidence of bacterial contamination.

When the monolayer is confluent, wash with 20 ml Y-1 phosphate saline solution. Add 1.5 ml 0.25% trypsin (prepared as described in Section 24.43). Hold at 35°C until cells have detached from the plastic surface. Add 3.5 ml fresh Y-1 cell medium and gently agitate to disperse cells. Add 1 ml of this suspension to 20 ml fresh Y-1 cell medium. (Transfer remaining 4 ml of this suspension to 16 ml fresh Y-1 medium in 75 sq cm flask to maintain the line, and incubate as described above.) Dispense 0.2 ml aliquots of Y-1 suspension with gentle agitation to each well of a sterile 96-well microtitration plate. Incubate 48 hr or longer at 35°C in CO_2 incubator until the monolayer in each well is almost complete.

Inoculate bacterial cultures in 15 ml of Syncase broth medium in a 200-ml flask. Incubate 20 hr at 35°C on a reciprocating shaker (225 rpm). Centrifuge cultures at $1200 \times g$ to remove bulk of cells. Sterilize supernatant by filtration through a 0.45-μm membrane filter. Dilute filtrate 1:5 in fresh Y-1 cell culture medium. Examine immediately or refrigerate (maximum 1 week at 4°C).

Remove medium from wells of microtitration plate and add 0.1 ml fresh Y-1 cell culture medium to each well. Add 0.05 ml of each diluted filtrate to wells. Positive control is 10 ng purified cholera enterotoxin dissolved in 0.05 ml Y-1 phosphate saline solution. Negative control is heated enterotoxin (30 min at 60°C). Incubate microtitration plates 20 hr at 35°C in a CO_2 incubator.

Examine microtitration plates at $150\times$ magnification by using an inverted stage microscope. Positive reaction is conversion of 75% or more of elongated cells into round, refractile cells. Background nonspecific rounding with known negative controls should be less than 2%.

Note: This test will be inapplicable if the culture produces a cytotoxin that causes detachment of the monolayer or other damage to mouse adrenal cells.

24.105   DNA Probe for Identifying the Heat-labile Toxin Gene

This method will identify pathogenic strains encoding a heat-labile toxin (LT) gene. Identification of the gene does not necessarily indicate an active product. The method assumes that a test sample of a ^{32}P-labeled cloned DNA probe for the LT gene has been constructed by the analyst or that it is available ready-made from another source. For example, the probe could be on the plasmid pEWD 299 that is maintained in *E. coli* C600. Plasmid maintenance and preparation, excision and electrophoretic separation, and in vitro radio-labeling of the LT gene fragment have been described by Hill.[25] Alternatively, a custom-synthesized oligodeoxyribonucleotide probe can be obtained commercially or an oligo DNA probe can be constructed in the laboratory by using manual or automated commercial synthesizers as discussed by Hill.[25]

The method given here involves the growth of suspected toxigenic *E. coli* colonies on filters and in situ lysis of the constituent cells, hybridization of the DNA probe to the lytically released LT DNA, and identification of hybridizing colony lysates by autoradiography.

24.1051   Colony hybridization filter preparation

Procedure for preparing colony hybridization filters. To test pure strains, inoculate 5 ml of BHI broth with cultures to be tested and incubate 18 to 24 hr at 37°C. Always include appropriate positive and negative control cultures. Prepare BHI agar in 15 × 100-mm petri plates and dry, inverted, 18 to 24 hr at 37°C.

From overnight broth cultures, inoculate agar plates, using orderly array of spots 9 to 10 mm apart to ensure that resulting colonies will not merge during growth. Record location of each culture; it is essential that resulting culture patterns, and ultimately the autoradiograms, can be unambiguously oriented. Because procedures may have to be repeated, prepare several plates. Incubate plates, inverted, for 18 to 24 hr at 37°C. Note the cultures failing to grow so that false-negative results will not be reported for these isolates.

If a mixed culture, such as that found in a food homogenate, is to be analyzed, streak for isolation on an appropriate medium. Ideally, positive and negative control cultures should be spotted on every plate, but with streak plates, this may not be feasible or even desirable. In lieu of placing control cultures on every plate, which could conceivably commingle with a test sample and compromise the analysis, prepare a series of "test strips" as follows.

Inoculate plates in an orderly array as detailed above, but place all required controls in a column and repeat the array in that column as necessary. After filter has been processed (see below), it may be cut into columns. Each time a hybridization is performed, this strip of controls may be added to the reaction so that it will experience the same hybridization, washing, and autoradiography conditions as the test sample.

Labile sterile Whatman No. 541 cellulose filters, 82 to 85 mm in diameter, using a soft lead pencil; mark each filter so that it can be oriented correctly after colonies have been replicated onto it. (Note: Similar manufactured filters may vary in their DNA binding properties so that high backgrounds may be observed.) If pure cultures are to be isolated by picking colonies from the replicated plate, use sterile Whatman No. 541 filters. Alternate No. 541 filters with other absorbent filters, wrap in foil, and autoclave. Handle with forceps dipped in ethanol and flamed. Use a sharp pencil whose tip has been dipped in ethanol for labeling. Be sure filters are properly marked so that the location of positive and negative controls can be determined with no doubt. Carefully apply sterile filter over colony array, pencil markings face down. To reduce formation of air pockets, wet an edge of the filter and roll it across the surface of the plate. Remove any air bubbles by gentle pressure with a spreading rod. The use of the spreader increases the efficiency of colony attachment to the filter, but do not use excessive pressure as the colonies may spread. Filters may be peeled from agar plates immediately, but stronger hybridization signals may be obtained if filters remain in place for 1 to 2 hr. (Note: The colony array is now a mirror image of the array used to inoculate the agar plate. Interpretation of autoradiograms (see below) may be easier if the film is reversed before it is compared to the original colony array.)

Lyse the colonies on the replication filters by placing the filters (colony side up) onto absorbent paper filters (such as Whatman No. 1 or S & S No. 597, about 85 mm diameter) contained in 15 × 100-mm glass petri plates. Wet these absorbent filters with 1.5 to 2.0 ml lysis mixture C before transferring colony-containing filters to them. Be sure that no air is trapped between the filters. Steam the filters in the glass plates for 3 to 5 min. It may be possible to lyse *E. coli* by microwaves. Transfer steamed filters to glass petri plates containing absorbent paper filters previously wetted with 1.5 to 2.0 ml lysis mixture.

Remove any air pockets. Keep filters horizontal when they are being transferred to prevent DNA from lysed colonies from running together. Let filters sit 5 to 10 min. If filters are not to be used immediately, air-dry at room temperature and store under a vacuum between absorbent paper. Filters have been stored in this manner for up to 1 year without a noticeable change in results.

Optional procedure for performing hybridization with multiple filters. Laboratories requiring the capability to process many isolates (filters) may use the following procedure to hybridize several filters at once for efficient use of radioactive label. The arrangement of cultures on the filters results in a space-saving arrangement in the X-ray film cassettes.

Spot culture with sterile applicator sticks or toothpicks into 60 × 60-mm array (6 columns by 8 rows), using a template that can be conveniently taped to the laboratory bench. After incubation of cultures, transfer colonies to Whatman No. 541 filter paper cut to 60 × 60 mm and marked for orientation. Lyse the colonies on the filters as described above, using NaOH and steam.

Cut fiberglass mesh screen (from ordinary household window screen, mesh size approximately 1.7 mm) to 60 × 60 mm. Boil screen squares in distilled water for about 30 min, rinse, and air-dry.

Stack up to 10 filters in a plastic petri dish with a fiberglass mesh square placed between each one. Add enough hybridization mix (see below) to cover each filter (about 2.8 ml per filter). Add a total of 1 million cpm of radioactive probe and conduct the hybridization as described in the next section.

Procedure for colony hybridization. Prepare 50 ml hybridization mixture B in plastic tube just before use. Boil 1.0 ml sonicated calf-thymus DNA 5 min in water bath and add to hybridization mixture B. Dispense 5 to 10 ml mixture into 100 × 15 or 20-mm plastic petri dish and add paper filter with lysed colony array. (Note: It is not necessary to preincubate the filters.) Ensure that filter is thoroughly soaked and covered by hybridization mixture. Since ^{32}P decays with a halflife of 14.2 days, calculate volume of DNA probe solution required to contain 1×10^6 cpm so that a standard amount of radioactivity can be used for each hybridization reaction. Add this amount to the filter containing the hybridization solution. Mix briefly and incubate overnight at the appropriate hybridization temperature. (Note: The hybridization and washing temperatures may vary with different probes. These temperatures depend primarily on the length and the base composition of the oligodeoxyribonucleotide. Although there are formulas for estimating these temperatures, the reaction conditions, at present, are best determined empirically.)

Wash hybridization filter(s) free of ^{32}P-labeled DNA probe that is not specifically bound to DNA in lysed colonies by removing filter from hybridization mixture and rinsing for 5 to 10 sec in a plastic petri dish containing about 10 ml $6\times$ standard saline citrate (SSC) prewarmed to the washing temperature. Drain and recover filter with $6\times$ SSC and incubate for 1 hr at the washing temperature. Again, drain plate, recover filter with $6\times$ SSC, and reincubate for 1 hr. Finally, rinse filter for 5 to 10 sec in $2\times$ SSC at room temperature.

Procedure for autoradiography. Mount filter with small pieces of tape to 8×10-inch piece of relatively stiff paper such as Whatman 3MM. Cover with plastic wrap to prevent contamination of intensifying screens in X-ray film holder. (Note: Static electricity often causes undesirable lines on autoradiogram. To reduce this problem, wipe plastic surface with damp paper to smooth out wrinkles, and let dry. The problem can also be alleviated by using stiffer plastic such as that found in a document holder.)

In darkroom, place film on top of plastic-covered filters in cassette film holder with intensifying screens. This film can be used with OC-series safelight. XAR-2 Kodak film is individually packaged with 8×10-inch size is well suited for this work. Put loaded film cassette into plastic bag before placing in freezer to prevent condensation from forming on cassette and possibly on film when it is removed from freezer. Place bag in freezer. Length of exposure will depend on how much radioactive DNA has bound to the filter. If handheld Geiger-Mueller counter is available, estimate the time. If a noticeable increase in background registers when counter is held over filter (i.e., 2 to 3 counts per sec), a positive reaction may be visible on the film after a 1-day exposure. The $-70°C$ temperature speeds exposure time because it stabilizes light-sensitive crystals in the film emulsion and so requires less exposure time than at room temperature.

After exposure, let cassette warm to room temperature before removing it from plastic bag. In darkroom, use X-ray developer to develop film under OC safelight. Usually 3 to 4 min of development at 20°C is sufficient. Rinse with water for 30 sec and fix for 5 min. After film has been fixed for 1 to 2 min, room lights may be turned on. Wash for 10 min in tap water, coat with Photo-flo™, if available, and hang film to dry. If spots are very faint, expose new film for longer period.

Interpretation of results. Colonies that possess the gene for *E. coli* LT should have bound the radioactively labeled toxin gene DNA. These colonies should expose the film and cause dark spots to appear. The more copies of the toxin gene present in a colony, the blacker and larger the spot. However, since colony size can vary (as can hybridization efficiency), this test is best used qualitatively and not quantitatively. If dark areas appear on the film where there are no colonies, the unbound radioactivity has probably not been completely washed away. Rewash the filter twice again under the original working conditions for 1 hr each time. Let filter dry and expose another film to it. Examine results from control cultures. A strongly positive control should be a dark spot. A negative control should show no darkening of the film or, at most, a very faint darkening. A weak control should show a spot of intermediate intensity but may, in fact, more closely resemble the strongly positive control. Based on intensity of the control spots, determine whether each culture contains the gene for *E. coli* LT.

Troubleshooting. The following factors could cause unsatisfactory autoradiograms:

1. Negative cultures caused by spontaneous plasmid loss;
2. Faulty colony hybridization filter preparation;
3. Faulty colony hybridization reaction conditions (incorrect hybridization mix, insufficient radioactivity);
4. Insufficient post-hybridization filter washing;
5. Faulty exposure and film development.

Possible remedies for the above sources of error include the following, respectively:

1. Use fresh isolates or isolates that have been stored correctly;
2. Prepare new filters;
3. Review procedures;
4. Rewash filters;
5. Check film and develop unexposed film as control and check processing solutions and temperature; also check cassette holder and intensifying screens for light leaks or damage; expose another film and develop. (Note: If all or most of the cultures appear to be positive, the DNA probe may not have been sufficiently purified away from other nucleotide sequences. Another preparation of probe DNA is required.)

24.106   Nitrocellulose Dot Enzyme Immunoassay for Heat-labile Toxin[45]

Enterotoxigenic *E. coli* (ETEC) implicated in diarrheal illnesses of humans and domestic animals produces either one or both of two different types of enterotoxins. The high molecular weight, heat-labile toxin (LT) cross-reacts immunologically with cholera toxin. The low molecular weight, heat-stable toxin (ST) is haptenic. These strains may also produce one or more fimbrial antigens that enable the cells to adhere to the mucosal surface of the intestine.

In the test described here for identifying *E. coli* LT, culture supernatants are spotted on a nitrocellulose membrane that binds the proteins contained in the supernatants. Remaining unbound sites on the membrane are blocked with a protein such as gelatin. Membranes with bound antigen are incubated with rabbit antibody to LT. After washing, the presence of any rabbit IgG on membranes is identified by a reaction with peroxidase-conjugated goat antibody to rabbit IgG. After a reaction with peroxidase substrate, culture supernatants containing LT show as purple dots on a white background.

24.1061   Storing cultures and preparing culture supernatants

For culture storage, inoculate 20 ml sterile trypticase soy broth (TSB) in 125-ml flasks with *E. coli* strains. Incubate overnight at 37°C. Add equal volume of sterile 80% glycerol, mix, and aseptically distribute 2.0-ml portions of culture into sterile screw-cap tubes. Store at −70°C.

To test for toxin production, inoculate test sample cultures and control cultures into 5.0 ml TSB in 50 ml flasks and incubate on shaker for 6 to 8 hr at 37°C. Transfer 0.1 ml of each culture into 5.0 ml of Casamino acid yeast-extract lincomycin broth. Incubate on shaker 16 to 20 hr at 37°C. Add 0.1 ml polymyxin B solution to each culture tube and incubate 30 min at 37°C. Centrifuge cultures and filter through Acrodisc membranes to obtain clear supernatants for LT and ST enzyme-linked immunosorbent assay (ELISA) assays. Store culture supernatants frozen until assay.

24.1062   ELISA procedure

1. Fill glass petri dish with 50 ml TBS. Handle nitrocellulose membrane with forceps and gloves. Mark membrane with pencil for future orientation. Place membrane at angle into buffer to wet membrane thoroughly. Remove after 10 min and place on filter paper for 5 min.

2. Dispense 2 μl of each culture supernatant including positive and negative control cultures to surface of membrane. Place tests 6 to 8 mm apart. Let membrane dry completely for 5 min after application of last test supernatant. About 75 culture supernatants can be analyzed on a single 9 cm diameter membrane.

3. Immerse membrane in 50 ml Tris buffered saline (TBS)-3% gelatin solution for 1 hr. Agitate solution intermittently or place on rotary shaker.

4. Remove membrane from TBS-3% gelatin and transfer to 50 ml of a solution of rabbit anti-LT antiserum diluted 1:100 in TBS-1% gelatin. Incubate 2 to 3 hr at 25°C with gentle agitation.

5. Briefly rinse membrane in 50 ml double-distilled water. Wash membrane by immersing for 5 min in 50 ml TBS-Tween. Repeat washing procedure three more times.

6. Transfer membrane from wash solution to 50 ml goat antirabbit IgG-

peroxidase conjugate diluted 1:3000 with TBS-1% gelatin. Incubate at 25°C for 2 hr with gentle agitation.

7. Remove and wash membrane as in 5, above.

8. Prepare peroxidase color development solution immediately before use. Transfer membrane from wash solution into color development solution. LT-positive spots will appear as purple dots within 5 min. Avoid prolonged color development beyond 15 to 30 min. If precipitate forms in color development solution, prepare fresh solution and use immediately. Immerse membrane in distilled water to stop color development.

24.1063   Interpretation of data

Test spots containing 1 ng or greater concentration of LT become visible as purple dots within 2 to 5 min. However, control cultures that are negative for LT may give a very faint spot if color development proceeds beyond 5 min. Since rabbits are constantly exposed to *E. coli*, their sera may contain some antibodies to *E. coli* components other than antibodies to LT. With high titer sera, the use of 1:200 or even 1:400 dilution in the reaction minimizes the low level background observed with LT-negative control cultures.

24.107   Infant Mouse Test for Heat-stable Toxin[12]

At least three heat-stable toxin (ST) moieties are produced by *E. coli*.[52] Two are differentiated by molecular weight and amino acid composition and produce a positive reaction in infant mice. One is important in human illness, the other in animals. The third ST does not react in infant mice, but does react in infant pigs. Consequently, these strains will be overlooked. All appear to stimulate guanylate cyclase. LT is nonreactive in infant mice under the conditions used for the ST assay.

Use the *E. coli* culture filtrates prepared as described in Section 24.104. Add 2 drops 2% Evans blue dissolved in 0.5% NaCl solution to each undiluted filtrate. Inject 0.1 ml filtrate percutaneously into the milk-enlarged stomachs of infant mice. Use four mice for each culture. Hold mice 3 hr at room temperature in a filter-paper-lined glass petri dish. Reject any mice showing dye in the peritoneal cavity and those that do not contain dye in the stomach. Sacrifice the remaining mice using chloroform vapor. Open abdomen and remove intestinal tract but not the stomach. Pool intestines of the mice inoculated with the same filtrate in a tared weighing vessel. Pool remainder of carcasses in another tared vessel. Weigh vessels on a balance accurate to 0.01 g. Calculate ratio of intestinal weight to remaining body weight. A ratio of 0.083 or greater is considered positive. A ratio of 0.074 is considered negative. Reexamine filtrates that give ratios of 0.075 to 0.083 because the significance of these values is questionable. Since ST-producing strains of animal significance also give a positive reaction, positive data must be evaluated in conjunction with serological data for identification of somatic and colonization antigens.

24.108   DNA Probe Detection of the Heat-stable Toxin Gene

The procedure described in Section 24.105 is applicable to strains with the ST gene given the appropriate ST gene probe.[25, 48]

24.109   Enzyme Immunoassay for Heat-stable Toxin[45]

A microtitration plate competitive enzyme immunoassay (ELISA) has been developed for identification of *E. coli* ST. Protein A labeled with horseradish peroxidase (HRP-PA) is used as a tracer of antitoxin in an assay in which free ST in culture fluids competes with immobilized ST for a limited quantity of antitoxin. HRP-PA measures the quantity of antibody bound to the immobilized ST. A decrease in binding of antibody, manifested by a decrease in color production of the substrate, indicates the presence of free ST in the culture fluid.

24.1091   *E. coli* ST assay procedure

Arrange plate to contain set of either 12 or 24 tests (including controls) in quadruplicate. Each set should contain five controls: a blank (culture medium that does not receive antibody); a sterile culture medium that receives antibody; supernatant from a known ST^- culture; and supernatant from known ST^+ culture used in duplicate.

24.1092   Sample preparation

See *E. coli* LT ELISA assay procedure (Section 24.106).

24.1093   ELISA procedure

1. Coat wells of plate with 0.1 ml ST in phosphate-buffered saline-merthiolate (PBS-M). Cover plate and incubate at room temperature overnight. Aspirate and wash wells five times with 0.25 ml PBS-M.
2. Add 0.25 ml PBS-M-rabbit serum albumin (RSA) to all wells and incubate at room temperature for 5 hr. Aspirate and rinse five times as in 1, above.
3. Add 0.05 ml test culture supernatant and 0.05 ml antiserum diluted in PBS-M-RSA to wells in quadruplicate, except for blank that received 0.05 ml PBS-M-RSA. Cover plate and incubate at room temperature overnight. Aspirate and rinse plate five times with 0.25 ml STM.
4. Add 0.1 ml of appropriate dilution of HRP-PA in PBS-M-gelatin (PBS-M-GEL) to wells. The HRP-PA conjugate should be present in excess. A concentration equivalent to 0.125 μg/ml protein A in conjugate is a useful working dilution. Cover plate and incubate 4 hr at room temperature. Aspirate and rinse wells as in 3, above. Shake any excess liquid from wells.

5. Add 0.1 ml ABTS substrate to 8 wells simultaneously with 8-channel dispenser. Fill whole plate immediately and record starting time. Cover plate and incubate 15 to 30 min at room temperature. Add 0.1 ml stopping reagent to wells in same order as substrate. Measure absorbance of developed color in spectrophotometer at 414 nm or in microtitration plate reader.

24.1094   Titration of ST

Prepare 1 mg/ml ST solution in PBS-M from anhydrous ST standard. Make dilutions of ST in PBS-M at concentrations of 0, 0.01, 0.05, 0.1, 0.5, 1, 5, and 10 μg/ml. Add 0.1 ml ST to wells of plate, placing each ST dilution in separate row of 12 wells. Proceed as in 1 and 2, above. Prepare antiserum in PBS-M-RSA at dilutions of 1:400, 1:800, and 1:1600. Add 0.1 ml of these dilutions to 4 columns of 8 wells so that each ST-coating concentration receives quadruplicate portions of each antiserum dilution. Incubate and follow remaining steps of procedure as defined in 3 through 5, above. Select optimal coating concentration from plot of absorbance values against concentration of ST used for coating. Select antibody dilution curve that has peak absorbance of 1 ± 0.2 absorbance units. Use this antibody dilution in test. Lowest ST concentration producing maximum absorbance represents dilution of ST for coating plate.

24.1095   Interpreting data

Determining whether a culture contains ST is based on the experimental data meeting two criteria: reproducibility of the test values must be acceptable, and duplicate positive (+) control values must not differ significantly. If both criteria are not met, the test samples must be reanalyzed. Examples of the statistical calculations involved in testing both criteria are available.[45]

24.10100   Isolation of Enterohemorrhagic *E. coli* (EHEC) and Tests for Its Toxins

Since the recognition of *E. coli* as a cause of hemorrhagic colitis in 1982[41] and hemolytic uremic syndrome in 1983,[27] development of methods for the isolation of the causative organism(s) from food is still in the formative stage and none has official approval. Three approaches have been used to identify *E. coli* O157:H7, the primary strain causing hemorrhagic colitis, from food: (1) sorbitol-MacConkey agar, (2) an immunoblot technique for verocytotoxins, and (3) an enzyme-labeled monoclonal antibody procedure.

24.10101   Isolation with sorbitol-MacConkey agar

Homogenize 10 g of test sample in 90 ml peptone water diluent. Prepare serial tenfold dilutions in peptone water diluent in accordance with anticipated level (up to 10^6/g). Pipette 1 ml of each dilution in duplicate onto the surface of dried sorbitol-MacConkey agar and spread material evenly across each plate. Incubate plates at 35°C and read after 18 hr. Sorbitol-negative colonies (typical of *E. coli* O157:H7) are pale compared with the bright pink sorbitol-positive colonies (most other *E. coli* strains). Test sorbitol-negative colonies against O157 and H7 antisera to confirm isolates' serotypes.

Precaution: This medium has been used successfully to isolate *E. coli* O157:H7 from stool specimens and has also been adopted for food isolation. However, high levels of contaminating coliform organisms will mask the O157 strains.

24.10102   Isolation with immunoblot for verocytotoxins

Add 25 g of test sample to 225 ml trypticase novobiocin (TN) broth in 1 L flasks and incubate with agitation (100 gyrations per min) at 37°C for 18 to 24 hr. Dilute enrichment culture to 10^{-7} in 0.01 M phosphate buffer at pH 7.5 and filter 1 ml of each dilution through HGMFs. Place each HGMF over 6 × 6 cm of wetted nitrocellulose paper on the surface of a TN agar plate and incubate at 37°C for 18 to 24 hr. Remove HGMF, place on a TN agar plate, and refrigerate if not processing immediately. Treat nitrocellulose papers by an immunoblot procedure to identify verocytotoxins. First, inactivate any free microbial peroxidase by washing papers twice with salts phosphate-buffered-saline (salts-PBS) solution, treating with 0.012 M sodium borohydride for 30 min, and rewashing three times with salts-PBS solution. Second, treat the washed papers with 1% bovine serum albumin (BSA) in salts-PBS solution for 1 hr with agitation (50 gyrations per min) at 37°C. Then suspend the papers in verocytotoxin rabbit antibody solution at 37°C for 1 hr with agitation (50 gyrations per min) at 37°C, and wash twice in 1% BSA in salts-PBS before soaking them in the same but fresh solution at 37°C, for 10 min. Repeat this washing procedure three times. Third, suspend the nitrocellulose papers in 1:1000 goat antiserum (to rabbit immunoglobulin G) conjugated with HRP at 37°C for 1 hr. Then, wash three times and incubate in salt-PBS as described above, and react with HRP color development solution at room temperature for 5 min with a final wash in deionized, distilled water. If purple-blue areas are present on the papers, align them with the corresponding HGMFs, and select colonies from the appropriate areas to be cultured on trypticase soy agar for characterization as *E. coli* O157:H7 by Biken tests,[13] verocytotoxicity,[13] and biochemical reactions.

24.10103   Isolation and enumeration with an enzyme-labeled monoclonal antibody

Homogenize 10 g of test sample in 90 ml peptone water (and prepare a 1:100 dilution if counts are expected to be high). Pipette 1-ml aliquots through disposable 100-μm prefilters and add to 10 ml peptone water filtered through HGMFs (Todd et al. Appl. Environ. Microbiol. 54:2536. 1988). Layer filters onto hemorrhagic coli (HC) agar and incubate at 43°C for 16 to 20 hr. Replicate colony growth onto other HGMFs using HGMF replicator. Incubate replicates on HC agar at 43°C for 16 to 20 hr and test original filters with conjugated antibody as follows: remove visible colony growth from filters by agitating (60 rpm) filters in distilled water for 10 min. Block unoccupied grid spaces by immersing filters in 3% gelatin-Tris buffered saline (TBS) for 30 min. After blocking, transfer HGMFs to antibody solution and agitate for 60 min at 60 gyrations per min. Remove excess antibody by rinsing rapidly in distilled water, then twice (7 min each) in a solution containing TBS Tween. Add HRP color development solution. After 15 to 30 min, rinse in distilled water and count colonies (purple dots). To eliminate *Salmonella* spp. of Group N, which cross-react with *E. coli* O157, take incubated replicate HGMFs and stain as above, using HRP-labeled Spicer-Edwards antisera instead of *E. coli* O157-labeled antisera (no purple dots should occur if *E. coli* O157 is present). To identify *E. coli* further, locate specific grids on replicate HGMFs that correspond to the purple dots and pick the colonies; make single line inoculations on fresh HGMFs that have been placed on HC agar and streak the picks onto HC agar; incubate plates at 43°C for 16 to 20 hr. Retest HGMF isolates with the enzyme-labeled monoclonal antibody procedure and if positive, recover pure cultures from the corresponding streaked HC agar. Determine *E. coli* O157 flagellar type with specific H antisera.

25.10104   Tissue culture test for verotoxin

Preparation of Verotoxin. Inoculate culture to 20 ml trypticase soy broth in 250-ml Erlenmeyer flask and incubate with agitation at 37°C for 20 to 24 hr. Centrifuge culture at 7000 × *g* for 30 min to sediment most bacteria. Filter supernatant through a 0.45-μm membrane to remove residual bacteria. Store at 4°C. Dilute filtrate 1:5 in PBS, pH 7.0, before use.

Preparation of Vero monolayers. Maintain Vero culture in MEME-L15 medium containing 2% milk serum, prepared as follows. Add dry milk to double-distilled water to final concentration of 10%. Add concentrate of gentamicin sulfate to level of 50 μg/ml. Stir 1 hr on magnetic stirrer at room temperature. With stirring, adjust pH to 4.5 with 1 N HCl. Filter through cheesecloth. Clarify by centrifugation at 2500 rpm for 15 min. Filter again through cheesecloth. Sterilize by filtration through 0.22 μm membrane. Add milk serum to give 2% concentration by volume in MEME-L15 medium. Incubate culture in 5% CO_2 incubator held at 36°C for 72 hr. Examine culture for purity and appearance of cells. If cells are normal and not contaminated, treat with trypsin (see Section 24.102) to remove monolayer. Suspend cells to a density of 10^5 per ml in cell growth medium. With gentle agitation, transfer 0.5-ml portions to 16-mm wells in sterile plastic dishes. Incubate 3 to 4 days at 36°C in CO_2 incubator. Examine for purity and appearance of cells. Remove spent medium and replace with 0.5 ml fresh medium.

1. Toxicity test. Add 0.05 ml diluted culture filtrate to well. For control, dilute trypticase soy broth 1:5 in PBS. Add 0.05 ml to well. Incubate 4 days at 36°C in CO_2 incubator.
2. Examine daily for cytopathic effects, i.e., rounding, shriveling, and detachment of cells. Potent preparations affect at least 50% of the monolayer cells. There should be a progressive increase in toxicity with increased incubation. Cytotoxicity, in contrast to the cytotonic effect of LT, is not reversible if the medium is changed and the monolayers are reincubated.

24.1020   Addendum. Recent advances.

Okrend *et al* (J. Food Prot. 53:249, 936. 1990) have developed a relatively sensitive cultural procedure. Twenty-five g of meat are blended in a modified EC broth containing reduced bile salts concentration (1.12 g/L), and novobiocin (20 mg/L) and incubated for 6 hr with shaking at 37°C or for 24 hr statically at 35°C; 0.1 ml amounts of several dilutions are spread over large (150 × 15 mm) MacConkey sorbitol agar (MSA) plates, and incubated at 42°C overnight. [A recent modification (Okrend et al. J. Food Prot. 53:941. 1990) substitutes MSA containing 5-bromo-4-chloro-3-indoxyl-β-D-glucuronide (BCIG) to help in selection of *E. coli* O157:H7 colonies, which are white or translucent (sorbitol negative, β-D-glucuronidase negative) compared with other organisms which show as red, blue or green colonies.] Sorbitol negative BCIG negative colonies are smeared onto EMB plates and stabbed into phenol red sorbitol agar containing MUG. On these media *E. coli* O157:H7 colonies should be sorbitol negative, MUG negative and have a typical *E. coli* metallic sheen. These are confirmed biochemically.

Finally, presumptive isolates are identified serologically with agglutination tests with O157 (Oxoid) and H7 antisera. These authors are also examining the 3M procedure (see below) for the best combination of the two methods.

Szabo *et al.* (Appl. Environ. Microbiol. 56:3546. 1990) have extended the use of the direct count HGMF-enzyme-linked-antibody procedure (24.10103) to foods other than meat. Recovery was good for vegetable and dairy products containing ≥ 10–20 cells/g. The exception is processed cheese, which is nonfilterable, unless treated with pronase. Disposable foam pipet pre-filters were found to improve detection and were recommended for all foods; otherwise, the original method remains the same.

Because *E. coli* O157:H7 appears to be present in some foods at very low levels, an enrichment method was also developed for better sensitivity (1 cell/g). TN broth, incubated at 43°C with shaking for 16–20 hr gave the best results for enrichment of meat (10 g in 90 ml), but TSB at 43°C with shaking was superior for bovine stool specimens. After incubation, 1-ml aliquots are filtered through HGMFs, which are then incubated on HC agar. The TN broth was also satisfactory for enriching dairy products and vegetables.

Dynatech Laboratories Inc., Chantilly, Virginia, is in the process of designing a kit (Q-Trol™ *E. coli* O157:H7 Detection Kit) which is based on a sandwich enzyme immunoassay procedure. Microtiter plates have wells coated with polyclonal antibodies to *E. coli* O157:H7. These antibodies bind any O157:H7 antigens present in the food samples tested. After washing to remove unbound material, antibody (against the bound antibody) conjugated to alkaline phosphatase is added to form an antibody-antigen-antibody enzyme complex. Unbound conjugate is removed by washing the wells and a colorimetric substrate is added to measure the enzyme activity. Samples with an optical density greater than or equal to the cut off value stated in the kit package are considered positive for *E. coli* O157:H7 antigens. The sensitivity is approximately 1 cell in 10 g, but there is no way of confirming tests by cultural means.

Another sandwich ELISA procedure using microtiter plates is being researched by Organon Teknika Corporation/Bionetics Research Institute (Rockville, Maryland). Monoclonal antibodies have been prepared against the *E. coli* O157 polysaccaride antigen and also against the H7 flagellar antigen. The O157 antibodies cross-react with group N salmonellae, but the H7 ELISA will be able to confirm any positive reactions with the O157 serum. At present, only pure culture work has been done with a sensitivity of 100,000 cells/ml of non-selective soy enrichment broth. Further research will focus on competing microorganisms and inoculated food samples to determine the effects of food components and other organisms on the growth and detection of the pathogen.

3M (Microbiology Products, 3M Center, St. Paul, Minnesota) is also developing a kit with a method based on its Petrifilm™ approach. A 25-g sample is preenriched in 225 ml of m TSB (TN broth) or mEC (Okrend *et al. op. cit*) and incubated for 6–8 hr at 36°C. One mL of the broths together with 1 mL each of 10^{-1} and 10^{-2} dilutions are added to PEC (Petrifilm *E. coli*) plates, which are then incubated for 18 h at 42°C. Most *E. coli* produce blue colonies with gas bubbles (glucuronidase positive). *E. coli* O157:H7 produces red colonies with gas bubbles, as do other coliforms. After incubation, the surface film together with the medium which sticks to the film (because of the guar gum present) is peeled back to expose the well. A proprietary reactive disk is placed in the well and the film is carefully replaced to allow transfer of antigens to the disk. After 2 minutes the film and the PEG medium are peeled back and kept for isolation of presumptive *E. coli* O157 colonies, and the disk removed from the well, washed briefly and exposed to affinity purified polyclonal O157 antibody conjugated to an *E. coli* phosphatase enzyme. After rinsing, a substrate is added to produce a permanent color reaction with any *E. coli* O157 antigens present recognized by small grey or black spots or circles. *Salmonella* group N antigens will also react with the O157 antibody but cause a different type of color reaction. Isolates can be obtained by aligning the stained disk with the original medium (PEC), and selecting the appropriate area for colony isolation and biochemical testing. The sensitivity of the test is one cell in 10 g of raw hamburger and one in 50 g with cooked hamburger.

Advancement in food methodology using existing verotoxin I and II detection systems that utilize monoclonal antibodies and DNA probes is expected shortly. Pollard *et al.*, (J. Clin. Microbiol. 28:540. 1990) have developed a method that uses the polymerase chain reaction to detect the genes for verotoxins I and II. This procedure is presently being considered for possible use in food samples.

Acknowledgment

This chapter is based on the text prepared by the late Ira J. Mehlman for the previous edition of this book.

24.11   REFERENCES

1. APHA. 1985a. "Laboratory Procedures for the Examination of Seawater and Shellfish," 5th ed. Am. Pub. Health Assoc., Washington, D.C.
2. APHA. 1985b. "Standard Methods for the Examination of Dairy Products," 15th ed. Am. Pub. Health Assoc., Washington, D.C.
3. APHA. 1985c. "Standard Methods for the Examination of Water and Wastewater," 16th ed. Am. Pub. Health Assoc., Washington, D.C.
4. Anderson, J. M. and Baird-Parker, A. C. 1975. A rapid and direct plate method for enumerating *Escherichia coli* biotype 1 in food. J. Appl. Bacteriol. 39: 111.
5. Andrews, W. H. 1986. Resuscitation of injured *Salmonella* spp. and coliforms from foods. J. Food Prot. 49: 62.
6. Andrews, W. H., Wilson, C. R., Poelma, P. L., Bullock, L. K., McClure, F. D., and Gentile, D. E. 1981. Interlaboratory evaluation of the AOAC method and the A-1 procedure for recovery of fecal coliforms from foods. J. Assoc. Off. Anal. Chem. 64: 1116.
7. AOAC. 1984. "Official Methods of Analysis," 14th ed. Assoc. of Official Analytical Chemists, Arlington, Va.
8. AOAC. 1985. Total coliform, fecal coliform and *Escherichia coli* in foods, hydrophobic grid membrane filter method. J. Assoc. Off. Anal. Chem. 68: 404.
9. Brenner, D. J., Davis, B. R., Steigerwalt, A. G., Riddle, C. F., McWhorter, A. C., Allen, S. D., Farmer III, J. J., Saitoh, Y., and Fanning, G. R. 1982a. Atypical biogroups of *Escherichia coli* found in clinical specimens and description of *Escherichia hermannii* sp. nov. J. Clin. Microbiol. 15: 703.
10. Brenner, D. J., McWhorter, A. C., Knutson, J. K. L., and Steigerwalt, A. G. 1982b. *Escherichia vulneris*: A new species of *Enterobacteriaceae* associated with human wounds. J. Clin. Microbiol. 15: 1133.
11. Burrows, W. and Musteikis, G. M. 1966. Cholera infection and toxin in the rabbit ileal loop. J. Infect. Dis. 116: 183.
12. Dean, A. G., Ching, Y., Williams, R. G., and Harden, L. B. 1972. Test for *Escherichia coli* enterotoxin using infant mice. Application in a study of diarrhea in children in Honolulu. J. Infect. Dis. 125: 407.
13. Doyle, M. P., and Schoeni, J. L. 1987. Isolation of *Escherichia coli* O157:H7 from retail fresh meats and poultry. Appl. Environ. Microbiol. 53: 2394.
14. DuPont, H. L., Formal, S. B., Hornick, R. B., Snyder, J. J., Libonati, J. P., Sheahan, D. G., LaBrec, E. H., and Kalas, J. P. 1971. Pathogenesis of *Escherichia coli* diarrhea. N. Engl. J. Med. 285: 1.

15. Entis, P. 1983. Enumeration of coliforms in nonfat dry milk and canned custard by hydrophobic grid membrane filter method: collaborative study. J. Assoc. Off. Anal. Chem. 66: 897.

16. Entis, P. 1984a. Enumeration of total coliforms, fecal coliforms and *Escherichia coli* in foods by hydrophobic grid membrane filter: collaborative study. J. Assoc. Off. Anal. Chem. 67: 812.

17. Entis, P. 1984b. Enumeration of total coliforms, fecal coliforms and *Escherichia coli* in foods by hydrophobic grid membrane filter: supplementary report. J. Assoc. Off. Anal. Chem. 67: 811.

18. Evans, D. G. and Evans, D. J. Jr. 1978. New surface-associated heat-labile colonization factor antigen (CFA/II) produced by enterotoxigenic *Escherichia coli* of serogroups O6 and O8. Infect. Immun. 21: 638.

19. Evans, D. G., Evans, D. J. Jr., Clegg, S., and Pauley, J. A. 1979. Purification and characterization of the CFA/I antigen of enterotoxigenic *Escherichia coli*. Infect. Immun. 25: 738.

20. Evans, T. M., Seidler, R. J., and LeChevallier, M. W. 1981. Impact of verification media and resuscitation on accuracy of the membrane filter total coliform enumeration technique. Appl. Environ. Microbiol. 41: 1144.

21. Ewing, W. H. 1986. "Edwards and Ewing's Identification of *Enterobactericeae*," 4th ed. Elsevier, New York, N.Y.

22. Feng, P. C. S. and Hartman, P. A. 1982. Fluorogenic assays for immediate confirmation of *Escherichia coli*. Appl. Environ. Microbiol. 43: 1320.

23. Hartman, P. A. 1988. MUG (glucuronidase) test for *Escherichia coli* in food and water. Proc. 5th International Symposium on Rapid Methods and Automation in Microbiology. Florence, Italy (in press).

24. Hartman, P. A. and Hartman, P. S. 1976. Coliform analyses at 30C. J. Milk Food Technol. 39: 763.

25. Hill, W. E. 1987. Detection of pathogenic bacteria by DNA colony hybridization. In "FDA Bacteriological Analytical Manual," 6th ed., Suppl. Assoc. of Official Analytical Chemists, Arlington, Va.

26. Holbrook, R., Anderson, J. M., and Baird-Parker, A. C. 1980. Modified direct plate method for counting *Escherichia coli* in foods. Food Technol. Aust. 32: 78.

27. Karmali, M. A., Steele, B. T., Petric, M., and Lim, C. 1983. Sporadic cases of hemolytic-uremic syndrome associated with faecal cytotoxin and cytotoxin producing *Escherichia coli* in stools. Lancet 1: 619.

28. Kauffman, P. E. 1981. Production and evaluation of antibody to the heat-stable enterotoxin from a human strain of enterotoxigenic *Escherichia coli*. Appl. Environ. Microbiol. 42: 611.

29. Kaysner, C. A. and Weagent, S. D. 1987. Limitations of the A-1 M method for fecal coliform enumeration in the Pacific Oyster (*Crassotrea gigas*). J. Assoc. Off. Anal. Chem. 70: 535.

30. Krieg, N. R. and Holt, J. G. eds. 1984. "Bergey's Manual of Systematic Bacteriology," Vol. 1. Williams and Wilkins, Baltimore, Md.

31. Krishnan, C., Fitzgerald, V. A., Dakin, S. J., and Behme, R. J. 1987. Laboratory investigation of outbreak of hemorrhagic colitis caused by *Escherichia coli* O157:H7. J. Clin. Microbiol. 25: 1043.

32. Lawton, W. C. 1955. A comparison of 32°C and 35°C as incubation temperatures for the coliform count of milk and cream. J. Milk Food Technol. 18: 288.

33. LeChevallier, M. W. and McFeters, G. A. 1984. Recent advances in coliform methodology for water analysis. J. Environ. Health 47: 5.

34. Levine, M. M. 1987. *Escherichia coli* that cause diarrhea: Enterotoxigenic, enteropathogenic, enteroinvasive, enterohemorrhagic, and enteroadherent. J. Infect. Dis. 155: 377.

35. Marshall, R. T., Case, R. A., Ginn, R. E., Messer, J. W., Peeler, J. T., Richardson, G. H., and Wehr, H. M. 1987. Update on standard methods for the examination of dairy products, 15th ed. J. Food Prot. 50: 711.

36. Mehlman, I. J., Simon, N. T., Sanders, A. C., Fishbein, M., Olson, J. C. Jr., and Read, R. B. Jr. 1975. Methodology for enteropathogenic *Escherichia coli*. J. Assoc. Off. Anal. Chem. 58: 283.

37. Mehlman, I. J., Eide, E. L., Sanders, A. C., Fishbein, M., and Aulisio, C. 1977. Methodology for recognition of invasive potential of *Escherichia coli*. J. Assoc. Off. Anal. Chem. 66: 546.

38. Moberg, L. J., Wagner, M. K., and Kellen, L. A. 1988. Fluorogenic assay for rapid detection of *Escherichia coli* in chilled and frozen foods: Collaborative study. J. Assoc. Off. Anal. Chem. 71: 589.

39. Mossel, D. A. A. 1985. Media for *Enterobacteriaceae*. Int. J. Food Microbiol. 2: 27.

40. Ray, B. 1986. Impact of bacterial injury and repair in food microbiology: Its past, present and future. J. Food Prot. 49: 651.

41. Riley, L. W., Remis, R. S., Helgerson, S. D., McGee, H. B., Davis, B. R., Herbert, R. J., Olcott, E. S., Johnson, L. M., Hargrett, N. J., Blake, P. A., and Cohen, M. L. 1983. Hemorrhagic colitis associated with a rare *Escherichia coli* serotype. N. Engl. J. Med. 308: 681.

42. Rippey, S. R., Chandler, L. A., and Watkins, W. D. 1987. Fluorometric method for enumeration of *Escherichia coli* in molluscan shellfish. J. Food Prot. 50: 685.

43. Sack, D. A. and Sack, R. B. 1975. Test for enterotoxigenic *Escherichia coli* using Y-1 adrenal cells in miniculture. Infect. Immun. 11: 334.

44. Sereny, B. 1957. Experimental keratoconjunctivitis in shigellosa. Acta Microbiol. Hung. 4: 367.

45. Shah, D. B., Wimsatt, J. C., and Kauffman, P. E. 1987. Enzyme linked immunosorbent assay (ELISA). In "FDA Bacteriological Analytical Manual." Assn. of Offic. Analyt. Chem., Arlington, Va.

46. Sharpe, A. N. and Peterkin, P. I. 1988. "Membrane Filter Food Microbiology: Innovation in Microbiology Research Studies Series." Research Studies Press, Letchworth, UK.

47. Sharpe, A. N., Rayman, M. K., Burgener, D. M., Conley, D., Loit, A., Milling, M., Peterkin, P. I., Purvis, U., and Malcolm, S. 1983. Collaborative study of the MPN, Anderson-Baird-Parker direct plating, and hydrophobic grid-membrane filter methods for the enumeration of *Escherichia coli* biotype I in foods. Can. J. Microbiol. 29: 1247.

48. So, M., Boyer, H. W., Betlach, M., and Falkow, S. 1976. Molecular cloning of an *Escherichia coli* plasmid that encodes for the production of heat-stable enterotoxin. J. Bacteriol. 128: 463.

49. Staples, S. T., Asher, S. E., and Gianella, R. A. 1980. Purification and characterization of heat-stable enterotoxin produced by a strain of *E. coli* pathogenic for man. J. Biol. Chem. 255: 4716.

50. Szabo, R. A., Todd, E. C. D., and Jean, A. 1986. Method to isolate *Escherichia coli* O157:H7 from food. J. Food Prot. 49: 768.

51. Weiss, K. F., Chopra, N., Stotland, P., Reidel, G. W., and Malcolm, S. 1983. Recovery of fecal coliforms and of *Escherichia coli* at 44.5, 45.0, 45.5°C. J. Food Prot. 46: 172.

52. Whipp, S. C., Moon, H. W., and Argenzio, R. A. 1981. Comparison of enterotoxic activities of heat-stable enterotoxins from class 1 and class 2 *Escherichia coli* of swine origin. Infect. Immun. 31: 245.

Chapter 25

SALMONELLA

Russell S. Flowers, Jean-Yves D'Aoust, Wallace H. Andrews, and J. Stan Bailey

25.1 GENERAL BASIS OF METHODS

25.11 Introduction

The incidence of salmonellosis appears to have increased during the past 20 years.[97] Estimates of human foodborne salmonellosis in this country vary from 740,000 to 5,300,000 cases annually.[121] Many experts agree that two key factors for reducing or, at the very least, for maintaining these figures are consumer education and implementation and maintenance of adequate laboratory quality control programs in the food industry.

Discussion of the consumer educational aspects of salmonellosis control is beyond the scope of this chapter, but optimal detection methods for a stringent laboratory quality control program will be reviewed in detail. Food processors do not want their companies' products involved in salmonellosis outbreaks because the consequences can be economically devastating. Industry has therefore implemented rigid quality control programs to minimize the risk of *Salmonella* contamination of its products. Pressures from the food industry in the last 5 years have played a significant part in the development, validation, and marketing of several diagnostic kits for the rapid detection of *Salmonella* in foods.

For years, the fluorescent antibody technique[4] offered the only Association of Official Analytical Chemists (AOAC)-approved alternative to the more tedious and labor-intensive conventional culture method[141] for *Salmonella*. Although this technique fulfilled a need at the time, excessively high rates of discrepant false-positive reactions occurred with the analysis of certain foods.

371

Thus, the food industry continued to seek more reliable rapid methods, particularly those that would provide "next-day" results.

High-technology companies in the private sector responded to the need by introducing a variety of techniques for the rapid detection of *Salmonella* in foods. These rapid methods are, by definition, screening methods, and they are highlighted in a subsequent section of this chapter. Presumptively positive results with such methods must be confirmed by the conventional culture method, but negative results may be considered definitive.

Rapid screening methods give presumptively positive results 1 to 2 days earlier than the conventional culture method. Considering the technological advancements of the past 5 years, methods providing "next-day" results or even "same-day" results may soon be a reality. The greatest obstacle to such methods presently is the need to pre-enrich food samples. Attempts at reducing this pre-enrichment period to less than 18 hr have not been successful.[27] The ultimate goal, of course, would be to detect *Salmonella* in a food suspension without requiring pre-enrichment.

25.12   General Description of Methods for the Isolation of *Salmonella* from Foods

25.121   Introduction

The examination of various types of food products for *Salmonella* requires methods different from those used in clinical laboratories. The need for such methods is due to the generally low numbers of salmonellae in foods and the frequently poor physiological state of these pathogens following exposure to stressful conditions during food processing or storage. Injured or debilitated salmonellae are resuscitated in a nonselective broth medium. Although qualitative recovery of foodborne *Salmonella* is generally sought, the analytical approach used in conventional methods can be adapted for the enumeration of salmonellae by the most probable number (MPN) technique.[113]

The reference procedure described hereafter for the isolation and identification of *Salmonella* (Section 25.5) has been adapted from the "Official Methods of Analysis" of the AOAC.[4] The biochemical and serological tests used to identify *Salmonella* are described in the reference procedure and are listed in Table 4.

The classification of the *Salmonella-Arizona* group of *Enterobacteriaceae* has been a source of confusion because of different systems of nomenclature.[41, 79, 90] The Enteric Bacteriology Laboratories at the Centers for Disease Control (CDC) recently introduced changes in their nomenclature of the *Salmonella-Arizona* group by incorporating the *Arizona* group[41] into the *Salmonella* genus.[19, 49, 88, 89] Table 1 summarizes the properties of the seven subspecies within the genus *Salmonella* defined on the basis of DNA hybridization studies.[19, 88, 89]

Many scientific journals require the nomenclature of microorganisms to comply with *Bergey's Manual of Systematic Bacteriology*.[84] *Bergey's* has taken a different approach from CDC and has adopted the position that the use of "species" names for *Salmonella* serovars is useful in many fields, so long as the serovars' names are not taxonomically equated with species. The nomenclature in this chapter and the classic definition of the genus *Salmonella* are as described in *Bergey's Manual of Systematic Bacteriology*.[90]

Not all serovars within the genus *Salmonella* are equally pathogenic to humans and animals, but all are important to public health, and isolation procedures should recover all serovars of *Salmonella*. Analysts should be thoroughly familiar with the various biochemical and serological characteristics involved in differentiating *Salmonella* from the other foodborne microorganisms.

25.122 Sampling

General directions for sample collection and handling are discussed in Chapter 2. Various organizations have suggested sampling plans that can be used specifically for *Salmonella*. One of these plans has been proposed by the National Academy of Sciences (NAS)[101] through the Committee on *Salmonella* of the National Research Council (NRC). Foods are categorized on the basis of hazards presented by the particular food: (1) the food or food ingredient is a significant potential source of *Salmonella*; (2) the manufacturing process does not include a controlled step that should kill *Salmonella* microorganisms; and (3) a potential exists for microbiological growth if the food is mishandled in distribution or by consumers. Considering these hazards, foods are placed in one of five categories:

Category I—foods intended for use by infants, the aged, and the infirm, the restricted population of high risk
Category II—foods that present the three hazards
Category III—foods with two hazards
Category IV—foods with one hazard
Category V—foods with none of the hazards

Criteria for acceptance of any particular lot of food are based on the results of analyses of a required number of 25-g analytical units, the actual portions of food analyzed. Each analytical unit is taken from a larger sample unit, usually a minimum of 100 g, the balance being set aside as a reserve. A series of random sample units make up the sample, and a sample that is representative of the lot is used to determine the acceptability of the entire lot of food. A food lot is defined as an identifiable unit of food produced and handled under uniform conditions, usually determined by a limited period of time. This sampling plan is based on the premise that the distribution of the *Salmonella* organisms within the lot is homogeneous. This premise implies that any analytical unit is as likely as any other analytical unit to contain *Salmonella*.

Table 1—Properties of the Seven Subspecies Within *Salmonella enterica* ("the *Salmonella-Arizona* Group")[a]

	Designation						
	Salmonella subspecies 1	*Salmonella* subspecies 2	*Salmonella* subspecies 3a	*Salmonella* subspecies 3b	*Salmonella* subspecies 4	*Salmonella* subspecies 5	*Salmonella* subspecies 6
DNA-hybridization group of Crosa et al.[19]	1	2	3	4	5	Not studied	6
Salmonella subgenus names formerly used	I	II	III	III	IV	V	
Genus according to Ewing[47]	*Salmonella*	*Salmonella*	*Arizona*	*Arizona*	*Salmonella*	*Salmonella*	*Salmonella*
Subspecies according to Le Minor et al.[89]	*enterica*	*salamae*	*arizonae*	*diarizonae*	*houtenae*	*bongori*	*indica*
Usually monophasic (Mono) or diphasic (Di) flagella	Di	Di	Mono	Di	Mono	Mono	Di
Usually isolated from humans and warm-blooded animals	+	−	−	−	−	+	+
Usually isolated from cold-blooded animals and the environment	−	+	+	+	+	+	+
Pathogenic for humans	+	+	+	+	+	+?	? unknown

Tests to differentiate the subspecies

Dulcitol fermentation	96[b]	90	0	1	0	variable
Lactose fermentation	1	1	15	85	0	? not given
ONPG Test	2	15	100	100	0	variable
Malonate utilization	1	95	95	95	0	0
Growth in KCN medium	1	1	1	1	95	0
Mucate fermentation	90	96	90	30	0	+
Gelatin hydrolysis[c]	–	+	+	+	+	+
D-Galacturonate fermentation[c]	–	+	–	+	+	+
Lysis by 01 bacteriophage[c]	+	+	–	+	–	+

[a] Adapted from Le Minor et al.[88, 89, 90]

[b] The numbers give the % positive for the tests after 2 days incubation at 35°C and are based on CDC data. The vast majority of the positive tests occur within 24 hr; reactions positive after 2 days are not considered.

[c] Based on the data of Le Minor et al.[88, 89, 90] + = 90% or more positive; – = 10% or less positive. The test for gelatin hydrolysis is the rapid "film" method at 35°C (almost all strains are negative by the tube method at 22°C within 2 days).

Source: Farmer et al.[49]

The NAS/NRC Committee proposed criteria for the acceptance of any particular food lot in the various categories:

Category I—60 analytical units tested and found negative, indicating a 95% probability of ≤1 *Salmonella* organism per 500 g of food in the lot tested

Category II—29 analytical units found negative, indicating ≤1 *Salmonella* organism per 250 g of food

Categories III, IV, V—13 analytical units found negative, indicating ≤1 *Salmonella* organism per 125 g of food

The International Commission on Microbiological Specifications for Foods (ICMSF)[72] proposed a general microbial sampling plan that also includes a sampling plan specific for *Salmonella*. Basically, any particular food is sampled according to its placement in 1 of 15 categories, or, "cases." Such placement depends on two factors: (1) type of microbial hazard involved and (2) anticipated conditions of handling and use of the food after sampling. The microbial hazard can range from no direct health hazard (e.g., spoilage or reduced shelf life) to severe hazard (e.g., suspected presence of *Clostridium botulinum*). Anticipated conditions of handling and use of the food can be reduced hazard (e.g., cooking prior to consumption), unchanged hazard (e.g., direct consumption of dried foods), or increased hazard (e.g., storage of thawed frozen food at ambient or high temperatures). The stringency of sampling varies directly with the case number assigned to the food.[72]

Under the ICMSF plan, food sampling for most *Salmonella* corresponds to Cases 10, 11, and 12 (decreased, unchanged, and increased hazard in use, respectively). The case number increases as the stringency of the criteria for acceptability of any particular food lot increases. However, foods suspected of containing *S. typhi*, *S. paratyphi*, or *S. cholerae suis* are assigned higher risk levels and are sampled with greater stringency (Cases 13, 14, or 15). In contrast, the NAS/NRC sampling plan recognizes an equally high degree of risk for all serovars and thus calls for greater sampling stringency than the ICMSF plan under most conditions. An added feature of the ICMSF plan, not found in the NAS/NRC plan, however, is the distinction made between sampling under normal (routine) and special (investigational) conditions, such as investigation of a foodborne outbreak. The ICMSF plan compares in stringency to the NAS/NRC plan only in the investigational mode.

The two sampling plans are nevertheless similar in that both recommend increasing the number of analytical units with increased health risk. In general, the assignment of a food to a particular category or case depends on the sensitivity of the consumer group, the history of the food, whether there is a step lethal to *Salmonella* microorganisms during processing or in the home, and the abuse potential of the product. The sensitivity of the consumer group and whether the food undergoes a step lethal to *Salmonella* during processing or in the home are most important to the Food and Drug Administration (FDA) in selecting a sampling plan for *Salmonella*. Accordingly, a sampling plan has been implemented, placing foods into one of three categories:

Category I—foods that would normally be placed in Category II, except that they are intended for consumption by the aged, the infirm, and infants (60 analytical units)

Category II—foods that would not normally be subjected to a process lethal to *Salmonella* between the time of sampling and consumption (30 analytical units)

Category III—foods that would normally be subjected to a process lethal to *Salmonella* between the time of sampling and consumption (15 analytical units)

Various studies have demonstrated that dry compositing (combining food samples into a single analytical unit)[70, 122] or wet compositing (combining pre-enrichment cultures of individual analytical units)[109, 120, 122] substantially reduces the analytical workload without compromising method sensitivity for detecting *Salmonella*. In the FDA sampling plan, up to 15 × 25-g analytical units may be combined and tested as a single 375-g composite unit. The presence of *Salmonella* in foods assigned to Categories I, II, or III may be determined by the analysis of 4, 2, or 1 composite unit(s), respectively.

25.123   Pre-enrichment

Salmonellae in dried, processed foods are often present in low numbers and in a debilitated condition. Moreover, the presence of non-*Salmonella* bacteria and substances indigenous to the food sample may interfere with the growth and recovery of *Salmonella*. It is generally accepted that pre-enrichment of processed foods in a nonselective broth medium facilitates detection of sublethally injured *Salmonella*. The ideal pre-enrichment broth should provide for the repair of cell damage, dilute toxic or inhibitory substances, and be of such nutritive capacity as to favor a higher ratio of *Salmonella* to non-*Salmonella* microorganisms.

Lactose broth is commonly used for pre-enrichment. Although most *Salmonella* do not utilize lactose, North[103] concluded that when competing lactose-utilizing bacteria are present in a food sample, a resulting drop in pH generates a bacteriostatic effect on competing microflora. Lactose broth is widely used in the United States, but it is not recommended for all products and it is only one of the many pre-enrichment broths recommended for use worldwide (Table 3). In addition to these common pre-enrichment media, Gomez et al.[66] developed a glucose-inorganic salts medium (M-9) for recovery of salmonellae stressed under extreme conditions of heat and dehydration and exposure to antibiotics.[65, 66, 77] However, Poelma et al.[108] found M-9 to be less efficient than lactose broth for recovery of *Salmonella* in artificially contaminated casein powder.

The method of sample rehydration may significantly influence the recovery of *Salmonella* from dry products. Ray et al.[113] and van Schothorst et al.[143] concluded that in a low osmotic environment, cells in dry products are less prone to osmotic injury during slow rehydration. Initial reconstitution of dried

Table 2—Analysis of Foods by Methods of the Bacteriological Analytical Manual and the Association of Official Analytical Chemists

Food	Pre-enrichment[a]	Preparation[b]
Dried egg yolk, egg white, and whole egg; pasteurized liquid and frozen eggs; powdered bread and pastry mixes; infant formulas; oral or tube feedings containing egg; coconut;[c] food dyes with pH ≥ 6.0 (10% aqueous solution); gelatin[d]	Lactose broth	Mix
Pasta (noodles, macaroni, spaghetti); egg rolls; cheese; dough; prepared salads; fresh, frozen, or dried fruits and vegetables; nut meats; crustaceans; fish; heated, processed, or dried meats, meat substitutes, meat by-products, animal substances, glandular products, meals (fish, meat, and bone); casein	Lactose broth	Blend
Nonpasteurized frozen egg products	None[e]	Mix 25 g/225 ml SC 25 g/225 ml TBG
Food dyes with pH < 6.0 (10% aqueous solution)	None[e]	Mix 25 g/225 ml TBG
Raw or highly contaminated meats and meat products	None[e]	Blend 25 g/225 ml SC 25 g/225 ml TBG
Nonfat dry milk and dry whole milk	Distilled water; add 0.45 ml 1% brilliant green solution	Mix
Dried active[f] and inactive yeast; black pepper, white pepper, celery seed and flakes, chili powder, cumin, paprika, parsley flakes, rosemary, sesame seed, thyme, and vegetable flakes.	Trypticase (tryptic) soy broth	Mix

Onion flakes and powder, garlic flakes and powder	Trypticase (tryptic) soy broth containing 0.5% K_2SO_3 (final concentration)	Mix
Allspice, cinnamon, oregano	Trypticase (tryptic) soy broth	Mix, using 1:100 sample/broth ratio
Clove	Trypticase (tryptic) soy broth	Mix, using 1:1,000 sample/broth ratio
Leafy condiments	Trypticase (tryptic) soy broth	Mix, using >1:10 sample/broth ratio
Candy and candy coating; chocolate	Reconstituted nonfat dry milk,[g] add 0.45 ml 1% brilliant green solution	Blend
Frosting and topping mixes	Nutrient broth	Mix
Frog legs		Immerse/rinse leg pairs (individual leg if ≥ 25g) and examine rinsings
Snails	See preparation	Immerse/rinse minimal 25-g analytical units individually in lactose broth, SC, and TBG and examine rinsings

[a] Unless specified otherwise, 25-g samples are pre-enriched in 225 ml of indicated medium.

[b] Unless specified otherwise, 1-ml volumes of incubated pre-enriched cultures are subcultured to 10-ml volumes of selenite cystine (SC) or tetrathionate (TBG) broth prepared by adding 10 ml of 0.1% brilliant green dye solution and 20 ml of iodine-potassium iodide solution to 1 L of tetrathionate broth base.

[c] Add up to 2.2 ml of Tergitol 7 or Triton X-100 to initiate foaming.

[d] Add 5 ml of 5% gelatinase solution.

[e] Pre-enrichment in lactose broth may provide improved recovery and is recommended (see Sec. 25.124).

[f] One-ml volumes of pre-enrichment cultures of dried active yeast are transferred to 10-ml volumes lauryl sulfate broth and TBG broth.

[g] Reconstituted nonfat dry milk is prepared by adding 100 g of nonfat dry milk to 1 L distilled water.

Table 3—Standard Cultural Media for Detection of Foodborne *Salmonella*[a]

Agency/Group	Pre-enrichment	Selective enrichment	Plating
AOAC[b] and APHA[c]	Lactose Brilliant green water Nonfat dry milk with brilliant green Tryptic (trypticase) soy Nutrient	TBG_{35} SC_{35}	BSA XLD HE
FDA[d]	same as AOAC/APHA	TBG_{35} SC_{35}	BSA XLD HE BSA BGS
HPB[e]	Nutrient Brilliant green water Trypticase soy Nonfat dry milk with brilliant green	TBG_{43} SC_{35}	BSA BGS
ICMSF[f]	Lactose Buffered peptone Brilliant green water Nonfat dry milk with brilliant green	TBG_{43} SC_{43}	BSA BGA third optional
ISO[g]	Buffered peptone	$MKTBG_{43}$ (changing to RV_{43}) SC_{35} SBG_{35}	BGA (compulsory) BSA (or other optional)
NAS[h]	Lactose Brilliant green water	TBG_{35} SC_{35}	BSA BGA BGS
USDA[i]	Lactose	TT_{35} SC_{35}	XLD BSA

[a] Adapted from D'Aoust, J.-Y.[24]
[b] Association of Official Analytical Chemists
[c] American Public Health Association
[d] U.S. Food and Drug Administration
[e] Health Protection Branch (Canada)
[f] International Commission on Microbiological Specifications for Food
[g] International Organization for Standardization
[h] National Academy of Sciences (U.S.)
[i] U.S. Department of Agriculture

milk for 30 min using a sample to broth ratio of 1:2, followed by dilution to 1:9, is recommended for increased *Salmonella* recovery.[3, 143]

Addition of surfactants to broth media has been used to aid in *Salmonella* recovery in foods with a high fat content. Supposedly, these surfactants disperse the lipid particles containing entrapped *Salmonella* organisms. Morris and Dunn[98] reported an increased recovery of *Salmonella* from pork sausage using Tergitol Anionic 7, but other studies have reported that the use of surfactants is unnecessary and may even be toxic to *Salmonella* bacteria.[32, 37, 112]

In the analysis of foods for *Salmonella*, pre-enrichment cultures are usually incubated for 18 to 24 hr at 35 to 37°C and then a portion is subcultured to one or more selective enrichment broths. The potential of using a shorter incubation period was investigated by D'Aoust and Maishment[27], but they found that incubation of pre-enrichment for 6 hr, rather than 24 hr, resulted in significantly high numbers of false-negative results. The impact of transfer volumes on method sensitivity has also been examined. Normally, one ml of pre-enrichment culture is inoculated into 9 ml of selective enrichment broth. Studies comparing the efficiency of subculturing smaller (0.1 ml)[27] or larger (2 ml and 10 ml)[27, 109] volumes demonstrated no significant difference in method sensitivity when pre-enrichment cultures were incubated overnight (18 to 24 hr).

25.124   Selective enrichment

Selective enrichment media contain selective ingredients that allow the proliferation of *Salmonella* and inhibit the growth of competing non-*Salmonella* microorganisms. Although selective enrichment media are customarily inoculated from the pre-enrichment media, raw or highly contaminated samples have been directly enriched in selective enrichment media.[63, 137, 138, 141] However, other studies[39, 60, 68] have shown that detection of *Salmonella* in raw meats and sewage materials was substantially greater with pre-enrichment than with direct enrichment. D'Aoust[24] concluded that direct enrichment of food samples heavily contaminated with competitive flora is not justified and may lead to false-negative results.

Although selenite broth[87], selenite broth modified by the addition of cystine (SC)[104] or brilliant green dye[124] are used for the detection of foodborne salmonellae, various modifications of tetrathionate broth have generally found wider application. These include TBG, the Mueller[99] tetrathionate broth as modified by Kauffmann;[78] TT, the formulation of Hajna and Damon;[67] Tet, as formulated by Rolfe,[117] and MKTBG, the Mueller-Kauffmann tetrathionate broth widely used in Europe.[39] The tetrathionate ($S_4O_6^=$) anions constitute the principal selective agent in these enrichment media and are most effective at a concentration of 0.03 M.[24, 83] Several studies have demonstrated toxicity of the TT, Tet, and MKTBG formulations of tetrathionate broth.[26] Therefore, the TBG formulation is recommended. Modified Rappaport medium[144, 145] is also used in food analyses, particularly in Europe where the medium recently replaced MKTBG in International Standards Organization (ISO) methodology. Some toxicity was reported with TT and Rolfe Tet. Use of two or more selective enrichment media provides greater recovery of *Salmonella* from different food products.[10, 25, 102]

Incubation temperature markedly affects productivity of selective enrichment broths by suppressing growth of competing microorganisms but not *Salmonella*. Although selective enrichment media are frequently incubated at 35° to 37°C, several studies[26, 39, 98, 123] have shown increased recovery of *Salmonella* following incubation of selective enrichments at 43°C. McCoy[93] and Aleksic et al.,[1] however, reported that incubation at 43°C, in some instances, prevented recovery of *Salmonella*. The use of SC incubated at 35°C and TT incubated at 43°C was shown to give maximal recoveries of *Salmonella* from poultry and pork products.[11]

Attempting to provide greater flexibility in the analytical protocol, D'Aoust et al.[31] investigated the potential of refrigerating pre-enrichment and selective enrichment media until they could be conveniently analyzed during a normal work week. Collaborative studies showed that refrigeration (4°C) of pre-enrichment and enrichment cultures did not adversely affect the detection of *Salmonella* in a variety of low- and high-moisture foods, thereby increasing the number of days on which *Salmonella* analyses could be initiated.[33]

25.125 Selective plating media

Selective plating media are formulated so that growth of *Salmonella* bacteria results in the formation of discrete colonies with concomitant repression of competing microflora. Separation of *Salmonella* from non-*Salmonella* bacteria is obtained through the incorporation of various dyes, bile salts, and other selective agents into the agar media. When non-*Salmonella* colonies appear on these media, they are generally distinguished by their ability or inability to produce hydrogen sulfide and to utilize one or more discriminating carbohydrates in the media.[26] Selective plating media that have been used for the isolation of *Salmonella* include brilliant green (BG),[85] BG sulfa,[105] bismuth sulfite (BS),[146] *Salmonella Shigella*,[36] MacConkey's,[91] desoxycholate citrate,[86] Hektoen enteric (HE),[82] Xylose lysine desoxycholate citrate (XLD),[130] Shanson's,[118] Rappold-Bolderdijk modified lysine iron,[110] lysine-iron-cystine,[115] MSRV,[34] and novobiocin-brilliant green-glucose.[35] None of these agars are ideal for all situations, justifying the recommendation in many reference methods for the use of two or more agar media.[4, 63, 76, 102, 142]

Since their original formulation, some of these agars have been modified by the addition of antibiotics, sulfa drugs, surfactants, and other chemical substances in an attempt to improve media selectivity and/or sensitivity. Gadberry and Highby[62] incorporated dimethylchlortetracycline hydrochloride into BG agar and reported inhibition of species of *Proteus*, *Providencia*, and *Citrobacter*. Sulfadiazine, sulfapyridine, or sulfanilamide reportedly improves

BG agar selectivity.[63, 95, 105, 149] Moats and Kinner[96] subsequently found that addition of a hydrogen sulfide detection system to BG agar aided in the identification of *Salmonella* colonies, particularly in the presence of large populations of competing microorganisms. Addition of novobiocin to XLD agar or HE agar improved media selectivity[69, 94, 116] and increased rates of *Salmonella* recovery.[94]

Variations in the preparation of the selective agars are common and can adversely affect media performance. Although Difco[36] recommends using freshly prepared plates of bismuth sulfite agar, Cook[14] reported that such plates were inhibitory to several *Salmonella* serovars; such inhibition decreased upon storage of prepared plates under refrigeration for up to 5 days before use. McCoy[93] found that freshly poured BS plates were too inhibitory for serovars other than *S. typhi*. D'Aoust[23] also reported that inoculated plates of freshly poured BS agar required incubation for 48 hr to yield *Salmonella* recoveries similar to those obtained on homologous refrigerated plates. When a manufacturer's directives for medium preparation differ from those described in a reference method, follow the reference method. Where such directives are not specified in the analytical method, the media should be prepared according to the manufacturer's instructions.

The selective plating media are inoculated by streaking a loopful of the enrichment culture onto the dry surface of prepared plates to obtain well-separated colonies. Plates are usually incubated at 35° or 37°C. Incubation at an elevated temperature (41.5°C) was reportedly advantageous in recovering different *Salmonella* serovars on BG agar and *S. typhi* on XLD and HE agars.[114, 148] Wilson et al.,[147] however, reported that incubation of BS agar plates at 43°C resulted in the appearance of small atypical *Salmonella* colonies and, in several instances, reduced method sensitivity. Earlier results had also shown significantly lower recoveries on BS plates incubated at 43°C than at 35°C.[61]

Inoculated plates are usually incubated 18 to 24 hr. BS agar plates should be observed after 24 hr of incubation, and any suspect *Salmonella* colony should be further screened biochemically and serologically. BS agar plates should be incubated up to 48 hr before making a final determination on the presence or absence of *Salmonella* in the test material.

25.126   Biochemical media

Biochemical screening media are nonselective and generally establish different biochemical traits of the test culture through color change(s) in the medium. Such data generally pertain to the production of hydrogen sulfide or to the utilization of one or more fermentable carbohydrates in the medium. Additionally, inoculated differential media also provide an inoculum for subsequent biochemical and serological testing.

Two differential agar tube media are widely used. Triple sugar iron (TSI) agar measures production of hydrogen sulfide and utilization of glucose, lactose, and sucrose,[126] whereas lysine iron (LI) agar monitors production of hydrogen sulfide and decarboxylation of lysine.[40] These two agars are usually used in combination and provide a preliminary biochemical screening of suspect cultures. It is important to recognize that some of the TSI reactions may be redundant with those observed on plating media. Cultures that appear to be contaminated on these agar tube media should be restreaked on an appropriate selective plating agar and a small portion of a single colony exhibiting typical characteristics transferred to the differential media for repeat testing. Among the other *Salmonella* differential media are dulcitol lactose iron agar;[131] malonate dulcitol lysine iron agar;[125] DMS agar;[12] dulcitol-malonate-phenylalanine agar;[46] and selective Padron-Dockstader agar.[106]

25.13   General Description for the Identification of *Salmonella*

25.131   Biochemical tests

Many biochemical tests are available for the characterization of cultural isolates obtained from food products. A comprehensive list of biochemical and nutritional characters of the family *Enterobacteriaceae* is found in *Bergey's Manual of Systematic Bacteriology*,[90] and many of these tests have been described in detail by Ewing.[47] Presumptive identification of typical *Salmonella* can be obtained from a minimal number of biochemical tests that may include urease, KCN, and indole. The urease, lysine decarboxylase, growth in KCN, and indole tests are generally sufficient for presumptive identification of salmonellae.[4, 142] Note: Final identification rests with serological tests, not biochemical tests, because *Salmonella* strains do not always produce typical biochemical reactions.

25.132   Commercial biochemical multitest systems or kits

Many biochemical tests are routinely used to differentiate members of the family *Enterobacteriaceae* and to characterize presumptive *Salmonella* isolates. Commercially available multitest systems or diagnostic kits are more convenient than conventional tube systems and generally provide reliable biochemical test results.[16, 17, 108] The API 20E, Minitek, and Enterotube received AOAC approval in 1978,[107] and the Micro-ID received first action approval in 1988.[80] Other miniaturized systems have shown a high degree of correlation with conventional tube tests but have not been subjected to AOAC collaborative studies. These and other diagnostic systems and kits are thoroughly reviewed in Chapter 39. Note: Complete identification of *Salmonella* should not be based solely on biochemical tests because strains do not always produce typical biochemical reactions (Tables 1 and 4).

25.133   Confirmatory serological tests

The genus *Salmonella* is characterized serologically by specific antigenic components.[47] The antigens are divided into somatic (O), flagellar (H), and capsular (K) antigens. The somatic (O) antigens are composed of lipopoly-saccharide complexes that are heat stable and resistant to alcohol and dilute acid. The proteinaceous flagellar (H) antigens are heat labile, whereas the surface K antigens consist of heat-sensitive polysaccharides that occur in the capsule or in the outer membrane of the bacteria. K antigens such as the Vi antigen tend to inhibit somatic (O) agglutination reactions and must be thermally denatured before undertaking somatic agglutination reactions. For further information concerning *Salmonella* antigens and antisera, see Edwards and Ewing,[41] Kauffmann,[79] and ICMSF.[74]

Since other members of the *Enterobacteriaceae* have related somatic (O) antigens, false-positive serological tests may be encountered, on occasion, upon testing unknown isolates with *Salmonella* antisera. This problem is diminished when more specific single factor or adsorbed antisera are used. Definitive serotyping of a culture should be performed by specially trained personnel working in a reference laboratory.

Concurrent serological confirmation and biochemical characterization of a single colony forming unit (CFU) by some biochemical kits can be completed within 8 to 24 hr.[16, 17]

25.14   Short Cultural Methods

Early attempts to reduce the time required for *Salmonella* analysis involved the use of short incubation times. Abbreviated incubation of pre-enrichment (≤6 hr) is desirable because it would allow presumptive identification of salmonellae 1 day earlier compared to standard culture methods employing 18 to 24-hr pre-enrichment. However, attempts to reduce pre-enrichment incubation to 6 hr resulted in an unacceptable number of false-negative results compared to 18 to 24-hr pre-enrichment.[24, 27]

Combining pre-enrichment and enrichment steps into a single analytical procedure also has been proposed to reduce analytical time. In this approach, selective agents were added to the pre-enrichment medium, either gradually through the use of time-release capsules[127] or by direct addition after 4-hr incubation.[128] The first study showed that the time-release capsule method was not effective in reducing analytical time required for analysis, presumably because of the inconsistency of the capsules. In a subsequent study, Sveum and Kraft[128] added selective agents to a nonselective basal medium after 4 hr of incubation and continued incubation for a total of 24 hr at 35°C. Results with heat-injured and freeze-injured salmonellae and with artificially contaminated foods compared favorably with the standard culture method. However, this novel approach has not found wide application, possibly because addition of selective agents after 4-hr incubation is inconvenient and could result in a longer workday (> 8 hr). The need for large quantities of selective agents to convert pre-enrichment cultures into selective enrichment broths would significantly increase analytical costs.

Reduced incubation of selective enrichment broths also has been investigated. One study utilizing a 6-hr selective step following overnight pre-enrichment yielded results similar to that obtained with a 24-hr selective step for feeds and feed ingredients.[33] However, use of a 6-hr enrichment with raw and processed foods resulted in a high percentage of false-negative results compared to that obtained after 24 hr of incubation (D'Aoust, personal communication).

The influence of reduced incubation time ($\leq$ 8 hr) on productivity of tetrathionate and Rappaport broths for detection of *Salmonella* in naturally and artificially contaminated foods was examined by Rappold et al.[111] Modified Rappaport broth identified a similar number of *Salmonella*-positive samples after 8 hr and 24 hr of incubation. With tetrathionate broth, all but 3 of 27 contaminated samples were positive after 8 hr of incubation. Thus, the use of reduced incubation of selective enrichment periods may provide adequate detection under certain conditions, but is not consistently reliable and is not recommended. Some evidence suggests that extended incubation (> 24 hr) of selective enrichment may improve detection,[39, 68, 145] but other data indicate no benefit and reduced recovery from extended (> 24 hr) selective enrichment.[24, 26, 33]

Although reduced incubation of enrichments may not always provide optimal conditions for isolation of salmonellae, some evidence shows that reduced enrichment can be productive when used in combination with rapid screening methods. For example, 6-hr selective enrichment procedures are employed in three rapid methods approved by the AOAC: hydrophobic grid membrane filtration,[43] enzyme immunoassay,[54, 57] and DNA-DNA hybridization.[56]

Most of the methods proposed for the rapid detection of *Salmonella* in foods are screening tests and designed to provide rapid negative results, but require culture confirmation whenever presumptive positive results are obtained. Ideally, a rapid screening method would be performed directly on the food product without the need for enrichment of the sample. However, none of the methods currently available possesses the required sensitivity to detect the low numbers of salmonellae usually encountered in foods. Most employ one or more enrichment steps whose purpose is the same as described in standard cultural methods; i.e., pre-enrichment allows for the recovery and growth of injured cells whereas selective enrichment favors the growth of salmonellae and inhibits the growth of competitive bacteria. Several methods also employ a third enrichment step (post-enrichment) in a nonselective broth medium that is designed to increase the number of salmonellae to levels detectable by the rapid assays.

25.15   Association, Agency, and International Methods

25.151   Association of Official Analytical Chemists (AOAC)

The primary objective of the AOAC is ". . . to obtain, improve, develop, test, and adopt uniform, precise, and accurate methods for the analysis of foods, drugs, feeds, fertilizers, pesticides, water, or any other substances affecting public health and safety, economic protection of the consumer, or quality of the environment. . . ."[4] To be adopted as official, a method must be (1) reliable, (2) practical, (3) available to all analysts, and (4) substantiated. The proposed method of analysis must be subjected to a collaborative study and the results from that study reviewed by an AOAC committee. If approved, the study is published in the AOAC's journal and the method is adopted as official. The recommended procedure for the analysis of various foods delineated in Section 25.5 is based on AOAC methods.

25.152   U.S. Food and Drug Administration (FDA)

This book[142] contains the microbiological methods used in FDA laboratories to analyze foods. These methods are currently considered to be the most useful to the FDA in enforcing the provisions of the Federal Food, Drug, and Cosmetics Act.[140] Methods having official AOAC status are included in this manual. The BAM and AOAC methods of preparing various foods for the isolation of *Salmonella* are listed in Table 2. Isolation and confirmation procedures are described in Sections 25.52 and 25.53.

25.153   Centers for Disease Control (CDC)

A manual[81] used in the CDC's course on *Salmonella* isolation procedures is available. Directions for sampling, isolation, and identification of *Salmonella* are provided.

25.154   United States Department of Agriculture (USDA)

The Agricultural Research Service publishes manuals for *Salmonella* analysis of poultry[18] and animal feeds.[137] Recommended test procedures are presented, followed by descriptions of serological and biochemical confirmatory test procedures.

The Poultry Division of the Agricultural Marketing Service publishes a laboratory handbook[139] that includes directions for the analysis of eggs and egg products.

The Food Safety and Inspection Service publishes a laboratory guidebook[138] that contains a comprehensive discussion of isolation and identification procedures for *Salmonella* in foods.

25.155   International organizations

Many organizations are concerned with microbiological criteria and safety of foods involved in international trade. Specifically, these agencies are involved in the collection and assessment of microbiological criteria for foods, and the development, study, and standardization of methods for the microbiological examination of foods. Figuring prominently in this area of endeavor are the

International Commission on Microbiological Specifications for Foods (ICMSF) (of the International Association of Microbiological Societies) and the Codex Alimentarius Commission (CAC), as well as temporary Expert Consultations of the Joint Food Standards Programme of the United Nations' Food and Agriculture Organization (FAO) and World Health Organization (WHO), and Technical Committee 34 of the International Organization for Standardization (ISO).

25.2 TREATMENT OF SAMPLE

25.21 Collection (see Chapter 2 and Section 25.122)

25.22 Holding (see Chapter 2)

25.23 Mixing and Homogenization

If the food product is frozen, thaw a suitable portion at 2° to 5°C for 18 hr before analysis, or, if rapid thawing is desired, thaw at <45°C for ≤15 min. If the food product is powdered, ground, or comminuted, mix it with a sterile spoon or other sterile equipment before withdrawing an analytical unit. A homogeneous suspension of most powdered products can be obtained by mixing the analytical unit and broth with a sterile glass rod or other appropriate sterile instrument. Homogeneous suspensions are obtained in some cases by shaking the food-broth mixture by hand or by using a mechanical shaker. Mechanical blending may be required if the food consists of large pieces. A blending time of 2 min at 8,000 rpm is usually satisfactory for most foods.

25.3 EQUIPMENT AND SUPPLIES

25.31 Equipment and Materials

1. Blender and sterile blender jars
2. Sterile 16-oz (500-ml) widemouthed, screw-cap jars, sterile 500-ml Erlenmeyer flasks, sterile 250-ml beakers, sterile glass or paper funnels of appropriate size, and, optionally, containers of appropriate capacity to accommodate composited samples
3. Sterile bent-glass spreader rods
4. Balance, with weights; 2,000-g capacity, sensitivity of 0.1 g
5. Balance, with weights; 120-g capacity, sensitivity of 5 mg
6. Incubator, 35°C
7. Water bath, 48° to 50°C
8. Sterile spoons or other appropriate instruments for transferring food specimens

9. Sterile culture dishes, 15 × 100 mm, glass or plastic
10. Sterile pipettes, 1 ml, with 0.01 ml graduations; 5 and 10 ml, with 0.1 ml graduations
11. Inoculating needle and inoculating loop (about 3 mm id), nichrome, platinum-iridium, or chromel wire
12. Sterile test or culture tubes, 16 × 150 mm and 20 × 150 mm; serological tubes, 10 × 75 mm or 13 × 100 mm
13. Test or culture tube racks
14. Vortex mixer
15. Sterile shears, large scissors, scalpel, and forceps
16. Lamp (for observing serological reactions)
17. Fisher or Bunsen burner
18. pH test paper (pH range 6 to 8) with maximum graduations of 0.4 pH units per color change
19. pH meter
20. Plastic bags, 28 × 37 cm, sterile, with resealable tape. (Items 20 to 22 are needed in the analysis of frog legs and rabbit carcasses.)
21. Plastic beakers, 4 L, autoclavable, for holding plastic bag during shaking and incubation
22. Mechanical shaker, any model that can be adjusted to give 100 excursions per min with a 4-cm (1 1/2-in) stroke, such as the Eberbach shaker with additional 33- and 48-cm clamp bars

25.32   Media and Reagents

For preparation of media and reagents, refer to Sections 46.115 to 46.128 in *Official Methods of Analysis.*[4]

1. Nonselective media for enrichment and propagation

    a. Lactose broth
    b. Nonfat dry milk (reconstituted)
    c. Trypticase soy broth
    d. M-broth
    e. GN-broth
    f. Nutrient broth
    g. Brain heart infusion (BHI) broth

2. Selective enrichment media

    a. Selenite cystine broth
    b. Tetrathionate broth

3. Selective isolation media

    a. Xylose lysine desoxycholate (XLD) agar
    b. Hektoen enteric (HE) agar

    c. Bismuth sulfite (BS) agar
    d. MacConkey agar

4. Media for biochemical characterization of isolates

    a. Triple sugar iron (TSI) agar
    b. Tryptone (tryptophane) (TSI) broth
    c. Trypticase (tryptic) soy broth
    d. Lauryl tryptose (LST) broth
    e. Trypticase soy-tryptose broth
    f. MR-VP broth
    g. Simmons citrate agar
    h. Urea broth
    i. Urea broth (rapid)
    j. Malonate broth
    k. Lysine iron agar (LIA) (Edwards and Fife)
    l. Lysine decarboxylase broth
    m. Motility test medium (semisolid)
    n. Phenol red carbohydrate broth
    o. Potassium cyanide
    p. Purple carbohydrate broth

5. Reagents

    a. Gelatinase solution, 5%
    b. Potassium sulfite powder, anhydrous
    c. Kovacs' reagent
    d. Voges-Proskauer (VP) test reagents
    e. Creatine phosphate crystals
    f. Potassium hydroxide solution, 40%
    g. 1 N sodium hydroxide solution
    h. 1 N hydrochloric acid
    i. Brilliant green dye solution, 1%
    j. Bromcresol purple dye solution, 0.2%
    k. Methyl red indicator
    l. Sterile distilled water
    m. Tergitol Anionic 7
    n. Triton X-100
    o. Physiological saline solution (sterile)
    p. Formalinized physiological saline solution
    q. *Salmonella* polyvalent somatic (O) antiserum
    r. *Salmonella* polyvalent flagellar (H) antiserum
    s. *Salmonella* somatic group (O) antisera: A, B, C_2, C_3, D_1, D_2, E_1, E_2, E_3, E_4, F, G, H, I, Vi, and other groups as appropriate
    t. *Salmonella* Spicer-Edwards flagellar (H) antisera

25.33   Additional Materials and Equipment

25.331   Fluorescent antibody (FA) technique

1. Fluorescent microscope with exciter filter (330 to 500 nm) and barrier filter (>400 nm)
2. Multiwell slides coated with fluorocarbon material (available from Cell-Line Associates, Minotola, NJ 08341 or Clinical Sciences, Inc., 30 Troy Road, Whippany, NJ 07981); slides may also be prepared as described in the AOAC method.[4]

25.332   Hydrophobic grid membrane filtration (HGMF)

1. Hydrophobic grid membrane filter (HGMF), polysulfone membrane filter with pore size of 0.45 μm and imprinted with nontoxic hydrophobic material in a grid pattern (QA Laboratories, Toronto, Canada), or equivalent
2. Filtration units for HGMF, equipped with 5-μm mesh prefilter to remove food particles during filtration; one unit is required for each test sample
3. Vacuum pump, water aspirator vacuum source is necessary
4. Manifold or vacuum flask

25.333   Immunodiffusion

Salmonella 1-2 TEST unit (BioControl Systems, Inc., Bothell, Washington)

25.334   Enzyme immunoassays

1. Multipipettes capable of delivering accurate amounts in ranges 50 to 250 μl
2. Waterbath, autoclave, or steamer capable of maintaining 100°C
3. Microtiter plate reader; specifications of instrument may vary with the assay and are described in the methods (Section 25.74)

25.335   DNA hybridization

1. Micropipettes capable of accurately dispensing 0.10 ml, 0.25 ml, and 0.75 ml
2. Waterbath capable of maintaining 65°C
3. Photometer to read absorbance at 450 nm in 12 × 75-mm test tubes
4. Dipstick holders and wash basins (available from Gene-Trak Systems, Framingham, MA 01701)

25.4   PRECAUTIONS AND LIMITATIONS OF REFERENCE AND RAPID METHODS

25.41   Sampling

Specific sampling plans for *Salmonella* have been in place for several years.[72, 101, 142] To maintain the statistical significance of these plans, they should be used exactly as directed, without modification. Particular attention should be given to instructions for sample compositing. The maximal number of 25-g analytical units that may be composited is 15, resulting in composites weighing 375 g. Increasing the number of composited units beyond 15 may result in decreased analytical sensitivity.

In applying the soak method for the analysis of low-moisture, powdered foods, be aware that composited samples of certain foods such as non-instant nonfat dry milk, dry whole milk, and soy flour are not readily wetted. In these cases, 25-g analytical units should not be composited but analyzed individually.

25.42   Media Preparation

Unreliable laboratory results can arise from improper preparation of laboratory media and absence of appropriate controls that form an integral part of sound laboratory quality assurance programs.

A positive medium control ensures that no substances in the laboratory medium are inhibitory to the salmonellae. This control is prepared by inoculating the medium with a suitable strain of *Salmonella* and proceeding through the entire analytical protocol used for test samples.

Two types of negative controls should be included. A negative medium control ensures that the prepared medium is not contaminated with salmonellae. The control is prepared by carrying a flask of the uninoculated medium through the analytical procedure used for test samples. A second negative control, the culture control, either demonstrates the appearance of competitive flora on various media or shows that these non-salmonellae will not grow on the selective media used in the test. This control is prepared by inoculating the initial medium with the non-salmonellae and carrying the medium through the entire procedure.

In addition to the above, the following specific points should be considered in the preparation of media for *Salmonella* isolation:

1. Potential toxicity of various lots of brilliant green dye should be determined using appropriate laboratory strains of salmonellae.
2. Flasks of tetrathionate broth should be shaken frequently during dispensing into culture tubes because calcium carbonate tends to settle.
3. Selenite cystine should be dispensed in 16×150-mm tubes to a depth of at least 5 cm, since this medium is most efficient in an environment of reduced oxidation-reduction potential.[106]

4. Plates of bismuth sulfite agar should be made the day before use since freshly prepared agar may be inhibitory for *Salmonella*. Prepared plates should be stored at 4° to 5°C and tempered to room temperature before use to avoid condensation of moisture on the surface.

5. Lysine iron agar slants should be prepared with a deep butt (4 cm) since lysine decarboxylation reactions are more reliable under microaerophilic conditions.

6. KCN should not be stored under refrigeration longer than 2 weeks since it may become unstable and give false-positive results.

7. TSI tubes should be capped loosely; otherwise erroneous reactions occur. By definition/convention, H_2S production by *Salmonella* is defined using TSI.

25.43 Conventional Culture Procedure

For the analysis of a test sample, the following specific points should be considered:

1. The actual rpm speed of a food blender should be determined by a tachometer or similar device. Use of a blending speed higher than that recommended in Section 25.23 may result in injury or death of *Salmonella* organisms. To avoid spillage, initiate blending at lowest speed for a few seconds, and then gradually increase to the recommended blending speed.

2. If it is necessary to thaw a frozen sample for analysis, waterbath temperature must not exceed 45°C.

3. Analysts should be aware that atypical *Salmonella* strains, e.g., *S. arizonae* and other lactose/sucrose-positive salmonellae biotypes, may be encountered on differential agar media. Lactose- and/or sucrose-positive cultures may resemble coliforms on HE, XLD, and TSI agars. TSI cultures with an acid slant should not be discarded as non-*Salmonella* but further screened biochemically and serologically.

4. The center of suspect *Salmonella* colonies on plating media should be picked lightly to avoid transfer of viable non-salmonellae that may lie under or adjacent to the suspect *Salmonella* colony.

5. TSI agar slants should be capped loosely during incubation for maintenance of aerobic conditions to prevent erroneous acid reactions on slant and excessive H_2S production in the butt of the tube. If heavy H_2S production masks the reaction in the butt, glucose utilization should be assumed.

6. Caps of inoculated lysine decarboxylase broth should be replaced tightly. Lysine decarboxylation occurs anaerobically, and exclusion of air will eliminate false-positive reactions resulting from oxidative deamination of peptones in the medium. For lysine iron agar and lysine decarboxylation broth reactions, only a distinct yellow color in the butt should

be considered negative. Cultures giving weak, indeterminate reactions in the decarboxylase broth medium should be retested by adding a few drops of 0.2% bromcresol purple dye and reading immediately.

7. If purity of the TSI agar culture is in doubt, streak the culture to MacConkey, HE, or XLD agar and repeat the TSI test using a well-isolated colony.

8. For each type of biochemical determination, a tube of uninoculated medium (negative medium control) should be included.

9. Only the AOAC-approved diagnostic kits described in Section 25.132 should be used for the rapid biochemical identification of *Salmonella*.

25.44   Rapid Screening Methods

25.441   Fluorescent antibody (FA) technique

1. This method is recommended only as a screening test for the presence of *Salmonella* because the antibodies may produce false-positive reactions by cross-reacting with other members of the *Enterobacteriaceae* and through nonspecific reactions. Consequently, presumptive FA-positive enrichment cultures must be streaked onto plating media and suspect colonies confirmed by biochemical and serological techniques described in Section 25.5. Interpretation of FA results is highly subjective and requires trained analysts.

2. The method is subject to variations in the preparation of smears, conjugate, and other reagents, and misalignment of the fluorescent microscope may lead to erroneous results.

25.442   Hydrophobic grid membrane filtration (HGMF) described in Section 25.72

1. The method, as approved by AOAC, is not applicable to the analysis of all foods, but is restricted to nonfat dry milk, powdered eggs, cheese powders, pepper, chocolate, and raw poultry meat.

2. In this technique, tetrathionate broth medium (10 ml) is inoculated with 0.1 ml of pre-enrichment culture instead of the more standard 1.0 ml transfer volume; larger volumes do not provide favorable *Salmonella* to non-*Salmonella* ratios in tetrathionate broths after a 6-hr incubation.

3. Tubes of tetrathionate broth are inoculated with a portion of pre-enrichment culture and incubated at 35° to 37°C in a waterbath, rather than in a convection incubator, because a full 6-hr incubation period is needed for *Salmonella* organisms to reach detectable levels.

4. Colonies on HGMF filters should be picked with a fully cooled sterile needle.

25.443   Immunodiffusion: 1-2 Test™ described in Section 25.73

1. This method is a screening test for foodborne *Salmonella*.
2. Nonmotile *Salmonella* strains will not be detected because the method is based on the migration of salmonellae in a semisolid medium.
3. The chamber plug that seals the opening between the motility chamber and the tetrathionate inoculation chamber must be removed prior to inoculation of the 1-2 Test. Failure to remove this plug will prevent *Salmonella* from migrating from the inoculation to the motility chamber.
4. The gel former tip, an interior protrusion of the cap of the motility chamber, must be cut off to prevent displacement of the added antibody solution.

25.444   Enzyme immunoassays (BioEnzaBead™, TECRA™, Q-Trol™ described in Section 25.74.)

Although commercially available kits differ in their sensitivity and specificity, the inherent limitations of these diagnostic tools are similar.

1. These methods are screening tests for the presence of *Salmonella* in foods. The antibodies employed may produce false-positive reactions through cross-reactions with other *Enterobacteriaceae* or as a result of nonspecific reactions. Presumptively positive ELISA samples must be confirmed by streaking homologous enrichment broths on appropriate plating media and identifying suspect colonies as described in Section 25.5.
2. Although antibodies used in these diagnostic kits are meant to react with all salmonellae, a small percentage of salmonellae reportedly produce false-negative results.[29]
3. Commercially available kits contain standardized reagents. Use of other materials or procedures may yield erroneous results.
4. Positive and negative controls are included in test kits and must be included with each group of test samples. Controls must fall within acceptable ranges to validate test results.

25.445   DNA hybridization (GENE-TRAK™, described in Section 25.75)

1. This method is a screening test for the presence of *Salmonella* in foods. Presumptively positive assays must be confirmed by streaking onto appropriate plating media and suspect colonies identified as described in Section 25.5.
2. Commercially available kits contain standardized reagents, and use of other materials or procedures may yield erroneous results.
3. Positive and negative controls are included in the test kits and must be included with each group of samples. Controls must fall within acceptable ranges to validate test results.

4. Reagents that contain sodium azide should be flushed down sinks with an abundant supply of water. Do not pipette reagents by mouth.

25.5 REFERENCE METHOD

This section contains the approved methods of the *Bacteriological Analytical Manual*[142] and the AOAC[4] for the isolation and identification of foodborne *Salmonella*.

Method of pre-enrichment and preparation of sample for each food are listed in Table 2.

25.51 Pre-enrichment

Aseptically open a sample container and add a 25-g sample into a sterile blender jar (1-L size) or a widemouthed container with screw cap or other suitable closure. Continue as directed under appropriate food section below.

25.511   Dried whole egg, dried egg yolk, and dried egg white[4]

1. Gradually add 225 ml of sterile lactose broth to the sample. Add a small portion (15 ml) of sterile lactose broth and mix with a suitable sterile stirrer to obtain a homogeneous suspension. Repeat this procedure three times and then add the remainder of the lactose broth. Stir until a lump-free suspension is obtained.
2. Cap the container securely and let stand at room temperature for 60 min.
3. Mix well by shaking and determine pH with appropriate test paper.
4. Adjust the pH, if necessary, to 6.8 ± 0.2 with 1 N sodium hydroxide or 1 N hydrochloric acid.
5. Loosen the container cap about one-quarter turn and incubate 24 ± 2 hr at 35°C.
6. Continue as directed under Section 25.52.

25.512   Nonfat dry milk and dry whole milk[4]

1. Add 225 ml of sterile distilled water to the sample and mix well.
2. Continue as directed under section 25.511, 2.
3. Add 0.45 ml of 1% aqueous brilliant green dye solution and mix well.
4. Loosen the container cap about one-quarter turn and incubate 24 ± 2 hr at 35°C.
5. Continue as directed under Section 25.52.

25.513   Dried active yeast[4]

1. Add 225 ml sterile trypticase (tryptic) soy broth, mix well, and allow yeast to form homogeneous suspension. (If pH is adjusted before yeast is evenly suspended, final pH will lie below target value.)

2. Continue as directed under Section 25.511, 2 to 5.
3. Continue as directed under Section 25.52.

25.514 Onion powder and garlic powder[4]

1. Add 225 ml sterile trypticase (tryptic) soy broth containing 0.5% potassium sulfite and mix well.
2. Continue as directed under Section 25.511, 2 to 5.
3. Continue as directed under Section 25.52.

25.515 Milk chocolate and edible casein[4]

1. Add 225 ml of sterile reconstituted nonfat dry milk (NFDM) (100 g dehydrated NFDM in 1 L of distilled water) to chocolate sample, or add 225 ml of sterile lactose broth to casein sample.
2. Blend each sample/broth mixture 2 min at 8,000 rpm and pour the homogenate into a sterile 500-ml jar.
3. Continue as directed under Section 25.511, 2.
4. Add 0.45 ml of 1% aqueous brilliant green dye to the chocolate homogenate and mix well.
5. Loosen the container cap about one-quarter turn and incubate 24 ± 2 hr at 35°C.
6. Continue as directed under Section 25.52.

25.52 Isolation of *Salmonella*

Tighten lid and gently shake incubated sample mixture; transfer replicate 1-ml portions to 10 ml selenite cystine and tetrathionate brilliant green broths. Incubate 24 ± 2 hr at 35°C.

Vortex enrichment culture tubes and streak 3-mm loops of selenite cystine culture on bismuth sulfite (BS), XLD, and HE agars.

Repeat plate inoculations with 3-mm loops of tetrathionate enrichment culture.

Incubate plates 24 ± 2 hr at 35°C.

Examine plates for suspect *Salmonella* colonies.

1. *HE agar.* Salmonellae generally produce blue-green to blue colonies with or without black centers. Strong H_2S-producing strains may produce colonies with large, glossy black centers or appear as completely black colonies. Atypical lactose-positive and/or sucrose-positive strains and coliforms produce salmon-colored colonies.
2. *BS agar.* Typical *Salmonella* colonies occur as black colonies with or without a metallic sheen. Medium surrounding *Salmonella* colonies gradually changes from brown to black with increased incubation to produce the so-called halo effect.

3. *XLD agar*. Typical salmonellae occur as pink colonies with or without black centers. Strong H_2S-producing strains may yield colonies with large, glossy black centers or appear as completely black colonies. Atypical lactose-positive and/or sucrose-positive *Salmonella* strains produce yellow colonies with or without black centers.

Inoculate two or more suspect colonies from each selective plating medium into triple sugar iron (TSI) and lysine iron (LIA) agars. BS agar plates with no suspect colonies or with no growth should be incubated for an additional 24 hr.

Touch the center of a suspect colony with a sterile inoculating needle and inoculate a TSI agar tube by streaking the slant and stabbing the butt. Without flaming the needle, inoculate an LIA agar tube by stabbing the butt twice and then streaking the slant.

Incubate TSI and LIA agar slants at 35°C for 24 ± 2 hr. *Salmonella* in TSI cultures typically produces alkaline (red) slant and acid (yellow) butt, with or without production of H_2S (blackening of agar). However, some lactose- and/or sucrose-positive salmonellae will produce atypical reactions; i.e., acid slant, acid butt with or without blackening. In LIA, *Salmonella* typically produces an alkaline (purple) butt. Consider only a distinct yellow butt as a negative reaction. Do not eliminate cultures that produce yellow (lysine negative) discoloration of the butt solely on the strength of this reaction because lysine negative biotypes have been reported. Most *Salmonella* cultures produce H_2S in LIA.

Re-examine 48-hr BS agar plates for suspect *Salmonella* colonies. Pick two or more of these colonies and continue procedure.

Retain all presumptive-positive TSI cultures (alkaline slant and acid butt) for further biochemical and serological testing, whether corresponding LIA reaction is positive (alkaline butt) or negative (acid butt). Do not exclude a TSI culture that appears to be non-*Salmonella* if the corresponding LIA is typical (alkaline butt) for *Salmonella*. Treat these cultures as presumptive-positive and submit them to further biochemical/serological examination. LIA is useful for the detection *S. arizonae* and atypical strains of *Salmonella* that utilize lactose and/or sucrose. Discard only cultures that appear not to be *Salmonella* on TSI agar (acid slant and acid butt) if corresponding LIA reactions are negative (acid butt) for *Salmonella*. Test retained presumed-positive TSI agar cultures as directed in Section 25.53 to determine if they are *Salmonella*. If original TSI cultures failed to indicate the presence of *Salmonella*, inoculate additional suspect colonies from appropriate selective agar plates into fresh TSI and LIA agar slants.

Apply biochemical and serological identification tests to three presumptive TSI agar cultures recovered from each set of plates streaked from selenite cystine and tetrathionate broth cultures. Examine a minimum of six TSI cultures for each 25-g analytical unit.

25.53   Identification of *Salmonella*

25.531   Mixed TSI cultures

Streak TSI agar cultures that appear to be mixed on MacConkey, HE, or XLD agar. Incubate plates 24 ± 2 hr at 35°C and examine plates for the presence of suspect *Salmonella* colonies.

1. *MacConkey agar.* Typical colonies appear transparent and colorless, sometimes with opaque center. *Salmonella* will clear areas of precipitated bile caused by lactose-fermenting microorganisms.
2. *HE agar.* See Section 25.52.
3. *XLD agar.* See Section 25.52.

Transfer at least two presumptive *Salmonella* colonies from the plates used to purify mixed TSI cultures to fresh TSI and LIA agar slants and proceed as described in Section 25.52.

25.532   Pure TSI cultures

1. *Urease test (conventional).* With a sterile needle, inoculate tubes of urea broth with growth from each presumptive-positive TSI culture and incubate 24 ± 2 hr at 35°C. An uninoculated negative control should be included because urea broth can produce a false-positive reaction (purple red) on standing.
2. *Optional urease test (rapid).* Transfer two 3-mm loops of growth from each presumptive-positive TSI culture into a tube of rapid urea broth. Incubate for 2 hr in a waterbath at 37 ± 0.5°C.

Most salmonellae are urease-negative; however, urease-positive cultures have been reported. Retain all cultures for further testing.

25.533   Serological screening with polyvalent flagellar (H) antisera or Spicer-Edwards

1. Perform the polyvalent flagellar (H) test at this point to eliminate false-positive TSI cultures, or later as described in Section 25.535. Inoculate growth from each urease-negative TSI agar slant into (1) brain heart infusion broth and incubate 4 to 6 hr at 35°C until visible growth occurs (to test on same day); or (2) trypticase (tryptic) soy-tryptose broth and incubate 24 ± 2 hr at 35°C (to test on following day). Add 2.5 ml formalinized physiological saline solution to 5 ml of either broth culture. Select two formalinized broth cultures from each 25-g analytical unit and test with *Salmonella* polyvalent flagellar (H) antisera. Mix 0.5 ml each of appropriately diluted *Salmonella* polyvalent flagellar (H) antiserum and formalinized antigen in a 10 × 75-mm or 13 × 10-mm serological test tube. Prepare a saline control by mixing 0.5 ml forma-

linized physiological saline solution with 0.5 ml formalinized antigen. Incubate mixtures in a waterbath at 48 to 50°C. Observe at 15-min intervals for flocculation and record final results after 1 hr. A positive tube reaction consists of agglutination/flocculation in the test mixture and absence of agglutination in the control tube. A negative reaction corresponds to absence of agglutination in both the test and control tubes. A nonspecific autoagglutination reaction produces agglutination in both the test and control tubes. Cultures giving such nonspecific results should be tested with Spicer-Edwards antisera.

2. The Spicer-Edwards serological test can be used as an alternative to the polyvalent flagellar (H) screening test. Perform Spicer-Edwards flagellar (H) antisera test using Spicer-Edwards antisera 1, 2, 3, 4, in addition to the en, L, and 1 complexes.

3. If both formalinized BHI broth cultures are serologically negative, repeat serological tests on additional broth cultures to obtain a minimum of two serologically positive cultures for additional serological and biochemical testing (Sections 25.533 and 25.536). If all TSI cultures from a given sample give negative serological flagellar (H) test results, check them for motility (Section 25.539).

25.534   Serological somatic (O) tests for *Salmonella*

(Pre-test all antisera with known *Salmonella* cultures.)

1. *Polyvalent somatic (O) test.* Using a wax pencil, mark off two sections about 1 × 2-cm each on the inside of a glass or plastic petri dish (15 × 100 mm). Commercially available sectioned slides may be used. Transfer a loopful of growth from a 24-hr TSI agar culture in the upper portion of both marked sections. Add 1 loopful of physiological saline solution to the lower portion of one section (control) and 1 drop of *Salmonella* polyvalent somatic (O) antiserum to the lower portion of the remaining section. With a sterile loop or needle, emulsify the culture in the saline solution; repeat for the test section using a sterile loop or needle. Tilt mixtures back and forth for 1 min and observe against a dark background in good illumination. Consider any degree of agglutination (clumping) as a positive reaction. A positive reaction consists of agglutination in the test but not in the control section. A negative reaction shows no agglutination in either the control or test section. A nonspecific reaction corresponds to agglutination in both the test and control sections.

2. *Somatic (O) group tests.* Test polyvalent (O)-positive cultures using individual group somatic (O) including Vi antisera. Cultures giving a positive Vi agglutination reaction should be examined as described in Section 46.126 of the *Official Methods of Analysis.*[4] Record cultures that agglutinate with individual somatic (O) antiserum as positive for that group.

25.535   Interpretation of serological tests

Cultures producing positive polyvalent flagellar (H) test (Section 25.533) or polyvalent somatic (O) test (Section 25.534) should be further tested to determine Spicer-Edwards reaction (Section 25.533) and somatic (O) group (Section 25.534), or biochemically typed using a rapid diagnostic kit (Section 25.132) or by traditional biochemical tests (Section 25.536).

If a specific somatic group (O) (Section 25.534) and Spicer-Edwards (Section 25.533) reactions are obtained on one or more TSI cultures, the sample is positive; additional biochemical testing may be performed but is not required.

TSI cultures that produce negative variable or nonspecific serological reactions should be tested biochemically by a rapid diagnostic kit (Section 25.132) or traditional methods (Section 25.537).

25.536   Biochemical testing of cultures

Following is a list of biochemical tests for identification of *Salmonella*; diagnostic kits for identification of *Enterobacteriaceae* may be substituted (Section 25.132).

1. *Lysine decarboxylase broth.* If the LIA test was satisfactory, it need not be repeated. Use lysine decarboxylase broth for definitive determination of lysine decarboxylase activity if culture gives doubtful LIA reaction. Inoculate broth with a small amount of growth from presumptive-positive TSI agar slant. Replace cap tightly and incubate 48 ± 2 hr at 35°C, but examine after 24 hr of incubation. *Salmonella* species produce an alkaline reaction (purple) throughout the medium. A negative test is indicated by yellow color throughout the medium. If the medium is discolored (neither purple or yellow), add a few drops of 0.2% bromcresol purple dye and repeat the reading.

2. *Phenol red dulcitol broth or purple broth base with 0.5% dulcitol.* Inoculate the broth with a small amount of growth from a presumptive-positive TSI agar culture. Replace the cap loosely and incubate 48 ± 2 hr at 35°C, but examine after 24 hr. Most *Salmonella* species give a positive test indicated by gas formation in an inverted fermentation vial and acidity (yellow) of the medium. Production of acid should be interpreted as a positive reaction. A negative test is indicated by the absence of gas formation and a red (phenol red) or purple (bromcresol purple) color throughout the medium.

3. *Tryptone (or tryptophan) broth.* Inoculate broth with small amount of growth from TSI agar culture. Incubate 24 ± 2 hr at 35°C and proceed as follows:

    a. *Potassium cyanide (KCN) broth.* Transfer 3-mm loopful of 24-hr tryptophan broth culture to KCN broth. Heat rim of tube so that good seal is formed when tube is stoppered with wax-coated cork.

Incubate 48 ± 2 hr at 35°C, but examine after 24 hr. Interpret growth (indicated by turbidity) as positive. Most *Salmonella* species do not grow in this medium, as indicated by lack of turbidity.

b. *Malonate broth.* Transfer a 3-mm loopful of 24-hr tryptone broth culture to malonate broth. Since occasional uninoculated tubes of malonate broth turn blue (positive test) on standing, include an uninoculated tube of this broth as control. Incubate 48 ± 2 hr at 35°C, but examine after 24 hr. Most *Salmonella* species give a negative test (green or unchanged color) in this broth.

c. *Indole test.* Transfer 5 ml of 24-hr tryptone broth culture to a sterile test tube and add 0.2 to 0.3 ml Kovacs' reagent. Most *Salmonella* cultures give a negative reaction (no deep red color at the surface of the broth). Record varying shades of orange and pink as indeterminate.

4. Classify as "confirmed" *Salmonella* those cultures that exhibit typical *Salmonella* reactions for tests no. 1 to 11, shown in Table 4, or produce a positive flagellar (H) agglutination test and typical biochemical profile in an acceptable biochemical identification kit (Section 25.132). If one TSI culture from a single 25-g analytical unit is identified as *Salmonella*, further testing of other TSI cultures from the same 25-g analytical unit is unnecessary. Cultures that contain demonstrable *Salmonella* flagellar (H) antigens but do not have biochemical characteristics of *Salmonella* should be purified (Section 25.531) and retested, beginning as in Section 25.532.

25.537   Additional biochemical tests

1. *Phenol red or bromcresol purple lactose broth.* Inoculate the broth with a small amount of growth from the TSI agar slant. Examine after 24 and 48 hr of incubation at 35°C. A positive reaction consists of acid production (yellow color with either phenol red or bromcresol purple) and gas production in the inverted fermentation vial. A negative reaction consists of a red (with phenol red) or purple (with bromcresol purple) color throughout the medium. Most *Salmonella* are lactose-negative.

2. *Phenol red or bromcresol purple sucrose broth.* Follow procedure described in Section 25.537, 1. Most *Salmonella* are sucrose-negative.

3. *MR-VP broth.* Inoculate the medium with a small amount of growth from each unclassified TSI agar slant (suspected to contain *Salmonella*) and incubate for 48 ± 2 hr at 35°C.

a. *VP test.* At room temperature, transfer 1 ml broth culture to a sterile test tube and incubate the remainder of the MR-VP broth for an additional 48 hr at 35°C. Add 0.6 ml alpha-naphthol and shake well. Add 0.2 ml 40% KOH solution and shake. To intensify and accelerate the reaction, add a few crystals of creatine; read reactions after

Table 4—Typical Biochemical and Serological Reactions of *Salmonella*

Test or Substrate	Positive	Negative	*Salmonella* species reaction[a]
1. Glucose (TSI)	yellow butt	red butt	+
2. Lysine decarboxylase (LIA)	purple butt	yellow butt	+
3. H₂S (TSI and LIA)	blackening	no blackening	+
4. Urease	purple-red color	no color change	−
5. Lysine decarboxylase broth	purple color	yellow color	+
6. Phenol red dulcitol broth	yellow color and/or gas	no gas; no color change	+[b]
7. KCN broth	growth	no growth	−
8. Malonate broth	blue color	no color change	−[c]
9. Indole test	red color at surface	yellow color at surface	−
10. Polyvalent flagellar test	agglutination	no agglutination	+
11. Polyvalent somatic test	agglutination	no agglutination	+
12. Phenol red lactose broth	yellow color and/or gas	no gas; no color change	−[d]
13. Phenol red sucrose broth	yellow color and/or gas	no gas; no color change	−
14. Voges-Proskauer test	pink-to-red color	no color change	−
15. Methyl red test	diffuse red color	diffuse yellow color	+
16. Simmons citrate	growth; blue color	no growth; no color change	V

[a] +, 90% or more positive in 1 or 2 days; −, 90% or more negative in 1 or 2 days; V, variable.
[b] Majority of *Salmonella* subspecies 3a, 3b, 4, and 6 are negative (see Table 1).
[c] Majority of *Salmonella* subspecies 2, 3a, and 3b are positive (see Table 1).
[d] Majority of *Salmonella* subspecies 3b are positive (see Table 1).

4 hr of incubation. Development of a pink to (ruby) red color throughout medium corresponds to a positive test. Most *Salmonella* cultures are VP-negative.

   b. *Methyl red test.* To 5 ml of MR-VP broth (96 hr) culture, add 5 to 6 drops of methyl red indicator. Read results immediately. Most *Salmonella* cultures give a positive test, as indicated by a diffuse red color in the medium. A distinct yellow color constitutes a negative test.

   c. *Simmons citrate agar.* Inoculate the agar with growth from the TSI agar slant, using a sterile needle. Inoculate by streaking the slant and stabbing the butt and incubate for 96 ± 2 hr at 35°C. A positive reaction consists of visible growth, usually accompanied by a color change from green to blue. Most *Salmonella* cultures are citrate-positive. A negative reaction shows little or no growth with no color change in the medium.

25.538   Identification of *Salmonella* cultures

Typical *Salmonella* cultures produce reactions described in Table 4 or a suitable biochemical profile in diagnostic kits and positive flagellar (H) agglutination tests. If neither of two TSI cultures carried through these tests confirms the isolates as *Salmonella*, perform tests on remaining TSI cultures from the same 25-g analytical unit.

   1. Confirm as *Salmonella* cultures producing specific Spicer-Edwards flagellar (H) test (Section 25.533) and somatic group (O) (Section 25.534) reactions.
   2. Confirm as *Salmonella* a culture identified as presumptive *Salmonella* according to the criteria in Table 4 or with a commercial biochemical kit and positive *Salmonella* somatic (O) and flagellar (H) tests.
   3. Discard cultures classified as non-*Salmonella* with commercial biochemical kits using data base-dependent numerical profiles and that fail to give positive flagellar (H) agglutination reactions. Also discard cultures that are negative for both somatic (O) and flagellar (H) and produce atypical reactions in biochemical tests (Table 4).
   4. Send cultures that do not conform to 1, 2, or 3 to a reference laboratory for definitive serotyping and identification.

25.539   Treatment of cultures giving negative flagellar (H) test

If biochemical reactions of a flagellar (H)-negative culture strongly suggest that it could be *Salmonella*, the negative flagellar agglutination may be the result of nonmotile organisms or insufficient development of flagellar antigen. Proceed as follows: Inoculate motility test medium held in a petri dish, using a small amount of growth from the TSI slant. Inoculate by lightly stabbing the medium once about 10 mm from the edge of plate. Do not stab to the bottom of the plate or inoculate any other portion of the plate. Incubate 24 hr at 35°C. If organisms have migrated 40 mm or more, retest as follows: Inoculate a 3-mm loopful of the growth that migrated farthest into trypticase soy-tryptose broth. Repeat polyvalent flagellar (H) or Spicer-Edwards (Section 25.533) serological tests. If cultures are not motile after the first 24 hr, incubate an additional 24 hr at 35°C; if still not motile, incubate up to 5 days at 25°C. Classify a culture as nonmotile if the tests remain negative. If a flagellar (H)-negative culture is strongly suspected as *Salmonella* on the basis of its biochemical reactions, the culture should be sent to a reference laboratory for serotyping and final identification.

25.6 INTERPRETATION OF DATA—REFERENCE METHOD

If no suspect colonies are observed on isolation media (Section 25.52), or if none of the suspect colonies picked from isolation media produce typical *Salmonella* reactions in TSI or LIA, then the sample is negative for *Salmonella*.

If presumptive-positive cultures are obtained in either TSI or LIA, a minimum of six cultures must be subjected to serological and biochemical confirmation tests. If fewer than six presumptive cultures are obtained, apply confirmation tests to all presumptive-positive cultures.

Confirm as *Salmonella* presumptive cultures that meet criteria 1 or 2 in Section 25.538. If one or more presumptive cultures meet either criterion, the sample is positive for *Salmonella*.

Discard as non-*Salmonella* cultures meeting criterion 3 in Section 25.538. If all presumptive cultures examined meet the criterion, the sample is negative.

If presumptive-positive cultures cannot be classified as "confirmed" or "non-*Salmonella*," additional tests should be performed[40] until the cultures can be definitively identified.

25.7 RAPID SCREENING TESTS

Acceptance of rapid screening methods as reliable alternatives to conventional culture methods for detection of *Salmonella* in foods generally arises from collaborative studies that establish the equivalence of standard cultural and rapid test methods.[2] Before the actual collaborative study is conducted, a thorough evaluation should be performed in the laboratory where the method originated, in some other laboratory, or preferably both. The purpose of the initial study is to compare the efficiency of the proposed method with that of the conventional method. The collaborative approach ensures that novel methods are thoroughly evaluated and that the technology is sound in the hands of the developers and other researchers.

One of the major criteria for acceptance of a rapid method is the rate of false-positive and false-negative reactions in relation to results obtained with a reference method. Positive results from rapid methods require cultural confirmation. If the screening methods are more productive than the standard culture method, positive assays may be obtained with the rapid method that cannot be confirmed culturally. Generally, these reactions are considered false-positives, but may in fact represent "true-positives" that cannot be confirmed because of failure of the confirmation procedure. In other cases, the rapid method may be as sensitive in detection of salmonellae as the cultural method but not produce identical results; i.e., neither method provides 100% detection, but false-negative rates are similar. In comparing data, consider that the basis for detection of *Salmonella* by the rapid methods may be different from that for isolation by culture methods.[50]

Positive results by culture methods require that three cultural conditions be met. First, a sufficient number of salmonellae must be present in at least one of the selective enrichment cultures to ensure that one or more *Salmonella* cells are streaked onto plates. Second, the relative proportion of salmonellae to other organisms capable of growth on the selective/differential isolation media must be such that at least one isolated colony of *Salmonella* can be obtained. Thus, the basis for obtaining positive results by culture is primarily selectivity, but the importance of pre-enrichment for resuscitation of injured cells cannot be minimized. This is clear from the lower productivity of "direct enrichment" (Section 25.124). Rapid screening methods require that a sufficient number of $>10^4$ salmonellae/ml be present to allow detection by DNA hybridization, serological, or biochemical tests. High numbers of competitors might inhibit growth of salmonellae to the level necessary for detection by the rapid methods as well as prevent isolation by standard culture conditions. However, under certain conditions sufficient numbers of salmonellae could develop to produce positive results by the rapid assays but not by the culture procedure because of large populations of competitive flora (e.g., swarming *Proteus*). Additionally, other conditions could allow cultural isolation of *Salmonella* present at levels below the threshold sensitivity of rapid methods. Although it may be unrealistic to expect 100% agreement between conventional culture and rapid assay results, the high sensitivity of standard cultural methods for *Salmonella*[2] will generally provide for a high agreement between rapid and conventional culture methods.

Rapid methods that have been evaluated collaboratively are discussed in sufficient detail below to facilitate performance of the tests.

25.71   Fluorescent Antibody Method[4]

Many of the rapid methods proposed for detection of salmonellae are based on immunological reactions. The fluorescent-antibody (FA) technique was the first immunological method applied to the detection of salmonellae. Thomason et al.[133] reported that the O, Vi and H antigens of *Salmonella typhi* could be stained with fluorescein-labeled antibodies and observed by fluorescence microscopy. With the advent of antisera of greater sensitivity and specificity, a protocol was developed for detection of salmonellae in foods.

The method was extensively evaluated and approved by AOAC in 1975. An historical summary of the development of the FA procedure has been published.[132] The AOAC-approved method employs a 24-hr pre-enrichment (for all foods but raw meat samples, which are placed directly in selective enrichment), and a 24-hr selective enrichment followed by a 4-hr post-enrichment.[48] Portions of the post-enrichment are then stained and examined for fluorescent cells. The presence of fluorescent cells morphologically typical of salmonellae constitutes a presumptive-positive result that must be confirmed by cultural methods. Negative results are generally available 1 day earlier than with conventional culture methods. Thomason[132] compiled data from three studies and indicated a 97.6% agreement between standard culture methods and FA, and a false-negative and false-positive rate of 0.1% and 2.3%, respectively. However, some laboratories observed much higher false-positive rates, especially with certain products.[132] It was also established that staining and reading of stained slides is both laborious and subjective, requiring a high degree of technical training and experience.

An FA system was developed to automate the staining and reading of slides.[100, 134] The system included a slide processor for automated staining and a fluorometer that read total fluorescent intensity of stained samples. However, the automated system failed to detect *Salmonella* in certain samples, and high numbers of false-positive results were reported. These shortcomings probably contributed to the reluctance of the food industry to accept the manual or automated versions of the FA procedure.

A detailed description of the FA method is not presented in this edition of the *Compendium of Methods for the Microbiological Examination of Foods* but appears in the previous edition[75] and in the 14th edition of *Official Methods of Analysis.*[4]

25.72 Hydrophobic Grid Membrane Filtration (HGMF)[5]

A major problem associated with the non-salmonellae analysis of foods by membrane filtration has been the limited counting range. One solution to the problem has been the introduction of the HGMF procedure.[119] The method uses a membrane filter impregnated with hydrophobic material in a grid pattern of 1,600 compartments. The hydrophobic material acts as a barrier, preventing the spread of "growth units" between adjacent compartments. The food test sample is prepared by blending or stomaching, and the appropriate dilution is filtered. The HGMF filter is then placed on a plate of appropriate agar. Following incubation, the number of occupied squares is counted and converted to a most probable number value using a formula specific for this method. A major advantage of HGMF over traditional membrane filtration is that a counting range in excess of three logarithmic cycles is possible on a single filter.

Problems associated with membrane filtration are the clogging of pores during filtration and interference with counting of organisms by food particles trapped on the membrane surface. The clogging problem was resolved through use of nonbactericidal enzymes and use of a prefilter to remove large particles of food before filtration.[45]

HGMF has found application in the qualitative analysis of foods for *Salmonella*. Entis et al.[44] reported the use of an HGMF method for the detection of *Salmonella* in foods that was subsequently subjected to an AOAC collaborative study. In the AOAC method,[4] approved for the analysis of six foods (nonfat dry milk, powdered eggs, cheese powders, pepper, chocolate, and raw poultry), the test sample was incubated in the appropriate pre-enrichment medium for 18 to 24 hr at 35°C. A 0.1-ml volume of the pre-enriched test sample was subcultured in 10 ml of tetrathionate broth. After 6 to 8 hr of incubation in a 35°C water-bath, a 1-ml portion of diluted (raw poultry) or undiluted (the other five foods) selective TBG enrichment was filtered through the HGMF. The filters were then placed on plates of selective lysine agar (SLA) or, in the case of nonfat dry milk, on plates of SLA and HE agar. Following incubation of the SLA (43°C) and the HE (35°C) agar plates for 24 hr, the filters were examined for *Salmonella*; suspect colonies, if present, were confirmed by the conventional AOAC culture method.[4]

The HGMF method indicates that SLA and HE plates need not be restreaked if an HGMF test result is presumptive-positive because the culture is already available for confirmation.[4] However, occasionally mixed cultures may be recovered from grids producing typical reactions. Thus, restreaking to obtain pure cultures may sometimes be required and is suggested, especially when membranes appear to be heavily contaminated with competing flora.

Use of the HGMF method has limitations. Its performance beyond the analysis of the six foods previously mentioned has not been fully assessed. Further, the use of a single selective enrichment and a single selective plating agar may preclude the detection of strains that are more readily recovered by other selective enrichment broths and/or selective agars. Lysine-negative *Salmonella* cultures will not be detected when SLA is the only selective plating agar used. Lysine-negative variants, however, occur primarily in the serovars *S. choleraesuis* and *S. parathyphi* A, which account for only a very small percentage of human *Salmonella* isolations.

25.73   Immunodiffusion[30, 52]

Detection of *Salmonella* in the self-contained and disposable Salmonella 1-2 TEST unit (BioControl Systems, Inc., Bothell, Washington) is based on the formation of an opaque zone or band when *Salmonella* bacteria are immobilized by polyvalent H (flagellar) antibodies in a semisolid motility medium. The clear, plastic device consists of two interconnected chambers: a motility chamber containing L-serine and a peptone-based, nonselective motility medium and an inoculation chamber containing L-serine and tetrathionate broth with brilliant green dye.

Most food samples are pre-enriched for 24 ± 2 hr at 35°C as described in the cultural reference method. The pre-enrichment culture is then seeded into the inoculation chamber of the 1-2 TEST system. Raw meats and other highly contaminated products are not pre-enriched but are placed directly in 9 volumes of tetrathionate broth with brilliant green dye for 24 ± 2 hr at 35°C. Pre-enriched samples of flour-containing products are subcultured overnight in 10 ml of tetrathionate broth with brilliant green dye. Enrichment cultures of raw meats and flour-containing products are then added to the inoculation chamber of the 1-2 TEST system.

Preparation of the 1-2 unit involves three steps. First, the TBG in the inoculation chamber is activated by the addition of 1 drop of iodine-iodide solution. Then 1 drop of a *Salmonella* antibody solution is added to the motility chamber. The blue-colored antibody preparation facilitates reading of the immobilization reaction.

Following removal of the chamber plug that seals the opening between the motility chamber and the inoculation chamber, a 0.1-ml portion of pre-enrichment (processed food), direct enrichment (raw meats), or enrichment (flour-based products) cultures is added to the inoculation chamber. Since raw meats, highly contaminated foods, and flour-containing products have undergone selective enrichment prior to inoculation into the 1-2 unit, it is noteworthy that these foods are being selectively enriched for a second time. Other foods are selectively enriched in the inoculation chamber of the 1-2 unit only.

Because the concentration of L-serine is higher in the inoculation chamber than in the motility chamber, recognition of this amino acid in the motility chamber by *Salmonella* is delayed, thereby allowing the organisms to establish relatively high levels before migration. When the concentration of L-serine in the inoculation chamber is reduced by metabolism, a concentration gradient is established, encouraging *Salmonella* to migrate into the motility medium.

The 1-2 unit is incubated for a minimum 14 hr at 35°C. Motile *Salmonella* organisms, if present, migrate from the inoculation chamber into the motility chamber. A visible band of precipitation occurs where motile *Salmonella* and diffusing antibody interface. Such presumptive-positive reactions are then confirmed by streaking a loopful of TBG from the inoculation chamber onto selective plating media as described by the manufacturer. Isolates are then confirmed using the reference method above.

In addition to yielding presumptive-positive results for processed foods and raw meat samples 1 day earlier than with the conventional culture method, the Salmonella 1-2 TEST offers other advantages. It is easy to use, requires no specialized training or sophisticated equipment, and is readily adaptable for use in laboratories that handle small or large numbers of test samples.

Because the detection of *Salmonella* by the 1-2 TEST is based on immuno-suppression of motility, nonmotile serovars such as *S. gallinarum* and *S. pullorum* and other variants will not be detected.

25.74   Enzyme immunoassays[53, 54, 57, 59]

Several enzyme immunoassays (EIA) have been proposed for detection of salmonellae in foods. Reviews on the types of EIAs and on the development of EIAs for detection of salmonellae in foods have been published.[71, 92, 131] Some of these methods have undergone collaborative study and have been approved by AOAC.[53, 54, 57, 59]

The first EIA method approved by AOAC was the BioEnzaBead™ method (Organon Teknika, Durham, N.C., formerly Litton Bionetics). Comparative studies on the productivity of this method based on the reaction of two antibodies, MOPC 467 and 6H4, with *Salmonella* antigens were conducted by D'Aoust and Sewell,[29] Eckner et al.,[38] Flowers et al.,[54] and Todd et al.[135, 136] The EIA method evaluated by Eckner et al.[38] employed a 24 ± 2-hr pre-enrichment, an 18-hr selective enrichment, and a 6-hr M-broth (35°C) post-enrichment. The EIA assay required less than 2 hr to complete. A total time of 72 hr, compared to a minimum of 96 hr for the AOAC culture method,[4] was required for presumptive results. A total of 1,289 samples, consisting of 760 artificially inoculated, 150 naturally contaminated, and 379 uninoculated controls, were tested by both the BioEnzaBead™ and AOAC culture methods. A total of 570 samples were positive by the culture method, whereas 568 of the 594 EIA positives were confirmed culturally. Examination of 26 food types showed no food-dependent differences (P > 0.05) between the two methods except cake mix and raw shrimp, where the EIA and AOAC methods, respectively, were significantly better. False-negative rates for EIA and the culture method were 3.4% and 3.1%, respectively. In 26 samples, positive EIA could not be confirmed by plating from M-broth cultures and were interpreted as false-positives (3.7%). However, some of these samples had been inoculated with *Salmonella*, which raised a question about the adequacy of the confirmation method. A subsequent study on the performance of BioEnzaBead™ for the detection of salmonellae in shrimp and related products also examined the reliability of plating from both the selective enrichment and M-broth cultures for the confirmation of EIA-positive reactions.[54] Analysis of 287 samples of raw chilled shrimp, frozen shrimp, cooked shrimp, raw lobster, and raw crabmeat yielded 129 and 134 positive results by the AOAC and EIA-confirmed procedures, respectively. Use of M-broth alone resulted in 112 confirmations compared with 127 confirmations from tetrathionate and selenite cystine enrichment cultures. No significant differences between the AOAC culture method and EIA-confirmed data at the 5% probability level were noted when both M-broth and homologous enrichment cultures were employed for confirmation. These findings demonstrate that the use of M-broth alone for confirmation reduced the number of confirmed positive results and that all three enrichment media should be used to confirm positive EIA readings.

Todd et al.[135, 136] compared the sensitivity of the BioEnzaBead™ method to the standard ISO culture procedure[76] for detection of *Salmonella* in naturally contaminated foods. These authors reported that of 211 samples analyzed, 134 were positive by both methods, 39 negative by both methods, 35 positive by EIA that could not be confirmed culturally, and 3 positive by culture but negative by EIA. The authors noted that all test samples had previously been found positive by the cultural method and suggested that the high incidence of EIA-positive but culture-negative samples may have resulted from greater EIA sensitivity.

Flowers et al.[53] reported on a collaborative study comparing the Bio-EnzaBead™ to the AOAC culture method. Twenty-five laboratories participated in the study, analyzing 12 samples of each of six food types. No significant difference appeared in the productivity of EIA and the culture procedure at the 5% probability level for any of the foods. Based on the results of this collaborative study[53] and an earlier comparative study,[38] the BioEnzaBead™ EIA method was approved by AOAC.[6] The approved method employed preenrichment in nonselective medium for 24 ± 2 hr at 35°C, selective enrichment in TBG/SC for 18 to 24 hr, post-enrichment in M-broth for 6 hr (35°C), and a centrifugation/heating step prior to performing the EIA procedure. Subsequent work indicated that the incubation period for selective enrichment could be reduced and the centrifugation step eliminated with low-moisture foods.[54] A collaborative study was performed to compare the efficiency of the modified *Salmonella* method with the AOAC culture method.[54] The modified method required 18 to 24-hr pre-enrichment, 6 to 8-hr selective enrichment, and 14 to 18-hr post-enrichment and heating prior to EIA. The minimum time to complete the modified method was 40 hr, compared with 48 hr for the longer EIA method and 96 hr for the AOAC culture method. Based on the results of the collaborative study, which indicated no significant difference ($P > 0.05$) in detection of *Salmonella* by the modified EIA and the AOAC culture method, the modified method was approved by AOAC.[57] Continuing work with the BioEnzaBead™ has shown that a few strains of salmonellae are not detected by the antibodies employed in these assays.[29] Also, it should be noted that cross-reaction with other non-salmonellae, notably *C. freundii*, may produce high false-positive rates[30] when these organisms are present in analytical samples.

The BioEnzaBead™ immunoassay originally used plastic-coated ferrous metal beads as the solid support phase. Monoclonal antibodies specific for *Salmonella* antigens were adsorbed onto the surface of the coated beads. The assay was initiated by dropping an antibody-coated metal bead into a microtiter dish well containing a heated extract of the food sample. Washing and subsequent steps in the assay were performed by moving the metal beads between plates containing wash solutions, conjugate, or substrate, using a magnetic transfer device. If *Salmonella* antigens were present in the sample, the conjugate would bind to the *Salmonella* antigens already attached to the antibody-coated bead. The beads were washed to remove any unbound conjugate and then placed in a substrate solution. Appearance of color indicated the presence of *Salmonella* antigen in the sample.

In 1988, this immunoassay was modified in favor of an antibody-coated microelisa 12-well strip-plate developed by Organon Teknika. This format (Salmonella-Tek™) offers several advantages over the bead assay, including the need for only one rather than the eight microtiter plates required by the bead assay and use of a more sensitive substrate. Small numbers of samples can be tested by removing only the required number of strip wells. In addition, more antibody molecules are bound to the well surfaces of the strip-plate, providing for greater method sensitivity.

The Salmonella-Tek™ strip-plate assay was compared with the Bio-EnzaBead™ method using both inoculated and naturally contaminated samples.[20] This study demonstrated equivalent results by the BioEnzaBead™ assay and the Salmonella-Tek™ plate assay to those obtained by the culture method. The Salmonella-Tek™ assay was more sensitive than the Bio-EnzaBead™ assay; i.e., it was capable of detecting lower levels of *Salmonella* in the post-enrichment cultures. Thus, the Salmonella-Tek™ assay can reliably replace the BioEnzaBead™ assay for detecting *Salmonella* in foods when the same enrichment protocol is employed. Consequently, it was recommended to AOAC that the Salmonella-Tek™ assay method replace the BioEnza-Bead™ method and that the BioEnzaBead™ method be discontinued.[20]

Both assays employ the same two *Salmonella*-specific antibodies and thus should offer similar degrees of specificity. The enrichment steps of the Salmonella-Tek™ and BioEnzaBead™ assay are similar. After boiling, portions of the cooled M-broth cultures are dispensed into the wells of the microelisa strips and incubated with agitation to allow capture of *Salmonella* antigens. The wells are then washed, and peroxidase-labeled conjugate binds to the captured *Salmonella* antigen (if present) to form an antibody-antigen-antibody-peroxidase complex. Unbound conjugate is removed from the wells by washing, and enzyme substrate is added. If a blue color develops, the sample is presumptive-positive for *Salmonella*. The reaction is stopped with an acid solution that turns the blue color to an intense yellow. The plates are read on an EIA reader; all presumptive-positives must be confirmed culturally.

Two other EIA techniques have undergone comparative and collaborative studies.

The TECRA™ EIA method (Bioenterprises Pty. Ltd., Roseville, N.S.W., Australia), in contrast to Salmonella-Tek™, utilizes polyclonal rather than monoclonal antibodies. The assay is performed in microtiter plates or strip wells and can be read visually or spectrophotometrically. TECRA™ detection of foodborne salmonellae was compared to the AOAC culture method. A total of 1,249 samples (21 food types) consisting of 800 inoculated samples, 399 uninoculated control samples, and 50 samples of naturally contaminated foods were analyzed for *Salmonella* by the AOAC culture method and the

TECRA™ procedure.[51] The false-positive rate for TECRA™ was 3.1%; raw turkey rather than processed food samples contributed most of the erroneous results. False-negative rates for EIA (0.2%) and culture (0.5%) were similar. The TECRA™ method was simple to perform, with no requirement for sophisticated instrumentation. Wash steps were performed manually, and assay results could be readily obtained visually, thereby eliminating the need for an EIA spectrophotometer.

These preliminary results led to an AOAC collaborative study.[58] A total of 634 food samples were analyzed by 14 laboratories using the AOAC culture and TECRA™ methods, with 96.7% agreement between the two methods. The false-negative rates for EIA and culture were 1.4% and 1.7%, respectively. The false-positive rate for TECRA™ was 4.1%; most unconfirmed positive EIA reactions occurred with raw turkey samples. Excluding turkey, the false-positive rate for EIA was 1.0%. Statistical analysis of the data indicated no significant difference between detection of *Salmonella* by EIA and culture methods (P > 0.05) for any of the foods analyzed. Based on the results of the collaborative[58] and comparative (unpublished) studies, the TECRA™ method was approved by AOAC.[8]

The Q-TROL™ *Salmonella* assay (Dynatech Laboratories, Inc., Chantilly, Va.) utilizes monoclonal antibodies and a fluorogenic reagent. More than 1,700 food samples were analyzed by the Q-TROL™ and AOAC culture methods.[59] False-negative rates for the Q-TROL™ and culture methods were 1.4% and 1.9%, respectively. The false-positive rate for the EIA assay was 4.9%.

A collaborative AOAC study of the Q-TROL™ method was performed in 13 laboratories.[59] No significant difference appeared in the proportion of samples positive by the EIA and culture procedures at the 5% confidence level for any of the foods analyzed. The level of agreement between the Q-TROL™ and the culture method was 98.5%, with false-negative rates of 0.8% and 1.1%, respectively. Based on the results of this study, the method was approved by AOAC.[9] Subsequently, a colorimetric enzyme assay using the substrate phenolphthalein monophosphate (PMP) and the enzyme alkaline phosphatase was developed and compared with the fluorogenic assay. The results indicated that the colorimetric assay was at least as sensitive as the previously approved fluorogenic assay.[22]

The extensive evaluations of the EIA methods clearly indicate that this technology is an attractive alternative to conventional culture methods for detection of salmonellae in foods. This analytical approach provides detection of salmonellae 1 day earlier than by conventional cultural methods, with low numbers of both false-negative and false-positive results for most processed products, although relatively high false-positive rates have been reported for some raw products.[28, 29, 38, 53] Advantages of the method include automation and a definitive end-point that contrasts with the subjective interpretation associated with culture methods.

25.75   DNA Hybridization

Genetic relatedness among related bacteria can be measured by the DNA-DNA hybridization (DNAH) technique that probes for unique nucleotide sequences in target organisms. The performance of a ^{32}P DNA hybridization assay for *Salmonella* in foods (GENE-TRAK Systems Framingham, Mass.) was compared to the AOAC culture method.[55] Analysis was made of 1,609 food samples consisting of inoculated, uninoculated control, and naturally contaminated samples representing 23 different foods. More than 20 *Salmonella* serovars were used to inoculate foods. The results showed that the sensitivity of the DNAH method compared favorably with the culture method under all test conditions and, in some cases, DNAH appeared to provide superior detection. False-negative rates for culture and DNAH were 5.9% and 1.8%, respectively. The false-positive rate for the DNAH assay was 5.3%.

A collaborative study among 11 laboratories compared the sensitivity of the ^{32}P DNAH procedure to the standard culture method for detection of *Salmonella* in six artificially contaminated foods: ground pepper, soy flour, dry whole egg, milk chocolate, nonfat dry milk, and raw deboned turkey.[56] Results of the DNAH method were significantly better than those of the standard culture method (P < 0.05) for the detection of *Salmonella* in turkey, with no significant difference (P > 0.05) between the methods for the other five foods. The agreement between DNAH and the culture method was 95.6% with a false-negative rate of 0.2% for DNAH and 5.9% for the culture method. The results of this collaborative study[55] and earlier comparative studies[53] led to an AOAC approval of the DNAH method for rapid detection of salmonellae in foods.[7] The isotopic DNAH method includes pre-enrichment (18 to 24 hr), 6-hr selective enrichment in TBG/SC, and a 12 to 16-hr post-enrichment in GN broth for processed foods and 18-hr enrichment in TBG + 6-hr GN for raw meats. After inoculation of the post-enrichment GN-broth with 0.1 ml of enrichment (TBG/SC) culture, both selective enrichments are incubated for 12 to 16 hr. A portion of the GN enrichment culture is then filtered, and the DNAH assay performed on the filters.

Positive reactions are reported when counts for the test filter are >500 cpm above the average of three negative control filters. The assay itself requires about 4 hr to perform, and the culture steps require a minimum of 42 hr. Thus, the total time required for the DNAH method is 46 hr. The DNAH assay is a screening method, and positive results must be confirmed by culture methods. Both post-enrichment and reincubated selective enrichment cultures are streaked to selective agar media for confirmation of positive DNAH assays.

Emswiler-Rose et al.[42] compared the DNAH method with conventional culture methods for detection of salmonellae in naturally contaminated ground beef; they found a false-positive rate of 3.7% by DNAH and no false-negative results for either DNAH or the culture method.

Subsequent to approval of the isotopic DNAH method, a non-isotopic, colorimetric DNAH method was developed.[21] The colorimetric assay employed DNA probes different from those used in the isotopic method. The target for the colorimetric assay probes is ribosomal RNA; i.e., the assay is based on hybridization of the DNA probes to target rRNA. The assay, which is carried out in an aqueous environment, involves hybridization between rRNA and *Salmonella*-specific oligonucleotide probes, capture of rRNA target:DNA probe hybrids onto a solid support, and a colorimetric end-point detection. Following pre-enrichment, selective enrichment, and post-enrichment of test samples as described above for the DNAH assay, bacteria are lysed and *Salmonella*-specific fluorescein-labeled detection and poly dA capture probes are added. The mixture is then incubated to allow hybridization of both probes to target rRNA, if present. A polydeoxythymidylic (poly dT)-coated plastic dipstick solid phase is then introduced into the hybridization solution. Base pairing between the poly dA tail sequence of the capture probe and the poly dT on the dipstick facilitates capture of the DNA probe:rRNA target hybrids onto the dipstick. Unbound labeled probe is removed by washing the dipstick, followed by incubation in a solution containing anti-fluorescein antibody (Ab) conjugated to horseradish peroxidase (HRP). The peroxidase conjugate binds to the fluorescein label on the hybridized detector probe. Unbound conjugate is washed away, and the dipstick is incubated in a substrate-chromogen solution. Reaction of HRP with substrate-chromagen results in development of a blue color. The enzyme:substrate reaction is stopped by addition of acid with a concomitant change in color from blue to yellow. Absorbance at 450 nm in excess of threshold value indicates the presence of *Salmonella* in the test samples.

The colorimetric DNAH assay can be completed in 2.5 hr following approximately 44 hr of culture enrichments. Chan et al.[13] compared the productivity of the colorimetric DNAH (cDNAH) method with the AOAC culture method.[4] One thousand samples representing 20 food types were analyzed in parallel by both methods. The false-negative rates were 0.8% and 2.2% for the cDNAH and culture methods, respectively. The false-positive rate for cDNAH was 0.8%. Based on the encouraging results of this study, an AOAC collaborative study was performed in 11 laboratories to validate the cDNAH method.[21] No significant difference appeared in the ability of the methods to detect salmonellae in any of the six artificially contaminated foods examined in this study.

25.8   REFERENCES

1. Aleksic, S., Rohde, R. and Quddus Khan, A. 1973. The isolation of *Salmonella* from human fecal specimens in selenite enrichment medium at incubation temperatures of 37°C or 43°C. Zbl. Bakt. Hyg, I Abt. Orig. A. 225: 27.
2. Andrews, W. H. 1985. A review of culture methods and their relation to rapid methods for the detection of *Salmonella* in foods. Food Technol. 39: 77.
3. Andrews, W. H., Wilson, C. R. and Poelma, P. L. 1983. Improved *Salmonella* species

recovery from nonfat dry milk pre-enriched under reduced rehydration. J. Food Sci. 48: 1162.

4. AOAC. 1984. "Official Methods of Analysis," 14th ed. (Supplements, 1986, 1987) Assn. Off. Anal. Chem., Arlington, Va.

5. AOAC, 1985. Changes in methods. *Salmonella* detection in foods: Hydrophobic grid membrane filter method. J. Assn. Off. Anal. Chem. 68: 405.

6. AOAC, 1986. Changes in methods. *Salmonella* in foods: Enzyme immunoassay screening method. J. Assn. Off. Anal. Chem. 69: 381.

7. AOAC, 1987. Changes in methods. *Salmonella* in foods: DNA hybridization method. J. Assn. Off. Anal. Chem. 70: 394.

8. AOAC, 1989. Changes in official methods. *Salmonella* in foods: Colorimetric polyclonal EIA screening method. J. Assn. Off. Anal. Chem. 72: 201.

9. AOAC, 1989. Changes in official methods. *Salmonella* in foods: Fluorogenic monoclonal EIA screening method. J. Assn. Off. Anal. Chem. 72: 203.

10. Bailey, J. S., Cox, N. A. and Thomson, J. E. 1981. Efficiency of selenite cystine and TT enrichment broths for the detection of *Salmonella*. J. Appl. Bacteriol. 51: 409.

11. Bailey, J. S., Chiu, J. Y., Cox, N. A. and Johnston, R. W. 1988. Improved selective procedure for detection of salmonellae from poultry and sausage products. J. Food Prot. 51: 391.

12. Bonev, S. I. 1976. DMS agar, a new composite tube medium for differentiation within the genus *Salmonella*. Int. J. Syst. Bacteriol. 26: 79.

13. Chan, S. W., Wilson, S. G., Johnson, A., Whippie, K., Shah, A., Wilby, A., Ottaviani, M., Vera-Garcia, M., Mozola, M. and Holbert, D. Comparative study of a colorimetric DNA hybridization assay and the conventional culture procedure for the detection of *Salmonella* in foods. J. Assn. Off. Anal. Chem. In press.

14. Cook, G. T. 1952. Comparison of two modifications of bismuth-sulphite agar for the isolation and growth of *Salmonella typhi* and *Salmonella typhimurium*. J. Path. Bacteriol. 64: 559.

15. Cox, N. A. and Mercuri, A. J. 1978. Recovery of salmonella from broiler carcasses by direct enrichment. J. Food Prot. 41: 521.

16. Cox, N. A. and Mercuri, A. J. 1979. Rapid biochemical testing procedures for *Enterobacteriaceae* in foods. Food Technol. 33: 57.

17. Cox, N. A., Bailey, J. S. and Thomson, J. E. 1983. Evaluation of five miniaturized systems for identifying *Enterobacteriaceae* from stock cultures and raw foods. J. Food Prot. 46: 914.

18. Cox, N. A., Thomson, J. E. and Bailey, J. S. 1983. Procedure for isolation and identification of *Salmonella* from poultry carcasses. Agricultural Handbook No. 603. Agric. Res. Serv., U.S. Dept. of Agriculture, Washington, D.C.

19. Crosa, J. H., Brenner, D. J., Ewing, W. H. and Falkow, S. 1973. Molecular relationships among the Salmonellae. J. Bacteriol. 115: 307.

20. Curiale, M. S., Klatt, M. J., Robison, B. J. and Beck, L. T. 1990. Comparison of colorimetric monoclonal enzyme immunoassay screening methods for detection of *Salmonella* in foods. J. Assn. Off. Anal. Chem. 73: 43.

21. Curiale, M. S., Klatt, M. J. and Mozola, M. A. 1990. Colorimetric deoxyribonucleic acid hybridization for rapid screening of *Salmonella* in foods. J. Assn. Off. Anal. Chem. 73: 248.

22. Curiale, M. S., Klatt, M. J., Gehle, W. E. and Chandonnet, H. 1990. Colorimetric and fluorometric substrate immunoassays for the detection of *Salmonella* in all foods: A comparative study. J. Assn. Off. Anal. Chem. 73: 961.

23. D'Aoust, J.-Y. 1977. Effect of storage conditions on the performance of bismuth sulfite agar. J. Clin. Microbiol. 5: 122.

24. D'Aoust, J.-Y. 1981. Update on pre-enrichment and selective enrichment conditions for detection of *Salmonella* in foods. J. Food Prot. 44: 369.

25. D'Aoust, J.-Y. 1984. Effective enrichment-plating conditions for detection of *Salmonella* in foods. J. Food Prot. 47: 588.

26. D'Aoust, J.-Y. 1989. *Salmonella*. In "Foodborne Bacterial Pathogens," ed. M. P. Doyle, 327. Marcel Dekker, New York.

27. D'Aoust, J.-Y. and Maishment, C. 1979. Pre-enrichment conditions for effective recovery of *Salmonella* in foods and feed ingredients. J. Food Prot. 42: 153.

28. D'Aoust, J.-Y. and Sewell, A. M. 1986. Detection of *Salmonella* by the enzyme immunoassay (EIA) technique. J. Food Sci. 51: 484.

29. D'Aoust, J.-Y. and Sewell, A. M. 1988. Detection of *Salmonella* with the BioEnzaBead™ enzyme immunoassay technique. J. Food Prot. 51: 538.

30. D'Aoust, J.-Y. and Sewell, A. M. 1988. Reliability of the immunodiffusion 1-2 Test™ system for detection of *Salmonella* in foods. J. Food Prot. 51: 853.

31. D'Aoust, J.-Y., Maishment, C., Burgener, D. M., Conley, D. R., Loit, A., Milling, M. and Purvis, U. 1980. Detection of *Salmonella* in refrigerated pre-enrichment and enrichment broth cultures. J. Food Prot. 43: 343.

32. D'Aoust, J.-Y., Maishment, C., Stotland, P. and Boville, A. 1982. Surfactants for the effective recovery of *Salmonella* in fatty foods. J. Food Prot. 45: 249.

33. D'Aoust, J.-Y., Beckers, H. J., Boothroyd, M., Mates, A., McKee, C. R., Moran, A. B., Sado, P., Spain, G. E., Sperber, W. H., Vassiliadis, P., Wagner, D. E. and Wiberg, C. 1983. ICMSF methods studies. XIV. Comparative study on recovery of *Salmonella* from refrigerated pre-enrichment and enrichment broth cultures. J. Food Prot. 46: 391.

34. De Smedt, J. M. and Bolderdijk, R. F. 1987. Dynamics of *Salmonella* isolation with modified semisolid Rappaport-Vassiliadis medium. J. Food Prot. 50: 658.

35. Devenish, J. A., Ciebin, B. W. and Brodsky, M. H. 1986. Novobiocin-brilliant green-glucose agar: New medium for isolation of salmonellae. Appl. Environ. Microbiol. 52: 539.

36. Difco Laboratories. 1984. "Difco Manual of Dehydrated Culture Media and Reagents for Microbiological and Clinical Laboratory Procedures," 10th ed. Difco Laboratories, Detroit, Mich.

37. Dockstader, W. B. and Groomes, R. J. 1970. Evaluation of surfactants for use in microbiological analyses. Bacteriol. Proc., Amer. Soc. Microbiol. 70th Annual Meeting, p. 6. Boston, Mass.

38. Eckner, K. F., Flowers, R. S., Robison, B. J., Mattingly, J. A., Gabis, D. A. and Silliker, J. H. 1987. Comparison of *Salmonella* BioEnzaBead™ immunoassay method and conventional culture procedure for detection of *Salmonella* in foods. J. Food Prot. 50: 379.

39. Edel, W. and Kampelmacher, E. H. 1973. Comparative studies on the isolation of "sublethally injured" salmonellae in nine European laboratories. Bull. Wld. Hlth. Org. 48: 167.

40. Edwards, P. R. and Fife, M. A. 1961. Lysine-iron agar in the detection of *Arizona* cultures. Appl. Microbiol. 9: 478.

41. Edwards, P. R. and Ewing, W. H. 1972. "Identification of *Enterobacteriaceae*," 3rd ed. Burgess Publ. Co., Minneapolis, Minn.

42. Emswiler-Rose, B., Bennett, B. and Okrend, A. 1987. Comparison of cultural methods and the DNA hybridization test for detection of salmonellae in ground beef. J. Food Sci. 52: 1726.

43. Entis, P. 1985. Rapid hydrophobic grid membrane filter method for *Salmonella* detection in selected foods: Collaborative study. J. Assn. Off. Anal. Chem. 68: 555.

44. Entis, P., Brodsky, M. H., Sharpe, A. N. and Jarvis, G. A. 1982. Rapid detection of *Salmonella* spp. in food by use of the ISO-GRID hydrophobic grid membrane filter. Appl. Environ. Microbiol. 43: 261.

45. Entis, P., Brodsky, M. H. and Sharpe, A. N. 1982. Effect of pre-filtration and enzyme treatment on membrane filtration of foods. J. Food Prot. 45: 8.

46. Eskenazi, S. and Littell, A. M. 1978. Dulcitol-malonate-phenylalanine agar for the identification of *Salmonella* and other *Enterobacteriaceae*. Appl. Environ. Microbiol. 35: 199.

47. Ewing, W. H. 1986. "Edwards and Ewing's Identification of *Enterobacteriaceae*," 4th ed., Elsevier Science Publ. Co., New York.

48. Fantasia, L. D., Schrade, J. P., Yoger, J. F. and Debler, D. 1975. Fluorescent antibody method for the detection of *Salmonella*: Development, evaluation, and collaborative study. J. Assn. Off. Anal. Chem. 58: 828.

49. Farmer, J. J., McWhorter, A. C., Brenner, D. J. and Morris, G. K. 1984. The *Salmonella-Arizona* group of *Enterobacteriaceae*: Nomenclature, classification, and reporting. Clin. Microbiol. Newsletter. 6: 63.

50. Flowers, R. S. 1985. Comparison of rapid *Salmonella* screening methods and the conventional culture method. Food Technol. 39: 103.

51. Flowers, R. S. and Klatt, M. J. 1987. Evaluation of a visual immunoassay for detection of *Salmonella* in foods. Inst. of Food Technol. Annual Meeting, Abstract 122. Dallas, Tex.

52. Flowers, R. S. and Klatt, M. J. 1989. Immunodiffusion screening method for detection of motile *Salmonella* in foods: Collaborative study. J. Assn. Off. Anal. Chem. 72: 303.

53. Flowers, R. S., Eckner, K. F., Gabis, D. A., Robison, B. J., Mattingly, J. A. and Silliker, J. H. 1986. Microbiological Methods. Enzyme immunoassay for detection of *Salmonella* in foods: Collaborative study. J. Assn. Off. Anal. Chem. 69: 786.

54. Flowers, R. S., Klatt, M. J., Robison, B. J., Mattingly, J. A., Gabis, D. A. and Silliker, J. H. 1987. Enzyme immunoassay for detection of *Salmonella* in low-moisture foods: Collaborative study. J. Assn. Off. Anal. Chem. 30: 530.

55. Flowers, R. S., Mozola, M. A., Curiale, M. S., Gabis, D. A. and Silliker, J. H. 1987. Comparative study of a DNA hybridization method and the conventional culture procedure for detection of *Salmonella* in foods. J. Food Sci. 52: 781.

56. Flowers, R. S., Klatt, M. J., Mozola, M. A., Curiale, M. S., Gabis, D. A. and Silliker, J. H. 1987. Microbiological Methods. DNA hybridization assay for detection of *Salmonella* in foods: Collaborative study. J. Assn. Off. Anal. Chem. 70: 521.

57. Flowers, R. S., Klatt, M. J., Robison, B. J. and Mattingly, J. A. 1988a. Evaluation of abbreviated enzyme immunoassay method for detection of *Salmonella* in low-moisture foods. J. Assn. Off. Anal. Chem. 71: 341.

58. Flowers, R. S., Klatt, M. J. and Keelan, S. L. 1988b. Visual immunoassay for detection of *Salmonella* in foods: Collaborative study. J. Assn. Off. Anal. Chem. 71: 973.

59. Flowers, R. S., Klatt, M. J., Keelan, S. L., Swaminathan, B., Gehle, W. D. and Chandonnet, H. E. 1989. Fluorescent enzyme immunoassay for rapid screening of *Salmonella* in foods: Collaborative study. J. Assn. Off. Anal. Chem. 72: 318.

60. Gabis, D. A. and Silliker, J. H. 1974. ICMSF methods studies. II. Comparison of analytical schemes for detection of *Salmonella* in high-moisture foods. Can. J. Microbiol. 20: 663.

61. Gabis, D. A. and Silliker, J. H. 1977. ICMSF methods studies. IX. The influence of selected enrichment broths, differential plating media, and incubation temperatures on the detection of *Salmonella* in dried foods and feed ingredients. Can. J. Microbiol. 23: 1225.

62. Gadberry, J. L. and Highby, S. N. 1970. An improved medium for the isolation of species of *Salmonella* and *Arizona* from animals. Pub. Hlth. Lab. 28: 157.

63. Galton, M. M., Lowery, W. D. and Hardy, A. V. 1954. *Salmonella* in fresh and smoked pork sausage. J. Infect. Dis. 95: 232.

64. Galton, M. M., Morris, G. K. and Martin, W. T. 1968. "Salmonellae in Foods and Feeds. Review of Isolation Methods and Recommended Procedures." Communicable Disease Center, Atlanta, Ga.

65. Gomez, R. F. and Sinskey, A. J. 1974. DNA breaks in rifampin-treated *Salmonella typhimurium* LT2 after exposure to nutritionally complex media. Nature 247: 211.

66. Gomez, R. F., Sinskey, A. J., Davies, R. and Labuza, T. P. 1973. Minimal medium recovery of heated *Salmonella typhimurium* LT2. J. Gen. Microbiol. 74: 267.

67. Hajna, A. A. and Damon, S. R. 1950. New enrichment and plating media for the isolation of *Salmonella* and *Shigella* organisms. Appl. Microbiol. 4: 341.

68. Harvey, R. W. S. and Price, T. H. 1977. Observations on pre-enrichment for isolating

salmonellas from sewage polluted natural water using Muller-Kauffmann tetrathionate broth prepared with fresh and desiccated ox bile. J. Appl. Bacteriol. 43: 145.

69. Hoben, D. A., Ashton, D. H. and Peterson, A. C. 1973. Some observations on the incorporation of novobiocin into Hektoen enteric agar for improved *Salmonella* isolation. Appl. Microbiol. 26: 126.

70. Huhtanen, C. N., Naghski, J. and Dellamonica, E. S. 1972. Efficiency of *Salmonella* isolation from meat-and-bone meal of one 300-g sample versus ten 30-g samples. Appl. Microbiol. 23: 688.

71. Ibrahim, G. F. and Fleet, G. H. 1985. Detection of salmonellae using accelerated methods. A review. Int. J. Food Microbiol. 2: 259.

72. ICMSF. 1974. "Microorganisms in Foods, 2. Sampling for Microbiological Analysis: Principles and Specific Applications." Intern. Comm. on Microbiolog. Spec. for Foods. Univ. of Toronto Press, Toronto, Ontario, Canada.

73. ICMSF. 1986. "Microorganisms in Foods, 2. Sampling for Microbiological Analysis: Principles and Specific Applications," 2nd ed. Intern. Comm. on Microbiolog. Spec. for Foods. Univ. of Toronto Press, Toronto, Ontario, Canada.

74. ICMSF. 1988. "Microorganisms in Foods, 1. Their Significance and Methods of Enumeration," 2nd ed. Intern. Comm. on Microbiolog. Spec. for Foods. Univ. of Toronto Press, Toronto, Ontario, Canada.

75. Insalata, N. F. and Chordash, R. A. 1984. Fluorescent antibody detection of salmonellae. In "Compendium of Methods for the Microbiological Examination of Foods," 2nd ed., ed. M. L. Speck, p. 327. Amer. Pub. Health Assn., Washington, D. C.

76. ISO 1981. "Microbiology—General Guidance for the Detection of *Salmonella*," Intern. Org. for Standardization 6579, Geneva, Switzerland.

77. Juven, B. J., Cox, N. A., Bailey, J. S., Thomson, J. E., Charles, O. W. and Shutze, J. V. 1984. Recovery of *Salmonella* from artificially contaminated poultry feeds in nonselective and selective broth media. J. Food Prot. 47: 299.

78. Kauffmann, F. 1935. Weitere Erfahrungen mit dem kombinierten Anreicherungsverfahren fur *Salmonella*-bacillen. Z. Hyg. Infektionskr. 117: 26.

79. Kauffmann, F. 1966. "The Bacteriology of *Enterobacteriaceae*." Williams and Wilkins Co., Baltimore, Md.

80. Keelan, S. L., Flowers, R. S. and Robison, B. J. 1988. Microbiological Methods. Multitest system for biochemical identification of *Salmonella, E. coli,* and other *Enterobacteriaceae* isolated from foods: Collaborative study. J. Assn. Off. Anal. Chem. 71: 968.

81. Kent, P. T., Thomason, B. M. and Morris, G. K. 1981. "Salmonellae in Foods and Feeds. Review of Isolation Methods and Recommended Procedures." Centers for Disease Control, Atlanta, Ga.

82. King, S. and Metzger, W. I. 1968. A new plating medium for the isolation of enteric pathogens. I. Hektoen enteric agar. Appl. Microbiol. 16: 577.

83. Knox, R., Gell, P. G. H. and Pollock, M. R. 1943. The selective action of tetrathionate in bacteriological media. J. Hyg. Camb. 43: 147.

84. Krieg, N. R. and Holt, J. G. 1984. "Bergey's Manual of Systematic Bacteriology," Vol. 1, Williams and Wilkins, Baltimore, Md.

85. Kristensen, M., Lester, V. and Jurgens, A. 1925. On the use of trypsinized casein, bromthymol-blue, brom-cresol-purple, phenol-red and brilliant-green for bacteriological nutrient media. Brit. J. Exp. Pathol. 6: 291.

86. Leifson, E. 1935. New culture media based on sodium desoxycholate for the isolation of intestinal pathogens and for the enumeration of colon bacilli in milk and water. J. Pathol. Bacteriol. 40: 581.

87. Leifson, E. 1936. New selenite enrichment media for the isolation of typhoid and paratyphoid (*Salmonella*) bacilli. Am. J. Hyg. 24: 423.

88. Le Minor, L., Vernon, M. and Popoff, M. 1982. Taxonomie des *Salmonella*. Ann. Microbiol. 133B: 223.

89. Le Minor, L., Vernon, M. and Popoff, M. 1982. Proposition pour une nomenclature des *Salmonella*. Ann. Microbiol. 133B: 245.

90. Le Minor, L. 1984. Genus III. *Salmonella*. In "Bergey's Manual of Systematic Bacteriology, Vol. 1.", ed. N. R. Krieg and J. G. Hold. p. 427. Williams and Wilkins, Baltimore, Md.

91. MacConkey, A. 1905. Lactose-fermenting bacteria in faeces. J. Hyg. 5: 333.

92. Mattingly, J. A., Robison, B. J., Boehm, A. and Gehle, W. D. 1985. Use of monoclonal antibodies for the detection of *Salmonella* in foods. Food Technol. 39: 90.

93. McCoy, J. H. 1962. The isolation of salmonellae. J. Appl. Bacteriol. 25: 213.

94. Moats, W. A. 1978. Comparison of four agar plating media with and without added novobiocin for isolation of salmonellae from beef and deboned poultry meat. Appl. Environ. Microbiol. 36: 747.

95. Moats, W. A. and Kinner, J. A. 1974. Factors affecting selectivity of brilliant green-phenol red agar for salmonellae. Appl. Microbiol. 27: 118.

96. Moats, W. A. and Kinner, J. A. 1976. Observations on brilliant green agar with an H_2S indicator. Appl. Microbiol. 31: 380.

97. Morris, G. K. 1986. *Salmonella* In "Progress in Food Safety," ed. O. Cliver and B. A. Cochrane, p. 46. Food Res. Inst., Univ. of Wisconsin-Madison.

98. Morris, G. K. and Dunn, C. G. 1970. Influence of incubation temperature and sodium heptadecyl sulfate (Tergitol No. 7) on the isolation of salmonellae from pork sausage. Appl. Microbiol. 20: 192.

99. Mueller, L. 1925. Un nouveau millieu d'enrichissement pour la recherche du Bacille typhique et des paratyphiques. Comp. Rendus Soc. Biol. 89: 434.

100. Munson, T. E., Schrade, J. P., Bisciello, N. B. Jr., Fantasia, L. D., Hartung, W. H. and O'Connor, J. J. 1976. Evaluation of an automated fluorescent antibody procedure for detection of *Salmonella* in foods and feeds. Appl. Environ. Microbiol. 31: 514.

101. NAS/NRC. 1969. "An Evaluation of the *Salmonella* Problem." Pub. 1683, Natl. Acad. of Sciences/Natl. Res. Council, Washington, D.C.

102. NAS/NRC. 1971. "Reference Methods for the Microbiological Examination of Foods." Subcomm. on Food Microbiol., Food Prot. Comm. Natl. Acad. of Sciences/Natl. Res. Council, Washington, D.C.

103. North, W. R. Jr. 1961. Lactose pre-enrichment method for isolation of *Salmonella* from dried egg albumen. Appl. Microbiol. 9: 188.

104. North, W. R. and Bartram, M. T. 1953. The efficiency of selenite broth of different compositions in the isolation of *Salmonella*. Appl. Microbiol. 1: 130.

105. Osborne, W. W. and Stokes, J. L. 1955. A modified selenite brilliant-green medium for the isolation of *Salmonella* from egg products. Appl. Microbiol. 3: 295.

106. Padron, A. P. and Dockstader, W. B. 1972. Selective medium for hydrogen sulfide production by salmonellae. Appl. Microbiol. 23: 1107.

107. Poelma, P. L., Romero, A. and Andrews, W. H. 1978. Comparative accuracy of five biochemical systems for identifying *Salmonella* and related foodborne bacteria: Collaborative study. J. Assn. Off. Anal. Chem. 61: 1043.

108. Poelma, P. L., Andrews, W. H. and Wilson, C. R. 1981. Comparison of methods for the isolation of *Salmonella* species from lactic casein. J. Food Sci. 46: 804.

109. Price, W. R., Olsen, R. A. and Hunter, J. E. 1972. *Salmonella* testing of pooled pre-enrichment broth cultures for screening multiple food samples. Appl. Microbiol. 23: 679.

110. Rappold, H. and Bolderdijk, R. F. 1979. Modified lysine iron agar for isolation of *Salmonella* from food. Appl. Environ. Microbiol. 38: 162.

111. Rappold, H., Bolderdijk, R. F. and De Smedt, J. M. 1984. Rapid cultural method to detect *Salmonella* in foods. J. Food Prot. 47: 46.

112. Ray, B. Jr., Jezeski, J. J. and Busta, F. F. 1971. Effect of rehydration on recovery, repair, and growth of injured freeze-dried *Salmonella anatum*. Appl. Microbiol. 22: 184.

113. Ray, B. Jr., Jezeski, J. J. and Busta, F. F. 1972. Isolation of salmonellae from naturally

contaminated dried milk products. III. Influence of pre-enrichment conditions. J. Milk Food Technol. 35: 670.

114. Read, R. B. and Reyes, A. L. 1968. Variation in plating efficiency of salmonellae on eight lots of brilliant green agar. Appl. Microbiol. 16: 746.

115. Reamer, R. H., Hargrove, R. E. and McDonough, F. E. 1974. A selective plating agar for direct enumeration of *Salmonella* in artificially contaminated dairy products. J. Milk Food Technol. 37: 441.

116. Restaino, L., Grauman, G. S., McCall, W. A. and Hill, W. M. 1977. Effects of varying concentrations of novobiocin incorporated into two *Salmonella* plating media on the recovery of four *Enterobacteriaceae*. Appl. Environ. Microbiol. 33: 585.

117. Rolfe, V. 1946. A note on the preparation of tetrathionate broth. Monthly Bull. of the Ministry of Health (U.K.) 5: 158.

118. Shanson, D. C. 1975. A new selective medium for the isolation of salmonellae other than *Salmonella typhi*. J. Med. Microbiol. 8: 357.

119. Sharpe, A. N. and Michaud, G. L. 1974. Hydrophobic grid-membrane filters: New approach to microbiological enumeration. Appl. Microbiol. 28: 223.

120. Silliker, J. H. 1969. "Wet compositing" as an approach to control procedures for the detection of salmonellae. Appendix D, In "An Evaluation of the *Salmonella* Problem." Commit. on *Salmonella*, p. 206. Natl. Acad. of Sciences/Natl. Res. Council Publ. 1683, Washington, D.C.

121. Silliker, J. H. 1982. The *Salmonella* problem: Current status and future direction. J. Food Prot. 45: 661.

122. Silliker, J. H. and Gabis, D. A. 1973. ICMSF Methods Studies. I. Comparison of analytical schemes for detection of *Salmonella* in dried foods. Can. J. Microbiol. 19: 475.

123. Silliker, J. H. and Gabis, D. A. 1974. ICMSF Methods Studies V. The influence of selective enrichment media and incubation temperatures on the detection of salmonellae in raw frozen meats. Can. J. Microbiol. 20: 813.

124. Stokes, J. L. and Osborne, W. W. 1955. A selenite brilliant green medium for the isolation of *Salmonella*. Appl. Microbiol. 3: 217.

125. Stroup, J. R. 1972. Malonate dulcitol lysine iron agar—a new differential medium for the identification of *Salmonella* subgenera I-III. J. Assn. Off. Anal. Chem. 55: 214.

126. Sulkin, S. E. and Willett, J. C. 1940. A triple sugar-ferrous sulfate medium for use in identification of enteric organisms. J. Lab. Clin. Med. 25: 649.

127. Sveum, W. H. and Hartman, P. A. 1977. Timed-release capsule method for the detection of salmonellae in foods and feeds. Appl. Environ. Microbiol. 33: 630.

128. Sveum, W. H. and Kraft, A. A. 1981. Recovery of salmonellae from foods using a combined enrichment technique. J. Food Sci. 46: 94.

129. Swaminathan, B., Alexio, J. A. G, and Minnich, S. A. 1985. Enzyme immunoassays for *Salmonella*: One-day testing is now a reality. Food Technol. 39: (3)83.

130. Taylor, W. I. 1965. Isolation of shigellae. I. Xylose lysine agars; new media for isolation of enteric pathogens. Am. J. Clin. Pathol. 44: 471.

131. Taylor, W. I. and Silliker, J. H. 1958. Isolation of salmonellae from food samples. III. Dulcitol lactose iron agar, a new differential tube medium for confirmation of microorganisms of the genus *Salmonella*. Appl. Microbiol. 6: 335.

132. Thomason, B. M. 1981. Current status of immunofluorescent methodology for salmonellae. J. Food Prot. 44: 381.

133. Thomason, B. M., Cherry, W. B. and Moody, M. D. 1957. Staining bacterial smears with fluorescent antibody. III. Antigenic analysis of *Salmonella typhosa* by means of fluorescent antibody and agglutination reactions. J. Bacteriol. 74: 525.

134. Thomason, B. M., Hebert, G. A. and Cherry, W. B. 1975. Evaluation of a semiautomated system for direct fluorescent antibody detection of salmonellae. Appl. Microbiol. 30: 557.

135. Todd, L. S., Roberts, D., Bartholomew, B. A. and Gilbert, R. J. 1986. Evaluation of an

enzyme immunoassay kit for the detection of salmonellae in foods and feeds. In Proc. 2nd World Congress Foodborne Infection and Intoxications, Vol. 1, p. 418. Berlin.

136. Todd, L. S., Roberts, D., Bartholomew, B. A. and Gilbert, R. J. 1987. Assessment of an enzyme immunoassay for the detection of salmonellae in foods and animal feeding stuffs. Epidem. Inf. 98: 301.

137. USDA. 1968. Recommended Procedure for the Isolation of *Salmonella* Organisms from Animal Feeds and Feed Ingredients, ARS 91-68. U.S. Dept. of Agric., Animal Health Division, Agric. Res. Serv., Hyattsville, Md.

138. USDA. 1974. "Microbiological Laboratory Guidebook." Food Safety and Inspection Serv., U.S. Dept. Agric., Washington, D.C.

139. USDA. 1984. Laboratory Methods for Egg Products. Agric. Market. Serv., U.S. Dept. Agric., Washington, D.C.

140. U.S. FDA. 1971. Federal Food, Drug, and Cosmetic Act, as amended, January 1971. Stock No. 1712-0126. Food and Drug Admin., U.S. Govt Print. Off., Washington, D.C.

141. U.S. FDA. 1978. Chap. VII In "Bacteriological Analytical Manual," 5th ed. p. 1, Food and Drug Admin., Washington, D.C.

142. U.S. FDA. 1984. Chap. VII In "Bacteriological Analytical Manual," 6th ed. p. 1, Food and Drug Admin., Washington, D.C.

143. Van Schothorst, M., Van Leusden, F. M., De Gier, E., Rijnierse, V. F. M. and Veen, A. J. D. 1979. Influence of reconstitution on the isolation of *Salmonella* from dried milk. J. Food Prot. 42: 936.

144. Vassiliadis, P., Pateraki, E., Papadakis, J. and Trichopoulos, D. 1974. Evaluation of the growth of salmonellae in Rappaport's broth and in Mueller-Kauffman's tetrathionate broth. J. Appl. Bacteriol. 37: 411.

145. Vassiliadis, P., Trichopoulos, D., Papoutsakis, G. and Pallandiou, E. 1979. A note on the comparison of two modifications of Rappaport's medium with selenite broth in the isolation of *Salmonellas*. J. Appl. Bacteriol. 46: 567.

146. Wilson, W. J. and Blair, E. M. Mcv. 1927. Use of a glucose bismuth sulphite iron medium for the isolation of *B. typhosus* and *B. proteus*. J. Hyg. 26: 374.

147. Wilson, C. R., Andrews, W. H. and Poelma, P. L. 1980. Recovery of *Salmonella* from milk chocolate using a chemically defined medium and five nondefined broths. J. Food Sci. 45: 310.

148. Wun, C. K., Cohen, J. R. and Litsky, W. 1972. Evaluation of plating media and temperature parameters in the isolation of selected enteric pathogens. Health Lab. Sci. 9: 225.

149. Yamamoto, R., Sadler, W. W., Adler, H. E. and Stewart, G. F. 1961. Comparison of media and methods for recovering *Salmonella typhimurium* from turkeys. Appl. Microbiol. 9: 76.

Chapter 26

SHIGELLA

James L. Smith and Robert L. Buchanan

26.1 INTRODUCTION

26.11 *Shigella* and Shigellosis

Shigellosis, also known as bacillary dysentery, is a localized ulcerative infection of the colon. The host range is limited to higher primates; there are no natural nonprimate hosts. Organisms of the genus *Shigella* are transmitted directly or through food or water contaminated by fecal matter. The infective dose is low, in the order of 10^1 to 10^4 cells/person. In the United States, shigellosis outbreaks are more frequently associated with consumption of contaminated food rather than water. This is in contrast to the occurrence of the disease in developing countries; the difference is probably due to the use of chlorinated water supplies in the United States.

The genus *Shigella* is grouped within the family *Enterobacteriaceae*. Shigellae are rod-shaped, gram-negative, nonmotile, facultatively anaerobic, catalase-positive (except for one serovar of *S. dysenteriae*), oxidase-negative, lactose-negative (except for a few strains), citrate-negative, and H_2S-negative. With a few exceptions, shigellae ferment sugars without producing gas. The mole percentage G + C of their DNA is 49 to 53.

There are four species of *Shigella*: *S. dysenteriae* (with 10 serovars), *S. flexneri* (with six serovars and a number of subserovars), *S. boydii* (with 15 serovars), and *S. sonnei*. The serovars and subserovars are antigenically distinct. On the basis of their DNA homology (70% to 100% related), *Shigella* and *Escherichia* form a single genus and are difficult to separate on the basis of biochemical tests, e.g., are gas-producing shigellae as well as *Escherichia coli* strains that are lactose-negative, nonmotile, or non-gas-producing. Further, there are *E. coli* strains that produce a shiga-like toxin. Thus, the separation between *E. coli* and *Shigella* is not clear.

423

The incubation period prior to the onset of symptoms for shigellosis is 12 to 50 hr after ingestion of the organisms. The duration of the disease is typically 4 days, but in severe cases, symptoms may persist for 10 to 14 days. A gastrointestinal syndrome is presented with diarrhea in a majority of the cases. There may be blood and mucus in stools and individuals may suffer from abdominal cramps, ulceration of the intestinal mucosa, and fluid loss. Proper fluid replacement appears to be the treatment of choice for most cases of shigellosis.

The chief contributing factor underlying foodborne shigellosis outbreaks is poor personal hygiene; an infected food handler failed to wash his or her hands thoroughly after defecating or after touching shigellae-contaminated materials (e.g., diapers from an infected infant). The second most important factor leading to foodborne shigellosis is improper holding temperature of contaminated foods, allowing growth of the organism to take place. Most reported outbreaks involved foods prepared and mishandled in food service establishments. After being contaminated by an infected individual, any food that is not heated, or not reheated after preparation, and that is easily temperature-abused should be considered a potential vehicle for a shigellosis outbreak.

Virulent strains of *Shigella* are invasive, i.e., they invade the epithelial cells of the intestinal mucosa. Invasiveness can be measured *in vivo* by observing the keratoconjunctivitis in the guinea pig cornea (Sereny test) or *in vitro* by invasion of HeLa cells. Virulent strains of *Shigella* spp. carry a 120 to 140 megadalton plasmid that is necessary for the expression of invasiveness. Deletion of the invasive genes from the plasmid or complete loss of the plasmid leads to loss of invasiveness.

Virulence is temperature dependent; cells grown at 30°C are not invasive, whereas those grown at 37°C are. The loss of virulence at 30°C is not due to the loss of the virulence plasmid but to the lack of expression of the invasive genes coded by the plasmid. Virulence-plasmid-containing *Shigella* strains grown at 30°C express virulence after 2 to 3 hr upshift to 37°C. Virulence-plasmid-containing shigellae present in foods kept in the cold are expected to behave as if they are not virulent; however, ingestion of the shigellae and subsequent growth of the organisms in the intestinal tract can allow the expression of their virulence properties. Therefore, storing food at low temperatures will not render shigellae avirulent.

Shigella species produce a potent exotoxin whose precise role in shigellosis is not understood completely. The toxin is cytotoxic to tissue culture cells and is enterotoxigenic (fluid accumulates in rabbit ileal loops). The mode of action of Shiga toxin involves the inhibition of protein synthesis in susceptible target cells in both mammalian and bacterial systems. More specifically, the toxin acts by inactivating large ribosomal subunits, resulting in cessation of peptide chain elongation. The genes for Shiga toxin biosynthesis are chromosomally located.

Enteroinvasive *E. coli* strains that produce keratoconjunctivitis in the guinea pig and invade HeLa cells harbor a 140 megadalton plasmid with a high degree of homology to the virulence plasmid of *Shigella* species. Certain strains of enteropathogenic *E. coli* (those strains that lack heat-labile or heat-stable enterotoxins and enteroinvasive capacity) and hemorrhagic *E. coli* produce toxins that can be neutralized by Shiga antitoxin.

For recent reviews concerning *Shigella*, see *Shigella* as a foodborne pathogen;[5, 17] Shiga and shiga-like toxins;[3, 8, 11] molecular genetics of virulence;[1] taxonomy;[15] and pathogenesis.[6]

26.12   Foods Implicated in Shigellosis

The foods most commonly implicated in shigellosis are salads. Contaminated potato salad is the most common cause of outbreaks, followed by other types of salads containing chicken, fish, or seafood. However, a variety of foods have been involved in *Shigella* outbreaks, including seafood, meat, and chicken dishes.[2, 17] The foods usually implicated contain ingredients, either cooked or raw, that are made into salads or other dishes not heated before consumption. Too often, the food is also temperature-abused before serving.

26.13   Growth and Survival of *Shigellae*

Food microbiologists commonly believe that *Shigella* species are fragile and not very resistant to environmental stresses. However, a survey of the literature indicates that shigellae are not particularly fragile and may survive for several days under adverse conditions.

For a review of shigellae growth and survival under a variety of conditions and in a variety of food products, see Smith.[17]

26.14   Detecting Injured Cells

One of the difficulties with the use of selective agars or enrichment broths for the isolation of *Shigella* species is that the media contain bile salts or desoxycholate, which inhibit the repair and detection of injured cells.[20] The presence of injured cells resulting from sublethal stress is a very real possibility in processed foods, particularly if the food has been underprocessed.[18] Injured cells cannot repair and produce colonies in the presence of toxic agents that are added to media to confer selectivity.

Tollison and Johnson[20] found that heat-injured *S. flexneri* cells did not produce colonies on tryptic phytone glucose agar (TPGA) containing desoxycholate or bile salts; uninjured cells, however, readily formed colonies on TPGA. These authors recommend plating dilutions of food samples suspected of containing injured shigellae onto a nonselective agar followed by incubation at 35°C for at least 8 hr to allow repair of injured cells. Then the nonselective agar was overlaid with a selective agar (containing bile salts or deoxycholate); the plates were further incubated until colonies formed.[20] For a discussion of injury and repair of injured microorganisms, see Smith and Palumbo[18] and Ray[13] and Chapter 7 of this book.

26.15   Isolating, Detecting, and Identifying *Shigella* Species

Smith[17] reviewed media used for the isolation and detection of *Shigella* from suspect foods. Speciation and identification of the suspect colonies from selective media are accomplished by the use of biochemical and serological techniques.[14, 22] Colicin and phage typing[15] and analysis of antibiotic resistance plasmids[19] can be used as epidemiological tools in studies of dysenteric outbreaks. Molecular biology techniques are also useful in *Shigella* studies. Virulent strains of *Shigella* as well as invasive strains of *E. coli* can be detected by use of an enzyme-linked immunosorbent assay[12] that depends on the presence of a virulence antigen. DNA probes have been used with success to identify virulent shigellae, i.e., those shigellae strains that contain the 120 or 140 megadalton virulence plasmid.[16, 23] These probes also react with enteroinvasive *E. coli* strains that contain a 140 megadalton virulence plasmid.

26.2   RECOMMENDED PROCEDURES

26.21   Culture Media and Reagents (Chapter 62)

Acetate differential agar
Decarboxylase medium Moeller plus lysine
Decarboxylase medium Moeller plus ornithine
Gram-negative broth, Hajna (GN)
Indicator broth with various sugars (carbohydrate fermentation media)
KCN broth base
KOH for Voges-Proskauer (VP) reaction
Kovac's reagent (indole)
MacConkey agar (MAC)
Malonate broth
Methyl red for MR test
Methyl red-Voges-Proskauer (MR-VP) medium
Motility test medium
Nutrient agar
Nutrient broth
Salmonella-Shigella agar (SS)
Selenite cystine broth (SC)
Simmons citrate agar
Triple sugar iron agar (TSI)
Tryptic soy broth
Tryptone (1%) broth for indole
Urea R$_{(apid)}$ broth
Xylose-lysine-desoxycholate agar (XLD)

26.22   Treatment of Food Samples

Foods suspected of containing shigellae should be analyzed as quickly as possible. If the food sample can be analyzed within 24 hr, it should be kept at 4°C; otherwise, the sample should be frozen until it can be tested. Sections 26.23 to 26.27 give examples of procedures that can be used to isolate and identify shigellae that may be present in foods.

26.23   Enrichment

Twenty-five g of the food sample (if frozen, the sample should be thawed) is added to a sterile stomacher bag containing 225 ml of sterile enrichment broth. When appropriate, the sensitivity of the analytical procedures can be increased through the use of additional analytical units or by compositing analytical units. This requires development of statistically valid sampling plans that incorporate the concepts and principles outlined by the International Commission on Microbiological Specifications for Foods.[7] Such sampling plans should include identification of consumer populations at risk and likelihood that the product will be consumed without further cooking. Using the stomacher, blend the mixture for up to 3 min until well homogenized (specific time will depend on the type of food). After blending, check the pH and if necessary adjust to 7.0 ± 0.2. Fold over and fasten the top of the bag and incubate at 35° to 37°C for 16 to 20 hr. Use two enrichment broths, such as GN and SC broths.

If the presence of injured shigellae is suspected, a different procedure must be followed since it is probable that the enrichment broths will prevent the detection of injured cells. Blend the food sample with 100 ml tryptic soy broth (check pH and adjust to 7.0, if necessary). Incubate the blended material at 35° to 37°C for 8 hr; then add 125 ml of double-strength enrichment broth to the broth-food mixture and blend 1 min. Incubate the stomacher bags at 35° to 37°C for an additional 16 to 20 hr. This procedure should permit the repair of injured cells before selective pressure is exerted.

26.24   Selective Media

Use a loop to streak aliquots of the enrichment broths onto selective agars. Use at least two, and preferably three, selective agars: (1) a low-selectivity medium such as MAC agar, (2) an intermediate-selectivity medium such as XLD agar, and (3) a high-selectivity medium such as SS agar. An agar of low selectivity allows the investigator to isolate fragile shigellae such as *S. dysenteriae* 1.[10] XLD, an agar of intermediate selectivity, is suitable for the isolation of most *Shigella* strains. A highly selective medium such as SS should be used when the background flora of the food product is high.[10] Using an agar from each of the selectivity groups enhances the chances of isolating shigellae from the suspect food product. Incubate the plates at 37°C and observe them periodically over 48 hr.

Shigellae appear as translucent, colorless, and non-lactose-fermenting colonies on MAC and SS agars. On XLD, shigellae appear as rose-colored colonies surrounded by rosy halos when viewed by transmitted light.

26.25   Biochemical Screening of Isolates from Selective Agars

Inoculate two or more well-isolated colonies from each selective plate into TSI agar slants by streaking the slant and stabbing the butt. Incubate slants at 37°C for 24 hr. (However, tubes should be kept in the incubator for several days in case a strain with slow fermentation characteristics has been isolated; see Table 1.) *Shigella* produces a red (alkaline) slant and a yellow (acid) butt with no production of gas or H_2S. If the culture appears contaminated on TSI slants, purify by plating on MAC and repeat TSI inoculation. If typical reactions are not obtained on TSI, test additional colonies from selective plates on TSI slants.

Inoculate the presumptive shigellae on TSI slants into Urea R broth and incubate at 37°C; observe at 2 to 3 hr. Since shigellae are urease-negative, retain those cultures that produce no color change in Urea R broth. Using growth from TSI slants, inoculate urease-negative organisms into nutrient broth tubes (to be used as a source of inoculum for further biochemical tests), nutrient agar slants (for determination of gram reaction), and motility agar tubes. Incubate all media at 37°C for 24 hr. Shigellae are gram-negative, nonmotile, non-encapsulated, and nonsporeforming rods occurring singly. Further biochemical tests are necessary to confirm the presence of *Shigella* species (Table 1).

26.26   Additional Tests

1. Serology (modified from Twedt[21]). Growth of presumptive *Shigella* from nutrient agar is treated with *Shigella* somatic group antibodies A, A_1, B, C, C_1, C_2, D, and A-D (Alkalescens-Dispar).

   Add 1 ml of 0.85% saline solution to each of two 24-hr nutrient agar slants and make a heavy suspension. Mark nine ½-inch squares in a petri dish with a wax pencil. Place a drop of cell suspension in the upper left-hand corner of each square and then place 0.05 ml of each antiserum into a square; in the ninth square place 0.05 ml saline as an autoagglutination control. Mix cell suspension into antisera by use of a disposable needle (use a different needle for each antibody); enhance agglutination by rocking petri dish gently. Agglutination may take as long as 3 to 4 min. A 4+ reaction will appear as a visible floc with clear fluid. In the event of a negative reaction, the cell suspension should be boiled for 30 min (to destroy interfering K antigen) and the agglutination repeated.

2. Virulence. The ability to bind Congo red from an agar medium has been shown to be associated with the virulence plasmid in *Shigella* species.[4] Streak organisms that behave as *Shigella* species onto plates of tryptic

Table 1—Selected Biochemical Characteristics of the Genus *Shigella* for Speciation[a]

Medium	Reaction (comments)
KCN broth	negative
malonate broth	negative
tryptone broth (indole)	positive or negative (*S. dysenteriae* 1, *S. flexneri* 6 and *S. sonnei* are negative; *S. dysenteriae* 2 is positive)
MR-VP medium	positive methyl red
	negative Voges-Proskauer
citrate agar	negative
decarboxylase medium	
with lysine	negative
with ornithine	negative
acetate differential agar	negative (some strains of *S. flexneri* 4a are positive)
indicator broth	
with glucose	acid (some strains of *S. flexneri* 6 and *S. boydii* 13 and 14 produce acid and gas)
with adonitol, xylose, cellobiose, dulcitol, inositol, salicin	no acid (*S. boydii* is variable on xylose)
with lactose	no acid (some strains of *S. flexneri* 2a and *S. boydii* 9 produce acid; *S. sonnei* produces acid after several days)
with sucrose	no acid (*S. sonnei* produces acid after several days)
with mannitol	acid (*S. dysenteriae* does not produce acid; some strains of *S. flexneri* 4a and 6 do not produce acid)
with raffinose	no acid (*S. flexneri* is variable; *S. sonnei* produces acid after several days)

[a]Adapted from Rowe and Gross (1984).[15]

soy broth containing 2% agar and 0.01% Congo red; incubate at 37°C for 24 to 48 hr. Virulent *Shigella* species take up the dye and appear as red colonies, while shigellae that have lost the virulence plasmid appear as white colonies.

26.27 Interpretation

1. Biochemical tests. Shigellae are gram-negative, nonmotile rods lacking urease. They do not utilize KCN, malonate, citrate, or acetate as sole carbon sources. Shigellae may be either indole* + or −, are MR+ and VP−, and do not decarboxylate lysine or ornithine. They produce acid from glucose and mannitol* but do not produce acid from adonitol, dulcitol, inositol, xylose*, cellobiose, lactose*, sucrose*, raffinose*, or salicin. Shigellae generally do not produce gas from sugar* (*see Table 1).

2. Serology. A positive agglutination with antibody A, A_1, B, C, C_1, C_2, D, or A-D suggests that the organisms are *Shigella* species. Final classification as species of *Shigella* should not depend on serology alone.

3. Virulence. Uptake of Congo red by shigellae indicates that the organisms contain the 140 megadalton virulence plasmid (120 megadaltons in *S. sonnei*) and are invasive pathogens. The ability to bind Congo red (CR^+) is a convenient marker to determine virulence in wild-type *Shigella* species since CR^+ and invasiveness generally coincide. Note, however, that these characteristics are not directly related, and it is potentially possible to isolate CR^- strains that are invasive.

26.3 PRECAUTIONS AND LIMITATIONS OF THE METHOD

Shigella species are P2 level pathogens (i.e., they are agents of moderate potential hazard to personnel) and must be treated accordingly by using the appropriate safety procedures for such organisms.[9] These safety procedures should include use of microbiological safety hoods, pipetting devices, food mixing systems that create minimal aerosols (use of stomacher rather than mechanical blenders), and proper decontamination and disposal procedures. *Shigella* is infectious at low numbers, and laboratory-acquired shigellosis should be suspected if laboratory personnel develop diarrhea after working with *Shigella* strains.

A sufficient number of colonies should be picked from the selective agar plates to ensure presence or absence of *Shigella*. Some *E. coli* strains behave quite similarly to *Shigella* species and may give confusing results. Except for *S. sonnei*, each species of *Shigella* includes several serovars, and not all serovars within a species behave similarly in biochemical tests. Culture media, reagents, and antisera should be subjected to quality control procedures since different lots may give varying results.

26.4 REFERENCES

1. Binns, M. M. 1985. Molecular genetics of virulence in *Shigella*. Microbiol. Sciences 2: 275.
2. Black, R. E., Craun, G. F., and Blake, P. A. 1978. Epidemiology of common-source outbreaks of shigellosis in the United States, 1961-1975. Am. J. Epidemiol. 108: 47.
3. Cantey, J. R. 1985. Shiga toxin—An expanding role in the pathogenesis of infectious diseases. J. Infect. Dis. 151: 766.
4. Daskaleros, P. A. and Payne, S. M. 1985. Cloning the gene for Congo red binding in *Shigella flexneri*. Infect. Immun. 48: 165.
5. Fehlhaber, K. 1981. Zur Bedeutung der Shigellen aus der Sicht tierarztlicher Lebensmittelhygiene. Mh. Vet.-Med. 36: 308.
6. Hale, T. H. and Formal, S. B. 1987. Pathogenesis of Shigella infections. Pathol. Immunopathol. Res. 6: 117.
7. International Commission on Microbiological Specifications for Foods. 1986. "Microorganisms in Foods 2. Sampling for Microbiological Analysis: Principles and Specific Applications." University of Toronto, Canada.

8. Keusch, G. T., Donohue-Rolfe, A., and Jacewicz, M. 1985. Shigella toxin and the patho-genesis of shigellosis. In "Microbial Toxins and Diarrhoeal Disease," p. 193. CIBA Found. Sympos. #112, Pitman, London.

9. Miller, B. M., ed. 1986. "Laboratory Safety: Principles and Practices." Am. Soc. for Micro-biol., Washington, D.C.

10. Morris, G. K. 1984. *Shigella*. In "Compendium of methods for the microbiological exami-nation of foods," ed. Speck, M. L. 2nd ed., p. 343. Am. Pub. Health Assoc., Washington, D.C.

11. O'Brien, A. D. and Holmes, R. K. 1987. Shiga and Shiga-like toxins. Microbiol. Rev. 51: 206.

12. Pal, T., Pacsa, A. S., Emody, L., Voros, S., and Selley, E. 1985. Modified enzyme-linked immunosorbent assay for detecting enteroinvasive *Escherichia coli* and virulent *Shigella* strains. J. Clin. Microbiol. 21: 415.

13. Ray, B. 1986. Impact of bacterial injury and repair in food microbiology: Its past, present and future. J. Food Prot. 49: 651.

14. Rowe, B. and Gross, R. J. 1981. The genus *Shigella*. In "The Prokaryotes," ed. Starr, M. P., Stolp, H., Truper, H. G., Balows, A., and Schlegel, H. G. Vol. II, p. 1248. Springer-Verlag, Berlin.

15. Rowe, B. and Gross, R. J. 1984. Genus II. *Shigella*. In "Bergey's Manual of Systematic Bacteriology," eds., Krieg, N. R. and Holt, J. G. Vol. 1. p. 423. Williams and Wilkins, Baltimore, Md.

16. Sethabutr, O., Hanchalay, S., Echeverria, P., Taylor, D. N., and Leksomboon, U. 1985. A non-radioactive DNA probe to identify *Shigella* and enteroinvasive *Escherichia coli* in stools of children with diarrhoea. Lancet (2), #8464: 1095.

17. Smith, J. L. 1987. *Shigella* as a foodborne pathogen. J. Food Prot. 50: 788.

18. Smith, J. L. and Palumbo, S. A. 1982. Microbial injury reviewed for the sanitarian. Dairy and Food Sanitation 2: 57.

19. Tacket, C. O., Shahid, N., Huq, M. I., Alim, A. R. M. A., and Cohen, M. L. 1984. Usefulness of plasmid profiles for differentiation of *Shigella* isolates in Bangladesh. J. Clin. Microbiol. 20: 300.

20. Tollison, S. B. and Johnson, M. G. 1985. Sensitivity to bile salts of *Shigella flexneri* sublethally heat stressed in buffer or broth. Appl. Environ. Microbiol. 50: 337.

21. Twedt, R. M. 1978. Shigella. In "FDA, Div. Microbiology, Bacteriological Analytical Man-ual," 5th ed., Chapter VIII. Off. Anal. Chemists, Washington, D.C.

22. Wilson, G. S. and Miles, A. 1975. "Topeley and Wilson's Principles of Bacteriology, Virology and Immunity," Vol. 1, 6th ed. Williams and Wilkins Co., Baltimore, Md.

23. Wood, P. K., Morris, J. G. Jr., Small, P. L. C., Sethabutr, O., Toledo, M. R. F., Trabulsi, L., and Kaper, J. B. 1986. Comparison of DNA probes and the Sereny test for identification of invasive *Shigella* and *Escherichia coli* strains. J. Clin. Microbiol. 24: 498.

Chapter 27

YERSINIA

Donald A. Schiemann and Georges Wauters

27.1 INTRODUCTION

There are three species of *Yersinia* with unquestionable pathogenicity for humans: *Yersinia pestis*, *Yersinia pseudotuberculosis*, and *Yersinia enterocolitica*. *Y. pestis* is the agent of plague; it has no common association with food, and, therefore, is not included in this discussion when reference is made to the genus alone. Several new species have been separated from *Y. enterocolitica* as this species was originally defined to represent what were sometimes called "*Yersinia enterocolitica*-like" bacteria or "environmental" strains (Table 1). The preponderance of data indicates that none of these new species are pathogenic for humans; however, there is not full agreement with this conclusion, particularly with regard to the species *Y. kristensenii* and possibly *Y. frederiksenii* too. Nevertheless, the emphasis in this chapter will be first on *Y. enterocolitica* as it is presently defined, which is often foodborne, and second on *Y. pseudotuberculosis*, which has a lower incidence and less obvious role in foodborne disease.

Yersinia is classified in the family *Enterobacteriaceae* and demonstrates the characteristics that define this family: gram-negative bacilli that are usually nitrate-reductase-positive, fermentative, oxidase-negative, and facultative with respect to oxygen requirements. *Yersinia* is usually urease-positive, and, when motile, is so at 25°C but not at 35°C. *Y. enterocolitica* can be differentiated from *Y. pseudotuberculosis* by a positive test for ornithine decarboxylase, fermentation of sucrose, and negative reactions for rhamnose and melibiose fermentation. *Y. enterocolitica* is more active biochemically at 25°C than at 35° to 37°C, giving, for example, a positive Voges-Proskauer test only at the

Table 1—Biochemical Tests for Differentiation of *Y. enterocolitica* and Related Species

Test (25°C)	*Y. enterocolitica*	*Y. kristensenii*	*Y. frederiksenii*	*Y. intermedia*	*Y. aldovae*	*Y. rohdei* Biotype 1	*Y. rohdei* Biotype 2
Voges-Proskauer	+	−	+	+	+	−	−
indole	V	V	+	+	−	−	−
Simmons citrate	−	−	V	V	+	V	+
acid from							
sucrose	+	−	+	+	−	+	+
L-rhamnose	−	−	+	+	+	−	−
D-melibiose	−	−	−	+	−	+	−
α-methyl-D-glucoside	−	−	−	+	−	−	−
D-raffinose	−	−	+	+	−	+	−
D-sorbitol	V	+	+	+	+	+	+

V = variable reactions; + = positive reactions; − = negative reactions.

lower temperature. *Y. enterocolitica* as originally defined proved to represent a heterogeneous group of bacteria, which encouraged the development of several biotyping schemes. Several correlations existed between biotype, serotype, and ecological characteristics. Some of these biotypes now have species status (Table 1); consequently, these original schemes have become outdated. Reference is often made to "biotype 1" to mean "environmental" and nonpathogenic strains of *Yersinia* without describing the biochemical tests or typing scheme applied. So-called "American strains" of serotype (serogroup, serovar) O:8, which are nearly always pathogenic, are, for example, biotype 1 (indole-positive) by one scheme, but biotype 2 (esculin- and salicin-negative) by another. It has been proposed recently that biotype 1 be divided into 1A (esculin- and salicin- rapidly positive), which are of environmental origin and nonpathogenic, and 1B (esculin- and salicin-negative), which are mostly of human origin and pathogenic.[46] Variants of biotype 3 defined by Bercovier et al.[6] as biotypes 3A and 3B have been identified in this new proposal as biotype 6, distinguishable by their proline peptidase activity (Table 2). These biotypes have recently been recognized as two new species called *Y. mollaretti* and *Y. bercovieri*.[48] Biotype 3 as it remains includes serotypes such as O:1,2,3 and O:5,27, which are lipase-negative and also indole-negative at 24 hr but often positive with longer incubation. A variant of this biotype has been described in Japan that is serotype O:3 and Voges-Proskauer-negative.[15]

The epidemiology of yersiniosis is quite different in North America, with

Table 2—Biotyping Scheme for *Y. enterocolitica*

Biochemical Test	Reaction for Biogroup						
	1A	1B	2	3	4	5	6[c]
lipase (Tween-esterase)	+	+	−	−	−	−	−
hydrolysis of esculin	+/−	−	−	−	−	−	−
indole	+	+	(+)	−	−	−	−
acid from							
xylose	+	+	+	+	−	V	+
salicin	+/−	−	−	−	−	−	−
trehalose	+	+	+	+	+	−	+
nitrate reduction	+	+	+	+	+	−	+
pyrazinamidase	+	−	−	−	−	−	+
β-D-glucosidase	+	−	−	−	−	−	−
Voges-Proskauer	+	+	+	+/−[a]	+	(+)	−
proline peptidase	V	−	−	−[b]	−	−	+

[a]A biotype of serotype O:3 found in Japan.
[b]Some chinchilla isolates may be positive.
[c]Recently recognized as two new species, *Y. mollaretii* and *Y. bercovieri*.[48]
+ = positive reactions; − = negative reactions; V = variable reactions; ( ) = delayed reactions.

the exception of eastern Canada, than in many other countries. Yersiniosis in the United States has been characterized by periodic foodborne outbreaks, whereas in eastern Canada, European countries, and Japan it is endemic. The serotypes (and biotypes) of *Y. enterocolitica* associated with human illness also vary between North America and these other countries. Where yersiniosis is endemic, serotype O:3 is most common, followed in incidence by O:9. Both of these can be found as normal throat flora in slaughter-age pigs and on fresh porcine tongues and in ground pork.[41, 44, 47] The situation is similar in eastern Canada, where, for some unknown reason, it differs from the remainder of North America.[33, 42]

Three of the four documented foodborne outbreaks in the United States involved serotype O:8,[9, 37, 40] which has been the most common serotype associated with human illness in the United States and western Canada.[42] Human carriers were the likely sources of the organism in two of these outbreaks. This serotype has only once been reported in pigs,[13] although there have been very few and limited surveys of porcine carriage in the United States. An outbreak in New York State in 1976 in schoolchildren was traced to contaminated chocolate milk.[9] Another outbreak in New York in July 1981 in a summer camp implicated chow mein and milk prepared from powdered milk.[37] The third outbreak occurred in the state of Washington between December 1981 and January 1982 and involved tofu (soybean curd).[40] Serotypes O:8 and O:21 ("O:Tacoma") were isolated from the food and water used in manufacturing the tofu. Between June and July 1982, a large multistate outbreak of enteritis was traced to pasteurized milk from a Memphis, Tenn., dairy plant.[39] The serotype of *Y. enterocolitica* involved in this outbreak, O:13a,13b, had been isolated previously only from ill monkeys. It was suggested that the organism originated from pigs and contaminated the outside of milk cartons placed in the same crates that had been previously used to transport outdated dairy products to the swine farm. Subsequently, it was demonstrated that *Y. enterocolitica* could survive for long periods on the outside of milk cartons.[38]

The most efficient procedures for recovering enteropathogenic bacteria from foods have incorporated at least one and often two enrichment steps before plating onto selective-differential agar media. A variety of enrichment methods have been described for recovery of *Y. enterocolitica* from foods. Their performance varies with the species and serotypes of *Yersinia* present in the food, and also with whether the judgment of performance is based on inclusiveness or specificity for a certain serotype.[28, 43, 47] This chapter therefore presents a choice of enrichment media and plating agars for isolating *Y. enterocolitica* from foods. Far less information is available on reliable methods for recovery of *Y. pseudotuberculosis* from foods. Consequently, the methods described here are taken from those that have been used for isolation of *Y. pseudotuberculosis* from tissue specimens and fecal material.

27.2   GENERAL CONSIDERATIONS

27.21   Treatment of Food Samples

Food samples should be collected aseptically and placed in sealed containers to prevent dehydration and contamination in transit and to protect handlers. If prompt delivery to the laboratory is not possible, refrigeration is preferable to freezing, which can result in cell injury and some death if the time is prolonged. *Yersinia* is a psychrotroph and can multiply to high numbers within a few days at refrigeration temperatures. An even greater concern is the multiplication of other psychrotrophic competitive bacteria that can hinder recovery of *Yersinia*.

Yersinia is relatively sensitive to acid conditions; therefore, acid foods and fermented products should be analyzed promptly. The pH of food homogenates should be monitored when analyzing acid foods and adjusted back to the starting pH if necessary.

27.22   Incubation Temperatures

"Cold enrichment" has commonly used 4°C as the incubation temperature, most likely because this temperature is conveniently available in laboratory refrigerators. Some work has suggested that enrichment at 10°C for 3 days or 15°C for 2 days will accomplish the same purpose in terms of competitive growth of *Yersinia*.[34] Some workers have reported success with primary enrichment at 25°C for 1 or 2 days, but this result is no doubt highly dependent on the nature and level of the background flora in the food sample. Selective enrichment media have nearly always been incubated at 25°C (room temperature).

Highly selective enteric plating media, such as *Salmonella-Shigella* (SS) agar, that have been used for isolation of *Yersinia* tend to be inhibitory at temperatures of 35° to 37°C. This inhibition can be overcome by incubation at 22° to 25°C, which extends the time required for colony development to 2 days. This inhibition could probably be reversed by supplementing the medium with 2.5 mM calcium or reducing the temperature slightly to 30° or 32°C, which still allows for colony development within 24 hr. Cefsulodin-irgasan-novobiocin (CIN) agar performs best at 32°C where it requires just 18 hr for colony development, although only a few strains are inhibited on the medium at 35°C. SS-desoxycholate (SSDC) agar, preferred by some workers for isolation of serotype O:3, is incubated at 30°C for 24 hr.[47]

27.23   Alkali Treatment

Yersinia is more resistant to high pH than other gram-negative bacteria. This property has been exploited for isolation of *Yersinia* by treating enrichment broths for a very short period to alkali (KOH) before plating them onto agar media.[3] The treatment decreases the background flora to a greater extent than any *Yersinia*, which then become the dominant flora on the agar medium. The technique therefore depends upon successful enrichment and only improves the probability of locating colonies of *Yersinia* among a mixed flora, which is a greater problem with an agar medium of low selectivity and poor differential properties. Evaluations of this technique have reported mixed success with both fecal specimens and foods.[29] We suggest that if alkali treatment is used, it should be in addition to secondary enrichment and not as a substitute for this step.

27.24   Isolation Procedures

Several procedures have been described for isolation of *Yersinia* from foods, and the selection of any one over another is likely to be influenced by the amount of comparative data available. It is quite possible that there are superior methods that go unrecognized only because they have not been examined with the same thoroughness as others. It does seem clear that if one is seeking serotype O:3 (and possibly O:9) only, then the choice of method will be different from the choice if one wishes to determine whether the food sample contains *Yersinia* of any species or type. We therefore suggest two different categories of isolation methods on this basis (Table 3). The bacteriologist can select the media and incubation conditions in each category.

27.3   EQUIPMENT, MATERIALS, AND REAGENTS

27.31   Equipment

Anaerobic chambers (for *Y. pseudotuberculosis*)
Blender with cups (or stomacher with bags)
Incubators (temperatures depending on methods used: 4°, 10°, 15°, 25°, 30°, 32°, and 35°C)
Stereomicroscope

27.32   Media (Chapter 62)

Bile esculin agar
Bile-oxalate-sorbose (BOS) broth
Carbohydrate fermentation broth (or Purple broth base) with (1.0%)—
α-methyl-D-glucoside
Melibiose
Rhamnose
Raffinose
Salicin
Sorbitol
Sucrose

Table 3—Enrichment and Plating Media with Incubation Conditions for Isolation of *Yersinia* from Foods

Primary Enrichment			Secondary Enrichment			Plating Agar		
Medium	Temp. (°C)	Time (days)	Medium	Temp. (°C)	Time (days)	Medium	Temp. (°C)	Time (hr)
A. Inclusive:[a]								
TSB	4	14–21	BOS	22–25	3–5	CIN[27]	32	18
PEM[30]	10	3				MAC	22–25	48
PBS	15	2						
	22–25	1						
B. Selective:[b]								
RAP	22–25	2–3	none			CIN[c]	32	18
ITC	25					SSDC	30	24
						MAC	22–25	48

[a]Temperature and corresponding time may be used for any of these media. Can be followed by KOH treatment before direct plating without secondary enrichment.

[b]Selective for serotype O:3 (and possibly O:9).

[c]Inhibitory for serotype O:3/biotype 3B (15), which can be recovered on VYE agar.[14]

See Section 27.32 for definitions of abbreviations.

Trehalose
Xylose
CIN agar or *Yersinia*-selective agar
Christensen's urea agar
Congo red acid-morpholinepropanesulfonic acid pigmentation (CRAMP) agar
Decarboxylase broth with (1.0%)—
  Arginine
  Lysine
  Ornithine
Eagle's minimum essential medium (MEM) with 10% fetal bovine serum
  (FBS)
Eosin methylene blue (EMB) agar
Irgasan-ticarcillin-chlorate (ITC) broth
Kligler iron agar (KIA)
MacConkey (MAC) agar
Magnesium oxalate (MOX) agar
Methyl red-Voges Proskauer (MR-VP) medium
Modified Rappaport (RAP) broth
Motility test medium
Nitrate broth
Peptone broth 1.0%
Disodium phosphate buffer $\frac{1}{15}$ M (pH 7.6)
Phosphate-buffered saline (PBS)
PBS with 1.0% sorbitol and 0.15% bile salts
Pre-enrichment medium (PEM)
Simmon's citrate agar
SSDC agar (*Yersinia* agar)
Triple sugar iron (TSI) agar
Trypticase soy broth (TSB)
Tryptone broth for indole

27.33 Reagents

Crystal violet
Potassium hydroxide 0.5%–sodium chloride 0.5%
Pyrazine carboxamide

27.4 SAFETY PRECAUTIONS

Y. enterocolitica and *Y. pseudotuberculosis* are human pathogens; therefore, cultures and food samples that may contain these organisms should be handled carefully. Disinfect any utensils used to transfer the food sample before washing or discard. Prepare food homogenates in blenders in a biological safety cabinet to contain aerosols. An alternative device for preparing homogenates that reduces the risk of aerosols is the stomacher. Disinfect homogenates and any glassware or stomacher bags used to hold homogenates by autoclaving or heating to boiling for 10 min before discarding. Avoid mouth pipetting of homogenates, liquid samples, enrichment broths, and other inoculated laboratory media. Several types of pipetting devices are available that are equally efficient and reduce the risks in mouth pipetting. Always insert the tip of the pipette below the rim of the vessel when discharging the material in order to avoid spillage and dispersion of aerosols. Place used pipettes completely submerged in a receptacle with a suitable disinfectant. Never store used pipettes or glassware dry! Treat spills with 1% sodium hypochlorite (household bleach diluted 1:5) or a quaternary ammonium compound prepared according to manufacturer's instructions. Cover the spilled area or material with the disinfectant and allow at least 10 min contact before removal. Take appropriate personal precautions when handling animals infected with *Yersinia*. Place animal carcasses in bags and destroy by incineration or autoclave before discarding with other wastes. Autoclave all soiled bedding, cages, and other materials coming into contact with infected animals before washing and returning to use.

27.5 PROCEDURES

27.51 *Yersinia enterocolitica*

27.511 Primary enrichment

Prepare a 1:10 homogenate of the food sample by weighing 25 g of food and adding it to 225 ml of a primary enrichment medium (Table 3). Prepare the homogenate by blending at low speed for 2 min, or in a stomacher (Tekmar Company, Cincinnati, OH) for the same time. Foods containing bones, pits, or other hard objects may break or puncture the plastic bags used in the stomacher. This risk can be reduced by using a double bag or a net liner designed to separate the liquid from solids for easier pipetting. Place the stomacher in a position where any spillage from broken bags can easily be disinfected and removed. Carefully transfer the homogenate from the blender cup to a sterile jar or flask for incubation. Stomacher bags may be incubated without removing the contents. Fold the top over and seal with a paper clip, then hold in an upright position by placing the bag inside a 1-L beaker. Incubate the homogenate at the temperature and for the time(s) you have chosen from Table 3.

27.512 Alkali treatment

The inclusive primary enrichment media may be treated with alkali by transferring 0.5 ml into a tube containing 4.5 ml of 0.5% KOH-0.5% NaCl. Mix quickly for 3 to 4 seconds and immediately streak with a 5-mm loop onto a plating agar. Do not use this method with the selective enrichment media (i.e., modified RAP and ITC broths).

27.513   Secondary enrichment

Inoculate BOS selective enrichment broth with one of the primary enrichment broths at a ratio of 1:100 (1 ml + 100 ml or 0.1 ml + 10 ml). Incubate BOS broth at 25°C and streak onto a plating agar after 3 and 5 days.

27.514   Plating agars

Streak the primary or secondary enrichment broths after incubation onto one or more of the plating agars identified in Table 3. After the appropriate incubation period, examine the plates for colonies resembling *Yersinia*. The use of a stereomicroscope with an oblique light source is very useful for differentiating colonies on MAC and SS (or SSDC) agars. On MAC agar, the colonies are 0.7 ± 0.2 mm at 32°C and 1.2 ± 0.2 mm at 25°C, are pinkish to colorless, have a smooth and entire edge, and may sometimes be rough or granular. On SSDC agar, colonies of *Yersinia* are about 1 mm in diameter, round, and opaque or colorless. Presumptive identification on CIN agar is greatly facilitated by using transmitted light. A wax pencil mark on the stage can be seen through the transparent border around a red "bullseye" that characterizes *Yersinia* colonies on this medium. There is considerable variation in colony morphology among species of *Yersinia* and serotypes of *Y. enterocolitica*.

Fukushima and Gomyoda[15] found CIN agar inhibitory for *Y. pseudotuberculosis* and serotype O:3/biotype 3B of *Y. enterocolitica*. Fukushima[14] subsequently developed a new medium called Virulent *Yersinia enterocolitica* (VYE) agar for recovery of serotype O:3/biotype 3B, which is more common in Japan, and for differentiation of avirulent strains of *Y. enterocolitica* by esculin hydrolysis.

Colonies are larger on agar media incubated at 25°C, and differential characteristics may be distorted by incubation beyond the recommended time. Strains carrying the virulence plasmid tend to form smaller colonies, especially at 35°C. It is advisable to select these smaller colonies for further testing since certain tests for virulence are plasmid-dependent.

27.515   Biochemical identification

Transfer at least two presumptive colonies to KIA slants. KIA is preferred over TSI since sucrose-positive *Yersinia* will give an acid/acid reaction on the latter medium and appear as lactose fermenters. It may be desirable to subculture first or at the same time to a nonselective medium incubated at 25°C where there is less risk of plasmid loss. Incubate the slants at 35°C for 18 to 24 hr. Transfer isolates giving a typical reaction (alkaline/acid without H_2S and little or no gas), using a heavy inoculum, from the KIA slant to a slant of Christensen's urea agar. Incubate urea agar slants at 35°C and read after 2 or 3 hr. Hold negative slants overnight. Urease-negative strains of *Y. entero-*

colitica have been described, but are rare and, according to available information, nonpathogenic.

Y. enterocolitica can be identified by subjecting urease-positive isolates to tests for citrate utilization and fermentation of sucrose, rhamnose, raffinose, melibiose, and α-methyl-D-glucoside. The species is sucrose-positive and negative in the other tests (Table 1). Other species of *Yersinia* can be identified with the tests listed in Table 1, and biotypes of *Y. enterocolitica* determined by the tests in Table 2. Biotyping can help in determining whether the isolate is a pathogenic strain of *Y. enterocolitica*.

27.516   Typing

Fifty-seven somatic heat-stable O factors have been identified and used for serotyping of *Y. enterocolitica* and related species.[45] A proposal has been made that the original serotyping scheme be revised to include 18 serogroups containing 20 O factors that appear to be limited to the species *Y. enterocolitica* as it was later defined.[1] Four new antigenic factors have been described recently and will be added to this scheme in the near future. Epidemiologic data and laboratory models of pathogenicity have identified the 12 serotypes listed in Table 4 as those that can include pathogenic varieties. The most common human serotypes usually present consistent and unique biotypes. On occasion, however, isolates from the environment may bear the same antigenic factors but differ biochemically and not demonstrate pathogenicity. Some serotypes, especially O:21 and O:4,32, are common in the environment, especially in water, but these isolates demonstrate different biotypes from

Table 4—Serotypes That Include Pathogenic Strains of *Y. enterocolitica*

Serotype O:	Occurrence			Distribution	
	Common	Occasional	Rare	World-wide	North America
3	X			X	
9	X			X[a]	
5,27 (5B)	X			X	
8	X				X
21 (O:Tacoma)		X			X
13a,13b		X			X
4,32		X			X[b]
1			X	X	
1,2,3			X	X	
2,3			X	X	
20			X		X
40			X		X

[a]Extremely rare in North America.
[b]Primarily from western region.

those associated with disease. Serotype is, therefore, a strong predictor of pathogenicity in the case of O:3, O:9, O:5,27, and O:8, and probably O:1, O:1,2,3, and O:2,3; but it is less reliable in the case of serotypes O:21 and O:4,32. It is important to distinguish serotype O:13a,13b, which is pathogenic, from O:7,13, which is different biochemically and never pathogenic. Only a few isolates of serotypes O:20 and O:40 have been described; therefore, no similar generalizations can be made.

New investigations on the flagellar (H) antigens of *Yersinia* have shown them to be useful for separating species.[2] Antisera against the flagellar antigens are not readily available, and these typing schemes have not demonstrated epidemiologic usefulness. Several different bacteriophage typing systems have been described, but none has been used for epidemiologic purposes.

27.517   Recognizing pathogenic *Yersinia*

As noted previously, most data indicate that only the species *Y. enterocolitica* includes pathogenic strains. Serotyping and biotyping of isolates within this species can be helpful in determining whether they are potential pathogens. Other indirect but simple markers of pathogenicity that can be determined in most laboratories include (Table 5): (1) calcium-dependent growth at 37°C; (2) autoagglutination at 35° or 37°C; (3) Congo red binding; (4) crystal violet binding at 37°C; (5) pyrazinamidase activity; and (6) salicin and esculin fermentation. Note that all but the last two of these tests are plasmid-dependent, and, therefore, may be lost during subculture. Some laboratories have reported difficulty with the Congo red binding method for identifying plasmid-positive strains. The test for salicin fermentation must be completed at 35°C and not read after 4 days' incubation. Rapid esculin hydrolysis at 25°C, which can often be seen on bile-esculin agar within hours with a heavy inoculum, is clear evidence of a nonpathogenic strain. Because of some weak salicin reactions observed in a few nonpathogenic strains (which may be because a lower incubation temperature was used), it has been suggested that the most reliable biochemical screening tests for pathogenicity are salicin, esculin, and pyrazinamidase. Pyrazinamidase activity is limited with rare exceptions to nonpathogenic strains.[17] None of these three biochemical tests is mediated by the virulence plasmid. Procedures for these tests are described in the references identified in Table 5.

Several animal models have been used to study the pathogenicity of *Yersinia* (Table 6). The response in some of these models is quite different between "American" strains (serotypes O:8, O:21) and "European" strains (serotypes O:3, O:9, O:5,27). The latter strains do not produce fatal infections in adult mice and gerbils or cause obvious conjunctivitis in guinea pigs. Alternative models to demonstrate pathogenicity in these serotypes include suckling mice, infant rabbits, mice that have been iron-overloaded or treated with an iron chelator, and invasiveness in cold-stressed mice. Procedures for the use of these animal models are described in the references identified in Table 6.

Table 5—Markers of Pathogenicity in *Y. enterocolitica*

Marker	Temperature (°C)	Plasmid mediated	Reference
calcium-dependent growth	37	yes	Gemski et al., 1980
autoagglutination	37	yes	Laird and Cavanaugh, 1980
reduced colony size	37 (25?)	yes	Lazere and Gemski, 1983
V and W antigens	37	yes	Carter et al., 1980
unique outer membrane proteins	37	yes	Portnoy et al., 1984
Congo red uptake	37 or 25	yes	Prpic et al., 1983
crystal violet binding	37	yes	Bhaduri et al., 1987
hydrophobicity	37	yes	Schiemann and Swanz, 1985
	25	no	Schiemann and Swanz, 1985
mannose-resistant hemagglutination		yes	Kapperud and Lassen, 1983
42–48 Mdal plasmid		yes	Portnoy et al., 1981
tissue culture:			
adhesion	37	?	Schiemann and Devenish, 1982
invasion[a]	37	no	Schiemann and Devenish, 1982
serum resistance	37	?	Chiesa and Bottone, 1983
salicin fermentation (negative)	37	no	Schiemann and Devenish, 1982
esculin hydrolysis (negative)	25	no	Schiemann and Devenish, 1982
pyrazinamidase (absent)	25	no	Kandolo and Nauters, 1985

[a]More efficient in bacteria grown at 25°C.

Table 6—Animal Models for Pathogenic Y. enterocolitica

Model	Plasmid encoded	Reaction with serotype:			Reference
		O:8	O:3	O:5,27	
guinea pig or mouse conjunctivitis in mice treated with iron chelator[a]	yes	+	±/–	±/–	Scheimann and Devenish, 1980
			+		Robins-Browne and Prpic, 1985
lethal infections in mice or gerbils in mice treated with iron chelator[a]	yes	+	–	–	Carter, 1975; Scheimann and Devenish, 1980
			+	+	Robins-Browne and Prpic, 1985
lethal infections in suckling mice	yes	+	+	+	Aulisio et al., 1980
systemic infections (spleen-positive) in cold-stressed mice[a]	yes	+	+	+	Bakour et al., 1985
intestinal colonization with signs of diarrhea and long-term fecal excretion in mice with oral infections	yes	+	+	+	Scheimann et al., 1981
diarrhea in infant rabbit with oral infection	yes	+	+		Pai et al., 1980
production of heat-stable enterotoxin in vitro	no	+	+	+	Pai et al., 1978

[a] Also demonstrated with strains of serotype O:9.

+ = positive reactions; – = negative reactions; ± = weak or erratic reactions.

27.52   *Y. pseudotuberculosis*

27.521   Enrichment

Prepare a 1:10 homogenate by weighing 25 g of the food sample and adding it to 225 ml of either $\frac{1}{15}$ M disodium phosphate buffer (pH 7.6) or 1% peptone broth. Use a blender at low speed or a stomacher for 2 min to prepare the homogenate.

27.522   Plating agars

Hold the food homogenate at 4°C for up to 4 weeks. At approximately weekly intervals, streak a loopful of the cold enrichment onto MAC, SS, or EMB agar. Prior to streaking, the enrichment media may be treated with alkali (see procedure above). Incubate the agar media at 22° to 25°C for 24 to 48 hr and a duplicate set of plates at 35°C. Prepare a second set of plates for anaerobic incubation at both temperatures. Some strains of *Y. pseudotuberculosis* require the lower temperature or anaerobic conditions.[8]

On MAC agar, colonies of *Y. pseudotuberculosis* are round, opaque or colorless, and 0.5 to 3 mm in diameter. Colonies develop more slowly on SS and EMB agars, and are pale pink on EMB agar.

27.523   Biochemical identification

Select at least two representative lactose-negative colonies from each of the agar media used and inoculate a TSI slant. Incubate overnight at 25°C. *Y. pseudotuberculosis* will give an alkaline (red)/acid (yellow) reaction without gas or H_2S production (indicated by blackening of medium). Test isolates giving typical reactions on TSI for urease production. *Y. pseudotuberculosis* can be identified by a positive test for urease, a negative test for citrate utilization, motility at 25° but not at 35°C, negative reactions for arginine, lysine, and ornithine decarboxylases and raffinose fermentation, and positive tests for melibiose and rhamnose fermentation. These sugars should be incubated at 25°C.

27.524   Typing

Y. pseudotuberculosis has been separated into six groups, type I through VI, on the basis of type-specific, thermostable, somatic O antigens. Subtypes A and B have been described for types I, II, IV, and V. Determination of serotype can be useful in epidemiological investigations. However, typing antisera are not readily available, and isolates must be submitted to a reference laboratory.

27.525   Pathogenicity

All isolates of *Y. pseudotuberculosis* should be considered potential pathogens. The organism is pathogenic in small animals, causing necrotizing, suppurative, granulomatous lesions in the liver, spleen, and lymph nodes. *Y. pseudotuberculosis* demonstrates several of the same markers of pathogenicity as do pathogenic strains of *Y. enterocolitica*, including the presence of a 42 to 48 Mdal plasmid, unique outer membrane proteins, autoagglutination, and calcium-dependent growth at 37°C, formation of V and W antigens, and penetration of epithelial cells in tissue cultures.

27.6   INTERPRETATION

Isolation of *Y. pseudotuberculosis* from any food would be cause for concern just because there is not sufficient information available to judge the true significance or predict the consequence of ingestion of this organism. Other species of *Yersinia* can be isolated with ease from many types of foods, especially raw vegetables and meats, if one uses a reasonably inclusive enrichment system. In most cases these isolates will represent related species of *Yersinia* or nonpathogenic forms of *Y. enterocolitica*. These organisms may mask the presence of pathogenic forms that are present in lower numbers or are weaker competitors. Consequently, isolation and identification alone of *Yersinia* without determination of species and application of some tests of pathogenicity have no meaning.

Tests for pathogenicity with models or markers that are plasmid-mediated may give negative results if the plasmid has been lost during isolation and subculture, something that occurs more readily during incubation at higher temperatures. This possibility can be minimized by incubating culture media whenever possible at lower temperatures and by selecting colonies of smaller size from plating agars. Food isolates identified as *Y. enterocolitica* that are negative in plasmid-mediated models should be examined for other markers of pathogenicity, or one should return to the original plating agar and select additional colonies for examination.

27.7   REFERENCES

1. Aleksic, S. and Bockemuhl, J. 1984. Proposed revision of the Wauters et al. antigenic scheme for serotyping of *Yersinia enterocolitica*. J. Clin. Microbiol. 20: 99.
2. Aleksic, S., Bockemuhl, J., and Lange, F. 1986. Studies on the serology of flagellar antigens of *Yersinia enterocolitica* and related *Yersinia* species. Zentralbl. Bakteriol. Mikrobiol. Hyg. [A] 261: 299.
3. Aulisio, C. C. G., Mehlman, I. J., and Sanders, A. C. 1980. Alkali method for rapid recovery of *Yersinia enterocolitica* and *Yersinia pseudotuberculosis* from foods. Appl. Environ. Microbiol. 39: 135.
4. Aulisio, C. C. G., Hill, W. E., Stanfield, J. T., and Morris, J. A. 1983. Pathogenicity of *Yersinia enterocolitica* demonstrated in the suckling mouse. J. Food Prot. 46: 856.
5. Bakour, R., Balligand, G., Laroche, Y., Cornelis, G., and Wauters, G. 1985. A simple adult-mouse test for tissue invasiveness in *Yersinia enterocolitica* strains of low experimental virulence. J. Med. Microbiol. 19: 237.

6. Bercovier, H., Brault, J., Barre, N., Treignier, M., Alonso, J. M., and Mollaret, H. H. 1978. Biochemical, serological, and phage typing characteristics of 459 *Yersinia* strains isolated from a terrestrial ecosystem. Curr. Microbiol. 1: 353.

7. Bhaduri, S., Conway, L. K., and Lachica, R. V. 1987. Assay of crystal violet binding for rapid identification of virulent plasmid-bearing clones of *Yersinia enterocolitica*. J. Clin. Microbiol. 25: 1039.

8. Bissett, M. L. 1981. Microbiological aspects of *Yersinia pseudotuberculosis*. In "Yersinia enterocolitica," ed. E. J. Bottone, p. 31. CRC Press, Inc., Boca Raton, Fl.

9. Black, R. E., Jackson, R. J., Tsai, T., Medvesky, M., Shayegani, M., Feeley, J. C., MacLeod, K. I. E., and Wakelee, A. M. 1978. Epidemic *Yersinia enterocolitica* infection due to contaminated chocolate milk. N. Engl. J. Med. 298: 76.

10. Carter, P. B. 1975. Pathogenicity of *Yersinia enterocolitica* for mice. Infect. Immun. 11: 164.

11. Carter, P. B., Zahorchak, R. J., and Brubaker, R. R. 1980. Plague virulence antigens from *Yersinia enterocolitica*. Infect. Immun. 28: 638.

12. Chiesa, C. and Bottone, E. J. 1983. Serum resistance of *Yersinia enterocolitica* expressed in absence of other virulence markers. Infect. Immun. 39: 469.

13. Doyle, M. P., Hugdahl, M. B., and Taylor, S. L. 1981. Isolation of virulent *Yersinia enterocolitica* from porcine tongues. Appl. Environ. Microbiol. 42: 661.

14. Fukushima, H. 1987. New selective agar medium for isolation of virulent *Yersinia enterocolitica*. J. Clin. Microbiol. 25: 1068.

15. Fukushima, H. and Gomyoda, M. 1986. Growth of *Yersinia pseudotuberculosis* and *Yersinia enterocolitica* biotype 3B serotype 03 inhibited on cefsulodin-irgasan-novobiocin agar. J. Clin. Microbiol. 24: 116.

16. Gemski, P., Lazere, J. R., and Casey, T. 1980. Plasmid associated with pathogenicity and calcium dependency of *Yersinia enterocolitica*. Infect. Immun. 27: 682.

17. Kandolo, K. and Wauters, G. 1985. Pyrazinamidase activity in *Yersinia enterocolitica* and related organisms. J. Clin. Microbiol. 21: 980.

18. Kapperud, G. and Lassen, J. 1983. Relationship of virulence-associated autoagglutination to hemagglutinin production in *Yersinia enterocolitica* and *Yersinia enterocolitica*-like bacteria. Infect. Immun. 42: 163.

19. Laird, W. J. and Cavanaugh, D. C. 1980. Correlation of autoagglutination and virulence of *Yersiniae*. J. Clin. Microbiol. 11: 430.

20. Lazere, J. R. and Gemski, P. 1983. Association of colony morphology with virulence of *Yersinia enterocolitica*. FEMS Microbiol. Lett. 17: 121.

21. Pai, C. H., Mors, V., and Toma, S. 1978. Prevalence of enterotoxigenicity in human and nonhuman isolates of *Yersinia enterocolitica*. Infect. Immun. 22: 334.

22. Pai, C. H., Mors, V., and Seemayer, T. A. 1980. Experimental *Yersinia enterocolitica* enteritis in rabbits. Infect. Immun. 28: 238.

23. Portnoy, D. A., Moseley, S. L., and Falkow, S. 1981. Characterization of plasmids and plasmid-associated determinants of *Yersinia enterocolitica* pathogenesis. Infect. Immun. 31: 775.

24. Portnoy, D. A., Wolf-Watz, H., Bolin, I., Beeder, A. B., and Falkow, S. 1984. Characterization of common virulence plasmids in *Yersinia* species and their role in the expression of outer membrane proteins. Infect. Immun. 43: 108.

25. Prpic, J. K., Robins-Browne, R. M., and Davey, R. B. 1983. Differentiation between virulent and avirulent *Yersinia enterocolitica* isolates by using Congo red agar. J. Clin. Microbiol. 18: 486.

26. Robins-Browne, R. M. and Prpic, J. K. 1985. Effects of iron and desferrioxamine on infections with *Yersinia enterocolitica*. Infect. Immun. 47: 774.

27. Schiemann, D. A. 1979. Synthesis of a selective agar medium for *Yersinia enterocolitica*. Can. J. Microbiol. 25: 1298.

28. Schiemann, D. A. 1982. Development of a two-step enrichment procedure for recovery of *Yersinia enterocolitica* from food. Appl. Environ. Microbiol. 43: 14.

29. Schiemann, D. A. 1983. Alkalotolerance of *Yersinia enterocolitica* as a basis for selective isolation from food enrichments. Appl. Environ. Microbiol. 46: 22.
30. Schiemann, D. A. 1987. *Yersinia enterocolitica* in milk and dairy products. J. Dairy Sci. 70: 383.
31. Schiemann, D. A. and Devenish, J. A. 1980. Virulence of *Yersinia enterocolitica* determined by lethality in Mongolian gerbils and by the Sereny test. Infect. Immun. 29: 500.
32. Schiemann, D. A. and Devenish, J. A. 1982. Relationship of HeLa cell infectivity to biochemical, serological, and virulence characteristics of *Yersinia enterocolitica*. Infect. Immun. 35: 497.
33. Schiemann, D. A. and Fleming, C. A. 1981. *Yersinia enterocolitica* isolated from throats of swine in eastern and western Canada. Can. J. Microbiol. 27: 1326.
34. Schiemann, D. A. and Olson, S. A. 1984. Antagonism by gram-negative bacteria to growth of *Yersinia enterocolitica* in mixed cultures. Appl. Environ. Microbiol. 48: 539.
35. Schiemann, D. A. and Swanz, P. J. 1985. Epithelial cell association and hydrophobicity of *Yersinia enterocolitica* and related species. J. Med. Microbiol. 19: 309.
36. Schiemann, D. A., Devenish, J. A., and Toma, S. 1981. Characteristics of virulence in human isolates of *Yersinia enterocolitica*. Infect. Immun. 32: 400.
37. Shayegani, M., Morse, D., DeForge, I., Root, T., Parsons, L. M., and Maupin, P. S. 1983. Microbiology of a major foodborne outbreak of gastroenteritis caused by *Yersinia enterocolitica* serogroup O:8. J. Clin. Microbiol. 17: 35.
38. Stanfield, J. T., Jackson, G. J., and Aulisio, C. C. G. 1985. *Yersinia enterocolitica:* Survival of a pathogenic strain on milk containers. J. Food Prot. 48: 947.
39. Tacket, C. O., Narain, J. P., Sattin, R., Lofgren, J. P., Konigsberg, C., Jr., Rendtorff, R. C., Rausa, A., Davis, B. R., and Cohen, M. L. 1984. A multistate outbreak of infections caused by *Yersinia enterocolitica* transmitted by pasteurized milk. J. Amer. Med. Assn. 251: 483.
40. Tacket, C. O., Ballard, J., Harris, N., Allard, J., Nolan, C., Quan, T., and Cohen, M. L. 1985. An outbreak of *Yersinia enterocolitica* infections caused by contaminated tofu (soybean curd). Am. J. Epidemiol. 121: 705.
41. Tauxe, R. V., Wauters, G., Goossens, V., van Noyen, R., Vandepitte, J., Martin, S. M., de Mol, P., and Thiers, G. 1987. *Yersinia enterocolitica* infections and pork: the missing link. The Lancet I(8542): 1129.
42. Toma, S. and Lafleur, L. 1981. *Yersinia enterocolitica* infections in Canada 1966 to August 1978. In "Yersinia enterocolitica," ed. E. J. Bottone, p. 183. CRC Press, Inc., Boca Raton, Fl.
43. Wauters, G. 1973. Improved methods for the isolation and the recognition of *Yersinia enterocolitica*. Contr. Microbiol. Immunol. 2: 68.
44. Wauters, G. 1979. Carriage of *Yersinia enterocolitica* serotype 3 by pigs as a source of human infection. Contr. Microbiol. Immunol. 5: 249.
45. Wauters, G. 1981. Antigens of *Yersinia enterocolitica*. In "Yersinia enterocolitica," ed. E. J. Bottone, p. 41. CRC Press, Inc., Boca Raton, Fl.
46. Wauters, G., Kandolo, K., and Janssens, M. 1987. Revised biogrouping scheme of *Yersinia enterocolitica*. Contr. Microbiol. Immunol. 9: 14.
47. Wauters, G., Goossens, V., Janssens, M., and Vandepitte, J. 1988a. New enrichment method for isolation of pathogenic *Yersinia enterocolitica* serogroup O:3 from pork. Appl. Environ. Microbiol. 54: 851.
48. Wauters, G., Janssens, M., Steigerwalt, A. G., and Brenner, D. J. 1988b. *Yersinia mollaretii* sp. nov. and *Yersinia bercovieri* sp. nov., formerly called *Yersinia enterocolitica* biogroups 3A and 3B. Int. J. Syst. Bacteriol. 38: 424.

Chapter 28

VIBRIO

Charles A. Kaysner, Mark L. Tamplin, and Robert M. Twedt

28.1 INTRODUCTION

28.11 Description of Genus

Members of the genus *Vibrio* are defined as gram-negative, asporogenous rods that are straight or have a single, rigid curve. They are motile; most have a single polar flagellum when grown in liquid medium. Most produce oxidase and catalase, and ferment glucose without producing gas.[31] Three species, *V. cholerae*,[3] *V. parahaemolyticus*,[73] and *V. vulnificus*,[51] are well documented human pathogens. A new species, *V. mimicus*,[13] formerly included in the species *V. cholerae* and distinguished primarily by its inability to ferment sucrose, also is a recognized pathogen. A growing body of evidence suggests that other species—*V. alginolyticus*,[56] *V. fluvialis*,[40] *V. metschnikovii*,[39] and *V. hollisae*[28]—possibly are pathogenic for humans.[6, 46, 72]

V. cholerae, the type species of the genus *Vibrio*, is the causative agent of cholera outbreaks and epidemics. It is characterized by various biochemical properties and antigenic types. It can be differentiated from other halophilic *Vibrio* species because its obligate requirement for Na^+ ion[63] can be satisfied by the trace amounts present in most media constituents. Most *V. cholerae* strains recovered from cholera cases contain a somatic antigen in common and include serotype O group 1.[24, 31] Strains that are agglutinable in Inaba or Ogawa classes of 01 antiserum are well documented human pathogens.

V. cholerae strains that are identical to, or closely resemble, clinical strains in biochemical characteristics but fail to agglutinate in anti-O1 serum are referred to as *V. cholerae* non-01.[87] Evidence indicates that non-01 strains are sometimes involved in cholera-like diarrheal disease.[6, 33] Indeed, the permeability factor produced by a non-01 strain recovered from surface water

451

during an investigation of cholera outbreak has been found biologically and immunologically indistinguishable from cholera toxin.[12, 65]

V. mimicus is a new species associated with diarrhea following consumption of raw or undercooked seafood.[13, 61] Isolated from samples during a search for *V. cholerae*, *V. mimicus* can be differentiated from that closely related pathogen by nonsucrose fermentation. The organism will appear as green colonies on thiosulfate citrate bile salts sucrose (TCBS) agar and will grow in most common media without added NaCl.

V. parahaemolyticus is a halophilic estuarine organism. All strains share a common H antigen, but to date 11 0 type and 65 K (capsular) antigens exist.[57] Pathogenic strains of *V. parahaemolyticus* are differentiated from nonpathogenic strains by the ability to produce a thermostabile direct hemolysin (TDH), whose production is termed the Kanagawa phenomenon.[58] The TDH gene has been cloned and sequenced.[49] A DNA probe is now available to test for the presence of the gene sequence in isolates from food samples.[50]

V. vulnificus can be differentiated from *V. parahaemolyticus*, which it resembles closely and mimics on TCBS agar, by several biochemical reactions, including *B*-galactosidase activity. Results of DNA reassociation studies confirm this halophile as a separate species.[10] Those few strains that fail to ferment lactose are nevertheless *B*-galactosidase-positive as measured by the ONPG assay.[17] Epidemiological and clinical investigations show that *V. vulnificus* causes septicemia and death following oral ingestion of seafood or after wound infections originating from the marine environment.[4, 51, 68]

V. metschnikovii (formerly referred to as enteric group 16) differs from all other *Vibrio* species in its lack of cytochrome oxidase.[39] Some strains (biotype II) of *V. fluvialis* sp. nov. (formerly called group F vibrios) produce gas during the fermentation of D-glucose.[40] *V. hollisae*, formerly group EF13 or enteric group 42, is a halophilic species that grows poorly if at all on TCBS agar and exhibits a delayed motility pattern (>48 hr) uncharacteristic of the other vibrios.[28] All three of these species have been isolated from human stools and/or patients with gastroenteritis.

28.12   Distribution and Sources of Contamination

28.121   V. cholerae

This organism is excreted in great numbers in the feces of cholera patients and convalescents. The disease is transmitted primarily by the fecal-oral route, indirectly through contaminated water supplies. Direct person-to-person spread is not common. Food supplies may be contaminated by the use of human excreta as fertilizer, or by freshening vegetables for market with contaminated water. Recent cholera outbreaks in Italy,[76] Louisiana,[5] Florida,[81] and Guam[45] are thought to have resulted from the consumption of raw, undercooked, contaminated, or recontaminated seafood. *V. cholerae* 01 (toxigenic and non-toxigenic) as well as non-01 strains have been isolated with increasing frequency from estuarine water and shellfish.[11, 29, 36] Indeed, accumulating evidence suggests that *V. cholerae* 01 is a component of the autochthonous flora of brackish water, estuaries, and salt marshes of coastal areas of the temperate zone,[5, 11, 29, 36] posing an ongoing hazard to public health.

28.122 *V. parahaemolyticus*

This organism is frequently isolated from coastal waters and seafoods in temperate zones throughout the world. It is the most frequent cause of foodborne disease in Japan, where many residents eat raw fish. A number of common-source gastroenteritis outbreaks attributed to *V. parahaemolyticus* have occurred in the United States. Following 14 outbreaks between 1971 and 1978, *V. parahaemolyticus* was isolated from both stool specimens and foods.[67, 75, 77-80] Foods implicated in the United States are crab, oyster, shrimp, and lobster that, unlike fish in Japan, were typically cooked before eating.[67, 75, 77-80] The resulting outbreaks probably were caused by gross mishandling practices, such as improper refrigeration, insufficient cooking, cross-contamination, or recontamination.

28.123 *V. vulnificus*

Recent interest in *V. vulnificus*, the causative agent of septicemic shock, has spurred ecological studies to determine its incidence in coastal waters of the United States.[37, 51, 69, 71] A review of cases has determined an association between septicemia and consumption of raw oysters. In most cases, oysters originated from Gulf Coast waters. This halophilic species will grow on or in many laboratory formulations of media that contain NaCl; a 0.5% minimum concentration is recommended.[51]

28.124 Other halophilic vibrios

V. alginolyticus, *V. fluvialis* sp. nov., *V. metschnikovii*, and *V. hollisae* are, like *V. parahaemolyticus*, *V. cholerae*, and *V. vulnificus*, recovered from brackish coastal waters, sediment, and sea life taken from the temperate estuarine environment.[6] These species appear to be normal components of that environment and have been associated with human illnesses.

28.13 Methods of Isolation

Vibrio species, like many other gram-negative bacteria, grow in the presence of relatively high levels of bile salts. They are facultatively aerobic and grow best in alkaline conditions. The strict halophilic nature of *V. parahaemolyticus* probably accounts for the fact that diseases caused by this organism were not documented in the United States until workers began examining foods and feces on appropriate media containing added salt. TCBS agar[38] has proved to be an excellent medium for the isolation of both *V. cholerae* and

V. parahaemolyticus. Although intralot variations have been noted,[48, 86] this medium supports good growth of both species and inhibits most nonvibrios. Recent formulations for selective agars for the isolation of *V. vulnificus* have proved effective.[8, 42]

28.2   GENERAL CONSIDERATIONS

28.21   Storage of Sample

The sample should be held under moderate refrigeration (about 7°C to 10°C) and analyzed as soon after collection as possible. This maximizes survival and recovery of vibrios and reduces the tendency for overgrowth by indigenous marine microflora. Despite the recognized fragility of the organisms to extremes of heat and cold, its survival is enhanced under mild refrigeration.[44, 70, 84] If frozen storage of the sample is required, a temperature of −80°C is recommended, if feasible.[7]

28.22   Special Media

Isolation from foods is facilitated by the use of special media. Glucose salt teepol broth (GSTB),[1] Horie arabinose ethyl violet broth (HAEB),[30, 52] and salt polymyxin broth (SPB)[59, 60] have been recommended as enrichment broths for isolating *V. parahaemolyticus* from foods. At present, no commercial source of teepol is available; thus the use of GSTB is limited to laboratories with a supply of this ingredient. Alkaline peptone water (APW) and gelatin phosphate salt (GPS) broth are used commonly for isolating *V. cholerae* from foods.[20, 53, 82] While no specific enrichment broth has been formulated for *V. vulnificus* isolation, APW has been used successfully.[37, 69] TCBS agar is designed especially for the isolation of *Vibrio*. Cellobiose-polymyxin-colistin (CPC)[42] and sodium dodecyl sulfate-polymyxin-sucrose (SDS)[8] selective agars have been designed to differentiate *V. vulnificus* from other vibrios. *V. cholerae* strains, except *V. cholerae* 01 classical biotype, will grow on both CPC and SDS agars, while most *V. parahaemolyticus* strains will not grow on CPC, but will grow on SDS agar. Media used for testing the biochemical reactions of *V. parahaemolyticus* should contain 2% to 3% NaCl. *V. vulnificus* requires NaCl for growth. A minimum of 0.5% NaCl, the concentration of most prepared media, is adequate.

28.23   Recommended Controls

Duplicate plating media should be used for *V. cholerae* because strains may vary in their growth characteristics. It is advisable in conducting the biochemical tests for *V. parahaemolyticus*, *V. cholerae*, and *V. vulnificus* to inoculate known positive control organisms to ensure appropriate reading of reactions.

28.3   EQUIPMENT, MATERIALS, AND REAGENTS

28.31   Media and Reagents (Chapter 62)

ABTS substrate solution
Alkaline peptone water (APW)
Cary-Blair transport medium
Casamino acids yeast extract (CAYE) broth
Cellobiose polymyxin colistin (CPC) agar
ELISA buffer
Gelatin agar
Gelatin phosphate salt (GPS) broth (agar)
Glucose salt teepol broth (GSTB)
Heart infusion broth, agar
Horie arabinose ethyl violet broth (HAEB)
Kligler iron agar (KIA)
Motility test medium
Mueller-Hinton agar
Peptone Tween salt (PTS) diluent
Phosphate buffered saline (PBS)
Protein A peroxidase conjugate
Salt polymyxin broth (SPB)
Sodium dodecyl sulfate polymyxin sucrose (SDS) agar
Thiosulfate citrate bile salts sucrose (TCBS) agar
T_1N_1 agar
Triple sugar iron (TSI) agar
Tryptic soy agar-magnesium sulfate-NaCl (TSAMS)
Trypticase soy broth (TSB), agar (TSA)
Vibrio parahaemolyticus sucrose agar (VPSA)
Wagatsuma agar
0.1 M Bicarbonate buffer

28.4   PRECAUTIONS

In *V. parahaemolyticus* outbreaks, the importance of stool, rectal swab, and vomitus specimens and samples of incriminated foodstuffs cannot be overemphasized. Usually, clinical specimens will contain Kanagawa-positive organisms. Clinical specimens must be obtained as early in the disease as possible because the duration of excretion of the pathogen is short.

A good selective enrichment broth has not been developed for *V. cholerae*. APW provides suitable enrichment for incubation periods of 6 to 8 hr, but other competing microflora may overgrow *V. cholerae* during longer enrichment periods of certain types of samples. Overnight periods (16 to 18 hr), although not desirable, have been used to facilitate sample analysis during work hours.

28.5 PROCEDURES

28.51   *V. cholerae*

28.511   Enrichment and plating

Weigh 25 g of sample into each of two tared jars (capacity approximately 500 ml). Products such as seafood or vegetables may be blended or cut into small pieces with scissors.

Add 225 ml APW to one jar and 225 ml GPS broth to the other. Thoroughly mix both samples.

Incubate each broth at 35° ± 2°C for 6 to 8 hr. For analysis of oysters, include a third tared jar with 25 g of product plus 225 ml APW. This jar should be incubated 6 to 8 hr at 42° ± 0.2°C in a water bath.[14] An enumeration technique by most probable number (MPN) may also be performed if desired (see Section 28.521 for procedure).

Prepare dried plates of two media; one should be TCBS agar, the other a nonselective medium, such as gelatin *or* GPS agar. CPC and SDS agars may also be included.

Transfer a 3 mm loopful from the surface growth of each broth culture to the surface of each of the two plating media, and streak in a manner that will yield isolated colonies.

Incubate the inoculated plating media overnight (18 to 24 hr) at 35° ± 2°C. Incubate CPC agar at 40° ± 2°C for 18 to 24 hr.

Subculture three or more typical colonies from each plating medium to T_1N_1 agar slants or motility test medium stabs. Incubate slants or stabs overnight at 35° ± 2°C.

Typical colonies of *V. cholerae* on TCBS agar are large (2 to 3 mm), smooth, yellow (occasional slow sucrose fermenters are green), and slightly flattened with opaque centers and translucent peripheries.

Typical colonies of *V. cholerae* on gelatin agar are transparent and usually have a characteristic cloudy zone around them that becomes more definite after a few minutes of refrigeration. Viewed in oblique light, *V. cholerae* colonies appear iridescent green to bronze colored and finely granular.

Typical colonies of *V. cholerae* on GPS agar are small and transparent with a cloudy halo. Satellite growth of nongelatinase-producing, non-*Vibrio* colonies may surround *V. cholerae* colonies on this medium.

Typical colonies of *V. cholerae* on CPC agar are small, smooth, opaque, and green to purple in color, with a purple background on extended incubation.

Typical colonies of *V. cholerae* on SDS agar are small, smooth, opaque, and yellow.

28.512   Confirmation

Kligler iron agar (KIA) reaction. Inoculate each suspect T_1N_1 agar culture to a tube of KIA by streaking the slant and stabbing the butt. Incubate the cultures overnight at 35° ± 2°C. *V. cholerae* cultures will have an alkaline (red) slant and an acid (yellow) butt, no gas, and no blackening (H_2S production) in the butt. Use of TSI agar is less desirable since *V. cholerae* ferments sucrose, resulting in an acid slant and acid butt. *V. mimicus* cultures do not ferment sucrose and will have an alkaline slant and an acid butt in TSI agar.

String test. The string test described by Smith[64] is a useful presumptive test for suspected strains of *V. cholerae*. All *V. cholerae* are positive. Emulsify a large colony or other inoculum from a T_1N_1 agar culture in a large drop of 0.5% sodium desoxycholate in 0.85% saline solution. Within 60 sec a mucoid mass forms, and this material strings when a loopful is lifted (up to 2 to 3 cm) from the slide.

Serologic agglutination test. Serotyping of *V. cholerae* passing the string test can be applied to the somatic or O antigens. Two major serotypes, Ogawa and Inaba, and one rarely encountered serotype, Hikojima, are recognized as human pathogens. All three types are seen in both the classical *V. cholerae* and the El Tor biotypes.

Mark off two sections about 1 × 2 cm on the inside of a glass petri dish or on a 2 × 3-inch glass slide.

Place a small amount of culture from a T_1N_1 agar slant directly onto the dish or slide in the upper part of each marked section.

Add one drop of 0.85% saline solution to the lower part of each marked section. With a sterile transfer loop or needle, emulsify the culture in the saline solution for one section, and repeat for the other section.

Add a drop of polyvalent *V. cholerae* 01 antiserum to one section of emulsified culture and mix with a sterile loop or needle. (The other section containing antigen only is the autoagglutination control.)

Tilt the mixture back and forth for one min and observe against a dark background. A positive reaction is indicated by a rapid, strong agglutination.

Test each culture with polyvalent antiserum and, if positive, test with Ogawa and Inaba antisera. The Hikojima serotype reacts with both antisera.

Monoclonal antibodies to the Inaba, Ogawa, and group 01 antigen are commercially available.

Biochemical tests. Table 1 shows the minimal number of characters needed to identify *V. cholerae* strains.[32] The ability of *V. cholerae* to grow in 1% tryptone without added NaCl differentiates it from other sucrose-positive vibrios.

28.513   Differentiation of El Tor and classical biotypes

Bacteriophage susceptibility. A modification of the method described by Mukerjee[47] is used. Inoculate a tube of T_1N_1 broth from each suspect T_1N_1 agar culture and incubate broth at 35° ± 2°C for 4 hr. Transfer each 4 hr broth culture to a Mueller-Hinton agar plate using a wire loop or cotton swab, to yield confluent growth. With a 3-mm platinum loop, superimpose one loopful of an appropriate test dilution of phage IV on the inoculated agar surface. Incubate overnight at 35° ± 2°C. Classical strains are sensitive; El Tor strains are resistant to the action of Mukerjee's phage IV.

Table 1—Minimal Number of Characters Needed to Identify *V. cholerae* Strains

	Reaction	Percentage Positive
gram-negative, asporogenous rod	+	100
oxidase	+	100
glucose, acid under a petrolatum seal	+	100
glucose, gas	−	0
D-mannitol, acid	+	99.8
meso-inositol, acid	−	0
hydrogen sulfide, black butt on TSI	−	0
L-lysine decarboxylase	+	100
L-arginine dihydrolase	−	0
L-ornithine decarboxylase	+	98.9
growth in 1% tryptone broth[a]	+	99.1

[a]No sodium chloride added.

Polymyxin-B sensitivity. A modification of the technique of Han and Khie[27] is used. Inoculate a Mueller-Hinton agar plate with a suspect 4 hr broth culture to yield a heavy discrete colonial growth. Dry the plate and place a 50 unit disc of polymyxin-B on the surface. Invert the plate, incubate overnight at 35° ± 2°C, and record the result. Classical strains are sensitive (≥ 12 mm zone); El Tor strains are resistant.

Other tests. Some additional tests useful for biotype differentiation are hemolysis of 1% sheep red blood cells,[19] chicken red blood cell agglutination,[21] and the Voges-Proskauer (VP) test.[18] El Tor biotypes are usually hemolytic to 1% sheep red blood cells, agglutinate chicken red blood cells, and give a positive VP reaction at 22°C.

28.514   Determination of enterotoxigenicity

Virulent and avirulent strains of *Vibrio* exist in the environment. Isolates that are determined, either biochemically, or serologically and biochemically, to be *V. cholerae* or *V. mimicus*, should be tested for the production of cholera enterotoxin (CT) or cytotoxin.

Y-1 mouse adrenal cell assay. CT has been shown to stimulate the enzyme adenylate cyclase with the production of cyclic adenosine monophosphate that ultimately influences several cellular processes. In the Y-1 cell assay, CT promotes the conversion of elongated fibroblast-like cells into round refractile cells.[55]

The maintenance and passage of cell cultures, preparation of microtiter assay plates, and conduct and interpretation of assay are carried out as in Chapter 24 of this book.

Inoculate test cultures from T_1N_1 slants to tubes of CAYE broth and incubate overnight at 30° ± 2°C. Inoculate a 10 ml portion of CAYE broth in a 50 ml Erlenmeyer flask from each stationary culture; incubate for 18 hr with shaking. Centrifuge each test culture; filter the supernatant through a 0.22 μm filter. Refrigerated filtrates may be stored for up to 1 week.

Add aliquots of 0.025 ml from each filtrate, both unheated and heated to 80°C for 30 min, to wells of the microtiter assay plate. In addition to filtrates from known toxigenic and nontoxigenic cultures, add 0.025 ml aliquots from preparations containing 1.0 and 0.1 ng CT/ml. Suppression of cell rounding by treatment of test filtrates with anti-CT serum is an advisable control for nonspecific reactions.

Immunological detection of enterotoxin. A solid phase-microtiter radioimmunoassay (RIA) test is used.[25] Polyvinyl microtiter plates are precoated with anti-CT serum diluted to an optimally effective concentration in phosphate buffered saline (PBS), pH 7.4. Incubate the plates 12 hr at room temperature, wash five times in PBS, fill the wells with 1% bovine serum albumin (BSA) in PBS, and reincubate for 12 hr. Remove BSA-PBS and wash twice with PBS.

Fill each well with 50 μl of culture filtrate prepared as in Section 28.514 above or with purified CT diluted in PBS with 1% BSA. Incubate the plates at room temperature overnight. Wash the wells five times with PBS.

To each well, add 50 μl ^{125}I-labeled anti-CT. After 4 hr incubation at 37°C wash the plates five times in PBS, cut them up, and place the separate wells in gamma-counting tubes for analysis.

The results are expressed as the ratio of residual counts in the sample well to the mean of residual counts in wells receiving BSA-PBS or sterile broth controls. A sample-to-control ratio of 1.7 or greater is considered positive.

Micro-ELISA procedure for detection of enterotoxin and cytotoxin. Grow vibrios in CAYE medium containing 45 μg lincomycin/ml with shaking as described in Section 28.514 for performance of Y-1 assay. Centrifuge culture at $9000 \times g$ for 20 min in refrigerated centrifuge and decant supernatant for testing. Supernatants need not be sterilized and may be frozen at $-20°C$ before use.

Coat each well of microtiter plate with 50 μl of appropriate dilution of antigen-specific coating antibodies. Make dilutions of antibody in 0.1 M bicarbonate buffer, pH 9.6. Cover and store at 4°C overnight. Block with 1% BSA for 1 hr at 37°C. Wash plates three times with 200 μl ELISA buffer and add 50 μl test supernatant to each well. Run positive controls (enterotoxin- or cytotoxin-positive bacterial strains) and negative controls (uninoculated growth medium). Cover and incubate plates for 1 hr at 37°C. Wash plates three times with 200 μl ELISA buffer and add 50 μl of appropriate dilution of antigen-specific secondary antibodies to each well. Make dilutions in ELISA buffer. Cover and incubate plates at 37°C for 1 hr. Wash plates three times with 200 μl ELISA buffer, and add 50 μl protein A-peroxidase solution to each well. Cover plates and incubate at 37°C for 1 hr. Wash plates three times with ELISA buffer, and add 100 μl of ABTS solution to each well. Cover and incubate plates at 37°C for 30 min.

Read optical density of each well at 410 nm using a spectrophotometer. Reincubate plates at 37°C to obtain darker reactions. Culture supernatants yielding an optical density greater than 0.1 are positive for production of either cholera enterotoxin or cytotoxin, depending on which specific antiserum was used. The final report should include biochemical and serological identification of the isolate and enterotoxicity results.

Toxins other than cholera enterotoxin produced by V. cholerae non 0-1. Spira and Daniel[65] described the isolation of *V. cholerae* non 0-1 strains that do not produce cholera enterotoxin from clinical cases of diarrhea. Madden et al.[41] also described clinical isolates of this nature and demonstrated that they are pathogenic for infant rabbits.[15, 22] Unpublished data of these authors indicate that these isolates will also cause diarrhea in adult rabbits inoculated according to the procedure described by Spira et al.[66] A heat-labile cytolysin produced by *V. cholerae* non-01 was found by McCardell et al.[43] to be cytotoxic to Y-1 mouse adrenal and Chinese hamster ovary cells, to be rapidly fatal upon intravenous injection into adult mice, and to cause fluid accumulation in rabbit ileal loops.

28.52   *V. parahaemolyticus*

The following analytical scheme for culturing *V. parahaemolyticus* is presented in two parts, one for seafood and another for clinical samples. The procedures differ only in the way the specimens are handled on the first day in the enrichment procedure. Thereafter they are identical.

28.521   Seafood samples

Enrichment, isolation, and enumeration. Weigh 50 g of seafood sample into a blender. Obtain surface tissues, gills, and gut of fish. Sample the entire interior of shellfish. For crustaceans such as shrimp, use the entire animal if possible; if it is is too large, select the central portion including gill and gut.

Add 450 ml PBS dilution water and blend for 1 min at 8,000 rpm. This constitutes the 1:10 dilution.

Prepare 1:100, 1:1000, 1:10,000 dilutions or higher, if necessary, in PBS.

Inoculate 3 × 10 ml portions of the 1:10 dilution into 3 tubes containing 10 ml of enrichment broth (GSTB, SPB, or HAEB)—2X concentration. This represents the 1 gm portion. Similarly, inoculate 3 × 1 ml portions of the 1:10, 1:100, 1:1000, and 1:10,000 dilutions into 10 ml of single-strength enrichment broth. If high numbers of *V. parahaemolyticus* are expected, the examination may start at the 1:10 dilution of product.

Incubate the tubes overnight at 35° ± 2°C.

Streak a 3 mm loopful from the top 1 cm of broth tubes containing the three highest dilutions of sample showing growth onto TCBS agar.

Incubate TCBS agar plates overnight at 35° ± 2°C.

V. parahaemolyticus appears as round, opaque, green or bluish colonies,

2 to 3 mm in diameter. Interfering, competitive *V. alginolyticus* colonies are large, opaque, and yellow.

When the blue-green colonies are finally identified biochemically as *V. parahaemolyticus* (see below), refer to the original positive dilutions in the enrichment broth and apply the 3-tube-MPN tables (Chapter 6) for final enumeration of the organism.

To detect injured *V. parahaemolyticus* in refrigerated and frozen seafood, a pre-enrichment of samples in nonselective medium has been recommended.[54] Inoculate sample dilutions into TSB or TSB containing 3% salt, incubate overnight at 35° ± 2°C, and then transfer to a selective medium, such as SPB.

Biochemical identification of isolates. Unless otherwise specified, all media in this section are prepared to contain 2% to 3% NaCl.

Transfer two or more suspicious colonies from TCBS agar with a needle to TSI agar slants. Streak the slant, stab the butt, and incubate overnight at 35° ± 2°C. Both *V. parahaemolyticus* and *V. vulnificus* produce an alkaline slant and an acid butt, but no gas or H_2S in TSI agar.

For TSB and TSA slants, inoculate both media and incubate overnight at 35° ± 2°C. These cultures provide inocula for other tests as well as material for the gram-stain and for microscopic examination. Both *V. parahaemolyticus* and *V. vulnificus* are gram-negative, pleomorphic organisms exhibiting curved or straight rods with polar flagella. Some strains of *V. parahaemolyticus* form unsheathed peritrichous flagella on solid media.

Inoculate a tube of motility test medium by stabbing the column of the medium to a depth of approximately 5 cm. Incubate overnight at 35° ± 2°C. A circular outgrowth from the line of stab constitutes a positive test. *V. parahaemolyticus* and *V. vulnificus* are motile.

Only motile, gram-negative rods that produce an acid butt and an alkaline slant on TSI agar and do not form H_2S or gas are examined further. The identifying characteristics of *V. parahaemolyticus* and *V. vulnificus* are shown in Table 2.

Biochemically, *V. parahaemolyticus* and *V. vulnificus* are phenotypically similar, but can be differentiated by differences on the ONPG, halophilism, cellobiose, and lactose reactions (Table 2). By using selected biochemical traits, *V. parahaemolyticus* and *V. vulnificus* can be distinguished from most interfering marine vibrios and other marine microorganisms[82] (Table 3).

Hydrophobic grid membrane filtration enumeration procedure (HGMF).[16] (See also Chapter 39.) Prepare a 1:10 dilution of seafood sample with peptone-tween-salt diluent (PTS), and blend 60 sec at high speed.

Filter 1.0 ml or other volume of homogenate through HGMF using sterile diluent as a carrier. With forceps, aseptically transfer the HGMF from the filtration apparatus to the surface of a dry tryptic soy agar magnesium sulfate (TSAMS) NaCl plate. Incubate 4 hr at 35°C.

With forceps, aseptically transfer the HGMF from the TSAMS to the sur-

Table 2—Identifying Characteristics of *V. parahaemolyticus* and *V. vulnificus*

Tests		Reactions of *V. parahaemolyticus*	*V. vulnificus*
gram stain		gram-negative	
morphology		curved/straight rods	
motility		+	+
TSI		K/A[a], H$_2$S ($-$), gas ($-$)	
Hugh-Liefson glucose (O/F medium)		fermentation ($+$), gas ($-$)	
oxidase		+	+
ONPG		$-$	+
arginine dihydrolase		$-$	$-$
lysine decarboxylase		+	+
ornithine decarboxylase		+	+
gelatin liquefaction		+	+
halophilism (% NaCl)	0	$-$	$-$
	6	+	+
	8	+	$-$
	10	$-$	$-$
growth at 42°C		+	+
Voges-Proskauer[b]		$-$	$-$
indole		+	+
acid production from:			
cellobiose		$-$	+
sucrose		$-$	$-$
maltose		+	+
mannitol		+	+
trehalose		+	+
lactose		$-$	+

[a]Alkaline slant/acid butt.
[b]Incubate at 30°C overnight.

face of a dry *Vibrio parahaemolyticus* sucrose agar (VPSA) plate. Invert plate and incubate at 42°C for 18 to 20 hr.

On VPSA, *V. parahaemolyticus* colonies will be green to blue. Other growth will be yellow due to sucrose fermentation. Count squares with green/blue colonies and calculate the MPN per g of seafood.

The apparatus, filters, and specific instructions may be obtained from QA Laboratories, Ltd., 135 The West Mall, Toronto, Canada, M9C 1C2; (416) 622-6705.

28.522   Clinical specimens

If the transit time from field to laboratory is more than 8 hr, place rectal swabs or swabs of fresh stool specimens in Cary-Blair transport medium.[9] In the laboratory, inoculate the swab onto TCBS agar and streak for isolation. Incubate the plate overnight at 35° ± 2°C.

Table 3—Scheme for Differentiating *V. parahaemolyticus* from Other Microorganisms

Test	Vibrio species						Aeromonas hydrophila	Plesiomonas shigelloides
	parahaemolyticus	vulnificus	alginolyticus	anguillarum	fluvialis	metschnikovii		
TCBS (green colony)	+	+	−	−	−	−	−	+
growth at 42°C	+	+	+	−	V	V	−	−
growth in media with								
0% NaCl	−	−	−	−	−	−	+	+
6% NaCl	+	+	+	+	+	+	−	−
8% NaCl	+	−	+	V	+	V	−	−
10% NaCl	−	−	+	−	−	−	−	−
lysine decarboxylase	+	+	+	−	−	V	−	+
arginine dihydrolase	−	−	−	V	+	+	V	+
ornithine decarboxylase	V	V	V	−	−	−	−	V
sucrose fermentation	−	−	+	+	+	+	V	−
lactose fermentation	−	+	−	−	−	V	V	V
mannitol fermentation	+	V	+	+	+	+	+	−
arabinose fermentation	+	−	−	−	+	−	V	−
Voges-Proskauer	−	−	+	V	−	+	V	−
ONPG reaction	−	+	−	ND	+	V	+	+

V = variable; ND = not determined.

Place the swab in a 10 ml tube of alkaline peptone water containing 3% NaCl. After 8 hr of incubation at 35° ± 2°C, streak a loopful onto TCBS agar. Incubate the plate overnight at 35° ± 2°C. Proceed as indicated under seafood samples (Section 28.521).

If transit time from field to laboratory is less than 8 hr, place stool specimen or rectal swab in alkaline peptone water containing 3% NaCl.

After 8 hr of incubation, streak a loopful onto TCBS agar. Incubate the plate overnight at 35° ± 2°C. Proceed as indicated under seafood samples (Section 28.521).

28.523   Serologic typing

V. parahaemolyticus possesses three antigenic components: H, O, and K. The H antigen is common to all strains of V. parahaemolyticus and is of little value in serotyping. The K, or capsular, antigen may be removed from the bacterial body by heating the isolate for 1 or 2 hr at 100°C. This process exposes the O, or somatic, antigen, which is thermostable. Since the K antigen masks the O antigen, it is necessary to remove the former by heating before performing the O agglutination tests.

There are 11 O group and 65 K antigens.[57] Five of the K antigens have been found to occur with either of two O group antigens; therefore, there are 70 recognized serotypes, as seen in Table 4.[57] Except for unusual clinical isolates, the Commission has recommended that additions to this scheme be avoided. Serologic tests by themselves are not used to identify V. parahae-

Table 4—Antigenic Scheme of V. parahaemolyticus (1986)[a]

O group	K type
1	1,25,26,32,38,41,56,58[b],64,69
2	3,28
3	4[b],5,6,7,29,30[b],31,33,37,43,45,48,54,57,58[b],59,65
4	4[b],8,9,10,11,12,13,34,42,49,53,55,63,67
5	15,17,30[b],47,60,61[b],68
6	18,46
7	19[b]
8	20,21,22,39,70
9	23,44
10	19[b],24,52,66,71
11	36,40,50,51,61[b]
Total	
11	65

[a]The antigenic scheme was first established by Sakazaki et al. and later extended by the Commission of the Serotyping of V. parahaemolyticus (Japan); K antigens, 2,14,16,29,35, and 62 were excluded by the Commission.[59]

[b]Occurs with more than one O group.

molyticus because of cross-reactions with many other marine organisms. On the other hand, during investigations of foodborne outbreaks, serologic tests become an indispensable epidemiologic tool.

Commercial Japanese *V. parahaemolyticus* diagnostic antiserum is available from Nichimen Co., 1185 Avenue of the Americas, 31st Floor, New York, NY 10036; (212) 719-1000. Because the antiserum is expensive, it is not recommended for small laboratories. To serotype, use the following procedure:

Determining the O group. Inoculate two TSA-3% NaCl slants and incubate at 35° ± 2°C for 24 hr. Wash one slant with 1 ml of a 3% NaCl-5% glycerol solution. Autoclave this suspension at 121°C at 15 lb for 1 hr. Centrifuge at 5,000 × g and resuspend cells in 3% NaCl. This yields the prepared O antigen.

On a plastic or glass plate, mark off 12 1-cm squares with a wax pencil, or purchase agglutination slides. Place a drop of heated O antigen in each square with a Pasteur pipette. Place a drop of O group antiserum in 11 squares representing all 11 groups. The twelfth square containing only O antigen is the autoagglutination control.

Mix all drops with a wire needle and rock back and forth for at least 2 min. A positive agglutination should be produced rapidly and completely. Weak and delayed reactions are considered negative. Frequently all 11 O groups will be negative, and the culture must be reported as O group-untypable.

Determining the K type. Wash down the second TSA-3% NaCl slant from Section 28.523 with 1 ml of 3% NaCl solution. This is the K antigen suspension.

The foregoing O group determination establishes the number and identity of the individual K types that could be associated with the specific O group. For example, if group O8 were found, one would test against monovalent K20, 21, 22, 39, and 70 antisera. Thus, five test squares plus one autoagglutination control square would be drawn with wax pencil on a plastic plate.

Repeat as in Section 28.523, and deliver a drop of K antigen to each square with a Pasteur pipette. Add one drop of specific antiserum to each square except the control square.

Mix and rock as in Section 28.523. The K type reactions, if positive, are rapid (1 to 2 min). Experience has shown that only 40% of all American seafood isolates are serotypable.[23]

28.524   Determining pathogenicity

Kato et al.[35] showed that *V. parahaemolyticus* isolates from the stools of patients with enteric infections are hemolytic on a special high-salt human blood agar, whereas *V. parahaemolyticus* isolates from seafood and marine water usually are not. Wagatsuma[85] later modified this special agar. To avoid confusion with the regular normal hemolytic activity of *V. parahaemolyticus* on conventional 5% sheep blood agar, the special agar was named Wagatsuma agar and the special hemolytic response the Kanagawa phenomenon.

The correlation has been well established that *V. parahaemolyticus* strains that cause illness in humans are almost always Kanagawa-positive and isolates recovered from seafood are almost always Kanagawa-negative.[58] In addition, extensive investigation in animal models suggests that the Kanagawa hemolysin is the primary virulence factor in *V. parahaemolyticus*.[74] The test should be performed with fresh isolates since an organism may lose this characteristic. During a *V. parahaemolyticus* epidemic, it is essential to perform a Kanagawa test on isolates from all patients and from the incriminated food to establish the causative serotype.

Kanagawa test. Inoculate suspect organism in TSB-3% NaCl and incubate overnight at 35° ± 2°C.

Drop a loopful of culture on a previously well-dried Wagatsuma blood agar plate. Several drops in a circular pattern may be made on a single plate. Plates may be divided into sections to test more than one isolate per plate. Include a known Kanagawa-positive strain on each plate.

Incubate at 35° ± 2°C and read in less than 24 hr. A positive test consists of beta hemolysis, a zone of transparent clearing of the blood cells around the area of growth. No observation made beyond 24 hr is valid.

28.53   *V. vulnificus*

28.531   Method

The analytical scheme for isolating *V. vulnificus* is a procedure previously used with success in several laboratories[37, 69, 88] for the analysis of oysters and environmental samples. No specific enrichment broths have been designed or evaluated for an enumeration procedure. The following method is derived from the procedure used for the isolation of *V. cholerae*.

28.532   Seafood samples

Enrichment, isolation, and enumeration. Prepare an initial 1:10 dilution of sample in PBS following the procedure for *V. parahaemolyticus* (Section 28.521). Prepare decimal dilutions in PBS.

Inoculate 3 × 1 ml portions of the dilutions into 3 tubes containing 10 ml APW. If low numbers are expected, 3 × 10 ml portions of the 1:10 dilution can be inoculated into 3 × 10 ml 2× APW. Incubate tubes 12 to 16 hr at 35° ± 2°C.

Streak a 3 mm loopful from the top 1 cm of APW tubes with growth onto TCBS, CPC, and SDS selective agars. Incubate TCBS and SDS agars overnight at 35° ± 2°C. Incubate CPC agar overnight at 40° ± 1°C.

On these media the appearance of *V. vulnificus* colonies is distinctive. On TCBS agar colonies are round, opaque, green to blue, and 2 to 3 mm in diameter. On SDS agar they are round, opaque, blue to brownish, and 2 to 3 mm in diameter with a blue, opaque halo around each colony. On CPC agar colonies are round, flat, opaque, yellow, and 1 to 2 mm in diameter.

Upon identification of *V. vulnificus*, refer to the original positive dilutions of APW and apply the 3-tube-MPN tables (Chapter 6) for final enumeration of the organism.

Biochemical identification of isolates. Unless otherwise specified, all media in this section are prepared to contain a minimum of 0.5% NaCl. Transfer two or more suspicious colonies with a needle from TCBS, CPC, and SDS agar plates to TSB, TSA, and TSI agar slants and motility medium described in Section 28.521. Biochemical reactions to differentiate *V. vulnificus* from *V. parahaemolyticus* can be found in Tables 2 and 3.

28.533   Determination of virulence[82]

V. vulnificus exhibits a variation in colonial morphology that is associated with virulence.[62] When selecting colonies from agar plates to test for virulence, select opaque rather than translucent colonies if both types are present. Translucent colonies are less virulent. Grow isolates in 50 ml heart infusion broth in 250 ml flasks on a shaker at 250 rpm at 37°C to early stationary phase (usually 8 to 12 hr).

Harvest 10 ml of cells by centrifugation (5000 × g for 10 min) and wash twice with 10 ml of sterile PBS. During this time inject four groups of five 20 g mice (18 to 22 g) with 250 μg of iron dextran per g of body weight by the intramuscular route.

Resuspend the washed cells in 10 ml sterile PBS and make decimal dilutions to 10^{-8}. Determine the viable count by standard plate methods using heart infusion agar. Viable cells should be approximately 10^9 per ml in 8 to 12 hr.

Approximately 2 hr after the injection of iron dextran, inject groups of five mice with approximately 10^0, 10^1, and 10^2 cells of *V. vulnificus* in 0.5 ml volume by the intraperitoneal route. Inject a fourth group of five mice with 0.5 ml of sterile PBS.

Observe the mice for 48 hr and count the number of deaths in each group. Calculate the LD_{50} value by the end point titration procedure in Table 5.

If a strain is virulent, all or nearly all mice will die and the LD_{50} will be <10 cells/20 g mouse. Avirulent strains have thus far not caused death in mice at $<10^6$ cells/mouse.

28.6   INTERPRETATION

The isolation of *V. parahaemolyticus* from seafood is not unusual.[2, 23, 26, 34, 59, 83] *V. parahaemolyticus* is a normal saprophytic inhabitant of the coastal marine environment and multiplies during the warm summer months.[26] In this period the organism is readily recovered from most of the seafood species harvested in coastal areas. The Japanese have separated the virulent from the avirulent strains of *V. parahaemolyticus* by means of the Kanagawa test.[85] Thus far, only one isolate from American seafood involved

Table 5—Calculation of LD₅₀ by Reed-Muench Method

Dilution	Bacterial cells/ml	# mice dead[a]	# mice survived[a]	Accum values		Mortality (%)
				dead	survived	
10^0	3×10^8	3	0	16	0	100
10^{-1}	3×10^7	3	0	13	0	100
10^{-2}	3×10^6	4	0	10	0	100
10^{-3}	3×10^5	3	0	6	0	100
10^{-4}	3×10^4	3	1	3	1	75[b]
10^{-5}	3×10^3	0	3	0	4	0
10^{-6}	3×10^2	0	4	0	8	0

[a]Arrows indicate direction of addition for accumulated values.

[b]The 50% end point in the above example lies between dilutions 10^{-4} (3×10^4 cells) and 10^{-5} (3×10^3 cells).

Fractional titer = (% mortality above 50% − 50%)/(% mortality above 50% − % mortality below 50%) = $(75 - 50)/(75 - 0) = 0.33$. Negative logarithm of LD₅₀ titer = $4.0 + 0.33 = 4.33$. LD₅₀ titer = $10^{-4.33}$ dilution. To find the number of bacterial cells in $10^{-4.33}$ dilution subtract $10^{-4.33}$ from $10^{8.48}$, which is 3×10^8 (number of cells in undiluted or original culture).

$$10^{8.48} - 10^{-4.33} = 10^{4.15} = 14,000 \text{ cells/ml}$$

Because mice were injected with 0.5 ml, the LD₅₀/0.5 ml now becomes 7000 cells.

in an outbreak has proved to be Kanagawa-positive.[67] However, these types have occurred with greater frequency in Japan and England. In most instances, *V. parahaemolyticus* Kanagawa-negative seafood strains do not cause human gastroenteritis.

In contrast, contamination of food with enterotoxigenic *V. cholerae* and with *V. vulnificus* constitutes an important finding from the standpoint of public health. The entire lot of contaminated food should be withheld from distribution until the appropriate health authorities are notified and an epidemiologic investigation can be undertaken.

28.7 REFERENCES

1. Akiyama, S., Takizawa, K., and Obara, Y. 1964. Study on enrichment broth for *Vibrio parahaemolyticus*. Ann. Rep. Kanagawa Pref. Inst. Public Health 13: 7.
2. Bartley, C. H. and Slanetz, L. W. 1971. Occurrence of *Vibrio parahaemolyticus* in estuarine waters and oysters of New Hampshire. Appl. Microbiol. 21: 965.
3. Barua, D. and Burrows, W., eds. 1974. "Cholera." W. B. Sanders Company, Philadelphia, Pa.
4. Blake, P. A., Merson, M. H., Weaver, R. E., Hollis, D. G., and Heublein, P. C. 1979. Disease caused by marine *Vibrio*. Clinical characteristics and epidemiology. New Engl. J. Med. 300: 1.
5. Blake, P. A., Allegra, D. T., Snyder, J. D., Barrett, T. J., McFarland, L., Caraway, C. T., Feeley, J. C., Craig, J. P., Lee, J. V., Puhr, N. D., and Feldman, R. A. 1980. Cholera— A possible endemic focus in the United States. New Engl. J. Med. 302: 305.
6. Blake, P. A., Weaver, R. E., and Hollis, D. G. 1980. Diseases of humans (other than cholera) caused by vibrios. Ann. Rev. Microbiol. 34: 341.
7. Boutin, B. K., Reyes, A. L., Peeler, J. T., and Twedt, R. M. 1985. Effect of temperature and suspending vehicle on survival of *Vibrio parahaemolyticus* and *Vibrio vulnificus*. J. Food Prot. 48: 875.
8. Bryant, R. G., Jarvis, J., and Janda, J. M. 1987. Use of sodium dodecyl sulfate-polymyxin B-sucrose medium for isolation of *Vibrio vulnificus* from shellfish. Appl. Environ. Microbiol. 53: 1556.
9. Cary, S. G. and Blair, F. B. 1961. New transport medium for shipment of clinical specimens. I. Fecal specimens. J. Bacteriol. 88: 96.
10. Clark, W. A. and Steigerwalt, A. G. 1977. Deoxyribonucleic acid reassociation experiments with a halophilic lactose-fermenting vibrio isolated from blood cultures. Int. J. Syst. Bacteriol. 27: 194.
11. Colwell, R. R., Seidler, R. J., Kaper, J., Joseph, S. W., Garges, S., Lockman, H., Maneval, D., Bradford, H., Roberts, N., Remmers, E., Huq, I., and Huq, A. 1981. Occurrence of *Vibrio cholerae* serotype 01 in Maryland and Louisiana estuaries. Appl. Environ. Microbiol. 41: 555.
12. Craig, J. P., Yamamoto, K., Takeda, Y., and Miwatani, T. 1981. Production of a cholera-like enterotoxin by a *Vibrio cholerae* non-01 strain isolated from the environment. Infect. Immun. 34: 90.
13. Davis, B. R., Fanning, G. R., Madden, J. M., Steigerwalt, A. G., Bradford, H. B. Jr., Smith, H. L. Jr., and Brenner, D. J. 1981. Characterization of biochemically atypical *Vibrio cholerae* strains and designation of a new pathogenic species, *Vibrio mimicus*. J. Clin. Microbiol. 14: 631.
14. DePaola, A., Motes, M. L., and McPhearson, R. M. 1988. Comparison of APHA and elevated temperature enrichment methods for recovery of *Vibrio cholerae* from oysters: collaborative study. J. Assn. Off. Anal. Chem. 71: 584.

15. Dutta, N. K. and Habbu, M. K. 1955. Experimental cholera in infant rabbits: A method for chemotherapeutic investigation. Br. J. Pharmacol. 10: 153.

16. Entis, P. and Boleszczuk, P. 1983. Overnight enumeration of *Vibrio parahaemolyticus* in seafood by hydrophobic grid membrane filtration. J. Food Prot. 46: 783.

17. Farmer, J. J. III. 1980. Revival of the name *Vibrio vulnificus* Int. J. Syst. Bacteriol. 30: 656.

18. Feeley, J. C. 1965. Classification of *V. cholerae* (*Vibrio comma*), including El Tor vibrios, by infrasubspecific characteristics. J. Bacteriol. 89: 665.

19. Feeley, J. C. and Pittman, M. 1963. Studies on the haemolytic activity of El Tor vibrios. Bull. WHO 28: 347.

20. Felsenfeld, O. 1965. Notes on food, beverages and fomites contaminated with *Vibrio cholerae*. Bull. WHO 33: 725.

21. Finkelstein, R. A. and Mukerjee, S. 1963. Hemagglutination: A rapid method for differentiating *Vibrio cholerae* and El Tor vibrios. Proc. Soc. Exp. Biol. Med. 112: 355.

22. Finkelstein, R. A., Norris, H. T., and Dutta, N. K. 1964. Pathogenesis of experimental cholera in infant rabbits. I. Observations on the intraintestinal infection and experimental cholera produced with cell-free products. J. Infect. Dis. 114: 203.

23. Fishbein, J., Mehlman, I. J., and Pitcher, J. 1970. Isolation of *Vibrio parahaemolyticus* from the processed meat of Chesapeake Bay blue crabs. Appl. Microbiol. 20: 176.

24. Gardner, A. D. and Venkatraman, K. V. 1935. The antigens of the cholera group of vibrios. J. Hyg. (London) 35: 262.

25. Greenberg, H. B., Sack, D. A., Rodriguez, W., Sack, R. B., Wyatt, R. G., Kalica, A. R., Horswood, R. L., Chanock, R. M., and Kapakian, A. Z. 1977. Microtiter solid-phase radioimmunoassay for detection for *Escherichia coli* heat-labile enterotoxin. Infect. Immun. 17: 541.

26. Hackney, C. R., Ray, B., and Speck, M. L. 1980. Incidence of *Vibrio parahaemolyticus* in and the microbiological quality of seafood in North Carolina. J. Food Prot. 43: 769.

27. Han, G. K. and Khie, T. 1963. A new method for the differentiation of *Vibrio comma* and *Vibrio El Tor*. Amer. J. Hyg. 77: 184.

28. Hickman, F. W., Farmer, J. J., Hollis, D. G., Fanning, G. R., Steigerwalt, A. S., Weaver, R. E., and Brenner, D. J. 1982. Identification of *Vibrio hollisae* sp. nov. from patients with diarrhea. J. Clin. Microbiol. 15: 395.

29. Hood, M. A., Ness, G. E., and Rodrick, G. E. 1981. Isolation of *Vibrio cholerae* serotype 01 from the eastern oyster *Crassostrea virginica*. Appl. Environ. Microbiol. 41: 559.

30. Horie, S., Saheki, K., Kozima, T., Nara, M., and Sekine, Y. 1964. Distribution of *Vibrio parahaemolyticus* in plankton and fish in the open sea. Bull. Jpn. Soc. Sci. Fish. 30: 786.

31. Hugh, R. and Feeley, J. C. 1972. Report (1966–1970) of the subcommittee on taxonomy of vibrios to the International Committee on Nomenclature of Bacteria. Int. J. Syst. Bacteriol. 22: 123.

32. Hugh, R. and Sakazaki, R. 1972. Minimal number of characters for the identification of *Vibrio* species, *Vibrio cholerae* and *Vibrio parahaemolyticus*. Public Health Lab. 30: 133.

33. Hughes, J. M., Hollis, D. G., Gangarosa, E. J., and Weaver, R. E. 1978. Non-cholera *Vibrio* infections in the United States. Clinical, epidemiologic, and laboratory features. Ann. Int. Med. 88: 602.

34. Kampelmacher, E. H., Van Noorle Jansen, L. M., Mossel, D. A. A., and Groen, F. J. 1972. A survey of the occurrence of *Vibrio parahaemolyticus* and *Vibrio alginolyticus* on mussels and oysters and in estuarine waters in the Netherlands. J. Appl. Bacteriol. 35: 431.

35. Kato, T., Obara, Y., Ichinoe, H., Nagashima, K., Akiyama, S., Takizawa, K., Matsuchima, A., Yamai, S., and Miyamoto, Y. 1965. Grouping of *Vibrio parahaemolyticus* with a hemolysis reaction. Shokuhin Eisei Kankyu 15: 83 (in Japanese).

36. Kaysner, C. A., Abeyta, C., Wekell, M. M., DePaola, A., Stott, R. F., and Leitch, J. M. 1987a. Incidence of *Vibrio cholerae* from estuaries of the United States West Coast. Appl. Environ. Microbiol. 53: 1344.

37. Kaysner, C. A., Abeyta, C., Wekell, M. M., DePaola, A., Stott, R. F., and Leitch, J. M. 1987b. Virulent strains of *Vibrio vulnificus* isolated from estuaries of the United States West Coast. Appl. Environ. Microbiol. 53: 1349.

38. Kobayashi, T., Enomoto, S., Sakazaki, R., and Kuwabara, S. 1963. A new selective isolation medium for pathogenic vibrios: TCBS agar. Jpn. J. Bacteriol. 18: 387.

39. Lee, J. V., Donovan, T. J., and Furniss, A. L. 1978. Characterization, taxonomy, and amended description of *Vibrio metschnikovii*., Int. J. Syst. Bacteriol. 28:99.

40. Lee, J. V., Shread, P., Furniss, A. L., and Bryant, T. N. 1981. Taxonomy and description of *Vibrio fluvialis* sp. nov. (synonym group F vibrios, group EF-6). J. Appl. Bacteriol. 50: 73.

41. Madden, J. M., Nematollahi, W. P., Hill, W. E., McCardell, B. A., and Twedt, R. M. 1981. Virulence of three clinical isolates of *Vibrio cholerae*, non-01 serogroup, in experimental enteric infections in rabbits. Infect. Immun. 33: 616.

42. Massad, G. and Oliver, J. D. 1987. New selective and differential medium for *Vibrio cholerae* and *Vibrio vulnificus*. Appl. Environ. Microbiol. 53: 2262.

43. McCardell, B. A., Madden, J. M., and Shah, D. B. 1985. Isolation and characterization of a cytolysin produced by *Vibrio cholerae* serogroup non-01., Can. J. Microbiol. 31: 711.

44. Matches, J. R., Liston, J., and Daneault, L. P. 1971. Survival of *Vibrio parahaemolyticus* in fish homogenate during storage at low temperatures. Appl. Microbiol. 21: 951.

45. Merson, M. H., Martin, W. T., Craig, J. P., Morris, G. K., Blake, P. A., Craun, G. F., Feeley, J. C., Camacho, J. C., and Gangarosa, E. J. 1977. Cholera on Guam, 1974. Amer. J. Epidemiol. 105: 349.

46. Morris, J. G. and Black, R. E. 1985. Cholera and other vibrioses in the United States. New Engl. J. Med. 312: 343.

47. Mukerjee, S. 1961. Diagnostic uses of cholera bacteriophages. J. Hyg. 59: 109.

48. Nicholls, K. M., Lee, J. V., and Donovan, T. J. 1976. An evaluation of commercial thiosulfate citrate bile salt sucrose agar (TCBS). J. Appl. Bacteriol. 41: 265.

49. Nishibuchi, M. and Kaper, J. B. 1985. Nucleotide sequence of the thermostabile direct hemolysin of *Vibrio parahaemolyticus*. J. Bacteriol. 162: 558.

50. Nishibuchi, M., Hill, W. E., Zon, G., Payne, W. L., and Kaper, J. B. 1986. Synthetic oligodeoxyribonucleotide probes to detect Kanagawa phenomenon-positive *Vibrio parahaemolyticus*. J. Clin. Microbiol. 23: 1091.

51. Oliver, J. D. 1981. The pathogenicity and ecology of *Vibrio vulnificus*. Marine Technol. Soc. J. 15: 45.

52. Peterson, E. H. 1979. Comparative study of procedures for quantification of *Vibrio parahaemolyticus* in seafoods. J. Food Prot. 42: 852.

53. Prescott, L. M. and Bhattacharjee, N. K. 1969. Viability of El Tor vibrios in common foodstuffs found in an endemic cholera area. Bull. WHO 40: 980.

54. Ray, B., Hawkins, S. M., and Hackney, C. R. 1978. Method for the detection of injured *Vibrio parahaemolyticus* in seafoods. Appl. Environ. Microbiol. 35: 1121.

55. Sack, D. A. and Sack, R. B. 1975. Test for enterotoxigenic *Escherichia coli* using Y 1 adrenal cells in miniculture. Infect. Immun. 11: 334.

56. Sakazaki, R. 1968. Proposal of *Vibrio alginolyticus* for the biotype 2 of *Vibrio parahaemolyticus*. Jpn. J. Med. Sci. Biol. 21: 359.

57. Sakazaki, R. and Shimada, T. 1986. Vibrio species as causative agents of food-borne infection. In "Developments in Food Microbiology-2," ed. R. K. Robinson, p. 123. Elsevier Applied Science Publishers, New York, N.Y.

58. Sakazaki, R., Tamura, K., Kato, T., Obara, Y., Yamai, S., and Hobo, K. 1968. Studies on the enteropathogenic facultatively halophilic bacteria, *Vibrio parahaemolyticus*. III. Enteropathogenicity. Jpn. J. Med. Sci. Biol. 21: 325.

59. Sakazaki, R., Karashimada, T., Yuda, K., Sakai, S., Sasakawa, Y., Yamazaki, M., Nakanishi, H., Kobayashi, K., Nishio, T., Okazaki, H., Doke, T., Shimada, T., and Tamura,

K. 1979. Enumeration of and hygienic standard of food safety for *Vibrio parahaemolyticus*. Arch. Lebensmittelhyg. 30: 103.

60. Sakazaki, R., Pivnick, H., Jarvis, G., Goddard, M., Asakawa, Y., Barrow, G., Beuchat, L., Colwell, R., Gleeson, T., Gray, R., Nakanishi, H., Sakai, S., Stavric, S., Takizawa, K., Tamura, K., Twedt, R., Vanderzant, C., and West, P. 1986. ICMSF Methods Studies. XVI. Comparison of Salt Polymyxin Broth with Glucose Salt Teepol Broth for enumerating *Vibrio parahaemolyticus* in naturally contaminated samples. J. Food Prot. 49: 773.

61. Shandera, W., Johnston, J. M., Davis, B. R., and Blake, P. A. 1983. Disease from infection with *Vibrio mimicus*, a newly recognized *Vibrio* species. Ann. Intern. Med. 99: 169.

62. Simpson, L. M., White, V. K., Zane, S. F., and Oliver, J. D. 1987. Correlation between virulence and colony morphology in *Vibrio vulnificus*. Infect. Immun. 55: 269.

63. Singleton, F. L., Attwell, R., Jangi, S., and Colwell, R. R. 1982. Effects of temperature and salinity on *Vibrio cholerae* growth. Appl. Environ. Microbiol. 44: 1047.

64. Smith, H. L. Jr. 1970. A presumptive test for vibrios: The "string" test. Bull. World Health Org. 42: 817.

65. Spira, W. M. and Daniel, R. R. 1979. Biotype clusters formed on the basis of virulence characters in non-0 group 1 *Vibrio cholerae*. In "Proc. 15th Joint Cholera Res. Conf., U.S.-Japan Coop. Med. Sci. Prog." Bethesda, Md., 1979, p. 440.

66. Spira, W. M., Sack, R. B., and Froelich, J. L. 1981. Simple adult rabbit model for *Vibrio cholerae* and enterotoxigenic *Escherichia coli* diarrhea. Infect. Immun. 32: 739.

67. Spite, G. T., Brown, D. F., and Twedt, R. M. 1978. Isolation of an enteropathogenic, Kanagawa-positive strain of *Vibrio parahaemolyticus* from seafood implicated in acute gastroenteritis. Appl. Environ. Microbiol. 35: 1226.

68. Tacket, C. O., Brenner, F., and Blake, P. A. 1984. Clinical features and an epidemiological study of *Vibrio vulnificus* infections. J. Infect. Dis. 149: 558.

69. Tamplin, M. L., Rodrick, G. E., Blake, N. J., and Cuba, T. 1982. Isolation and characterization of *Vibrio vulnificus* from two Florida estuaries. Appl. Environ. Microbiol. 44: 1466.

70. Thomson, W. K. and Thacker, C. L. 1973. Effect of temperature on *Vibrio parahaemolyticus* in oysters at refrigerator and deep freeze temperatures. Can. Inst. Food Sci. Technol. J. 6: 156.

71. Tilton, R. C. and Ryan, R. W. 1987. Clinical and ecological characteristics of *Vibrio vulnificus* in the Northeastern United States. Diagn. Microbiol. Infect. Dis. 6: 109.

72. Tison, D. L. and Kelly, M. T. 1984. *Vibrio* species of medical importance. Diagn. Microbiol. Infect. Dis. 2: 263.

73. Twedt, R. M. 1989. *Vibrio parahaemolyticus*. In "Foodborne Bacterial Pathogens," ed. M. P. Doyle, p. 544. Marcel Dekker, Inc., New York, N.Y.

74. Twedt, R. M., Peeler, J. T., and Spaulding, P. L. 1980. Effective ileal loop dose of Kanagawa-positive *Vibrio parahaemolyticus*. Appl. Environ. Microbiol. 40: 1012.

75. U.S. HEW/PHS/CDC. 1973a. Morbid. Mortal. Weekly Rep. 22: 231. U.S. Dept. Health, Ed. & Welfare. U.S. Pub. Health Service, Washington, D.C.

76. U.S. HEW/PHS/CDC. 1973b. Morbid. Mortal. Weekly Rep. 22: 300. U.S. Dept. Health, Ed. & Welfare. U.S. Pub. Health Service, Washington, D.C.

77. U.S. HEW/PHS/CDC. 1973c. Morbid. Mortal. Weekly Rep. 22: 418. U.S. Dept. Health, Ed. & Welfare. U.S. Pub. Health Service, Washington, D.C.

78. U.S. HEW/PHS/CDC. 1975. Morbid. Mortal. Weekly Rep. 24: 109, 115. U.S. Dept. Health, Ed. & Welfare. U.S. Pub. Health Service, Washington, D.C.

79. U.S. HEW/PHS/CDC. 1978a. Morbid. Mortal. Weekly Rep. 27: 65. U.S. Dept. Health, Ed. & Welfare. U.S. Pub. Health Service, Washington, D.C.

80. U.S. HEW/PHS/CDC. 1978b. Morbid. Mortal. Weekly Rep. 27: 345. U.S. Dept. Health, Ed. & Welfare. U.S. Pub. Health Service, Washington, D.C.

81. U.S. HEW/PHS/CDC. 1980. Morbid. Mortal. Weekly Rep. 29: 601. U.S. Dept. Health, Ed. & Welfare. U.S. Pub. Health Service, Washington, D.C.

82. U.S. HEW/PHS/FDA. Division of Microbiology. 1984. "Bacteriological Analytical Manual." 6th ed. Chap. 12–13. Assoc. of Off. Anal. Chem., Arlington, Va.

83. Van den Broek, M. J. M., Mossel, D. A. A., and Eggenkamp, A. E. 1979. Occurrence of *Vibrio parahaemolyticus* in Dutch mussels. Appl. Environ. Microbiol. 37: 438.

84. Vanderzant, C. and Nickelson, R. 1972. Survival of *Vibrio parahaemolyticus* in shrimp tissue under various environmental conditions. Appl. Microbiol. 23: 34.

85. Wagatsuma, S. 1968. A medium for the test of the hemolytic activity of *Vibrio parahaemolyticus*. Media Circle 13: 159.

86. West, P. A., Russek, E., Brayton, P. R., and Colwell, R. R. 1982. Statistical evaluation of a quality control method for isolation of pathogenic *Vibrio* species on selected thiosulfate-citrate-bile salts-sucrose (TCBS) agars. J. Clin. Microbiol. 16: 1110.

87. West, P. A., Brayton, P. R., Bryant, T. N., and Colwell, R. R. 1986. Numerical taxonomy of vibrios isolated from aquatic environments. Int'l. J. System. Bacteriol. 36: 531.

88. Williams, L. A. and Larock, P. A. 1985. Temporal occurrence of *Vibrio* species and *Aeromonas hydrophila* in estuarine sediments. Appl. Environ. Microbiol. 50: 1490.

Chapter 29

CAMPYLOBACTER

Norman J. Stern, Charlotte M. Patton, Michael P. Doyle,
Chong E. Park, and Barbara A. McCardell

29.1 INTRODUCTION

Campylobacter jejuni, C. coli, and *C. lari* are carried in the intestinal tract of animals and, therefore, contaminate foods of animal origin. *C. jejuni* is recognized as a leading cause of acute bacterial gastroenteritis in humans, and eating foods of animal origin has been associated with many of these illnesses. *C. coli* and *C. lari* also are recognized causes of gastroenteritis but less frequently than *C. jejuni*. Because these campylobacters are recognized causes of human diarrheal disease, the presence of any of these species in food represents a potential hazard to human health. For simplicity's sake these three species will be collectively referred to as the *C. jejuni* group unless otherwise noted.

29.11 Description of the Organisms

As of 1989 the genus *Campylobacter* consisted of 18 species, subspecies, and biovars, with 17 names officially recognized by the International Committee on Systematic Bacteriology[100] and one species name proposed but not official[98] (unofficial names are placed in quotation marks). The taxonomic status of the genus is in flux and is likely to continue changing for some time to come. At least nine species appear to be important in human disease. This number includes *C. pylori*, the agent of human gastritis,[66] whose genetics are only distantly related to *Campylobacter*[94] and which is now classified as *Helicobacter pylori*.

Campylobacters grow at between 25°C and 43°C, are gram-negative, motile, curved or spiral rods, are oxidase-positive, and do not ferment or oxidize carbohydrates. The campylobacters can be broadly placed into two groups on the basis of the catalase test. The catalase-positive campylobacters are most frequently associated with human disease; however, the catalase-negative species "*C. upsaliensis*" also appears to be related to human disease.[81] Consequently, the isolation of a catalase-negative *Campylobacter* from foods should be pursued and the strains characterized.

The campylobacters are generally inactive in many conventional biochemical tests and identification is based on only a few morphological and biochemical features. With certain strains, species identification is based on the results of only one test, and in some cases definitive identification is not possible with routinely available laboratory tests.

29.12   Pathology

Diarrheal symptoms in *C. jejuni* infections may vary from profuse watery diarrhea (cholera-like) to frankly bloody diarrhea containing mucus and white blood cells (dysentery-like). Although the mechanisms by which *C. jejuni* produces disease are as yet largely undefined, several factors such as toxins, motility, and adherence have been described as possible virulence factors. It has been proposed that *C. jejuni* colonizes human intestinal mucus in a manner similar to that of the spiral bacteria of the normal microbiota.[62, 63] These bacteria have a spiral morphology, are microaerophilic, and can penetrate deeply into intestinal crypts. The adaptation to the intestinal mucus niche may be an important determinant of virulence for *C. jejuni*. Motility may also be an important virulence factor for *C. jejuni*.[18, 42, 104] *C. jejuni* infections that result in a dysentery-like disease suggest that some strains of the species may be invasive.[49] The profuse watery diarrhea observed in some *Campylobacter* infections may indicate that these strains could be enterotoxigenic. Certain strains of *C. jejuni* produce a toxin immunologically related to cholera toxin (CT) and *Escherichia coli* heat-labile toxin (LT).[46, 47, 53, 68] *C. jejuni* cytotoxins have been described.[77] The *Campylobacter* toxin produces cytotonic changes in tissue culture cells via stimulation of cyclic AMP production.[67, 97] The role of the cytotoxin in pathogenesis has not been defined, but animals challenged with cytotoxin-positive strains have more severe diarrhea than those given cytotoxin-negative strains.[77] The presence of cytotoxin is also correlated with patients having bloody diarrhea.[54]

The lack of an easy-to-use, inexpensive animal model that mimics human infections has seriously hampered the identification of virulence factors in *C. jejuni*. Although many animal models have been proposed,[10, 17, 30, 42, 51, 62, 96, 99, 104] none has gained wide acceptance.

29.13   Distribution and Epidemiology

C. jejuni has been isolated from individuals with gastroenteritis throughout the world.[8, 19, 23, 50, 61, 75, 84, 87, 89, 105] *C. jejuni* is often isolated from patients with diarrhea at greater isolation rates than reported for *Salmonella* spp. The prevalence of *C. jejuni* infection on college campuses in the United States is 10 and 46 times more frequent than *Salmonella* and *Shigella* infection, respectively.[114] Research indicates that as few as 500 cells of *C. jejuni* can produce illness in humans.[5, 90]

Foods of animal origin are the primary vehicles involved in human infection. The sources of the other *Campylobacter* species implicated in human disease, i.e., *C. hyointestinalis*, "*C. upsaliensis*," *C. cinaedi*, *C. fennelliae*, and *C. pylori (H. pylori)*, have not been determined. Unpasteurized milk has been by far the most commonly implicated vehicle in foodborne outbreaks of *C. jejuni* enteritis.[9, 14, 29, 59, 85, 86, 91, 116, 117, 122] *C. jejuni* can cause a mastitis in cows,[60] and two reports suggest that the presence of *C. jejuni* in the implicated raw milk resulted from udder excretion rather than from fecal contamination.[41, 44]

Although raw milk is a frequently reported vehicle of outbreaks of *Campylobacter* enteritis, epidemiologic studies of sporadic cases have revealed that mishandled poultry is more important than raw milk in transmitting *C. jejuni* enteritis.[22, 32, 37, 115] Several outbreaks also have been associated with eating poultry.[15, 45, 72] For these reasons public health authorities now believe that poultry is the most prominent vehicle in transmission of *Campylobacter* enteritis within the United States.

29.2   GENERAL CONSIDERATIONS

29.21   Methods of Isolation

Because *C. jejuni* does not grow below 30°C and is sensitive to normal atmospheric concentrations of oxygen, only small numbers of campylobacters may be present in foods. Hence, selective enrichment is needed to detect the few culturable cells of *C. jejuni* that may be present. Large sample size, selective enrichment broth, suitable microaerobic conditions, and selective isolation media or filtration techniques are important for isolating campylobacters from foods. Various selective enrichment broth systems,[13, 25, 79, 92, 121] selective isolation agar media[8, 12] and methods to produce a microaerobic atmosphere[52] have been developed for the isolation of *C. jejuni*. These systems will be discussed. Enrichment-filtration techniques with incubation at 37°C[69] have also been reported that increase the isolation of *C. jejuni* and allow growth of other *Campylobacter* species of human health concern.

29.22   Treatment of Sample

Food samples must be processed rapidly to ensure optimum isolation of *C. jejuni*, which is sensitive to many environmental conditions. Methods of analyzing samples that address the fragile nature of the organism should take the following facts into consideration: The optimum temperature for growth is 42°C to 43°C, and thermal inactivation occurs at 48°C. Heat injury and repair of *C. jejuni* occurs at 46°C,[76] and the existence of an injured, viable, but nonculturable form of the organism has been reported.[93] *C. jejuni* will not survive the minimum pasteurization treatment (63°C for 30 min or 71.7°C for 15 sec) for milk or milk products, hence a *Campylobacter*-free product should be anticipated with good manufacturing practices.[28, 34] Similar observations have been made regarding heat inactivation of campylobacters in meat products.[6, 33, 56, 108]

C. jejuni grows at temperatures between 30°C and at or below 45°C and is not likely to grow in foods held under typical storage conditions. The organism dies more quickly at 25°C than at either 4°C or 30°C.[6, 24] Reports indicate that *C. jejuni* survives best in foods held at refrigeration temperature,[20, 57, 108] but it is highly susceptible to freezing conditions.[1, 33, 36, 74, 108, 109] Survival of the organism under frozen conditions is enhanced with cryoprotective agents.[7, 108] Also, freeze-stressed *C. jejuni* may not be culturable from contaminated frozen foods,[88] a concern addressed by Park and Sanders[78] in their enrichment procedure.

C. jejuni is very sensitive to sodium chloride.[26, 35] The optimum concentration for recovery or enumeration of *C. jejuni* is 0.5% NaCl. Although *C. jejuni* dies more rapidly in the presence of sodium chloride, the organism can persist for weeks in refrigerated (4°C) foods with 6.5% salt. Campylobacters are also quite sensitive to drying conditions, although they survive for up to 6 weeks at 4°C in an environment of 14% or less relative humidity.[27] In laboratory media, *C. jejuni* grows well at pH 5.5 to 8.0. Optimal growth is in the pH range of 6.5 to 7.5, while no growth occurs at pH 4.9 or lower.[24] Lactic and acetic acids can be used to reduce the number of campylobacters on chicken broiler halves.[110]

Campylobacters are both microaerophilic and capnophilic, that is, the organism grows best under conditions of reduced atmospheric concentrations of oxygen and under high carbon dioxide concentrations. The optimum atmospheric composition for growth of *C. jejuni* is 5% oxygen, 10% carbon dioxide, and 85% nitrogen.[11, 52] At 4°C, the organism survives optimally in the presence of 0.01% sodium bisulfite in an atmosphere of 100% nitrogen.[57] Recovery of *C. jejuni* from inoculated unpasteurized milk is improved by the addition of reducing agents.[58] Survival of *C. jejuni* on refrigerated meat is similar irrespective of the packaging treatment.[36, 112, 120]

29.3 MEDIA AND REAGENTS

29.31 Media (Chapter 62)

29.311 Nonselective media for checking purity and propagation and testing tolerance to certain chemicals and antimicrobial compounds

Brucella-FBP agar[31]
Brucella-FBP broth
Semisolid Brucella-FBP medium

29.312   Selective isolation agars

Butzler's agar[80]
Campy-BAP[8] (Blaser's agar)
Campylobacter charcoal differential agar (CCDA)—Preston blood-free
   medium[43]
Skirrow's agar[101]

29.313   Enrichment broths

Doyle and Roman[25]
Park and Sanders[78]
Preston enrichment broth[13]
Wesley broth[121]

29.314   Semisolid media for maintenance, storage, and transport of
          cultures

Cary-Blair transport medium
Wang's transport/storage medium[119]

29.315   Media for taxonomic criteria

Fermentation base for *Campylobacter*
Nitrate broth (heart infusion broth + 0.002% potassium nitrate)
Oxidation-fermentation medium for *Campylobacter* (O-F)
Semisolid (0.16% agar) brucella (albimi) medium
Trimethylamine N-oxide (TMAO) medium
Triple sugar iron (TSI) agar

29.316   Additional media

Brucella broth
Heart infusion agar (HIA) slant
Heart infusion agar + 5% difibrinated rabbit blood (HIA-RB)
Heart infusion broth (HIB)
Nutrient broth

29.32   Reagents

Catalase test
Cephalothin—30 µg/disc
Gram stain with carbol fuchsin counterstain
Hippurate hydrolysis
Lead acetate paper strip
McFarland No. 1 turbidity standard
Nalidixic acid—30 µg/disc
Nitrate reduction
Oxidase test
Ryuflagella stain[55]

29.4 PROCEDURES

29.41 General Sampling Protocol

Appropriate sample handling and transport must be emphasized when attempting to isolate *C. jejuni* from foodstuffs. Improper handling or storage of samples before testing may negate the value of a sensitive isolation procedure. The organism is sensitive to oxygen and storage at room temperature. Therefore, if the samples are improperly handled before testing, the value of any isolation procedure is compromised.

Optimally, the food sample should be stored in an oxygen-free environment (100% N_2) with 0.01% sodium bisulfite, and held under refrigeration. Under these conditions the organism will survive 10 times longer than when the same strain is held in a bisulfite-free medium exposed to air at 25°C.[57] Storing meat samples at 4°C with an equal amount of Cary-Blair diluent results in little change in *Campylobacter* spp. viability during 14 days of storage and may be used as a transport and storage procedure.[108]

To optimize recovery of *C. jejuni* from foods, cultures from both food samples and enrichment cultures should be streaked onto selective agar plates. Both CCDA[43] and Campy-BAP[8] media are commonly used with *C. jejuni* isolation from foods. After the media have been poured into plates, they should not be excessively exposed to light[48] and should be dried to limit moisture on the agar before streaking.

29.411 Surface rinse technique

This procedure is useful for sampling poultry carcasses and moderately large pieces of foods (see Chapter 2). Place the unmascerated sample (1 to 2 kg) in a sterile plastic bag with 250 ml of Brucella broth or other appropriate broth and rinse the surface by shaking and massaging. Filter the broth/rinse suspension through two layers of cheesecloth. Centrifuge the filtrate at 16,000 x *g* for 10 min at 4°C. Discard the supernatant fluid and suspend the pellet in 2 to 5 ml of enrichment broth.

29.412 Swab sample technique

This procedure is useful for sampling surfaces of very large animal carcasses and equipment (see Chapter 2). Dip a sterile swab into enrichment broth and remove excess moisture. Take a representative sample by wiping the surface of the sample with the moistened swab. Return the swab to the enrichment broth or directly inoculate a plate of selective agar by rotating the swab over a 3 to 5 cm² area and streak for isolation with a sterile loop.

29.42 Direct Plating Before Enrichment

Transfer two or three loops of the above centrifuged broth/rinse suspension of the sample to the surface of each of two selective isolation agar plates

(Section 29.312) and streak for isolated colonies. Swab samples should be directly inoculated to two selective agar plates. If the foods will be added directly to enrichment broth (e.g., raw milk or ground beef), concentrating the associated microflora by washing and centrifuging will provide a sample for direct plating.

Incubate the agar plates in a microaerobic atmosphere (5% O_2, 10% CO_2, 85% N_2) at 42°C for 48 hr. The plates can be inspected for characteristic colonies after 18 to 24 hr, but must be reincubated under the same conditions for an additional day if typical colonies are not observed. Typically on moist media, C. jejuni growth swarms, which is a useful diagnostic growth characteristic; however, this type of confluent growth makes it difficult to obtain isolated colonies. Individual colonies can be obtained by cultivating the culture on dry plates. Dry plates can be obtained by holding plates overnight at room temperature in the absence of light, or by adding 4 drops of glycerol to a filter paper kept in the vessel containing the plates.[107]

29.43   Selective Isolation Agar Media

Several selective agar media can be used for isolating C. jejuni from foods. Most prominent among these selective media are the Campy-BAP formulation,[8] the modified CCDA-Preston blood-free medium,[43] the "Butzler" formulation,[21, 80] and the "Skirrow" formulation.[101] One comparison of selective agar media indicated that the Campy-BAP medium was more effective for recovering C. jejuni in ground beef than either the Skirrow or Butzler formulations, whereas Butzler's medium was more selective for the organism than the other two formulations.[107] In our experience, the Preston blood-free medium provides excellent selectivity and allows for good quantitative recovery (Stern, unpublished results).

29.44   Selective Broth Enrichment and Plating

Enrichment culture is needed when small numbers of culturable C. jejuni are present in foods.[106] Several effective enrichment broths have been developed for this purpose. The Doyle and Roman[25] enrichment broth consists of Brucella broth to which supplements are added. The supplemental lysed horse blood can be excluded from the medium when testing for C. jejuni in certain meats, such as ground beef.[110] The broth (90 or 100 ml) is inoculated with 10 or 25 g of food, respectively, and incubated with agitation under a microaerobic atmosphere at 42°C for 16 to 18 hr. The enrichment culture is plated onto selective media, and the plates are incubated at 42°C for up to 48 hr under microaerobic conditions. The procedure can detect as few as two cells of C. jejuni per g of inoculated meat with an accuracy of 96%.[111]

A second enrichment procedure for isolating C. jejuni from chicken carcasses was originally described by Park et al.[79] This enrichment has been modified,[78] and now takes into account the high sensitivity of the organism to freezing (Chapter 7). The procedure involves resuscitation of the organism for 3 to 4 hr at 31°C to 32°C in a microaerobic environment without shaking. Subsequently, the enrichment culture is supplemented with antibiotics, held at 35°C to 37°C for 1 to 2 hr, and is further incubated at 42°C for an additional 40 to 42 hr with agitation.

Another selective enrichment medium[121] developed for isolating *C. jejuni* from poultry products consists of tryptose, yeast extract, and other supplements. The enrichment medium is reportedly particularly effective in inhibiting *Pseudomonas aeruginosa*. In addition, an enrichment medium has been described[12] and has been reported to be useful in the isolation of *C. jejuni* from foods.

The Doyle and Roman method[25] has been reported more effective than the original procedure described by Park et al.[79] in recovering *C. jejuni* from chicken carcasses. The Doyle and Roman procedure[25] was reported to give the highest rates of detection[4] and has also been reported as more effective in suppressing microbial competitors.[95] However, a rigorous comparison between the enrichment procedures still is required before one method can be considered superior to another.

29.45   Microaerobic Requirements

C. jejuni is a strict microaerophile,[103] and this requirement must be taken into account in using enrichment and plating procedures. Approaches to obtain microaerobic conditions include atmosphere exchange,[40] atmosphere-generating systems,[16] and even the use of an "Alka-Seltzer" (TM) gas-generating system.[83] The use of candle jars is not as effective for growing campylobacters as the other approaches described above.

29.451   Enrichment cultures

The most effective means for providing a microaerobic atmosphere in flasks with enrichment broth is by introducing a mixture of 5% O_2, 10% CO_2, 85% N_2 from a gas cylinder. The normal atmosphere can be evacuated by a standard laboratory vacuum system (about 15 mm Hg). The gas mixture may be introduced through a side arm of a flask or through a rubber stopper fitted with a short glass tube in the top of a flask. A tube and clamp are attached to the short glass tube or side arm to transfer and retain the gas in the flask. The stopper can be held in place with a screw cap that allows the glass tube to pass through. This additional cap will prevent the rubber stopper from popping out during the increase in gaseous pressure that occurs during incubation at 42°C. Introduce the gas slowly from the cylinder into the flask, tighten the clamp, and gently swirl the flask to incorporate the microaerobic gas mixture into the enrichment broth. Release the clamp for a short interval to equalize the gaseous pressure, and repeat the entire procedure twice.

An alternative approach is to place the enrichment medium and sample in cotton-plugged flasks into an anaerobic jar. The air content of the jar is evacuated and refilled with the microaerobic gas mixture. If agitation is required for enrichment, the entire anaerobic jar can be shaken. Park et al.[79] used a continual flow of the microaerobic gas mixture through the enrichment broth vessel. This method requires hook-up of tubes to the vessel and uses substantial amounts of gas.

29.452   Selective agar plates

A container to hold agar plates and a means to introduce and maintain the microaerobic atmosphere are also required. An anaerobe jar or a self-sealing bag with a portal for introducing the gas mixture can be used. As with the enrichment flasks, the microaerobic gas mixture should be introduced and evacuated from the container several times to ensure an optimal environment for growth of *C. jejuni*. Exchange of the gas mixture can be accomplished by creating a vacuum in the vessel or, when using plastic bags, by expelling the atmosphere through a small opening in the zipper of the bag. The container with the petri plates is then placed into a 42°C incubator.

29.453   Media supplement

Enhancing the aerotolerance of *Campylobacter* spp. is also advisable to optimize recovery of the organism from foodstuffs. Supplementing the growth media with 0.025% each of ferrous sulfate, sodium metabisulfite and sodium pyruvate (FBP) increases the oxygen tolerance of *C. jejuni*.[31, 38, 39, 113]

29.46   Isolation

Select *Campylobacter*-like colonies from each selective agar medium. Colonies on blood-supplemented or charcoal-based media are smooth, convex, and glistening with a distinct edge or flat, translucent, shiny, and spreading with an irregular edge; colorless to greyish or light cream; usually 1 to 2 mm in diameter but can range from pinpoint to 4 to 5 mm in diameter; and nonhemolytic on blood agar. Growth may be confluent without distinct colonies.

Make a wet-mount preparation of a broth culture of a colony and examine for morphology and motility by dark-field or phase-contrast microscope. *C. jejuni* cells are curved, S-shaped, gull-winged or spiral rods, 0.2 to 1 μm wide, and 0.5 to 5 μm long with darting or corkscrew-like motility. Cells in older cultures may be coccoid and nonmotile.

Prepare thin smears of young cultures and gram-stain by standard procedures, but use Ziehl-Neelsen's carbol-fuchsin stain as the counterstain (Chapter 62). Carbol-fuchsin stains *Campylobacter* better than safranin. Flagella can be demonstrated by staining with the method of Kodaka et al.[55] Cells have a single flagellum at one or both ends of the cell.

29.5   IDENTIFICATION TESTS

Select a single colony from the primary isolation medium, and transfer it to a plate of HIA-RB. Incubate plate in a microaerobic atmosphere at 42°C until growth is adequate, usually 24 hr. Transfer the fresh culture to 5 ml of HIB, and adjust the density of cells to match a McFarland No. 1 turbidity standard (Chapter 62). Use the cell suspension in HIB to inoculate tubes and plates of media for biochemical and growth tests.

Inoculate tubes of glucose fermentation base, nitrate, glycine, NaCl, cysteine, and HIA slant with 2 drops (approximately 0.1 ml) of cell suspension using a Pasteur pipette. Place a lead acetate paper strip over the cysteine medium for detection of H_2S. Incubate tubes in a microaerobic atmosphere at 35°C to 37°C for 3 days with the caps loose.

Inoculate two HIA-RB plates to test for growth at 25°C and 42°C by saturating a fiber-tipped swab with the broth suspension and making a single streak across each plate. Use a fresh surface of the swab for each plate by rotating the swab one-half of a turn. Four isolates can be inoculated to each plate. Incubate plates in a microaerobic atmosphere at each temperature for 3 days.

Inoculate the entire surface of an HIA-RB plate with a swab soaked with the bacterial suspension. Place discs of nalidixic acid (30 μg) and cephalothin (30 μg) on the plate and incubate in a microaerobic atmosphere at 35°C to 37°C until zones of inhibition of growth around the disks can be measured, usually within 24 hr.

Inoculate the remaining tubes of media, TSI, O-F base with and without glucose, and TMAO with an inoculating needle with a small amount of growth from the HIA-RB plate. Streak heavily the slant of TSI medium and stab the butt one time. Stab the O-F and TMAO media three times in the upper one-third of the medium. Include in the TMAO test a tube of medium inoculated with a strain of *C. lari* (positive control) and an uninoculated tube of medium. Incubate tubes of TSI and O-F media in a microaerobic atmosphere at 35°C–37°C for 3 days with caps loose. Incubate TMAO tubes in an anaerobic atmosphere for 7 days with caps loose.

29.51   *Campylobacter* Test Methodology

29.511   Catalase test

Add several drops of 3% hydrogen peroxide to 24 to 48 hr growth on the HIA slant. Production of any bubbles is considered positive. Confirm negative results by suspending growth in a drop of 3% hydrogen peroxide on a slide, and examine for bubbles with hand lens or dissecting microscope. (Media with body fluids can give false-positive reactions.)

29.512   Oxidase test

Place a piece of filter paper in an empty petri dish and spread a loopful of growth in a line 3 to 5 mm long on the pad. Add 1 to 2 drops of reagent to the growth. A dark purple color that develops within 10 sec is considered positive.

29.513   Nitrate reduction

To a 3-day culture growing in nitrate broth, add an equal volume (5 drops from Pasteur pipette) of solutions A and B. Development of a red color within 1 to 2 min is a positive result indicating production of nitrite from nitrate. If no color develops, add a small amount of powdered zinc to the tube. Development of a red color in 5 to 10 min with zinc indicates nitrates are present (negative test). No color with zinc indicates nitrates have been reduced to other compounds or to nitrogen as indicated by gas in the insert tube (positive test).

29.514   Glucose utilization

Fermentation is indicated by a red color (acid production) in fermentation broth with Andrade's indicator. Oxidation is indicated by a yellow color (acid production) in the O-F medium with phenol red indicator. O-F medium will be yellow (acid) when removed from the microaerobic atmosphere due to absortion of CO_2. To read O-F reactions, let tubes stand in room atmosphere until O-F control becomes neutral or alkaline, usually in 1 to 2 hr.

29.515   H₂S production

TSI agar. Any blackening of the medium indicates H_2S production. *Lead acetate strip.* Brownish-black coloration of the strip is a positive test. Record the degree of blackening from trace to 4 +. Lead acetate strips are more sensitive than sulfide indicators in media. Some strains may be positive by the strip procedure and negative in TSI medium.

29.516   Glycine and NaCl tolerance

Any growth, usually in the top 10 mm of the medium, is considered positive.

29.517   Temperature tolerance

Substantive growth in the line of inoculum across the HIA-RB plate is considered positive. A trace of growth that is difficult to distinguish from initial inoculum is not considered positive. Incubate replicate plates at 42°C and 25°C under microaerobic atmosphere.

29.518   Antimicrobial discs

Any zone of inhibition around disks indicates the organism is sensitive to the antimicrobial. Measure and record diameter of zone.

29.519   TMAO

Growth away from the stab or dispersed in the medium is considered positive. Compare with controls.

29.510   Hippurate hydrolysis

Prepare 1% sodium hippurate in sterile distilled water, dispense in 0.4 ml amounts in 13 × 100-mm screw cap tube, and freeze at −20°C until used. Emulsify in a thawed tube of sodium hippurate a large loopful of 18-to-24 hr growth from a HIA-RB plate. Incubate suspension in a 37°C waterbath for 2 hr.

After incubation, overlay 0.2 ml of 3.5% ninhydrin solution in a 1:1 mixture of acetone and butanol. (Store ninhydrin solution in the dark at room temperature.) Reincubate tube in a water bath at 37°C for 10 min. Development of a crystal violet color is a positive result. A colorless or light to medium purple is considered negative.

29.52   Test Interpretations

29.521   Catalase

C. jejuni is catalase positive.

29.522   Oxidase

C. jejuni is oxidase positive.

29.523   Nitrate reduction

C. jejuni will reduce nitrate.

29.524   Glucose utilization

C. jejuni will neither ferment nor oxidize glucose.

29.525 H_2S production

C. jejuni produces detectable H_2S with the lead acetate test, whereas H_2S production is negative with TSI agar.

29.526   Glycine and NaCl tolerance

C. jejuni will grow in the presence of 1% glycine but will not grow in 3.5% NaCl.

29.527   Temperature tolerance

C. jejuni will grow at 42°C but will not grow at 25°C.

29.528   Antimicrobial discs

C. jejuni and *C. coli* are susceptible to nalidixic acid and resistant to cephalothin, whereas *C. lari* is resistant to both nalidixic acid and to cephalothin.

29.529   TMAO

C. jejuni and *C. coli* will not grow in this medium.

29.5210   Hippurate hydrolysis

C. jejuni is positive for hippurate hydrolysis, whereas *C. coli* and *C. lari* are negative.

29.53   Identification Criteria

Table 1 summarizes characteristics useful in identifying the catalase-positive campylobacters associated with foods. From a practical standpoint in the food microbiology laboratory, separating *C. jejuni* and *C. coli* may not be necessary. The thermophilic campylobacters (*C. jejuni*, *C. coli*, and *C. lari*) grow well at 42°C, do not grow at 25°C, and *C. lari* strains are resistant to nalidixic acid. Isolates of *C. lari* that are sensitive to nalidixic acid have been reported. Anaerobic growth in 0.1% TMAO may be used to separate these strains from *C. jejuni* and *C. coli*. Hippurate hydrolysis is the most reliable test for separating *C. jejuni* and *C. coli*. *C. jejuni* strains are positive in this test. Strains with unclear or negative results by the ninhydrin method for hippurate hydrolysis can be tested by the more sensitive gas liquid chromatography procedure.[55, 71] Other methods to separate *C. jejuni* and *C. coli* have been described,[102] but hippurate hydrolysis appears to correlate best with genetic classification of the species. Hippurate-negative isolates of *C. jejuni* have been reported and probably occur infrequently.[118] *C. fetus* subsp. *fetus* grows at 25°C. This feature separates *C. fetus* subsp. *fetus* from the thermophilic campylobacters. Details of characteristics and methods to identify other *Campylobacter* spp. can be found elsewhere.[2, 3, 70, 71]

29.54   Serotyping

Strains of *C. jejuni*, *C. coli*, and *C. lari* can be serotyped for epidemiologic studies. Two systems are in common use, one for soluble heat-stable antigens identified by an indirect hemagglutination procedure for unabsorbed antisera[82] and one for heat-labile antigens using a slide agglutination technique and absorbed antisera.[64] The heat-stable serotyping scheme employs antisera to 42 *C. jejuni* and 18 *C. coli* strains. The heat-labile serotyping system has 108 serotypes, 63 *C. jejuni*, 37 *C. coli*, and 8 *C. lari*. Commercial antisera are not readily available for either serotyping system. Serotyping can be obtained on request from the *Campylobacter* Reference Laboratory, Centers for Disease Control, for strains from outbreaks and for approved studies.

29.55   Stock Culture Maintenance

The fragility of *C. jejuni* requires that special care be taken in stock culture maintenance. To prepare a stock culture, inoculate a heavy loopful of the

Table 1—Characteristics of Campylobacter Species

Species	Growth					Nalidixic Acid	Cephalothin	Biochemical Reaction						
	25°C	42°C	1% Glycine	3.5% NaCl	0.1% TMAO			Oxidase	Catalase	Glucose Utilization	NO$_3$ Reduction	H$_2$S, TSI	H$_2$S, paper strip	Hippurate Hydrolysis
C. jejuni	−	+	+	−	−	S	R	+	+	−	+	−	+	+[a]
C. coli	−	+	+	−	−	S	R	+	+	−	+	D	+	−
C. lari	−	+	+	−	+	R	R	+	+	−	+	−	+	−
C. fetus subsp. fetus	+	D	+	−	D	R	S	+	+	−	+	−	+	−
C. fetus subsp. venerealis	+	−	−	−	−	R	S	+	+	−	+	−	+	−

[a]Hippurate-negative C. jejuni strains have been reported.

+ = 90% or more of strains are positive; − = 90% or more of strains are negative; D = 11% to 89% of strains are positive; S = susceptible;
R = resistant.

strain into semisolid brucella broth in a screw cap test tube. Loosen the caps to allow exchange of the atmosphere. Grow the culture to mid-log phase, i.e., for approximately 24 hr at 42°C. Cultures may be stored up to 1 month at 4°C in a microaerobic atmosphere or in a vacuum. Wang et al.[119] described a semisolid (0.15% agar) brucella medium with 10% sheep blood for storing the organism. Studies revealed the organism survived in this medium at 25°C for at least 3 weeks. Nair et al.[73] described an egg-based medium that maintained viability of *C. jejuni* for over 3 months when held at 4°C. This medium was superior to Wang's preservation medium when cultures were held at 27°C. Cary-Blair medium with 0.16% agar has also been shown to be a useful medium for storing *C. jejuni*.[65]

For long-term storage, grow *C. jejuni* on brucella agar with FBP supplement in a microaerobic atmosphere for 24 hr at 42°C, suspend in a diluent and concentrate by centrifugation, and re-suspend the pellet in brucella broth with 15% glycerol. Small quantities (1 to 2 ml) of this thick bacterial suspension can be stored in tightly sealed vials for several years when held at −70°C. Cultures can also be lyophilized in skim milk and stored indefinitely at −20°C.

29.6 INTERPRETATION

C. jejuni is a fragile organism that is readily inactivated by methods used to eliminate other enteropathogens from foods. In spite of this fragility, the organism causes millions of cases of gastroenteritis in the United States each year. This discrepancy can usually be explained by the cross-contamination of either utensils or the ready-to-eat product with contaminated raw foods, especially those of animal origin. Experience has shown that bacterial disease is often transmitted when a contaminated raw food enters the food preparation area.

The best available means to protect health at this time is through consumer education and reinforcement of hygienic practices. Care is required to segregate raw foods and processing utensils from any food or material that comes directly or indirectly into contact with the consumer. This approach will diminish and prevent many cases of campylobacteriosis. The paramount goal, however, should be to eliminate *C. jejuni* from animals used for production of food. Preventing the organism from colonizing animals used for food would prevent contamination of meat products, and would greatly reduce potential for foodborne transmission.

29.7 REFERENCES

1. Barrell, R. A. E. 1984. The survival of *Campylobacter jejuni* in red meats stored at different temperatures. Int. J. Food Microbiol. 1: 187.
2. Barrett, T. J., Patton, C. M., and Morris, G. K. 1988. Differentiation of *Campylobacter* species using phenotypic characterization. Lab. Med. 19: 96.

3. Benjamin, J., Leaper, S., Owen, R. J., and Skirrow, M. B. 1983. Description of *Campylobacter laridis*, a new species comprising the nalidixic acid resistant thermophilic *Campylobacter* (NARTC) group. Curr. Microbiol. 8: 231.

4. Beuchat, L. R. 1987. Efficacy of some methods and media for detecting and enumerating *Campylobacter jejuni* in frozen chicken meat. J. Appl. Bacteriol. 62: 217.

5. Black, R. E., Levine, M. M., Clements, M. L., Hughes, T. P., and Blaser, M. J. 1988. Experimental *Campylobacter jejuni* infection in humans. J. Infect. Dis. 157: 472.

6. Blankenship, L. C. and Craven, S. E. 1982. *Campylobacter jejuni* survival in chicken meat as a function of temperature. Appl. Environ. Microbiol. 44: 88.

7. Blankenship, L. C., Craven, S. E., Chiu, J. Y., and Krumm, G. W. 1983. Sampling methods and frozen storage of samples for detection of *Campylobacter jejuni* on freshly processed broiler carcasses. J. Food Prot. 46: 510.

8. Blaser, M. J., Berkowitz, I. D., LaForce, F. M., Cravens, J., Reller, L. B., and Wang, W.-L. L. 1979. Campylobacter enteritis: Clinical and epidemiologic features. Ann. Intern. Med. 91: 179.

9. Blaser, M. J., Cravens, J., Powers, B. W., LaForce, F. M., and Wang, W.-L. L. 1979. Campylobacter enteritis associated with unpasteurized milk. Am. J. Med. 67: 715.

10. Blaser, M. J., Duncan, D. J., Warren, G. H., and Wang, W.-L. L. 1983. Experimental *Campylobacter jejuni* infection of adult mice. Infect. Immun. 39: 908.

11. Bolton, F. J. and Coates, D. 1983. A study of the oxygen and carbon dioxide requirements of thermophilic campylobacters. J. Clin. Pathol. 36: 829.

12. Bolton, F. J., Hutchinson, D. N., and Coates, D. 1984. Blood-free selective medium for isolation of *Campylobacter jejuni* from feces. J. Clin. Microbiol. 19: 169.

13. Bolton, F. J. and Robertson, L. 1982. A selective medium for isolating *Campylobacter jejuni/coli*. J. Clin. Pathol. 35: 462.

14. Brieseman, M. A. 1984. Raw milk consumption as a probable cause of two outbreaks of *Campylobacter* infection. N. Z. Med. J. 97: 411.

15. Brouwer, R., Mertens, M. J. A., Siem, T. H., and Katchaki, J. 1979. An explosive outbreak of campylobacter enteritis in soldiers. Antonie van Leeuwenhoek J. Microbiol. Serol. 45: 517.

16. Buck, G. E., Fojtasek, C., Calvert, K., and Kelly, M. T. 1982. Evaluation of the CampyPakII gas generator system for isolation of *Campylobacter fetus* subsp. *jejuni*. J. Clin. Microbiol. 15: 41.

17. Caldwell, M. B., Walker, R. I., Stewart, S. D., and Rogers, J. E. 1983. Simple adult rabbit model for *C. jejuni* enteritis. Infect. Immun. 42: 1176.

18. Caldwell, M. B., Guerry, P., Lee, E. C., Burans, P., and Walker, R. I. 1985. Reversible expression of flagella in *Campylobacter jejuni*. Infect. Immun. 50: 941.

19. Chowdhury, M. N. H. and Mahgoub, E.-S. 1981. Gastroenteritis due to *Campylobacter jejuni* in Riyadh, Saudi Arabia. Trans. Roy. Trop. Med. Hyg. 75: 359.

20. Christopher, F. M., Smith, G. C., and Vanderzant, C. 1982. Examination of poultry giblets, raw milk, and meat for *Campylobacter fetus* subsp. *jejuni*. J. Food Prot. 45: 260.

21. Dekeyser, P., Gossuin-Detrain, M., Butzler, J. P., and Sternon, J. 1972. Acute enteritis due to related *Vibrio*: First positive stool cultures. J. Infect. Dis. 125: 390.

22. Deming, M. S., Tauxe, R. V., Blake, P. A., Dixon, S. E., Fowler, B. S., Jones, T. S., Lockamy, E. A., Patton, C. M., and Sikes, R. O. 1987. Campylobacter enteritis at a university: Transmission from eating chicken and from cats. Am. J. Epidemiol. 126: 526.

23. DeMol, P. and Bosmans, E. 1978. Campylobacter enteritis in central Africa. Lancet i: 604.

24. Doyle, M. P. and Roman, D. J. 1981. Growth and survival of *Campylobacter fetus* subsp. *jejuni* as a function of temperature and pH. J. Food Prot. 44: 596.

25. Doyle, M. P. and Roman, D. J. 1982. Recovery of *Campylobacter jejuni* and *Campylobacter coli* from inoculated foods by selective enrichment. Appl. Environ. Microbiol. 43: 1343.

26. Doyle, M. P. and Roman, D. J. 1982. Response of *Campylobacter jejuni* to sodium chloride. Appl. Environ. Microbiol. 43: 561.

27. Doyle, M. P. and Roman, D. J. 1982. Sensitivity of *Campylobacter jejuni* to drying. J. Food Prot. 45: 507.

28. Ehlers, J. G., Chapparo-Serrano, M., Richter, R. L., and Vanderzant, C. 1982. Survival of *Campylobacter fetus* subsp. *jejuni* in Cheddar and cottage cheese. J. Food Prot. 45: 1018.

29. Finch, M. J. and Blake, P. A. 1985. Foodborne outbreaks of campylobacteriosis: The United States experience, 1980–1982. Am. J. Epidemiol. 122: 262.

30. Fitzgeorge, R. B., Baskerville, A., and Lander, A. P. 1981. Experimental infection of rhesus monkeys with a human strain of *Campylobacter jejuni*. J. Hyg. 86: 343.

31. George, H. A., Hoffman, P. S., Smibert, R. M., and Krieg, N. R. 1978. Improved media for growth and aerotolerance of *Campylobacter fetus*. J. Clin. Microbiol. 8: 36.

32. Gill, C. O. and Harris, L. M. 1982. Survival and growth of *Campylobacter fetus* subsp. *jejuni* on meat and in cooked foods. Appl. Environ. Microbiol. 44: 259.

33. Gill, C. O. and Harris, L. M. 1984. Hamburgers and broiler chickens as potential sources of human campylobacter enteritis. J. Food Prot. 47: 96.

34. Gill, K. P. W., Bates, P. G., and Lander, K. P. 1981. The effect of pasteurization on the survival of *Campylobacter* species in milk. Br. Vet. J. 137: 578.

35. Hanninen, M. L. 1981. The effect of NaCl on *Campylobacter jejuni/coli*. Acta Vet. Scand. 22: 578.

36. Hanninen, M. L., Korkeala, H., and Pakkala, P. 1984. Effect of various gas atmospheres on the growth and survival of *Campylobacter jejuni* on beef. J. Appl. Bacteriol. 57: 89.

37. Harris, N. V., Thompson, D., Martin, D. C., and Nolan, C. M. 1986. A survey of *Campylobacter* and other bacterial contaminants of pre-market chicken and retail poultry and meats, King County, Washington. Am. J. Publ. Health 76: 401.

38. Hoffman, P. S., Krieg, N. R., and Smibert, R. M. 1979a. Studies of the microaerophilic nature of *Campylobacter fetus* subsp. *jejuni*. I. Physiological aspects of enhanced aerotolerance. Can. J. Microbiol. 25: 1.

39. Hoffman, P. S., George, H. A., Krieg, N. R., and Smibert, R. M. 1979b. Studies of the micro-aerophilic nature of *Campylobacter fetus* subsp. *jejuni*. II. Role of exogenous superoxide anions and hydrogen peroxide. Can. J. Microbiol. 25: 8.

40. Holdeman, L. V., Cato, E. P., and Moore, W. E. C. eds. 1977. "Anaerobe Laboratory Manual," 4th ed. Virginia Polytechnic Institute and State U., Blacksburg, Va.

41. Hudson, P. J., Vogt, R. L., Brondum, J., and Patton, C. M. 1984. Isolation of *Campylobacter jejuni* from milk during an outbreak of campylobacteriosis. J. Infect. Dis. 150: 789.

42. Humphrey, C. D., Montag, D. M., and Pittman, F. E. 1985. Experimental infections of hamsters with *Campylobacter fetus jejuni*. J. Infect. Dis. 151: 485.

43. Hutchinson, D. N. and Bolton, F. J. 1984. An improved blood-free selective medium for isolation of *Campylobacter jejuni* from faecal specimens. J. Clin. Pathol. 37: 956.

44. Hutchinson, D. N., Bolton, F. J., Hinchliffe, P. M., Dawkins, H. C., Horsley, S. D., Jessop, E. G., Robertshaw, P. A., and Counter, D. E. 1985. Evidence of udder excretion of *Campylobacter jejuni* as the cause of milk-borne *Campylobacter* outbreak. J. Hyg. 94: 205.

45. Istre, G. R., Blaser, M. J., Shillam, P., and Hopkins, R. S. 1984. *Campylobacter enteritis* associated with undercooked barbecued chicken. Am. J. Publ. Health 74: 1265.

46. Johnson, W. M. and Lior, H. 1984. Toxins produced by *Campylobacter jejuni* and *Campylobacter coli*. Lancet i: 229.

47. Johnson, W. M. and Lior, H. 1986. Cytotoxic and cytotonic factors produced by *Campylobacter jejuni*, *Campylobacter coli*, and *Campylobacter laridis*. J. Clin. Microbiol. 24: 275.

48. Juven, B. J. and Rosenthal, I. 1985. Effect of free-radical and oxygen scavengers on photochemically generated oxygen toxicity and on the aerotolerance of *Campylobacter jejuni*. J. Appl. Bacteriol. 59: 413.

49. Kapperud, G. K. and Bukholm, G. 1987. Expression of *Campylobacter jejuni* invasiveness in cell cultures coinfected with other bacteria. Infect. Immun. 55: 2816.

50. Kazmi, R. R., Hafeez, A., and Kazmi, S. U. 1986. Isolation of *Campylobacter jejuni* from

diarrheal stool specimens in Karachi. Abstracts Annu. Meet. Am. Soc. Microbiol. C82, p. 341.

51. Kazmi, S. U., Roberson, B. S., and Stern, N. J. 1984. Animal-passed, virulence-enhanced *Campylobacter jejuni* causes enteritis in neonatal mice. Curr. Microbiol. 11: 159.

52. Kiggins, E. M. and Plastridge, W. N. 1956. Effect of gaseous environment on growth and catalase content of *Vibrio fetus* cultures of bovine origin. J. Bacteriol. 72: 397.

53. Klipstein, F. A. and Engert, R. F. 1984. Properties of crude *Campylobacter jejuni* heat-labile enterotoxin. Infect. Immun. 45: 314.

54. Klipstein, F. A., Engert, R. F., Short, H. B., and Schenk, E. A. 1985. Pathogenic properties of *Campylobacter jejuni*: assay and correlation with clinical manifestations. Infect. Immun. 50: 43.

55. Kodaka, H., Lombard, G. L., and Dowell, V. R. Jr. 1982. Gas-liquid chromatography technique for detection of hippurate hydrolysis and conversion of fumarate to succinate by micro-organisms. J. Clin. Microbiol. 16: 962.

56. Koidis, P. and Doyle, M. P. 1983a. Survival of *Campylobacter jejuni* in fresh and heated red meat. J. Food Prot. 46: 771.

57. Koidis, P. and Doyle, M. P. 1983b. Survival of *Campylobacter jejuni* in the presence of bisulfite and different atmospheres. Eur. J. Clin. Microbiol. 2: 384.

58. Koidis, P. and Doyle, M. P. 1984. Procedure for increased recovery of *Campylobacter jejuni* from inoculated unpasteurized milk. Appl. Environ. Microbiol. 47: 455.

59. Korlath, J. A., Osterholm, M. T., Judy, L. A., Forfang, J. C., and Robinson, R. A. 1985. A point-source outbreak of campylobacteriosis associated with consumption of raw milk. J. Infect. Dis. 152: 592.

60. Lander, K. P. and Gill, K. P. W. 1980. Experimental infection of the bovine udder with *Campylobacter coli/jejuni*. J. Hyg. 84: 421.

61. Lauwers, S., DeBoeck, M., and Butzler, J. P. 1978. Campylobacter enteritis in Brussels. Lancet i: 604.

62. Lee, A., O'Rourke, J. L., Barrington, P. J., and Trust, T. J. 1986. Mucus colonization as a determinant of pathogenicity in intestinal infection by *Campylobacter jejuni*: A mouse cecal model. Infect. Immun. 51: 536.

63. Lee, A., Logan, S. M., and Trust, T. J. 1987. Demonstration of a flagellar antigen shared by a diverse group of spiral-shaped bacteria that colonize intestinal mucus. Infect. Immun. 55: 828.

64. Lior, H., Woodward, D. L., Edgar, J. A., Laroche, L. J., and Gill, P. 1982. Serotyping of *Campylobacter jejuni* by slide agglutination based on heat-labile antigenic factors. J. Clin. Microbiol. 15: 761.

65. Luechtefeld, N. W., Wang, W.-L. L., Blaser, M. J., and Reller, L. B. 1981. Evaluation of transport and storage techniques for isolation of *Campylobacter fetus* subsp. *jejuni* from turkey cecal specimens. J. Clin. Microbiol. 13: 438.

66. Marshall, B. 1983. Unidentified curved bacilli on gastric epithelium in active chronic gastritis. Lancet i: 1273.

67. McCardell, B. A., Madden, J. M., and Lee, E. C. 1984a. *Campylobacter jejuni* and *Campylobacter coli* production of a cytotonic toxin immunologically similar to cholera toxin. J. Food Prot. 47: 943.

68. McCardell, B. A., Madden, J. M., and Lee, E. C. 1984b. Production of cholera-like toxin by *Campylobacter jejuni/coli*. Lancet i: 448.

69. Megraud, F. 1987. Isolation of *Campylobacter* spp. from pigeon feces by a combined enrichment-filtration technique. Appl. Environ. Microbiol. 53: 1394.

70. Morris, G. K. and Patton, C. M. 1985. *Campylobacter*. In "Manual of Clinical Microbiology," 4th ed. eds. E. H. Lennette, A. Balows, and W. J. Hausler, Jr. Amer. Soc. for Microbiol., Washington, D.C.

71. Morris, G. K., El Sherbeeny, M. R., Patton, C. M., Kodaka, H., Lombard, G. L., Edmonds, P., Hollis, D. G., and Brenner, D. J. 1985. Comparison of four hippurate hydrolysis methods for identification of thermophilic *Campylobacter* sp. J. Clin. Microbiol. 22: 714.

72. Mouton, R. P., Veltkamp, J. J., Lauwers, S., and Butzler, J. P. 1982. Analysis of a small outbreak of campylobacter infections with high morbidity. In *"Campylobacter*-Epidemiology, pathogenesis and biochemistry,"* ed. D. G. Newell, p. 129. MTP Press Ltd., Lancaster, England.

73. Nair, G. B., Chowderhury, S., Das, P., Pal, S., and Pal, S. C. 1984. Improved preservation medium for *Campylobacter jejuni.* J. Clin. Microbiol. 19: 298.

74. Oosterom, J., DeWilde, G. J. A., DeBoer, E., DeBlaauw, L. H., and Karman, H. 1983. Survival of *Campylobacter jejuni* during poultry processing and pig slaughtering. J. Food Prot. 46: 702.

75. Pai, C. H., Sorger, S., Lackman, L., Sinai, R. E., and Marks, M. I. 1979. *Campylobacter* gastroenteritis in children. J. Pediatr. 94: 589.

76. Palumbo, S. A. 1984. Heat injury and repair in *Campylobacter jejuni.* Appl. Environ. Microbiol. 48: 477.

77. Pang, T., Wong, P. Y., Puthucheary, D., Sihotang, K., and Chang, W. K. 1987. In-vitro and in-vivo studies of a cytotoxin from *Campylobacter jejuni.* J. Med. Microbiol. 23: 193.

78. Park, C. E. and Sanders, G. W. 1989. A sensitive enrichment procedure for the isolation of *Campylobacter jejuni* from frozen foods. Abstr. Fifth International Workshop on Campylobacter Infections. Puerto Vallarta, Mexico.

79. Park, C. E., Stankiewicz, Z. K., Lovett, J., Hunt, J., and Francis, D. W. 1983. Effect of temperature, duration of incubation, and pH of enrichment culture on the recovery of *Campylobacter jejuni* from eviscerated market chickens. Can. J. Microbiol. 29: 803.

80. Patton, C. M., Mitchell, S. W., Potter, M. E., and Kaufmann, A. F. 1981. Comparison of selective media for primary isolation of *Campylobacter fetus* subsp. *jejuni.* J. Clin. Microbiol. 13: 326.

81. Patton, C. M., Shaffer, N., Edmonds, P., Barrett, T. J., Lambert, M. A., Baker, C., Perlman, D. M., and Brenner, D. J. 1989. Human disease associated with *"Campylobacter upsaliensis"* (Catalase-negative or weakly positive *Campylobacter* spp. in the United States). J. Clin. Microbiol. 27: 66.

82. Penner, J. L. and Hennessey, J. N. 1980. Passive hemagglutination technique for serotyping *Campylobacter fetus* subsp. *jejuni* on the basis of soluble heat-stable antigens. J. Clin. Microbiol. 12: 732.

83. Pennie, R. A., Zunino, J. N., Rose, C. E., and Guerrant, R. L. 1984. Economical, simple method for production of the gaseous environment required for cultivation of *Campylobacter jejuni.* J. Clin. Microbiol. 20: 320.

84. Piscoya-Hermosa, Z. A. 1985. Aislamiento y caracterizacion fenotipica de *Campylobacter jejuni* en Lima, Peru-Determinacion de biotipos. Master's thesis, Faculty of Science and Philosophy, University of Peru-Cayetano Heredia, Tingo Maria, Peru.

85. Porter, I. A. and Reid, T. M. S. 1980. A milk-borne outbreak of *Campylobacter* infection. J. Hyg. 84: 415.

86. Potter, M. E., Blaser, M. J., Sikes, R. K., Kaufmann, A. F., and Wells, J. G. 1983. Human *Campylobacter* infection associated with certified raw milk. Am. J. Epidemiol. 117: 475.

87. Rajan, D. P. and Mathan, V. I. 1982. Prevalence of *Campylobacter fetus* subsp. *jejuni* in healthy populations in southern India. J. Clin. Microbiol. 15: 749.

88. Ray, B. and Johnson, C. 1984. Survival and growth of freeze-stressed *Campylobacter jejuni* cells in selective media. J. Food Safety 6: 183.

89. Ringertz, S., Rockhill, R. C., Ringertz, O., and Sutomo, A. 1980. *Campylobacter fetus* subsp. *jejuni* as a cause of gastroenteritis in Jarkata, Indonesia. J. Clin. Microbiol. 12: 538.

90. Robinson, D. A. 1981. Infective dose of *Campylobacter jejuni* in milk. Br. Med. J. 282: 1584.

91. Robinson, D. A., Edgar, W. J., Gibson, G. L., Matchett, A. A., and Robertson, L. 1979. Campylobacter enteritis associated with consumption of unpasteurised milk. Br. Med. J. 1: 1171.

92. Rogol, M., Shpak, B., Rothman, D., and Sechter, I. 1985. Enrichment medium for isolation of *Campylobacter jejuni-Campylobacter coli.* Appl. Environ. Microbiol. 50: 125.

93. Rollins, D. M. and Colwell, R. 1986. *Campylobacter* dormancy under environmental conditions. Appl. Environ. Microbiol. 52: 531.
94. Romaniuk, P. J., Zoltowska, B., Trust, T. J., Lane, D. J., Olsen, G. J., Pace, N. R., and Stahl, D. A. 1987. *Campylobacter pylori*, the spiral bacterium associated with human gastritis, is not a true *Campylobacter* sp. J. Bacteriol. 169: 2137.
95. Rothenberg, P. J., Stern, N. J., and Westhoff, D. C. 1984. Selected enrichment broths for recovery of *Campylobacter jejuni* from foods. Appl. Environ. Microbiol. 48: 78.
96. Ruiz-Palacios, G. M., Escamilla, E., and Torres, N. 1981. Experimental *Campylobacter* diarrhea in chickens. Infect. Immun. 34: 250.
97. Ruiz-Palacios, G. M., Torres, J., Torres, N. I., Escamilla, E., Ruiz-Palacios, B. R., and Tamayo, J. 1983. Cholera-like enterotoxin produced by *Campylobacter jejuni*: characterization and clinical significance. Lancet ii: 250.
98. Sandstedt, K. and Ursing, J. 1986. *Campylobacter upsaliensis*, a new species, formerly the CNW group. Abst. XIV International Congress of Microbiology, P.B8-17, p. 61.
99. Sanyal, S. C., Islam, K. M. N., Neogy, P. K. B., Islam, M., Speelman, P., and Huq, M. I. 1984. *Campylobacter jejuni* diarrhea model in infant chickens. Infect. Immun. 43: 931.
100. Skerman, V. B. D., McGowan V., and Sneath, P. H. A. 1980. Approved lists of bacterial names. Int. J. Syst. Bacteriol. 30: 225.
101. Skirrow, M. B. 1977. Campylobacter enteritis: a "new" disease. Br. Med. J. 2: 9.
102. Skirrow, M. B. and Benjamin, J. 1980. '1001' Campylobacters: Cultural characteristics of intestinal campylobacters from man and animals. J. Hyg. Camb. 85: 427.
103. Smibert, R. M. 1984. *Campylobacter*. In "Bergey's Manual of Systematic Bacteriology." eds. N. R. Krieg and J. G. Holt, p. 11. Williams and Wilkins, Baltimore, Md.
104. Stanfield, J. T., McCardell, B. A., and Madden, J. M. 1987. *Campylobacter* diarrhea in an adult mouse model. Microbiol. Pathogen. 3: 155.
105. Steele, T. W. and McDermott, S. 1978. Campylobacter enteritis in south Australia. Med. J. Aust. 2: 404.
106. Stern, N. J. 1981. *Campylobacter fetus* ssp. *jejuni*: recovery methodology and isolation from lamb carcasses. J. Food Sci. 46: 660.
107. Stern, N. J. 1982. Selectivity and sensitivity of three media for the recovery of inoculated *Campylobacter fetus* ssp. *jejuni* from ground beef. J. Food Safety 4: 169.
108. Stern, N. J. and Kotula, A. W. 1982. Survival of *Campylobacter jejuni* inoculated into ground beef. Appl. Environ. Microbiol. 44: 1150.
109. Stern, N. J., Green, S. S., Thaker, N., Krout, D. J., and Chiu. J. 1984. Recovery of *Campylobacter jejuni* from fresh and frozen meat and poultry collected at slaughter. J. Food Prot. 47: 372.
110. Stern, N. J., Rothenberg, P. J., and Stone, J. M. 1985. Enumeration and reduction of *Campylobacter jejuni* in poultry and red meats. J. Food Prot. 48: 606.
111. Stern, N. J., Hernandez, M. P., Blankenship, L., Deibel, K. E., Doores, S., Doyle, M. P., Ng, H., Pierson, M. D., Sofos, J. N., Sveum, W. H., and Westhoff, D. C. 1985. Prevalence and distribution of *Campylobacter jejuni* and *Campylobacter coli* in retail meats. J. Food Prot. 48: 595.
112. Stern, N. J., Greenberg, M. D., and Kinsman, D. M. 1986. Survival of *Campylobacter jejuni* in selected gaseous environments. J. Food Sci. 51: 652.
113. Stern, N. J., Kazmi, S. U., Roberson, B. S., Ono, K., and Juven, B. J. 1988. Response of *Campylobacter jejuni* to combinations of ferrous sulphate and cadmium chloride. J. Appl. Bacteriol. 64: 247.
114. Tauxe, R. V., Deming, M. S., and Blake, P. A. 1985. *Campylobacter jejuni* infections on college campuses: a national survey. Am. J. Publ. Health 75: 659.
115. Tauxe, R. V., Hargrett-Bean, N., Patton, C. M., and Wachsmuth, I. K. 1988. Campylobacter infections in the United States, 1982–1986. Morbid. Mortal. Weekly Rep. 37: S52, p 1–13.
116. Taylor, D. N., Porter, B. W., Williams, C. A., Miller, H. G., Bopp, C. A., and Blake,

P. A. 1982. Campylobacter enteritis: a large outbreak traced to commercial raw milk. West. J. Med. 137: 365.

117. Tosh, F. E., Mullen, G. A., and Wilcox, D. E. 1981. Outbreak of *Campylobacter* enteritis associated with raw milk—Kansas. Morbid. Mortal. Weekly Rep. 30: 218.

118. Totten, P. A., Patton, C. M., Tenover, F. C., Barrett, T. J., Stamm, W. E., Steigerwalt, A. G., Lin, J. Y., Holmes, K. K., and Brenner, D. J. 1987. Prevalence and characterization of hippurate-negative *Campylobacter jejuni* in King County, Washington. J. Clin. Microbiol. 25: 1747.

119. Wang, W.-L. L., Luechtefeld, N. W., Reller, L. B., and Blaser, M. J. 1980. Enriched brucella medium for storage and transport of cultures of *Campylobacter fetus* subsp. *jejuni*. J. Clin. Microbiol. 12: 479.

120. Wesley, R. D. and Stadelman, W. J. 1985. The effect of carbon dioxide packaging on detection of *Campylobacter jejuni* from chicken carcasses. Poultry Sci. 64: 763.

121. Wesley, R. D., Swaminathan, B., and Stadelman, W. J. 1983. Isolation and enumeration of *Campylobacter jejuni* from poultry products by a selective enrichment method. Appl. Environ. Microbiol. 46: 1097.

122. Wright, E. P., Tillett, H. E., Hague, J. T., Clegg, F. G., Darnell, R., Culshaw, J. A., and Sorrell, J. A. 1983. Milk-borne campylobacter enteritis in a rural area. J. Hyg. 91: 227.

Chapter 30

AEROMONAS HYDROPHILA GROUP

Samuel Palumbo, Carlos Abeyta, and Gerard Stelma, Jr.

30.1 INTRODUCTION

30.11 General Characteristics of the Genus

Aeromonas hydrophila, a member of the *Vibrionaceae* family, is a facultative, anaerobic, gram-negative rod often found in the environment, particularly in water and sewage. General characteristics of *A. hydrophila* include
these: motility by a single polar flagellum; metabolism of glucose by both
fermentative and respiratory pathways; positive catalase and oxidase tests;
production of exoenzymes such as amylase, protease, phospholipase, and
DNase; resistance to the vibriostatic agent 0/129; and lack of the enterobac-
terial common antigen.[98] Popoff[98] lists four species in the genus *Aeromonas:*
A. hydrophila, *A. sobria*, *A. caviae*, and *A. salmonicida*. The genus also can
be differentiated into two broad groups: the *A. hydrophila* group, consisting
of *A. hydrophila*, *A. caviae*, and *A. sobria*, and the *A. salmonicida* group,
consisting of *A. salmonicida* and its subspecies. The *A. hydrophila* group is
characterized by growth at 37°C and motility; *A. salmonicida* does not grow
at 37°C, is nonmotile, and is a pathogen of salmonid fish. In addition, *A.
salmonicida* usually produces a brown pigment. There is, however, one report
of a motile aeromonad that produces a dark red-brown pigment.[111] The *A.
hydrophila* group is collectively referred to as motile aeromonads or mesophilic *Aeromonas*. It is this group that is of interest and importance to human
public health.

30.12 Ecology

A. hydrophila was first reported by Sandrelli,[113] who isolated the organism
from frogs. Motile aeromonads occur widely in aquatic environments,[50] both

fresh and saline waters. Its name translates simply as a "water-loving, gas-producing" bacterium. Aeromonads were once thought to be absent from the marine environment;[43] however, numerous investigators have found strains of *Aeromonas* in marine systems that interface with fresh and saline waters.[2, 3, 24, 50, 61, 142] *Aeromonas* may not be truly indigenous to the marine environment, but may have a transient existence after entering salt water via rivers or sewage inputs.[106] Motile aeromonads also occur widely in sludge and sewage.[71, 117]

Motile aeromonads are not considered normal inhabitants of the human gastrointestinal tract.[42, 69, 77] The fecal carriage rate of *A. hydrophila* in asymptomatic hospitalized patients varies from 0% to 8%.[20, 83, 140] This suggests that motile aeromonads are transient inhabitants of the human intestinal tract and that humans are not the major contributors of the organism to the environment, although aeromonads that are shed can multiply in sewage lines to significant numbers prior to discharge into the receiving waters.[53]

Motile aeromonads are also present in both chlorinated and unchlorinated waters.[14, 21, 70, 125] Low levels of the organism have been found in chlorinated approved drinking water that is free of *E. coli*.[14] Multiple regression analysis determined that growth of motile aeromonads in chlorinated water was related to water temperature and free chlorine content. The association of warm temperatures with high levels of motile aeromonads is also observed in surface waters in the United States.[36, 50, 119] Motile aeromonads isolated from chlorinated drinking waters in the United States have been shown to possess virulence factors[70] that may be related to enteric disease. Epidemological studies suggest that the incidence of *Aeromonas*-associated gastroenteritis peaks during the warmer months when the highest levels of motile aeromonads are present in the aquatic habitats.[14]

Foods that come in direct contact with water are likely sources of motile aeromonads, with fish and seafood products most often contaminated. The organism has been isolated worldwide from wild fish and pond-cultured edible and ornamental fish. *A. hydrophila* was first reported as associated exclusively with diseased fish.[129] The organism is not known to be part of the intestinal flora and tissue of healthy fish.[9, 51, 89, 122, 135, 144] However, *A. hydrophila* is easily isolated from retail market finfish. Shellfish, particularly oysters, represent another known reservoir of the organism.[1, 2, 3, 65, 92]

Motile aeromonads have been associated with refrigerated animal products such as chicken, beef, pork, lamb, dairy products, raw milk, and vegetables.[15, 31, 57, 63, 87, 88, 92, 124] The predominant organism found in these foods is *Pseudomonas* spp., with the motile aeromonads present in lower numbers. Palumbo et al.[92] did, however, observe a poultry sample in which the motile aeromonad count was 10% of the total aerobic flora after 1 week's storage at 5°C. The organism has been isolated from modified-atmosphere-packaged meats after prolonged refrigerated storage. Enfors et al.[31] isolated 10^6 *A. hydrophila*/cm^2 from nitrogen-packaged cuts of pork; in contrast, the organism was not recovered in air-packed cuts. In the case of raw milk, motile aero-monads were not detected at the time of purchase; however, after 1 week's storage at 5°C, the organism reached levels of 10^3 to 10^4/ml.[92]

30.13 Epidemiology

Aeromonas spp. were associated with diseases of cold-blooded animals long before they were considered to be pathogenic to humans. *A. salmonicida* is strictly a parasite of fish under natural conditions and is the cause of fish furunculosis in salmon and trout;[98] this organism is not pathogenic to humans.[98, 137] Motile aeromonads (the *A. hydrophila* group) can cause "red-leg" disease in amphibians and are considered responsible for diseases in reptiles, fishes, and snails.[98]

For many years, the *A. hydrophila* group has been associated with such extraintestinal infections in humans as wound infections,[29, 139, 143] septi-cemia,[23, 133, 134, 139] and meningitis.[29, 30, 101] Wound infections caused by *Aeromonas* spp. are directly associated with traumatic exposure to water or soil[23, 143] or to shucking of shellfish.[37] *Aeromonas* wound infections in healthy adults remain localized.[23] However, in compromised individuals wound infections may lead to septicemia, sometimes resulting in death.[143] Most cases of sep-ticemia and meningitis attributed to *Aeromonas* spp. have occurred in immu-nocompromised patients, usually victims of leukemia or cirrhosis.[23, 29, 48, 143] Sepsis has also been reported in patients with sickle cell anemia or those undergoing hemodialysis.[143] The patients' gastrointestinal tracts are consid-ered to be the usual source of the organism in disseminating infections.[143] Another source of motile aeromonads may be asymptomatic human carriers, particularly those working as food handlers. The fatality rate of patients with *Aeromonas* sepsis is about 62%.[23]

Recently, motile aeromonads also have been associated with gastroenter-itis.[4, 41, 44, 53, 56, 58, 83, 134] Two types of diarrhea have been attributed to these organisms: a "cholera-like" illness, characterized by watery stools, and a less common "dysentery-like" illness, characterized by blood and mucus in the stools.[44] Both types of diarrhea are usually mild and self-limiting,[137] but either may be chronic or severe.[19, 40, 47, 54, 58, 104, 110] Epidemiological data implicating motile aeromonads as causative agents of diarrhea include more frequent isolations of the organism from diarrheal stools than from normal stools[4, 44] and the occurrence of large numbers of the organism only in diarrheal stools.[139] *Aeromonas* gastroenteritis is observed most frequently in individuals who are immunocompromised[54, 107, 121] or are receiving antibiotic therapy.[54, 86] How-ever, motile aeromonads have been identified as the primary agents of gas-troenteritis in a number of patients with no underlying disorders,[19, 40, 41, 47, 58, 104] including individuals with severe cases of both cholera-like[16, 19, 47] and dysentery-like illness.[104] Although *Aeromonas*-associated diarrhea has been observed in healthy individuals of all age groups, it is most frequently observed in the very young or in older adults.[4, 44, 83]

30.14   Pathogenicity

No known characteristic (property or trait) distinguishes enteropathogenic motile aeromonad isolates from those that are nonvirulent. However, there is evidence that motile aeromonads produce both cytotoxic and cytotonic enterotoxins. Asao et al.[8] purified a β-hemolysin, which was also cytotoxic to Vero cells and caused fluid accumulation in the rabbit ileal loop (RIL). Antiserum to the purified hemolysin completely neutralized the RIL activity of several isolates,[131] demonstrating that the β-hemolysin alone can cause the changes in intestinal permeability associated with diarrhea. Ljungh et al.[73, 74] partially purified a cytotonic (cholera-like) enterotoxin, which had activities similar to cholera toxin in tissue cultures, was active in the RIL, and was stable to treatment at 56°C for 10 min. This toxin, however, was not serologically related to cholera toxin. Chakroborty et al.[18] reported cloning the gene for a cytotonic enterotoxin similar to the one described by Ljungh et al.[73, 74] A cholera toxin cross-reactive site was reported by Rose et al.[109] to reside on the cytotoxin molecule and by Schultz and McCardell[118] to reside on the cytotonic enterotoxin molecule. The confusion concerning these toxins needs to be clarified before the pathogenicity of specific isolates can be assessed accurately. Since purified hemolysin produced cytotonic-like reactions in tissue culture even after heating at 56°C and thus can be mistaken for cytotonic enterotoxin,[12] it will be necessary to isolate strains that do not produce hemolysin.

Assessment of the pathogenicity of *Aeromonas* isolates will also require the identification of additional factors, such as the ability to adhere to the intestinal mucosa and invasiveness. This was made evident by the results of a human feeding study in which known enterotoxic clinical strains caused diarrhea in only 2 of 56 volunteers.[85] One reason for the failure of these strains to cause diarrhea in most of the volunteers was offered by Kirov et al.[64] They observed that piliated environmental isolates shift toward nonpiliated forms once the intestine is infected; therefore, the nonpiliated forms isolated from stools would be noninfective when used in challenge studies.

Little is known about the properties of motile aeromonads associated with disseminating infections. However, it seems likely that such strains would be invasive. Supporting evidence for this hypothesis is found in the observation that *A. sobria*, the most virulent species,[58] is also the most invasive.[141] The β-hemolysin, which is highly lethal to mice,[8] also could be a factor.

30.15   Isolation Media

The isolation of the *A. hydrophila* group has been extensively studied by clinical microbiologists, and many media have been developed for their isolation from stool specimens. The methods and literature were reviewed by von Graevenitz and Bucher.[138] Additional media have been developed recently for clinical use; these include sheep blood agar with 30μg ampicillin/ml,[5, 34,]

[45, 84] sheep blood with no antibiotics,[59] and sheep blood with 10μg ampicillin/ml. Altorfer et al.[5] described the usefulness of cefsulodin-Irgasan-novobiocin (CIN) agar for the simultaneous detection of both *Aeromonas* spp. and *Yersinia* spp. Many of the media developed for use with stool specimens have also been used with water and environmental samples.[49, 79, 106, 123]

Since isolating bacteria from food presents distinct problems (different background microflora, need for quantitative recovery, and the possibility of injured cells), media developed for the clinical laboratory often must be modified or new media developed for use with foods. As part of a survey on the incidence of *Aeromonas* spp. in retail fresh foods of animal origin, one of us (SP[92]) found that clinical media were not suitable because of low recoveries of the organism and difficulties in distinguishing the *A. hydrophila* group from the background microflora. To correct these problems, Palumbo et al.[92] formulated a new medium, starch ampicillin (SA) agar, with starch hydrolysis as the differential trait (few bacteria in food are capable of hydrolyzing starch) and ampicillin (final level, 10μg/ml) to suppress the background microflora. SA agar has proved useful for the quantitative detection of the *A. hydrophila* group in retail fresh foods of animal origin[92, 132] and fresh vegetables.[15]

Lachica (personal communication, 1990) has developed a modification of the SA agar, which he found useful in studying the fate of *A. hydrophila* in foods held under different temperature conditions. Other media and procedures have been evaluated for the isolation of the *A. hydrophila* organisms from foods. Stern et al.[132] compared various media for the isolation of *Aeromonas* spp. from ground beef and animal feces and found that SA agar was optimal with respect to selectivity and the ability to differentiate *Aeromonas* spp. from other resident microflora. Nishikawa and Kishi,[90] when studying the recovery of motile *Aeromonas* from foods and environmental specimens, observed swarming of *Proteus* when they employed SA agar and formulated a new medium with starch hydrolysis as the differential system and bile salts and brilliant green as inhibitory substances. They obtained quantitative recovery of motile aeromonads using artificially contaminated samples. Abeyta et al.[3] studied the recovery of *A. hydrophila* from oysters frozen for 1½ years at −72°C. In their recovery studies, they found that tryptic soy broth + 30μg/ml ampicillin (TSBA) was the best enrichment broth and MacConkey agar gave the best recovery of the *A. hydrophila* group organisms.

Enrichment broths are often used in the recovery of different pathogens from food either when low numbers are encountered (and especially in the presence of a large background microflora) or when injured organisms are anticipated. The enrichment broth permits repair of damaged cells, which can then form colonies on selective agars. In the case of recovering *A. hydrophila* from oysters mentioned above,[3] the TSBA probably allowed repair of injured cells.

Von Graevenitz and Bucher[138] have recommended the use of the general-purpose alkaline peptone water (APW) for enrichment of the *A. hydrophila* group and as specifically useful in the isolation of the *A. hydrophila* group from environmental samples and, in particular, feces.[45, 82] APW in conjunction with low temperature (5°C) has been found useful for the enrichment of *Yersinia enterocolitica*, also. Hunter and Burge[57] used APW in the isolation of *A. caviae* from ice cream.

Membrane filter techniques are useful for the isolation and quantitation of bacteria, including motile aeromonads[49, 106] from aquatic environments, especially when they occur in low numbers. Rippey and Cabelli[106] employed trehalose in a primary medium as the fermentable carbohydrate and ampicillin and ethanol as selective inhibitors. After 20 hr of incubation at 37°C, an *in situ* mannitol fermentation followed by an *in situ* oxidase test was used to differentiate *A. hydrophila* from other organisms present in fresh waters. Their procedure gave recoveries that exceeded other procedures, with greater confirmation rates and fewer negative samples.

One factor that often complicates the quantitative recovery of bacteria from foods is the presence of injured cells (Chapter 7). The phenomenon of injury has not yet been studied in *A. hydrophila*. Since injury has been studied and does occur in the closely related genera of *Vibrio*[30, 103] and *Plesiomonas*,[81] and since *Aeromonas* spp. present in foods may be exposed to the same stresses that injure other foodborne pathogens, injury should also be of concern in the recovery of the *A. hydrophila* group.

30.16   Characterization and Speciation in the Genus *Aeromonas*

Bacteria may be recognized as belonging to the genus *Aeromonas* by biochemical tests and thus easily separated from other closely related organisms. In the past, motile aeromonads were often confused biochemically with the family *Enterobacteriaceae*. The oxidase test is an easy and useful test to separate *Vibrionaceae* and *Enterobacteriaceae*. Differentiation of the genera within the family *Vibrionaceae* can be accomplished by biochemical reactions (Table 1). Two tests for differentiating *Vibrio* and *Aeromonas* are O/129 sensitivity and salt requirement. Sensitivity to the water-soluble vibriostatic agent 2, 4-diamino-6, 7-diisopropyl pteridine (O/129) phosphate is determined by disk sensitivity testing on nutrient agar containing 0.5% (wt/vol) NaCl. Disks containing either 10 μg or 150 μg of O/129 phosphate are used. Any zone of inhibition around the 150 μg disk is read as sensitive. *Aeromonas* spp. are resistant to O/129 at both levels. Growth at different concentrations of NaCl (e.g., 0% and 1%) is determined in 1% tryptone broth incubated for 24 to 48 hours at 35°C. *Aeromonas* spp. will grow in the broth with and without NaCl, whereas *Vibrio* spp. require NaCl for growth.

The *A. hydrophila* group is a phenotypically and genetically heterogeneous taxon. Various authors have divided the species *A. hydrophila* into such groups as *A. punctada*, *A. formicans*, *A. liquefaciens*, *A. anaerogenes*, *A. proteolytica*, and, more recently, *A. caviae* and *A. sobria*.[28, 33, 70, 75, 78, 99, 114, 115, 116, 120, 128] The complexity of the problem was recently shown by Popoff

Table 1—Differentiation of the Genus *Aeromonas* from Other Genera of the Family *Vibrionaceae* Encountered in Foods[98]

Test	Aeromonas	Vibrio	Plesiomonas
oxidase	+	+	+
gas from glucose	+	−	−
inositol (acid)	−	−	+
mannitol (acid)	+	+	−
ornithine decarboxylase[a]	−	D	+
Na+ required for growth	−	+	−
production of exoenzymes	+	D	−
amylase	+	−	−
gelatinase	+	+	−
lipase	+	−	−
growth on thiosulfate-citrate-bile salt-sucrose agar	−	+	−
inhibition by 0/129			
10 μg	R	D	D
150 μg	R	S	S

[a]*Aeromonas veronii* is ornithine decarboxylase +. This organism has become recognized in the clinical laboratory as a cause of diarrhea[52]; its occurrence in foods is unknown at present.
+ = positive; − = negative; D = different biotypes; R = resistant; S = sensitive.

et al.,[100] who found that *A. hydrophila* could be divided into distinct groups based on DNA-DNA hybridization. From DNA hybridization studies, motile aeromonad species exhibit DNA/DNA homology values of 35% to 50% with 8% to 12% divergence.[10] These DNA hybridization values are consistent with the criteria required to define groups at a species level rather than subspecies level. In contrast, the nonmotile *A. salmonicida* group appears to be a genetically homogeneous group, with very high homology values.[75]

Biochemical characteristics of the motile aeromonads have been studied by numerous investigators.[27, 28, 32, 43, 76, 96, 99, 126] Besides those mentioned previously, the genus *Aeromonas* has the following characteristics: Gram-negative straight rods measuring 0.3 μm to 1.0 μm in diameter and 1.0 μm to 3.5 μm in length; motile by a single polar flagellum in liquid medium (peritrichous flagella may occur on solid media in young cultures); failure to ferment inositol; reduction of nitrate to nitrite; absence of ornithine decarboxylase; hydrolyze starch, gelatin, o-nitrophenyl-β-D-galactopyranoside, DNA, and RNA; hydrogen sulfide not produced from thiosulfate; growth from 45°C to as low as 0°C in some strains, with an optimum at 28°C; NaCl tolerance from 0% to 4%; found at pH values from 5.2 to 9.8.

Popoff et al.[100] determined that, although the motile aeromonads could not be speciated based on DNA hybridization studies, they could be divided into three species—*A. hydrophila*, *A. caviae*, and *A. sobria*—based on biochemical reactions[99, 100] (Table 2). Properties that are important for distinguishing

Table 2—Differentiation among the Motile *Aeromonas* Species

Characteristic/biochemical test[a]	*A. hydrophila*	*A. caviae*	*A. sobria*
esculin hydrolysis	+	+	−
growth in KCN broth	+	+	−
L-arginine utilization	+	+	−
L-lysine utilization	+	−	+
L-arabinose utilization	+	+	−
fermentation of salicin	+	+	−
fermentation of sucrose	+	+	+
fermentation of mannitol	+	+	+
breakdown of inositol	−	−	−
acetoin from glucose (Voges-Proskauer reaction)	+	−	D
gas from glucose	+	−	+
indole production	+	+	+
Beta-hemolysis[b]	+	−	+
H₂S from cysteine	+	−	+

[a]incubation temperature 28° to 30° C.[98,99]
[b]Human red blood cells in tryptic soy agar.[136]
+ = positive; − = negative; D = different biotypes.

among the three species are esculin hydrolysis, growth in KCN broth, salicin fermentation at 30°C or room temperature, and production of gas from glucose. Another test used by some investigators to differentiate among the three motile aeromonads is production of H_2S from thiosulfate. Motile aeromonads do not produce H_2S from thiosulfate, but some strains do produce H_2S from cysteine.[60, 98] It is suggested that all motile aeromonads may produce H_2S in small amounts and the usefulness of testing for H_2S is limited.[98]

As discussed above, biochemical reactions are very important in biotyping or speciating motile aeromonad isolates. Identifying isolates biochemically requires a large number of test media.[99] Various rapid test systems have been developed to aid microbiologists in identifying their isolates. Some of the systems that have been successfully used with isolates of motile aeromonads include API 20E,[108, 127] API ZYM,[46] PASCO MIC-ID system,[105] and Mast-ID 15 system.[55] The developers and manufacturers of these systems have large data bases of biochemical reactions for different isolates, and these data bases can be called upon to aid in identifying isolates. The accuracy and reliability of the systems vary, but "typical" isolates, which are more than 90% of them, can be easily and readily identified.

Kaper et al.[60] described a single-tube medium for the rapid presumptive identification of *A. hydrophila*. It also offered good differentiation of *Klebsiella, Proteus,* and other enterics. The reactions that could be observed in the single tube were fermentation of mannitol and inositol, ornithine decarboxylation and deamination, indole production, motility, and H_2S production from sodium thiosulfate and cysteine. They found this medium useful in identifying environmental isolates of the *A. hydrophila* group.

The temperature at which the biochemical tests are incubated is important, especially when using one of the above rapid systems. Microbiologists should use the temperature at which the cultures in the system's data base were incubated. Altwegg et al.[6] observed differences in the decarboxylase activity of motile aeromonad isolates as a function of both medium and temperature, with 29°C being the best to retain two important biochemical reactions in these organisms: ornithine negativity and arginine positivity. Ewing et al.[32, 33] also reported differences in other biochemical reactions depending on temperature. Popoff and Veron[99] incubated all their test media at 30°C; because their scheme is recognized as the definitive one, this temperature should be used in determining the biochemical activity of isolates. Work by one of us (Palumbo, unpublished data) has indicated that, for various food isolates of motile aeromonads, many biochemical reactions are negative when incubated at 37°C compared with incubation at 28°C.

In addition to biochemical tests, clinicians and epidemiologists often use other tests to characterize isolates from different sources. These tests permit tracing the epidemiological patterns of the organism. Some of these tests and techniques have been applied to clinical and environmental isolates of motile aeromonads and undoubtedly can be applied to food isolates. These tests include phage typing[39] [phage typing has also been used for diagnostic purposes in studies of *A. salmonicida*;[97] there have been studies on immunization of salmonid fishes against *A. salmonicida*[130]], serotyping,[26, 38, 68, 94, 112] and esterase[95] and haemagglutination[13, 22, 66] patterns. The motile aeromonads are antigenically heterogeneous and have been extensively reviewed.[11, 27, 33, 67, 72, 80, 102, 120] The antigenic studies have dealt primarily with the serologic specificity of extracellular antigens and the diversity of somatic and flagellar antigens. Ewing and coworkers[32, 33] found 12 O antigenic groups and one H antigenic group among 71 *A. hydrophila* studied. The presence of K antigens, partially inhibiting the O agglutination, has also been reported.[25] *A. salmonicida* also has been studied serologically.[62]

The profiles of outer membrane proteins also appear as a potential means of distinguishing isolates of *A. hydrophila* from different sources.[7] Canonica and Pisano[17] analyzed the fatty acid methyl esters obtained from clinical isolates of motile aeromonads and observed the presence of two hydroxy fatty acid species: 3-hydroxy-12:0 and 3-hydroxy-14:0. The 3-hydroxy-12:0 fatty acid was unique to the clinical isolates and thus permitted separation of motile aeromonads of clinical origin from nonclinical isolates. This approach might prove useful when applied to food isolates. Figura and Guglielmetti[35] describe testing motile *Aeromonas* isolates for production of a CAMP-like factor. *A. hydrophila* strains were positive whether tested aerobically or anaerobically,

A. sobria strains were positive only under aerobic conditions, and *A. caviae* strains were always negative.

30.2   GENERAL CONSIDERATIONS

30.21   Handling of Samples

Since *A. hydrophila* group organisms are capable of ready growth in fresh foods of both animal[92] and plant[8] origin at 5°C, the food samples should be processed as soon as possible upon arrival at the laboratory. Motile aeromonads are somewhat sensitive to pH values below 5.5; therefore, acidic foods should be processed soon after arrival in the laboratory. The ability to withstand freezing has not been studied in motile aeromonads, though Abeyta et al.[3] were able to isolate *A. hydrophila* from oysters held frozen for 1½ years at −72°C. An enrichment technique may be necessary when analyzing frozen foods for the presence of *A. hydrophila* group organisms.

30.3   EQUIPMENT, MATERIALS, AND REAGENTS

30.31   Equipment

Incubator, 28°C
Stomacher

30.32   Media (Chapter 62)

Alkaline peptone water
Bile salts brilliant green starch (BBGS)
DNase test agar or toluidine blue agar
Kaper's medium
Modified SA agar
Nutrient agar
Peptone (0.1%)
SA agar
Tryptic soy agar (TSA)
Tryptic soy broth + 30 mg/L ampicillin (TSBA)

30.33   Reagents (Chapter 62)

Ascorbic acid
Gram stain
Kovac's reagent
Lugol's iodine solution
1% N,N,N′,N′ tetramethyl-p-phenylenediamine dihydrochloride
3% Hydrogen peroxide
Vibriostatic 0/129 discs (10 μg)

30.4   PROCEDURES

The following procedures are suggested for isolating and quantitating motile aeromonads from foods. Since, at this point, there is no officially accepted methodology (BAM 6th Ed., 1984), these procedures are based on our experience in handling various foods and various media and techniques used for the *A. hydrophila* group.

30.41   Sampling

Aseptically weigh 25 g of the food into a stomacher bag, add 225 ml of sterile peptone (0.1%) water, and blend for 2 to 3 min in a stomacher laboratory mixer. Further dilute peptone water as needed and surface plate 0.1 ml portions onto media described below. Use sterile bent glass rods to distribute the sample dilutions evenly over the surface of the media.

Another procedure may be used; however, we have not had any direct experience with it. In this procedure the food samples are weighed into special stomacher filter bags (spiral systems, Bethesda, Md.) and the samples prepared as above. By use of the special filter bags, the food samples and dilutions can then be plated using a spiral plater (Spiral Systems, Bethesda, Md.) and the number of *A. hydrophila* can be determined quantitatively by an appropriate calculation.

30.42   Inoculation of Media

SA agar[92] and modified SA agar (Lachica, personal communication, 1990) are recommended. BBGS agar is suggested by the investigators who formulated it as being useful for samples in which large numbers of *Proteus* spp. might be encountered.

After inoculating these media with appropriate dilutions of the food samples, incubate the plates at 28°C overnight (24 hr maximum). After incubation, flood SA and BBGS agar plates with 5 ml of Lugol's iodine solution. Count typical colonies (5 mm, yellow to honey-colored on SA agar) surrounded by a clear zone of hydrolyzed starch against a black background as *A. hydrophila* groups. Suspect colonies must be picked at this step for verification since the iodine is rapidly lethal to the cells. On overcrowded plates, the growth can be scraped off with a sterile loop and zones counted to provide an estimate of the number of *A. hydrophila* colonies. On the modified SA agar, *A. hydrophila* colonies are surrounded by a light halo against a blue background; the iodine solution is not needed.

30.43   Enrichment Media

In instances when small numbers of *A. hydrophila* are anticipated or when injured cells are suspected, use an enrichment broth. The two recommended enrichment broths are APW[137] and TSBA (Difco).[3] The enrichment media can be inoculated with a 25-g sample of food or dilutions of the original 1/10 slurry prepared in the stomacher bag. Incubation at 28°C is recommended. When quantitation is desired, either of the suggested enrichment broths can be incorporated into a most probable number (MPN) procedure in which various dilutions are employed in a 3- or 5-tube method. After 24 hr, streak portions of the broths onto the above three plating media, and observe plates after 24 hr at 28°C. Score plates as positive or negative for typical *A. hydrophila* colonies, and obtain a quantitative estimate of the number of *A. hydrophila* in the original sample using MPN tables (Chapter 6).

30.44   Verification of Isolates as *A. hydrophila*

In our experience, amylase-producing colonies from SA agar plates have all been verified as belonging to the *A. hydrophila* group. The following procedure allows investigators to verify food isolates as the *A. hydrophila* group.

Pick typical *A. hydrophila* colonies from SA agar and streak them onto plates of nutrient agar (Difco), tryptic soy agar (Difco), or any other suitable growth medium that does not contain carbohydrate; also streak a plate of DNase test agar. Test the suspected colonies from the SA plate for amylase activity by placing a drop of Lugol's iodine on each colony. If the colonies are amylase-positive, incubate the two plating media for 24 hr at 28°C. Before incubation, place a disk of 0/129 in a heavy streak area so that zones of inhibition can be seen.

Nutrient agar (or TSA) plates are used for several procedures: (a) to determine if a pure culture was obtained from the initial streaking; (b) to perform a gram stain (*A. hydrophila* group organisms are short gram-negative rods); (c) to perform a catalase test (a few drops of 3% H_2O_2 are added to an isolated colony; bubbles formed indicate a positive reaction); and (d) to test resistance to the vibriostatic agent 0/129 (*A. hydrophila* is not inhibited by the compound).

Further verification of the isolates can be easily accomplished by inoculating into a tube of Kaper's medium[60] (5-ml amounts incubated at 35°C). After 18 to 24 hr, read the tubes. A typical *A. hydrophila* group reaction is alkaline band at top, acid butt, motility +, H_2S −, and indole + (add 2 drops of Kovac's reagent to the tube and look for a red/scarlet color). The isolate also can be inoculated into the API 20E series test strip and reactions read after 24 hr. Identify by comparing the isolate's biochemical reactions with a reference table and by using a numerical key. The company can be contacted directly for help in identifying cultures giving atypical reactions.

30.5   INTERPRETATIONS

The exact significance of organisms of the *A. hydrophila* group in foods is not known. They can readily be isolated, often in high numbers, from a wide variety of fresh foods and from various water supplies. They are recognized as pathogens in select groups of individuals such as immunocompromised persons and patients with underlying malignancies, young children, and travelers in third-world countries. *A. hydrophila* cultures isolated from the environment and from clinical specimens often possess factors and traits that are associated with virulence in other gram-negative bacteria, including enterotoxin formation, hemolysin, serum resistance, and haemagglutinins. These organisms are able to grow at 5°C. They can be destroyed readily by heat,[93] irradiation,[91] and other processes as well. However, if present, they can grow competitively in many foods (including vacuum-packaged meats) and will easily tolerate up to 2% NaCl and pH values above 6.0.

30.6 REFERENCES

1. Abeyta, C. Jr. 1987. Unpublished data. U. S. Food and Drug Admin., Seafood Products Research Center, Seattle, Wash.
2. Abeyta, C. Jr., Kaysner, C. A., and Wekell, M. M. 1986. Media evaluation for recovery of *Aeromonas hydrophila* from West Coast estuaries. No. Q 86, Abstr. of the 86th Annual Meeting of the Amer. Soc. for Microbiol., Washington, D.C., March 23–28, 1986.
3. Abeyta, C. Jr., Kaysner, C. A., Wekell, M. M., Sullivan, J. J., and Stelma, G. N. 1986. Recovery of *Aeromonas hydrophila* from oysters implicated in an outbreak of foodborne illness. J. Food Protect. 49: 643.
4. Agger, W. A., McCormick, J. D., and Gurwith, M. J. 1985. Clinical and microbiological features of *Aeromonas hydrophila* associated diarrhea. J. Clin. Microbiol. 21: 909.
5. Altorfer, R., Altwegg, M., Zollinger-Iten, J., and von Graevenitz, A. 1985. Growth of *Aeromonas* spp. on Cefsulodin-Irgasan-Novobiocin agar selective for *Yersinia enterocolitica*. J. Clin. Microbiol. 22: 478.
6. Altwegg, M., von Graevenitz, A., and Zollinger-Iten, J. 1987. Medium and temperature dependence of decarboxylase reactions in *Aeromonas* spp. Curr. Microbiol. 15: 1.
7. Aoki, T. and Holland, B. I. 1985. The outermembrane proteins of the fish pathogens *Aeromonas hydrophila, Aeromonas salmonicida* and *Edwardsiella tarda*. FEMS Microbiol. Letters. 27: 299.
8. Asao, T., Kinoshito, Y., Kozaki, S., Uemura, T., and Sakaguchi, G. 1984. Purification and some properties of *Aeromonas hydrophila* hemolysin. Infect. Immun. 46: 122.
9. Boulanger, Y., Lallier, R., and Cousineau, G. 1977. Isolation of enterotoxigenic *Aeromonas* from fish. Can. J. Microbiol. 23: 1161.
10. Brenner, D. J., Fanning, G. R., and Steigerwalt, A. G. 1972. Deoxyribonucleic acid relatedness among species of *Erwinia* and between *Erwinia* species and other enterobacteria. J. Bacteriol. 110: 12.
11. Bullock, G. L. 1966. Precipitation and agglutination reactions of aeromonads isolated from fish and other sources. Bull. Off. Int. Epizoot. 68: 805.
12. Bunning, V. K., Crawford, R. G., Stelma, G. N. Jr., Taylor, L. O., and Johnson, C. H. 1986. Melanogenesis in murine B16 cells exposed to *Aeromonas hydrophila* cytotoxic enterotoxin. Can. J. Microbiol. 32: 814.
13. Burke, V., Cooper, M., and Robinson, J. 1986. Haemagglutination patterns of *Aeromonas* spp. related to species and source of strains. Aust. J. Exp. Biol. Med. Sci. 64: 563.
14. Burke, V., Robinson, J., Gracey, M., Peterson, D., and Partridge, K. 1984. Isolation of *Aeromonas hydrophila* from a metropolitan water supply: Seasonal correlation with clinical isolates. Appl. Environ. Microbiol. 48: 361.
15. Callister, S. M. and Agger, W. A. 1987. Enumeration and characterization of *Aeromonas*

hydrophila and *Aeromonas caviae* isolated from grocery store produce. Appl. Environ. Microbiol. 53: 249.

16. Campbell, J. D. and Houston, C. H. 1985. Effect of cultural conditions on the presence of a cholera-toxin cross-reactive factor in culture filtrates of *Aeromonas hydrophila*. Curr. Microbiol. 12: 101.

17. Canonica, F. P. and Pisano, M. A. 1985. Identification of hydroxy fatty acids in *Aeromonas hydrophila*, *Aeromonas sobria*, and *Aeromonas caviae*. J. Clin. Microbiol. 22: 1061.

18. Chakroborty, T., Montenegro, M. A., Sanyal, S. C., Helmuth, R., Bulling, E., and Timmis, K. N. 1984. Cloning of enterotoxin gene from *Aeromonas hydrophila* provides conclusive evidence of production of a cytotonic enterotoxin. Infect. Immun. 46: 435.

19. Champsaur, H., Andremont, A., Mathieu, D., Rottman, E., and Auzepy, P. 1982. Cholera-like illness due to *Aeromonas sobria*. J. Infect. Dis. 145: 248.

20. Chatterjee, B. D. and Neogy, K. N. 1972. Studies on *Aeromonas* and *Plesiomonas* species isolated from cases of choleraic diarrhea. Ind. J. Med. Res. 60: 520.

21. Clark, J. A., Burger, G. A., and Sabatinos, L. E. 1982. Characterization of indicator bacteria in municipal raw water, drinking water and new main water samples. Can. J. Microbiol. 28: 1002.

22. Crichton, P. B. and Walker, J. W. 1985. Methods for the detection of haemagglutinins in *Aeromonas*. J. Med. Microbiol. 19: 273.

23. Davis, W. A. III, Kane, J. G., and Garagusi, V. F. 1978. Human *Aeromonas* infections: A review of the literature and a case report of endocarditis. Medicine 57: 267.

24. Davis, J. W. and Sizemore, R. K. 1981. Nonselectivity of Rimler-Shotts medium for *Aeromonas hydrophila* in estuarine environments. Appl. Environ. Microbiol. 42: 544.

25. Demeuron, P. A. and Peduzzi, R. 1979. Caracterisation de souches du genre *Aeromonas* isolees chez des poissons d'eau douce et quelques reptiles. Zentralbl. Vet. 266: 153.

26. Dooley, J. S. G., Lallier, R., and Trust, T. J. 1986. Surface antigens of virulent strains of *Aeromonas hydrophila*. Vet. Immun. Immunopathol. 12: 339.

27. Eddy, B. P. 1960. Cephalotrichous, fermentative gram-negative bacteria: The genus *Aeromonas*. J. Appl. Bacteriol. 23: 216.

28. Eddy, B. P. 1962. Further studies on *Aeromonas*. I. Additional strains and supplementary biochemical tests. J. Appl. Bacteriol. 25: 137.

29. Ellison, R. T. and Mostow, S. R. 1984. Pyogenic meningitis manifesting during therapy for *Aeromonas hydrophila* sepsis. Arch. Intern. Med. 144: 2078.

30. Emswiler, B. S., Pierson, M. D., and Shoemaker, S. P. 1976. Sublethal heat stress of *Vibrio parahaemolyticus*. Appl. Environ. Microbiol. 32: 792.

31. Enfors, S. O., Molin, G., and Ternström, A. 1979. Effect of packaging under carbon dioxide, nitrogen, or air on the microbial flora of pork stored at 4°C. J. Appl. Bacteriol. 47: 197.

32. Ewing, W. H., Hugh, R., and Johnson, J. G. 1961. Studies on the *Aeromonas* group. U. S. Depart. Health, Ed. and Welfare, Centers for Disease Control, Atlanta, Ga.

33. Ewing, W. H., Hugh, R., and Johnson, J. G. 1961. Studies on the *Aeromonas* group. In "Public Health Service Monograph." Centers for Disease Control, Atlanta, Ga.

34. Figura, N. 1985. A comparison of various media in the detection of *Aeromonas* spp. from stool samples. Boll. Ist. Sieroter. Milan. 64: 167.

35. Figura, N. and Guglielmetti, P. 1987. Differentiation of motile and mesophilic *Aeromonas* strains into species by testing for a CAMP-like factor. J. Clin. Microbiol. 25: 1341.

36. Fliermans, C. B., Gorden, R. W., Hazen, T. C., and Esch, G. W. 1977. *Aeromonas* distribution and survival in a thermally altered lake. Appl. Environ. Microbiol. 33: 114.

37. Flynn, T. J. and Knepp, I. G. 1987. Seafood shucking as an etiology for *Aeromonas hydrophila* infection. Arch. Intern. Med. 147: 1816.

38. Fricker, C. R. 1987. Serotyping of mesophilic *Aeromonas* spp. on the basis of lipopolysaccharide antigens. Lett. Appl. Microbiol. 4: 113.

39. Geiger, D. and Geiger, W. 1986. Comparaison au moyen de la lysotypie entre souches d'*Aeromonas* de pisciculture et souches isolees de l'homme. Schweiz. Z. Hydrol. 48: 161.

40. Gelbart, S. M., Prabhudesai, M., and Magee, S. M. 1985. A case report: *Aeromonas sobria* gastroenteritis in an adult. Am. J. Clin. Pathol. 83: 389.

41. George, W. L., Nakata, M. M., Thompson, J., and White, M. L. 1985. *Aeromonas*-related diarrhea in adults. Arch. Intern. Med. 145: 2207.

42. George, W. L., Jones, M. J., and Nakata, M. M. 1986. Phenotypic characteristics of *Aeromonas* species isolated from adult humans. J. Clin. Microbiol. 23: 1026.

43. Gibson, D. M., Hendrie, M. S., Houston, N. C., and Hobbs, G. 1977. The identification of some gram negative heterotrophic aquatic bacteria. In "Aquatic Microbiology," eds. F. A. Skinner and J. M. Shewan, p. 135. Academic Press, Inc., New York, N.Y.

44. Gracey, M., Burke, V., and Robinson, J. 1982. *Aeromonas*-associated gastroenteritis. Lancet 2(8311): 1304.

45. Gray, S. J. 1984. *Aeromonas hydrophila* in livestock: Incidence, biochemical characteristics and antibiotic susceptibility. J. Hyg. (Camb.) 92: 365.

46. Gray, S. J. 1987. Characterisation of *Aeromonas sp.* in the API ZYM system. Med. Lab. Sci. 44: 287.

47. Gurwith, M., Bourque, C., Cameron, E., Forrest, G., and Green, M. 1977. Cholera-like diarrhea in Canada. Arch. Intern. Med. 137: 1461.

48. Harris, R. L., Fainstein, V., Elting, L., Hopfer, R. L., and Bodey, G. P. 1985. Bacteremia caused by *Aeromonas* species in hospitalized cancer patients. Rev. Infect. Dis. 7: 314.

49. Havelaar, A. H., During, M., and Versteegh, J. F. M. 1987. Ampicillin-dextrin agar medium for the enumeration of *Aeromonas* species in water by membrane filtration. J. Appl. Bacteriol. 62: 279.

50. Hazen, T. C., Fliermans, C. B., Hirsch, R. P., and Esch, G. W. 1978. Prevalence and distribution of *Aeromonas hydrophila* in the United States. Appl. Environ. Microbiol. 36: 731.

51. Heuschmann-Brunner, G. 1978. Aeromonads of the "hydrophila-punctata" group in fresh water fishes. Arch. Hydrobiol. 83: 99.

52. Hickman-Brenner, F. W., MacDonald, K. L., Steigerwalt, A. G., Fanning, G. R., Brenner, D. J., and Farmer, J. J. III. 1987. *Aeromonas veronii*, a new ornithine decarboxylase-positive species that may cause diarrhea. J. Clin. Microbiol. 25: 900.

53. Holmberg, S. D. and Farmer, J. J. III. 1984. *Aeromonas hydrophila* and *Plesiomonas shigelloides* as causes of intestinal infections. Rev. Infect. Dis. 6: 633.

54. Holmberg, S. D., Schell, W. L., Fanning, G. R., Wachsmuth, I. K., Hickman-Brenner, F. W., Blake, P. A., Brenner, D. J., and Farmer, J. J. III. 1986. *Aeromonas* intestinal infections in the United States. Ann. Intern. Med. 105: 683.

55. Holmes, B. and Dawson, C. A. 1987. Evaluation of Mast-ID 15 system for identifying *Enterobacteriaceae*, some *Vibrionaceae*, and *Acinetobacter*. J. Clin. Pathol. 40: 1168.

56. Honda, T., Sato, M., Nishimura, T., Higashitsutsumi, M., Fakai, F., and Miwatani, T. 1985. Demonstration of cholera toxin-related factor in cultures of *Aeromonas* species by enzyme-linked immunosorbent assay. Infect. Immun. 50: 322.

57. Hunter, P. R. and Burge, S. H. 1987. Isolation of *Aeromonas caviae* from ice-cream. Lett. Appl. Microbiol. 4: 45.

58. Janda, J. M., Bottone, E. J., and Reitano, M. 1983. *Aeromonas* species in clinical microbiology: Significance, epidemiology, and speciation. Diagn. Microbiol. Infect. Dis. 1: 221.

59. Janda, J. M., Dixon, A., Raucher, B., Clack, R. B., and Bottone, E. J. 1984. Value of blood agar for primary plating and clinical implications of simultaneous isolation of *Aeromonas hydrophila* and *Aeromonas caviae* from a patient with gastroenteritis. J. Clin. Microbiol. 20: 1221.

60. Kaper, J., Seidler, R. J., Lockman, H., and Colwell, R. R. 1979. Medium for the presumptive identification of *Aeromonas hydrophila* and *Enterobacteriaceae*. Appl. Environ. Microbiol. 38: 1023.

61. Kaper, J. B., Lockman, H., and Colwell, R. R. 1981. *Aeromonas hydrophila* ecology and toxigenicity of isolates from an estuary. J. Appl. Bacteriol. 50: 359.
62. Karlsson, K. A. 1964. Serologische studien von *Aeromonas salmonicida*. Zentralbl. Bakteriol. Parasitenkd. Infektionskr. Hyg. Ankh. Abt. I Orig. A. 194: 73.
63. Kielwein, G., Gerlach, R., and Johne, H. 1969. Prevalence of *A. hydrophila* in raw milk. Arch. Lebensmittelhyg. 20: 34.
64. Kirov, S. M., Rees, B., Wellock, R. C., Goldsmid, J. M., and van Galen, A. D. 1986. Virulence characteristics of *Aeromonas* spp. in relation to source and biotype. J. Clin. Microbiol. 24: 827.
65. Konuma, H., Suzuki, A., Kawanishi, T., Takayama, S., Mizushima, K., Takaku, H., and Yamada, M. 1975. Distribution of microbial flora in oysters. J. Food Hyg. Soc. Japan 16: 422.
66. Kozaki, S., Kurokawa, A., Asao, T., Kato, K., Uemura, T., and Sakaguchi, G. 1987. Enzyme-linked immunosorbent assay for *Aeromonas hydrophila* hemolysins. FEMS Microbiol. Letters 41: 147.
67. Kulp, W. L. and Borden, D. G. 1942. Further studies on *Proteus hydrophila*, etiological agent in "red-leg" disease of frogs. J. Bacteriol. 44: 673.
68. Lallier, R. 1984. Antigenic differentiation of pili from non-virulent and fish-pathogenic strains of *Aeromonas hydrophila*. J. Fish Dis. 7: 509.
69. Lautrop, H. 1961. *Aeromonas hydrophila* isolated from human feces and its possible pathological significance. Acta Pathol. Microbiol. Scand. Suppl. 144–152: 299.
70. LeChevallier, M. W., Evans, T. M., Seidler, R., Daily, O. P., Merrell, B. R., Rollins D. M., and Joseph, S. W. 1982. *Aeromonas sobria* in chlorinated drinking water supplies. Microb. Ecol. 8: 325.
71. LeClerc, H. and Buttiaux, R. 1962. Frequence des *Aeromonas* dans l'eaux d'alimentation. Ann. Inst. Pasteur, Paris 103: 97.
72. Liu, P. V. 1961. Observations of the specificities of extracellular antigens of the genus *Aeromonas* and *Serratia*. J. Gen. Microbiol. 24: 145.
73. Ljungh, A., Wretlind, B., and Möllby, R. 1981. Separation and characterization of enterotoxin and two hemolysins from *Aeromonas hydrophila*. Acta Pathol. Microbiol. Scand., Sect. B 89: 387.
74. Ljungh, A., Enroth, P., and Wadström, T. 1982. Cytotoxic enterotoxin from *Aeromonas hydrophila*. Toxicol. 20: 787.
75. Macinnes, J. L., Trust, T. J., and Crosa, J. H. 1979. Deoxyribonucleic acid relationships among members of the genus *Aeromonas*. Can. J. Microbiol 25: 579.
76. McCarthy, D. H. 1975. "The bacteriology and taxonomy of *Aeromonas liquefaciens*." Technical Report Series, Fish Diseases Laboratory, Ministry of Agriculture, Weymouth, Dorset.
77. McCracken, A. W. and Barkley, R. 1972. Isolation of *Aeromonas* species from clinical sources. J. Clin. Pathol. 25: 970.
78. Merkel, J. R., Traganza, E. D., Mukherjee, B. B., Griffin, T. B., and Prescott, J. M. 1964. Proteolytic activity and general characteristics of a marine bacterium, *Aeromonas proteolytica* a sp. N. J. Bacteriol. 87: 1227.
79. McCoy, R. H. and Pilcher, K. S. 1974. Peptone beef extract glycogen agar, a selective and differential *Aeromonas* medium. J. Fish. Res. Board Can. 31: 1553.
80. Miles, E. M. and Miles, A. A. 1951. The identity of *Proteus hydrophilus* Bergey *et al.* and *Proteus melanovogenes* Miles and Halnah and their relation to the genus *Aeromonas* Kluyver and Van Niel. J. Gen. Microbiol. 5: 298.
81. Miller, M. L. and Koburger, J. A. 1986. Evaluation of inositol brilliant green bile salts and Plesiomonas agars for recovery of *Plesiomonas shigelloides* from aquatic samples in a seasonal survey of the Suwannee River estuary. J. Food Protect. 49: 274.
82. Millership, S. E. and Chattopadhyay, B. 1984. Methods for the isolation of *Aeromonas hydrophila* and *Plesiomonas shigelloides* from faeces. J. Hyg. (Camb.) 92: 145.

83. Millership, S. E., Curnow, S. R., and Chattopadhyay, B. 1983. Faecal carriage rate of *Aeromonas hydrophila*. J. Clin. Pathol. 36: 920.

84. Mishra, S., Nair, G. B., Bhadra, R. K., Sikder, S. N. and Pal, S. C. 1987. Comparison of selective media for primary isolation of *Aeromonas* species from human and animal feces. J. Clin. Microbiol. 25: 2040.

85. Morgan, D. R., Johnson, P. C., Dupont, H. L., Satterwhite, T. K., and Wood, L. V. 1985. Lack of correlation between known virulence properties of *Aeromonas hydrophila* and enteropathogenicity for humans. Infect. Immun. 50: 62.

86. Moyer, N. P. 1987. Clinical significance of *Aeromonas* species isolated from patients with diarrhea. J. Clin. Microbiol. 25: 2044.

87. Myers, B. R., Marshall, R. T., Edmondson, J. E., and Stringer, W. C. 1982. Isolation of pectinolytic *Aeromonas hydrophila* and *Yersinia enterocolitica* from vacuum-packaged pork. J. Food Protect. 45: 33.

88. Nagel, C. W., Simpson, K. L., Ng, H., Vaughn, R. H., and Stewart, G. F. 1959. Microorganisms associated with spoilage of refrigerated poultry. Food Technol. 14: 21.

89. Nieto, T. P., Toranzo, A. E., and Barja, J. L. 1984. Comparison between the bacterial flora associated with fingerling rainbow trout cultured in two different hatcheries in the north-west of Spain. Aquaculture 42: 193.

90. Nishikawa, Y. and Kishi, T. 1987. A modification of bile salts brilliant green agar for isolation of motile *Aeromonas* from foods and environmental samples. Epidem. Inf. 98: 331.

91. Palumbo, S. A., Jenkins, R. K., Buchanan, R. L., and Thayer, D. W. 1986. Determination of irradiation D-values for *Aeromonas hydrophila*. J. Food Protect. 49: 189.

92. Palumbo, S. A., Maxino, F., Williams, A. C., Buchanan, R. L., and Thayer D. W. 1985. Starch-ampicillin agar for the quantitative detection of *Aeromonas hydrophila*. Appl. Environ. Microbiol. 50: 1027.

93. Palumbo, S. A., Williams, A. C., Buchanan, R. L., and Phillips, J. G. 1987. Thermal resistance of *Aeromonas hydrophila*. J. Food Protect. 50: 761.

94. Peduzzi, R., de Meuron, P. A., and Grimaldi, E. 1983. Investigation of *Aeromonas* isolated from water; a serological study using Ouchterlony and immunoelectrophoresis techniques. Experientia 39: 924.

95. Picard, B., and Goullet, P. H. 1987. Epidemiological complexity of hospital aeromonas infections revealed by electrophoretic typing of esterases. Epidem. Inf. 98: 5.

96. Popoff, M. 1969. Etude sur les *Aeromonas salmonicida*. I. Caracteres biochimiques et antigeniques. Rech. Vet. 3: 49.

97. Popoff, M. 1971. Interet diagnostique d'un bacteriophage specifique des *Aeromonas salmonicida*. Ann. Rech. Vet. 2: 137.

98. Popoff, M. 1984. Genus III. *Aeromonas* Kluyver and Van Niel 1936, 398. In "Bergey's Manual of Systematic Bacteriology," eds. N. R. Kreig and J. G. Holt, Vol. I, p. 545. Williams and Wilkins, Baltimore, Md.

99. Popoff, M. and Veron, M. 1976. A taxonomic study of the *Aeromonas hydrophilia-Aeromonas punctata* group. J. Gen. Microbiol. 94: 11.

100. Popoff, M., Coynault, C., Kiredjian, M. and Lemelin, M. 1981. Polynucleotide sequence relatedness among motile *Aeromonas* species. Curr. Microbiol. 5: 109.

101. Qadri, S. M. H., Gordon, L. P., Wende, R. D., and Williams, R. C. 1976. Meningitis due to *Aeromonas hydrophila*. J. Clin. Microbiol. 3: 102.

102. Rao, V. B. and Foster, B. G. 1977. Antigenic analysis of the genus *Aeromonas*. Texas J. Sci. 29: 85.

103. Ray, B., Hawkins, S. M., and Hackney, C. R. 1978. Method for the detection of injured *Vibrio parahaemolyticus* in seafoods. Appl. Environ. Microbiol. 35: 1121.

104. Rhaman, A. F. M. S. and Willoughby, J. M. T. 1980. Dysentery-like syndrome associated with *Aeromonas hydrophila*. Br. Med. J. 281: 976.

105. Rhoden, D. L., Schable, B., and Smith, P. B. 1987. Evaluation of PASCO MIC-ID system for identifying gram-negative bacilli. J. Clin. Microbiol. 25: 2363.
106. Rippey, S. R. and Cabelli, V. J. 1979. Membrane filter procedure for enumeration of *Aeromonas hydrophila* in fresh waters. Appl. Environ. Microbiol. 38: 108.
107. Roberts, I. M., Parenti, D. M., and Albert, M. B. 1987. *Aeromonas hydrophila*-associated colitis in a male homosexual. Arch. Intern. Med. 147: 1502.
108. Robertson, E. A. and MacLowry, J. D. 1974. Mathematical analysis of the API Enteric 20 profile register using a computer diagnostic model. Appl. Microbiol. 28: 691.
109. Rose, J. M., Houston, C. W., Florent, G., Dixon, J. D., and Kurosky, A. 1985. Characterization of a cytotoxic factor produced by *Aeromonas hydrophila*. B-164. Abstracts of the 86th Annual Meeting of the American Society for Microbiology, Las Vegas, Nev., March 3–7, 1985.
110. Rosner, R. 1964. *Aeromonas hydrophila* as the etiologic agent in a case of severe gastroenteritis. Am. J. Clin. Pathol. 42: 402.
111. Ross, A. J. 1962. Isolation of a pigment-producing strain of *Aeromonas liquefaciens* from silver salmon (*Orcorhynchus kisutch*). J. Bacteriol. 84: 590.
112. Sakazaki, R. and Shimada, T. 1984. O-serogrouping scheme for mesophilic *Aeromonas* strains. Japan J. Med. Biol. 37: 247.
113. Sandrelli, G. 1891. Uber einen neuen Mikroorganismes des Wassers, welcher fur Tiere mit veraenderlicher und konstanter Temperature Pathogen ist. Zentralbl. Bakteriol. Parasitenk. Infektionskr. Hyg. Abt. 192: 222.
114. Schubert, R. H. W. 1969. Infrasubspecific taxonomy of *Aeromonas hydrophila* (Chester 1901) Stanier 1943. Zentralbl. Bakteriol. Parasitenk. Infektionsk. Hyg. Orig. Abt. 1, 211: 406.
115. Schubert, R. H. W. 1969. *Aeromonas hydrophila* subsp. *proteolytica* (Merkel et al. 1964) Comb. Nov. Zentralbl. Bakteriol. Parasitenk. Infektionsk. Hyg. Abt. 1, Orig. 211: 409.
116. Schubert, R. H. W. 1974. Genus II *Aeromonas*. In "Bergey's Manual of Determinative Bacteriology," 8th ed., eds. R. E. Buchanan and N. E. Gibbons, p. 345. Williams and Wilkins, Baltimore, Md.
117. Schubert, R. H. W., Shafer, E., and Meiser, W. 1972. Vergleichende Untersuchungen uber die Eliminierung von Poliomyelitis-Impfvirus und Aeromonaden an einer halbtechnischen belebtschlammanlage des Grossen erftverbandes in Bergheim. Gas Wasserf. 113: 132.
118. Schultz, A. J. and McCardell, B. A. 1988. DNA homology and immunological cross-reactivity between *Aeromonas hydrophila* cytotonic toxin and cholera toxin. J. Clin. Microbiol. 26: 57.
119. Seidler, R. J., Allen, D. A., Lockman, H., Colwell, R. R., Joseph, S. W., and Daily, O. P. 1980. Isolation, enumeration, and characterization of *Aeromonas* from polluted waters encountered in diving operations. Appl. Environ. Microbiol. 39: 1010.
120. Shaw, D. H. and Hodder, H. J. 1978. Lipopolysaccharides of motile Aeromonads; Core oligosaccharide analysis as an aid to taxonomic classification. Can. J. Microbiol. 24: 864.
121. Sherlock, C. H., Burdge, D. R., and Smith, J. A. 1987. Does *Aeromonas hydrophila* preferentially colonize the bowels of patients with hematologic malignancies? Diagn. Microbiol. Infect. Dis. 7: 63.
122. Shotts, E. B., Kleckner, A. L., Gratzek, J. B., and Blue, J. L. 1976. Bacterial flora of aquarium fishes and their shipping waters imported from southeast Asia. J. Fish. Res. Board Can. 33: 732.
123. Shotts, E. B. Jr. and Rimler, R. 1973. Medium for the isolation of *Aeromonas hydrophila*. Appl. Microbiol. 26: 550.
124. Simard, R. E., Zee, J. and L'Heureux, L. 1984. Microbial growth in carcasses and boxed beef during storage. J. Food Protect. 47: 773.
125. Slade, P. J., Falah, M. A., and Al-Ghady, A. M. R. 1986. Isolation of *Aeromonas hydro-*

phila from bottled waters and domestic water supplies in Saudi Arabia. J. Food Protect. 49: 471.

126. Smith, I. W. 1963. The classification of *Bacterium salmonicida*. J. Gen. Microbiol. 33: 263.
127. Smith, P. B., Tomfohrde, K. M., Rhoden, D. L., and Balows, A. 1972. API System: A multitube micromethod for identification of *Enterobacteriaceae*. Appl. Microbiol. 24: 449.
128. Snieszko, S. F. 1957. Genus IV. *Aeromonas* Kluyver and Van Niel. 1936. In "Bergey's Manual of Determinative Bacteriology," 7th ed., eds. R. S. Breed, E. G. D. Murray, and N. R. Smith, p. 189. Williams and Wilkins, Baltimore, Md.
129. Snieszko, S. F. and Bullock, G. L. 1976. Disease of freshwater fishes caused by bacteria of the genera *Aeromonas, Pseudomonas*, and *Vibrio*. FDL-40. USK1, FWS. 10 pp.
130. Spence, K. D., Fryer, J. L., and Pilcher, K. S. 1965. Active and passive immunization of certain salmonid fishes against *Aeromonas salmonicida*. Can. J. Microbiol. 11: 397.
131. Stelma, G. N., Johnson, C. H., and Spaulding, P. 1986. Evidence for the direct involvement of β-hemolysin in *Aeromonas hydrophila* enteropathogenicity. Current Microbiol. 14: 71.
132. Stern, N. J., Drazek, E. S., and Joseph, S. W. 1987. Low incidence of *Aeromonas* sp. in livestock feces. J. Food Protect. 50: 66.
133. Travis, L. B. and Washington, J. A. II. 1986. The clinical significance of stool isolates of *Aeromonas*. Am. J. Clin. Pathol. 85: 330.
134. Trust, T. J. and Chipman, D. C. 1979. Clinical involvement of *Aeromonas hydrophila*. Can. Med. Assoc. J. 120: 942.
135. Trust, T. J. and Sparrow, R. A. H. 1974. The bacterial flora in the alimentary tract of freshwater salmonid fishes. Can. J. Microbiol. 20: 1219.
136. Turnbull, P. C. B., Lee, J. V., Miliotis, M. D., Van De Walle, S., Koornhof, H. J., Jeffery, L., and Bryant, T. N. 1984. Enterotoxin production in relation to taxonomic grouping and source of isolation of *Aeromonas* species. J. Clin. Microbiol. 19: 175.
137. von Graevenitz, A. 1985. *Aeromonas* and *Plesiomonas*. In "Manual of Clinical Microbiology," 4th ed., eds. E. H. Lennette, A. Balows, W. J. Hausler, Jr., and H. J. Shadomy, p. 278. American Society for Microbiology, Washington, D.C.
138. von Graevenitz, A. and Bucher, C. 1983. Evaluation of differential and selective media for isolation of *Aeromonas* and *Pleisomonas* from human feces. J. Clin. Microbiol. 17: 16.
139. von Graevenitz, A. and Mensch, A. H. 1968. The genus *Aeromonas* in human bacteriology. Report of 30 cases and review of the literature. N. Engl. J. Med. 278: 245.
140. von Graevenitz, A. and Zinterhofer, L. 1970. The detection of *Aeromonas hydrophila* in stool specimens. Health Lab. Sci. 7: 124.
141. Watson, I. M., Robinson, J. O., Burke, V., and Gracey, M. 1985. Invasiveness of *Aeromonas* spp. in relation to biotype, virulence factors and clinical features. J. Clin. Microbiol. 22: 48.
142. Williams, L. A. and LaRock, P. A. 1985. Temporal occurrence of *Vibrio* species and *Aeromonas hydrophila* in estuarine sediments. Appl. Environ. Microbiol. 50: 1490.
143. Wolff, R. L., Wiseman, S. L., and Kitchens, S. C. 1980. *Aeromonas hydrophila* bacteremia in ambulatory immunocompromised hosts. Am. J. Med. 68: 238.
144. Wolke, R. E. 1975. In "The Pathology of Fishes," eds. W. E. Ribelin and G. Migaki, p. 33. U. of Wisconsin Press, Madison, Wis.

Chapter 31

PLESIOMONAS SHIGELLOIDES

John A. Koburger and Cheng-I Wei

31.1 INTRODUCTION

31.11 Description

Plesiomonas shigelloides is an opportunistic pathogen.[1, 4, 11, 21] Controversy exists as to its role as an enteropathogen.[2, 8, 9, 10, 26, 27] While much of the earlier information concerning this organism came from foreign literature, recent studies from the United States are now supporting the role of *P. shigelloides* as a primary pathogen in diarrheal episodes.[10, 23] Many of these cases can be associated with the consumption of uncooked mollusks or with foreign travel.[10, 25]

Symptoms caused by *P. shigelloides* are typical of those associated with a gram-negative infection. The incubation period ranges from 1 to 2 days, and the symptoms can include diarrhea, abdominal pain, nausea, fever, headache, and vomiting and may last 10 days or longer.[10] The attacks are usually self-limited, and treatment involves replacement of fluids and electrolytes.[9] If antibiotic therapy is indicated, consider recent studies reporting that *Plesiomonas* is sensitive to ciprofloxacin, enoxacin, tetracycline, trimethoprim, and chloramphenicol.[23, 24]

Plesiomonas shigelloides is a motile, oxidase- and catalase-positive, facultative gram-negative rod.[28] It is the only species within the genus and was previously known as *Aeromonas shigelloides*.[16] The other genera within the family Vibrionaceae, *Aeromonas* and *Vibrio*, can be separated by routine biochemical tests. *Plesiomonas* can be misidentified as a member of the Enterobacteriaceae if care is not taken to conduct an oxidase test during the identification procedures.[3, 10] Also, some strains of *P. shigelloides* are antigenically related to *Shigella sonnei*.[3, 10] Attempts at grouping the plesiomonads by biotyping appear to be of limited value.[16] Various studies have reported on the serological profile of *P. shigelloides*[2, 29]; however, antisera are not commercially available. Rapid identification kits have been useful in the identification of *Plesiomonas*.[14, 20]

With the increased interest in *P. shigelloides*, a number of studies have reported on the mechanism by which it may cause diarrhea in humans.[12, 13, 26] In a study of 29 strains of plesiomonads, 24 were shown to produce a cholera-like toxin when tested in Chinese hamster ovary cells.[7] Activity of sterile filtrates could be removed by heating or by preincubation of the filtrates with cholera antitoxin. In contrast, another report indicated that the plesiomonads may be enteroinvasive.[10] To further confound the problem, in a study of 33 healthy volunteers, ingestion of 1×10^3 to 4×10^9 organisms did not result in any clinical manifestation of a disease.[8] Further insight into various aspects of this organism may be gained from a number of published reviews.[9, 10, 15, 16, 32]

31.12   Ecology

Isolation of *P. shigelloides* has been reported worldwide. Various mammals, birds, fish, and environmental sites have been mentioned.[2, 9, 30, 31, 33] Isolations from humans have been reported for both symptomatic and asymptomatic individuals.[2, 3, 9, 32] Fresh and brackish water is usually an excellent source of this organism, as are fresh-water fish.[2, 15, 31] A number of studies have shown a seasonal effect on isolation rates from these sources as well as an increase in the reported cases of diarrhea during the warmer seasons.[2, 30] It has been reported that some isolates can grow in broth containing 5% sodium chloride and at a pH as low as 4 and as high as 9. The isolates could not grow at a temperature of 5°C nor at 50°C. Pasteurization at 60°C for 30 min readily destroyed the plesiomonads tested.[18]

31.13   Isolation and Identification

Our experience has shown that *P. shigelloides* does not grow on some media (thiosulfate citrate bile salts sucrose agar, TCBS), grows slowly on others (inositol brilliant green bile salts agar, IBB) and grows well on others (Plesiomonas agar, PL). Species differences, an injury phenomenon, nutritional demands, and lack of tolerance to certain media components complicate any attempt at recommending one simple procedure for isolating this organism.

Early isolations of *P. shigelloides* were usually accomplished with enteric agars.[2, 19, 30, 31, 32, 33] Salmonella Shigella, EMB, MacConkey, and XLD are a few that have been used. It is quite tolerant to bile salts and brilliant green. Because lactose is generally only slowly fermented, the plesiomonads appear as lactose-negative on solid media, including triple sugar iron (TSI) agar. Because of their apparent lack of competitiveness and nutritional dependency, enrichment techniques are of only limited usefulness for the plesiomonads.[6] Direct plating of the sample should always be done, and, depending on the needs of the analyst, an enrichment step can be employed. Selenite, gram-negative (GN) broth, alkaline peptone water (APW), tetrathionate, and various bile broths have been evaluated with differing success.[5, 22, 31] Success following enrichment is probably a reflection of the nature of the sample, including the presence of other organisms as well as the incubation temperature.[5, 6]

P. shigelloides shares many characteristics with both the *Vibrionaceae* and the *Enterobacteriaceae*. However, once an oxidase test is conducted and found to be positive, further separation and identification is fairly rapid. Classical biochemical testing is conducted to confirm identity of the organism. Table 1 summarizes some of the characteristics of the plesiomonads. Complete descriptions of the plesiomonads are reported elsewhere.[15, 16, 28]

Our laboratory uses the following protocol when isolating the plesiomonads. Samples, depending upon consistency and expected numbers, are diluted and directly surface streaked to IBB and PL agars.[17] One to 10 grams of sample are added to 90 ml of tetrathionate broth. Plates are incubated at

Table 1—Some Identifying Characteristics of *Plesiomonas shigelloides*

Character	Reaction
Gram stain	− rod
motility	lophotrichous flagella
oxidase	+
catalase	+
glucose	acid no gas
gelatinase	−
arginine dihydrolase	variable
lysine decarboxylase	+
ornithine decarboxylase	+
nitrate to nitrite	+
deoxyribonuclease	−
string test	−
0/129 sensitivity	sensitive
acid from lactose	variable
sucrose	−
mannitol	−
inositol	+
arabinose	−
xylose	−
urease	−
citrate	−
growth at 42C	+
halophilism 0% NaCl	+
3% NaCl	+
6% NaCl	−

35°C and the enrichment broths at 40°C. Following 24 hr of incubation, suspect colonies are picked from the plates to TSI slants and inositol gelatin medium (deep stab).[17] The enrichment broths are streaked to the isolation media and the plates incubated at 35°C for 24 hr. Isolates that are alkaline over acid without gas or hydrogen sulfide on TSI, produce acid but no gas from inositol, and do not hydrolyze gelatin are tested for oxidase. If the organism is oxidase-positive and a gram-negative rod, it is *Plesiomonas*.

31.2   EQUIPMENT, MATERIALS, AND SOLUTIONS (Chapter 62)

Materials in general are as for the *Enterobacteriaceae*.

Alkaline peptone water (APW) (0.1%)
Brilliant green lactose bile (BGLB) agar
Inositol brilliant green bile (IBB) salts agar
Inositol gelatin deeps
MacConkey agar
Oxidase reagent
Peptone water (0.1%)
PL agar
Salmonella shigella (SS) agar
Tetrathionate broth (without iodine)
Triple sugar iron (TSI) agar

Plesiomonads appear as yellow colonies on IBB agar and pink on PL agar. In inositol gelatin deeps, plesiomonads will turn the medium yellow and will not hydrolyze the gelatin.

31.3   PROCEDURE

31.31   Selective Agar

Prepare dried plates of two of the following media: MacConkey, brilliant green lactose bile agar, PL, SS, or IBB. If the sample is fluid, transfer a 0.5 mm loopful to the surface of duplicate plates of each medium and streak for isolation. If the sample is solid, prepare a 1:10 dilution in 0.1% peptone water and streak. Incubate at 35°C for 24 hr.

31.32   Enrichment Broth

Transfer a 10 g sample to 90 ml tetrathionate broth without iodine and incubate at 40°C for 24 hr. Following enrichment, streak to duplicate plates of two of the above selective media and incubate plates at 35°C for 24 hr.

31.33 Identification

Pick three typical colonies from each of the selective media into TSI and inositol gelatin deeps. Incubate at 35°C for 24 hr. *Plesiomonas* appears as alkaline over acid with no gas or hydrogen sulfide in TSI, will ferment inositol without gas, and will not hydrolyze gelatin. Conduct an oxidase test and gram stain from the TSI slant.

31.34 Precautions

A known wild-type isolate as well as an ATCC strain should be tested concurrently with the unknown isolates to ensure accuracy of media reactions. While *P. shigelloides* is not highly infectious, reasonable care should be taken when working with this organism.

31.4 REFERENCES

1. Appelbaum, P. C., Bowen, A. J., Adhikari, M., Robins-Browne, R. M., and Koornhof, H. J. 1978. Neonatal septicemia and meningitis due to *Aeromonas shigelloides*. J. Pediatr. 92: 676.
2. Arai, T., Ikejima, N., Itoh, T., Sakai, S., Shimada, T., and Sakazaki, R. 1980. A survey of *Plesiomonas shigelloides* from aquatic environments, domestic animals, pets, and humans. J. Hyg. (Camb.) 84: 203.
3. Bhat, P., Shanthakumari, S., and Rajan, D. 1974. The characterization and significance of *Plesiomonas shigelloides* and *Aeromonas hydrophila* isolated from an epidemic of diarrhoea. Ind. J. Med. Res. 62: 1051.
4. Dahm, L. J. and Weinberg, A. G. 1980. *Plesiomonas (Aeromonas) shigelloides* septicemia and meningitis in a neonate. South. Med. J. 73: 393.
5. Freund, S. M., Koburger, J. A., and Wei, C. I. 1988. Enhanced recovery of *Plesiomonas shigelloides* following an enrichment technique. J. Food Prot. 51: 110.
6. Freund, S. M., Koburger, J. A., and Wei, C. I. 1988. Isolation of *Plesiomonas shigelloides* from oysters using tetrathionate broth enrichment. J. Food Prot. 51: 925.
7. Gardner, S. E., Fowlston, S. E., and George, W. L. 1987. In vitro production of cholera toxin-like activity by *Plesiomonas shigelloides*. J. Infect. Dis. 156: 720.
8. Herrington, D. A., Tzipori, S., Robins-Browne, R. M., Tall, B. D., and Levine, M. M. 1987. In vitro and in vivo pathogenicity of *Plesiomonas shigelloides*. Infect. Immun. 55: 979.
9. Holmberg, S. D. and Farmer, J. J. 1984. *Aeromonas hydrophila* and *Plesiomonas shigelloides* as causes of intestinal infections. Rev. Infect. Dis. 6: 633.
10. Holmberg, S. D., Wachsmuth, I. K., Hickman-Brenner, F. W., Blake, P. A., and Farmer, J. J. 1986. *Plesiomonas* enteric infections in the United States. Ann. Intern. Med. 105: 690.
11. Ingram, C. W., Morrison, A. J., and Levitz, R. E. 1987. Gastroenteritis, sepsis, and osteomyelitis caused by *Plesiomonas shigelloides* in an immunocompetent host: Case report and review of the literature. J. Clin. Microbiol. 25: 1791.
12. Janda, J. M. 1987. Effect of acidity and antimicrobial agent-like compounds on viability of *Plesiomonas shigelloides*. J. Clin. Microbiol. 25: 1213.
13. Johnson, W. M. and Lior, H. 1981. Cytotoxicity and suckling mouse reactivity of *Aeromonas hydrophila* isolated from human sources. Can. J. Microbiol. 27: 1019.
14. Jorgensen, J. H., Dyke, J. W., Helgeson, N. G. P., Cooper, B. H., Redding, J. S., Crawford, S. A., Andruszewski, M. T., and Prowant, S. A. 1984. Collaborative evaluation of the

Abbott Advantage System for identification of frequently isolated nonfermentative or oxidase-positive gram-negative bacilli. J. Clin. Microbiol. 20: 899.

15. Koburger, J. A. 1988. *Plesiomonas shigelloides*. In "Foodborne Bacterial Pathogens," ed. M. P. Doyle, p. 311. Marcel Dekker, Inc. New York, N.Y.

16. Miller, M. L. and Koburger, J. A. 1985. *Plesiomonas shigelloides*: An opportunistic food and waterborne pathogen. J. Food Prot. 48: 449.

17. Miller, M. L. and Koburger, J. A. 1986. Evaluation of Inositol Brilliant Green Bile Salts and Plesiomonas agars for recovery of *Plesiomonas shigelloides* from aquatic samples in a seasonal survey of the Suwannee River estuary. J. Food Prot. 49: 274.

18. Miller, M. L. and Koburger, J. A. 1986. Tolerance of *Plesiomonas shigelloides* to pH, sodium chloride and temperature. J. Food Prot. 49: 877.

19. Millership, S. E. and Chattopadhyay, B. 1984. Methods for the isolation of *Aeromonas hydrophila* and *Plesiomonas shigelloides* from faeces. J. Hyg. (Camb). 92: 145.

20. Overman, T. L. and Overley, J. K. 1986. Feasibility of same-day identification of members of the Family *Vibrionaceae* by the API 20E system. J. Clin. Microbiol. 23: 715.

21. Penn, R. G., Giger, D. K., Knoop, F. C., and Preheim, L. C. 1982. *Plesiomonas shigelloides* overgrowth in the small intestine. J. Clin. Microbiol. 15: 869.

22. Rahim, Z. and Kay, B. A. 1988. Enrichment for *Plesiomonas shigelloides* from stools. J. Clin. Microbiol. 26: 789.

23. Reinhardt, J. F. and George, W. L. 1985. *Plesiomonas shigelloides*-associated diarrhea. J. Am. Med. Assoc. 253: 3294.

24. Reinhardt, J. F. and George, W. L. 1985. Comparative in vitro activities of selected antimicrobial agents against *Aeromonas* species and *Plesiomonas shigelloides*. Antimicrob. Agents Chemother. 27: 643.

25. Rutala, W. A., Sarubbi, F. A. Jr., Finch, C. S., MacCormack, J. N., and Steinkraus, G. E. 1982. Oyster-associated outbreak of diarrheal disease possibly caused by *Plesiomonas shigelloides*. Lancet 1: 739.

26. Sanyal, S. C., Saraswathi, B., and Sharma, P. 1980. Enteropathogenicity of *Plesiomonas shigelloides*. J. Med. Microbiol. 13: 401.

27. Sanyal, S. C., Singh, S. J., and Sen, P. C. 1975. Enteropathogenicity of *Aeromonas hydrophila* and *Plesiomonas shigelloides*. J. Med. Microbiol. 8: 195.

28. Schubert, R. H. W. 1984. Genus IV *Plesiomonas*, In "Bergey's Manual of Systematic Bacteriology," eds. N. R. Krieg and J. G. Holt, Vol. 1, p. 548. Williams and Wilkins, Baltimore, Md.

29. Shimada, T. and Sakazaki, R. 1978. On the serology of *Plesiomonas shigelloides*. Jap. J. Med. Sci. Biol. 31: 135.

30. Tsukamoto, T., Kinoshita, Y., Shimada, T., and Sakazaki, R. 1978. Two epidemics of diarrhoeal disease possibly caused by *Plesiomonas shigelloides*. J. Hyg. (Camb.) 80: 275.

31. Van Damme, L. R. and Vandepitte, J. 1980. Frequent isolation of *Edwardsiella tarda* and *Plesiomonas shigelloides* from healthy Zairese freshwater fish: A possible source of sporatic diarrhea in the tropics. Appl. Environ. Microbiol. 39: 475.

32. Vandepitte, J., Makulu, A., and Gatti, F. 1974. *Plesiomonas shigelloides* survey and possible association with diarrhoea in Zaire. Ann. Soc. Belge. Med. Trop. 54: 503.

33. Winsor, D. K., Bloebaum, A. P., and Mathewson, J. J. 1981. Gram-negative, aerobic, enteric pathogens among intestinal microflora of wild turkey vultures (*Cathartes aura*) in West Central Texas. Appl. Environ. Microbiol. 42: 1123.

Chapter 32

ENTEROCOCCI

Paul A. Hartman, Robert H. Deibel, and Linda M. Sieverding

32.1 INTRODUCTION

Classification of the enterococci is in a state of flux. In the second edition of this book,[10] all streptococci of fecal origin that produce group D antigen were considered enterococci. These included *Streptococcus avium*, *S. bovis*, *S. faecalis* (and its varieties *liquefaciens* and *zymogenes*), and *S. faecium* (and its varieties *casseliflavus* and *durans*). Mundt (1986) included only *S. avium*, *S. faecalis*, *S. faecium*, and *S. gallinarum* in the most recent edition of *Bergey's Manual*;[34] *S. bovis* and *S. equinus* were placed in a group of "Other Streptococci."[23] Recent molecular biology studies (including oligonucleotide cataloging of 16S rRNA and DNA-DNA and DNA-rRNA hybridization), combined with physiological studies, resulted in a more elaborate classification,[39] wherein a new genus, *Enterococcus*, was established. Members of this genus are *E. avium*, *E. casseliflavus*, *E. durans*, *E. faecalis*, *E. faecium*, *E. gallinarum*, *E. hirae*, *E. malodoratus*, and *E. mundtii* (Table 1). All these bacteria usually grow at 45°C, in 6.5% NaCl, and at pH 9.6; most grow at 10°C. *S. bovis* and *S. equinus*, which are negative in two or more of these properties, were assigned to a miscellaneous group of "Other Streptococci."[39] Almost all (99%) are susceptible to vancomycin, and very few (less than 1%) produce gas from glycerol.[1]

The enterococci have conventionally been identified by physiological as well as serological methods. When the former are employed, a spectrum of characteristics (Table 1) must be examined because no single, two, or three traits will establish a definitive identification.[9] Identification medium formulations and interpretations of tests have been described by Facklam and Collins.[15] All enterococci, as well as *S. bovis* and *S. equinus*, produce group D antigen, although presence of this antigen is difficult to demonstrate with some isolates.

Table 1—Some Characteristics of the Enterococci and Group D Fecal Streptococci.[a]

Species	G + C content (mole %)	Serological group	PYR (see text)	Growth, 10°C	Growth, 45°C	Growth, 6.5% NaCl	Growth, pH 9.6	Hydrol. of arginine	Hydrol. of esculin	Hydrol. of hippurate	Acid from arabinose	Acid from glycerol	Acid from melezitose	Acid from melibiose	Acid from sorbitol	Acid from sorbose	Acid from tagatose	Motility	Yellow pigment	H_2S produced
E. avium	39–40	D + Q	+	+	+	+	+	−	+	−	+	v	+	v	+	+	+	−	−	+
E. casseliflavus	41–45	D	+	+	+	+	+	v	+	v	+	v	−	+	v	−	(−)	+	+	−
E. durans	38–40	D	+	+	+	+	+	+	+	v	−	−	−	v	−	−	+	−	−	−
E. faecalis	37–40	D	+	+	+	+	+	+	(+)	v	−	(+)	(+)	−	(+)	+	(−)	−	−	−
E. faecium	37–40	D	+	+	+	+	+	+	+	(−)	+	−	(−)	v	v	−	(+)	−	−	−
E. gallinarum	39–40	D	+	+	+	+	+	+	+	(+)	+	−	−	+	−	−	v	+	−	−
E. hirae	37–38	D	+	+	+	+	+	+	+	(−)	−	−	v	(+)	+	−	−	−	−	nd
E. malodoratus	40–41	D	+	+	+	+	+	−	+	−	+	−	−	+	v	+	−	−	−	+
E. mundtii	38–39	D	+	+	+	+	+	+	+	−	+	−	−	+	v	−	−	−	+	nd
S. bovis	36–38	D	−	−	+	−	−	−	+	−	v	−	nd	nd	−	nd	nd	−	−	−
S. equinus	36–39	D	−	−	+	−	−	−	+	−	−	−	nd	nd	−	nd	nd	−	−	−

[a]All are gram-positive, catalase-negative, facultatively anaerobic cocci or coccobacilli. Note that "false-positive" and "false-negative" test reactions can be obtained, depending on the sensitivity of the assay that is used.[19]

+ = positive; (+) = most strains positive; − = negative; (−) = most strains negative; v = variable; nd = not determined (but probably would be H_2S-negative). Differential characteristics of Enterococcus spp. are listed in references[3, 6, 7, 12, 14, 15, 16, 18, 20] and by L. M. Sieverding (unpublished data). See Facklam and Collins (1989) for abbreviated identification schemes, including those for three new species (E. pseudoavium, E. raffinosus, and E. solitarius).

Generally, the *Enterococcus* habitat is the intestinal contents of both warm- and cold-blooded animals, including insects.[33] Some enterococci have adapted to an epiphytic relationship with growing vegetation. None of the enterococci can be considered as absolutely host specific, although some species evidence a degree of host specificity.

Enterococcus faecalis and *E. faecium* are relatively heat resistant and characteristically may survive traditional milk pasteurization procedures. *Enterococcus faecium* is markedly heat tolerant and is a spoilage agent in marginally processed canned hams. Most of the enterococci are relatively resistant to freezing, and, unlike *Escherichia coli*, they readily survive this treatment.

In the past, some investigators have associated food poisoning outbreaks with these bacteria,[24] but definitive experiments with unequivocal positive results were lacking until recently, when several enterococci were implicated as causes of diarrheal diseases in neonatal animals.[12] Other enterococci, especially those that are resistant to chemotherapeutic agents, can cause serious illness in humans.[26]

32.2   GENERAL CONSIDERATIONS

An abundance of media has been advocated for the selective isolation and/or quantitation of enterococci.[25] Many selective agents, incubation conditions, and combinations of these have been described, but all have one or more shortcomings. The media and methods that are available presently lack selectivity, differential ability, quantitative recovery, relative ease of use, or a combination of these to various degrees. Some strains of fecal streptococci from anaerobic environments, for example, initiate growth only in the presence of elevated levels of CO_2 until the cultures have been adapted to an aerobic environment.[30] Therefore, a compromise must be reached in the selection of a general-purpose medium for the recovery of enterococci from foods. In food microbiology, *E. faecalis* and *E. faecium* are the most common enterococci encountered. This undoubtedly influences the rationale of employing KF streptococcal agar for the estimation of enterococci in foods.[28] The selectivity of KF streptococcal agar is not absolute,[13] quantitative recovery is less than ideal, and preparation of the medium necessitates an aseptic addition of an indicator. Nevertheless, many industry and regulatory agencies have accepted KF agar for the quantitative estimation of enterococci in nondairy foods. For dairy products, a more selective medium or higher incubation temperature (45°C) may be necessary to reduce background growth of lactobacilli and lactic streptococci.

KF streptococcal agar[28] is a selective differential medium that employs sodium azide as the chief selective agent and triphenyltetrazolium chloride (TTC) for differential purposes. The medium contains a relatively high concentration of maltose (2.0%) and a small amount of lactose (0.1%). Most, but not all, enterococci and streptococci ferment these sugars. The intensity of TTC reduction varies. *E. faecalis* reduces the compound to its formazan derivative, imparting a deep red color to the colony. Other group D enterococci and streptococci, if they grow on KF agar, are feebly reductive and the colonies appear light pink. (Tetrazolium reactions of *E. hirae*[18] and *E. malodoratus*[6] have not been described.) Most other lactic acid bacteria are partially or completely inhibited; however, some strains of *Pediococcus*, *Lactobacillus*, and *Aerococcus* may grow, producing light pink colonies. A "repair-detection" procedure[22] should be considered when the enterococcal population of a food may contain a large proportion of injured cells (Chapter 7).

KF streptococcal medium is available commercially with or without agar. A broth is available for the most probable number (MPN) procedure to detect low numbers of enterococci, but the MPN procedure is rarely used for foods.

KF streptococcal agar contains azide, which is inhibitory to many strains of *S. bovis* and *S. equinus* and possibly some of the newly named *Enterococcus* spp. Therefore, an alternative procedure[32] that permits the recovery of a wider variety of enterococci from foods is included in this section. This alternative procedure, fluorogenic gentamicin-thallous-carbonate (fGTC) agar, utilizes inhibitors other than azide. Dyed starch and a fluorogenic substrate are included to impart differential qualities to the medium. Enterococcal counts from foods may be two or more orders of magnitude higher on fGTC agar than on KF agar. Further, the incubation period for fGTC agar is only 18 to 24 hr whereas it is 48 hr for KF agar. Neither KF nor fGTC agars have been tested for recoveries of some of the newly named enterococci, and the performance of both media should be reevaluated in the light of recent advances in enterococcal classification.

As in other microbiological plating procedures, sample preparation is important. For example, dried foods are often reconstituted and immediately diluted and plated. In one study,[41] however, the optimum procedure of sample preparation involved the addition of 25 ml of 0.1% peptone water diluent to 25 g of dry food in a sterile pint jar. The jar was "swirled" and allowed to remain at 4°C for 60 min. Then 200 ml of sterile peptone water were added to the jar and mixed to obtain a final 1:10 dilution. Enterococcal counts of dried soup mix were increased by 42% by using the "swirl-hold-dilute" method.[41]

32.3 EQUIPMENT, MATERIALS, AND REAGENTS (Chapter 62)

Bile-esculin agar[16]
Brain Heart Infusion broth (BHI)
Filter-sterilized 1% aqueous triphenyltetrazolium chloride (TTC)
Fluorogenic gentamicin-thallous-carbonate (fGTC) agar[32]
Hydrogen peroxide (3%)
KF streptococcus (KF streptococcal) agar[28]
Long-wave (365-nm) ultraviolet light
6.5% salt medium (BHI + 6.0% NaCl)

32.4 PRECAUTIONS

Many foods contain from small to large numbers of enterococci, especially *E. faecalis* and *E. faecium*. Certain varieties of cheese and, occasionally, fermented sausage may contain more than 10^6 organisms per g. Relatively low levels, 10^1 to 10^3 per g, are common in a wide variety of other foods. The shelf life of sliced, prepackaged ham (and sometimes other similarly prepared cured meats) may be dictated by controlling the initial numbers of contaminating enterococci.

Many investigators have reported a lack of correlation between *Enterococcus* and *E. coli* counts, and the unreliability of *Enterococcus* counts as a reflection of fecal contamination is established. The ability of enterococci to grow in food processing plants, and possibly other environments, long after their introduction, as well as the observation that enterococci can establish extraintestinal epiphytic relationships, reinforces these observations.

No acceptable levels of enterococci can be stated because *Enterococcus* counts vary with product, holding conditions, time of storage, and other factors. In general, enterococci serve as a good index of sanitation and proper holding conditions. However, the entire history of each product must be established and the culture medium and conditions must be standardized before setting specific criteria.

32.5 ENUMERATION OF ENTEROCOCCI

32.51 KF Streptococcal Agar[28]

Prepare the sample for culturing by the pour plate method as directed in Chapter 4 or Section 32.2 above. Dispense 1 ml of decimal dilutions into duplicate petri plates. If a low count is expected, the accuracy and sensitivity may be increased by plating 1 ml of a 1:10 dilution into each of 10 petri plates, in which case the total number of colonies on the 10 plates represents the count per g of food. Add 12 to 15 ml of KF agar cooled to 45°C, and allow to solidify. Incubate the plates for 48 ± 2 hr at 35° ± 1°C. Using a dissecting microscope with a magnification of 15 diameters or a colony counter, count all red and pink colonies. Report this number as the KF enterococcal count.

32.52 fGTC Agar[32]

Prepare plates as directed in Section 32.51 above. Add 12 to 15 ml of fGTC agar[32] cooled to 45°C, and allow to solidify. Incubate the plates for 18 to 24 hr at 35° ± 1°C. Observe for starch hydrolysis (a zone of clearing around a colony under visible light) and fluorescence (a zone of bright bluish fluorescence when the opened plate is held under a long-wave ultraviolet (UV) lamp). Three phenotypic groups are identifiable: (1) starch hydrolysis and fluorescence, indicative of *S. bovis*, (2) no starch hydrolysis but fluorescence, indicative of *E. faecium* and related biotypes, and (3) no starch hydrolysis or fluorescence, indicative of *E. faecalis, E. avium, S. equinus*, and other streptococci.[32] Use all colonies to calculate the fGTC enterococcal count, which can be divided, if desired, into subgroups based on starch hydrolysis and fluorescence.

32.6   CONFIRMATION OF ENTEROCOCCI

32.61   Conventional Procedures

If confirmation is desired, pick 5 to 10 typical colonies and transfer each into a separate tube of brain heart infusion (BHI) broth. Incubate at 35°C for 18 to 24 hr. Prepare gram-stained smears of the BHI cultures and observe for typical enterococcal morphology (gram-positive cocci, elongated, in pairs and occasionally short chains). Test for catalase activity by adding 1 ml of 3% hydrogen peroxide to a culture and observe for the generation of oxygen bubbles. Enterococci are catalase-negative, and no reaction should occur. Caution: Do not test for catalase activity directly on azide-containing media such as KF streptococcal agar. Observe for growth and blackening on bile-esculin agar[13] after incubation for 24 hr at 35°C. Examine for growth in BHI broth containing 6.5% NaCl after incubation for 72 hr at 35°C. Test for growth at 45°C in BHI broth that has been tempered to 45°C prior to incubation. Note: If growth in the salt-containing medium and growth at 45°C are to be determined, subcultures must be inoculated before testing for catalase.

S. equinus and *S. bovis* are not enterococci, but they can be of fecal origin. Most do not grow at 10°C, in media containing 6.5% NaCl, or at pH 9.6, but all should grow at 45°C. An excellent confirmatory test for enterococci/fecal streptococci is the ability of an isolate to grow on bile-esculin agar. Enterococci and group D streptococci tolerate bile (grow on bile-esculin agar) and hydrolyze esculin.[13] Esculin is 6,7-dihydroxycoumarin-β-D-glucoside. Some bacteria produce an "esculinase" (β-D-glucosidase) that hydrolyzes esculin and releases esculetin (6,7-dihydroxycoumarin); the esculetin reacts with Fe^{+3} in the medium to form a dark brown or black complex.

32.62   Rapid Methods

A 15-min "esculinase" test was devised using *p*-nitrophenyl-β-D-glucopyranoside as the substrate for β-D-glucosidase ("esculinase") determination,[42] and a 4-hr combined sodium chloride tolerance-esculin hydrolysis test also has been described.[37]

Another rapid confirmatory test is the PYR test (Table 1), which detects the ability of a culture to hydrolyze pyrrolidonyl-β-naphthylamide (L-pyroglutamic acid-β-naphthylamide). Hydrolysis of this aminopeptidase substrate is detected by formation of a reddish color within 2 min of addition of PYR reagent. Of the streptococci, only *S. pyogenes* (group A) and the enterococci are positive; *S. bovis* and *S. equinus* are negative.[16, 20] Prepackaged PYR test reagents are available[38] (Strep-A-Chek, E-Y Laboratories, Inc., 107 North Amphlett Blvd., San Mateo, CA 94401; Identicult-AE, Scott Laboratories, Inc., 771 Main St., West Warwick, RI 02893; Roscoe Diagnostica, 2630 Taastrup, Denmark).

Convenient tri-plates, quad-plates, and tubed[29] media for key identification tests are available from many suppliers of prepared media. A RapID STR kit (Vitek Systems, 595 Anglum Drive, Hazelwood, MO 63042)[2, 45] may also be time-saving. This kit is similar to the API-20S (Analytab Products, Div. Sherwood Medical, 200 Express St., Plainview, NY 11803).[1, 8, 17, 19, 21, 27, 36] The efficacy of this kit and the data bank used with it are based on isolates from human clinical material; the efficiency may differ when isolates from other animals or food are studied.[36] See Chapter 39 for general precautions.

32.63   Automated Identification

Both the Vitek AutoMicrobic gram-positive identification system[1, 17] and the General Diagnostics Autobac system[4] can be used. The latter system includes only bile-esculin agar and salt broth to confirm whether an isolate is or is not an *Enterococcus* or group D *Streptococcus*; the Autobac system makes no attempt to speciate. An impedance method that will detect 10 to 100 "fecal streptococci" in dry milk within 18 hr has been described.[43] See Chapter 39 for descriptions of these systems.

32.64   Serological tests

If serological confirmation is deemed necessary, commercial grouping sera are available from BBL Microbiology Systems, Becton Dickinson Co., Cockeysville, MD 21030 and Wellcome Reagents Div., Burroughs Wellcome Co., Research Triangle Park, NC 27709. A variety of serological kits is available: BBL Strep typing kit; Bacto Strep Grouping Kit, Difco Laboratories, P.O. Box 1058, Detroit, MI 48232; Streptex, Wellcome Reagents[5, 20, 35, 38, 40]; SeroSTAT, Scott Laboratories, Inc., 771 Main St., West Warwick, RI 02893[5, 31, 38, 44]; Strepslide, NCS Diagnostics, Inc., 1051 Clinton Ave., Buffalo, NY 14206; and Phadebact, Pharmacia Diagnostics, 800 Centennial Ave., Piscataway, NJ 08854.[5, 20, 35, 38] These kits vary in efficacy, and false-negative group D reactions are common. Consult the references listed before using these kits.

It is often difficult to demonstrate the presence of the group D antigen in some strains; only 77% of 188 *Enterococcus* strains tested were positive.[15] The method of group antigen preparation is important.[11, 35]

32.7   REFERENCES

1. Appelbaum, P. C., Jacobs, M. R., Heald, J. I., Palko, W. M., Duffett, A., Crist, R., and Naugle, P. A. 1984. Comparative evaluation of the API 20S system and the AutoMicrobic system gram-positive identification card for species identification of streptococci. J. Clin. Microbiol. 19: 164.

2. Appelbaum, P. C., Jacobs, M. R., Palko, W. M., Frauenhoffer, E. E., and Duffett, A. 1986. Accuracy and reproducibility of the IDS RapID STR system for species identification of streptococci. J. Clin. Microbiol. 23: 843.

3. Bridge, P. D. and Sneath, P. H. A. 1982. *Streptococcus gallinarium* sp. nov. and *Streptococcus oralis* sp. nov. Intl. J. Syst. Bacteriol. 32: 410.

4. Brown, L. H., Peterson, E. M., and de la Maza, L. M. 1983. Rapid identification of enterococci. J. Clin. Microbiol. 17: 369.

5. Chang, G. T. and Ellner, P. D. 1983. Evaluation of slide agglutination methods for identifying group D streptococci. J. Clin. Microbiol. 17: 804.

6. Collins, M. D., Jones, D., Farrow, J. A. E., Kilpper-Bälz, R., and Schleifer, K. H. 1984. *Enterococcus avium* nom. rev., comb. nov.; *E. casseliflavus* nom. rev., comb. nov.; *E. durans* nom. rev., comb. nov.; *E. gallinarium* comb. nov.; and *E. malodoratus* sp. nov. Intl. J. Syst. Bacteriol. 34: 220.

7. Collins, M. D., Farrow, J. A. E., and Jones, D. 1986. *Enterococcus mundtii* sp. nov. Intl. J. Syst. Bacteriol. 36: 8.

8. Colman, G. and Ball, L. C. 1984. Identification of streptococci in a medical laboratory. J. Appl. Bacteriol. 57: 1.

9. Deibel, R. H. 1964. The group D streptococci. Bacteriol. Rev. 28: 330.

10. Deibel, R. H. and Hartman, P. A. 1984. The enterococci. In "Compendium of Methods for the Microbiological Examination of Foods," 2nd ed., ed. M. L. Speck, p. 405. American Public Health Assn., Washington, D.C.

11. Elliott, S. D., McCarty, M., and Lancefield, R. C. 1977. Teichoic acids of group D streptococci with special reference to strains from pig meningitis (*Streptococcus suis*). J. Exper. Med. 145: 490.

12. Etheridge, M. E., Yolken, R. H., and Vonderfecht, S. L. 1988. *Enterococcus hirae* implicated as a cause of diarrhea in suckling rats. J. Clin. Microbiol. 26: 1741.

13. Facklam, R. R. and Moody, M. D. 1970. Presumptive identification of group D streptococci: The bile-esculin test. Appl. Microbiol. 20: 245.

14. Facklam, R. R. and Carey, R. D. 1985. The streptococci and aerococci. In "Manual of Clinical Microbiology," 4th ed., ed. E. A. Lennette, A. Balows, W. J. Hausler, Jr., and H. J. Shadomy, p. 154. Amer. Soc. for Microbiol., Washington, D.C.

15. Facklam, R. R. and Collins, M. D. 1989. Identification of *Enterococcus* species isolated from human infections by a conventional test scheme. J. Clin. Microbiol. 27: 731.

16. Facklam, R. R., Thacker, L. G., Fox, B., and Eriquez, L. 1982. Presumptive identification of streptococci with a new test system. J. Clin. Microbiol. 15: 987.

17. Facklam, R., Bosley, G. S., Rhoden, D., Franklin, A. R., Weaver, N., and Schulman, R. 1985. Comparative evaluation of the API 20S and AutoMicrobic gram-positive identification systems for non-beta-hemolytic streptococci and aerococci. J. Clin. Microbiol. 21: 535.

18. Farrow, J. A. E. and Collins, M. D. 1985. *Enterococcus hirae*, a new species that includes amino acid assay strain NCDO 1258 and strains causing growth depression in young chickens. Intl. J. Syst. Bacteriol. 35: 73.

19. Fertally, S. S. and Facklam, R. 1987. Comparison of physiologic tests used to identify non-beta-hemolytic aerococci, enterococci, and streptococci. J. Clin. Microbiol. 25: 1845.

20. Gordon, L. P., Damm, M. A. S., and Anderson, J. D. 1987. Rapid presumptive identification of streptococci directly from blood cultures by serologic tests and the L-pyrrolidonyl-β-naphthylamide reaction. J. Clin. Microbiol. 25: 238.

21. Groothuis, D. G., Elzenaar, C. P., and Van Silfhout, A. 1986. An evaluation of the API-20 Strep system (Rapid-Strep system). Syst. Appl. Microbiol. 8: 137.

22. Hackney, C. R., Ray, B., and Speck, M. L. 1979. Repair detection procedure for enumeration of fecal coliforms and enterococci from seafoods and marine environments. Appl. Environ. Microbiol. 37: 947.

23. Hardie, J. M. 1986. Other streptococci. In "Bergey's Manual of Systematic Bacteriology,"

ed. P. H. A. Sneath, N. S. Mair, M. E. Sharpe, and J. G. Holt, Vol. 2, p. 1068. Williams and Wilkins, Baltimore, Md.

24. Hartman, P. A., Reinbold, G. W., and Saraswat, D. S. 1966. Indicator organisms—A review. II. The role of enterococci in food poisoning. J. Milk Food Technol. 28: 344.

25. Hartman, P. A., Petzel, J. P., and Kaspar, C. W. 1986. New methods for indicator organisms. In "Foodborne Microorganisms and Their Toxins: Developing Methodology," ed. M. D. Pierson and N. J. Stern, p. 175. Marcel Dekker, Inc., New York, N.Y.

26. Hoffman, S. A. and Moellering, R. C. Jr. 1987. The enterococcus: "Putting the bug in our ears." Ann. Intern. Med. 106: 757.

27. Jorgensen, J. H., Crawford, S. A., and Alexander, G. A. 1983. Rapid identification of group D streptococci with the API 20S system. J. Clin. Microbiol. 17: 1096.

28. Kenner, B. A., Clark, H. F., and Kabler, P. W. 1961. Fecal streptococci. I. Cultivation and enumeration of streptococci in surface waters. Appl. Microbiol. 9: 15.

29. Kim, M. J., Weiser, M., Gottschall, S., and Randall, E. L. 1987. Identification of *Streptococcus faecalis* and *Streptococcus faecium* and susceptibility studies with newly developed antimicrobial agents. J. Clin. Microbiol. 25: 787.

30. Latham, M. J., Sharpe, M. E., and Weiss, N. 1979. Anaerobic cocci from the bovine alimentary tract, the amino acids of their cell wall peptidoglycans and those of various species of anaerobic *Streptococcus*. J. Appl. Bacteriol. 47: 209.

31. Levchak, M. E. and Ellner, P. D. 1982. Identification of group D streptococci by SeroSTAT. J. Clin. Microbiol. 15: 58.

32. Littel, K. J. and Hartman, P. A. 1983. Fluorogenic selective and differential medium for isolation of fecal streptococci. Appl. Environ. Microbiol. 45: 622.

33. Mundt, J. O. 1982. The ecology of the streptococci. Microb. Ecol. 8: 355.

34. Mundt, J. O. 1986. Enterococci. In "Bergey's Manual of Systematic Bacteriology," ed. P. H. A. Sneath, N. S. Mair, M. E. Sharpe, and J. G. Holt, Vol. 2, p. 1063. Williams and Wilkins, Baltimore, Md.

35. Poutrel, B. 1983. Comparative evaluation of commercial latex agglutination and coagglutination reagents for groups B, C, and D mastitis streptococci. Amer. J. Vet. Res. 44: 490.

36. Poutrel, B. and Ryniewicz, H. Z. 1984. Evaluation of the API 20 Strep system for species identification of streptococci isolated from bovine mastitis. J. Clin. Microbiol. 19: 213.

37. Qadri, S. M. H., Flournoy, D. J., and Qadri, S. G. M. 1987. Sodium chloride-esculin hydrolysis test for rapid identification of enterococci. J. Clin. Microbiol. 25: 1107.

38. Rappaport, T., Sawyer, K. P., and Nachamkin, I. 1988. Evaluation of several commercial biochemical and immunologic methods for rapid identification of gram-positive cocci directly from blood cultures. J. Clin. Microbiol. 26: 1335.

39. Schleifer, K. H. and Kilpper-Bälz, R. 1987. Molecular and chemotaxonomic approaches to the classification of streptococci, enterococci and lactococci: A review. Syst. Appl. Microbiol. 10: 1.

40. Shlaes, D. M., Toossi, Z., and Patel, A. 1984. Comparison of latex agglutination and immunofluorescence for direct Lancefield grouping of streptococci from blood cultures. J. Clin. Microbiol. 20: 195.

41. Ting, W.-T. and Banwart, G. J. 1985. Enumeration of enterococci and aerobic mesophilic plate count in dried soup using three reconstitution methods. J. Food Prot. 48: 770.

42. Trepeta, R. W. and Edberg, S. C. 1987. Esculinase (β-glucosidase) for the rapid estimation of activity in bacteria utilizing a hydrolyzable substrate, *p*-nitrophenyl-β-D-glucopyranoside. Antonie van Leeuwenhoek 53: 273.

43. Tsang, N., Firstenberg-Eden, R., and Lamb, M. 1987. Assessment of the microbial quality of dairy powder using the impedance technique. Dairy Food Sanit. 7: 516. (abstract).

44. Vanzo, S. J. and Washington, J. A. II. 1984. Evaluation of a rapid latex agglutination test for identification of group D streptococci. J. Clin. Microbiol. 20: 575.

45. You, M. S. and Facklam, R. R. 1986. New test system for identification of *Aerococcus*, *Enterococcus*, and *Streptococcus* species. J. Clin. Microbiol. 24: 607.

Chapter 33

STAPHYLOCOCCUS AUREUS

Gayle A. Lancette and Sita R. Tatini

33.1   INTRODUCTION

The growth of *Staphylococcus aureus* in foods presents a potential public health hazard since many strains of *S. aureus* produce enterotoxins that cause food poisoning if ingested. Among the reasons for examining foods for *S. aureus* are the following: (a) to confirm that this organism may be the causative agent of foodborne illness; (b) to determine whether a food or food ingredient is a potential source of enterotoxigenic staphylococci, and (c) to demonstrate postprocessing contamination, which usually is due to human contact with processed food or exposure of the food to inadequately sanitized food-processing surfaces. Foods subjected to postprocess contamination with enterotoxigenic types of *S. aureus* represent a significant hazard because of the absence of competitive organisms that normally restrict the growth of *S. aureus* and the production of enterotoxins.

Foods commonly associated with staphylococcal food poisoning are meat (beef, pork, and poultry) and meat products (ham, salami, hotdogs), salads (ham, chicken, potato), cream-filled bakery products, and dairy products (cheese). Many of these items are contaminated during preparation in homes or foodservice establishments and subsequently mishandled (improper refrigeration) prior to consumption. In processed foods, contamination may result from human, animal, or environmental sources. Therefore, the potential for enterotoxin development is greater in foods that are exposed to temperatures that permit the growth of *S. aureus*. This is especially true for fermented meat and dairy products. Though the potential is there, it is only when improper fermentation takes place that the development of staphylococcal enterotoxin occurs.

In processed foods in which *S. aureus* is destroyed by processing, the presence of *S. aureus* usually indicates contamination from the skin, mouth, or nose of food handlers. This contamination may be introduced directly into foods by process line workers with hand or arm lesions caused by *S. aureus* coming into contact with the food, or by coughing and sneezing, which is common during respiratory infections. Contamination of processed foods also may occur when deposits of contaminated food collect on or adjacent to processing surfaces to which food products are exposed. When large numbers of *S. aureus* are encountered in processed food, it may be inferred that sanitation, temperature control, or both were inadequate.

In raw foods, especially animal products, the presence of *S. aureus* is common and may not be related to human contamination. Staphylococcal contamination of animal hides, feathers, and skin is common and may or may not result from lesions or bruised tissue. Contamination of dressed animal carcasses by *S. aureus* is common and often unavoidable. Raw milk and unpasteurized dairy products may contain large numbers of *S. aureus*, usually a result of staphylococcal mastitis.

The significance of the presence of *S. aureus* in foods should be interpreted with caution. This normally relates to the capacity of certain types of *S. aureus* to produce enterotoxins when conditions permitting growth prevail. As a result of such conditions, large numbers of *S. aureus* usually will be present in the food. The presence of large numbers of the organism in food is not, however, sufficient cause to incriminate a food as the vector of food poisoning. The potential for staphylococcal intoxication cannot be ascertained without testing the enterotoxigenicity of the *S. aureus* isolate and/or demonstrating the presence of staphylococcal enterotoxin in food. Neither the absence of *S. aureus* nor the presence of small numbers is complete assurance that a food is safe. Conditions inimical to the survival of *S. aureus* may result in a diminished population or death of viable microbial cells, while sufficient toxin remains to elicit symptoms of staphylococcal food poisoning. For example, outbreaks of illness with convincing epidemiological evidence to suggest staphylococcal food poisoning have been attributed to dried skim milk from which viable cells of *S. aureus* could not be isolated.[4]

The method to be used for the detection and enumeration of *S. aureus* depends to some extent on the reason for conducting the test. Foods suspected to be vectors of staphylococcal food poisoning frequently contain a large population of *S. aureus*, in which case a highly sensitive method will not be required. A more sensitive method may be required to demonstrate an unsanitary process or postprocess contamination, since small populations of *S. aureus* may be expected. Usually *S. aureus* may not be the predominant species present in the food, and, therefore, selective inhibitory media generally are employed for isolation and enumeration.

33.2   GENERAL CONSIDERATIONS

33.21   Techniques for Isolation and Enumeration

Enrichment isolation and direct plating are the most commonly used approaches for detecting and enumerating S. aureus in foods. Enrichment procedures may be selective[2, 46, 59] or nonselective.[31] Nonselective enrichment is useful for demonstrating the presence of injured cells, whose growth is inhibited by toxic components of selective enrichment media. Enumeration by enrichment isolation may be achieved by determining either an indicated number or the most probable number (MPN) of S. aureus present. Common MPN procedures use three tubes or five tubes for each dilution.[3, 31]

For enumeration, samples may be applied to a variety of selective media in various ways: surface spreading, drop plates, and pour plates have all been used in direct plating procedures. Surface spreading and drop plate procedures are advantageous in that the form and appearance of surface colonies are somewhat more characteristic than the subsurface colonies encountered with pour plates. More of the sample can be tested using surface spreading techniques than by using drop plates; thus, the surface spreading technique is more sensitive than drop plates. The principal advantage of pour plates is that greater sample volumes can be used. The relative precision of the various direct plating techniques for enumeration of S. aureus has not been established.

Since the same types of selective media frequently are employed in both enrichment and direct plating, the relative sensitivity of the two procedures depends largely on the sample volumes. Larger volumes of sample normally are used in enrichment tubes, but equivalent volumes can be used in direct plating procedures by increasing the number of replicate plates. The relative precision of the two procedures for enumeration of S. aureus has not been established, but generally the plate counting procedures are more precise.

33.22   Screening Food Products for Excessive Growth of S. aureus

In certain processed foods, conditions in the early stages of processing may permit growth of S. aureus to high numbers ($\geq 1,000,000$/g or ml). Subsequent processing such as smoking, cooking, and fermentation, followed by aging or drying, may result in a diminished population due to death of S. aureus. Enumeration of S. aureus may not be useful in reflecting the enterotoxin hazard because enterotoxins are much more stable to these conditions than are S. aureus. Such situations may necessitate actual testing for enterotoxins, which is expensive and involved. While this may be justifiable in foods involved in food poisoning, it may not be necessary for routine quality control purposes. Testing foods for thermonuclease as an indicator of staphylococcal growth to levels of $\geq 1,000,000$/g or ml and of the likely presence of enterotoxins serves as a rapid screening procedure.[18, 37, 51, 54, 55, 56, 68, 69] Few organisms other than S. aureus produce thermonuclease; namely, S. hyicus subspecies hyicus, group

D streptococci, and *Bacillus* species.[56] However, the thermonucleases of the latter two are less heat-stable than that of *S. aureus*; *S. aureus* thermonuclease survives heating at 100°C for 100 min, whereas thermonuclease of streptococci and bacilli are substantially inactivated under these conditions.[56] Various foods naturally contaminated with *S. aureus* and enterotoxins showed presence of detectable levels of thermonuclease.[13, 18, 54, 68, 69, 71]

33.23   Media Commonly Used for Isolation

Selective media employ various toxic chemicals, which are inhibitory for *S. aureus* to a varying extent as well as to competitive species. The adverse effect of selective agents is more acute in processed foods containing injured cells of *S. aureus*. A toxic medium may help prevent overgrowth of *S. aureus* by competing species. The two selective toxic chemicals most frequently used in staphylococcal isolation media are sodium chloride (NaCl) and potassium tellurite (K_2TeO_3). Various concentrations of these agents have been used, ranging from 5.5% to 10% NaCl and from 0.0025% to 0.05% K_2TeO_3. Other chemicals such as ammonium sulfate, sorbic acid, glycine, lithium chloride, and polymyxin frequently are combined with NaCl and K_2TeO_3. Sodium azide alone or in combination with NaCl and neomycin also has been used in selective isolation media. Media containing identical selective agents at the same concentrations may vary further with respect to pH. Additional differences in media are contributed by combinations of selective agents and by the inclusion of different combinations of diagnostic features.

The principal diagnostic features of contemporary media include (a) the ability of *S. aureus* to grow in the presence of 7.5% or 10% NaCl;[3, 17, 47] (b) the ability to grow in the presence of 0.01% to 0.05% K_2TeO_3 in combination with 0.2% or 0.5% lithium chloride, and from 0.12% to 1.26% glycine,[6, 26, 50, 76, 77] or 40 µg/ml polymyxin;[20, 21] (c) the ability of *S. aureus* to reduce K_2TeO_3, producing black colonies,[1, 6, 62, 77] aerobically and anaerobically;[26, 73] (d) the colonial form, appearance and size; (e) the pigmentation of colonies; (f) coagulase activity and acid production in solid medium;[52] (g) the ability of *S. aureus* to hydrolyze egg yolk;[41, 70] (h) the production of phosphatase;[76] (i) the production of thermonuclease;[13, 14, 22, 44, 56] and (j) growth at 42° to 43°C on selective agar.[49, 74] Media used in the detection and enumeration of *S. aureus* may employ one or more of these diagnostic features.

33.24   Tests Used for Identification

Sometimes additional diagnostic features may be required to confirm *S. aureus* colonies because the inhibitors used may not completely prevent growth of other organisms, such as bacilli, micrococci, streptococci, and some yeasts. Microscopic morphology helps to differentiate bacilli, streptococci, and yeasts from staphylococci, which form irregular or grape-like clusters of cocci. Staphylococci may be further differentiated from streptococci on the basis of the catalase test, with the former being positive. Additional features are needed to differentiate staphylococci further from micrococci. Usually, staphylococci are lysed by lysostaphin[44, 61] but not by lysozyme, and they can grow in the presence of 0.4 μg/ml of erythromycin. Micrococci are not lysed by lysostaphin,[44] may be lysed by lysozyme, and will not grow in the presence of erythromycin. In a deep stab culture micrococci will grow at the surface, whereas most staphylococci grow throughout the agar. Staphylococci will grow and produce acid from glucose and mannitol anaerobically,[7, 67] whereas micrococci do not. Staphylococcal cells contain teichoic acids in the cell wall and do not contain aliphatic hydrocarbons in the cell membrane, whereas the reverse is true with micrococci.[8] Further, the G + C content (mole percentage) of staphylococci is 30 to 40 and 66 to 75 for micrococci.[5] Testing for some of these features is difficult, time-consuming, and expensive, and usually is not required for routine detection and enumeration procedures.

S. aureus is differentiated from the 20 other staphylococcal species by a combination of the following features: colonial morphology and pigmentation, production of coagulase, thermonuclease, acetoin, β-galactosidase, phosphatase and alpha toxin (hemolysis), acid from mannitol, maltose, xylose, sucrose and trehalose, novobiocin resistance, presence of ribitol teichoic acid, protein A, and clumping factor in the cell wall.[7, 22, 27, 40] The ultimate species identification may be established by DNA-DNA hybridization with reference strains.

The confirmation procedure most frequently used to establish the identity of S. aureus is the coagulase test. Coagulase is a substance that clots plasma of human and other animal species. Differences in suitability among plasmas from various animal species have been demonstrated.[53] Human[72] or rabbit plasma is most frequently used for coagulase testing and is available commercially. The use of pig plasma sometimes has been found advantageous, but it is not widely available. Coagulase production by S. aureus may be affected adversely by physical factors, such as culture storage conditions, pH of the medium, and desiccation. The extent to which the production of coagulase may be impaired by the toxic components of selective isolation media has not been demonstrated clearly.

As noted above, thermonuclease is also frequently used as a simple, rapid, and practical test for routine identification of S. aureus.[42, 43, 75] However, the use of the coagulase and/or thermonuclease test may result in erroneous species designation from a taxonomic standpoint. Two species, S. intermedius[29] and S. hyicus[24] subspecies hyicus are both coagulase and thermonuclease positive. However, the latter species can easily be differentiated from S. aureus on the basis of the clumping factor test.[27] The enterotoxigenicity of non-S. aureus species is not completely established. Coagulase and/or thermonuclease negative staphylococci are being reported to be enterotoxigenic.[10, 23, 48] This necessitates testing directly for enterotoxigenicity of cultures, which is not yet practical and has other limitations (see Chapter 34).

Presence of clumping factor in cells is another unique feature of *S. aureus*. It can be used to distinguish tube-coagulase-positive *S. aureus* from other tube-coagulase-positive species such as *S. hyicus* subspecies *hyicus*. Clumping factor present in *S. aureus* cells binds to fibrinogen or fibrin present in human or rabbit plasma, resulting in agglutination of cells. This is referred to as slide coagulase, bound coagulation, or agglutination. Clumping of cells in this test is very rapid (less than 2 min) and the results are more clearcut than 1+ or 2+ clotting in the tube coagulase test. Clumping factor can be detected using commercially available latex agglutination reagents.[57] Latex particles coated with rabbit plasma containing fibrinogen and IgG react, respectively, with clumping factor and protein A. However, protein A present in the cell wall of *S. hyicus* subspecies *hyicus* from swine does not interfere and give false positive results in the slide agglutination test using SeroSTAT Staph reagents (Scott Laboratories, Fiskeville, RI). All protein A-positive, tube-coagulase-positive, *S. hyicus* subspecies *hyicus* strains showed no clumping or agglutination of cells when mixed with rabbit plasma EDTA or SeroSTAT reagents.[27]

33.3 PRECAUTIONS AND LIMITATIONS OF METHODS

Many factors affect the usefulness and reliability of *S. aureus* detection and enumeration procedures. Among the more important factors are (a) physiological state of the organism, (b) competitive position of *S. aureus* in the sample menstruum, and (c) limitations of isolation media.

It has been demonstrated that the growth of injured cells of *S. aureus* is restricted by many of the selective isolation media used. Media satisfactory for detecting the presence of *S. aureus* in animal lesions, excretory products, and nonprocessed foods may not be adequate for analyzing processed foods. Factors such as heating, freezing, desiccation, ripening, and storage, which are common elements of food processing, have been shown to affect the growth of *S. aureus*[9] adversely. The extent of cellular injury inflicted during processing depends on the type and severity of treatment.

The importance of the physiological state of *S. aureus* to the selection of media for use in isolation and enumeration procedures is receiving increased attention. Frequently used staphylococcal isolation media that may restrict the growth of sublethally heated cells are mannitol salt agar, Vogel and Johnson agar, egg yolk azide agar, phenolphthalein phosphate agar containing polymyxin, milk-salt agar, tellurite glycine medium, staphylococcus medium number 110, and tellurite polymyxin egg yolk agar.[1, 16, 19, 28, 35, 36, 38, 64, 65] Selective media containing salt were more satisfactory than the media containing tellurite and tellurite azide in recovering *S. aureus* presumably injured by the ripening process of cheese.[64] Metabolically impaired cells that survive the toxic chemicals of selective media also may fail to show typical appearance.

Agents used in contemporary media to improve the recovery of stressed cells include (a) sodium pyruvate or catalase, which acts to prevent cell death from hydrogen peroxide accumulation during aerobic growth and repair;[15] (b) Tween 80 for repair of damaged cell membranes where lipid and phospholipid are located;[33] (c) a combined supplement of 0.05% (wt/vol) Tween 80 and 0.1% $MgCl_2 \cdot 6H_2O$, where Mg^{2+} may be required for repair of damaged ribosomes as a consequence of Mg^{2+} loss after stress;[34, 35, 43] and (d) phosphatidyl choline (2 mg/ml medium) or lecithin, which acts similar to egg yolk for increasing enumeration of heat injured S. aureus.[1]

Limitations in detection and enumeration methods are generally those associated with limitations of the isolation media in supporting growth of S. aureus and suppressing growth of competing species. In addition to variations contributed by the competition for growth media nutrients, procedural efficiency may be affected by other factors, such as acid-base changes and production of growth-limiting products, antibiotics, bacteriocins, bacteriophages, and the microflora of food products. It is generally conceded that none of the staphylococcal isolation media will prevent growth of all competing species without restricting growth of some S. aureus. Among the sources of variation shown to affect media efficiency significantly are (a) type of food examined, (b) the relative competitive position of S. aureus, and (c) the strain of S. aureus involved.[21]

Diagnostic criteria used in most staphylococcal isolation media make visual colony identification of S. aureus impossible without further testing. The physiology of S. aureus is diverse, and not all strains of the species demonstrate similar activity. For example, not all biotypes have the capacity to hydrolyze egg yolk, a common diagnostic feature in many detection and enumeration procedures.[25, 41] Considerable divergence also has been demonstrated in the response of various strains to the chemical agents used in selective isolation media. This diversity may lead to considerable confusion regarding the suitability of various isolation media.

Instability has been shown in certain of the physiological traits demonstrated by this species. Variability has been attributed to both physiological and genetic factors. The frequency with which physiological traits may change, and the elements stimulating such change, have not been demonstrated clearly. In applying the customary procedures for detection and enumeration of S. aureus possible variation in certain physiological traits should be considered. Some of the usual diagnostic features characteristic of the species may not always be displayed.

33.31   Treatment of Samples

Procedures for sample collection, shipment, and preparation described in Chapter 2 should be observed.

Conclusions regarding the potential hazard of foods in noncommercial or opened commercial containers in which the presence of S. aureus has been detected should be made with considerable caution. Correlation of biotypes isolated from food containers and from food poisoning victims should be established.

33.32   Handling Stock Cultures

Stock cultures of the following properly identified organisms should be maintained for testing the quality of media and reagents:

S. aureus. (ATCC 12600) A coagulase positive biotype with the combined characteristics of egg yolk hydrolysis and pigment production is preferable.

S. epidermidis. (ATCC 14990)

S. hyicus subspecies *hyicus.* (ATCC 11249)

Micrococcus spp.—*M. caseolyticus* or *M. varians* (ATCC 15306)

Storage of stock cultures on laboratory media that results in desiccation of the media, and thus requires frequent transfer of stock cultures, should be avoided to lessen the risk of loss of certain diagnostic traits.

33.33   Recommended Controls

Each batch of medium prepared for isolation and enumeration of *S. aureus* should be tested for sterility, productivity, and suitability of diagnostic criteria. To test sterility, pour melted solid media into sterile plates and incubate 45 to 48 hr at 35° to 37°C. Liquid media also should be incubated 45 to 48 hr at 35° to 37°C.

Media productivity testing may be accomplished by determining counts of *S. aureus* obtained in 18 to 24 hr broth cultures grown in a noninhibitory medium such as brain heart infusion (BHI) broth. Enumeration should be accomplished on noninhibitory solid plating media such as BHI agar. The isolation medium being tested for productivity should give counts not significantly less (20%) than the noninhibitory medium.

Each prepared batch of medium should be streaked with known cultures of *S. aureus* to test for appropriate diagnostic characteristics, such as colony size and appearance, pigmentation, and egg yolk reaction.

Each lot of coagulase plasma or latex reagents should be tested with known cultures of *S. aureus*, *S. epidermidis*, and *S. hyicus* subsp. *hyicus* to determine the suitability of the plasma for distinguishing positive and negative reactions.

33.4   EQUIPMENT, REAGENTS, AND MEDIA

33.41   Equipment and Supplies

Glass spreading rods: sterile, fire polished, hockey or hoe shaped, approximately 3 to 4 mm diameter, 15 to 20 cm long, with an angled spreading surface 45 to 55 mm long.

Drying cabinet or incubator for drying surfaces of agar plates and for checking thermonuclease positive colonies.

33.42   Reagents (Chapter 62)

Coagulase plasma containing EDTA. (Plasma derived from blood for which EDTA was used as the anticoagulant, or to which is added 0.1% EDTA (wt/ vol).

(a) Rabbit plasma (fresh or desiccated)
(b) Porcine plasma (fresh or desiccated)
(c) Commercial latex reagents for slide agglutination tests
(d) Gram stain reagents.

33.43   Media (Chapter 62)

Baird-Parker agar
Baird-Parker agar containing rabbit plasma fibrinogen
Baird-Parker agar without egg yolk
Brain heart infusion agar
Brain heart infusion broth
Pork plasma fibrinogen overlay agar
Toluidine blue DNA agar
Trypticase soy or tryptic soy agar
Trypticase soy or tryptic soy broth
Trypticase soy or tryptic soy broth (double strength)
Trypticase soy or tryptic soy broth containing 20% NaCl
Trypticase soy or tryptic soy broth containing 10% NaCl and 1% sodium pyruvate

33.5   PROCEDURES

33.51   Repair-Selective Enrichment Procedure[31]

This procedure is recommended for testing processed foods likely to contain a small population of injured cells.

Prepare food samples by the procedure described in Chapter 2. Transfer 50 ml of a 1:10 dilution of the sample into 50 ml of double-strength trypticase soy broth. Incubate 3 hr at 35° to 37°C.

Add 100 ml of single-strength trypticase soy broth containing 20% NaCl. Incubate for 24 ± 2 hr at 35° to 37°C.

Transfer 0.1 ml aliquots of culture to duplicate plates of a Baird-Parker agar and spread inoculum to obtain isolated colonies. Incubate the plates for 46 ± 2 hr at 35° to 37°C.

Select two or more colonies suspected to be S. aureus (Section 33.54) from each plate and subject to coagulase test (Section 33.56) or clumping factor test (Section 33.57). Report results as S. aureus present or absent in 5 g of food, as indicated by results of coagulase or clumping factor testing.

33.52   Selective Enrichment Procedure[3]

This procedure is recommended for detecting small numbers of *S. aureus* in raw food ingredients and nonprocessed foods expected to contain a large population of competing species.

Prepare food samples by the procedure described in Chapter 2.

Inoculate three tubes of trypticase soy broth containing 10% NaCl and 1% sodium pyruvate at each test dilution with 1 ml aliquots of decimal sample dilutions. Maximum dilution of sample tested must be high enough to yield a negative endpoint. Incubate 48 ± 2 hr at 35°C.

Using a 3 mm inoculating loop, transfer 1 loopful from each growth-positive tube to dried Baird-Parker agar plates. Vortex-mix tubes before streaking if growth is visible only on bottom or sides of tubes. Streak plates to obtain isolated colonies. Incubate 48 ± 2 hr at 35°C.

From each plate showing growth, pick ≥1 colony suspected to be *S. aureus* (Section 33.54) and subject to coagulase (Section 33.56) or clumping factor (Section 33.57) testing. Report most probable number (MPN) of *S. aureus*/ gram from tables of MPN values (Chapter 6).

33.53   Surface Plating Procedure[2]

This procedure is recommended for the detection of *S. aureus* in raw or processed food. The sensitivity of this procedure may be increased by using larger volumes (>1 ml) distributed over >3 replicate plates.

Prepare food samples by the procedure given in Chapters 2 and 4. Plating of two or more decimal dilutions may be required to obtain plates with the desired number of colonies per plate.

For each dilution to be plated, aseptically distribute 1 ml of sample suspension on three plates of Baird-Parker agar (e.g., 0.4, 0.3, and 0.3 ml). Spread the inoculum over the surface of the agar using sterile, bent glass spreading rods. Avoid the extreme edges of the plate. Keep the plates in an upright position until the inoculum is absorbed by the medium (about 10 min on properly dried plates). If the inoculum is not readily absorbed, plates may be placed in an incubator in an upright position for about 1 hr before inverting. Invert plates and incubate 45 to 48 hr at 35° to 37°C.

Select a plate containing 20 to 200 colonies unless plates at only lower dilutions (>200 colonies) have colonies with the typical appearance of *S. aureus*. If several types of colonies are observed that appear to be *S. aureus*, count the number of colonies of each type and record counts separately. When plates at the lowest dilution plated contain <20 colonies, they may be used. If plates containing >200 colonies have colonies with the typical appearance of *S. aureus* and typical colonies do not appear on plates at higher dilutions, use these plates for enumeration of *S. aureus*, but do not count nontypical colonies.

Select one or more colonies of each type counted and test for coagulase production or clumping factor. Coagulase or clumping factor positive cultures may be considered *S. aureus.*

Add the number of colonies on triplicate plates represented by colonies giving a positive coagulase or clumping factor test, and multiply the total by the sample dilution factor. Report this number as *S. aureus* per g of product tested.

33.54   Description of *S. aureus* Colonies

On Baird-Parker agar,[6] *S. aureus* colonies are usually ≥1.5 mm in size on uncrowded plates, jet black to dark gray, smooth, convex, with entire margins, with off-white edges, and may show an opaque zone and/or a clear halo extending beyond the opaque zone. Select one or more of each colony type for coagulase or clumping factor test.[57]

33.55   Direct Enumeration of Coagulase and Thermonuclease Positive *S. aureus*

This procedure is recommended for raw or processed foods. The sensitivity of the procedure may be increased by plating larger inoculum volumes (>1 ml) distributed over three or more replicate plates.

Prepare two or more decimal dilutions of food. Spread 1 ml of sample suspension of each dilution equally over three plates of Baird-Parker agar without egg yolk[30] or Baird-Parker agar containing rabbit plasma-fibrinogen tellurite[14, 39] to which 0.5 ml of 20% sodium pyruvate[32] was added just prior to use and then dried by incubating at 50°C for 1 hr. Keep the plates in an upright position until the inoculum is completely absorbed at 35° to 37°C.

If Baird-Parker agar containing no egg yolk is used, dispense 8 ml of tempered pork plasma-fibrinogen overlay agar[30] onto each plate. While this overlay is poured, the plates must be on a horizontal surface. After the overlay agar solidifies, invert and incubate plates for 45 to 48 hr at 35° to 37°C.

Select plates containing 20 to 200 colonies and count all black colonies showing the opaque fibrin halos (coagulase-positive) surrounding the colonies.[14, 30, 39] Incubate these plates at 65°C for 2 hr and then overlay each plate with 10 ml of melted toluidine blue DNA agar and let solidify. After solidification, incubate plates at 37°C for 4 hr.

Count all colonies showing pink halos against blue background as thermonuclease-positive. Add all colonies that showed both fibrin halos (coagulase-positive) and pink (thermonuclease-positive) halos, multiply by the sample dilution factor, and report as *S. aureus* per g or ml of product tested.

33.56   Coagulase Test

Transfer suspected *S. aureus* colonies to small tubes containing about 2 ml BHI broth and emulsify thoroughly.

Withdraw 1 loopful of resulting culture suspension and transfer to trypticase or tryptic soy agar slants. Incubate culture suspensions and slants 18 to 24 hr at 35° to 37°C. Keep slant cultures at room temperature for ancillary or repeat tests in case the coagulase test results are questionable.

Add 0.5 ml coagulase plasma with EDTA to 0.2 ml of each broth culture in a 10 × 75 mm tube and mix thoroughly. Incubate at 35° to 37°C and examine periodically during a 6 hr interval for clot formation. A 3+ or 4+ clot formation (Figure 1) is considered a positive reaction for *S. aureus*.[58, 63] Small or poorly organized clots (1+ and 2+) should be confirmed by performing the ancillary tests listed below. Recheck doubtful coagulase test results on broth cultures that have been incubated at 35° to 37°C for more than 18 hr but less than 48 hr. Assure culture purity before rechecking coagulase test results. Do not store rehydrated plasma longer than 5 days (at 2° to 8°C).

33.57 Clumping Factor

Using a loopful of growth from an 18- to 24-hr trypticase or tryptic soy agar slant, prepare a smooth heavy suspension of cells in saline. This can be done by placing two drops of saline, one for test and one for control, adjacent to each other on a microscope slide. Transfer cells from the loop to each drop and mix. To one suspension, add one drop of rabbit plasma EDTA or latex coated plasma (such as SeroSTAT reagent). To the remaining suspension, add one drop of saline to serve as a control. Tilt slide to mix and read

TYPES OF COAGULASE TEST REACTIONS

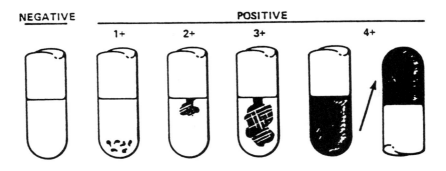

NEGATIVE	NO EVIDENCE OF FIBRIN FORMATION
1+ POSITIVE	SMALL UNORGANIZED CLOTS
2+ POSITIVE	SMALL ORGANIZED CLOT
3+ POSITIVE	LARGE ORGANIZED CLOT
4+ POSITIVE	ENTIRE CONTENT OF TUBE COAGULATES AND IS NOT DISPLACED WHEN TUBE IS INVERTED

Fig. 1 — Types of Coagulase Test Reactions

agglutination pattern within 2 min. Clumping with plasma or latex and no clumping with saline control indicates a positive test. The latex system gives a more rapid reaction (within a few seconds) and bigger clumps than rabbit plasma EDTA.

33.6 ADDITIONAL TESTS

33.61 *S. aureus* Speciation

If anomalies are encountered during testing, additional testing may be required to establish speciation of *S. aureus*. The following tests are usually adequate:

33.611 Microscopic examination

A Gram stain of *S. aureus* cultures will produce gram-positive cocci, 0.8 to 1.0 μm in diameter, occurring singly, in pairs, or most typically in irregular clusters resembling clusters of grapes.

33.612 Catalase reaction

Cultures of *S. aureus* are catalase-positive.

33.613 Production of thermonuclease[45]

Boil a portion of the culture growth used for coagulase test for 15 min and use for thermonuclease test. Cut 2-mm or larger wells in toluidine blue DNA agar plates and fill with boiled culture growth using a Pasteur pipette. Touching the bottom of the well will usually draw enough liquid to fill the well to level; if not, retouch the liquid with the pipette till it does. It may be necessary to refill the pipette before retouching. Trial test will indicate how much liquid to fill the pipette with prior to touching the bottom of the well. Incubate plates at 37°C for 4 hr or 50°C for 2 hr. Pink halos extending 1 mm beyond the well are considered positive for thermonuclease and considered to be *S. aureus*. Include positive and negative controls using *S. aureus* (ATCC 12600) and *S. epidermidis* (ATCC 14990), respectively.

33.614 Susceptibility to lysostaphin[44]

Use unboiled culture growth utilized for coagulase test. Mix 0.1 ml of cell suspension with 0.1 ml of lysostaphin (dissolved in a 0.02 M phosphate buffer containing 2% NaCl) to give a final concentration of 25 μg lysostaphin/ml. To another portion of 0.1-ml cell suspension, add 0.1 ml of phosphate buffer with NaCl (negative control). Also include *S. aureus* (ATCC 12600) as a positive control and *Micrococcus varians* (ATCC 15306) as a negative control in the assay. Partial or complete clearing of cell turbidity in test and positive cultures with no clearing in negative control is considered positive. *S. aureus* is lysed (clearing) by lysostaphin.

33.615   Anaerobic utilization of glucose and mannitol[67]

Follow the procedures recommended by the Subcommittee on Taxonomy of Staphylococci and Micrococci. Include controls of *S. aureus* (ATCC 12600) and *M. varians* (ATCC 15306). *S. aureus* will utilize glucose and usually mannitol anaerobically; *M. varians* will not.

33.616   Commercial identification products

Rapid identification kits available commercially may also be used. However, care must be taken in interpreting results of nontypical strains.

33.62   *S. aureus* as an Agent in Foodborne Illness[60]

Bacteriophage typing of *S. aureus* by the methods of Blair and Carr[11] or Blair and Williams[12] may be useful in elucidating the epidemiology of staphylococcal food poisoning outbreaks. A basic set of 22 phages for typing cultures of human origin is recommended by the Subcommittee on Phage-Typing of Staphylococci.[66]

33.7   THERMONUCLEASE ASSAY[54, 55, 68]

Sensitivity of this procedure may be increased by using sample sizes larger than 20 g.

Blend 20 g of food and 5 g of nuclease-free nonfat dry milk with 40 ml of distilled water in a blender for 3 min at high speed. (Omit addition of nonfat dry milk when testing products such as dry milk and cheeses. When testing fruit-filled dairy products, include nonfat dry milk.) Adjust the pH of the slurry to 3.8 with 1N HCl. Centrifuge under refrigeration for 15 min at 7,000 to 10,000 rpm or prechill the slurry to 5°C and centrifuge at room temperature using a table-top centrifuge at 7,000 rpm.

Decant the supernatant and add 0.05 ml of cold 3M trichloroacetic acid to each ml, mix and centrifuge as above. Decant and discard the supernatant.

Resolubilize the precipitate by adjusting the pH to 8.5 with 0.2N NaOH using a combination microglass electrode. The final volume of this should not exceed 2 ml. Boil the solution for 15 min or longer (up to 90 min) if a greater specificity is needed.

Assay for thermonuclease by filling 2 mm wells cut in toluidine blue DNA agar and incubate at 37°C for 4 hr. A pink halo extending 1 mm beyond the well is considered positive for thermonuclease regardless of the actual size of the zone. This indicates that *S. aureus* has grown to levels $>2 \times 10^6$/g in the product. Test such positive samples for enterotoxins (Chapter 34).

33.8 REFERENCES

1. Andrews, G. P. and Martin, S. E. 1978. Modified Vogel and Johnson agar for *Staphylococcus aureus*. J. Food Prot. 41: 530.
2. AOAC. 1984. "Official Methods of Analysis," 14th ed., p. 971. Assn. Off. Anal. Chem., Washington, D.C.
3. AOAC. 1987. Changes in Methods. *Staphylococcus aureus* in Foods. J. Assn. Off. Anal. Chem. 70: 393.
4. Armijo, R. D., Henderson, A., Timothee, R., and Robinson, H. B. 1957. Food poisoning outbreaks associated with spray-dried milk—An epidemiologic study. Amer. J. Pub. Health 47: 1093.
5. Auletta, A. E. and Kennedy, E. R. 1966. Deoxyribonucleic acid base composition of some members of the *Micrococcaceae*. J. Bacteriol. 20: 483.
6. Baird-Parker, A. C. 1962. An improved diagnostic and selective medium for isolating co-agulase-positive staphylococci. J. Appl. Bacteriol. 25: 12.
7. Baird-Parker, A. C. 1965. The classification of staphylococci and micrococci from worldwide sources. J. Gen. Microbiol. 38: 363.
8. Baird-Parker, A. C. 1970. The relationship of cell wall composition to the current classification of staphylococci and micrococci. Int. J. Sys. Bacteriol. 20: 483.
9. Baird-Parker, A. C. and Davenport, E. 1965. The effect of recovery medium on the isolation of *Staphylococcus aureus* after heat treatment and after storage of frozen or dried cells. J. Appl. Bacteriol. 28: 390.
10. Bautista, L. and Taya, P. 1988. A quantitative study of enterotoxin production by sheep milk staphylococci. Appl. Environ. Microbiol. 54: 566.
11. Blair, J. E. and Carr, M. 1960. The techniques and interpretation of phage typing of staphylococci. J. Lab. Clin. Med. 55: 650.
12. Blair, J. E. and Williams, R. E. O. 1961. Phage typing of staphylococci. Bull. World Health Org. 24: 771.
13. Batish, V. K., Ghodeker, D. R., and Ranganathan, B. 1978. The thermostable deoxyribonuclease (DNase) test as a rapid screening method for detection of staphylococcal enterotoxin in milk and milk products. Microbiol. Immunol. 22: 437.
14. Boothby, J., Genigeorgis, C., and Fanelli, M. H. 1979. Tandem coagulase/thermonuclease agar method for the detection of *Staphylococcus aureus*. Appl. Environ. Microbiol. 37: 298.
15. Brewer, D. G., Martin, S. E., and Ordal, Z. J. 1977. Beneficial effects of catalase or pyruvate in a most-probable-number technique for the detection of *Staphylococcus aureus*. Appl. Environ. Microbiol. 34: 797.
16. Busta, F. F. and Jezeski, J. J. 1963. Effect of sodium chloride concentration in an agar medium on growth of heat-shocked *Staphylococcus aureus*. Appl. Microbiol. 11: 404.
17. Chapman, G. H. 1945. The significance of sodium chloride in studies of staphylococci. J. Bacteriol. 50: 201.
18. Chesbro, W. R. and Auborn, K. 1967. Enzymatic detection of the growth of *Staphylococcus aureus* in foods. Appl. Microbiol. 15: 1150.
19. Collins-Thompson, D. L., Hurst, A., and Aris, B. 1974. Comparison of selective media for the enumeration of sublethally heated food-poisoning strains of *Staphylococcus aureus*. Canad. J. Microbiol. 20: 1072.
20. Crisley, F. D., Angelotti, R., and Foter, M. J. 1964. Multiplication of *Staphylococcus aureus* in synthetic cream fillings and pies. Pub. Health Reports 79: 369.
21. Crisley, F. D., Peeler, J. T., and Angelotti, R. 1965. Comparative evaluation on five selective and differential media for the detection and enumeration of coagulase-positive staphylococci in foods. Appl. Microbiol. 13: 140.
22. Cunningham, L., Catlin, B. W., and De Garilhe, M. Privat. 1956. A deoxyribonuclease of *Micrococcus pyrogens*. J. Amer. Chem. Soc. 78: 4642.
23. Danielsson, M. L. and Hellberg, B. 1977. The biochemical activity of enterotoxin and non-enterotoxin producing staphylococci. Acta Vet. Scand. 18: 266.

24. Devriese, L. A., Hajek, V., Oeding, P., Meyer, S. A., and Schleifer, K. H. 1978. *S. hyicus* (sompolinsky 1953) comb. nov. and *S. hyicus* subsp. *chromogenes* subsp. Nov. Intl. J. Syst. Bacteriol. 28: 482.

25. DeWaart, J., Mossel, D. A. A., ten Broeke, R., and Van De Moosdyk, A. 1968. Enumeration of *Staphylococcus aureus* in foods with special reference to egg-yolk reaction and mannitol negative mutants. J. Appl. Bacteriol. 31: 276.

26. Giolitti, G. and Cantoni, C. 1966. A medium for the isolation of staphylococci from foodstuffs. J. Appl. Bacteriol. 29: 395.

27. Gomez, M. and Tatini, S. R. Evaluation of latex slide agglutination test for rapid enumeration of *Staphylococcus aureus* from foods. (To be published, 1991.)

28. Gray, R. J. H., Gaske, M. A., and Ordal, Z. J. 1974. Enumeration of thermally stressed *Staphylococcus aureus* MF 31. J. Food Sci. 39: 844.

29. Hajek, V. 1976. *Staphylococcus intermedius*, a new species isolated from animals. Intl. J. Syst. Bacteriol. 26: 401.

30. Hauschild, A. H. W., Park, C. E., and Hilheimer, R. 1979. A modified pork plasma agar for the enumeration of *Staphylococcus aureus* in foods. Can. J. Microbiol. 25: 1052.

31. Heidelbaugh, N. D., Rowley, D. B., Powers, E. M., Bourland, C. T., and McQueen, J. L. 1973. Microbiological testing of skylab foods. Appl. Microbiol. 25: 55.

32. Holbrook, R., Anderson, J. M., and Baird-Parker, A. C. 1969. The performance of a stable version of Baird-Parker's medium for isolating *Staphylococcus aureus*. J. Appl. Bacteriol. 32: 187.

33. Hurst, A. 1977. Bacterial injury: A review. Can. J. Microb. 23: 935.

34. Hurst, A. and Hughes, A. 1978. Stability of ribosomes of *Staphylococcus aureus* S6 sublethally heated in different buffers. J. Bacteriol. 133: 564.

35. Hurst, A., Hughes, A., and Collins-Thompson, D. L. 1974. The effect of sublethal heating of *Staphylococcus aureus* at different physiological ages. Can. J. Microbiol. 20: 765.

36. Iandolo, J. J. and Ordal, Z. J. 1966. Repair of thermal injury of *Staphylococcus aureus*. J. Bacteriol. 91: 134.

37. Ibrahim, G. F. and Baldock, A. K. 1981. Thermostable deoxyribonuclease content and enterotoxigenicity of cheddar cheese made with subnormal starter activity. J. Food Prot. 44: 644.

38. Jackson, H. and Woodbine, M. 1963. The effect of sublethal heat treatment on the growth of *Staphylococcus aureus*. J. Appl. Bacteriol. 26: 152.

39. Julseth, R. M. and Dudley, R. P. 1973. Improved methods for enumerating staphylococci and detecting staphylococcal enterotoxin in meat foods. In "19th European Meeting of Meat Research Workers," Vol. II, p. 511. Centre Technique de la chareuterie, Paris, France.

40. Kloos, W. E. and Jorgersen, J. H. 1985. Staphylococci. In "Manual of Clinical Microbiology," 4th ed., p. 143. Amer. Soc. Microbiol., Washington, D.C.

41. Koskitalo, L. D. and Milling, M. E. 1969. Lack of correlation between egg yolk reaction in staphylococcus medium 110 supplemented with egg yolk and coagulase activity of staphylococci isolated from cheddar cheese. Canad. J. Microbiol. 15: 132.

42. Lachica, R. V. 1980. Accelerated procedure for the enumeration and identification of foodborne *Staphylococcus aureus*. Appl. Environ. Microbiol. 39: 17.

43. Lachica, R. V. 1984. Egg yolk-free Baird-Parker medium for the accelerated enumeration of foodborne *Staphylococcus aureus*. Appl. Environ. Microbiol. 48: 870.

44. Lachica, R. V. F., Hoeprich, P. D., and Genigeorgis, C. 1971. Nuclease production and lysostaphin susceptibility of *Staphylococcus aureus* and other catalase-positive cocci. Appl. Microbiol. 21: 823.

45. Lachica, R. V. F., Hoeprich, P. D., and Genigeorgis, C. 1972. Metachromatic agar-diffusion microslide technique for detecting staphylococcal nuclease in foods. Appl. Microbiol. 23: 168.

46. Lancette, G. A. and Lanier, J. 1987. Most probable number method for isolation and

enumeration of *Staphylococcus aureus* in foods: Collaborative Study. J. Assn. Off. Anal. Chem. 70: 35.

47. Lewis, K. H. and Angelotti, R. 1964. Examination of Foods for Enteropathogenic and Indicator bacteria. PHS Pub. No. 1142, p. 98. U.S. Govt. Print. Off., Washington, D.C.

48. Lotter, L. P. and Genigeorgis, C. A. 1977. Isolation of coagulase-positive variants from coagulase-negative enterotoxigenic staphylococci. Zbl. Bakt. Hyg., I. Abt. Orig. A239, 18.

49. Mintzer-Morgenstern, L. and Katzenelson, E. 1982. A simple medium for isolation of co-agulase-positive staphylococci in a single step. J. Food Prot. 45: 218.

50. Moore, T. D. and Nelson, F. E. 1962. The enumeration of *Staphylococcus aureus* on several tellurite-glycine media. J. Milk Food Technol. 25: 124.

51. Niskanen, A. and Koiranen, L. 1976. Effect of starter culture on staphylococcal enterotoxin and thermonuclease production in dry sausage. Appl. Environ. Microbiol. 31: 11.

52. Orth, D. S. and Anderson, A. W. 1970. Polymyxin-coagulase-mannitol-agar. I. A selective isolation medium for coagulase-positive staphylococci. Appl. Microbiol. 19: 73.

53. Orth, D. S., Chugg, L. R., and Anderson, A. W. 1971. Comparison of animal sera for suitability in coagulase testing. Appl. Microbiol. 21: 420.

54. Park, C. E., El Derea, H. B., and Rayman, M. K. 1978. Evaluation of staphylococcal thermonuclease (TNase) assay as a means of screening foods for growth of Staphylococci and possible enterotoxin production. Can. J. Microbiol. 24: 1135.

55. Park, C. E., El Derea, H. B., and Rayman, M. K. 1979. Effect of nonfat dry milk on recovery of staphylococcal thermonuclease production. Can. J. Microbiol. 25: 44.

56. Park, C. E., De Melo Serrano, A., Landgraf, M., Huang, J. C., Stankiewicz, Z., and Rayman, M. K. 1980. A survey for microorganisms for thermonuclease production. Can. J. Microbiol. 26: 532.

57. Pennell, D. R., Rott-Petri, J. A., and Kurzynski, T. A. 1984. Evaluation of three commercial agglutination tests for the identification of *Staphylococcus aureus*. J. Clin. Microbiol. 20: 614.

58. Rayman, M. K., Park, C. E., Philpott, J., and Dodd, E. C. D. 1975. Reassessment of the coagulase and thermostable nuclease tests as means of identifying *Staphylococcus aureus*. Appl. Microbiol. 29: 451.

59. Rayman, M. K., Devoyod, J. J., Purvis, U., Kusch, D., Lanier, J., Gilbert, R. J., Till, D. G., and Jarvis, G. A. 1978. ICMSF methods studies. X. An international comparative study of four media for the enumeration of *Staphylococcus aureus* in foods. Can. J. Microbiol. 24: 274.

60. Saint-Martin, M., Charest, G., and Desranleau, J. M. 1951. Bacteriophage typing in inves-tigations of staphylococcal food-poisoning outbreaks. Canad. J. Pub. Health. 42: 351.

61. Schindler, C. A. and Schuhardt, V. T. 1964. Lysostaphin: A new bacteriolytic agent for the staphylococcus. Proc. Nat. Acad. Sci. 51: 414.

62. Sinell, H. J. and Baumgart, J. 1966. Selektionahrboden zu Isolierung von Staphylokokken aus Lebensmitteln. Zentralbl. Bakteriol. Parasitenk. Infektionskr. Hug: Abt. Orig. 197: 447.

63. Sperber, W. H. and Tatini, S. R. 1975. Interpretation of the tube coagulase test for iden-tification of *Staphylococcus aureus*. Appl. Microbiol. 29: 502.

64. Stiles, M. E. 1977. Reliability of selective media for recovery of staphylococci from cheese. J. Food Prot. 40: 11.

65. Stiles, M. E. and Witter, L. D. 1965. Thermal inactivation, heat injury, and recovery of *Staphylococcus aureus*. J. Dairy Sci. 48: 677.

66. Subcommittee on Phage-Typing of Staphylococci. 1970. Report to the international com-mittee on nomenclature of bacteria. Int. J. Syst. Bacteriol. 21: 167.

67. Subcommittee on Taxonomy of Staphylococci and Micrococci. 1965. Recommendations. Int. Bull. Bacteriol. Nomenclature Taxonomy. 15: 109.

68. Tatini, S. R. 1981. Thermonuclease as an indicator of staphylococcal enterotoxins in food. In "Antinutrients and Natural Toxicants in Foods," ed. R.L. Ory, p. 53. Food and Nutrition Press, Inc., Westport, Conn.

69. Tatini, S. R., Cords, B. R., and Gramoli, J. 1976. Screening for staphylococcal enterotoxins in food. Food Technol. 30(4): 64, 66, 70, 72, and 73.
70. Tirunarayanan, M. O. and Lundbeck, H. 1968. Investigations on the enzymes and toxins of staphylococci. Acta Pathol. Microbiol. Scandinav. 73: 429.
71. Todd, E., Szabo, R., Roberu, H., Gleeson, T., Park, C., and Clark, D. S. 1981. Variation in counts, enterotoxin levels and TNase in Swiss type cheese contaminated with *Staphylococcus aureus*. J. Food Prot. 44: 839.
72. Turner, F. S. and Schwartz, B. S. 1958. The use of lyophilized human plasma standardized for blood coagulation factors in the coagulase and fibrinolytic tests. J. Lab. Clin. Med. 52: 888.
73. Van Dorne, H., Baird, R. M., Hendriksz, D. T., Van Der Kreck, D. M., and Pauwels, H. P. 1981. Liquid modification of Baird Parker's medium for the selective enrichment of *Staphylococcus aureus*. Antonie van Leeuwenhoek J. Microbiol. Serol. 47: 267.
74. Van Dorne, H., Pauwels, P., and Mossel, D. A. A. 1982. Selective isolation and enumeration of low numbers of *Staphylococcus aureus* by a procedure that relies on elevated temperature culturing. Appl. Environ. Microbiol. 44: 1459.
75. Van Schouwenberg-Van Foeden, A. W. J., Stadhouders, J., and Jans, J. A. 1978. The thermonuclease test for assessment of coagulase-positive with a normal acidity development. Neth. Milk Dairy J. 32: 217.
76. Williams, M. L. B. 1972. A note on the development of a polymyxin-mannitol phenolphthalein diphosphate agar for the selective enumeration of coagulase-positive staphylococci in foods. J. Appl. Bacteriol. 35: 139.
77. Zebovitz, E. J., Evans, J. B., and Niven, C. F. Jr. 1955. Tellurite-glycine agar: A selective plating medium for the quantitative detection of coagulase-positive staphylococci. J. Bacteriol. 70: 686.

Chapter 34

STAPHYLOCOCCAL ENTEROTOXINS

R. W. Bennett, S. Notermans, and S. R. Tatini

34.1 INTRODUCTION

34.11 General Information

Of the various metabolities produced by the staphylococci, the enterotoxins pose the greatest risk to consumer health. Enterotoxins are proteins produced by some strains of staphylococci,[6] which, if allowed to grow in foods, may produce enough enterotoxin to cause illness when the contaminated food is consumed. Although the true incidence is not known, staphylococcal enterotoxins are a leading cause of foodborne illness. The most common symptoms are vomiting and diarrhea, which occur 2 to 6 hours after ingestion of the toxin. The illness is relatively mild, usually lasting only a few hours to 1 day; however, in some instances the illness is severe enough to require hospitalization.

The need to identify enterotoxins in food encompasses two areas: foods that have been incriminated in foodborne illness and foods that are suspected of containing enterotoxin. In the former situation, the presence of enterotoxin in a suspect food confirms staphylococcal food poisoning. In the latter situation, the presence or absence of the enterotoxin determines the marketability of the product. The latter cannot be overemphasized because of the difficulty in preventing staphylococcal contamination of some types of foods and food ingredients. Routine testing of certain types of foods for the presence of enterotoxins, however, is not the basis for good manufacturing practices. Because toxin presence is only discernible at levels of 10^6 *Staphylococcus aureus* cells/g of product, emphasis must be more rigidly placed on preventing the contamination and subsequent outgrowth of *S. aureus* in food products.

The methods for identifying enterotoxins involve the use of specific antibodies (polyclonal or monoclonal).[38, 51, 52] The fact that there are several antigenically different enterotoxins (A to E) complicates their identification because each one must be assayed separately. Another problem is that unidentified enterotoxins exist for which antibodies are not available for *in vitro* serology. These unidentified toxins, however, appear to be responsible for only a small percentage of food poisoning outbreaks.

34.12 Sensitivity Requirements

The amount of enterotoxin required to cause illness in humans is not known; however, information from food poisoning outbreaks indicates that individuals experiencing illness probably consumed less than 1.0 μg of enterotoxin A, the serotype most frequently involved in staphylococcal foodborne illness.[13] The minimum level measurable with the microslide gel double diffusion technique is 30 to 60 ng of enterotoxin per 100 g of food; chromatographic and concentration procedures must be used before serological assay.[3] The microslide test method is approved by the Association of Official Analytical Chemists (AOAC)[1] and is the guide for testing new methods. It should also be the guide for those using the methods presented in this chapter.

34.13 Serological Assay Methods

A number of methods employing specific antibodies have been used to identify and measure enterotoxins. For food extracts, the method used should be equal in sensitivity (about 0.05 μg enterotoxin per ml) to the microslide method, which is used to identify enterotoxin in extraction-concentration procedures and is the method used by the Food and Drug Administration (FDA). To obtain this sensitivity, extracts must be concentrated from 100 g of food to about 0.2 ml. Any method less sensitive than the microslide is inadequate. Methods such as radioimmunoassay (RIA), agglutination, and enzyme-linked immunosorbent assay (ELISA) require less concentration or no concentration of the food extracts; thus they are less time-consuming and more sensitive.

The reversed passive hemagglutination method[46] presents two main problems: It is impossible to absorb enterotoxin antibodies from all of the antisera preparations onto red blood cells, and some food materials produce nonspecific agglutination of cells. However, more recently developed methods using latex[40] as a substitute for red blood cells appear promising as a serological tool for the identification of the staphylococcal enterotoxins.

The RIA method[16, 18, 26] probably will not be used widely in the routine microbiological laboratory because of the need for radioactively labeled purified toxins and the handling of radioactive materials; however, it may still be used in specialty and research laboratories. Several ELISA methods[23, 29, 31, 36, 44, 47, 49] have been proposed to identify enterotoxins in foods, although except for the polyvalent ELISA (section 34.352), their specificity has not been studied exhaustively. As a result, they should be used with the recommended controls. Of the ELISA methods proposed, the "sandwich" ELISA appears to be the method of choice, and the reagents necessary for its use are commercially available. Several of these methods are presented in this chapter.

34.14   Enterotoxigenicity of Staphylococcal Strains

Examining of staphylococci for enterotoxin production is helpful for identifying enterotoxin in foods and desirable for examining strains isolated from various sources. The methods outlined here are designed to determine the minimum amount of enterotoxin produced by a strain that could cause food contamination. A relatively simple and easily performed method is the membrane-over-agar[25] technique for enterotoxin production (see section 34.311) and the optimum sensitivity plate (OSP)[43] method for serological assay. The amount of enterotoxin produced with the membrane-over-agar method is adequate for testing with the OSP, although it is not as sensitive as the microslide. This system gives results equivalent to those obtainable with the monkey feeding test in designating a strain as enterotoxigenic.[42]

An alternative method for the production of toxin is the sac culture method of Donnelly et al.[19] Although it is the best method for the production of all the staphylococcal enterotoxins, this method is somewhat more cumbersome and time-consuming to set up than the membrane-over-agar method.[25] The OSP method can be used for determination of the enterotoxins with this method of production.

The semisolid agar method (see section 34.311) is an AOAC-approved method and is used by FDA for the production of enterotoxin. It is simple to perform and requires a minimum of items commonly found in the routine analytical laboratory. A smaller amount of enterotoxin is produced by this method than by the other two methods, and the microslide must be used to identify adequate levels of enterotoxin in order to classify a strain as enterotoxigenic. Although the microslide is more sensitive than the OSP, it is more difficult for inexperienced operators to achieve consistent results because it is a micro system. To determine the presence of enterotoxin in culture fluid, latex agglutination or ELISA methods can be applied as well, although commercial kits generally recommend broth media, which are comparable in enterotoxin production to the semisolid agar.[12] It should be remembered, however, that *S. aureus* in pure culture may produce substances that react nonspecifically with the immunoglobulin used.

The enterotoxigenicity of staphylococcal strains may also be determined by DNA hybridization techniques.[39] The nucleotide sequences of enterotoxin serotypes A, B, and C have been determined[8, 9, 27]; therefore, oligonucleotides can be synthesized and used as DNA probes to demonstrate the potential expression of toxin production by an organism.

34.15   Enterotoxin in Foods

The major problem in identifying enterotoxin in foods is the small amount that may be present in foods incriminated in food poisoning outbreaks. Marketable foods should contain no enterotoxin. Toxins can be identified if the counts are, or at some time were, $\geq 10^6$ staphylococci cells/g. Such high counts are not acceptable; therefore, instead of routinely testing products for the presence of toxins, rules of good manufacturing practices emphasize avoiding contamination and outgrowth of *S. aureus*. An additional problem may occur with thermally processed foods if toxins are rendered serologically inactive during processing.[2] However, serological activity can be restored with 6.0 M urea.[50] These procedures are available through FDA. To identify such small amounts of toxin, a very sensitive procedure or a satisfactory means of concentrating the food extract must be available. The sensitivity of the RIA and ELISA is such that food extracts seldom need to be concentrated; however, with the microslide, the extract must be concentrated from 100 g (or less) of food to 0.2 ml. At the same time, interfering substances must be removed from the extract.[3]

Two methods are presented for extraction and concentration of the enterotoxin in foods: the method of Casman and Bennett (see section 34.42) developed for use by FDA with minor modifications,[3, 54] requiring 5 to 6 days to complete (including serological testing); and the method developed by the Food Research Institute to shorten the assay time (see section 34.41). With this method, results equivalent to those of Casman and Bennett can be obtained on the third day. If latex agglutination or ELISA methods are used to identify toxins in foods, extraction procedures are simplified.

34.2   TREATMENT OF SAMPLES

Food to be analyzed should be kept refrigerated or frozen and should not be allowed to stand at room temperature except during handling. This is particularly true of foods that contain live organisms. Foods involved in poisoning outbreaks should be collected and refrigerated as soon as possible to avoid mishandling.

34.3   ENTEROTOXIN PRODUCTION BY STAPHYLOCOCCAL ISOLATES

Determining the enterotoxigenicity of *S. aureus* isolated from food, food ingredients, or the food processing environment can be a significant step in predicting the toxin serotype (A–E) in foods incriminated in foodborne intoxications. A number of methods[12, 19, 43] have been developed for the laboratory production of the staphylococcal enterotoxins. The membrane-over-agar,[43] sac culture,[19] and semisolid agar[12] methods are recommended for obtaining culture fluid for testing. Some commercial kits propose the use of simple broth such as brain heart infusion (BHI). The semisolid agar method is the one approved by the AOAC[1] for the laboratory production of the staphy-lococcal enterotoxins. The isolates are grown, the cells are removed by cen-trifugation, and the culture fluid is examined to determine whether entero-toxin has been produced by the optimum sensitivity method,[43] microslide gel double diffusion (section 34.312), reversed passive latex agglutination (section 34.322), or the ELISA (sections 34.332, 34.342, and 34.352).

34.31 Semisolid Agar[12] Microslide Method[14] (AOAC-approved method)

34.311   Enterotoxin production (semisolid agar)

1. Special equipment, supplies, and media

   a. Test tubes
      Test tubes (25 × 200 mm) are used to sterilize medium in 25-ml lots. Tubes containing medium may be stored until needed.
   b. Centrifuge
   c. Centrifuge tubes
   d. Agar
   e. Media
      Medium normally used is BHI broth, although other media such as 3% N-Z Amine A plus 1% yeast extract are satisfactory.
   f. Barium chloride and sulfuric acid
      $BaCl_2$ and H_2SO_4 are used to make the No. 1 McFarland standard for inoculum comparison.

2. Preparation of materials

   a. Agar medium
      Add 0.7% agar to BHI broth at pH 5.3 (0.7 g/100 ml). Dissolve agar by minimal boiling. Distribute medium in 25-ml quantities in test tubes (25 × 200 mm) and autoclave at 121°C for 10 min. Store the medium in test tubes. Pour it aseptically into petri dishes (15 × 100 mm). (Alternative procedure: Dissolve agar by autoclaving batchwise and pour 25-ml quantities into petri dishes.)
   b. Turbidity standard
      Prepare turbidity standard No. 1 of the McFarland nephelometer scale[33] by mixing 1% $BaCl_2$ with 99 parts of 1% H_2SO_4 in distilled water.

3. Production of enterotoxin

   a. Inoculum
      Pick representative colonies (5 to 10 for each culture), transfer each to nutrient agar (or comparable medium) slant, and grow 18 to 24 hr at 35°C. Add loopful of growth from agar slant to 3 to 5 ml of sterile distilled water or saline. Turbidity of the suspension should

be approximately equivalent (by visual examination) to the turbidity standard (approximately 3×10^8 organisms/ml). Spread four drops of aqueous suspension over entire surface of agar medium with a sterile spreader.

b. Incubation
Incubate plates at 35°C to 37°C for 48 hr (pH of culture should be approximately 8.0 or higher).

c. Enterotoxin recovery
Transfer contents of petri dish to a 50-ml centrifuge tube with an applicator stick or equivalent. Centrifuge 10 min at $32,000 \times g$. Test the supernatant fluid for enterotoxin using the microslide method.

34.312   Enterotoxin testing (microslide)

1. Special equipment, supplies, and reagents

a. Electrician's tape
Although either Scotch Brand vinyl plastic electrical tape No. 33, 3M Company, or Homart plastic tape 3/4 inch wide (Sears, Roebuck and Company) are recommended, any good-quality electrician's plastic tape should be satisfactory. The tape must be able to stick to the glass slides and not be readily removable with repeated washings.

b. Plexiglas template
The templates are made from plexiglas (Figure 1).

c. Silicon grease
Use silicone grease (Dow Corning), silicone lubricant spray (available at hardware stores), Lubriseal, or similar lubricant to coat the template so that it can be removed from the microslide after development without disrupting the layer of agar on which it is resting.

d. Petri dishes
The 20×150-mm size is convenient for incubation of slides.

e. Platform for filling templates
A Cordis Laboratories viewer with frosted glass over the lighted area is ideal for observing the presence of bubbles and removing them from the wells.

f. Capillary pipettes
Pasteur capillary pipettes (9-inch) are essential for applying the enterotoxin reagents and food materials to microslides.

g. Incubator
Any incubator or storage device that can be held constant at temperatures from 25°C to 37°C will suffice.

h. Fluorescent lamp
Any fluorescent desk lamp to which the microslide can be held at an oblique angle is adequate.

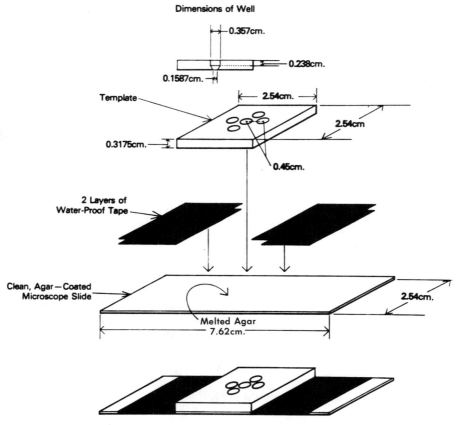

Figure 1 — Microslide assembly with diagram for preparation and specifications for plastic template.

i. Staining equipment

A Wheaton horizontal staining dish with removable slide rack, or Coplin jars can be used to stain microslides.

j. Enterotoxins

Crude enterotoxin preparations are adequate for the microslide test as long as only one enterotoxin precipitate line is obtained with the antiserum specific to that enterotoxin. These preparations may be obtained from Toxin Technology, Inc., 845 East Johnson St., Madison, WI 53703.

k. Enterotoxin antisera

Specific antisera to each of the enterotoxins that give only one line in the microslide with the respective crude enterotoxin are necessary.

These materials are readily available through Toxin Technology, Inc.

   l. Agar

   m. Thimersol (Merthiolate; ethylmercurithiosalicylate)

   n. Sodium barbital

Any reagent-grade sodium barbital may be used.

   o. Thiazine Red-R

This stain enhances precipitate lines in the microslide and can be obtained from a number of sources. Colour index No. 14780: Matheson, Coleman and Bell, Norwood, OH 45212. An alternative stain, which some investigators prefer to the Thiazine Red-R, is Woolfast Pink RL: American Hoechst Corp., Route 202-206, Bridgewater, NJ 08807.

   p. Synthetic sponge (strips, H_2O saturated)

2. Preparation of standards

   a. Enterotoxins

Dilute enterotoxin preparations according to specific instructions supplied with them. Reagents must be balanced, i.e., the concentration of the enterotoxin must be adjusted to that of the antiserum, so that a line of precipitate will appear approximately halfway between the antigen and antiserum wells in the microslide. If they are out of balance, lines may not appear or may be difficult to observe. The solution used to dissolve and dilute the enterotoxin should be prepared according to the manufacturer's instructions.

   b. Enterotoxin antisera (section 34.312, 1k)

3. Recommended controls

Enterotoxin reagents should be used at concentrations that give a visible line halfway between the antigen and antibody wells. The test can be made more sensitive by reducing the concentration of the reagents so that a line is visible only after staining or enhancement. The amount of enterotoxin necessary to give visible lines varies with the antisera, but normally a visible line can be obtained with 0.25 to 0.50 μg enterotoxin/ml of enterotoxin solution. It is essential that, under the conditions of the test, only one line be observed with the control reagents. A set of slides should be prepared that contains the antiserum and reference enterotoxin only.

4. Procedures

   a. Agar for coating slides

Add 2 g of agar to 1 liter of boiling distilled water and heat with stirring until solution becomes clear. Pour 30 ml into 6-oz prescription bottles or other suitable containers. Store at room temperature. The agar can be remelted until all is used.

b. Gel diffusion agar for slides

Add 12 g agar to 988 ml boiling sodium barbital saline buffer (0.9% NaCl, 0.8% sodium barbital, 1:10,000 merthiolate) adjusted to pH 7.41; continue boiling until agar dissolves, filter quickly with suction through two layers of filter paper, and store in 15- to 25-ml quantities in 4-oz prescription bottles. Remelting more than twice may break down the purified agar.

c. Slides

Wash microscope slides, 3 × 1 inch, in detergent solution, rinse thoroughly in tap water followed by distilled water, air dry, and store in dust-free containers. Slides must be scrupulously clean or the agar will not adhere to the glass and will tear when the template is removed.

d. Taping the slides

Wrap a 9.5- to 10.5-cm length (length needed will depend on how much the operator stretches the tape in applying it) of black plastic electrician's insulating tape twice around each end of the slide, about 0.5 cm from each end with a 2-cm space between the two strips. Stretch the tape slightly and press down firmly while wrapping it around the slide to avoid air bubbles. The finishing edge should end where the starting edge begins.

e. Rewashing slides

Wash slides after taping as described in section 34.312, 4c.

f. Precoating

Wipe area between tapes with 95% ethanol, using a small stick with piece of absorbent cotton twisted on the end. Cover surface between tapes with two drops of 0.2% agar (held at approximately 100°C) with a 1-ml pipette, and rotate slide to cover surface evenly. If agar forms beads instead of spreading evenly, rewash the slide. Air dry slides on a flat surface in a dust-free atmosphere.

g. Petri dishes for slides

Place two strips of synthetic sponge (approximately 0.5 × 0.5 × 2.5 inches) or two 3-inch strips of synthetic sponge opposite each other around the periphery of 15-cm petri dishes. Saturate strips with distilled water, pouring off any excess. Dishes will hold up to four slides and can be used repeatedly as long as the sponge or cotton is kept saturated with water.

h. Template

Spread a thin uniform film of silicone grease or other suitable lubricant on bottom of template. If too little lubricant is applied, the template cannot be removed easily from the agar layer; if too much is applied, the template will not stay firmly in place and precipitate lines will be distorted. If using silicone spray, spray the silicone on a piece of cotton on the end of a stick and wipe bottom surface of template, keeping coat as thin as possible. Before reusing templates, wash them in a warm detergent solution with a piece of cheesecloth to remove silicone, being careful not to nick or scratch the template. Rinse templates thoroughly with tap and distilled water to remove any traces of detergent.

i. Preparation of microslide (see Figure 1)

Place 0.45 to 0.50 ml of 1.2% melted agar (held at 80°C to 90°C) on precoated slide area between the tape and immediately lay the silicone-coated template on the agar by placing one edge on the edge of the tape on one side and bringing it down onto the edge of the tape on the other side. After the agar solidifies, place slides in petri dishes. Temperature of agar should be such that agar does not begin to harden before template can be put into place. Take care not to force agar into bottom of wells of the template.

j. Stain solution

If using Thiazine Red-R stain, dissolve 100 mg Thiazine Red-R in 100 ml of 1% acetic acid. If using Woolfast Pink RL, dissolve 1 g in 100 ml of the following solution: 5% trichloracetic acid, 1% acetic acid, and 25% ethanol in distilled water.

k. Preparation of record sheet

Draw pattern of holes of template in a notebook or use a rubber stamp of the hole pattern. Indicate materials that are placed in each well.

l. Addition of reagents and test materials to slides

Partially fill a capillary pipette by capillary action with the solution to be added. Remove excess liquid by touching pipette to edge of tube. Slowly lower pipette into well to be filled until it touches agar surface. (This leaves a small drop of liquid in bottom of well.) Refill capillary pipette with more reagent, lower into well, and fill well to convexity. (Do not overfill because of the danger of mixing reagents from different wells.) Place antiserum in center well of templates, standard enterotoxin reagent in upper and lower wells, and unknowns in the other two wells. Figure 2 shows the reagent arrangement for the bivalent and monovalent systems.

Apply reagents carefully to avoid formation of air bubbles in bottom of wells. All bubbles must be removed so that reagents make proper contact with agar layer. Remove bubbles by inserting end of heat-sealed capillary pipette to bottom of well. This operation and filling of wells are best done against a lighted background. Place slides in petri dishes as soon as possible to avoid undue evaporation of liquid from wells. An alternative method is to add reagents to slides without removing them from petri dishes.

m. Slide incubation

Incubate slides for 48 to 72 hr at room temperature or for 24 hr at 37°C.

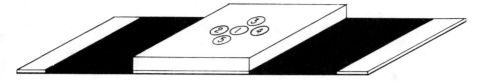

(1) Bivalent

   1. Combination Antisera
      (e.g., Anti A and B)
   2. Prepn under test
   3. Ref. enterotoxin (e.g., Type A)
   4. Prepn under test
   5. Ref. enterotoxin (e.g., Type B)

(2) Monovalent

   1. Antiserum (e.g., Anti A)
   2. Dilns of prepn under test
   3. Ref. enterotoxin (e.g., type A)
   4. Dilns of prepn under test
   5. Dilns of prepn under test

Figure 2—Arrangement of antiserum (antisera) and homologous reference enterotoxin(s) when assaying preparation(s) under test for presence of two serologically distinct enterotoxins simultaneously (bivalent detection system) or when assaying dilutions of a preparation under test (monovalent detection system).

n. Reading the slide

Remove template by sliding it to one side; clean slide with a momentary dip into water. Examine slide by holding it at an oblique angle against a fluorescent desk lamp. If precipitate lines are faint or none are visible, immerse slides in 1% cadmium acetate for 5 to 10 min, or immerse rinsed slide directly into Thiazine Red-R solution for 5 to 10 min. Alternative procedure: Place slides in a Wheaton jar filled with distilled water and extract with stirring for 30 min. Place slides in Woolfast Pink RL stain for 20 min at room temperature. Rinse off excess dye and destain in distilled water for 30 min or until stain is adequately washed out.[17]

o. Interpretation of data

Typical results (Figure 3): The control toxin should always give one precipitate line between antigen and antibody wells, as shown in Diagram 1, with toxin in wells 1 and 3, and water or unknowns containing no toxin in wells 2 and 4. The formation of a line by the unknown that joins with the control line, as illustrated in Diagrams 2 (wells 2 and 4) and 3 (well 2), shows that the unknown contains toxin at the concentration in the controls. The unknown in well 4 of Diagram 3 contains no toxin of the type present in the controls. The unknown in well 2 of Diagram 4 contains a smaller amount of enterotoxin than is present in the controls, and the unknown in well 4 contains a larger amount than is present in the controls. The unknown in well 2 of Diagram 5 contains much less toxin than is in the controls; the unknown in well 4 contains a much larger amount

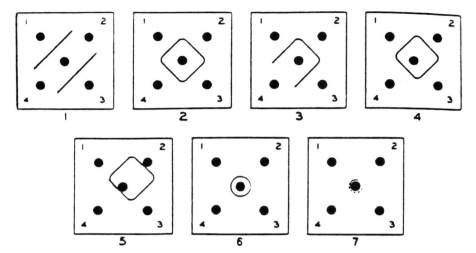

Figure 3—Typical results obtained with the microslide test. See interpretation of data.

than is in the controls. Both unknowns in Diagram 6 contain more enterotoxin than is present in the controls, and both unknowns in Diagram 7 contain much more. In the latter case the unknown should be diluted and the slide rerun because the excess toxin has prevented the formation of the control line.

Atypical results: Occasionally results are difficult to interpret, especially for the less experienced operator (Figure 4). In Diagram 1, the reference lines do not meet or cross the lines produced by the unknown in wells 2 and 4. It is impossible to interpret these results positively; hence, the slide should be made again. Frequently extraneous lines are produced by unknowns, as shown in Diagrams 2 and 3. Lines from unknowns (wells 2 and 4) that join with control lines (wells 1 and 3) show unknowns to be positive. The unknowns in Diagram 3 (wells 2 and 4) are negative because there are no joining lines. The extraneous lines are artifacts that are sometimes produced by unknowns. The results illustrated in Diagram 4 cannot be interpreted as positive because the lines extend beyond those produced by the controls, even though the latter lines do not cross the unknown lines. This type of slide should also be made again. The results shown in Diagrams 5 and 6 indicate channeling of the serum under the template because of improper contact between the template and the agar layer. The results shown in Diagram 5 indicate that the unknowns in wells 2 and 4 are positive because their lines join with the control lines. The results shown in Diagram 6 cannot be interpreted as positive for the unknown in well 4, and the slide should be made again. The partially double ring in Diagram 7 is a result of movement of the template during filling or development. The results indicate the presence of enterotoxin in the unknowns (wells 2 and 4), but to be certain the slide should be made again. The haze around the unknowns in Diagram 8 (wells 2 and 4) is occasionally encountered with food extracts. Such results are very difficult, if not impossible, to interpret. The haze results from the presence of contaminating substances (usually proteins) remaining in the concentrated extract. This problem may be remedied by additional $CHCl_3$ extractions, or possibly longer treatment with trypsin.

p. Preserving the slide[17, 32]

Thiazine Red-R staining: Rinse away any reactant liquid remaining on the slide by dipping the slide momentarily in water and immersing it for 10 min in each of the following baths: 0.1% Thiazine Red-R in 1% acetic acid, 1% acetic acid, 1% acetic acid, and 1% acetic acid containing 1% glycerol. Drain excess fluid from the slide, and dry it in a 35°C incubator if it is to be stored as a permanent record. After prolonged storage, lines of precipitation may not be visible until slide is immersed in water.

Woolfast Pink RL staining: Place slides in a Wheaton jar filled with distilled water and extract, stirring for 30 min. Place slides in Woolfast Pink RL stain for 20 min at room temperature. Rinse off excess dye and destain in distilled water for 30 min or until stain is adequately washed out.[32]

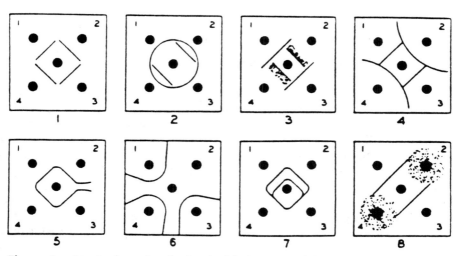

Figure 4—Atypical results obtained with the microslide test. See interpretation of data.

34.32   Enterotoxin Testing (Reverse Passive Latex Agglutination Assay — RPLA)[40]

34.321   Enterotoxin production

Use culture growth obtained by membrane-over-agar, sac culture, or semi-solid agar (section 34.311) methods for enterotoxin testing by RPLA.

34.322   Enterotoxin testing by RPLA

1. Special equipment and supplies

   a. SET-RPLA kit (Oxoid U.S.A., Inc., 9017 Red Branch Rd., Columbia, MD 21045; code TD900)
   b. Microtiter plates (V-well) and lids or clear plastic wrap
   c. Disposable membrane filtration unit — low protein binding type (millipore)
   d. Microtiter pipette with tips (to deliver 25 μl)

2. Preparation of materials

   a. SET-RPLA kit provides all the reagents required except those listed in section 34.322, 1b, c, and d.
   b. When using growth from section 34.311 or other methods, no additional treatment is required; otherwise, use millipore filter to remove cells from culture growth and use filtrate for enterotoxin testing.

3. Enterotoxin assay

   a. Follow directions given in kit.
   b. Dispense 25 μl of diluent from kit into each well of the microtiter plate (five rows by eight columns); four rows for enterotoxins A, B, C, and D, and the fifth row for control latex; seven columns for enterotoxin test sample, and the eighth for positive enterotoxin control and latex control.
   c. Add 25 μl of culture growth to the first well of each row (five rows).
   d. Mix and transfer 25 μl to the second, third, fourth, fifth, sixth, and seventh wells successively. Discard 25 μl from the seventh well.
   e. Add 25 μl of diluent to the eighth well of each row, respectively.
   f. Vigorously shake the suspensions of latex-coated antibody for each enterotoxin (A, B, C, and D) and control latex.
   g. Add 25 μl of the respective latex to the wells of each row (A, B, C, D, and control latex).
   h. Add 25 μl of enterotoxin solution to the eighth well; A for the first row, B for the second, C for the third, D for the fourth, and control latex for the fifth row, respectively.
   i. Mix contents of each well by tilting or agitating the plate.
   j. Cover plate with a lid, or wrap entire plate in clear plastic wrap

(such as Saran® wrap) or place plate in a moist chamber to prevent evaporation.

k. Leave plates undisturbed at room temperature for 20 to 24 hr.

4. Interpretation of test result

Read test result by observing each well for agglutination or lack of it (Figure 5). Lack of agglutination (negative test) results in a tightly packed button. When viewed from top of well, the button would look like a pinpoint. A positive test result is indicated by no button. Degree of agglutination (small to no button) indicates the amount of enterotoxin present in the test sample. Use a black background while reading the test result. Positive control (eighth well) for each enterotoxin should show no button, and the eighth well (fifth row) with control latex should show a button. Positive reaction in this well indicates reaction(s) from interfering substances. If control latex and test samples (in wells of fifth row) are positive at the same dilution, the test is considered negative. If the test sample is positive at a higher dilution than the control latex well in the fifth row, it is considered positive. Sensitivity of the RPLA is about 0.25–0.5 ng/ml.[41] The reciprocal of the dilution multiplied by the sensitivity indicates the amount of enterotoxin/ml. A negative test result by RPLA means enterotoxins A, B, C, or D were not found. Cultures could still be positive for unknown enterotoxins or for enterotoxin E, which is encountered at less than 1% frequency.[53]

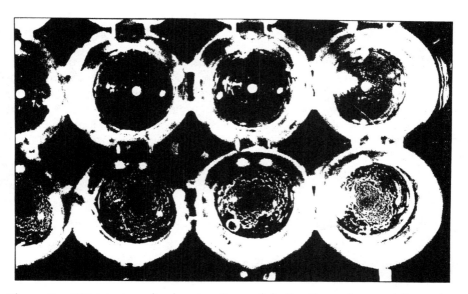

Figure 5 — RPLA test results showing "smooth button" negatives and "granular dispersed" positives.

34.33   ELISA Method (Microtiter-Plate)[37]

34.331   Enterotoxin production

Production of enterotoxin can be carried out as described under section 34.311 or by other methods.[7] However, because of the sensitivity of the ELISA, a more simplified production method is possible. Strains of *S. aureus* are inoculated in Erlenmeyer flasks containing BHI broth. After incubation with shaking at 37°C for 48 hr, the culture fluid is tested for the presence of enterotoxin.

1. Special equipment, supplies, and media

   a. Erlenmeyer flasks (100 ml)
   b. Centrifuge (section 34.311, 1b)
   c. Artiflex
   d. Media (the medium normally used is BHI broth)

2. Preparation of materials
   Add 10 ml of BHI broth to each Erlenmeyer flask, cover flask with double layer of artiflex, and autoclave at 120°C for 15 min.

3. Production of enterotoxin
   Inoculate *S. aureus* strains to be tested into each Erlenmeyer flask. Incubate flasks at 37°C with shaking (200 rpm). After 48 hr, centrifuge the culture fluid (20,000 × *g*) and test the supernatant for the presence of enterotoxin. Store the supernatant at −20°C.

34.332   Enterotoxin testing (ELISA)

Different enzyme immunoassays have been developed during the last decade. The sandwich ELISA has been used with some success for identification of enterotoxins. With this technique, antibodies are coated onto a solid matrix (wells of a microtiter tray). After incubation of the test sample, the amount of adsorbed enterotoxin is measured by using enzyme-labeled antibodies. The enzyme activity is proportional to the concentration of the enterotoxin. For labeling, different enzymes can be applied using different conjugation procedures. ELISA kits for identification of enterotoxin are commercially available (W. Bommeli, Langgrasstrasse 7, CH-3012 Bern, Switzerland). Follow manufacturer's instructions.

1. Special equipment, supplies, and reagents

   a. Polyvinyl microtiters trays
       Different trays are available. Trays of Cooke, Dynatech Cat. No. M25-001-2601, give satisfactory results.
   b. Shaker
       A small rotary shaker such as GFL type 3015 is acceptable.

c. Washing equipment
Various types of washing equipment are commercially available, such as the Ultrawash II made by Dynatech.
d. Spectrophotometer
e. Reagents
   (1) coating buffer (0.07 M phosphate buffer, pH 7.2, containing 0.15 M NaCl)
   (2) sample dilution buffer (coating buffer containing 0.05% (V/V) Tween 20 and 1% (W/V) bovine serum albumin)
   (3) washing buffer (coating buffer containing 0.05% (V/V) Tween 20)
   (4) IgG anti-enterotoxin A, B, C, D, and E
   (5) IgG anti-enterotoxin A, B, C, D, and E conjugated with peroxidase (horseradish peroxidase, Sigma type VI, R2 230; 0.3 M sodium bicarbonate; 1% fluordinitrobenzene in absolute ethanol; 0.8 M sodium periodate in distilled water; 0.16 M ethylene glycol; 0.01 M carbonate buffer, pH 9.5; 0.01 M phosphate buffer, pH 7.2, containing 0.15 M NaCl)
   (6) enzyme substrate (3,3',5,5'-tetramethylbenzidine; dimethylsulfoxide; 0.1 M sodium acetate/citric acid buffer, pH 6.0; 30% H_2O_2)
   (7) 2 M H_2SO_4
   (8) staphylococcal enterotoxins, commercially available from, among others, Toxin Technology, Inc., 845 East Johnson St., Madison, WI 53703.

2. Preparation of materials

   a. IgG anti-enterotoxin A, B, C, D, and E
   Polyclonal antibodies must be produced by immunization of sheep with highly purified enterotoxins. Sheep antibodies are advantageous because they do not react with protein A, an IgG-interfering substance produced by S. aureus.[27] Both the coating IgG and the enzyme-labeled IgG may be of the same lot. For production of highly purified enterotoxins, immunization of sheep and isolation of IgG are necessary.[10, 11, 15, 35, 45] Monoclonal antibodies can be produced according to the methods described by Thompson et al.[51] If the ELISA is carried out with monoclonal antibodies for coating, enzyme-labeled monoclonal antibodies that recognize a different epitope of the enterotoxin must be used. Furthermore, only monoclonal antibodies that neutralize the enterotoxin in vivo may be used.[38]
   b. Conjugation procedure (IgG peroxidase)
   The conjugation procedure developed by Nakane and Kawaoi[34] is suitable. In this procedure, peroxidase-aldehyde is prepared and then conjugated with the IgG. Dissolve 5 mg of horseradish per-

oxidase in 1.0 ml of 0.3 M sodium bicarbonate. Add 0.1 ml 1% fluordinitrobenzene dissolved in absolute ethanol. Mix gently at room temperature. After 1 hr add 1 ml 0.8 M sodium periodate dissolved in distilled water. Mix gently at room temperature, and after 30 min add 1 ml of 0.16 M ethylene glycol. Mix gently for 1 hr at room temperature. Dialyze the solution against 0.01 M carbonate buffer at pH 9.5 for 1 day with several changes of the buffer at 4°C. This solution may be kept up to a month at 4°C. Add 5 mg of IgG (powder) to 3 ml of the peroxidase-aldehyde solution. Mix gently for 2 to 3 hr. Dialyze against 0.01 M phosphate buffered saline, pH 7.2, at 4°C. The conjugates obtained can be freeze dried in 1% bovine serum albumin and 2% lactose and stored at 4°C; they remain stable for more than 1 yr.

c. Enzyme substrate

Prepare a solution of 42 mM 3,3',5,5'-tetramethylbenzidine in dimethylsulfoxide. From this stock solution, add 1 ml dropwise under gentle shaking to 100 ml of 0.1 M sodium acetate/citric acid buffer, pH 6.0. Just before use, add 7 μl of 30% H_2O_2 to 100 ml of buffer. Keep stock solution in the dark.

3. Procedures

a. Coating

Add 0.1 ml of IgG anti-enterotoxin diluted in coating buffer to each well of microtiter tray. Check concentration by checkerboard titration. However, almost 2 to 5 μg of IgG/ml is the optimal concentration. Incubate tray(s) overnight in rotary shaker (60 rpm) at room temperature. Avoid evaporation of contents of plates. Wash trays intensively with washing buffer.

b. Incubation of test samples

Add 0.1 ml of sample diluted in sample dilution buffer to each well. Incubate at room temperature for 60 min in rotary shaker (60 rpm). Wash trays intensively with washing buffer.

c. Conjugate incubation

Add 0.1 ml of conjugate (IgG peroxidase) diluted in sample dilution buffer to each well. Check concentration by checkerboard titration. Incubate at room temperature for 60 min on rotary shaker. Wash trays intensively with washing buffer.

d. Substrate reaction

Add 0.1 ml of enzyme substrate to each well and incubate for 30 min at room temperature. Stop the enzyme reaction with 0.05 ml of 2 M H_2SO_4; then measure the absorbance at 445 nm.

34.333   Recommended controls

Some immunoassays produce nonspecific reactions, which occur if substances other than the antigen bind to the antibodies used in the assay. Bacterial proteins able to react with the Fc-region of immunoglobulins have been found in a number of staphylococcal and streptococcal strains.[28, 30] False results may also be caused by lysozyme present in certain foods.[20] These reactions can be avoided by adding neutral IgG to the test sample.[21] However, for reliable results it is necessary to check for false-positive and false-negative results. The addition of a known quantity of enterotoxin can easily prevent false-negative results. False-positive results are more difficult to determine. The most appropriate method is as follows: Dilute a test sample giving a positive ELISA result until a clear positive ELISA reaction is obtained, then add a small quantity of IgG anti enterotoxin (1 to 5 μg/ml). After incubation for about 15 min at room temperature, test again by the ELISA. If the test sample contains enterotoxin, it will be neutralized by the added small quantity of IgG and the ELISA reaction will be negative.

34.34   ELISA Method (Polystyrene Ball)[22, 23]

This enzyme immunoassay is a commercial kit (SET-EIA, Toxin Technology, Inc., 845 East Johnson St., Madison, WI 53703), which reportedly can be used to semiquantitatively and quickly identify SET-A, SET-B, SET-C, and SET-D. SET-A and SET-D are the most common toxin serotypes encountered in food poisoning outbreaks. SET-B and SET-C are found less frequently, and SET-E is rarely seen. Therefore, SET-E has been omitted from this kit. The SET-EIA is designed to identify toxins in foods and culture fluids. This kit consists of color-coded polystyrene balls coated with antibodies specific for enterotoxins A, B, C, and D. Polystyrene balls used as negative controls are coated with immunoglobulins from normal rabbit serum (NRS). The extract suspected of containing toxin(s) is incubated with the antibody-coated balls overnight and the balls are washed with buffer to remove unbound nonspecific proteins.

The balls are placed individually into tubes and are incubated with phosphatase-labeled second antibody (enzyme-conjugate). After the balls are washed, they are exposed to p-nitrophenyl phosphate (PNPP) substrate, which is colorless. If a test sample contains one or more of the specific enterotoxin serotypes, it will bind to its own specific antibody ball while the other balls will remain free. Phosphatase-labeled antibodies bound to the ball(s) will cleave PNPP to the yellow compound p-nitro-phenolate. The intensity of the yellow color, which is measured photometrically at 405 nm, is proportional to the antigen concentration in the suspect extract.

The optical density of the negative control balls differentiates positive and negative values. The detection limit of this test is between 0.1 and 1.0 ng of enterotoxin/ml of extract, depending on the type of food specimen.

34.341   Enterotoxin production (SET-EIA)

1. Special equipment, supplies, and media (section 34.311, 1)
2. Preparation of materials (section 34.311, 2)

3. Production of enterotoxin (section 34.321, 3, semisolid agar or broth)

   a. Mix 0.4 ml of culture fluid with 20.0 µl NRS from kit to avoid interference of protein A, which nonspecifically binds immunoglobulin G, and incubate 30 min at room temperature.

   b. Add 3.6 ml of TRIS NaCl Tween (0.01 M TRIS; 0.5 M NaCl; 0.1% Tween 20, pH 7.5; 0.1% sodium azide) to produce a 1:10 dilution.

   c. Centrifuge (section 34.311, 1c) the treated mixture if turbidity occurs.

34.342   Enterotoxin testing (polystyrene ball-ELISA)

1. Special equipment, supplies, and reagents
Items in commercial kit:
SET-EIA Packages (Cat. No. 40010) are sufficient for 10 × 4 determinations and 20 controls.

   a. SET-A plastic balls, 10
   b. SET-B plastic balls, 10
   c. SET-C plastic balls, 10
   d. SET-D plastic balls, 10
   e. Control plastic balls, 20 (coated with rabbit immunoglobulins free of SET-antibodies)
   f. Anti SET-A enzyme conjugate, 2 × 4 ml
   g. Anti SET-B enzyme conjugate, 2 × 4 ml
   h. Anti SET-C enzyme conjugate, 2 × 4 ml
   i. Anti SET-D enzyme conjugate, 2 × 4 ml
   j. NRS
   k. Stock wash solution, 100 ml 10× concentrated NaCl-Tween: 0.14 M NaCl, 0.1% Tween 20
   l. Substrate buffer, 80 ml
   m. 20 mg PNPP, 10 tablets
Supplementary reagents:
   n. SET (A, B, C, D) culture supernatant, 1 µg/ml (Cat. No. 40060)
   o. Color-coded plastic tubes (red, blue, green, black, white) (Cat. No. 4-0070)
Reagents and equipment not provided in the commercial kit:
   p. Forceps (for transferring plastic balls)
   q. Screw-cap vials, 25- to 50-ml content
   r. Spectrophotometer, absorbance 405 nm
   s. Calculator (to determine standard deviation)
   t. Shaker, 100 rpm
   u. Aspirator with section cannula
   v. Reservoir for wash solution

2. Preparation of materials
Prepare all reagents, diluted and/or mixed, in accordance with specific instructions of supplier.

a. Preparation of wash solution
Prepare wash solution by diluting NaCl-Tween, 10× concentrate (section 34.342, 1k) 1:10 with distilled water.
b. Preparation of substrate solution
Dissolve one tablet of PNPP into 8.0 ml substrate buffer (section 34.342, 1l)

3. Preparation of standards
Prepare all standards in accordance with supplier's instructions.
4. Precautions and limitations
Adhere to precautions specified by kit supplier.

a. Unopened reagents are stable to expiration date on container labels.
b. Do not freeze SET-culture supernatant (section 34.342, 1n)
c. Use plastic tubes instead of glass tubes after conjugation step because of nonspecific uptake of conjugate by glass.
d. Protect substrate solution (section 34.342, 2b) from light and use within 1 day after preparation.

5. Recommended controls
If a spectrophotometer is used, negative controls aid in refining the interpretation of results.
Negative controls are evaluated once a day for a given kind of test sample (e.g., cheese or culture fluids). The negative value is then acceptable for similar materials. However, if a test sample is different in constitution, additional negative controls must be included. The mean value [x] and the standard deviation [s] are calculated from the absorbances of the four control balls (section 34.342, 1e); [x + 3s] represents the threshold value (99% confidence limit). To calculate a more accurate threshold value of a certain enterotoxin type, at least four control balls of the same type must be processed.

6. Procedures

a. Addition of culture fluid or food extract to antibody-coated plastic balls
Place one coated plastic ball of each SET—A, B, C, and D—and four NRS control plastic balls (section 34.342, 1e) into a vial (25 to 50 ml) that has been washed with NaCl-Tween. Add 4 ml of pretreated diluted culture fluid (section 34.341, 3a and 3b) or about 20 ml of food extract to the eight balls.
b. Incubation of plastic balls and test sample
Lay vial on shaker and agitate for about 100 rpm at room temperature from 4 hr (culture fluids) to overnight (food extracts).
c. Washing the plastic balls
Wash plastic balls twice with 1:10 dilution of the 10× concentrated stockwash solution (section 34.342, 1k). Transfer plastic balls into

respective color-coded polystyrene tubes. Wash balls in tubes one more time with wash solution (1:10 dilution of stock) to destroy binding sites on inner surface of polystyrene tubes.

d. Addition of enzyme-conjugate
    Add 0.5 ml of each SET enzyme conjugate A–D (section 34.342, 1f–i) to their respective tubes. Similarly process each of the four NRS control balls with one of the four conjugates.

e. Incubation of the conjugate-treated balls
    Incubate the balls in their respective tubes for 6 hr at room temperature without shaking.

f. Washing the conjugate-treated balls
    Wash the balls with wash solution (section 34.342, 2a) in the tubes by filling tubes completely with wash solution; remove wash using a cannula attached to an aspirator.

g. Addition of substrate
    Add 1 ml of freshly prepared substrate solution (section 34.342, 2b) to each tube containing a plastic ball and incubate for 60 min at room temperature. If numerous test samples are to be examined, terminate the reaction by adding 100 μl of 2N NaOH to each tube after 60-min incubation.

h. Reading and interpreting results
    A positive test for the presence of a staphylococcal enterotoxin serotype(s) is indicated when the phosphatase-labeled antibodies bound to the ball cleave PNPP to the yellow compound p-nitrophenolate. The intensity of the yellow color is proportional to the enterotoxin concentration and can be measured photometrically at 405 nm. The absorbance of the negative control balls serves as a threshold for the discrimination of positive and negative values. The detection limits range from 0.1 to 1.0 ng SET/ml.

34.35   Semi-Solid Agar[14]-ELISA (Polyvalent Visual Immunoassay)

See section 34.311.

This visual immunoassay provides a rapid (4-hr), sensitive (1.0 ng/ml or g), specific screening test for the simultaneous identification of any of the enterotoxins (A–E) that have been established as serological entities. However, the kit cannot be used to determine specific toxin serotypes. This ELISA is performed in a "sandwich" configuration (Figure 6). The kit is commercially available (Biotechnology Australia Pty. Ltd., 28 Barcoo St., P.O. Box 20, Roseville, N.S.W. 2069, Australia) and has performed well in studies evaluating enterotoxin presence in a variety of foods.[4, 5]

34.351   Enterotoxin production

1. Special equipment, supplies and media (section 34.311, 1)
2. Preparation of materials (section 34.311, 2)

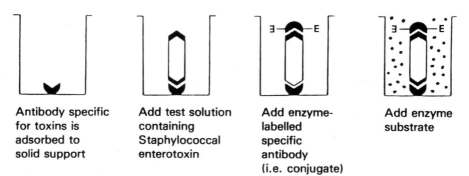

| Antibody specific for toxins is adsorbed to solid support | Add test solution containing Staphylococcal enterotoxin | Add enzyme-labelled specific antibody (i.e. conjugate) | Add enzyme substrate |

Figure 6—Typical double antibody "sandwich" ELISA scheme.

3. Production of enterotoxin (section 34.311, 3)
4. For determining the enterotoxigenicity of *S. aureus* isolates from foods or other sources, take 5.0 ml of the culture fluid (section 34.311, 3c), add 100 µl of sample additive, and mix thoroughly.
5. Remove a 200-µl aliquot of the additive-treated culture fluid and add to prewashed Removawells®.

34.352   Enterotoxin testing (polyvalent visual ELISA)

1. Special equipment, supplies, and reagents

   a. Materials supplied in kit:
       Reagent
       Wash concentrate
       Sample additive
       Positive control
       Negative control
       Conjugate diluent
       Conjugate
       Substrate diluent
       Substrate
       Stop solution
       Anti-SET antibody-coated Removawell® strips (48 wells) in resealable pouch
       Removawell® holder for securing individual wells or strips
       Instruction booklet
       Sample record sheet
       Colour Comparator
   Accessory materials and equipment to be supplied by user:
       Absorbent cotton
       Pipette (50 to 200 µl)
       Pipette (5 to 50 µl)

Tips, plastic
35°C to 37°C incubator
Plastic film wrap or sealable plastic container
Omnimixer (or other comparable homogenizer for the preparation of food slurries)
pH paper (range 0 to 14)
Tris buffer (0.25 M; prepare by using 30.28 g Tris per liter; pH 8)
Sodium hydroxide solution (1 M NaOH)
Hydrochloric acid (concentrated Hydrochloric)
Plastic squeeze bottle (500 ml)
Bench centrifuge
Deionized or distilled water
Sodium hypochlorite
Disposable plastic syringes (approximately 25 ml)

2. Preparation of materials (reagents)
   a. Reconstitution of wash solution
      Dilute wash concentrate with distilled or deionized water in a reagent bottle per kit instructions. This solution, referred to as the wash solution, is to be used for washing the wells. Wash solution should also be used for diluting positive control when required.
   b. Reconstitution of conjugate
      Add 5 ml conjugate diluent to conjugate and allow to rehydrate at room temperature by gently mixing. This solution is referred to as reconstituted conjugate.
   c. Reconstitution of substrate
      Add substrate diluent to the substrate. Be sure that the contents have dissolved and are at room temperature before use.
      CAUTION: Toxicity and hazard information on active ingredient are not available.
      These reagents are stable for 56 days if stored at 2°C to 8°C.

3. General precautions
   a. Note the expiration date of the kit. This is the last date on which the product can be reconstituted. All reagents must be prepared carefully and the date of reconstitution entered on the outside label of the box. Once reconstituted, the kit should be used within 56 days. All components must be refrigerated (2°C to 8°C) when not actually being used. DO NOT FREEZE.
   b. The components in the SET visual immunoassay are intended for use as an integral unit; therefore, components of different batch numbers should not be mixed.
   c. A new pipette tip must be used for each sample. Care must be taken not to cross-contaminate wells. If plastic troughs are used to dispense conjugate and substrate, they must always be kept separate.

d. The positive and negative controls must be run each time an assay is performed.
e. A trough containing 2% sodium hypochorite should be prepared and used for the disposal of all toxin-containing samples.
f. Unused Removawell® strips should always be stored in the pouch provided and re-sealed with tape after each use.

4. Recommended controls

a. Positive toxin control
Prepare the toxin control by making a 1:100 dilution of positive control in wash solution (conveniently, 50 μl to 5 ml) in a polypropylene tube. Run the positive toxin control whenever an assay is performed to indicate that all reagents are functional and the assay has been conducted correctly. Discard any unused diluted toxin control into the sodium hypochlorite solution.

b. Negative food control
Use a food of the same type as the suspect food, but which is known to be free of enterotoxin. Prepare the negative food control in exactly the same way as the suspect food. This control will indicate that washing of the wells has been adequate and will ensure that no food components will interfere with the test results.
If a negative food control is not available, use the negative control provided in the kit. No dilution is necessary.

c. Positive food control (optional)
Add an aliquot of the positive control to a known negative food product to act as a positive food control.
Homogenize the negative food product (10 g) as described under "Food Sample Preparation." Add a 100-μl aliquot of the positive control and rehomogenize to ensure thorough mixing. Continue sample preparation in the usual way. Assay this extract at the same time as the suspect food samples.

5. Procedures

a. Secure the desired number of Anti-SET Ab-coated Removawells® in the holder provided, allowing one well for each food sample, one well for the negative control, and one well for the positive control. An additional well will be required if the optional positive food control was prepared.
b. Fill each well with wash solution and let stand for 10 min at room temperature (20°C to 25°C).
c. Empty the wells by quickly inverting the holder, and remove any residual liquid by *firmly* striking the holder face-down on a paper towel several times.
d. Transfer 200-μl aliquots of the controls and samples (food extracts

or culture fluids) into individual wells, recording the position of each sample on the sample record sheet provided. Cover the wells and incubate for 2 hr at 35°C to 37°C. NOTE: The wells must be covered to prevent evaporation. It is suggested that plastic film or a sealed plastic container be used.

e. Wash the wells with a squeeze bottle filled with wash solution as follows:

(1) Press Removawells® firmly into holder.

(2) Quickly invert holder, emptying contents into a trough containing a solution of 2% sodium hypochlorite.

(3) Remove any residual liquid by *firmly* striking the holder face-down on a paper towel several times.

(4) Completely fill each well with wash solution.

(5) Repeat steps 5e(1)–5e(4) three more times. Finally, empty the wells according to steps 5e(2) and 5e(3).

f. Add 200 µl reconstituted conjugate into each well. Cover tray and incubate for 1 hr at room temperature (20°C to 25°C).

g. Empty wells and wash them thoroughly five times according to the procedure in steps 5e(1)–(4). Empty the wells and remove residual liquid as described in steps 5e(2) and 5e(3).

h. Add 200 µl reconstituted substrate to each well. Leave at room temperature (20°C to 25°C) for a minimum of 30 min until the positive control has reached an absorbance greater than 1.0 or a color darker than panel no. 2 on the Colour Comparator. Color development tends to concentrate around the edge of the wells. It is important to tap the sides of the plate *gently* to mix the contents before reading the result to obtain accurate absorbance readings.

i. Incubate the substrate-treated wells for 30 to 45 min at 20°C to 25°C.

j. Add 20 to 25 µl of stop solution to each well. Tap the sides of the plate *gently* to mix contents. The assay is now complete and results may be determined visually or with a microtiter tray reader.

k. Interpretation of ELISA results

Place tray on white background; then compare individual test well with the Colour Comparator provided in the kit. The positive toxin control (and positive food control, if used) should give a strong green color, indicating that all reagents are functional. If the negative control is significantly darker than the "negative" panels on the Colour Comparator, the washing step was probably inadequate and the assay must be repeated.

A sample is considered positive when the following criteria are met:

(1) The negative control is within the negative range on the Colour Comparator, and

(2) The sample has a color within the negative range on the Colour Comparator.

Read the absorbance of the samples at 414 ± 10 nm using a microtiter tray reader. Prepare the dual-wavelength reader blank against air and set the second "reference" wavelength at 490 ± 10 nm. Prepare a single-wavelength instrument blank according to the manufacturer's instructions. The positive toxin control should give an absorbance of at least 1.0, indicating that all reagents are functional.

If the negative control has an absorbance greater than 0.2, the tray washing was probably inadequate and the assay must be repeated. Refer to Troubleshooting Guide provided in the kit instruction booklet.

A sample is considered positive if an absorbance value of 0.2 or more is obtained.

A sample is considered negative if an absorbance value less than 0.2 is obtained.

34.4   ENTEROTOXIN IDENTIFICATION OF FOODS

At present, the most sensitive precipitation method generally available for the identification of enterotoxin is the microslide, which is sensitive to 50 ng/ml. To identify the small amounts of enterotoxin that may be present in foods, concentrate the extract from 100 g of food to 0.2 ml. Make extractions with buffer solution and absorb the enterotoxin from the extract with ion exchangers. Elute the toxin from the exchangers and concentrate with polyethylene glycol to 0.2 ml of eluate. Two extraction-concentration methods are presented: the Reiser et al. method[42] (section 34.41) and the Casman and Bennett method[3, 54] (section 34.42). Results obtained with the two methods are equivalent, but the Reiser et al. method requires 3 days, whereas the Casman and Bennett method requires 5 to 6 days.

Some recently developed rapid methods for identifying enterotoxins in foods described in this chapter are the reversed passive latex agglutination (section 34.32); microtiter plate-ELISA (section 34.33), polystyrene ball-ELISA (section 34.34), and the polyvalent (A–E serotypes) visual ELISA (section 34.35), a serological screening tool.

34.41   The Reiser, Conaway, and Bergdoll Method[42]

34.411   Special equipment, supplies, and reagents

1. pH meter
   The pH at which the extraction is done and the pH of the buffers used in the CG-50 extraction procedure are important. The pH adjustments usually are made within ± 0.1 pH unit.
2. Omnimixer
   An Omnimixer (Sorvall) is convenient for grinding food directly in the stainless steel centrifuge tubes.

3. Refrigerated centrifuge

   Food extracts are centrifuged at relatively high speeds at 5°C in a refrigerated centrifuge, such as a Sorvall RC-2B, which can reach speeds of 20,000 rpm. The lower the centrifuge speed, the more difficult the clarification of extracts.

4. Centrifuge tubes

   285-ml stainless steel centrifuge bottles (Sorvall No. 530)

5. Magnetic stirrer

   A magnetic stirrer keeps test samples agitated during pH adjustments, dialysis, etc.

6. Filter cloth

   At various stages in the procedures, food is filtered through several layers of coarse material, such as cheesecloth, placed in a funnel. Wetting the cheesecloth before placing it in the funnel reduces adherence of food to the cloth. The coarse material allows rapid flow with efficient removal of food particles, the chloroform layer, etc.

7. Amberlite CG-50 ion exchange resin

   The extract is purified partially by absorption onto Amberlite CG-50 ion exchange resin (100 to 300 mesh) (Mallinckrodt Chemical Works, St. Louis, MO 63160).

8. Polyethylene glycol

   Food extracts are concentrated with polyethylene glycol (Carbowax 20,000) (Union Carbide Corp., Chemical Division, 230 North Michigan Ave., Chicago, IL 60638)

9. Lyophilizer

   The extract is finally concentrated by freeze-drying, which conveniently reduces the volume to 0.2 ml and completely recovers the extract.

10. Dialysis tubing

    Cellulose casing of $1\frac{1}{8}$ inches flat width and an average pore diameter of 48 Angstrom units is used.

11. Chloroform

    The food extract is treated with $CHCl_3$ (several times in some instances) to remove lipids and other substances that interfere with the concentration of the extract to small volumes.

12. Trypsin

    The extract is treated with trypsin to eliminate extraneous proteins carried through the concentration procedures (crude trypsin Type II) (Sigma Chemical Co., P.O. Box 14508, St. Louis, MO 63178).

34.412   Recommended controls[6]

For food extractions, add a small amount of enterotoxin (0.25 to 0.50 μg) per 100 μg of uncontaminated food of the same type being examined for enterotoxin. This control will indicate whether the test is sensitive enough to detect the small amounts of enterotoxin that may be present. If known, the type of enterotoxin that may be present in the food can be used as the control. If not, then enterotoxin A is the recommended control. Crude enterotoxins can be used as the controls.

34.413   Procedures

Prepare a 30% polyethylene glycol (PEG) 20,000 MW solution by adding 3 g of PEG for each 7 ml of distilled water. Cut a piece of dialysis tubing (⅛ inch flat width) long enough to accommodate the volume of food extract to be concentrated. Soak tubing in two changes of distilled water to remove glycerol coating. Tie one end of tubing with two knots close together. Fill tube with distilled water and test for leaks by squeezing the filled sac while holding the untied end tightly closed. Empty the sac and place it in distilled water until use.

Suspend 100 g resin in 1.5 liters of distilled water, adjust to pH 12 with 5 N NaOH, and stir for 1 hr at room temperature. Let resin settle and decant supernatant fluid. Resuspend resin in distilled water, let resin settle, and decant. Repeat this washing until pH is that of the distilled water. Resuspend resin in distilled water, adjust pH to 2.0 with 6 N HCl, and stir for 1 hr. Let resin settle and decant supernatant fluid. Resuspend resin in distilled water, let resin settle, and decant. Repeat this washing procedure until pH is that of the distilled water. Suspend resin in 0.0005 M sodium phosphate buffer at pH 5.6. If pH is below 5.4, add 5 N NaOH and stir until the pH is corrected.

34.414   Extracting enterotoxin from food

1. Place a 100-g test sample of food in a 285-ml stainless steel centrifuge bottle with 140 ml distilled water and grind to even consistency (1 to 2 min) with a Sorvall Omnimixer.
2. Blend 10 ml 1.0 M HCl into the mixture (pH 4.5 to 5.0). For meat products, add only 5 ml of HCl; the pH should not drop below 4.5.
3. Centrifuge at 27,300 × g at 5°C for 20 min. Pour supernatant fluid (some of which may be quite viscous) into a beaker.
4. Adjust pH to 7.5 with 5 N NaOH. Extract with $CHCl_3$ (1 ml/10 ml test sample) by mixing with a magnetic stirrer for 3 to 5 min.
5. Transfer test sample to stainless steel centrifuge bottle, and centrifuge at 27,300 × g at 5°C for 20 min. Filter slowly through cheesecloth placed in a glass funnel to trap $CHCl_3$.
6. Adjust pH to 4.5 with 6 N HCl. Centrifuge as above to remove any precipitate. Remove supernatant fluid.
7. Adjust pH to 7.5 with 5 N NaOH and recentrifuge if any precipitate forms.
8. Add about 20 ml settled Amberlite CG-50 ion exchange resin, pH 5.4 to 5.9, per 100 g of original test sample. Measure resin by decanting buffer and transferring settled resin to a 20-ml beaker with a spatula.

After enough resin has been removed from the stock supply, add decanted buffer back and store resin at 5°C.

9. Stir mixture with a magnetic stirrer at 5°C for 1 hr. Remove resin from the liquid by filtration through cheesecloth in a Buchner funnel (Coors No. 1) with suction.

10. Wash resin in funnel with 200 ml of a 1:10 dilution of 0.15 M sodium phosphate-buffered 0.9% NaCl, pH 5.9. Discard the wash.

11. Resuspend resin in 30 ml of 0.15 M Na_2HPO_4 in 0.9% NaCl. Adjust pH to 6.8 with 5 N NaOH.

12. Stir mixture with a magnetic stirrer at 5°C for 45 min to elute enterotoxin from resin. Filter with suction through filter paper in a Buchner funnel. Wash resin on filter paper with a small amount of phosphate NaCl buffer. Discard resin.

13. Into the eluate stir 1 g of purified agar and continue stirring at 5°C for 1 hr. Filter mixture through a glass fiber filter (Type E) (Gelman Instrument Co., P.O. Box 1448, Ann Arbor, MI) in a Buchner funnel. Discard agar.

14. Place eluate into a dialysis tube (3 cm flat width). Place dialysis tube into PEG overnight.

15. Remove sacs from PEG and wash outside of sacs with warm tap water. Place sacs in warm tap water for 10 to 20 min to loosen toxin adhering to walls of sac.

16. Empty contents of sacs into 15-ml centrifuge tubes (Corex high speed, Corning No. 8441). Rinse sacs three times with distilled water, keeping final volume to 5 ml or less.

17. Add 0.5 ml of $CHCl_3$ to centrifuge tube and mix contents vigorously (a Vortex mixer serves this purpose very well).

18. Centrifuge test sample at 34,800 × g at 5°C for 10 min. Decant water layer to a test tube (18 × 100 mm) and freeze dry.

19. Dissolve dried test sample in 0.2 ml of a 1% trypsin suspension in distilled water. Digest for at least 30 min at room temperature.

20. Test for enterotoxin by the microslide method.

34.415   Precautions and limitations

The food to be tested must be ground to a very fine consistency for adequate extraction of toxin. This is particularly important for foods such as cheese, in which enterotoxin may be present throughout and not just on the surface. As much as possible of the nonsoluble food materials must be removed to eliminate their interference in the extraction procedures, such as in the CG-50 absorption process. The number of chloroform extractions needed to remove extraneous materials in the food depends on whether the extract can be concentrated to 0.2 ml and be of a consistency that can be applied readily to the microslide. One of the critical points is the ionic strength of the enterotoxin solution to which the CG-50 resin is added (section 34.414, 8). Instructions should be followed closely; if the ionic strength is too high, the toxin will not be absorbed completely, or possibly not at all.

This method cannot be used to recover the enterotoxin quantitatively, particularly at the levels usually found in foods involved in food poisoning outbreaks. One need not be too concerned about the amount recovered as long as the quantity is sufficient to determine the presence of 0.125 to 0.250 µg enterotoxin in 100 g of food.

34.42   The Casman and Bennett Method[3, 54] (AOAC-approved)

34.421   Special equipment, supplies, and reagents

1. Refrigerated cabinet or cold room
   Part of the extraction procedures, such as the carboxymethyl cellulose (CMC) column extraction, is done at about 5°C, primarily because the column is allowed to run overnight. This type of space is useful for storing food materials and extracts, thus eliminating the need for a refrigerator.
2. Waring blender
   The foods must be ground into a slurry for adequate extraction of enterotoxin.
3. pH meter
   The pH at which the extraction is done is important, as is the pH of the buffers used in the CMC column. The pH adjustments usually are made within ± 0.1 pH unit.
4. Refrigerated centrifuge (section 34.411, 3)
5. Centrifuge tubes (section 34.411, 4)
6. Magnetic stirrer (section 34.411, 5)
7. Filter cloth (section 34.411, 6)
8. Carboxymethyl cellulose
   The extract is purified partially by absorption onto CMC Whatman CM 22, 0.6 meq/g (H. Reeve Angel, Inc., 9 Bridewell Place, Clifton, NJ). Soluble extractants are removed by this step.
9. Polyethylene glycol (section 34.411, 8)
10. Lyophilizer (section 34.411, 9)
11. Chromatographic tube
    The enterotoxin in the food is partially purified by using CMC, with elution in a chromatographic tube. For this purpose, a 19-mm inside diameter column, e.g., chromaflex plain with stopcock, size 234 (Kontes Glass Company, Vineland, NJ) is recommended.
12. Dialysis tubing (section 34.411, 10)
13. Separatory funnels
    Separatory funnels of various sizes are needed in the $CHCl_3$ extractions and with the chromatographic column.

14. Glass wool

Glass wool makes ideal plugs for use in the chromatographic columns.

15. Chloroform

The food extract is treated with $CHCl_3$ (several times in some instances) to remove lipids and other substances that interfere with the concentration of the extract to small volumes.

34.422   Recommended controls[6]

See section 34.412.

34.423   Procedures

1. Polyethylene glycol (PEG) solution (section 34.413)
2. Dialysis tubing (section 34.413)
3. Separatory funnel

Attach a piece of latex tubing (approximately 24 inches) to the lower end of a 2-liter separatory funnel. Attach a piece of glass tubing in a No. 3 rubber stopper to the other end of the latex tubing. Place the separatory funnel in a ring stand above the chromatographic column.

4. Carboxymethyl cellulose column

Suspend 1 g of CMC in 100 ml of 0.005 M sodium phosphate buffer, pH 5.7, in a 250-ml beaker. Adjust pH of CMC suspension with 0.005 M H_3PO_4. Stir suspension intermittently for 15 min, recheck pH, and readjust to pH 5.7 if necessary. Pour suspension into the 1.9-cm chromatographic tube, and let CMC particles settle. Withdraw liquid from column through stopcock to within about 1 inch of surface of settled CMC. Place a loosely packed plug of glass wool on top of CMC. Pass 0.005 M sodium phosphate buffer, pH 5.7, through column until washing is clear (150 to 200 ml). Check pH of last wash. If pH is not 5.7, continue washing until the pH of wash is 5.7. Leave enough buffer in column to cover CMC and glass wool to prevent column from drying out.

34.424   Extracting enterotoxin from food

1. Grind 100 g of food material in a Waring blender at a high speed for 3 min with 500 ml of 0.2 M NaCl.
2. Adjust pH to 7.5 with 1 N NaOH or HCl if food material is highly buffered, and 0.1 N and 0.1 N NaOH or HCl if food material is weakly buffered (e.g., custards). Let slurry stand for 10 to 15 min, recheck pH, and readjust if necessary.
3. Transfer slurry to two 285-ml stainless steel centrifuge bottles. Centrifuge at 27,300 × g for 20 min at 5°C. Lower speeds with longer centrifuging time can be used, but clearing of some food materials is not as effective. Separation of fatty materials is ineffective unless centrifugation is done at refrigeration temperature.

4. Decant supernatant fluid into 800-ml beaker through cheesecloth or other suitable filtering material placed in a funnel.

5. Reextract residue with 125 ml of 0.2 M NaCl by blending for 3 min. Adjust pH to 7.5 if necessary.

6. Centrifuge at 27,300 × g for 20 min at 5°C. Filter supernatant through cheesecloth, and pool filtrate with the original extract.

7. Place pooled extracts into a dialysis sac. Immerse sac into 30% PEG at 5°C until volume is reduced to 15 to 20 ml or less (normally an overnight procedure).

8. Remove sac from PEG and wash outside thoroughly with cold tap water to remove any PEG adhering to sac. Soak in distilled water for 1 to 2 min and 0.2 M NaCl for a few minutes.

9. Pour contents into small beaker. Rinse inside of sac with 2 to 3 ml of 0.2 M NaCl by running the fingers up and down the outside of the sac to remove material adhering to sides of tubing. Repeat rinsing until rinse is clear. Keep the volume as small as possible.

10. Adjust pH of extract to 7.5. Centrifuge at 32,800 × g for 10 min. Decant supernatant fluid into a graduated cylinder to measure volume.

11. Add extract with ¼ to ½ volume of $CHCl_3$ to a separatory funnel. Shake vigorously 10 times through a 90-degree arc.

12. Centrifuge $CHCl_3$ extract mixture at 32,800 × g for 10 min at 5°C. Return fluid layers to separatory funnel. Draw off $CHCl_3$ layer from bottom of separatory funnel and discard.

13. Measure volume of water layer and dilute with 40 volumes of 0.005 M sodium phosphate buffer, pH 5.7. Adjust pH to 5.7 with 0.005 M H_3PO_4 or 0.005 M Na_2HPO_4. Place diluted solution in the 2-liter separatory funnel.

14. Place stopper (attached to bottom of separatory funnel) loosely into top with liquid from separatory funnel. Tighten stopper in top of tube and open stopcock of separatory funnel. Let fluid percolate through CMC column at 5°C at 1 to 2 ml per min by adjusting flow rate with stopcock at the bottom of column. Adjust flow rate so that percolation can be completed overnight. If all liquid has not passed through the column during the night, stop the flow when the liquid level reaches the glass wool layer. If all the liquid has passed through overnight, rehydrate the column with 25 ml of distilled water.

15. After percolation is complete, wash CMC column with 100 ml of 0.005 M sodium phosphate buffer (1 to 2 ml/min), stopping the flow when liquid level reaches glass wool layer. Discard wash.

16. Elute enterotoxin from CMC column with 200 ml of 0.05 M sodium phosphate buffer, pH 6.5 (0.05 M phosphate-0.5 M NaCl buffer, pH 6.5), at a flow rate of 1 to 2 ml/min at room temperature. Force last of liquid from CMC by applying air pressure to top of chromatographic tube.

17. Place eluate in a dialysis sac. Place sac in 30% PEG at 5°C and concentrate almost to dryness.
18. Remove sac from PEG and wash (as in section 34.424, 8). Soak sac in 0.2 M phosphate buffer, pH 7.4. Remove concentrated material from sac by rinsing five times with 2 to 3 ml of 0.01 M sodium phosphate buffer, pH 7.4 to 7.5.
19. Extract concentrated solution with CHCl₃ (as described in section 34.424, 11). Repeat CHCl₃ extractions until precipitate is so lacy that it falls apart in the CHCl₃ layer in the cheesecloth.
20. Place extract in a short dialysis sac (approximately 6 inches). Place sac in 30% PEG and let it remain until all liquid has been removed from inside sac (usually overnight).
21. Remove sac from PEG and wash outside with tap water. Place sac in distilled water for 1 to 2 min.
22. Remove contents by rinsing inside of sac with 1-ml portions of distilled water. Keep volume below 5 ml.
23. Place rinsings in a test tube (18 × 100 mm) or other suitable container and freeze dry.
24. Dissolve freeze-dried test sample in as small an amount of 0.2 M NaCl as possible (0.1 to 0.15 ml).
25. Check for enterotoxin by the microslide method.

34.425   Precautions and limitations

The food to be tested must be ground to a very fine consistency for adequate extractions of toxin. This is particularly important for foods such as cheese, in which enterotoxin may be present throughout and not just on the surface. As much as possible of the nonsoluble food materials must be removed to eliminate their interference later in the extraction procedures, such as in the CMC absorption process. The number of chloroform extractions needed to remove extraneous materials in the food depends on whether the extract can be concentrated to 0.2 ml and be of a consistency that can be applied readily to the microslides.

The method cannot be used to recover the enterotoxin quantitatively, particularly at the levels usually found in foods involved in food poisoning outbreaks. At the level of 1 μg or less per 100 g of food, the recovery is very low, probably 10 to 20%. One need not be too concerned about the amount recovered as long as the quantity is sufficient to determine the presence of 0.125 to 0.250 μg enterotoxin in 100 g of food.[3]

34.43   The Reverse Passive Latex Agglutination Assay (RPLA)

34.431   Special equipment, supplies, and reagents

1. SET-RPLA Kit (code TD900) (Oxoid U.S.A., Inc., 9018 Red Branch Road, Columbia, MD 21045)

    a. Blender
    b. pH meter
    c. Refrigerated centrifuge
    d. Microtiter plates (V-well) and lids or plastic wrap
    e. Microtiter pipette with tips (to deliver 25 μl)
    f. Centrifuge tubes

2. Preparation of materials

    a. Blend solid or semisolid food with an equal volume of saline (0.85% NaCl) for 2 min at high speed.
    b. Adjust pH to 4.6 with 1 N HCl.
    c. Centrifuge at 27,000 × g for 15 to 30 min at 4° to 5°C.
    d. Decant liquid (middle layer) and adjust pH to 7.0 to 7.5 with 1 N NaOH.
    e. If this liquid is not clear, extract with chloroform by mixing with five parts of chloroform.
    f. Centrifuge as in step c, above, for 10 min and use the supernatant for enterotoxin assay.
    g. For liquid foods such as milk, simply adjust pH to 4.6 as in step b, above, and follow steps c–f.
    h. Use the clear supernatant liquid for enterotoxin assay by the RPLA test.

Although RPLA kit directions do not call for steps b–g, these steps were found to minimize nonspecific reactions.[3] Extraction of enterotoxin as described and the use of RPLA identified 4 to 20 ng of enterotoxins/ml or 0.4 to 2 μg of enterotoxins/100 ml or g of food[53] and 1 ng/ml without chloroform extraction or dilution of enterotoxin during extraction with fermented dairy products.[24]

3. Enterotoxin assay by RPLA
Follow directions given in kit or those described in section 34.322, 3.

4. Interpretation of assay result
Absence of a pinpoint-type button in the test sample well and its presence in the eighth well of row 5 of microtiter plates indicates presence of enterotoxin of the respective type. Interfering substances other than enterotoxin may give a positive test result with control latex,[41] but if such material is present at lower levels than the enterotoxin of the test sample, a higher dilution than the control latex well will give a positive test result. A negative test result means lack of enterotoxins A, B, C, or D. Presence of enterotoxin E or unknown enterotoxins may not be determined by this assay. Frequency of occurrence of enterotoxin E is less than 1%.[53]

34.44   Enterotoxin Detection in Foods by ELISA

The ELISA is an appropriate method for identifying enterotoxin in food.[22, 23, 37, 47] With this method, quantities of 0.1 μg of enterotoxin in 100 g of food can easily be recovered. Because of the sensitivity of the ELISA, only a simple extraction procedure is needed to identify small quantities. Fluids such as milk can be tested without extraction. Solid or semisolid foods are blended with equal amounts of a buffer solution. After centrifuging, the extract is tested for the presence of enterotoxin. For some foods, however, such a simple extraction is not always possible. In case of extracts containing fat, an additional chloroform extraction is needed. If dry foods such as cereals or mealy products are to be tested, more extraction buffer must be used; for the sensitive detection of enterotoxin in such products, the extract must be concentrated.

34.441   Extraction procedure

34.4411   Special equipment, supplies, and reagents

1. Waring blender
   A Waring blender is convenient for grinding foods.
2. Refrigerated centrifuge (section 34.411, 3)
   The food extracts are centrifuged at relatively high speed at 5°C in a refrigerated centrifuge that can reach $30,000 \times g$.
3. Lyophilizer (section 34.411, 9)
   If necessary, extract can be finally concentrated by freeze drying.
4. PBS-extraction buffer (0.1 M phosphate buffer, pH 7.2, containing 0.15 M NaCl).
5. Chloroform ($CHCl_3$)
   If necessary, the food extract can be treated with $CHCl_3$ to remove lipids and other substances that may interfere with detection of the enterotoxin by ELISA.

34.4412   Recommended controls[3]

Addition of a small amount of enterotoxin (0.1 μg/100 g) to a part of the test sample is recommended as a control. This control will indicate whether the test is sensitive enough to detect the small amounts of enterotoxin that may be present in the food. If the type of enterotoxin present is unknown, mixtures of enterotoxin A, B, C, D, and E (each in a quantity of 0.1 μg/100 g) should be added. This procedure is a control in case of a negative test sample. To control positive test samples for the presence of enterotoxin, see ELISA procedure (section 34.352).

34.4413   Extracting enterotoxin from food (microtiter plate)

1. Place 100 g of food in a Waring blender and add 100 ml of phosphate-buffered saline (PBS) extraction. (Depending on the type of food, more than 100 ml buffer may be necessary.)

2. Blend mixture at high speed for 2 min and centrifuge at 27,300 × g at 5°C for 20 min. Pour supernatant fluid into a beaker.
3. If necessary, extract supernatant with $CHCl_3$ (1 ml/100 ml sample) by mixing with a magnetic stirrer for 3 to 5 min. Centrifuge mixture at 27,300 × g at 5°C for 20 min. Filter slowly through cheesecloth placed on a glass funnel to trap the $CHCl_3$.
4. If necessary, freeze dry the extract. Dissolve freezer-dried sample in a small amount of PBS containing 0.05% Tween 20.
5. Check extraction fluids obtained after steps 2, 3, and 4, above, for the presence of enterotoxin by ELISA (section 34.35).

34.4414   Precautions and limitations

The food to be tested must be ground to a very fine consistency for adequate extraction of toxin. Because 0.1 M phosphate buffer, pH 7.2, was used as extraction buffer, the pH of the ground product need not be controlled. A check of the pH is necessary only on acidified products. A pH of 6.0 must be adjusted to pH 7.0 by adding 1 M NaOH. The homogenate must be blended after the pH is adjusted. Because of the simple extraction procedure, the method is quantitative. Note, however, that recovery of enterotoxin depends on the food product tested.

34.45   Identification of Toxin in Foods by ELISA-Polystyrene Ball

34.451   Special equipment, supplies, and reagents

1. Distilled water or PBS
2. Centrifuge (section 34.411, 3); centrifuge tubes (section 34.411, 4)
3. 5 N hydrochloric acid
4. 5 N sodium hydroxide
5. Waring blender
   Foods must be ground into a slurry for effective extraction of enterotoxin.
6. pH meter
7. Hydrophilic tissue (laboratory wipe)
   This material is used to remove the fat layer.
8. Chloroform
9. NRS
   This serum is necessary to avoid interference by staphylococcal protein A, which nonspecifically binds immunoglobin G.
10. Tween 20

34.452   Preparation of materials

All materials for the extraction of staphylococcal enterotoxin from foods should be prepared in accordance with the recommendations of the supplier.

34.453   Extracting enterotoxin from food

Some products, such as milk, do not require extraction.

1. Mix one part food, about 100 g (or less if 100 g is not available) with one part of distilled water or PBS and homogenize for 10 min in a Waring blender (section 34.451, 5).
2. Centrifuge (section 34.411, 3) slurry at 10,000 × g for 20 min. If this speed is not obtained, longer centrifugation may be required to clarify extract. (Steps 1 and 2 are required for such foods as rice, minced meat, and macaroni.)
3. Adjust pH of slurry to 4.5 by adding 5 N HCl.
4. If turbidity occurs, centrifuge at 10,000 × g for 20 min as in step 2, above.
5. Collect the extract. If initial acid precipitation yields a sediment, repeat acid treatment (pH 4.5) and centrifugation.
6. Collect extract and filter through wet hydrophilic tissue (section 34.451, 7) to remove fat layer.
7. Some food extracts, such as macaroni, may require addition of $CHCl_3$ (1 ml/10 ml test sample) by stirring for 10 min. Separate and discard $CHCl_3$.
8. Independent of the pretreatment of the extract, the final pH of the extract must be 7.5. Add Tween 20 to a final concentration of 0.25%.
9. Treat 20 ml or less of the food extract with NRS (section 34.451, 9) to a final concentration of 2.5% and incubate 30 min at room temperature.
10. Centrifuge mixture again if turbidity occurs.
11. Assay extract for toxin by the polystyrene ball-ELISA (section 34.34).

34.46   Polyvalent ELISA Screening Methods for Foods

34.461   Special equipment, supplies, and reagents

See section 34.352, 1.

34.462   Recommended controls

See section 34.352, 4.

34.463   Extraction of enterotoxin from food

Food extracts should be prepared immediately before testing.

1. Milk and milk powder
   Reconstitute milk powder (10 g) by mixing with 50 ml 0.25 M Tris, pH 8. Treat reconstituted milk powder in the same way as fluid milk samples.
   For milk samples (10 ml), be sure that pH is in the range of 7.0 to 8.0; then add 200 μl sample additive and mix thoroughly. Use 200-μl aliquot of this solution to perform the ELISA (section 34.35).

2. Dehydrated food ingredients
Prepare food samples as follows:

   a. Add 50 ml 0.25 Tris, pH 8, to 10 g of food sample and homogenize for about 3 min.
   b. Centrifuge the sample for about 10 min in a bench centrifuge at 1,000 to 3,000 × g.
   c. Prepare a disposable plastic syringe (25 ml) by inserting a plug of absorbent cotton wool (about 0.5 cm thick). Then pump about 5 ml distilled water through to ensure tight packing. Remove plunger and carefully pump solution through, collecting the eluate.
   d. Take 5 ml of eluate; be sure pH is in the range of 7 to 8; then add 100 μl sample additive and mix thoroughly.
   e. Test 200 μl of sample in ELISA (section 34.35).

3. Cheeses

   a. Add 20 ml H₂O to 10 g of food sample and homogenize for about 3 min.
   b. Adjust pH to 4 (pH paper) with concentrated HCl.
   c. Centrifuge sample for about 10 min in a bench centrifuge (1,000 to 3,000 × g).
   d. Pour supernatant into disposable plastic syringe (25 ml) by inserting a plug of absorbent cotton wool (about 0.5 cm thick); then pump 5 ml distilled water through to ensure tight packing. Remove plunger and pour in the supernatant; then insert plunger and carefully pump solution through, collecting the eluate.
   e. Take 5 ml of eluate, add NaOH until pH is in the range of 7 to 8; then add 100 μl sample additive and mix thoroughly.
   f. Test 200 μl of sample in ELISA (section 34.35).

4. Other foods
Prepare food samples other than those described above as follows:

   a. Add 20 ml 0.25 M Tris, pH 8, to 10 g of food sample and homogenize for about 3 min.
   b. Centrifuge sample for about 10 min in a bench centrifuge at 1,000 to 3,000 × g.
   c. Prepare disposable plastic syringe (25 ml) by inserting a plug of absorbent cotton wool (about 0.5 cm thick). Then pump 5 ml distilled water through to ensure tight packing. Remove plunger and pour in supernatant; then insert plunger and carefully pump solution through, collecting the eluate.
   d. Take 5 ml of eluate; be sure pH is in the range of 7 to 8; then add 100 μl (four drops) sample additive and mix thoroughly.
   e. Test 200 μl of sample in ELISA (section 34.35).

34.5   REFERENCES

1. Association of Official Analytical Chemists. 1984. Official Methods of Analysis, 14th Ed. AOAC, Arlington, Va.

2. Bennett, R. W. and M. R. Berry, Jr. 1987. Serological reactivity and in vivo toxicity of *Staphylococcus aureus* enterotoxins A and D in selected canned foods. J. Food Sci. 52: 416–418.

3. Bennett, R. W. Archer, D. L., and Lancette, G. 1988. Modified procedure to eliminate elution of food proteins during seroassay for staphylococcal enterotoxins. J. Food Safety 9: 135–143.

4. Bennett, R. W., Ash, M., and Atrache, V. 1989. Visual screening with enzyme immunoassay for staphylococcal enterotoxins in foods: An interlaboratory study. AOAC Abstracts. 1989:72.

5. Bennett, R. W. and Atrache, V. 1989. Applicability of visual immunoassay for simultaneous indication of staphylococcal enterotoxin serotype presence in foods. ASM Abstracts, 1989: 323, p-28.

6. Bergdoll, M. S. 1972. The enterotoxins. In "The Staphylococci," ed. J.O. Cohen. p. 301–331. John Wiley and Sons, New York.

7. Bergdoll, M. S. and Bennett, R. W. 1984. Staphylococcal enterotoxins. In "Compendium of Methods for the Microbiological Examination of Foods," ed. M.L. Speck. p. 428–457. Am. Pub. Health Assn., Washington, D.C.

8. Betley, M. J. and Nekalanos, J. J. 1988. Nucleotide sequence of the type A staphylococcal enterotoxin gene. J. Bacteriol. 170: 34–41.

9. Bohach, G. A. and Schlievert, P. M. 1987. Nucleotide sequence of the staphylococcal enterotoxin C1 gene and relatedness to other pyrogenic toxins. Mol. Gen. Genet. 209: 15–20.

10. Borja, C. R. and Bergdoll, M. S. 1967. Purification and partial characterization of enterotoxin C produced by *Staphylococcus aureus* strain 137. Biochemistry 6: 1467–1473.

11. Borja, C. R., Fanning, E., Huang, I.-Y., and Bergdoll, M. S. 1972. Purification and some physiochemical properties of staphylococcal enterotoxin E. J. Biol. Chem. 247: 2456–2463.

12. Casman, E. P. and Bennett, R. W. 1963. Culture medium for the production of staphylococcal enterotoxin A. J. Bacteriol. 86: 18–23.

13. Casman, E. P., Bennett, R. W., Dorsey, A. E., and Issa, J. A. 1967. Identification of a fourth staphylococcal enterotoxin—Enterotoxin D. J. Bacteriol. 94: 1875–1882.

14. Casman, E. P., Bennett, R. W., Dorsey, A. E., and Stone, J. E. 1969. The microslide gel double diffusion test for the detection and assay of staphylococcal enterotoxins. Health Lab Sci. 6: 185–198.

15. Chu, F. S., Thadhani, K., Schantz, E. J., and Bergdoll, M. S. 1966. Purification and characterization of staphylococcal enterotoxin A. Biochemistry 5: 3281–3289.

16. Collins, W. S., Johnson, A. D., Metzger, J. F., and Bennett, R. W. 1973. Rapid solid-phase radioimmunoassay for staphylococcal enterotoxin A. Appl. Microbiol. 24: 774–777.

17. Crowle, A. J. 1958. A simplified micro double-diffusion agar precipition technique. J. Lab. Clin. Med. 52: 784–787.

18. Dickie, N., Yano, Y., Par, C., Robern, H., and Stavric, S. 1973. Solid-phase radio immunoassay of staphylococcal enterotoxins in food. Proceedings of Staphylococci in Foods Conference, Pennsylvania State University, University Park, Pa.

19. Donnelly, C. B., Leslie, J. E., Black, L. A., and Lewis, K. H. 1967. Serological identification of enterotoxigenic staphylococci from cheese. Appl. Microbiol. 15: 1382–1387.

20. Essink, A. W. G., Arkesteijn, S. J. M. W., and Notermans, S. 1985. Interference of lysozyme in the sandwich enzyme-linked immunosorbent assay (ELISA). J. Immunol. Methods 80: 91–96.

21. Fey, H. 1983. Nachweis von Staphylokokken Enterotoxinen in Lebensmitteln. Schweiz. Gesellschaft fur Lebensmittelhygiene, Schniffenreihe Heft 13: 51–67.

22. Fey, H. and Pfister, H. 1983. A diagnostic kit for the detection of staphylococcal enterotoxins

(SET) A, B, C, and D (SEA, SEB, SEC, SED). 2nd Int. Symp. Immunoenzym. Tech., Cannes, 1983. In "Immunoenzymatic Techniques," ed. Avrameas et al. Elsevier, Amsterdam.

23. Freed, R. C., Evenson, M. L., Reiser, R. F., and Bergdoll, M. S. 1982. Enzyme-linked immunosorbent assay for detection of staphylococcal enterotoxins in foods. Appl. Environ. Microbiol. 44a: 1349–1355.

24. Hamama, A. and Tatini, S. R. 1992. Hygienic quality of traditional Moroccan dairy products. Int. J. Food Microbiol. (In press).

25. Jarvis, A. W. and Lawrence, R. C. 1970. Production of high titers of enterotoxins for the routine testing of staphylococci. Appl. Microbiol. 19: 698–699.

26. Johnson, H. M., Bukovic, J. A., and Kauffman, P. E. 1973. Staphylococcal enterotoxins A and B: Solid-phase radioimmunoassay in food. Appl. Microbiol. 26: 309–313.

27. Jones, C. L. and Khan, S. A. 1986. Nucleotide sequence of the enterotoxin B gene from *Staphylococcus aureus*. J. Bacteriol. 166: 29–33.

28. Jurgens, D., Sterzik, B., and Fehrenbach, F. J. 1987. Unspecific binding of group B streptococcal cocytolysin (cAMP factor) to immunoglobulins and its possible role in pathogenicity. J. Exp. Med. 165: 720–732.

29. Kauffman, P. E. 1980. Enzyme immunoassay for staphylococcal enterotoxin A. J. Assoc. Off. Anal. Chem. 63: 1138–1143.

30. Koper, J. W., Hagenaars, A. B., and Notermans, S. 1980. Prevention of crossreactions in the enzyme-linked immunosorbent assay (ELISA) for detection of *Staphylococcus aureus* enterotoxin type B in culture filtrates and foods. J. Food Safety 2: 35–45.

31. Kuo, J. K. S. and Silverman, G. J. 1980. Application of enzyme-linked immunosorbent assay for detection of staphylococcal enterotoxins in foods. J. Food Prot. 43: 404–407.

32. Lumpkins, E. D., Sr. 1972. Methods for staining and preserving agar gel diffusion plates. Appl. Microbiol. 24: 499–500.

33. McFarland, J. 1907. The nephelometer: An instrument for estimating the number of bacteria in suspensions used for calculating the opsonic index and for vaccines. JAMA 49: 1176–1178.

34. Nakane, P. K. and Kawaoi, A. 1974. Peroxidase-labeled antibody. A new method of conjugation. J. Histochem. Cytochem. 22: 1084–1091.

35. Notermans, S. and Dufrenne, J. B. 1982. A simple purification method for enterotoxin F produced by *Staphylococcus aureus* and some properties of the toxin. Antonie van Leeuwenhoek; J. Microbiol. Serol. 48: 447–455.

36. Notermans, S., Verjans, H. L., Bol, J., and Van Schothorst, M. 1978. Enzyme-linked immunosorbent assay (ELISA) for determination of *Staphylococcus aureus* enterotoxin type B. Health Lab. Sci. 15: 28–31.

37. Notermans, S., Boot, R., Tips, P. D., and Denooij, M. P. 1983. Extractions of staphylococcal enterotoxins (SE) from minced meat and subsequent detection of SE with enzyme-linked immunosorbent assay (ELISA). J. Food Prot. 46: 238–241.

38. Notermans, S., Boot, R., and Tatini, S. R. 1987. Selection of monoclonal antibodies for detection of staphylococcal enterotoxins in heat processed foods. Int. J. Food Microbiol. 5: 49–55.

39. Notermans, S., Heuvelman, K. J., and Wernars, K. 1988. Synthetic enterotoxin B DNA probes for detection of enterotoxigenic *Staphylococcus aureus* strains. Appl. Environ. Microbiol. 54: 531–533.

40. Oda, T. 1978. Application of SP-Sephadex chromatography to the purification of staphylococcal enterotoxins A, B, C_2. Jpn. J. Bacteriol. 33: 743–752.

41. Park, E. E. and Szabo, R. 1986. Evaluation of the reversed passive latex agglutination (RPLA) test kit for detection of staphylococcal enterotoxins A, B, C, and D in food. Can. J. Microbiol. 32: 723–727.

42. Reiser, R., Conaway, D., and Bergdoll, M. S. 1974. Detection of staphylococcal enterotoxin in foods. Appl. Microbiol. 27: 83–85.

43. Robbins, R., Gould, S., and Bergdoll, M. S. 1974. Detecting the enterotoxigenicity of *Staphylococcus aureus* strains. Appl. Microbiol. 28: 946–950.
44. Saunders, G. C. and Bartlett, M. L. 1977. Double-antibody solid-phase enzyme immunoassay for the detection of staphylococcal enterotoxin A. Appl. Environ. Microbiol. 34: 518–522.
45. Shinagawa, K., Kunita, N., and Sakaguchi, S. 1975. Simplified methods for purification of staphylococcal enterotoxin A and C and preparation of anti-enterotoxin sera. Jpn. J. Bacteriol. 30: 683–692.
46. Silverman, S. J., Knott, A. R., and Howard, M. 1968. Rapid, sensitive assay for staphylococcal enterotoxin and a comparison of serological methods. Appl. Microbiol. 16: 1019–1023.
47. Simon, E. and Terplan, G. 1977. Nachweis von staphylokokken enterotoxin B Mittels ELISA-test. Zentralbl. Veterinaermed. Reihe B. 24: 842–844.
48. Soo, H. M., Tatini, S. R., and Bennett, R. W. 1973. Thermal inactivation staphylococcal enterotoxins A and D. Abstr. Annu. Meet. Am. Soc. Microbiol., p. 1.
49. Stiffler-Rosenberg, G. and Fey, H. 1978. Simple assay for staphylococcal enterotoxins A, B, and C: Modification of enzyme-linked immunosorbent assay. J. Clin. Microbiol. 8: 473–479.
50. Tatini, S. R. 1976. Thermal stability of enterotoxins in food. J. Milk Food Technol. 39: 432–438.
51. Thompson, N. E., Bergdoll, M. S., Meyer, R. F., Bennett, R. W., Miller, L., and Macmillan, J. D. 1985. Monoclonal antibodies to the enterotoxins and to the toxic shock syndrome toxin produced by *Staphylococcus aureus*. In "Monoclonal Antibodies," eds. A. J. L. Macario and E. C. Macario, Vol. II, p. 23–59. Academic Press, Orlando, Fla.
52. Thompson, N. E., Razdan, M., Kuntsmann, G., Aschenbach, J. M., Evenson, M. L., and Bergdoll, M. S. 1986. Detection of staphylococcal enterotoxins by enzyme-linked immunosorbent assays and radioimmunoassays: Comparison of monoclonal and polyclonal antibody systems. Appl. Environ. Microbiol. 51: 885–890.
53. Wieneke, A. A. and Gilbert, R. J. 1987. Comparison of four methods for the detection of staphylococcal enterotoxin in foods from outbreaks of food poisoning. Int. J. Food Microbiol. 4: 135–143.
54. Zehren, V. L. and Zehren, V. F. 1968. Examinations of large quantities of cheese for staphylococcal enterotoxin A. J. Dairy Sci. 51: 635–644.

Chapter 35

BACILLUS CEREUS

Stanley M. Harmon, J.M. Goepfert,* and Reginald W. Bennett

35.1 INTRODUCTION

Bacillus cereus is widely distributed in nature and can be isolated from a variety of foods. However, unless it is able to grow, its presence is not significant to human health. Consumption of food containing more than 10^5 viable *B. cereus* cells/g has resulted in outbreaks of food poisoning[3, 4, 11] and the establishment of specifications for various food ingredients by food manufacturers. Foods incriminated in outbreaks of *B. cereus* poisoning include boiled and fried rice, cooked pasta, cooked meats, cooked vegetables, soups, salads, puddings, and vegetable sprouts.

Two types of illness have been attributed to the consumption of food contaminated with *B. cereus*. The "diarrheal syndrome" is characterized by abdominal pain and diarrhea. It has an incubation period of 8 to 16 hr and symptoms that last 12 to 24 hr. The "emetic syndrome" is characterized by an acute attack of nausea and vomiting within 1 to 5 hr after a meal. Diarrhea is not a predominant feature in this type of illness, but it does occur in some cases. The diarrheal type of illness is caused by a protein enterotoxin with a molecular weight of approximately 38,000–50,000.[21, 22] The diarrheagenic toxin is inactivated by heating for 5 min at 56°C. The purified enterotoxin has been reported to cause increased vascular permeability in the skin of rabbits and a positive fluid accumulation response in the rabbit ligated ileal loop test.[18] This entity is antigenic and can be used to raise specific antibodies in rabbits for use in diagnostic tests. A microslide gel-diffusion assay for detection and quantitation of the diarrheagenic factor has been described[1, 2] and a commercial, reversed passive latex agglutination (RPLA) test kit may soon be available.

*Deceased

593

The symptoms experienced by patients in emetic syndrome outbreaks are apparently caused by a completely different toxin. This has not been fully purified, but the active substance has a molecular weight of <10,000, is very heat stable (withstanding 120°C for more than 1 hr), and is produced as a cell-free component in broth cultures.[22] The emetic activity of strains incriminated in emetic syndrome outbreaks has been demonstrated experimentally by monkey feeding[16] and in kittens by intravenous injection of heated culture fluids.[2] Preliminary results indicate that a tissue culture assay using HEp-2 cells may also be useful for the detection and quantitation of the emetic toxin.[9]

35.11   Taxonomic Position of *Bacillus cereus*

The work of Smith et al.[19] and Gordon et al.[5] has brought a measure of order to the diversity of strains and species in the genus *Bacillus B. cereus* is classified as a large-celled species of Group 1 (species with a cell width greater than 0.9 µm and whose spores do not appreciably swell the sporangium). Whether *B. anthracis*, *B. thuringiensis*, and *B. cereus* var. *mycoides* should be accorded species status or considered varieties of *B. cereus* is arguable. Certainly they are closely related, and, for all practical purposes, the other members of this group differ from *B. cereus* by only a single characteristic that may be lost with repeated culturing, viz., pathogenicity for animals by *B. anthracis*, production of an endotoxin crystal by *B. thuringiensis*, and rhizoid growth by *B. cereus* var. *mycoides*. Consequently, absolute separation of this group into distinct species is not possible in all instances. Nevertheless, the typical characteristics of *B. cereus* strains seem to be quite stable and the other biotypes usually can be readily differentiated from them when the variant properties are evident.[6] In this chapter, each will be considered a distinct species (except the rhizoid strains) and procedures will be described for distinguishing the other biotypes from typical *B. cereus*.

35.12   Characteristics of *B. cereus* and Culturally Similar Species

The salient features of the four biotypes of the *B. cereus* group are summarized in Table 1. Some caution is necessary in applying and interpreting tests for identification purposes, since even within a species, variability and strain heterogeneity are common. It should also be noted that some tests are more valuable or more easily performed than others and for that reason are advocated for identification of *B. cereus* in Section 35.23. The term egg yolk reaction is used to describe the turbidity developed in egg yolk or in agar containing egg yolk. The responsible agent is an extracellular substance(s) referred to in some cases as egg yolk turbidity factor, lecithinase, or phospholipase.

Although it has been established that *B. cereus* does produce a phospholipase C, there is some evidence that the turbidity developed in egg yolk may be due to a more complex series of events than the action of a single enzyme.[13]

Table 1—Characteristics of *Bacillus cereus* and Culturally Similar Species

Feature	*B. cereus*	*B. cereus* var. *mycoides*	*B. thuringiensis*	*B. anthracis*[a]
Gram stain	+	+	+	+
catalase	+	+	+	+
egg yolk reaction	±	±	±	(+)
motility	±	−	±	−
acid from mannitol	−	−	−	−
hemolysis (sheep RBC)	+	(+)	+	−
rhizoid growth	−	+	−	−
toxin crystals produced	−	−	+	−
anaerobic utilization of glucose	+	+	+	+
reduction of nitrate	±	+	+	+
VP reaction	+	+	+	+
tyrosine decomposition	+	(+)	+	(+)
resistance to lysozyme	+	+	+	+

[a]Additional tests are required to identify this species.[15]
+ = positive; ± = usually positive but occasionally may be negative; (+) = often weakly positive; − = negative.

Quantitation of *B. cereus* in a given sample is obtained with a simple surface plating technique. In the United States and in many parts of Europe, use is made of (a) the ability of *B. cereus* organisms to produce turbidity surrounding colonies growing on agar containing egg yolk, and (b) the resistance of *B. cereus* to the antibiotic polymyxin B to create a selective and differential plating medium. At least four such media have been described, and in three of them mannitol is incorporated to enhance differentiation.[8, 10, 17, 20] The PEMBA medium of Holbrook and Anderson[8] is apparently in wide use in the United Kingdom and a few other countries, but reports in the United States and Canada have been critical of its performance.[7, 20] Blood agar overlaid with polymyxin B has also been employed by some investigators, especially for the examination of stools.[12] Colonies of appropriate morphology that show the characteristic alteration of the surrounding medium are considered to be presumptive *B. cereus*. Confirmatory tests include microscopic examination of sporulating cultures and a variety of other determinations as described in Section 35.23.

35.13   Treatment of Sample

1. Collection
   The object is to obtain a representative sample of the material to be examined (Chapter 2).

2. Holding

There are no data available to suggest that refrigeration of samples will cause a reduction in the number of viable *B. cereus* (Chapter 2).

3. Homogenization and dilution

The surface plating procedure is used. See Chapter 2 for details on dilution of fluid materials, homogenization, and dilution of solid or semisolid samples. Also see Chapter 4 for preparation of surface plates.

4. Heat shocking

The spores of many, if not most, strains of *B. cereus* germinate readily on the plating media used for enumeration. In most cases, heat shocking treatment is not needed to enhance germination. Sometimes the investigator may desire only a spore count, or for other reasons may wish to use a heat-shock procedure. In such cases, the temperature-time treatment of 70°C for 15 min is recommended.

35.14 Special Equipment and Supplies

It is sometimes necessary to identify the group to which a particular *Bacillus* sp. isolate belongs. A smear made from a sporulating culture is examined to determine whether the spore has distended the sporangium. This can be determined most easily by dark-field examination of the smear under oil immersion at 600 to 1200X. Alternatively, a regular laboratory bright-field microscope equipped with a 90 to 100X oil immersion objective can be used to examine stained preparations. Cell size is also quite important; the cell width of *B. cereus* and culturally similar species usually exceeds 0.9 μm.

35.15 Special Reagents and Media (Chapter 62)

Colbecks egg yolk broth
Egg yolk emulsion 50%
Kim-Goepfert (KG) agar[10]
Mannitol yolk polymyxin (MYP) agar[17]
Polymyxin B sulfate

35.16 Additional Media and Reagents (Chapter 62)

Alpha-napthol solution
BC motility medium
Basic fuchsin stain
Creatine
40% Potassium hydroxide
L-tyrosine agar
Lipid globule stain (Burdon)
Lysozyme broth
Methanol
Modified Voges-Proskauer (VP) broth

Nitrate broth
Nitrite test reagents (method 2)
Nutrient agar
Phenol red dextrose broth
Spore stain (Ashby's)
Trypticase soy polymyxin broth
Trypticase soy sheep blood agar

35.17   Controls

It is advisable to have at least one strain each of *B. cereus*, *B. cereus* var. *mycoides*, and *B. thuringiensis* available so that the analyst can become familiar with the reactions obtained on the different media and thus learn to recognize the specific traits that differentiate them. Suitable cultures for this purpose can be obtained from the American Type Culture Collection, Rockville, MD. Prototype strains of the "emetic syndrome" and "diarrheal syndrome" types of *B. cereus* are available from the National Collection of Type Cultures, London, England, UK, as Numbers 11143 and 11145, respectively.

35.18   Precautions and Limitations

35.181   General

Several limitations are common to the plating media described above. *B. cereus* colonies on both KG and MYP agar may show various types of colonial morphology. Those most commonly seen on KG agar are round, flat, dry, with a ground glass appearance; they may be translucent or creamy white. Less commonly, but by no means rarely, colonies may be rather amorphous with highly irregular edges. In these cases the central portion of the colony is usually white, while the perimeter is translucent. The colonies on MYP agar are similar except that the colonies and surrounding medium are pink because of the failure of *B. cereus* to ferment mannitol.

Most commonly, *B. cereus* produces a very strong reaction in egg yolk agar that is characterized by a wide zone of turbidity surrounding the individual colonies after 20 to 24 hr of incubation. Quite frequently zones from individual colonies will coalesce if many *B. cereus* are present, and estimating the true number of "zone forming colonies" is difficult. This situation often develops when more *B. cereus* colonies appear on a plate. For this reason, the countable zone forming colony range on these media is reduced to 10 to 100 rather than the 30 to 300 normally used in most quantitative plating analyses. It should be noted also that these media are not 100% selective and that other organisms (mostly *Bacillus* spp.) are often encountered. Frequently, some colonies will be moist or almost mucoid in appearance, and, when viewed from the underside of the plate, will appear to have a zone of precipitate immediately beneath, though not extending beyond, the border of the colony. These colonies are not *B. cereus*, and the investigator should be concerned only with colonies having the typical morphology with, or infrequently without, a zone of turbidity surrounding them. Neither of these media is especially proficient for enumerating *B. cereus* in feces, particularly if there are fewer than 100,000 cells/g of feces. It has been suggested that blood agar overlaid with polymyxin B is a more appropriate plating medium for the isolation of *B. cereus* from fecal samples,[12] taking advantage of the characteristic colonial morphology and hemolytic activity of these organisms on blood agar. Although human and horse blood have been used successfully, our experience indicates that both rabbit and sheep blood are suitable alternatives.

35.182   Specific

1. MYP agar

This medium has been widely used in Europe and the United States for enumeration of *B. cereus*. On this medium, *B. cereus* is differentiated from most commonly occurring *Bacillus* spp. by its inability to ferment mannitol and its usual production of lecithinase. However, acid produced by colonies other than *B. cereus* often diffuses throughout the agar, making it difficult to distinguish mannitol-fermenting from nonfermenting organisms. Suspect colonies must be transferred to a fresh medium to ascertain their true character. *B. cereus* often sporulates poorly on MYP agar, and the transfer to a medium promoting sporulation is necessary before proceeding with the identification.

2. KG agar

This medium is equally sensitive and selective but is used much less frequently than MYP agar. KG agar was formulated to promote free spore formation within the 20- to 24-hr incubation period. This feature allows the direct confirmation of zone-forming organisms as Group 1 bacilli by means of microscopic examination, and the immediate differentiation of *B. cereus* from *B. thuringiensis* by visualization of the endotoxin crystal in sporulated cells of the latter organism. An additional advantage to KG agar is that Group 2 bacilli, such as *B. polymyxa*, which produce lecithinase, are unable to form lecithinase under the rather nutritionally poor conditions imposed by KG agar. Because of their similarity in composition and operating principles, the PEMBA medium of Holbrook and Anderson[8] or PEMPA medium of Szabo et al.[20] may be substituted for KG agar.

35.2   PROCEDURE

35.21   Sample Collection, Preparation, and Dilution (Chapter 2)

Inoculate duplicate predried MYP or KG agar plates with suitable dilutions (usually 10^{-1} to 10^{-6}) by spreading 0.1 ml of food homogenate over the entire plate surface with a bent glass rod or "hockey stick." Use a separate inoculating rod sterilized by autoclaving for each dilution. After spreading, allow the inoculum to dry and incubate the plates at 30°C to 32°C for 20 to 24 hr.

After incubation, examine the plates for typical colonies, which are usually surrounded by a precipitate caused by lecithinase activity. Colonies on MYP agar will be pink to violet, indicating that mannitol is not fermented. The number of such colonies multiplied by the reciprocal of the dilution that the countable plate represents is the presumptive *B. cereus* count. Remember that the dilution factor is tenfold higher than the sample dilution since only 0.1 ml was plated.

35.22 Most Probable Number Technique

A most probable number (MPN) technique is a suitable alternative to the direct plate count for examining foods that are expected to contain fewer than 1000 *B. cereus* per gram.[14] In this method, 3 tubes each of trypticase soy polymyxin broth are inoculated with 1 ml of the 1:10, 1:100, and 1:1000 dilutions of food homogenate. Incubate the tubes at 30°C for 48 hr and examine them for dense growth typical of *B. cereus*. Streak presumptive positive tubes on MYP agar, and select characteristic colonies for confirmation as *B. cereus*. The confirmed *B. cereus* count is determined using the appropriate MPN table (Chapter 6) on the basis of the number of tubes at each dilution in which *B. cereus* was detected.

35.23 Confirmatory Tests

Confirmatory tests are necessary to establish the identity of presumptive colonies as *B. cereus*. Two groups of tests are described which may be used, depending on the extent of identification desired. The first group of tests (Section 35.232) is designed to differentiate the typically reacting strains of *B. cereus* from other members of the *B. cereus* group when a clear-cut result has been obtained on MYP or KG agar. Since the results obtained on the plating media with members of the *B. cereus* group are so characteristic, other *Bacillus* species are unlikely to be mistaken for them. Therefore, the rapid confirmatory test of Holbrook and Anderson[8] can be substituted for the biochemical tests described in Section 35.233 unless the isolates are atypical or must be more definitely identified for regulatory purposes.

35.231 Rapid confirmatory test

Colonies from MYP agar to be tested should be subcultured on nutrient agar slants and incubated at 30°C for 24 hr; those from KG agar may be tested directly. The objectives are to determine vegetative cell, sporangium, and spore morphology and to demonstrate the presence of lipid globules within the vegetative cell. A staining procedure that combines the spore stain of Ashby and the intracellular lipid stain of Burdon is used as an aid in these determinations. Smears are made from the center of 1-day-old colonies or from the edge of 2-day-old colonies, air dried, and heat fixed with minimal flaming. The slide is placed over boiling water and flooded with 5% malachite green (heating slides at least twice at 1-min intervals with a bunsen burner until steam is seen is an acceptable alternative). After 2 min, the slide is washed, blotted dry, and stained with 0.3% wt/vol Sudan black B in 70% ethanol for 20 min. The stain is poured off and the slide blotted dry and washed with reagent grade xylene for 5 to 10 sec. The slide is blotted immediately and counterstained for 20 sec with 0.5% wt/vol of safranin. The stained slides are examined microscopically under oil immersion for the presence of lipid globules within the cytoplasm (stained dark blue) and central-to-subterminal spores that do not obviously swell the sporangium. Spores are usually pale to mid-green, contrasting with the red vegetative cells. The presence of intracellular lipid globules and typical spores is a good indication that isolates from MYP or KG agar are members of the *B. cereus* group. These properties, however, are not unique to *B. cereus*; therefore, the rapid confirmatory test must always be used in conjunction with more specific tests described below before an identification can be made.

35.232   Differentiating members of the *B. cereus* group

1. Motility tests. Semisolid BC motility medium or direct microscopic examination may be used to determine motility. BC motility medium is inoculated by stabbing down the center with a 3 mm loopful of culture and incubating for 18 to 24 hr at 30°C. Motile strains produce diffuse growth out into the medium away from the stab. Nonmotile strains (except *B. cereus* var. *mycoides*) grow only in and along the stab. Rhizoid strains of *B. cereus* var. *mycoides* usually produce characteristic fuzzy growth in semisolid media because of the expansion of the filamentous growth, but they are not motile by means of flagella. Doubtful results should be confirmed by the alternative microscopic motility test. This test is performed by adding 0.2 ml of sterile distilled water to a nutrient agar slant, which is then inoculated with a 3 mm loopful of culture. After incubation at 30°C for 6 to 8 hr, a loopful of liquid culture from the base of the slant is suspended in a drop of water on a clean slide, covered with a cover slip, and examined immediately for motility. *B. cereus* and *B. thuringiensis* are usually actively motile, whereas *B. anthracis* and the typically rhizoid strains of *B. cereus* var. *mycoides* are nonmotile.

2. Rhizoid growth. To test for rhizoid growth, a predried nutrient agar plate is inoculated near the center with a 2 mm loopful of culture and incubated for 24 to 48 hr at 30°C. If the culture is rhizoid, root or hairlike structures will develop up to several centimeters from the point of inoculation. This property is characteristic only of strains that are classified as *B. cereus* var. *mycoides*.

3. Hemolytic activity. To test for hemolytic activity, the bottom of a standard trypticase soy sheep blood agar plate is marked into six or eight equal segments. Each segment is labeled and inoculated near its center by gently touching the agar surface with a 2 mm loopful of culture. The plate is then incubated at 30° to 32°C for 24 hr and checked for hemolytic activity as indicated by a zone of complete hemolysis surrounding the growth. *B. cereus* is usually strongly hemolytic, whereas *B. thuringiensis* and *B. cereus* var. *mycoides* are often weakly hemolytic, or produce hemolysis only under the growth. *B. anthracis* is usually nonhemolytic. Caution: Nonmotile, nonhemolytic cultures could be *B. anthracis* and should be handled with special care.

4. Detection of toxin crystals. The endotoxin crystals of *B. thuringiensis* may be detected by phase-contrast microscopy, but are probably most conveniently detected by staining as follows: A nutrient agar slant is inoculated with a loopful of culture, incubated at 30°C for 24 hr, and then held at room temperature for 2 or 3 days to permit sporangiolysis. A smear is made on a clean slide, air dried, and lightly heat fixed. The smear is further fixed by flooding the slide with methanol. After 30 sec, the methanol is poured off and the slide is dried thoroughly by passing it through a flame. The smear is stained by flooding the slide with 0.5% aqueous basic fuchsin or TB carbol fuchsin ZN and gently heating the slide from below until steam is seen. After 1 or 2 min, the slide is heated again until steam is seen, held for 30 sec, and the stain is poured off. The slide is rinsed thoroughly in tap water, dried without blotting, and examined under oil immersion with a microscope for the presence of free spores and darkly stained tetragonal toxin crystals. Free toxin crystals are usually abundant within 3 days but will not be detectable by staining until the sporangia have lysed. *B. thuringiensis* produces endotoxin crystals that usually can be detected by staining. Other members of the *B. cereus* group do not produce such crystals.

5. Interpreting results. On the basis of test results, those isolates that are actively motile, strongly hemolytic, and do not produce rhizoid growth or endotoxin crystals should be tentatively identified as *B. cereus*. Nonmotile or weakly hemolytic strains of *B. cereus* may occasionally be encountered. These strains can be differentiated from *B. anthracis* by their resistance to penicillin and gamma bacteriophage.[15] Noncrystalliferous variants of *B. thuringiensis* and nonrhizoid strains derived from *B. cereus* var. *mycoides* cannot be differentiated from *B. cereus* by the tests described. When implicated in food poisoning, such isolates should be tested for enterotoxigenicity by biological or serological assays.[1, 2, 9, 22]

35.233 Biochemical tests

In some instances, identification of isolates with a greater degree of certainty may be desired. The following tests are recommended because they confirm the most salient characteristics of the *B. cereus* group and virtually eliminate the possibility of confusing strains of this group with any other *Bacillus* species.

1. Reactions on MYP agar. This test can usually be omitted if the isolates were picked from MYP agar and the reactions of all isolates were typical. However, the test should be included with isolates from KG agar to test for mannitol fermentation. The bottom of each plate should be marked into 6 or 8 equal segments. Each segment is labeled and inoculated near its center by touching the agar with a 2 mm loopful of culture. The plate is incubated at 30°C to 35°C for 24 hr and checked for lecithinase production as indicated by a zone of precipitate surrounding growth. Mannitol is not fermented if the growth and surrounding medium are pink. *B. cereus* and other members of the *B. cereus* group usually produce lecithinase but do not ferment mannitol.

2. Anaerobic glucose fermentation. The ability of isolates to metabolize glucose anaerobically is determined by inoculating phenol red dextrose broth with a loopful of culture and incubating the tube in an anaerobic jar at 35°C for 24 hr. A color change from red to yellow indicates that acid was produced. Acid is produced from glucose anaerobically by *B. cereus* and other members of the *B. cereus* group.

3. Nitrate reduction. Nitrates are usually reduced to nitrite by *B. cereus* and other members of the *B. cereus* group. Nitrate broth is inoculated and incubated at 35°C for 24 hr. Nitrite is detected by adding 0.25 ml each of sulfanilic acid and alpha-naphthol solutions. An orange color that develops within 10 min indicates the presence of nitrite.

4. VP test. Acetylmethylcarbinol is produced from glucose by members of the *B. cereus* group. Modified VP medium is inoculated and incubated at 35°C for 48 hr. The presence of acetylmethylcarbinol is determined by adding 0.2 ml of 40% potassium hydroxide and 0.6 ml of 5% alcoholic alpha-naphthol solution to 1 ml of culture in a test tube. Addition of a few crystals of creatine speeds the positive reaction, development of a purple color within 15 min.

5. Tyrosine decomposition. The ability of *B. cereus* and culturally similar species to decompose tyrosine is determined by inoculating a slant of nutrient agar containing 0.5% tyrosine and incubating for 48 to 72 hr at 35°C. Decomposition of tyrosine as indicated by clearing of the medium immediately under the growth, is caused by dissoluton of tyrosine crystals. This clearing progresses to a depth of 3 or 4 mm after 3 days of incubation. *B. cereus* and other members of the *B. cereus* group (except *B. anthracis*) readily decompose tyrosine.

6. Lysozyme resistance. The ability of isolates to grow in the presence of lysozyme is determined by inoculating nutrient broth containing a final concentration of 0.001% lysozyme. Growth that develops during 48 hr of incubation at 35°C indicates that the organism is resistant to lysozyme. *B. cereus* as well as other members of the *B. cereus* group are resistant to lysozyme.

35.3   INTERPRETATION OF DATA

Colonies from MYP and KG agar that meet the criteria defined in Section 35.232 should be provisionally identified as *B. cereus*. Isolates that also fulfill all criteria listed in Section 35.233 may be definitively identified as *B. cereus* (except as noted in Section 35.232.5), e.g., large gram-positive bacilli that produce lecithinase, are negative for mannitol fermentation on MYP agar, grow and produce acid from glucose anaerobically, reduce nitrate to nitrite (a few strains are negative), produce acetylmethylcarbinol, decompose L-tyrosine, grow in the presence of 0.001% lysozyme, exhibit motility, are hemolytic, and do not produce endotoxin crystals or rhizoid growth.

The plate count of such colonies, or the most probable number, times the dilution factor is the confirmed *B. cereus* count.

35.4   REFERENCES

1. Bennett, R. W. 1985. Serological and biological activities of *Bacillus cereus* diarrheal toxin. Seminar on *Bacillus cereus* enterotoxins: current concepts and developments. Ann. Meet. Am. Soc. Microbiol., Las Vegas, Nev., March 30, 1985.
2. Bennett, R. W. and Harmon, S. M. 1988. *Bacillus cereus* food poisoning. In "Laboratory Diagnosis of Infectious Diseases: Principles and Practices," ed. A. Balows, W. J. Hausler, Jr., and E. Lennette. p. 830. Springer-Verlag, New York, N.Y.
3. Gilbert, R. J. 1979. *Bacillus cereus* gastroenteritis. In "Food-borne Infections and Intoxications," 2nd ed., eds. H. Riemann and F. L. Bryan. p. 495. Academic Press, New York, N.Y.
4. Goepfert, J. M., Spira, W. M., and Kim, H. U. 1972. *Bacillus cereus*: Food poisoning organism. A review. J. Milk Food Technol. 35: 213.
5. Gordon, R. E., Haynes, W. C., and Hor-Nay Pang, C. 1973. The genus *Bacillus*. USDA Agriculture Handbook, No. 427, Washington, D.C.
6. Harmon, S. M. 1982. New method for differentiating members of the *Bacillus cereus* group. J. Assoc. Off. Anal. Chem. 65: 1133.
7. Harmon, S. M., Kautter, D. A., and McClure, F. D. 1984. Comparison of selective plating media for enumeration of *Bacillus cereus* in foods. J. Food Prot. 47: 65.
8. Holbrook, R. and Anderson, J. M. 1980. An improved selective diagnostic medium for the isolation and enumeration of *Bacillus cereus* in foods. Can. J. Microbiol. 26: 753.
9. Hughes, S., Bartholomew, B., Hardy, J. C., and Kramer, J. M. Potential application of a HEP-2 cell assay in the investigation of *Bacillus cereus* emetic-syndrome food poisoning. FEMS Microbiol. Lett. In press.
10. Kim, H. U. and Goepfert, J. M. 1971. Enumeration and identification of *Bacillus cereus* in foods. I. 24-hour presumptive test medium. Appl. Microbiol. 22: 581.
11. Kramer, J. M. and Gilbert, R. J. 1989. *Bacillus cereus* and other *Bacillus* species. In "Food-borne Bacterial Pathogens," ed. M. Doyle, p. 21. Marcel Dekker, New York, N.Y.
12. Kramer, J. M., Turnbull, P. C. B., Munshi, G., and Gilbert, R. J. 1982. Identification and characterization of *Bacillus cereus* and other *Bacillus* species associated with food poisoning. In "Isolation and Identification Methods for Food Poisoning Organisms," ed. J. E. L. Corry, F. Roberts, and F. A. Skinner, p. 261. Soc. Appl. Bacteriol. Tech. Ser. No. 17, Academic Press, London and New York.
13. Kushner, D. J. 1957. An evaluation of the egg yolk reaction as a test for lecithinase activity. J. Bacteriol. 73: 297.
14. Lancette, G. A. and Harmon, S. M. 1980. Enumeration and confirmation of *Bacillus cereus* in foods; collaborative study. J. Assoc. Off. Anal. Chem. 63: 581.

15. Leise, J. A., Carter, C. H., Friedlander, H., and Freed, S. N. 1959. Criteria for identification of *Bacillus anthracis*. J. Bacteriol. 77: 655.

16. Melling, J., Capel, B. J., Turnbull, P. C. B., and Gilbert, R. J. 1976. Identification of a novel enterotoxigenic activity associated with *Bacillus cereus*. J. Clin. Pathol. 29: 938.

17. Mossel, D. A. A., Koopman, M. J., and Jongerius, E. 1967. Enumeration of *Bacillus cereus* in foods. Appl. Microbiol. 15: 650.

18. Shinagawa, K. 1986. Personal Communication. Dept. of Veterinary Medicine, Iwate University, Morioka, 020, Japan.

19. Smith, N. R., Gordon, R. E., and Clark, F. E. 1952. Aerobic sporeforming bacteria. USDA Monograph No. 16, Washington, D.C.

20. Szabo, R. A., Todd, E. C. D., and Rayman, M. K. 1984. Twenty-four hour isolation of *Bacillus cereus* in foods. J. Food Prot. 47: 856.

21. Thompson, N. E., Ketterhagen, M. J., Bergdol, M. S., and Shantz, E. J., 1984. Isolation and some properties of an enterotoxin produced by *Bacillus cereus*. Infect. Immun. 43: 887.

22. Turnbull, P. C. B. 1986. *Bacillus cereus* toxins. In "Pharmacology of Bacterial Toxins," eds. F. Dorner and J. Drews, p. 397. Pergamon Press, Oxford, England.

Chapter 36

CLOSTRIDIUM BOTULINUM AND ITS TOXINS

Donald A. Kautter, Haim M. Solomon, Donald E. Lake,
Dane T. Bernard, and Daniel C. Mills

36.1 INTRODUCTION

Clostridium botulinum is a species of anaerobic, sporeforming, rod-shaped bacteria that produces a protein with a characteristic neurotoxicity. Severe food poisoning, botulism, results from the consumption of botulinal toxin (botulin) produced in food in which this organism has grown.

Antigenic types of *C. botulinum* are identified on the basis that their toxins are neutralized completely by the homologous type of antitoxin only, and that cross-neutralization by heterologous antitoxin types is absent or minimal. The seven recognized types are designated A, B, C, D, E, F, and G. Five of these apparently produce only one type of toxin, but all are given type designations corresponding to their toxin production. Types C and D cross-react with antisera to each other because they each produce more than one toxin and have at least one common toxic component. Type C produces predominantly C1 toxin with lesser amounts of C2 or only C2, and type D produces predominantly type D toxin along with smaller amounts of C2 toxin. The production of more than one type of toxin may be a more common phenomenon than previously realized. There is a slight reciprocal cross-neutralization of types E and F, and recently one strain of *C. botulinum* has been shown to produce a mixture consisting mostly of type A toxin and a small amount of type F toxin.

Botulism as a type of food poisoning in humans is rare, but case fatality is high. In the United States, 908 outbreaks have been recorded from 1899 through 1986. These have involved 2,210 cases and caused 1,030 deaths. Of outbreaks in which the toxin type was determined, 335 were due to type A, 94 to type B, 63 to type E, and 3 to type F[15] plus CDC reports presented at the Annual Meetings of the Interagency Botulism Research Coordinating Committee (IBRCC). The implicated foods of two outbreaks contained both A and B toxins. The limited number of reports that consider C or D toxin to be the causative agent of human botulism have not received general acceptance. On the other hand, all except types F and G, about which little is known, are important causes of animal botulism. Human botulism also may be caused by wounds infected with *C. botulinum* in which the organism grows and elaborates its toxin, but this is a rare occurrence. Gastrointestinal symptoms are usually absent in such cases.

Infant botulism, usually seen in infants 6 weeks to 6 months of age, was first recognized as a distinct clinical entity in 1976. This form of botulism results from growth and neurotoxin production by *C. botulinum* within the intestinal tract of infants rather than from ingestion of preformed toxin. It is usually caused by *C. botulinum* types A or B, but a few cases have resulted from other toxin types. Infant botulism has been diagnosed in most states of the United States and in every populated continent except Africa. In 1987, when the number of infant botulism cases diagnosed worldwide since its recognition reached a total of approximately 700, 90 infant botulism cases were reported in the United States, with 43 from California, more than any other state. This high number is probably due in part to greater surveillance and recognition in the medical and laboratory communities there.[1, 4-6, 11, 15]

Constipation almost always occurs in infant botulism and usually precedes characteristic signs of neuromuscular paralysis by a few days or weeks. There is a broad range of severity of illness. Some infants show only mild weakness, lethargy, and reduced feeding and do not require hospitalization. Many have shown more severe symptoms, such as weakened suck, swallowing, and cry; generalized muscle weakness; and diminished gag reflex with a pooling of oral secretions. Generalized muscle weakness and loss of head control in some infants reaches such a degree of severity that the patient appears "floppy." In some hospitalized cases, respiratory arrest has occurred, but most were successfully resuscitated, and with intensive supportive care have ultimately recovered. As a result, case-fatality rate for this form of botulism is low (2%). The routine therapy for infant botulism until recovery occurs is intensive supportive care, which usually requires at least several weeks of hospitalization.[1]

Definitive diagnosis of infant botulism depends on demonstration of toxin and/or organisms in the feces. *C. botulinum* has been recovered from patients' feces for as long as 5 months after onset of illness, and toxin for as long as 4 months. Although testing of serum is very useful for establishing the diagnosis of botulism in adults, it is of limited value in infants. In a recently reported study, toxin was found in the serum of only 9 of 67 (13%) culture-positive infant botulism patients.[5]

Honey is a known source of *C. botulinum* spores implicated in some cases of infant botulism. In studies of honey, up to 13% of the test samples contained low numbers of *C. botulinum* spores.[6] For this reason the U.S. Food and Drug Administration, the U.S. Centers for Disease Control, and the American Academy of Pediatrics recommend that honey not be fed to infants under the age of 1 year.

The organism *C. botulinum* is distributed widely in soils and in sediments of oceans and lakes, so that foods may be contaminated with it from many possible sources. The finding of type E in aquatic environments by many investigators correlates with the tracing of most cases of type E botulism to contaminated fish or other seafoods in which the organism has grown. Types A and B are most commonly encountered terrestrially, and the important vehicles of botulism caused by these two types are foods liable to be contaminated with soils. In the United States these foods have been primarily home-canned vegetables, but in Europe meat products also have been important vehicles.

C. botulinum cultures fall into three distinct groups by properties other than toxin types, with each group composed only of strains having similar cultural and physiological characteristics. Organisms of types C and D are nonproteolytic, being unable to digest coagulated egg white or meat, and have a common metabolic pattern that sets them apart from all the others. Cultures of the other types fall into two additional groups distinct from one another on the basis of proteolysis. All type A strains and some B and F strains are proteolytic, whereas all type E strains and the remaining type B and F strains are nonproteolytic. Type G shows slow proteolytic activity.

Optimum temperature for growth and toxin production of the proteolytics is close to 35°C, while that for the nonproteolytics is approximately 26° to 28°C. Nonproteolytic types B, E, and F can produce toxin at refrigeration temperature (3° to 4°C). Toxins of the nonproteolytics do not manifest maximum potential toxicity until they are activated with trypsin; toxins of the proteolytics generally occur in fully, or close to fully, activated form. These and other differences are important in epidemiological and laboratory considerations of botulism outbreaks.

Measures to prevent botulism include reduction of the microbial contamination level, acidification, reduction of moisture level, and destruction of all *C. botulinum* spores in the food. Heat is the most common method of destruction; properly processed canned foods do not contain viable *C. botulinum*. The greater incidence of botulism from home-canned foods than from commercially canned foods undoubtedly reflects the commercial canners' greater awareness and better control of the heating required.

A food may contain viable *C. botulinum* spores and still not be able to cause botulism. As long as the organisms do not grow, toxin is not synthesized (see Chapter 60). Many foods satisfy the nutritional requirements of *C. botulinum*, but not all provide the necessary anaerobic conditions. Many canned foods and many meat and fish products meet both nutritional and anaerobic requirements. However, growth in otherwise suitable foods is prevented if the product, naturally or by design, is acidic, has low water activity, a high sodium chloride concentration, an inhibitory sodium nitrite concentration, or two or more of these in combination. Unless the temperature is very precisely controlled and kept below 3°C, refrigeration will not prevent growth and toxin formation by nonproteolytic strains. Moreover, the usual vehicles of botulism are foods processed to prevent spoilage that are not usually refrigerated. Botulinal toxin is heat-labile; therefore, botulism can be prevented by heating all processed foods thoroughly, e.g., boiling for 10 min before serving.[3, 7-10, 13, 14]

36.2 TREATMENT OF SPECIMENS

Clinical diagnosis of botulism is most effectively confirmed in the laboratory by demonstrating botulinal toxin in the blood, feces, or vomitus of the patient. Specimens must be collected before the patient is treated with botulinal antitoxin. In foodborne botulism, identifying the causative food as soon as possible is important to prevent further cases.

36.21 Foods[3, 9, 15, 16]

Foods should be refrigerated until tested, except for unopened canned foods, which, unless badly swollen and in danger of bursting, need not be refrigerated.

Before testing, record identifying data such as product, manufacturer or home canner, source, type of container and size, labeling, manufacturer's batch, lot, or production code, and condition of container.

Clean and mark container with laboratory identification, disinfect, and open aseptically for sampling. Carefully avoid aerosols (see Section 36.61).

Check for ingredients which, by their presence or concentration in the product, could be lethal for mice by intraperitoneal route of administration; for example, a high salt concentration (as in anchovies).

36.22 Clinical Specimens[2, 3, 4, 15]

All clinical specimens should be collected as soon as botulism is suspected and before botulinal antitoxin is administered.

1. Serum

    Collect enough blood (15 to 20 ml) to provide at least 10 ml of serum for toxin neutralization tests. Allow blood to clot; centrifuge, and remove serum to a sterile vial or test tube with a leakproof cap. Examine immediately or refrigerate at 4°C until tested. Examination of posttreatment blood serum is also helpful to evaluate antitoxin therapy.

2. Feces

    Collect 50 g of the patient's feces (1 to 2 g from infants) in a sterile,

unbreakable, leakproof container. Preferably use a screwcap widemouth plastic bottle. Seal caps with waterproof tape. Cardboard containers are not satisfactory. Refrigerate specimens at 4°C until examined. A "soap-suds" enema should not be given before the feces are collected, since the soap may inactivate the toxin. If a passed stool is not available, the physician should be consulted to obtain a specimen by very carefully using a sterile water enema.
3. Miscellaneous clinical materials

Specimens of materials such as vomitus, gastric washings, cerebro-spinal fluid, or tissues obtained at autopsy should be collected in sterile, leakproof containers and refrigerated at 4°C.

36.3 SPECIAL EQUIPMENT AND SUPPLIES

36.31 Culture and Isolation of *C. botulinum*

Anaerobic jars, i.e., Gaspak or Case (nitrogen replacement)
Bunsen burner, micro-incinerator or electric incinerator
Clean dry towels
Culture tube racks
Mechanical pipetting device (never pipette by mouth)
Microscope (phase-contrast or bright-field)
Microscope slides
Refrigerator
Sterile can opener (bacti-disc or puncture type)
Sterile culture tubes (at least a few should have screwcaps)
Sterile forceps
Sterile mortar and pestle
Sterile 100 mm petri dishes
Sterile pipettes
Sterile sample jars
35°C incubator
Transfer loops
26°C incubator

36.32 Toxin Identification and Assay

(Sterility of equipment is desirable, but not absolutely necessary except as noted.)

Centrifuge tubes (some sterile for separation of patient's serum from clot)
Mice (about 15 to 20 g)
Mortar and pestle
Mouse cages, feed, etc.
1 ml or 2.5 ml inoculating syringes with 25 gauge 5/8-inch needles for inoc-ulation of mice

Refrigerated high-speed centrifuge
Sterile 25 to 50 ml syringes with 18 to 20 gauge 1 1/2-inch needles to obtain blood from patients
Sterile vials for storage of serum
37°C waterbath
Trypsin (Difco 1:250)

36.4   MEDIA AND REAGENTS

36.41   Culture and Isolation Procedures

Absolute ethanol
Alcoholic solution of iodine (or other suitable disinfectant)
Cooked meat medium (CMM) (liver or beef heart)
Gram stain, crystal violet, or methylene blue solutions
Liver, veal, egg yolk agar or anaerobic egg yolk agar
Sterile culture media (Chapter 62)
Sterile gel phosphate buffer, pH 6.2
Trypticase-peptone-glucose-yeast (TPGY) extract or with trypsin (TPGYT) broth. Use TPGYT as an alternative only when the organism involved is strongly suspected to be a nonproteolytic strain of types B, E, or F.

36.42   Toxin Identification and Assay

Gel phosphate buffer, pH 6.2
Monovalent antitoxins, types A through F (may be obtained from the Centers for Disease Control, Atlanta Ga. 30333)
Physiological saline
Trypsin solution (prepared from Difco 1:250 trypsin):
1 N hydrochloric acid.
1 N sodium hydroxide

36.5   PRECAUTIONS AND LIMITATIONS OF METHODS

Botulinal toxin is heat-labile. Store test samples and cultures under refrigeration. In addition, the pH of the toxic material must be controlled to keep it slightly acidic since botulinal toxin is less stable at alkaline pH.

When performing toxicity tests in mice, take care to distinguish between the symptoms of botulism and other causes of death, such as high concentrations of salt, acid, protein degradation products, or other toxic substances that may be present in the food being tested.

Be careful to avoid the creation of aerosols.

Never pipette by mouth. Use one of several mechanical pipetting devices available for this purpose.

Autoclave all glassware and utensils coming in contact with contaminated or potentially contaminated samples before handling them.

Botulinal toxins are among the most lethal proteins known; the specific toxicity of type A neurotoxin is 1×10^8 mouse LD_{50}/mg protein. Symptoms of botulism (paralysis of throat, eyes, respiratory musculature, etc.) are the result of toxin inhibiting the release of the acetylcholine neurotransmitter at peripheral synapses. Laboratory personnel who expect to be exposed to the toxin on a routine basis should be immunized with toxoid (available from the Centers for Disease Control, Atlanta, Ga).

36.6   PROCEDURE FOR IDENTIFYING VIABLE *C. BOTULINUM*[3, 9, 15, 16]

36.61   Opening Canned Foods

Sanitize the uncoded end of the can with an effective disinfectant. Allow a contact time of a few min, then remove the disinfectant and wipe the sanitized area with a sterile, dry towel. If the can is swollen, position the can so that the side seam is away from the analyst. A container with buckled ends should be chilled before opening and flamed with extreme caution to avoid bursting the can. Flame-sterilize the sanitized can end with a Bunsen burner by directing the flame down onto the can until the visible moisture film evaporates. Avoid excessive flaming, indicated by scorching and blackening of the inside enamel coating. Remove a disc of metal from the center area of the flamed end with a flame-sterilized or autoclaved bacti-disc cutter. Remove a disc about 5 cm in diameter, except from 202 diameter cans, where a 3-cm disc is satisfactory (see Chapter 60).

36.62   Solid Foods

Transfer foods with little or no free liquid aseptically to a sterile mortar. Add an equal amount of gel phosphate buffer solution and grind with a sterile pestle in preparation for inoculation. Alternatively, small pieces of the product may be inoculated directly into the enrichment broth using sterile forceps, or placed in a stomacher bag and pummeled with an equal volume of gel phosphate buffer.

36.63   Liquid Foods

Inoculate liquid foods directly into the culture media, using sterile pipettes.

36.64   Reserve Test Sample

After culturing, aseptically remove a reserve portion of the test sample to a sterile jar for later tests.

36.65. Examining a Product for Appearance and Odor

Note any evidence of decomposition, but do not taste the product under any circumstance. Record observations.

36.66   Preparation of Enrichment Cultures

1. Preparation of broth media. Before inoculation, unless the enrichment media are freshly prepared, heat broth media in flowing steam or boiling water for 15 min. After heating, cool rapidly to room temperature in cold water without agitation.
2. Inoculation of enrichment media. Inoculate 1 to 2 g of solid or 1 to 2 ml of liquid food per 15 ml of enrichment broth. Inoculate 2 tubes of CMM, either beef heart or chopped liver broth, and 2 tubes of TPGY broth. Introduce the inoculum slowly below the surface of the broth.
3. Incubation. Incubate the inoculated CMM at 35°C and the TPGY enrichment broth at 26° to 28°C.
4. Examination of cultures. After 7 days of incubation, examine each culture for turbidity, the production of gas, and the digestion of the meat particles. Note the odor. Examine the culture microscopically, by a wet mount preparation under high-power, phase-contrast microscopy, or a stained smear (gram stain, crystal violet, or methylene blue) with bright field illumination. Observe the morphology of the organisms in the preparation and note the existence of clostridial cells, the occurrence and relative extent of sporulation, and the location of spores within the cells. At this time, test each culture for toxin, and, if it is demonstrated, determine the toxin type according to the procedure described in Sections 36.72 and 36.73. The highest concentration of botulinal toxin is usually present after the period of active growth. In general, 7 days of incubation are necessary to reach maximal toxin levels. An enrichment culture showing no growth at 7 days should be incubated an additional 10 days to permit possible delayed germination of spores of *C. botulinum* before the culture is discarded.

   For pure culture isolation, gently mix and transfer 1 to 2 ml of the culture at peak sporulation to a sterile screwcap tube and refrigerate.

36.67   Isolation of Pure Cultures

1. Alcohol treatment. The possibility of isolating *C. botulinum* in pure culture from a mixed flora in the enrichment culture is greatly improved if spores are present. To 1 to 2 ml of a culture showing some sporulated cells (or the retained test sample), add an equal volume of filter-sterilized absolute ethanol in a sterile screwcap tube. Mix the alcohol with the culture, and incubate the mixure at room temperature for fig. hour. Streak plates of the recovery medium as described in Section 36.67.3.
2. Heat treatment. An alternative procedure to the alcohol method is to heat 1 to 2 ml of the enrichment culture sufficiently to destroy the

vegetative cells but not the spores of *C. botulinum* present. For a non-proteolytic type, however, do not use heat; for a proteolytic type, heat at 80°C for 10 to 15 min.

3. Plating. Streak the alcohol- or heat-treated culture on petri dishes containing either liver, veal, egg yolk agar, or anaerobic egg yolk agar (Chapter 62) in order to obtain well-separated colonies. Dilution of the culture may be necessary before plating in order to select well-isolated colonies. To prevent spreading of the colonies, the plates must be well dried. Alternatively, untreated enrichment cultures or stool can be streaked directly to isolate *C. botulinum* on one of the selective differential plating media recently developed.[11, 12]

4. Incubation. Incubate the streaked plates anaerobically at 35°C for about 48 hr. A Case Anaerobic Jar or the Gaspak system is adequate to obtain anaerobiosis. Other anaerobic systems also can be used.

5. Selection of typical colonies. After anaerobic incubation, select about 10 well-separated and typical colonies per plate. Colonies of *C. botulinum* may be raised or flat, smooth or rough; they commonly show spreading and have an irregular edge. On egg yolk medium the colonies usually exhibit a surface irridescence when examined by oblique light. This luster zone is due to lipase activity and is often referred to as a pearly layer; it usually extends beyond and follows the irregular contour of the colony. Besides the pearly layer, colonies of *C. botulinum* types C, D, and E are ordinarily surrounded by a zone (2 to 4 mm) of a yellow precipitate caused by lecithinase activity. Colonies of types A and B generally show a smaller zone of precipitation. However, considerable difficulty in picking toxin-producing colonies may be experienced since certain other members of the genus *Clostridium*, which do not elaborate toxin, produce colonies with characteristics similar to those of *C. botulinum*.

Inoculate each colony into a tube of sterile broth by means of a sterile transfer loop. For nonproteolytic *C. botulinum*, inoculate TPGY or TPGYT broth; for the proteolytic types, inoculate CMM. Incubate the inoculated tubes for 7 days as previously described; then test for toxin as described in Section 36.72. If toxin is demonstrated, determine the toxin type (Section 36.73). Restreak the toxin-producing culture in duplicate on egg yolk agar medium. Incubate one of the plates anaerobically and the other aerobically at 35°C. If colonies typical of *C. botulinum* only are found after 48 hr on the plate incubated anaerobically, and no growth is found on the plate incubated aerobically, the culture may be pure. Failure to isolate *C. botulinum* from at least one of the colonies selected means that its prevalence among the mixed flora in the enrichment culture is probably low. Sometimes the numbers can be increased enough to permit isolation by repeated serial transfer through additional enrichment steps.

6. Storage. Store the pure culture in the sporulated state under refrigeration.

36.7   IDENTIFYING BOTULINAL TOXIN IN FOODS[3, 9, 15, 16]

36.71   Preparing Food

After sampling for viable *C. botulinum*, remove a portion of the food for toxicity testing. Store the remainder in a refrigerator. Centrifuge test samples containing suspended solids in the cold and use the supernatant fluid for the toxin assay. Test liquid foods directly.

Extract solid food with an equal volume of gel phosphate buffer. Macerate the food and buffer with a prechilled mortar and pestle or mix in a stomacher. Centrifuge to remove the solids. Wash out emptied containers suspected of having contained toxic foods with a few ml of gel phosphate buffer. Do not use too much liquid as the toxin may be diluted below the determination level.

36.72   Toxicity Determinations in Foods or Culture

Toxins of nonproteolytic types, if present in the food, may need trypsin activation to be determined. Therefore, treat a portion of the food supernatant fluid, liquid food, TPGY, or cooked meat culture with trypsin before testing for toxin. Do not treat TPGYT cultures with trypsin. At the same time, test another portion of supernatant fluid extract, TPGY, or cooked meat culture, for toxin without trypsin treatment, since the fully active toxin of a proteolytic strain, if present, may be degraded by trypsin. The same is true if TPGYT containing the fully activated toxin of a nonproteolytic strain is further trypsinized.

To trypsinize, adjust a portion of the supernatant fluid to pH 6.2 with 1N sodium hydroxide or HCl. To 1.8 ml of each supernatant fluid, add 0.2 ml of an aqueous trypsin solution and incubate at 37°C for 1 hr with occasional gentle agitation. Prepare trypsin solution by placing 1 g of 1:250 trypsin (Difco) in a clean culture tube and adding 10 ml of sterile distilled water. Agitate from time to time and keep at room temperature until as much of the trypsin as possible has been dissolved. Check the pH of the trypsin solution and adjust to pH 6.0, if necessary.

Dilute a portion of the untreated fluid or culture 1:2, 1:10, and 1:100 in gel phosphate buffer. Make the same dilutions of each trypsinized test sample fluid or culture. Inject separate pairs of mice intraperitoneally (IP) with 0.5 ml of the undiluted fluid and with 0.5 ml of each dilution, using a 1.0 ml or 2.5 ml syringe with a 25 gauge 5/8-inch needle. Repeat this for the trypsinized test samples. Heat 1.5 ml of the untreated supernatant fluid or culture at 100°C for 10 min, cool, and inject each of two mice with 0.5 ml of the undiluted fluid.

Observe all of the mice periodically for 48 hr for symptoms of botulism and record deaths. If all of the mice die at the dilutions used, repeat, using higher dilutions to determine the end point, or the minimum lethal dose

(MLD) as an estimate of the amount of toxin present. The MLD is contained in the highest dilution killing both mice (or all mice inoculated). From this, the number of MLD per ml may be calculated.

It is very important to observe the mice closely for signs of botulinal intoxication during the first 24 hr after inoculation. Death of mice without clinical signs of botulism is not sufficient evidence that the material injected contained botulinal toxin.

Typical botulism symptoms in mice in sequence are ruffling of the fur, labored but not rapid breathing, weakness of the limbs, gasping for breath (opening of lower jaw), and death due to respiratory failure. Mice that die immediately after injection usually were injured on injection or react to some toxic substance other than botulinal toxin (e.g., ammonia, high salt concentration). Mice that die after 12 hours with closed, matted eyes are generally killed by infection, not toxin, and do not have the typical symptoms of botulism. Either of the latter can obscure the presence of botulinal toxin. Infectious bacteria can be removed by filtration, although this may also lower the toxin titer. If necessary, chemical agents, including medications used in treatment of patients, may be removed by dialysis. However, if neither type of treatment reveals the presence of toxin, subcultures may have to be relied upon, the results may remain indeterminate, or the product did not contain botulinal toxin.

36.73   Typing Toxin

In determining the type of toxin, either the untreated or trypsin-treated fluid may be used, provided that it was lethal to mice. Use the preparation that gave the higher MLD. If the trypsinized fluid is to be used, prepare a freshly trypsinized fluid. The continued action of trypsin may destroy the toxin.

Rehydrate the lyophilized vials of antitoxin and dilute the monovalent antitoxins to types A, B, E, and F in physiological saline to contain 1 international unit per 0.5 ml. Prepare enough of this solution to inject each of two mice with 0.5 ml of the antitoxin for each dilution of the toxic preparation to be tested.

Protect separate groups of mice by injecting each mouse with 0.5 ml of one of the above antitoxins 30 min to 1 hr before injecting them with the suspected toxic preparation. Inject both the unprotected and protected mice with a sufficient number of dilutions to cover a range of at least 10, 100, and 1000 MLD below the previously determined endpoint of toxicity. Observe the mice for 48 hr for symptoms of botulism, and record deaths.

An alternative procedure is to perform the test as described in Section 36.81.

If the toxin is not neutralized, repeat the test using monovalent antitoxins to types C and D, and a pool of types A through F.

36.8   IDENTIFYING BOTULINAL TOXIN IN CLINICAL SPECIMENS[3, 5, 15]

36.81   Toxin Neutralization Tests

Botulinal toxins in clinical specimens are identified by injecting mice with the suspect specimen alone, and the same specimen mixed with one or more botulinal antitoxins. If botulinal toxin is present in sufficient quantity to be determined, mice receiving the unneutralized toxin will die, and mice receiving the toxin neutralized by the specific antitoxin will survive. Although botulinal intoxication usually kills mice within 6 to 24 hr after inoculation, deaths may be delayed if the quantity of toxin is near the minimum lethal concentration. Therefore, the animals should be observed for 48 hr before recording as negative in the case of food.

36.82   Identification of Botulinal Toxin in Serum

Prepare serum-antitoxin mixtures as follows:

Patient's serum	Normal serum or antitoxin
1.2 ml	0.3 ml normal serum
1.2 ml	0.3 ml anti-A
1.2 ml	0.3 ml anti-B
1.2 ml	0.3 ml anti-E
1.2 ml	0.3 ml anti-F
1.2 ml	0.3 ml polyvalent
	(anti-A, B, C, D, E, F)

Because of limited volume of serum obtainable from infants, only anti-A and B, together with the normal serum control, should be tested initially.

Incubate mixtures in a 37°C waterbath for 30 min.

Inoculate 0.5 ml of the serum-antitoxin mixtures IP into each of two mice (15 to 20 g) for each test mixture. Each mouse, therefore, receives 0.4 ml of the patient's serum and 0.1 ml of normal serum or antitoxin.

Observe mice at intervals for 48 hr, note clinical signs, and record deaths or survivors.

If no toxin is found by using 0.4 ml of patient's serum per mouse, repeat the test using larger mice (25 to 30 g) inoculated with 0.8 ml of patient's serum mixed with 0.1 ml of normal serum per mouse. To do this, add 2.4 ml of patient's serum to the same amount of normal serum or antitoxin used before and inject each mouse with 0.9 ml of the mixture using the same scheme as outlined above. Do not inject mice with a total volume larger than 1.0 ml since excessive amounts of normal serum can cause death. Trypsinization of the patient's serum is not necessary for demonstration of toxin.

If all of the mice inoculated with the test mixtures described above develop signs suggestive of botulism and die, it is possible that type G, or an unidentified toxin, is involved. In this case, the patient's serum should be submitted to a reference laboratory for additional tests. At present, type G antitoxin is not available commercially.

If mice were protected only by neutralization of the toxin with the polyvalent antitoxin, repeat the test using monovalent type C, type D, and type F, the polyvalent antitoxin, and the normal test mixtures. If the mice receiving the polyvalent antitoxin mixture are the only survivors again, test the other combinations of monovalent antitoxins to determine if multiple toxin types are present. To estimate the quantity of botulinal toxin in the patient's serum, prepare dilutions (1:2; 1:4, etc.) with gel phosphate buffer and determine the MLD. Inoculate groups of mice with each dilution of the patient's serum, 0.5 ml IP per mouse.

36.83   Identifying Botulinal Toxin in Feces

Recent experience from the investigation of several botulism outbreaks has revealed that examination of feces for botulinal toxin is a valuable diagnostic procedure. This is especially true of infant botulism.

Homogenize 10 to 15 g of feces (1 to 2 g from infants) in an equal quantity (wt/vol) of gel phosphate buffer with a chilled mortar and pestle. Cover and refrigerate at 4°C for 6 to 18 hr to extract toxin.

After refrigeration, centrifuge (12,000 × g) at 4°C for 20 min and remove the liquid for a toxin neutralization test. If the extract is not clear, clarify by repeating the centrifugation procedure.

Prepare the following mixtures:

Feces from Adults

Extract of Feces	Treatment
1.0 ml	none
1.0 ml	heated*
1.0 ml	0.25 ml 0.5% trypsin
1.0 ml	0.25 ml anti-A
1.0 ml	0.25 ml anti-B
1.0 ml	0.25 ml anti-E
1.0 ml	0.25 ml anti-F
1.0 ml	0.25 ml polyvalent (anti-ABCDEF)

Feces from Infants

Extract of Feces	Treatment
1.0 ml	none
1.0 ml	heated*
1.0 ml	0.25 ml 0.5% trypsin
1.0 ml	0.25 ml anti-A
1.0 ml	0.25 ml anti-B
1.0 ml	0.25 ml polyvalent

*A portion of the extract is heated in a boiling water bath for 10 min; botulinum toxin is heat-labile.

Incubate the mixture in a 37°C water bath for 30 min.

Inoculate 0.5 ml of the extract-trypsin and extract-antitoxin mixtures and 0.4 ml of the others IP into two mice (15 to 20 g) for each test mixture.

If toxin is demonstrated only with the trypsinized specimen, repeat the neutralization tests using trypsinized extract. Add 1.5 ml of 0.5% trypsin to 6 ml of extract, and incubate the mixture at 37°C for 30 min.

Prepare the following extract-antitoxin mixtures:

Extract	Antitoxin
1.25 ml	0.25 ml anti-A
1.25 ml	0.25 ml anti-B
1.25 ml	0.25 ml anti-E
1.25 ml	0.25 ml anti-F
1.25 ml	0.25 ml anti-ABCDEF

Incubate and inoculate into two mice per mixture as before, but give each mouse 0.6 ml.

Observe the mice at intervals for 48 hr; note clinical symptoms of botulism and record deaths and survivors. Mice injected with the heated extract should survive. Interpret the results of the tests and perform repeat tests, if required, as described above, for identification of botulinal toxin in serum.

36.84   Miscellaneous Clinical Specimens

Tests for botulinal toxin in cerebrospinal fluid, urine, and other body fluids are performed as described for serum (Section 36.82) after centrifugation, if necessary, to clarify the liquids.

Dilute vomitus and gastric washings 1:1 with gel phosphate buffer (Chapter 62) before clarification by centrifugation and performance of the toxin neutralization tests.

Grind tissues with an equal volume of gel phosphate buffer using a sterile chilled mortar and pestle. Cover and refrigerate at 4°C for 12 to 18 hr. After refrigeration, centrifuge (12,000 × g) at 4°C, remove the liquid and perform a toxin neutralization test as described for feces (Section 36.83). Omit the heated extract-serum mixture.

36.85   Preparing Fecal Cultures

Enrichment cultures from feces are prepared as described for foods in Sections 36.66.1 and 36.66.2 by inoculating 0.5 to 1.0 ml of the chilled homogenate from Section 36.83 into two tubes of CMM, one of which is cooled as described and the other equilibrated at 80°C before inoculation. Hold the latter at 80°C for 10 min after inoculation. Incubate both cultures at 35°C for 7 days.

1. Toxin testing. Test for toxin in fecal cultures and type as in Sections 36.72 and 36.73 or 36.83.

2. Isolation of pure cultures. At the time enrichment cultures are tested for toxicity, or when there is evidence of sporulation, streak cultures on *Clostridium botulinum* isolation agar (CBI). To obtain well-isolated colonies, dilute with gel phosphate buffer, if necessary.
3. Incubation. Incubate as in Section 36.67.4.
4. Selection of typical colonies. Select several well-isolated colonies, test for toxicity, type, and check for purity as in Section 36.67.5.

36.9 INTERPRETING DATA

Laboratory tests required in an actual or potential botulism outbreak are designed to identify botulinal toxin and/or the organism in foods and clinical specimens. Toxin in a food means that the product, if consumed without thorough heating, could cause botulism. In clinical specimens, it means that a clinical diagnosis of botulism is consistent with the laboratory findings. The presence of viable *C. botulinum* but no toxin in specimens has a different meaning. In foods, the observation by itself is not proof that the food in question caused botulism, and in clinical specimens it does not necessarily mean that the patient has botulism. The presence of toxin in the food is required for an outbreak of botulism to occur. Ingested organisms may be found in the alimentary tract, but they are considered unable to multiply and produce toxin in vivo except in infants and in a very few adults who have received antibiotics. Assuming proper handling of specimens to prevent toxin inactivation, failure to find toxin means that a discernible level is not present.

Presence of botulinal toxin and/or organisms in low-acid (i.e., above pH 4.6) canned foods means that the items were underprocessed or were contaminated through postprocessing leakage. These failures occur more frequently in home processed than in commercially canned foods. Swollen containers are more likely than normal containers to contain botulinal toxin since the organism produces gas during growth. The rare occurrence of toxin in a flat can may imply that the seams were loose enough to allow gas to escape. Botulinal toxin in canned foods is usually type A or proteolytic type B, since spores of the proteolytics can be among the more heat-resistant of bacterial spores. Spores of the nonproteolytics, types B, E, and F, generally have low heat resistance, and do not normally survive even mild heat treatment, but can also be present in canned foods through postprocessing leakage.

The protection of mice from botulism and death with one of the monovalent botulinal antitoxins confirms the presence of botulinal toxin and determines the serological type of toxin. However, there is a slight degree of cross-neutralization between types E and F. For example, type E antitoxin at a concentration of 1000 anti-MLD will commonly neutralize 2 or 3 MLD of type F toxin. If low levels of type F toxin are present, mice protected with monovalent type E and those protected with monovalent type F antitoxin may all survive. It may also happen, if low levels of toxin are present, that the food may be toxic on initial testing, but may be nontoxic on subsequent testing.

If the mice are not protected by one of the monovalent botulinal antitoxins, (1) there may be too much toxin in the food, (2) there may be more than one type of toxin, or (3) deaths may be due to some other cause. This situation requires retesting at a higher dilution of toxin and the use of mixtures of A, B, C, D, E, and F antisera in place of the monovalent antiserum.

If both the heated and unheated supernatant fluids are lethal to mice, the deaths are probably not due to botulinal toxin. However, it is possible that a toxic substance not destroyed by heat may mask the presence of botulinal toxin. If the botulinal toxin is present in large quantities, further dilution may eliminate the heat-stable toxin and still allow the botulinal toxin to act.

When injecting mice to determine the presence and type of botulinal toxin, the following are helpful in interpreting results:

1. Mice injected with botulinal toxin may become hyperactive before symptoms of botulism occur.
2. The first 24 hr after injection are critical since 90% to 95% of mice will die within this time.

   Typical symptoms of botulism (ruffled hair, labored breathing, weakness of limbs, paralysis of hind legs, total paralysis with gasping for breath) and death may occur within 4 to 6 hr.
3. Unless typical botulism symptoms are evident, death of mice occurring after 24 hr, or only in those receiving the 1:5 but not in any higher dilution, may be due to nonspecific causes.

36.10 REFERENCES

1. Arnon, S. S. 1987. Infant botulism. In "Pediatrics," 18th ed., eds. A. M. Rudolph and J. I. E. Hoffman, p. 490. Appleton & Lange, Norwalk, Conn.
2. Dezfulian, M., McCroskey, L. M., Hatheway, C. L., and Dowell, V. R. 1981. Selective medium for isolation of *Clostridium botulinum* from human feces. J. Clin. Microbiol. 13: 526.
3. Dowell, V. R., and Hawkins, T. M. 1974. "Laboratory Methods in Anaerobic Bacteriology, CDC Laboratory Manual." PHS Pub. No. 1803, U.S. Dept. of Health, Ed., and Welfare. U.S. Pub. Health Serv., Washington, D.C.
4. Hatheway, C. L. 1979. Laboratory procedures for cases of suspected infant botulism. Rev. Infect. Dis. 1: 647.
5. Hatheway, C. L., and McCroskey, L. 1987. Examination of feces and serum for diagnosis of infant botulism in 336 patients. J. Clin. Microbiol. 25: 2334.
6. Hauschild, A. H. W., Hilsheimer, R., Weiss, K. F., and Burke, R. B. 1988. *Clostridium botulinum* in honey, syrups, and dry infant cereals. J. Food Prot. 51: 892.
7. Herzberg, M., ed. 1970. Toxic microorganisms: Mycotoxins. Botulism. Proceedings of the 1st U.S.-Japan Conf. U.S.-Japan Coop. Prog. In "Natural Resources." U.S. Dept. of the Interior, Washington, D.C.
8. Ingram, M., and Roberts, T. A., eds. 1967. "Botulism 1966." Chapman and Hall, London, England.

9. International Commission on Microbiological Specifications for Foods. 1978. "Microorganisms in Foods 1," 2nd ed. U. of Toronto Press, Toronto, Canada.
10. Lewis, K. H., and Cassel, K. Jr., eds. 1964. "Botulism. Proceedings of a Symposium." U.S. Dept. of Health, Ed., and Welfare. Pub. Health Serv., Washington, D.C.
11. Mills, D. C., Midura, T. F., and Arnon, S. S. 1985. Improved selective medium for the isolation of lipase-positive *Clostridium botulinum* from feces of human infants. J. Clin. Microbiol. 21: 947.
12. Silas, J. C., Carpenter, J. A., Hamdy, M. K., and Harrison, M. A. 1985. Selective and differential medium for detecting *Clostridium botulinum*. Appl. Environ. Microbiol. 50: 1110.
13. Smith, L. D. S., and Holdeman, L. V. 1968. "The pathogenic anaerobic bacteria." Charles C. Thomas, Springfield, Ill.
14. Stumbo, C. R. 1973. "Thermobacteriology in food processing," 2nd ed. Academic Press, Inc., New York, N.Y.
15. U.S.HEW/PHS/CDC. 1979. "Botulism in the United States 1899–1977." Pub. No. (CDC) 74-8279, U.S. Dept. of Health, Ed., and Welfare, Pub. Health Serv., Washington, D.C.
16. U.S.HHS/PHS/FDA. 1984. Chapter 18. "Bacteriological Analytical Manual," 6th ed. Assn. of Offic. Analyt. Chem., Arlington, Va.

Chapter 37

CLOSTRIDIUM PERFRINGENS

Ronald G. Labbe and Stanley M. Harmon

37.1   INTRODUCTION

The methods included in this chapter are useful for direct quantitation of the colony-forming units of *Clostridium perfringens* in food or feces and for detection and quantitation of *C. perfringens* enterotoxin in feces of food poisoning patients. The cultural methods recommended are generally accepted as the most effective for this purpose. They are in essential conformance with those adopted as official by the Association of Official Analytical Chemists (AOAC) and by the International Standards Organization. The reversed passive latex agglutination (RPLA) method for enterotoxin has been evaluated extensively in the United Kingdom[3] and in the United States,[12, 17] but a full-scale collaborative study has not yet been done.

37.11   Food Poisoning and Enterotoxin Formation

C. perfringens food poisoning is one of the most common types of human foodborne illness.[24] The foods usually involved are cooked meat or poultry products containing large numbers of viable cells. A heat-labile enterotoxin produced only by sporulating cells[5] induces the major symptom of diarrhea in perfringens poisoning. The enterotoxin appears to be released *in vivo* in the intestine by the sporulating organism. Although the enterotoxin is generally not preformed in the food, the foods in which conditions are favorable for sporulation may contain enterotoxin.[4, 29]

37.12   Importance of Cell Numbers

C. perfringens is not uncommon in raw meats, poultry, dehydrated soups and sauces, raw vegetables, and certain other foods or food ingredients. Thus, its mere presence in foods may be unavoidable. In food poisoning outbreaks, demonstration of hundreds of thousands or more organisms per gram in a suspect food supports a diagnosis of perfringens poisoning when substantiated by clinical and epidemiological evidence. The value of enumerating *C. perfringens* spores in feces of food poisoning patients as a means of confirming outbreaks has also been confirmed.[13]

C. perfringens cells may lose viability if suspect foods are frozen or held under prolonged refrigeration before analysis, thereby making it difficult to incriminate the organism in food poisoning outbreaks.[37] In such cases, gram-stained smears of food remnants or homogenates should be examined for the presence of large-celled bacilli typical of *C. perfringens*. The alpha-toxin method may be used to estimate nonviable populations of *C. perfringens*.[10] Foods responsible for food poisoning outbreaks usually contain a large enough number of cells to be readily detectable by direct microscopic examination.

Spores of different strains of *C. perfringens* may vary widely in their heat resistance. Some may withstand 100°C for several hours, whereas others are inactivated by a few minutes or less at the same temperature. In most environments, heat-sensitive strains outnumber heat-resistant strains. Both heat-resistant and heat-sensitive strains may cause food poisoning. Since *C. perfringens* does not sporulate in food, or does so only rarely, food should not be heated before the organism is enumerated. In feces only elevated levels of spores of *C. perfringens* are of diagnostic value. Heating a suspension of feces is recommended for detection of *C. perfringens* to eliminate competitive organisms such as members of the family *Enterobacteriaceae*.

37.13 Selective Differential Media

Several solid media have been devised for quantitation of *C. perfringens*, including neomycin blood agar,[36] sulfite polymyxin sulfadiazine (SPS) agar,[1] tryptone sulfite neomycin (TSN) agar,[26] Shahidi Ferguson perfringens (SFP) agar,[33] D-cycloserine blood agar,[7] oleandomycin polymyxin sulfadiazine perfringens (OPSP) agar,[8] tryptose sulfite cycloserine (TSC) agar,[15] egg yolk-free tryptose sulfite cycloserine (EY-free TSC) agar,[19] and trypticase-soy-sheep blood (TSB) agar.[14] The selectivity of these media is derived from the incorporation of one or more antibiotics that inhibit certain anaerobes or facultative anaerobes. With the exception of the blood agars, the media contain iron and sulfite. Clostridia reduce the sulfite to sulfide which reacts with the iron to form a black iron sulfide precipitate. Black colonies are presumptive *C. perfringens* and must be confirmed by additional tests.

The selectivity of TSN and SPS media results in the inhibition of some strains of *C. perfringens*. SPS also is unsatisfactory because many strains fail to form colonies that are distinguishably black. Although the selectivity of SFP and neomycin blood agars is limited, these media may be adequate when *C. perfringens* is the predominant organism. The selectivity of OPSP agar also may be of limited use with some facultative anaerobes. D-cycloserine blood agar may be useful for the selective isolation of *C. perfringens*, although it has not been tested for routine isolation of the organism from foods. TSC agar, or its modified form, EY-free TSC agar, has been documented as the most useful of the media for quantitative recovery of *C. perfringens*, with adequate suppression of the growth of practically all facultative anaerobes.[9, 20]

SFP, OPSP, and TSC also contain egg yolk for differential purposes. The lecithinase of *C. perfringens* hydrolyzes egg yolk lecithin and produces an opaque halo around the black colonies. However, other sulfite-reducing clostridia or other facultative anaerobes may produce a similar reaction. In some instances the egg yolk reaction of *C. perfringens* alpha-toxin may be masked by that of other organisms. In addition, false-negative *C. perfringens* colonies without detectable halos may occur on the plates.[19] EY-free TSC agar which is not dependent on alpha-toxin production for its differential utility is an improvement over TSC agar.[19, 21]

TSC agar contains egg yolk and must be used for surface plating. EY-free TSC agar is used in pour plates. The methods described here for quantitation of *C. perfringens* use TSC agar or EY-free TSC agar. The EY-free TSC may give results as good as or better than those of TSC agar. For outbreak stool samples, the EY-free TSC and TSB agars are superior to elevated-temperature (46°C) most probable number (MPN) methods for enumeration of *C. perfringens* spores.[14] TSB agar is reported to be preferable for the examination of stools because it is easier to use, and on it, most food poisoning strains can be more readily distinguished from other microorganisms that may be present.[14]

37.14 Rapid Methods for Detecting *C. perfringens* Enterotoxin

A number of serological assays have been reported for the rapid detection of enterotoxin. The most rapid methods available are the enzyme-linked immunosorbent assays (ELISA[2, 22, 23, 28, 31, 32, 38]) and RPLA,[12] marketed by Oxoid U.S.A., Inc., Columbia, Md. 21045. A rapid and inexpensive slide latex agglutination assay has also been reported,[27] but requires the coating of latex beads with immunoglobulin. The RPLA method is easier to perform than the ELISA, which requires special test reagents and equipment not generally available.[3, 17]

To determine the enterotoxigenicity of *C. perfringens* from food or feces, it is necessary to induce sporulation of the organism. A number of sporulation media have been proposed. The two recommended here are the modified[13] AEA medium of Taniguti[35] and the modified[13] medium of Duncan and Strong.[6, 25]

37.2 SAMPLING

For routine sampling of foods, *C. perfringens* spores or vegetative cells are enumerated by direct plating. In cases of outbreaks, fecal samples are examined for *C. perfringens* enterotoxin by RPLA and for *C. perfringens* spores by enumeration. Remnants of foods are examined microscopically to determine the type of analysis to be performed.

37.21   Maintaining Viability of Vegetative Cells

Generally it is recommended that outbreak food samples to be tested for *C. perfringens* be analyzed immediately, or refrigerated and tested as soon as possible, but not frozen. Loss of viability of some strains that occurs during refrigeration may be even greater when the cells are frozen. Foods that must be stored for more than 48 hr or shipped to the laboratory should be treated with buffered glycerol salt solution to give a 10% final concentration of glycerol and stored frozen at $-55°$ to $-60°C$ until the sample is analyzed. Treated samples shipped with dry ice show a minimal loss of viability of *C. perfringens*.[18] Fecal samples can be stored at $-20°C$ for several months with only minimal reductions in the spore count.[16]

37.3   EQUIPMENT AND SUPPLIES

37.31   Isolation and Quantitation

Air incubator 35 to 37°C.

Anaerobic containers or anaerobic incubator with equipment and materials for obtaining anaerobic conditions. These may be anaerobic devices in which the air is replaced 3 or 4 times with $90\% \ N_2 + 10\% \ CO_2$, or those in which oxygen is catalytically removed.

Colony counter with a piece of white tissue paper over the counting background area to facilitate counting black colonies.

Sterile blender jar, container and motor, or stomacher, or sterile mortar and pestle and sterile sand. The blender or stomacher is preferable.

Vortex mixer

Water bath

37.32   Reversed Passive Latex Agglutination for Quantitation of *C. perfringens* Enterotoxin

A kit for the detection of *C. perfringens* enterotoxin by RPLA in feces and culture fluids is available from Oxoid U.S.A., 9017 Red Branch Road, Columbia, Md. 21045. Additional materials required for performing the test include the following:

Microtiter plate (V-type)

Dropper (25 μl) or micropipet

Diluter (25 μl)

Centrifuge

37.4   SPECIAL REAGENTS AND MEDIA (Chapter 62)

37.41   Isolation and Quantitation

Chopped liver broth
Cooked meat medium (CMM) (Difco)
Fermentation medium
Fluid thioglycollate medium (Difco)
Lactose gelatin
Modified AEA sporulation medium
Modified Duncan Strong (DS) medium
Motility-nitrate medium
Nitrate reduction reagents (Method 1)
0.1% peptone water diluent
Phosphate-buffered saline (PBS)
Physiological saline (0.85% sodium chloride)
TSC agar, EY-free TSC agar, or TSB agar
Trypticase peptone glucose yeast extract broth (buffered)

37.5   RECOMMENDED CONTROLS

37.51   Direct Quantitation

For the selective differential media for quantitation of *C. perfringens*, use a control strain of the organism to validate the performance of the media. This control strain may also be useful when typical *C. perfringens* colonies have not been observed on the medium.

37.52   Reversed Passive Latex Agglutination

Sensitized and control latex, control enterotoxin and diluent are included in the Oxoid commercial kit.

37.6   PRECAUTIONS AND LIMITATIONS OF METHODS

37.61   Isolation and Quantitation

37.611   TSC, EY-free TSC, and TSB agar

Each medium appears to be suitable for enumeration of *C. perfringens*. However, some strains of *C. perfringens* may not produce distinguishable halos via the egg yolk reaction on TSC agar. Therefore, the absence of a halo around a black colony does not eliminate the possibility of the strain being *C. perfringens*. The halo of one colony also may be masked by the halo of another colony. TSB has the advantage of yielding information on the hemolytic activity of isolates, but it is not suitable for the examination of foods unless D-cycloserine is incorporated to impart selectivity.

37.612   Contamination with other sulfite-reducing clostridia

Other sulfite-reducing clostridia that produce black colonies and are egg-yolk positive can grow in TSC and EY-free TSC agar, including *Clostridium bifermentans, C. botulinum, C. paraperfringens (C. baratii), C. sardiniense (C. absonum),* and *C. sporogenes.*

37.613   Contamination with group D *Streptococcus*

Enterococci may be present in high numbers in some foods. In media other than those containing D-cycloserine, the overgrowth of these organisms may interfere with or prevent the isolation of *C. perfringens.* Incorporating D-cycloserine into TSC and EY-free TSC agar effectively inhibits growth of most enterococci.

37.614   Confirmation of the presumptive plate count

Presumptive sulfite-reducing colonies of *C. perfringens* from the selective differential media have often been confirmed by their nonmotility and their ability to reduce nitrate to nitrite. A variety of clostridia have these properties, including *C. celatum,*[19] *C. paraperfringens (C. baratii),* and *C. sardiniense (C. absonum).*[29] These species usually can be distinguished from *C. perfringens* by their inability to liquefy gelatin within 44 hr in lactose gelatin medium and by their inability to produce acid from raffinose within 3 days.

37.62   Reversed Passive Latex Agglutination

Because of interference from other components of the extract, it is often necessary to dilute the fecal extract 1:60 or more before enterotoxin can be quantitated.

37.7   PROCEDURE

37.71   Isolation and Quantitation

In some instances, it may be desirable to isolate *C. perfringens* from food samples contaminated with a very low number of cells. An enrichment procedure using chopped liver broth or trypticase peptone glucose yeast extract broth (buffered) may be used. Inoculate about 2 g of food sample into 15 to 20 ml of medium. Incubate the sample at 35° to 37°C for 20 to 24 hr. Positive tubes show turbidity and gas production. Streak TSC agar plates containing egg yolk to obtain presumptive *C. perfringens.*

37.72   Anaerobic Total Plate and Spore Count

1. Preparation of food and fecal homogenate

   Blend for 2 min at slow speed (or homogenize with stomacher or macerate with sterile sand) a 10 to 20 g food sample with 0.1% peptone to obtain a 1:10 dilution. For fecal specimens, homogenize 1.0 g (or 1 ml liquified stool) in 9 ml of 0.1% peptone in screw cap tubes. Homogenize on a vortex mixer. For spore counts, heat homogenates in screw cap tubes in a water bath at 75°C for 20 min before diluting and plating.

2. Preparation of dilutions

   Prepare serial decimal dilutions (through at least 10^{-7}) using 0.1% peptone dilution blanks.

3. Plating procedures

   Make duplicate spread platings of each dilution using 0.1 ml amounts on TSC agar. After the agar has dried slightly, overlay the surface with 5 ml (or more) of EY-free TSC agar. If EY-free TSC agar is used as the plating medium, make duplicate pour plates of each dilution, using 1.0 ml of diluted culture per plate. After the pour plates solidify, cover with an additional 5 ml (or more) of EY-free TSC agar.

4. Incubation

   Incubate the plates upright and anaerobically for 18 to 20 hr at 35° to 37°C.

5. Presumptive *C. perfringens* plate count

   Select plates containing, preferably, 20 to 200 black colonies, which may be surrounded by a zone of precipitate on the TSC agar but not on the EY-free TSC agar. Count all black colonies and calculate the average number of colonies in the duplicate plates.

37.73   Confirmation of *C. perfringens*

Select five representative black colonies (10 for official analyses) from TSC agar and stab inoculate motility-nitrate and lactose gelatin media in parallel using a stiff inoculating needle with a hook at the tip. Transfer colonies from crowded or contaminated plates to fluid thioglycollate medium. Incubate 18 to 20 hr at 35°C and streak on TSC agar to obtain pure cultures (as described in Section 37.73.1) before proceeding with confirmation.

1. Obtaining pure cultures

   Inoculate a portion of each selected black colony into a tube of buffered TPGY broth or fluid thioglycollate medium. Incubate for 4 hr in a water bath at 46°C or overnight at 35° to 37°C. After incubation examine microscopically for the presence of large gram-positive rods typical of *C. perfringens*. Endospores usually are not produced in this medium. Streak the culture onto TSC agar and incubate anaerobically for 24 hr at 35° to 37°C to obtain isolated colonies. Typical colonies are yellowish gray, 1 to 2 mm in diameter, usually surrounded by an opaque zone caused by lecithinase production. These colonies then may be picked and inoculated into fluid thioglycollate medium. For longer term storage, cultures can be grown and kept frozen in Difco CMM.

2. Motility nitrate reduction test

Stab inoculate each fluid thioglycollate medium culture into motility nitrate medium. The medium recommended contains 0.5% each of glycerol and galactose to improve the consistency of the nitrate reduction reaction with different strains of the organism.[19] Incubate the inoculated medium at 35° to 37°C for 24 hr. Read for motility. Since *C. perfringens* is nonmotile, growth should occur only along the line of inoculum and not diffuse away from stab. Test for reduction of nitrate to nitrite. A red or orange color indicates reduction of nitrate to nitrite. If no color develops, test fluid thioglycollate for residual nitrate by addition of powdered zinc.

3. Lactose gelatin medium

Stab inoculate suspect colony into lactose gelatin medium. Incubate at 35° to 37°C for 24 to 44 hr. Lactose fermentation is indicated by gas bubbles and a change in color of the medium from red to yellow. Gelatin usually is liquefied by *C. perfringens* within 24 to 44 hr.[19]

4. Carbohydrate fermentation

Subculture isolates that do not liquify gelatin within 44 hr, or are atypical in other respects, into fluid thioglycollate medium. Incubate the cultures for 18 to 24 hr at 35° to 37°C, make gram-stained smear, and check for purity. If pure, inoculate a tube of fermentation medium containing 1% salicin and a tube of fermentation medium containing 1% raffinose with 0.15 ml of thioglycollate culture of each isolate. Incubate inoculated media at 35° to 37°C for 24 hr and check for production of acid. To test for acid, transfer 1 ml of culture to a test tube or spot plate and add 2 drops of 0.04% bromthymol blue. A yellow color indicates that acid has been produced. Reincubate cultures for an additional 48 hr and retest for the production of acid. Salicin is rapidly fermented with the production of acid by culturally similar species such as *C. paraperfringens* (*C. baratii*), *C. sardiniense* (*C. absonum*), and *C. celatum*, but usually not by *C. perfringens*. Acid is produced from raffinose within 3 days by *C. perfringens* but is not produced by culturally similar species. The typical cultural reactions of each species are shown in Table 1.

37.74   Detection of Enterotoxin in Feces and Culture Supernatants by Reversed Passive Latex Agglutination

Prepare fecal extracts as described in Section 37.72.1, except homogenize the sample in nine parts (wt/vol) of physiological saline or PBS and centrifuge to remove insoluble solids.

Subculture isolates to be tested for enterotoxin in CMM (Difco) and incu-

Table 1—Characteristics of *Clostridium perfringens* and Culturally Similar Species[a]

Species	Number of strains	Motility-nitrate medium		Lactose-gelatin medium		Fermentation medium	
		Motility	Nitrite	Acid/gas	Gelatin liquefied	Salicin (24 h)	Raffinose (72 h)
C. perfringens Type A	38	−	4+	AG/T	+(48 h)	−	A
C. perfringens Type A	3	−	4+	AG/T	+(48 to 72 h)	(AG)	A
C. absonum	4	+	(+)	AG/CS	−	AG	−
C. baratii	2	−	3+	AG/CS	−	AG	−
C. celatum	2	−	2+	A/CS	−	A	−
C. paraperfringens	10	−	3+	AG/CS	−	AG	−
C. sardiniense	8	±	(+)	AG/CS	−	AG	−

[a]Determined using buffered supplemented motility-nitrate medium,[11] lactose-gelatin,[19] and Spray's fermentation medium.[34]

A = acid; AG = acid and gas; T = turbid; CS = clear with sedimented cells; + = positive; (+) = weak; − = negative.

bate for 1 or 2 days at 37°C. Mix the cooked meat culture with a Vortex mixer and transfer 2 to 3 drops to 10 ml of freshly steamed fluid thioglycollate medium. Heat the inoculated medium in a water bath at 75°C for 10 min and incubate for 18 hr at 37°C. Subculture 0.5 ml of this culture in fresh fluid thioglycollate and incubate for 4 hr at 37°C. Use the 4-hr subculture to inoculate (1% to 5% vol/vol) 15 ml of modified AEA sporulation medium or modified DS medium. Incubate the inoculated spore broth for 18 to 24 hr at 37°C. For best results, incubate AEA medium in an anaerobic jar or incubator. Check the resulting culture for spores by using a phase-contrast microscope or by examining stained smears. Fewer than 5 mature spores per field is not considered good sporulation. Retest such cultures in another sporulation medium. Centrifuge a portion of the sporulated culture for 15 min at 10,000 $\times$ g and test the cell-free culture supernatant for enterotoxin.

The procedures, including controls for detecting and quantitating enterotoxin by RPLA, are those specified by the manufacturer of the test kit. Enterotoxin levels as low 2 ng/ml can be reliably detected using this method. It is usually desirable to screen samples for the presence of enterotoxin over a broad range of dilutions before attempting to quantitate it precisely, e.g., a tenfold dilution series to 10^{-6}. Typically, fecal extracts are positive at dilutions from 10^{-2} to 10^{-5}. Culture supernatants are usually positive at dilutions from 10^{-3} to 10^{-6}.

To screen samples for enterotoxin, make a series of tenfold dilutions of the sample in the diluent provided with each kit. Transfer 25 µl of each dilution to two separate wells in adjacent rows of a "V" type microtiter plate. Add 25 µl of sensitized latex beads (coated with specific antibody to enterotoxin) to each well of the first row and 25 µl of control latex to the adjacent row. Mix the contents using a minishaker (Dynatech Corp., Alexandria, Va. 22314) or by stirring with clean flat toothpicks. Avoid spilling or mixing the contents of different wells. Cover the plate to minimize evaporation and incubate at room temperature (22° to 24°C) for 24 hr. If enterotoxin is present, it reacts with specific antibodies on the sensitized latex to give an agglutination pattern that can be scored from $1+$ to $3+$. The values obtained can be used to estimate the amount of enterotoxin in the sample. Control latex coated with normal immunoglobins usually does not react with substances in the test sample, so the beads sediment to a compact pellet at the bottom of the test wells. A positive result with the sensitized latex and a negative result with control latex is a positive indication that *C. perfringens* enterotoxin is present in the sample. A lyophilized preparation of enterotoxin is provided with each kit for confirming the reactivity of the sensitized latex and nonreactivity of the control latex. A precise indication of the amount of enterotoxin present in samples is usually not required for routine work. This can, however, be determined with an accuracy of approximately 50% by assuming that the sensitivity of the RPLA test is about 2 ng/ml of sample. After determinig the approximate end point of activity by screening samples, repeat the assay using a two-fold series of dilutions within the appropriate range. The reciprocal of the highest dilution that yields a positive reaction with the sensitized latex and a negative result with the control latex divided by 2000 gives the indicated amount of enterotoxin in μg/ml of undiluted extract or culture fluids. If more accurate results are desired, use an enterotoxin standard whose reactivity has been determined by other serological assays to determine the specific activity of the sensitized latex supplied with the test kit.

37.75   Detection of Enterotoxin in Feces by Reversed Passive Latex Agglutination

Prepare fecal extracts as described in Section 37.72, except centrifuge homogenized sample for 30 min at 15,000 × g to remove insoluble solids.

The procedures are those specified by the manufacturer of the RPLA kit. Prepare serial twofold dilutions of the test sample. However, to conserve reagents, conduct a preliminary trial using fecal extracts at dilutions of 1:10, 1:100, and 1:1000 using the diluent provided in the test kit.

37.8   INTERPRETATION OF DATA

37.81   Quantitation of *C. perfringens* Populations Based on Confirmed Anaerobic Plate Counts

Cultures obtained from presumptive *C. perfringens* black colonies on selective, differential TSC or EY-free TSC medium are confirmed as *C. perfringens* if they are nonmotile, reduce nitrate, ferment lactose, liquefy gelatin within 44 hr, and produce acid from raffinose. Calculate the number of viable *C. perfringens* per gram of food sample as follows: multiply the presumptive plate count by the reciprocal of the dilution plated and then by the ratio of the colonies confirmed as *C. perfringens* to total colonies tested. (Note: If the surface plating method is used, the result must be multiplied by 10 since only 0.1 ml was tested.)

37.9   REFERENCES

1. Angelotti, R., Hall, H. E., Foter, M. J., and Lewis, K. H. 1962. Quantitation of *Clostridium perfringens* in foods. Appl. Microbiol. 10: 193.
2. Bartholomew, B., Stringer, M., Watson, G., and Gilbert, R. 1985. Development and application of an enzyme-linked immunosorbent assay for *Clostridium perfringens* type A enterotoxin. J. Clin. Pathol. 38: 222.
3. Berry, P. R., Stringer, M. F., and Uemura, T. 1986. Comparison of latex agglutination and ELISA for the detection of *Clostridium perfringens* type A enterotoxin in feces. Lett. Appl. Microbiol. 2: 101.
4. Craven, S. E., Blankenship, L. C., and McDonel, J. L. 1981. Relationship of sporulation, enterotoxin formation, and spoilage during growth of *Clostridium perfringens* Type A in cooked chicken. Appl. Microbiol. 41: 1184.

5. Duncan, C. L. 1973. Time of enterotoxin formation and release during sporulation of *Clostridium perfringens*, type A. J. Bacteriol. 113: 932.
6. Duncan, C., and Strong, D. 1969. Improved medium for sporulation of *Clostridium perfringens*. Appl. Microbiol. 16: 82.
7. Fuzi, M., and Csukas, Z. 1969. New selective medium for the isolation of *Clostridium perfringens*. Acta Microbiol. Acad. Sci. Hung. 16: 273.
8. Hanford, P. M., and Cavett, J. J. 1973. A medium for the detection and enumeration of *Clostridium perfringens* (*welchii*) in foods. J. Sci. Food Agric. 24: 487.
9. Harmon, S. M. 1976. Collaborative study of an improved method for the enumeration and confirmation of *Clostridium perfringens* in foods. J. Assoc. Off. Anal. Chem. 59: 606.
10. Harmon, S. M., and Kautter, D. A. 1976. Estimating population levels of *Clostridium perfringens* in foods based on alpha toxin. J. Milk Food Technol. 39: 107.
11. Harmon, S. M., and Kautter, D. A. 1978. Media for confirming *Clostridium perfringens* from food and feces. J. Food Prot. 41: 626.
12. Harmon, S. M., and Kautter, D. A. 1986. Evaluation of a reversed passive latex agglutination test kit for *Clostridium perfringens* enterotoxin. J. Food Prot. 49: 523.
13. Harmon, S. M., and Kautter, D. A. 1986. Improved media for sporulation and enterotoxin production by *Clostridium perfringens*. J. Food Prot. 49: 706.
14. Harmon, S. M., and Kautter, D. A. 1987. Enumeration of *Clostridium perfringens* spores in human feces: Comparison of four culture media. J. Assn. Off. Anal. Chem. 70: 994.
15. Harmon, S. M., Kautter, D. A., and Peeler, J. T. 1971. Improved medium for enumeration of *Clostridium perfringens*. Appl. Microbiol. 22: 688.
16. Harmon, S. M., Kautter, D. A., and Hatheway, C. L. 1986. Enumeration and characterization of *Clostridium perfringens* spores in the feces of food poisoning patients and normal controls. J. Food Prot. 49: 23.
17. Harmon, S. M., Hatheway, C. L., Peterson, E. H., Ransome, G., and Wimsatt, J. 1987. Interlaboratory study of a reversed passive latex agglutination test kit for *Clostridium perfringens* enterotoxin. Abstracts of the 101st Annual Meeting, Assn. Off. Analyt. Chem., p. 84.
18. Harmon, S. M., and Placencia, A. M. 1978. Method for maintaining viability of *Clostridium perfringens* in foods during shipment and storage: Collaborative study. J. Assoc. Off. Anal. Chem. 61: 785.
19. Hauschild, A. H. W., and Hilsheimer, R. 1974. Evaluation and modifications of media for enumeration of *Clostridium perfringens*. Appl. Microbiol. 27: 78.
20. Hauschild, A. H. W., and Hilsheimer, R. 1974. Enumeration of food-borne *Clostridium perfringens* in egg yolk-free typtose-sulfite cycloserine agar. Appl. Microbiol. 27: 521.
21. Hauschild, A. H. W., Gilbert, R. J., Harmon, S. M., O'Keefe, M. F., and Vahlefeld, R. 1977. ICMSF methods studies. VIII. Comparative study for the enumeration of *Clostridium perfringens* in foods. Can. J. Microbiol. 23: 884.
22. Jackson, S. G., Yip-Chuck, D. A., and Brodsky, M. H. 1985. A double antibody sandwich-immunoassay for *Clostridium perfringens* type A enterotoxin detection in stool specimens. J. Immunol. Methods. 83: 141.
23. Jackson, S. G., Yip-Chuck, D. A., and Brodsky, M. H. 1986. Evaluation of the diagnostic application of an enzyme immunoassay for *Clostridium perfringens* type A enterotoxin. Appl. Environ. Microbiol. 52: 969.
24. Labbe, R. 1989. *Clostridium perfringens*. In "Foodborne Bacterial Pathogens." ed. M. Doyle, p. 191. Marcel Dekker, New York, N.Y.
25. Labbe, R. G., and Rey, D. K. 1979. Raffinose increases sporulation and enterotoxin production by *Clostridium perfringens* type A. Appl. Microbiol. 37: 1196.
26. Marshall, R. S., Steenbergen, J. F., and McClung, L. S. 1965. Rapid technique for the enumeration of *Clostridium perfringens*. Appl. Microbiol. 13: 559.
27. McClane, B. A., and Snyder, J. 1987. Development and preliminary evaluation of a slide latex agglutination assay for the detection of *Clostridium perfringens* type A enterotoxin. J. Immunol. Methods 100: 131.

28. McClane, B. A., and Strouse, R. J. 1984. Rapid detection of *Clostridum perfringens* type A enterotoxin by enzyme-linked immunosorbent assay. J. Clin. Microbiol. 19: 112.
29. Naik, H. S., and Duncan, C. L. 1977. Enterotoxin formation in foods by *Clostridium perfringens* type A. J. Food Safety: 1: 7.
30. Nakamura, S., Shimamura, T., Hayase, M., and Nishida, S. 1973. Numerical taxonomy of saccharolytic clostridia, particularly *Clostridium perfringens*-like strains: Description of *Clostridium absonum* sp. n. and *Clostridium paraperfringens*. Int. J. Syst. Bacteriol. 23: 419.
31. Notermans, S., Heuvelman, C., Beckers, H., and Uemura, T. 1984. Evaluation of the ELISA as a tool in diagnosing *Clostridium perfringens* enterotoxin. Zentralbl. Bakt. Hyg., I. Abt. Orig. B. 179: 225.
32. Olsvik, U., Granum, P. E., and Berdal, B. 1982. Detection of *Clostridium perfringens* type A enterotoxin by ELISA. Acta Pathol. Microbiol. Immunol. Scand. Sect. B 90: 445.
33. Shahidi, S. A., and Ferguson, A. R. 1971. New quantitative, qualitative, and confirmatory media for rapid analysis of food for *Clostridium perfringens*. Appl. Microbiol. 21: 500.
34. Spray, R. S. 1936. Semisolid media for cultivation and identification of the sporulating anaerobes. J. Bacteriol. 32: 135.
35. Taniguti, T. 1969. Sporulation media for *Clostridium perfringens*: A method with a new medium (AEA medium) for sporulation of *Clostridium perfringens* and some properties of formed spores. J. Food Hyg. Soc. Jpn. 9: 219.
36. Thatcher, F. S., and Clark, D. S. 1968. "Microorganisms in Foods: Their Significance and Methods of Enumeration." p. 128. U. of Toronto Press, Toronto, Canada.
37. Traci, P. A., and Duncan, C. L. 1974. Cold shock lethality and injury in *Clostridium perfringens*. Appl. Microbiol. 28: 815.
38. Wimsatt, J., Harmon, S. M., and Shah, D. 1986. Detection of *Clostridium perfringens* enterotoxin in stool specimens and culture supernatants by enzyme-linked immunosorbent assay. Diagn. Microbiol. Infect. Dis. 4: 307.

Chapter 38

LISTERIA

C. W. Donnelly, R. E. Brackett, S. Doores, W. H. Lee, and J. Lovett

38.1 INTRODUCTION

38.11 Description and Taxonomy of the Genus

Listeria monocytogenes was first definitively described by Murray et al.[81] in connection with an epizootic among laboratory-raised guinea pigs and rabbits. The researchers succeeded in both isolating the organism from the diseased animals and reinfecting healthy animals, thus establishing the pathogenesis of the organism. They named the organism *Bacterium monocytogenes* after the mononucleosis-like illness it produced. The following year, Pirie[87] described a similar epizootic in wild gerbils termed "Tiger River Disease" characterized by marked liver involvement; hence, Pirie's name for the isolate, *Listerella hepatolytica*. A third manifestation of listeriosis in animals was shown by Gill,[40] who found *L. monocytogenes* to be the cause of circling disease, an encephalitic condition in domesticated sheep. Nyfeldt[82] first reported listeriosis as a causative agent of an infectious mononucleosis-like disease in humans, and Burn[14] similarly described the first human cases of perinatal infection.

L. monocytogenes is a short, gram-positive, nonsporeforming rod-shaped bacterium that appears coccoidal in older cultures, leading to frequent misidentification.[100] It thrives under anaerobic to microaerophilic conditions, preferring a 10% carbon dioxide environment. *Listeria* multiplies over a wide range of temperatures, from 3° to 45°C with an optimum temperature range of 30° to 37°C, but it is considered a psychrotolerant foodborne pathogen.[114] The organism grows over a pH range of 5.0 to 9.6, but also survives in food products with pH levels outside of these parameters.[19] Growth occurs in some

637

media containing 10% NaCl with survival in 25.5% salt at 4°C.[79] The colonies produce a blue-green sheen on tryptose agar medium when viewed by obliquely transmitted light.[47] The production of β-hemolysis on blood agar plates has been closely linked with pathogenicity.[39] Characteristic umbrella-shaped growth occurs in tubed motility media when incubated at 25°C rather than at 35°C, and tumbling motility is exhibited in wet mounts. Seven serotypes are associated with this organism; however, foodborne outbreaks are thus far limited to serotype 4b.

Presumptive identification of *Listeria* focuses upon colony morphology, Gram reaction, tumbling motility, catalase reaction, and for *L. monocytogenes*, β-hemolysis. *Listeria* show the following biochemical reactions: catalase positive; oxidase negative; fermentation of carbohydrates to acid but not gas; esculin and sodium hippurate hydrolysis; methyl red positive; ammonia production from arginine; and negative reactions for hydrogen sulfide production, indole, nitrate reductase, gelatin liquefaction, and starch and urea hydrolysis.[70]

Members of the genus *Listeria* have been misidentified as *Corynebacterium* spp., *Haemophilus influenza*, *Erysepilothrix* spp., *Pneumococcus* spp., and *Streptococcus* spp. Cultural similarities to *Staphylococcus* spp. have been demonstrated by the abundance of new *Listeria* isolation media containing selective and differential agents designed to recover staphylococci.[11]

Species of *Listeria* can be separated by several taxonomic tests and physiologic reactions previously mentioned. In the eighth edition of Bergey's Manual,[101] four *Listeria* species were defined—*monocytogenes*, *denitrificans*, *grayi*, and *murrayi*. The latest edition[100] adds the species *L. innocua*, *L. seeligeri*, *L. welshimeri*, and *L. ivanovii*; however, three species described in the eighth edition—*denitrificans*, *grayi*, *murrayi*—have been relegated to a different taxonomic status. *L. denitrificans* is renamed *Jonesia denitrificans* based on differences in growth and biochemical characteristics, 16S RNA cataloging, and DNA homology to other species of the genus.[92, 112] The two species *L. murrayi* and *L. grayi* are classified in a new genus, *Murraya*, as *M. grayi* subsp. *murrayi* and *M. grayi* subsp. *grayi*, respectively.[104]

38.12   Ecology

L. monocytogenes has been isolated from numerous environmental sources, such as silage, soil, decaying vegetation, sewage, damp earth, straw, and feces.[1, 50, 67, 109, 110, 111, 113] Welshimer and Donker-Voet[113] suggested that *Listeria* exists in a saprophytic environment involving plants and soil that serves as a reservoir for later infections transmitted to animals and humans.[109] Gray[49, 50] postulated the link between feeding poorly made silage and the onset of encephalitis in ruminant animals. Although Olson et al.[83] did not show a clear relationship between continuous feeding of silage to sheep and the development of listeriosis, Donnelly[26] demonstrated an increase in listeriosis in cows fed poor-quality silage in which the pH level tended toward neutrality.

Listeria is ubiquitous and has been found in association with a wide variety of fish, birds, and mammals.[48, 52] Despite the routine isolation of the organism from the environment, only sporadic and epizootic outbreaks occur, suggesting that certain environmental or host circumstances are necessary before an outbreak is realized.[51, 56] In humans, incidence rates have ranged from 0.6% to 70% of the population.[58, 89] The carrier rate of the general public is believed to be 5%.[4]

38.13   Disease Syndrome

The disease listeriosis is a frequent cause of abortions in cattle and sheep; in humans, symptoms are manifest as septicemia, encephalitis, and circulatory monocytosis.[56] Although birds are susceptible to listeriosis, no symptoms or lesions appear.[48] In cases of milkborne infection, the organism is excreted into milk in an intracellular state within bovine neutrophils and macrophages.[13, 32] There are conflicting reports concerning the development of mastitis in cows that shed *Listeria* into milk.[24, 56] Cattle and sheep shed *L. monocytogenes* in feces and manure, and these materials, along with spoiled silage, have been used as fertilizer without benefit of composting.[62] Manure, spoiled silage, and soil may be the most significant sources of transmission of listeric infections to animals.

In women, *Listeria* may be harbored in the genital tract[53] and may be transmitted transplacentally from infected amniotic fluid and vaginal discharge to infants.[98] Infants may suffer from Granulomatosis infantisepticum, a necrotic disease affecting the internal organs. Infections may occur *in utero* as septicemia during early pregnancy or as meningitis later in gestation. Depending upon the stage of gestation, fetuses may succumb to spontaneous abortion or stillbirth or may be born with severe meningitis from which recovery is unlikely, despite rigorous antibiotic therapy. In maternal cases of listeriosis, the mother is usually mildly affected, exhibiting flu-like illness, whereas the fetus becomes profoundly infected.[8] Human infections as well as *in utero* infections can be successfully treated with tetracyclines.[98] In adults, septicemia, meningitis, endocarditis, conjunctivitis, pharyngitis, and flu-like illnesses are known to be manifestations of infection by *L. monocytogenes*. High-risk groups susceptible to infection are pregnant women, neonates, patients with neoplastic disease, or those treated with corticosteroids or antimetabolites or having other diseases that confer an immunocompromised state.[62] Suggestions have been made that persons suffering from chronic disorders such as diabetes, alcoholism, or heart disease may also be at higher risk.[72] Listeriosis appears to be an uncommon opportunistic infection in AIDS patients, although reported cases have increased.[6, 46, 73, 90] Occupationally, cutaneous listeriosis appears to be associated primarily with veterinarians and farm animal handlers.[16, 84] While transmission occurs from mother to child through the transplacental barrier, transmission from the environment to animals and animals to humans is not well understood.

38.14   Epidemiology

In North America, three outbreaks of infection caused by *L. monocytogenes* serotype 4b have been documented. In 1981, an outbreak involving 7 adults and 34 infants was recorded in the Maritime provinces of Canada where coleslaw was implicated as the vehicle of transmission. The cabbage used in the manufacture of the coleslaw was harvested from fields known to be fertilized by both composted and noncomposted manure from sheep, two of which had died from ovine listeriosis. Furthermore, the cabbage was held under refrigerated conditions for several months prior to manufacture of the coleslaw. Therefore, a combination of prolonged cold storage of cabbage and no heat treatment coupled with the use of ovine-infected manure fertilizer led to this incident.[97] Two adults (29%) and 17 infants (49%) died despite aggressive supportive care; all mothers recovered.

The second outbreak occurred in Massachusetts in 1983.[36] Pasteurized whole and 2% milk were implicated, although both products underwent pasteurization procedures with times and temperatures in excess of legal requirements. Of the 7 newborns and 42 adults affected, all adults had preexisting illnesses causing immunosuppression or were taking immunosuppressive drugs. Fourteen patients died (29% mortality). No *Listeria* were recovered from the finished product, but some were isolated from the raw milk and milk filters. These latter isolates, however, did not prove to match the epidemic serotype involved in the outbreak.

The third outbreak in 1985 implicated Mexican-style cheese as the vehicle of transmission.[57] A total of 145 cases occurred with 46 deaths (32% mortality); 88 (62%) of the afflicted individuals were pregnant Hispanic women.[68] Again *L. monocytogenes* serotype 4b was implicated. In this instance, the cheese was most likely manufactured from a combination of raw and pasteurized milk. *L. monocytogenes* was ubiquitous in the cheese plant environment, and the pH of the finished product was 6.6. Both of these factors were suspected of contributing heavily to the incident.

38.15   Foods Contaminated by *Listeria monocytogenes*

Two of the three outbreaks of listeriosis that have received considerable attention have involved contaminated dairy products. *L. monocytogenes* has been shown to survive but not necessarily grow during the manufacture of cottage,[95] Cheddar[93] and Camembert cheeses[94] when the organism is added to milk following pasteurization. Survival has also been shown during the spray-drying process of nonfat dry milk.[31]

Further investigation regarding the first outbreak, involving coleslaw, demonstrated that *L. monocytogenes* could grow on shredded cabbage.[7, 19] It is well established that *L. monocytogenes* displays rapid growth on processed meat products, including sliced chicken, turkey, ham, bologna, and bratwurst.[41] Khan et al.[60] and Leasor and Foegeding[64] have also demonstrated the ability of *Listeria* to grow in liquid eggs held at refrigeration temperatures.

38.16   Heat Resistance

Numerous researchers have described the heat resistance of the organism. Early work by Barber[3] and Potel[88] had indicated that *Listeria* could not survive pasteurization. Later studies by Bearns and Girard[5] demonstrated that *Listeria* could survive the time-temperature treatment of 61.7°C for 35 min if initial loads exceeded 50,000 per ml. Following the Massachusetts outbreak,[36] additional studies have examined the heat tolerance of this organism. Bradshaw et al.[9] found that under the conditions of their experiments, *L. monocytogenes* had a $D_{71.7°C}$ of 0.9 sec (range 0.8 to 1.1 sec) in milk. The heat resistance was shown to increase when the organism was heated in previously sterilized milk.[10] In either instance, pasteurization at 71.1°C for 15 sec would be more than adequate to inactivate levels of *L. monocytogenes* normally present in raw milk.[34] Donnelly et al.[28] also showed that the method for determining thermal resistance in earlier studies[5] could influence the numbers of survivors and advocated the use of sealed ampules rather than test tubes as heating vessels. Doyle et al.[32] and Fernandez-Garayzabal et al.[35] recovered *Listeria* from inoculated milk following heat-treatment in a pilot scale high-temperature short-time (HTST) unit using more extensive enrichment procedures.

Because *L. monocytogenes* has been shown to reside intracellularly within macrophages and neutrophils in bovine milk, several reports have questioned whether this location could provide a protective effect and thus confer a higher than usual heat resistance. Rigorous studies by Bunning et al.,[12, 13] have found that this was not the case.

38.17   Detection and Confirmation of *Listeria*

Numerous media have been examined for their ability to selectively isolate *Listeria* species. Successful isolation depends upon choosing a method sensitive to the recovery of low-level contamination (e.g., $<10^2$ *Listeria* per ml) coupled with the ability to repair injured organisms. Many procedures employ pre- or secondary enrichment media incubated at 35°C and 4°C followed by plating on selective/differential agars. Numerous taxonomic tests are required for confirmation.[69]

Further definition of the species can be demonstrated by DNA colony hybridization,[21] β-hemolysin gene probe,[22] enzyme immunosorbent assay,[33] plasmid DNA typing,[80] fluorescent antibody technique,[61] fatty acid analysis,[96] flow cytometry,[27, 29] Micro ID,[91] and Minitek or Vitek procedures.[30] Phage typing can be used in presumptive analysis[2, 77, 107] and appears to show close association with serological type.[105]

38.2   GENERAL CONSIDERATIONS

38.21   Methods of Isolation

Almost all of the methods developed for isolation of *L. monocytogenes* use one or both of two distinct characteristics of the bacterium. These characteristics are the abilities of *Listeria* to grow at refrigeration temperatures and to display resistance to many antibiotics. The earliest isolation methods[54] used a cold enrichment technique to allow *L. monocytogenes* to grow at the expense of non-psychrotrophic bacteria. Although this technique may require weeks or months to isolate *L. monocytogenes*, it is still among the most successful. Because time is often critical, the use of antimicrobial agents has replaced cold enrichment to select for *L. monocytogenes* in recent years.

The type of food will likely influence not only the populations of *L. monocytogenes* present but the type and populations of contaminants with which one must contend. Thus, the choice of media must sometimes be tailored to the type of food being analyzed.[42, 44, 45] This is particularly true if one is directly plating food samples on a selective medium, as discussed below.

Three general types of methods are presently being used to analyze foods for *L. monocytogenes*. The first and least-used of these is direct plating of a food suspension onto a selective solid medium. This technique offers the advantage of allowing the analyst to quantify the populations of *L. monocytogenes* cells in the food directly. Unfortunately, direct plating can detect only ≥ 100 per g *L. monocytogenes* in foods, not smaller numbers. For the detection of low numbers of *L. monocytogenes*, enrichment procedures must be employed. Media that work best for this purpose usually incorporate various antibiotics in a phenylethanol[66, 70, 74] or Baird-Parker[11] agar base. Antibiotics used most often include acriflavin, nalidixic acid, cycloheximide, and moxalactam. Among the best media for direct plating[17, 18] are LiCl-phenylethanol-moxalactam agar,[66] modified Vogel-Johnson agar (MVJ),[11] and Despierres agar.[23] Of these, MVJ provides the most easily recognizable *L. monocytogenes* colonies in the presence of contaminants.[11, 17, 18] Several modified versions of the Oxford agar developed by Curtis et al.,[20] such as Modified Oxford medium (MX) (38.31) or PalCam[106] are gaining in popularity for *Listeria* isolation because they are more inhibitory to *Enterococcus faecalis* by the use of 15 g per L LiCl.[20]

The second and most popular method uses one or more enrichment steps followed by plating onto a selective agar and is the basis for both the U.S. Food and Drug Administration (FDA)[70] and the U.S. Department of Agriculture (USDA), Food Safety and Inspection Service (FSIS)[76] isolation methods. The food is usually mixed with an enrichment broth and allowed to incubate for 24 to 48 hr. After incubation, a portion of the enrichment mixture is either again mixed with an enrichment broth or plated onto the final isolation agar. Enrichment broths are usually nutritious liquid media that employ various antimicrobial agents to which *L. monocytogenes* is resistant. The most common antimicrobial agents include nalidixic acid, acriflavin, and cycloheximide. Isolation agars include those used for direct plating, although less selective agars[17, 42] have also been used successfully.

The third group of methods used to analyze food for *L. monocytogenes* are the so-called rapid methods. These procedures go beyond traditional identification methods in that they also apply recently developed genetic and immunological techniques to reduce identification time. The use of enzyme immunosorbent assays[33] and DNA probes[21, 22] has been reported, and commercial kits are available for both (Section 38.53). Flow cytometry also shows promise for routine use as more specific antibodies become available and required equipment becomes more affordable.[27, 29] Rapid methods are faster than conventional methods and quite reliable. The main drawback and time constraints to the rapid methods developed thus far are the requirement for a pre-enrichment step to obtain sufficient cell density (see Chapter 39).

38.22   Treatment of Sample

Food samples should be stored and shipped at 4°C, and analyzed for *L. monocytogenes* as soon as possible. *L. monocytogenes* can grow slowly at refrigeration temperature. Therefore, samples should not be stored for prolonged times under refrigeration unless one specifically wishes to accomplish a cold enrichment.[70] Although *L. monocytogenes* is quite resistant to freezing,[43] freezing may cause drastic reduction of *L. monocytogenes* in certain foods. For this reason, frozen storage is recommended only when immediate analysis or refrigerated handling is not possible.

The growth of *L. monocytogenes* in refrigerated foods is not uniform, and foods should be sampled where growth of this organism is concentrated. For example, the growth of *L. monocytogenes* in soft cheeses like Brie is concentrated near the subsurface. In vacuum-packaged meats, the growth of *L. monocytogenes* is concentrated on or near the surface of the packaging film and thus can be detected fairly easily if sampled near the surface.[65] The growth of *L. monocytogenes* in refrigerated foods tends to be very spotty and erratic; thus one should sample a large number of retail samples to get an accurate assessment of the extent of contamination.

38.3   MEDIA, REAGENTS, AND EQUIPMENT

38.31   Media

Brain heart infusion
Columbia blood agar base
FDA *Listeria* enrichment broth (LEB)
University of Vermont (UVM) broth
HL agar
Lithium-phenylethanol-moxalactam (LPM) agar
Methyl red-Voges Proskauer (MR-VP) medium
Modified McBride agar (MMA)
Modified Oxford medium (MX)
Motility test medium

Neutralizing buffer
Nitrate broth
Nitrate reduction medium
Nutrient broth
Purple carbohydrate fermentation broth base
Triple sugar iron agar (TSI)
Trypticase soy agar (TSA)
Trypticase soy broth
Trypticase soy agar-yeast extract (TSA-YE)
Trypticase soy broth-yeast extract (TSB-YE)
TSA blood agar
Urea broth

38.32   Reagents

Defibrinated horse blood (Gibco Life Sciences #L20103)
Bile esculin
Dextrose
CAMP test cultures
        Staphylococcus—ATCC 25723, CIP 5710, NCTC 7428
        Rhodococcus equi—NCTC 1621
B lysin discs (Remel, Leneka, Kan)
Gram stain kit
Moxalactam, Eli Lilly & Co., Distra, or Sigma M-1900
Potassium phosphate buffer, 0.1 M, pH 6.0
Hydrogen peroxide (H_2O_2), 3%
Isopropanol, 70%
CO_2
Fetal calf serum
Maltose
Mannitol
Rhamnose
Xylose
MR-VP reagents
      (1) alpha-naphthol solution, 5 g per 100 ml absolute alcohol
      (2) potassium hydroxide solution, 40 g per 100 ml distilled H_2O
      (3) Methyl red indicator: 0.1 g methyl red in 300 ml 95%
ethanol made up to 500 ml in distilled water.
    Oxidase reagents—1 g N,N,N^1,N^1-tetramethyl-*p*-phenylenediamine·2HCl
in 100-ml distilled water.
    Nitrate reduction reagents
      (1) Reagent A—0.8 g sulfanilic acid in 100-ml 5 N acetic acid
      (2) Reagent B—0.5 g alpha-naphthylamine in 100-ml 5 N acetic
   acid

(3) Zinc powder
Acriflavin (Sigma)
Nalidixic acid (Sigma)
Cycloheximide (Sigma)
Polyvalent Antiserum (Difco)
    Type 1
    Type 4

38.33 Equipment

Balance—gram range
Chisel, steel, small
Cover slips, glass
Dissecting microscope
Erlenmeyer flask, 500 ml
Fermentation tubes (Durham)
Filter paper, Whatman 541
Forceps
Gauze pad, 3" × 3", sterile
Grease pencil or magic marker
Immersion oil (for microscope)
Incubators, 20° to 25°C; 30°C and 35°C
Inoculating loop
Inoculating needle
Inoculating needle, pure platinum
Lamp, fluorescent desk
Lamp with AO 653 Reichert light (or Bausch and Lomb Illuminator Light)
Microscope, inverted
Microscope slide, glass
Microscope, phase with 40× objective
Mirror, concave
Mixer, Vortex
Needle, 26 gauge, ⅜ inch
Pans, aluminum pie
Petri plates
pH meter
Pipettes (25 ml, 10 ml, 1 ml)
Scissors, steel
Sponge, 3" × 5", sterile with no anionic detergents
Sticks, glass hockey
Stomacher Model 400 (Tekmar, Cincinnati, Ohio) and sterile bags
Swabs, sterile cotton
Syringe, tuberculin, sterile, disposable
Tubes, 16 × 125 mm, screw-capped
Twist-tie for sealing plastic bags

38.4   PRECAUTIONS AND LIMITATIONS OF THE METHODS

Various methods differ in their ability to recover *L. monocytogenes* cells.[18, 42, 44, 45] In most cases, a particular medium will sacrifice either sensitivity or selectivity. This is particularly true if cells have been sublethally stressed by harsh treatments such as heating. The most selective media, such as LPM or MVJ, are poor at recovering injured cells. On the other hand, media that provide good recovery of injured cells, such as gum-based nalidixic acid (GBNA) agar, are often plagued with contaminants. In general, one should use the least selective medium possible. Foods that may contain injured *L. monocytogenes* cells and high populations of contaminants will almost certainly require pre-enrichment to allow the injured *L. monocytogenes* to recover.

The highly virulent nature of *L. monocytogenes* and the high mortality rates of listeriosis demand strict safety precautions. Laboratory supervisors should insist that standard good laboratory safety practices be followed.[78] Laboratory personnel should be especially mindful of generating aerosols during blending and mixing procedures and be meticulous in rinsing work areas often with bactericidal solutions. In addition, pregnant women or other immunocompromised personnel should be prohibited from entering laboratories in which *L. monocytogenes* will be analyzed. Individuals under medication should seek medical advice to determine whether their particular medications are known to compromise immunity.

38.5   PROCEDURES

Rapid progress is being made in the isolation of *L. monocytogenes* from foods and food manufacturing environments. Methodology has advanced from the long and cumbersome cold enrichment procedure to the relatively rapid procedure used by Lovett et al.[70, 71] Even more rapid procedures, promising to shorten the isolation and identification process to a few days, are employing monoclonal antibodies (ELISA methods) and DNA probes.

38.51   Enrichment and Direct Plating Methods

Detection of *L. monocytogenes* in foods is not difficult. Low numbers of the organism are commonly isolated from raw milk, meats, vegetables, seafoods, and the food processing environment.[71, 75] Enrichment procedures are used to isolate low numbers of *L. monocytogenes* from dairy and vegetable products (Sections 38.512, 38.514) and meats (Section 38.513), and food samples with ≥100/gram *L. monocytogenes* can be enumerated by direct plating on MX agar (38.516).

At the time of this writing, two methods are widely used in the United States to isolate low numbers of *L. monocytogenes* in foods. The FDA method is often used to examine dairy products and vegetables.[70] The USDA method[76] is widely used to recover *L. monocytogenes* from meat products and environmental swabs. The main difference between the USDA and FDA methods is that the USDA method uses a two-stage enrichment procedure, whereas the FDA method uses a single enrichment step. Also, the revised USDA procedure uses MX agar, yielding black *Listeria* colonies, so it is no longer necessary to use 45° transillumination to identify "blue" *Listeria* colonies.

38.511   Resuscitation for the isolation of injured *L. monocytogenes*

Injured *L. monocytogenes* are sublethally stressed as a result of exposure to heat,[11, 13, 42, 43, 102] freezing,[42, 43] or acid.[7] These injured cells and possibly intracellular bacteria may not grow in the selective media described in this chapter. The degree to which the particular selective medium suppresses the injured bacterial cell would vary depending on the medium's ingredients and also on the extent of the stress or injury. Sublethally stressed *L. monocytogenes* require resuscitation in a nonselective medium at a temperature favoring repair of sublethal injury. These parameters have not been fully determined, although media such as nutrient broth or TSA at temperatures of 25°C and 4°C have been used. Injured *L. monocytogenes* not detected by conventional enrichment procedures may resuscitate and grow to high numbers in foods stored at refrigeration temperatures, thus presenting a consumer health problem.

38.512   FDA's enrichment procedure for the isolation of *L. monocytogenes* from dairy foods

For liquid samples, pipette a 25-ml sample into 225 ml enrichment broth (LEB)[71] in a 500-ml flask and mix well by shaking. For solid samples, weigh 25 g into a Stomacher 400 bag and add 225 ml LEB. Mix the sample by stomaching for 2 min, and incubate the mixture in the plastic bag at 30°C. After incubation for 24 hr and again at 48 hr, the LEB culture is streaked onto modified McBride agar with cycloheximide (MMA)[71] and onto LPM agar[66] (53 Federal Register 44148, Nov. 1, 1988). MMA and LPM plates are incubated at 35°C for 48 hr and presumptive *Listeria* colonies are selected under 45° transillumination (Section 38.521). Colonies presumptively identified as *Listeria* on MMA are purified by restreaking on trypticase soy agar with yeast extract (TSA-YE). Colonies on TSA-YE incubated at 30°C for 24 to 48 hr are further identified according to the procedure in 38.52. A summary of the FDA method[70] is presented in Figure 1.

38.513   USDA's enrichment procedure for isolation of *L. monocytogenes* from meat products

The surfaces of meat packages are disinfected by swabbing with 70% isopropanol or 3% H_2O_2 before opening. Meat samples are cut into small pieces with either sterilized steel chisels, scissors, or forceps on a sterilized aluminum

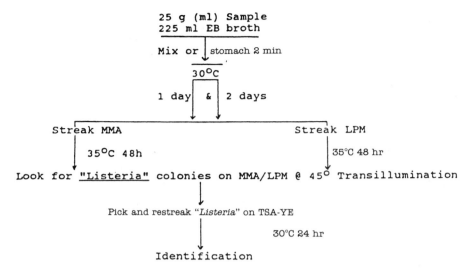

Figure 1—Schematic presentation of the FDA enrichment method for the isolation of low numbers of *L. monocytogenes* from dairy products.

pie pan. Twenty-five grams of meat samples are weighed into a sterile Stomacher 400 bag and 225 g of the primary enrichment broth (UVM) are added to the bag (Figure 2). The mixture is stomached for 2 min and closed with a wire twist-tie with some air trapped in the bag. To guard against leakage, the sample bag is placed inside another bag or beaker during incubation at 30°C for 24 hr. Following incubation, 0.1 ml of the UVM culture is pipetted into 10 ml of Fraser's secondary enrichment broth, and this is incubated at 35°C for 24 and 40 hr. After incubation, dip a sterile cotton swab into the Fraser's broth and swab and streak an MX agar plate as shown in Figure 2. MX agar is incubated at 35°C and examined for typical round *Listeria* colonies surrounded by a black zone. Incubate the MX agar for another day to detect a few slow growing *Listeria* strains. To purify suspect *Listeria* colonies as well as to identify β-hemolytic *Listeria* colonies from MX agar, touch 5 or 6 colonies simultaneously on MX agar with a soft pure platinum needle and streak these for isolation on HL agar (Section 38.522). The USDA FSIS isolation scheme is presented in Figure 3; presumptive *Listeria* isolates are identified according to the procedures outlined in Section 38.52.

38.514   Enrichment for isolation of *L. monocytogenes* from fruits and vegetables

Little work has been done on the detection of *L. monocytogenes* in fruits and vegetables. The most recent work is that of Hao et al.[55] designed to isolate *L. monocytogenes* from refrigerated cabbage. They examined several

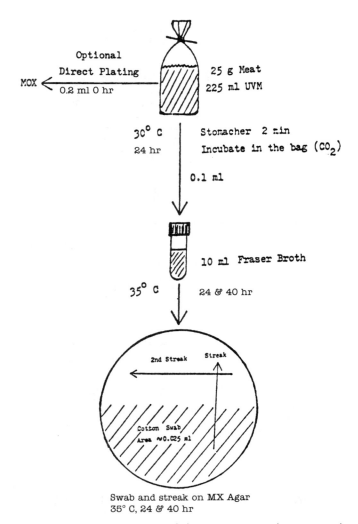

Figure 2—Schematic presentation of the USDA enrichment method for the isolation of low numbers of L. monocytogenes from meat products.

enrichment and isolation media. The enrichment broth of Lovett et al.[71] was found acceptable, and McBride's *Listeria* agar was recommended for isolation. Other media systems were also acceptable. Introduction of another medium will be avoided by using that already described.

Add 25 g fruit or vegetable to 225 ml LEB[71] in a stomacher 400 bag. Since surface contamination is likely to be the most important source of *L. monocytogenes*, remove for sampling primarily surface cuts whenever possible in these samples, which must be subdivided for analysis. Stomach for 2 min and

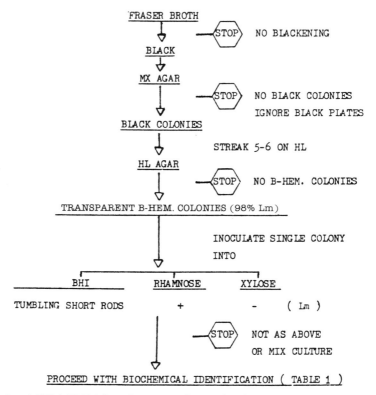

Figure 3—USDA FSIS identification schema for the isolation of *Listeria monocytogenes*.

incubate the mixture in the stomacher bag at 30°C for 7 days. At 1 and 7 days, streak culture onto MMA as described in Section 38.512.

38.515   Enrichment procedure for isolating *L. monocytogenes* from the environment by swabbing

L. monocytogenes is persistent on food processing machinery and in the food processing plant environment.[38] It can be detected by swabbing surfaces with a sterile 3″ × 3″ sponge or gauze moistened with Difco's Neutralizing Buffer.[38] (Caution: Some sponges contain anionic detergents, which inhibit the growth of *L. monocytogenes*. Each lot of sponges must be pretested for inhibition of *L. monocytogenes*.) Gauzes and sponges are placed into 100 ml of LEB or UVM (Figures 1 and 2). Continue as outlined in Section 38.513 for isolation of *Listeria*.

38.516   Enumeration of *L. monocytogenes* from foods by direct plating

Both the FDA and USDA enrichment procedures yield only qualitative data with respect to the presence or absence of *Listeria* in a sample. A great deal more information can be gained from routine enrichment tests (Figures 1 and 2) by surface plating 0.2 ml of the LEB or UVM blended suspension at 0 hr onto an MX agar plate. Most of the routine food samples yield negative plates by direct plating, but the presence of *Listeria* colonies by direct plating on MX agar indicates serious *Listeria* contamination problems, and colonies can be counted and identified as in Section 38.523. Samples implicated in cases of human listeriosis should always be tested by the enrichment procedure and also by direct surface plating of several decimal dilutions of the blended sample at 0 hr in MX agar in order to obtain an accurate count of *L. monocytogenes* in the samples. Samples expected to contain less than 100 per g of *L. monocytogenes* can be counted by the most probable number (MPN) procedure.

The FDA also employs MX agar plates for the direct plating and identification of high counts of *L. monocytogenes* in food samples with a listeriolysin-specific DNA probe after transferring the colonies from the MX agar to Whatman 541 filter paper (see Section 38.53).

Listeria that have grown in foods during manufacturing or storage under favorable conditions can be enumerated by plating 0.2 ml of the 1:10 dilution of a food in UVM or LEB onto MX agar (see Figure 2). When high counts are anticipated, decimal dilutions may be directly plated. Colonies are visible after 24 hr incubation at 30°C and can be easily counted after 40 hr incubation. Colonies can be identified on isolation agars as described in Section 38.52.

38.52   Identification of *L. monocytogenes* Colonies from Isolation Agars

38.521   Recognition of *Listeria* colonies by 45° transillumination

Colonies appearing as typical *Listeria* on LPM, MMA, and TSA-YE should be examined using a dissecting or inverted microscope arranged for 45° transillumination (see Section 38.33). Not all light sources and mirrors work for the proper 45° transillumination of *L. monocytogenes* colonies. Best results are obtained using the AO 653 (Reichert 653) or Bausch and Lomb illuminator light with a variable focus lens in conjunction with either a plane or concave mirror (Figure 4a). Alternatively, a more stable 45° transillumination without using a mirror can be achieved by using the AO 653 light and a low power (25×) invert microscope such as Leitz Diavert (Figure 4b). For proper 45° transillumination, place a piece of white filter paper on the microscope stage and focus the AO 653 light by adjusting the distance of the light as well as the focusing lens until a sharp image of the lamp filament appears on the filter paper. Check the microscope arrangement routinely using a 20-hr *L. monocytogenes* culture on LPM agar.

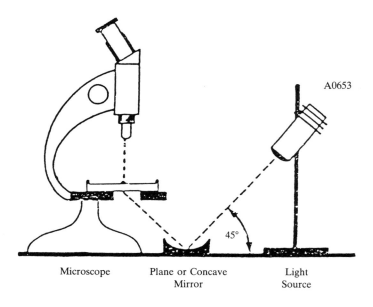

Microscope   Plane or Concave   Light
                    Mirror   Source

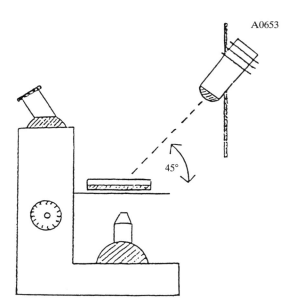

Figure 4—Examination of MMA and LPM plates for *Listeria* colonies using 45°
transillumination; 4a. using an illuminator light with a variable focus
lens in conjunction with a plane or concave mirror; 4b. using a
low-power invert microscope.

Depending on the size of the colony, *Listeria* colonies are dense white to iridescent white appearing as crushed glass. Small colonies tend to be blue. Non-*Listeria* tend to be yellowish or orange. With some experience, one can readily distinguish *Listeria* from other bacterial colonies. Typical *Listeria* colonies are picked from MMA agar and restreaked for purity on TSA-YE agar. Colonies on LPM agar are restreaked for purity on TSA-YE agar.

38.522   Detection of β-hemolytic *Listeria* on HL agar

After incubation at 35°C for 16 to 24 hr in 5% CO_2 (optional), surface-streaked *L. monocytogenes*, *L. seeligeri*, and *L. ivanovii* form distinctive hemolytic colonies on HL agar that can be viewed with a fluorescent desk lamp as shown in Figure 5. The β-hemolytic zone is not visible when viewed with a bacterial colony counter. The characteristic blue color of *Listeria* colonies can be observed by tilting the HL plate at an oblique angle to the light source. The colony characteristic of β-hemolytic *Listeria* on HL agar is unique, and no other β-hemolytic non-*Listeria* bacterial colonies look similar. When coupled with tumbling motility and rhamnose and xylose reactions, this appearance provides a presumptive-positive identification of *L. monocytogenes* in 4 to 5 days (Figure 3). Further identification of isolated colonies is outlined in Section 38.523.

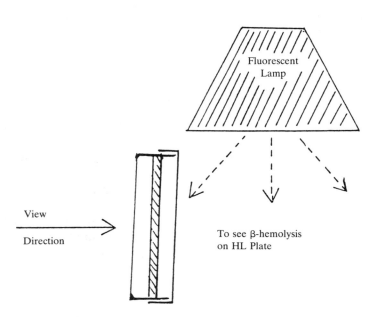

Figure 5 — Proper viewing of *Listeria* β-hemolysis on HL agar.

38.523   Biochemical and CAMP test identification of *L. monocytogenes*

Well-isolated *Listeria* colonies on TSA-YE agar or *B*-hemolytic colonies on HL agar are inoculated individually into 5 ml BHI broth and incubated overnight at 20° to 25°C. Wet mounts of young cultures examined with a phase microscope (oil immersion objective) permit observation of the characteristic slow tumbling motility and the short-rod morphology of these cultures. If a BHI culture appears contaminated (i.e., mixed rods, cocci, etc.), the culture should be restreaked for purity before proceeding with the biochemical identification. The BHI cultures are used to inoculate all biochemical cultures, the motility medium, and the CAMP test. The biochemical tests and staining reactions are listed in Table 1. *L. monocytogenes* are β-hemolytic, motile, CAMP-positive, gram-positive, rod-shaped organisms. Biochemically, *L. monocytogenes* are catalase-positive and oxidase- and urea-negative, ferment TSIA slants with an acid slant and acid butt, are O/F-positive for glucose, display growth and hydrolysis in bile esculin broth, are MR-VP-positive, do not reduce nitrate, do not ferment mannitol or xylose, but do ferment rhamnose.

The FDA procedure for detection of hemolysis requires stabbing of sheep blood agar plates and reading a zone of hemolysis around the stab in 48 hr at 35°C. The USDA procedure uses a culture streaked onto HL agar.

Inoculate motility medium from the BHI culture. Incubate for 7 days at room temperature and observe daily. *Listeria* are motile, forming a typical umbrella-shaped growth pattern that may be observable in 2 days.

The CAMP reaction or a zone of enhanced β-hemolysin interaction between *L. monocytogenes*, *L. seeligeri*, and *L. ivanovii* and *Staphylococcus aureus* (ATCC 25723, CIP 5710, or NCTC 7428) or *Rhodococcus equi* (NCTC 1621) is tested in an 8-ml thick plate of blood agar base containing 5% sheep's blood. Alternatively, a version of the CAMP test uses commercially prepared β-lysin discs. In this test, the disc is placed in the center of the TSA blood plate (8 ml thickness), and 4 or 5 *Listeria* cultures are streaked as radiating lines from the disc. Very sharp interaction between the cultures and the disc can be observed after overnight incubation at 35°C. All three species of *Listeria* mentioned above are CAMP-positive to the β-lysin discs, but only *L. ivanovii* forms a continuous β-hemolytic line on the TSA blood plate. A summary of the *Listeria* species characteristics is presented in Table 1. Some natural *Listeria* isolates do not fit all identification patterns of Table 1. These isolates can be tested for mouse virulence (Section 38.55). *Listeria* cultures may be preserved for a long time as a suspension in filter-sterilized fetal calf serum at −70°C or for several months in Difco motility medium stored at 4°C.

38.53   Rapid Detection Methods

A number of rapid methods are available to test for the presence of *Listeria* in a variety of food and environmental samples. Farber and Speirs[33] described

Table 1—Biochemical Identification and Differentiation of *Listeria* Species.[69]

	β-hemolysis	Tumbling motility	CAMP—*s. aureus*	CAMP—*Rhodococcus*	Umbrella motility	Gram reaction	Catalase	Oxidase	Urea	TSI	Glucose O/F	Bile esculin	MR-VP	NO₂	Mannitol	Xylose	Rhamnose
L. monocytogenes	+	+	+	−	+	+	+	−	−	a/a	+/+	+	+/+	−	−	−	+
L. seeligeri	+	+	+	−	+	+	+	−	−	a/a	+/+	+	+/+	−	−	+	−
L. ivanovii	+	+	+	+	+	+	+	−	−	a/a	+/+	+	+/+	−	−	+	−
L. innocua	−	+	−	−	+	+	+	−	−	a/a	+/+	+	+/+	−	−	−	+/−
L. grayi	−	+	−	−	+	+	+	−	−	a/a	+/+	+	+/+	−	+	−	−
L. murrayi	−	+	−	−	+	+	+	−	−	a/a	+/+	+	+/+	−	+	−	+/−

+ = positive reaction within 48 hr

− = negative reaction within 48 hr

a/a = acid slant/acid butt

O/F = oxidative, fermentative utilization of glucose

the use of enzyme-linked immunosorbent assay (ELISA) to detect *Listeria* in raw milk. This procedure involved the use of monoclonal antibodies specific for *Listeria* flagellar antigens. Flow cytometry[27, 29] has also been used to analyze milk samples rapidly for the presence of *Listeria*. Datta et al.[21, 22] reported development of an *L. monocytogenes*-specific DNA probe. This probe has been successfully used in conjunction with a direct plating procedure to quantitate *L. monocytogenes* in foods. The aforementioned rapid procedures are not available commercially. Two promising tests, however, are commercially available. The first, available from GENE-TRAK Systems (Framingham, Mass.) is a nucleic acid hybridization assay based on detection of unique *Listeria* 16S RNA sequences.[63] The original detection format was isotopic; it has since been revised to a colorimetric, non-isotopic detection format. Total assay time, including cultural enrichment, can be less than 2.5 days. The second rapid commercial assay is *Listeria*-tek, available from Organon-Technica (Durham, N.C.). *Listeria*-tek is an ELISA-based assay that employs two monoclonal antibodies specific to *Listeria*.[15] Total assay time required to perform this test is 40 hr. These two commercially available assays are useful as screening techniques because they react positively to samples containing any *Listeria* species. Their chief disadvantage is cost.

Fraser and Sperber[37] recently reported on a simple, cost-effective method to establish the presence of *Listeria* spp. presumptively. This method employs Fraser broth, a modification of USDA secondary enrichment broth containing lithium chloride and ferric ammonium citrate. Esculin hydrolysis, indicative of the presumptive presence of *Listeria*, is noted by observing blackening in the broth. Presumptive detection of *Listeria* can be accomplished within 48 hr using Fraser broth. This procedure has been shown to correlate well with the FDA procedure for detecting *L. monocytogenes* in ice cream products.

38.54 Serology

The numerous serologic variants among the O and H antigens are characterized according to various schemes. Paterson[86] described four basic serotypes based upon heat-labile "H" antigens. Donker-Voet[25] expanded this listing to 17 serovars.

L. monocytogenes can be serotyped using commercially available antisera as polyvalent O, type 1, and type 4 (Difco, Detroit, MI). The procedure to demonstrate specificity to other serotypes is more complex.

Specific O and H antigens can be prepared according to the methods of Bennett (personal communication) and Seeliger and Hohne.[99] Specific antiserum is produced by immunizing rabbits intravenously with increasing amounts of antigen over a 3- to 4-day period. The animals are exsanguinated when titers of 1:6000 and 1:6400 are achieved for O-antisera and H-antisera, respectively. Antisera are absorbed to remove unwanted antibodies and evaluated for titer, quality, and cross-serotype reactivity.

38.55   Pathogenicity Models

Pathogenicity within the genus *Listeria* is restricted to two species, *L. monocytogenes* and *L. ivanovii*. A number of models have been used to demonstrate the pathogenic potential of *L. monocytogenes* and *L. ivanovii* isolates. These models have included mouse pathogenicity,[71] the Anton test,[52] and inoculation of the chorioallantois membrane of chicken embryos.[103] The FDA employs mouse pathogenicity to demonstrate conclusively the virulence potential of isolates. Five mice per strain are inoculated intraperitoneally with 0.1 ml of diluted, washed culture containing approximately 10^9 *Listeria*. Pathogenic strains will kill mice within 5 days.[71]

Attempts have been made to study *Listeria* virulence without using an animal model. Pathogenic *Listeria* species are primarily distinguished from non-pathogenic *Listeria* strains on the basis of hemolysin production. Parrisius et al.[85] demonstrated that human pathogenic *Listeria* strains produce at least two distinct toxins, alpha- and beta-listeriolysin. In 26 of 28 isolates examined, β-hemolysis was the result of beta-listeriolysin production. Gaillard et al.[39] conclusively demonstrated the role of hemolysin in *Listeria* virulence by obtaining a hemolysin-negative mutant through insertion of a transposon Tn1545 into a virulent strain of *L. monocytogenes*, which rendered the strain totally avirulent. However, Kathariou et al.[59] reported that although hemolytic activity was lost through transposon mutagenesis with a concomitant loss of virulence in the mouse, hyperhemolytic variants, Hly^{+++}, were no more virulent in a mouse model than hemolytic variants, Hly^+.

38.6   INTERPRETATION OF DATA

Several problems have been encountered in interpreting the finding of *L. monocytogenes* in food and environmental samples. The cultural methods for the selection of *Listeria* are not entirely adequate and yield only qualitative results. Because of the difficult sampling procedures, a negative result does not necessarily ensure the absence of *Listeria*. Newer and emerging methods may help to alleviate this problem.

The entire physiology of *L. monocytogenes* is subject to intense scrutiny, primarily focusing on its behavior in foods and its survivability in adverse conditions.[108] While it is not unusual to recover *Listeria* from raw products, foods that undergo some type of heat processing during manufacture or are classified as "ready-to-eat" and are not expected to undergo any further cooking are required to be *L. monocytogenes*-free. Because of the psychrotrophic nature, refrigeration cannot be relied upon as the primary means of preservation.

Postprocessing contamination is presumed to result from environmental contamination. Where this occurs, more effective means to control environmental contamination as well as better processing methods should be instituted.

The interaction of *L. monocytogenes* and humans is not well understood.[49, 50] Host resistance, portal of entry, and infective dose play key roles in the acquisition of the organism. Neither the minimum infective dose nor the lethal dose for humans in known. For this reason, a zero tolerance level is now required.

Control of *L. monocytogenes* in the environment is being achieved presently with the institution of good manufacturing practices specifically designed to minimize contamination of *L. monocytogenes* as well as other foodborne pathogens.

38.7 REFERENCES

1. Al-Ghazali, M. R. and Al-Azawi, S. K. 1986. Detection and enumeration of *Listeria monocytogenes* in a sewage treatment plant in Iraq. J. Appl. Bacteriol. 60: 251.
2. Audurier, A., Rocourt, J. and Courtieu, A. L. 1977. Isolement et caracterisation de bacteriophages de *Listeria monocytogenes*. Ann. Microbiol. (Inst. Pasteur) 128A: 185.
3. Barber, M. 1939. A comparative study of *Listerella* and *Erysipelothrix*. J. Pathol. Bacteriol. 48: 11.
4. Barza, M. 1985. Listeriosis and milk. N. Engl. J. Med. 312(7): 438.
5. Bearns, R. E. and Girard, K. F. 1958. The effect of pasteurization on *Listeria monocytogenes*. Can. J. Microbiol. 4: 55.
6. Beninger, P. R., Savoia, M. C. and Davis, C. E. 1988. *Listeria monocytogenes* meningitis in a patient with AIDS-related complex. J. Infect. Dis. 158: 1396.
7. Beuchat, L. R., Brackett, R. E., Hao, D. Y.-Y. and Conner, D. E. 1986. Growth and thermal inactivation of *Listeria monocytogenes* in cabbage and cabbage juice. Can. J. Microbiol. 32: 791.
8. Bojsen-Moller, J. 1972. Human listeriosis. Acta Pathol. Microbiol. Scand. Suppl. 229: 1.
9. Bradshaw, J. G., Peeler, J. T., Corwin, J. J., Hunt, J. M., Tierney, J. T., Larkin, E. P. and Twedt, R. M. 1985. Thermal resistance of *Listeria monocytogenes* in milk. J. Food Prot. 48: 743.
10. Bradshaw, J. G., Peeler, J. T., Corwin, J. J., Hunt, J. M. and Twedt, R. M. 1987. Thermal resistance of *Listeria monocytogenes* in dairy products. J. Food Prot. 50: 543.
11. Buchanan, R. E., Stahl, H. G. and Archer, D. L. 1987. Improved plating media for simplified, quantitative detection of *Listeria monocytogenes* in foods. Food Microbiol. 4: 269.
12. Bunning, V. K., Crawford, R. G., Bradshaw, J. G., Peeler, J. T., Tierney, J. T. and Twedt, R. M. 1986. Thermal resistance of intracellular *Listeria monocytogenes* cells suspended in raw bovine milk. Appl. Environ. Microbiol. 52: 1398.
13. Bunning, V. K., Donnelly, C. W., Peeler, J. T., Briggs, E. H., Bradshaw, J. G., Crawford, R. G., Beliveau, C. M. and Tierney, J. T. 1988. Thermal inactivation of *Listeria monocytogenes* within bovine macrophages. Appl. Environ. Microbiol. 54: 364.
14. Burn, C. G. 1936. Clinical and pathological features of an infection caused by a new pathogen of the genus *Listerella*. Am. J. Pathol. 12: 341.
15. Butman, B. T., Plank, M. C., Durham, R. J. and Mattingly, J. A. 1988. Monoclonal antibodies which identify a genus-specific *Listeria* antigen. Appl. Environ. Microbiol. 54: 1564.
16. Cain, D. B. and McCann, V. L. 1986. An unusual case of cutaneous listeriosis. J. Clin. Microbiol. 23: 976.
17. Cassiday, P. K., Brackett, R. E. and Beuchat, L. R. 1989. Evaluation of three newly developed direct plating media to enumerate *Listeria monocytogenes* in foods. Appl. Environ. Microbiol. 55: 1645.

18. Cassiday, P. K., Brackett, R. E. and Beuchat, L. R. 1989. Evaluation of ten selective direct-plating media for enumeration of *Listeria monocytogenes* in hams and oysters. Food Microbiol. 6: 113.

19. Conner, D. E., Brackett, R. E. and Beuchat, L. R. 1986. Effect of temperature, sodium chloride, and pH on growth of *Listeria monocytogenes* in cabbage juice. Appl. Environ. Microbiol. 52: 59.

20. Curtis, G. D. W., Mitchell, R. G., King, A. F. and Griffin, E. J. 1989. A selective differential medium for the isolation of *Listeria monocytogenes*. Lett. Appl. Microbiol. 8: 95.

21. Datta, A. R., Wentz, B. A. and Hill, W. E. 1987. Detection of hemolytic *Listeria monocytogenes* by using DNA colony hybridization. Appl. Environ. Microbiol. 53: 2256.

22. Datta, A. R., Wentz, B. A., Shook, D. and Trucksess, M. 1988. Synthetic oligonucleotide probes for detection of *Listeria monocytogenes*. Appl. Environ. Microbiol. 54: 2933.

23. Despierres, M. 1971. Isolation of *Listeria monocytogenes* in a medium inhibitory to *Streptococcus faecalis*. Ann. Inst. Pasteur 121: 493.

24. Donker-Voet, J. 1962. My view on the epidemiology of *Listeria* infections. In "Second Symposium on Listeric Infection," ed. M. L. Gray, p. 133. Montana State College, Bozeman, Mont.

25. Donker-Voet, J. 1972. *Listeria monocytogenes*: Some biochemical and serological aspects. Acta Microbiol. Acad. Sci. Hung. 19: 287.

26. Donnelly, C. W. 1986. Listeriosis in dairy products. Why now and why milk? Hoards Dairyman July 25, p. 663.

27. Donnelly, C. W. and Baigent, G. J. 1986. Method for flow cytometric detection of *Listeria monocytogenes* in milk. Appl. Environ. Microbiol. 52: 689.

28. Donnelly, C. W., Briggs, E. H. and Donnelly, L. S. 1987. Comparison of heat resistance of *Listeria monocytogenes* in milk as determined by two methods. J. Food Prot. 50: 14.

29. Donnelly, C. W., Baigent, G. J. and Briggs, E. H. 1988. Flow cytometry for automated analysis of milk containing *Listeria monocytogenes*. J. Assn. Off. Anal. Chem. 71: 655.

30. Doores, S., Marshall, C. and Amelang, J. 1988. Comparison of the FDA procedure with Minitek and Vitek AMS for the identification of *Listeria* species. Abstr. P-7, Ann. Meet. of the Amer. Soc. for Microbiol.

31. Doyle, M. P., Meske, L. M. and Marth, E. H. 1985. Survival of *Listeria monocytogenes* during the manufacture and storage of nonfat dry milk. J. Food Prot. 48: 740.

32. Doyle, M. P., Glass, K. A., Beery, J. T., Garcia, G. A., Pollard, D. J. and Schultz, R. D. 1987. Survival of *Listeria monocytogenes* in milk during high-temperature, short-time pasteurization. Appl. Environ. Microbiol. 53: 1433.

33. Farber, J. M. and Speirs, J. I. 1987. Monoclonal antibodies directed against the flagellar antigens of *Listeria* species and their potential in EIA-based methods. J. Food Prot. 50: 479.

34. FDA. 1978. Grade A pasteurized milk ordinance. 1978 recommendations. Pub. Health Serv./Food and Drug Admin. Pub. 229 (Rev. 1983), U.S. Govt. Print. Office, Washington, D.C.

35. Fernandez-Garayzabal, J. F., Dominguez-Rodriguez, L., Vazquez-Boland, J. A., Rodriguez-Ferri, E. F., Briones-Dieste, V., Blanco-Cancelo, J. L. and Suarez-Fernandez, G. 1987. Survival of *Listeria monocytogenes* in raw milk treated in a pilot plant size pasteurizer. J. Appl. Bacteriol. 63: 553.

36. Fleming, D. W., Cochi, S. L., MacDonald, K. L., Brondum, J., Hayes, P. S., Plikaytis, B. D., Holmes, M. B., Audurier, A., Broome, C. V. and Reingold, A. L. 1985. Pasteurized milk as a vehicle of infection in an outbreak of listeriosis. N. Engl. J. Med. 312: 404.

37. Fraser, J. A. and Sperber, W. H. 1988. Rapid detection of *Listeria* spp. in food and environmental samples by esculin hydrolysis. J. Food Prot. 51: 762.

38. Gabis, D. A., Flowers, R. S., Evanson, D. and Faust, R. E. 1989. A survey of 18 dry

dairy product processing plant environments for *Salmonella, Listeria*, and *Yersinia*. J. Food Prot. 52: 122.

39. Gaillard, J.-L., Berche, P. and Sansonetti, P. 1986. Transposon mutagenesis to study the role of hemolysin in the virulence of *Listeria monocytogenes*. Infect. Immun. 52: 50.

40. Gill, D. A. 1937. Ovine bacterial encephalitis (Circling Disease) and the bacterial genus *Listerella*. Aust. Vet. J. 13: 46.

41. Glass, K. A. and Doyle, M. P. 1989. Fate of *Listeria monocytogenes* in processed meat products during refrigerated storage. Appl. Environ. Microbiol. 55: 1565.

42. Golden, D. A., Beuchat, L. R. and Brackett, R. E. 1988. Evaluation of selective direct-plating media for their suitability to recover uninjured, heat-injured, and freeze-injured *Listeria monocytogenes* from foods. Appl. Environ. Microbiol. 54: 1451.

43. Golden, D. A., Beuchat, L. R. and Brackett, R. E. 1988. Inactivation and injury of *Listeria monocytogenes* as affected by heating and freezing. Food Microbiol. 5: 17.

44. Golden, D. A., Beuchat, L. R. and Brackett, R. E. 1988. Direct plating technique for enumeration of *Listeria monocytogenes* in foods. J. Assn. Off. Anal. Chem. 71: 647.

45. Golden, D. A., Brackett, R. E. and Beuchat, L. R. 1990. Efficacy of direct plating media for recovering *Listeria monocytogenes* from foods. Int. J. Food Microbiol. 10: 143.

46. Gould, I. A., Belok, L. C. and Handwerger, S. 1986. *Listeria monocytogenes*: A rare cause of opportunistic infection in the Acquired Immunodeficiency Syndrome (AIDS) and a new cause of meningitis in AIDS. A case report. AIDS Res. 2: 231.

47. Gray, M. L. 1957. A rapid method for the detection of colonies of *Listeria monocytogenes*. Zentralbl. Bakteriol. Abt. 1, Orig. A. 169: 373.

48. Gray, M. L. 1958. Listeriosis in fowls—A review. Avian Dis. 2: 296.

49. Gray, M. L. 1960. A possible link in the relationship between silage feeding and listeriosis. J. Am. Vet. Med. Assn. 136: 205.

50. Gray, M. L. 1960. Isolation of *Listeria monocytogenes* from oat silage. Science 132: 1767.

51. Gray, M. L. 1964. Infections due to *Listeria monocytogenes* in wildlife. Trans. North Am. Wildl. Nat. Resour. Conf. 29: 202.

52. Gray, M. L. and Killinger, A. H. 1986. *Listeria monocytogenes* and listeric infections. Bacteriol. Rev. 30: 309.

53. Gray, M. L. and McWade, D. H. 1964. The isolation of *Listeria monocytogenes* from the bovine cervix. J. Bacteriol. 68: 634.

54. Gray, M. L., Stafseth, H. J., Thorp, F. Jr., Scholl, L. B. and Riley, W. F. Jr. 1948. A new technique for isolating listerellae from bovine brain. J. Bacteriol. 55: 471.

55. Hao, D. Y.-Y., Beuchat, L. R. and Brackett, R. E. 1987. Comparison of media and methods for detecting and enumerating *Listeria monocytogenes* in refrigerated cabbage. Appl. Environ. Microbiol. 53: 955.

56. Hyslop, N. St. G. and Osborne, A. D. 1959. Listeriosis: A potential danger to public health. Vet. Rec. 71: 1082.

57. James, S. M., Fannin, S. L., Agee, B. A., Hall, B., Parker, E., Vogt, J., Run, G., Williams, J., Lieb, L., Salminen, C., Prendergast, T., Werner, S. B. and Chin, J. 1985. Listeriosis outbreak associated with Mexican-style cheese. Morb. Mort. Wk. Rep. 34(24): 357.

58. Kampelmacher, E. H. and van Noorle Jansen, L. M. 1972. Further studies on the isolation of *L. monocytogenes* in clinically healthy individuals. Zentralbl. Bakteriol. Abt. 1, Orig. A. 221: 70.

59. Kathariou, S., Roucourt, J., Hof, H. and Goebel, W. 1988. Levels of *Listeria monocytogenes* hemolysin are not directly proportional to virulence in experimental infections of mice. Infect. Immun. 56: 534.

60. Khan, M. A., Palmas, C. V., Seaman, A. and Woodbine, M. 1973. Survival versus growth of a facultative psychrotroph in meat and products of meat. Zentralbl. Bakteriol. Hyg. 1. Abt. Orig. B. 157: 277.

61. Khan, M. A., Seaman, A. and Woodbine, M. 1977. Immunofluorescent identification of *Listeria monocytogenes*. Zentralbl. Bakteriol. Abt. 1, Orig. A. 239: 62.

62. Killinger, A. H. 1970. Listeriosis. In "Diseases Transmitted from Animals to Man," 6th ed., eds. W. T. Hubbert, W. F. McCulloch, and P. R. Schnurrenburger, p. 282. Thomas, Springfield, Ill.

63. Klinger, J. D. 1988. Isolation of *Listeria*: A review of procedures and future prospects. Infection 16 (suppl.): 98.

64. Leasor, S. B. and Foegeding, P. M. 1988. Growth and inactivation of *Listeria monocytogenes* F5069 and Scott A in liquid whole egg. Abstr. 168, Ann. Meet. of the Inst. of Food Technologists.

65. Lee, W. H. 1989. Screening test to detect *Listeria* ($\geq 100/g$) in food. P-325, Ann. Meet. of the Amer. Soc. for Microbiol.

66. Lee, W. H. and McClain, D. 1986. Improved *Listeria monocytogenes* selective agar. Appl. Environ. Microbiol. 52: 1215.

67. Lehnert, C. 1960. Die Tenazitat von *Listeria monocytogenes* in der Aussenwelt. Zentralbl. Bakteriol. Abt. 1, Orig. A. 180: 350.

68. Linnan, M. J., Mascola, L., Xiao, D. L., Goulet, V., May, S., Salminen, C., Yonekura, L., Fannin, S., Hayes, P., Weaver, R., Feeley, J. and Broome, C. V. 1986. An investigation of listeriosis in southern California, 1985. Abstr. C-391, Ann. Meet. of the Amer. Soc. for Microbiol.

69. Lovett, J. 1988. Isolation and enumeration of *Listeria monocytogenes*. Food Technol. 42: 172.

70. Lovett, J. and Hitchins, A. D. 1989. *Listeria* isolation. Bacteriological Analytical Manual, 6th ed., Supplement, Sept. 1987 (Second Printing 1989): 29.01.

71. Lovett, J., Francis, D. W. and Hunt, J. M. 1987. *Listeria monocytogenes* in raw milk: Detection, incidence, and pathogenicity. J. Food Prot. 50: 188.

72. Mair, N. S. 1968. Human listeriosis. In "Some Diseases of Animals Communicable to Man in Britain," ed. O. Graham-Jones, p. 221. Pergamon Press, London.

73. Mascola, L., Lieb, L., Chiu, J., Fannin, S. L. and Linnan, M. J. 1988. Listeriosis: An uncommon opportunistic infection in patients with acquired immunodeficiency syndrome. A report of five cases and a review of the literature. Am. J. Med. 84: 162.

74. McBride, M. E. and Girard, K. F. 1960. A selective method for the isolation of *Listeria monocytogenes* from mixed bacterial populations. J. Lab. Clin. Med. 55: 153.

75. McClain, D. and Lee, W. H. 1988. Development of a USDA-FSIS method for isolation of *Listeria monocytogenes* from raw meat and poultry. J. Assn. Off. Anal. Chem. 71: 660.

76. McClain, D. and Lee, W. H. 1989. FSIS method for the isolation and identification of *Listeria monocytogenes* from processed meat and poultry products. Lab. Comm. No. 57, Revised May 24, 1989. U.S. Dept. of Agric., FSIS, Microbiol. Div., Beltsville, Md.

77. McLauchlin, J., Audurier, A. and Taylor, A. G. 1986. The evaluation of a phage-typing system for *Listeria monocytogenes* for use in epidemiological studies. J. Med. Microbiol. 22: 357.

78. Miller, B. M., ed. 1986. "Laboratory Safety: Principles and Practices." Amer. Soc. for Microbiol., Washington, D.C.

79. Mitscherlich, E. and Marth, E. H., eds. 1984. "Microbial Survival in the Environment: Bacteria and Rickettsiae Important in Human and Animal Health," p. 219. Springer Verlag, Heidelberg.

80. Mottice, S., Robinson, W. and Reimer, L. G. 1987. Plasmid typing for the epidemiological characterization of *Listeria monocytogenes*. Abstr. C-206, Ann. Meet. of the Amer. Soc. for Microbiol.

81. Murray, E. G. D., Webb, R. A. and Swann, M. B. R. 1926. A disease of rabbits characterized by a large mononuclear leucocytosis caused by a hitherto undescribed bacillus *Bacterium monocytogenes* (n.sp.). J. Pathol. Bacteriol. 29: 404.

82. Nyfeldt, A. 1929. Etiologie de la mononucleose infectieuse. Compt. Rend. Soc. Biol. 101: 590.

83. Olson, C. Jr., Bagdonas, V., Rollins, C. L. and Blore, I. C. 1953. The relation of silage to listeriosis in sheep. Am. J. Vet. Res. 14: 202.

84. Owen, C. R., Meis, A., Jackson, J. W. and Stoenner, H. G. 1960. A case of primary cutaneous listeriosis. N. Engl. J. Med. 262: 1026.

85. Parrisius, J., Bhakdi, S., Roth, M., Tranum-Jensen, J., Goebel, W. and Seeliger, H. P. R. 1986. Production of listeriolysin by beta-hemolytic strains of *Listeria monocytogenes*. Infect. Immun. 51: 314.

86. Paterson, J. S. 1940. The antigenic structure of organisms of the genus *Listerella*. J. Pathol. Bacteriol. 51: 427.

87. Pirie, J. H. H. 1927. A new disease of veld rodents, "Tiger River Disease." Pub. S. Afr. Inst. Med. Res. 3: 163.

88. Potel, J. 1951. Die Morphologie, Kultur und Tierpathogenitat des *Corynebacterium infantisepticum*. Zentralbl. Bakteriol. Abt. 1, Orig. A. 156: 490.

89. Ralovich, B. 1986. Listeriosis research: Present situation and perspective. Ann. Immunol. Hung. 26: 911.

90. Read, E. J., Orenstein, J. M., Chorba, T. L., Schwartz, A. M., Simon, G. L., Lewis, J. H. and Schulof, R. S. 1985. *Listeria monocytogenes* species and small cell carcinoma of the rectum: An unusual presentation of the Acquired Immunodeficiency Syndrome. Am. J. Clin. Pathol. 83: 385.

91. Robinson, B. J., Donlevy, T., Keelan, S. and Flowers, R. S. 1988. Use of Micro-ID and selected biochemical tests to rapidly identify *Listeria* sp. and *Listeria monocytogenes*. Abstr. P-35, Ann. Meet. of the Amer. Soc. for Microbiol.

92. Rocourt, J., Wehmeyer, U. and Stackebrandt, E. 1987. Transfer of *Listeria denitrificans* to a new genus, *Jonesia* gen. nov., as *Jonesia denitrificans* comb. nov. Int. J. Syst. Bacteriol. 37: 266.

93. Ryser, E. T. and Marth, E. H. 1987. Behavior of *Listeria monocytogenes* during the manufacture and ripening of Cheddar cheese. J. Food Prot. 50: 7.

94. Ryser, E. T. and Marth, E. H. 1987. Fate of *Listeria monocytogenes* during the manufacture and ripening of Camembert cheese. J. Food Prot. 50: 372.

95. Ryser, E. T., Marth, E. H. and Doyle, M. P. 1985. Survival of *Listeria monocytogenes* during manufacture and storage of cottage cheese. J. Food Prot. 48: 746.

96. Sasser, M. and Roy, M. 1988. Fatty acid analysis for rapid identification of the species of *Listeria* and related bacteria. Abstr. P-44, Ann. Meet. of the Amer. Soc. for Microbiol.

97. Schlech, W. F., Lavigne, P. M., Bortolussi, R. A., Allen, A. C., Haldane, E. V., Wort, A. J., Hightower, A. W., Johnson, S. E., King, S. H., Nicholls, E. S. and Broome, C. V. 1983. Epidemic listeriosis—Evidence for transmission by food. N. Engl. J. Med. 308: 203.

98. Seeliger, H. P. R. and Finger, H. 1976. Listeriosis. In "Infectious Diseases of the Fetus and Newborn Infant," eds. J. S. Remington and J. O. Klein, p. 333. W. B. Saunders Company, Philadelphia, Penn.

99. Seeliger, H. P. R. and Hohne, K. 1979. Serotyping of *Listeria monocytogenes* and related species. In "Methods in Microbiology," eds. T. Bergen and J. R. Norris, p. 31. Academic Press, London.

100. Seeliger, H. P. R. and Jones, D. 1986. Genus *Listeria pirie*. In "Bergey's Manual of Systematic Bacteriology," 9th ed., ed. P. A. Sneath, Vol. 2, p. 1235. Williams and Wilkins, Baltimore, Md.

101. Seeliger, H. P. R. and Welshimer, H. J. 1974. *Listeria*. In "Bergey's Manual of Determinative Bacteriology," 8th ed., eds. R. E. Buchanan and N. E. Gibbons, p. 593. Williams and Wilkins, Baltimore, Md.

102. Smith, J. L. and Archer, D. L. 1988. Heat-induced injury in *L. monocytogenes*. J. Indust. Microbiol. 3: 105.

103. Steinmeyer, S., Schoen, R. and Terplan, G. 1987. Investigation of the pathogenicity of *Listeria* strains isolated from food, by injection into fertile hen's eggs. Archiv fur Lebensmittelhygiene. 38: 95.

104. Stuart, S. E. and Welshimer, H. J. 1974. Taxonomic reexamination of *Listeria pirie* and transfer of *Listeria grayi* and *Listeria murrayi* to a new genus *Murraya*. Int. J. Syst. Bacteriol. 24: 177.

105. Sword, C. P. and Pickett, M. J. 1961. The isolation and characterization of bacteriophages from *Listeria monocytogenes*. J. Gen. Microbiol. 25: 241.

106. Van Netten, P., Perales, I. and Curtis, G. D. W. 1989. Liquid and solid selective differential media for the detection and enumeration of *L. monocytogenes* and other *Listeria* spp. Internat. J. Food Microbiol. 8: 299.

107. Watson, B. B. and Eveland, W. C. 1965. The application of the phage-fluorescent antiphage staining system in the specific identification of *Listeria monocytogenes*. I. Species specificity and immunofluorescent sensitivity of *Listeria monocytogenes* phage observed in smear preparations. J. Inf. Dis. 115: 363.

108. Wehr, H. M. 1987. *Listeria monocytogenes*—A current dilemma. J. Assn. Off. Anal. Chem. 70: 769.

109. Weis, J. and Seeliger, H. P. R. 1975. Incidence of *Listeria monocytogenes* in nature. Appl. Microbiol. 30: 29.

110. Welshimer, H. J. 1960. Survival of *Listeria monocytogenes* in soil. J. Bacteriol. 80: 316.

111. Welshimer, H. J. 1968. Isolation of *Listeria monocytogenes* from vegetation. J. Bacteriol. 95: 300.

112. Welshimer, H. J. 1981. The genus *Listeria* and related organisms. In "The Procaryotes," Vol. 11., eds. M. P. Starr, H. Stolp, H. G. Truper, A. Balows, and H. G. Schlegel, p. 1680. Springer Verlag, New York.

113. Welshimer, H. J. and Donker-Voet, J. 1971. *Listeria monocytogenes* in nature. Appl. Microbiol. 21: 516.

114. Wilkins, P. O., Bourgeois, R. and Murray, R. G. E. 1972. Psychrotrophic properties of *Listeria monocytogenes*. Can. J. Microbiol. 18: 543.

Chapter 39

RAPID METHODS AND AUTOMATION

Paul A. Hartman, Bala Swaminathan, Michael S. Curiale,
Ruth Firstenberg-Eden, Anthony N. Sharpe, Nelson A. Cox,
Daniel Y. C. Fung, and Millicent C. Goldschmidt

39.1 INTRODUCTION

Methods for the detection, enumeration, isolation, and characterization of microorganisms in foods are changing rapidly. Increased emphasis is being placed on new methods that are convenient and produce results rapidly. These new methods are often more sensitive, specific, and accurate than are conventional techniques. They may also offer savings of space and materials or other advantages. Automation, or the use of commercial products that have been subjected to rigorous quality control, can result in reduction of human errors and savings in labor costs. On the other hand, automation will not replace the knowledgeable microbiologist, who must still function as the final judge of the data, who must be aware of the limitations of each rapid or automated method, and who may need to perform tests manually if instrumentation malfunctions. All these factors must be considered in balancing benefits of a method against its cost.

It is important for the user of a microbiological method to understand the basic premises and principles behind it, its advantages and disadvantages, and its strengths and weaknesses. In the diverse array of methods now available, one or more of these elements may be obscure. The purpose of this chapter is to present the general, fundamental concepts and procedures common to selected rapid methods and automated techniques. Some are sophisticated; others are simple. Examples are provided where appropriate, but not all applications of the methods described here are given in this chapter. Details for performing rapid or automated assays for specific microorganisms or groups of microorganisms appear in many other chapters in this book.

665

A carefully selected list of references follows each method summary, and a list of manufacturers, with addresses, appears at the end of this chapter.

39.2 IMMUNOASSAYS

39.21 Introduction

Immunoassay refers to the qualitative or quantitative determination of antigen or antibody in a specimen by an immunological reaction.[3] Conventional tube- and slide-agglutination assays have been used to identify and characterize bacteria since the turn of the century. The development of new and highly sensitive configurations of immunoassays, the development of mechanical devices to automate tedious steps in the procedures, partially or completely, and to measure the final reaction objectively (Section 39.95), and the introduction of techniques to construct antibodies of predetermined specificity (hybridoma technology) have greatly increased the use of immunoassays for the rapid detection of microorganisms. In fact, immunoassays are among the most commonly used techniques in clinical, food, and environmental microbiology for rapidly detecting pathogenic bacteria.

39.22 Immunoassay Techniques

39.221 Immunofluorescence

The immunofluorescence technique was the first type of immunoassay used to detect bacteria in biological specimens.[5] Immunofluorescence kits for detecting *Salmonella* in foods[22] have been commercially available for at least 10 years. In this method, bacteria from an enrichment culture are fixed to a microscope slide and the fixed cells are treated with fluorescein-conjugated somatic (O) and flagellar (H) antibodies specific for *Salmonella*. After excess reagent is removed, the slide is observed under a fluorescence microscope for cells with fluorescent cell walls and/or flagella. Although immunofluorescence is a useful tool in the research laboratory, it is not used in most food microbiology laboratories because final evaluation of the reaction is performed by microscopic examination, which is tedious. Further, trained and experienced personnel are needed to obtain reliable results. Attempts to automate the procedure have not been successful,[2, 15] but improved imaging devices might lead to successful automation of immunofluorescent techniques.[4, 17]

39.222 Coagglutination (agglutination-enhancement)

The coagglutination (agglutination-enhancement) technique is becoming popular in clinical microbiology[6, 7, 10, 11] because it is simple, rapid, moderately sensitive, and does not require instrumentation. The most common type of agglutination-enhancement method is the latex agglutination technique. Antibody (or antigen) can be immobilized on inert latex particles by either passive adsorption or covalent bonding. Latex reagents prepared in this manner are stable for as long as 1 year when stored at 4°C. The test is performed as follows: After centrifugation of an enrichment culture, the pellet containing bacteria of interest is resuspended in an appropriate buffer. A drop of the bacterial suspension is placed on a slide. A drop of the sensitized latex reagent is added and mixed thoroughly with the specimen. The slide is rocked for 1 to 5 min and then visually examined under a high-intensity lamp for agglutination. The sensitivity of the latex agglutination test for bacteria is generally in the range of 10^7–10^8 cells per ml. It is important to perform appropriate controls each time to ensure that the sensitized latex has retained reactivity and to detect false-positives caused by spontaneous agglutination of the sensitized latex. Latex agglutination has not yet been fully exploited in food microbiology, although tests for *Escherichia coli* toxins[9] and enzymes[12] and for *Salmonella* and *Shigella*[14] have been described.

In reverse passive latex agglutination (RPLA), an antibody immobilized on latex particles is allowed to react with an antigen in test tubes or wells of microtitration plates. If an antigen-antibody complex forms, a diffuse pattern is observed at the bottom of the tube or well. In the absence of an antigen-antibody reaction, a ring or "button" is observed.[10] RPLA tests have been developed for several bacterial toxins (see Table 1).

39.223   Immunoaffinity chromatography[23]

A monoclonal or polyclonal antibody to the target molecule—for example, aflatoxin B1—is immobilized on a solid inert support contained in a minicolumn. A sample suspected to contain the target antigen is allowed to flow through the column. The target molecule is retained while other materials are removed by extensive washing. The retained target molecule is eluted by changing the composition of the mobile phase and quantitated by an appropriate method—for example, fluorometry.

39.224   Immunoimmobilization

Immunoimmobilization is a procedure that takes advantage of the immobilization of motile bacterial cells in a semisolid medium by a specific antibody directed against the flagella of the bacteria. Motile bacteria traverse the semisolid medium until they meet the antiflagellar antibody diffusing from the opposite direction. A visible arc of immobilization forms at the antibody/bacterial interface; this arc indicates that target bacteria are present.[21] An immunoimmobilization-based test for detecting *Salmonella* in foods is commercially available[7] (BioControl Systems, Inc.). Immunoimmobilization has also been applied to the detection of *Escherichia coli* 0157:H7, a cause of hemorrhagic colitis.[8] The immunoimmobilization technique is applicable only to the detection of flagellated bacteria.

Table 1.—Commercially Available Immunoassay Test Kits

Target antigen	Immunoassay format	Kit manufacturer	AOAC approval
Antibody to *Trichinella spiralis*	heterogeneous enzyme immunoassay	Idetek, Inc.	No
Aflatoxins, other mycotoxins	sandwich immunoassay	Neogen Corp.	Yes
	sandwich immunoassay	AgriTech System, Inc.	No
	immunoaffinity column	Oxoid U.S.A., Inc.	No
	immunoaffinity column	Vicam	No
	immunoaffinity column	Cambridge Naremco	No
	competitive immunoassay	Environmental Diagnostics, Inc.	No
	column—TLC	Spectrochrom, Ltd.	No
	column—fluorescence	Rialdon Diagnostics	No
	antibody-isotope competition	Penicillin Assays, Inc.	No
	sandwich immunoassay	Organon Teknika Corp.	No
	sandwich immunoassay	IDEXX Corp.	No
	sandwich immunoassay	International Diagnostic Systems Corp.	No
Bacillus cereus	reverse passive latex agglutination	Oxoid U.S.A., Inc.	No
Campylobacter jejuni	latex agglutination	Becton Dickinson Microbiology Systems	No

Clostridium perfringens enterotoxin	reverse passive latex agglutination	Oxoid U.S.A., Inc.	No
Listeria	heterogeneous enzyme immunoassay	Organon Teknika	Yes
	heterogeneous enzyme immunoassay	3M Medical-Surgical Div.	No
Salmonella	immunofluorescence	Difco Laboratories	Yes
	immunofluorescence	Clinical Sciences, Inc.	Yes
	immunoimmobilization	BioControl Systems, Inc.	Yes
	heterogeneous enzyme immunoassay	Bioenterprises Pty, Ltd.	No
	heterogeneous enzyme immunoassay	Dynatech Laboratories, Inc.	Yes
	heterogeneous enzyme immunoassay	Organon Teknika	Yes
	heterogeneous enzyme immunoassay	3M Medical-Surgical Div.	No
	heterogeneous enzyme immunoassay	SmithKline Beckman Corp.	No
	latex agglutination	Oxoid U.S.A., Inc.	No
	latex agglutination	Stauffer Chemical Co.	No
Staphylococcus aureus	latex agglutination	Wellcome Diagnostics Div.	No
Staphylococcal enterotoxins	reverse passive latex agglutination	Oxoid U.S.A., Inc.	No
Vibrio cholerae cholera toxin and *Escherichia coli* heat-labile toxin	reverse passive latex agglutination	Oxoid U.S.A., Inc.	No

Note: The use of trade names and commercial sources is for identification only and does not imply endorsement by the Public Health Service or by the U.S. Department of Health and Human Services.

39.225   Enzyme immunoassay

Enzyme immunoassay (EIA), also known as enzyme-linked immunosorbent assay (ELISA), has become the most commonly used format for the immunological detection of microorganisms and their metabolites (toxins). EIA depends on three principles: (1) the exquisite specificity of antigen-antibody reactions, (2) biological amplification of the antigen-antibody reaction by an enzyme, and (3) the antibody's ability to retain its immunoreactivity after conjugation with an enzyme. Traditional immunoassays that used polyclonal antibodies often suffered from shortcomings caused by the presence of antibodies cross-reactive to bacteria other than the target organism and from batch-to-batch variations in antibody specificity. Cross-reactive antibodies can be removed by extensive, laborious, and time-consuming absorptions, but antibody titers are concurrently reduced. The introduction of hybridoma technology,[13] and adaptation of this technology for producing specific monoclonal antibodies to bacterial surface antigens and toxins,[20] revolutionized the field of enzyme immunoassays. Monoclonal antibody-based immunoassays are available for foodborne pathogens such as *Salmonella*, *Campylobacter*, and *Listeria*, as well as aflatoxins and other microbial toxins (Table 1).

39.23   Configurations of Enzyme Immunoassays

Enzyme immunoassays can be divided into two major categories: *homogeneous* enzyme immunoassays, which do not require separation of excess reactants from products, and *heterogenous* enzyme immunoassays, which do require separation of excess reactants from immune complexes.

The *homogeneous* enzyme immunoassay was developed by Rubenstein et al.[18] In this assay, an enzyme-labeled ligand competes with a free ligand from the sample for a few antibody sites to form an antibody-ligand complex. The enzyme-labeled antibody-ligand complex has very little enzyme activity because of either steric hindrance or allosteric inhibition caused by the antibody. In the absence of free ligand in a sample, all enzyme-labeled ligand will be complexed with the antibody, thereby causing very little conversion of substrate. When free ligand is present in the sample, however, competition for the antibody does occur, leaving more enzyme-ligand complex in the mixture. Thus, the enzyme activity will be directly proportional to the concentration of ligand in the sample. *Homogeneous* enzyme immunoassays have been generally used for several therapeutically important drugs, hormones, and other small molecules. In food microbiology, they have been applied to mycotoxin detection. Their advantages are that they are very rapid (completed in 1 to 15 min), simple to perform (two steps), and highly amenable to automation. Difficulty in adapting the assay for large molecules, relative lack of assay sensitivity, and susceptibility to interference from non-ligand sample components are some disadvantages of the *homogeneous* enzyme immunoassay. For additional information on *homogeneous* enzyme immunoassays and their various configurations, refer to the excellent monograph by Ngo and Lenhoff.[16]

The *heterogeneous* enzyme immunoassay requires separation of an antigen/antibody-enzyme complex from the excess reactants and takes 2 to 3 hr to complete. The assay, however, is more versatile than *homogeneous* enzyme immunoassays and suffers less from interference from material present in biological samples. The sandwich *heterogeneous* noncompetitive enzyme immunoassay, which uses a capture antibody to remove and immobilize the target antigen from a biological specimen and a second antibody (usually labeled with an enzyme) to detect the immobilized antigen, is most commonly used for detecting microorganisms. Therefore, the two-site *heterogeneous*, noncompetitive enzyme immunoassay will be described here. A description of the sandwich immunoassay follows; other studies[3, 19, 24] give information on other configurations of enzyme immunoassays.

39.24   The Sandwich Immunoassay

The target antigen (protein, carbohydrate, microorganism, etc.) must have at least two antibody-binding sites. Whenever possible, the two antibodies used in the assay should react with different epitopes (sites) on the antigen. The steps taken to perform this type of EIA (Figure 1) are discussed below.

Step 1. A capture antibody is immobilized on a solid matrix (e.g., a well of a polystyrene microtitration plate or titanous hydroxide) by either passive adsorption or covalent bonding. A coating buffer consisting of 0.5 *M* carbonate buffer, pH 9.6, is widely used. The binding of antibody to polystyrene is primarily through hydrophobic interactions, and maximal binding occurs at a pH close to the isoelectric point of the protein. Unlike polyclonal antibodies, which are heterogeneous mixtures of proteins with a range of isoelectric points, a monoclonal antibody is a homogeneous protein with a single isoelectric point. Therefore, a monoclonal antibody will tend to precipitate completely out of solution at its isoelectric point. Because monoclonal antibodies differ in their isoelectric points, experiments must be conducted with buffers of different ionic strengths and pH values to determine appropriate coating conditions for each antibody and application. The capture antibody is usually used at concentrations ranging from 1 to 10 μg per ml in coating buffer. The antibody is allowed to bind for 2 to 4 hr at room temperature or overnight at 7°C. Usually, less than 1% of the antibody binds to the polystyrene, so the antibody solution may be recovered and used again.

Step 2. After removal of the antibody solution, several sites remain available on the polystyrene matrix for additional protein binding. If these sites are not blocked, proteins added in subsequent steps will bind to the solid phase and interfere with the assay results. Commonly used blocking agents are bovine serum albumin (BSA), gelatin, and casein; concentrations of 0.5% to 2.0% are generally used. Another approach to avoiding nonspecific binding

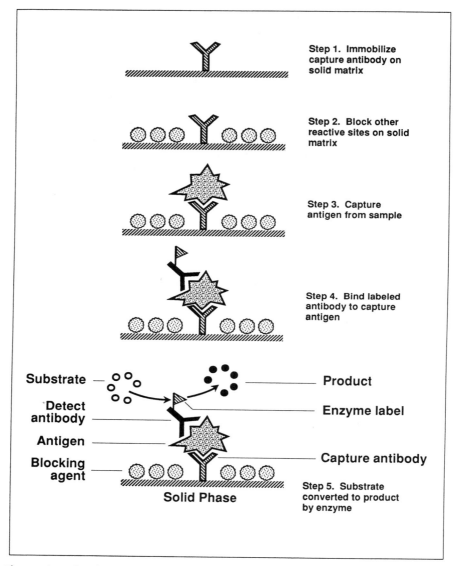

Figure 1.—Configuration of a Sandwich Immunoassay.

of proteins in subsequent steps is to include a wetting agent such as Tween 20 in all steps after coating; however, BSA-blocking is more common. An added advantage of BSA is that it may stabilize the monoclonal antibody used as the capture antibody. Plates that have been coated with a specific antibody and blocked may be rinsed, dried, and stored in a desiccator at 4°C for up to 1 year without loss of activity.

Step 3. To perform an assay, an activated plate is removed from storage and brought to ambient temperature. The sample is suitably prepared for the assay. This preparation may involve heating the sample or treating it with formaldehyde if the antibody reacts only with heated or formalinized antigen. If the antigen concentration in the sample is suspected to be below the threshold of the assay, concentration of the target antigen by centrifugation or filtration may be necessary before heat or chemical treatment. Treated antigen preparation is added to the wells and allowed to incubate for 15 min to 4 hr at an appropriate temperature to permit binding of the antigen to the capture antibody. Most incubations are done at 37°C, although no evidence indicates that this is the optimum temperature for the antigen/antibody reaction. At the end of the incubation, unbound substances are removed by discarding the contents of the microtitration plate, and the plate is washed with a buffer such as 0.01 M phosphate-buffered saline (PBS) pH 7.2, containing a nonionic detergent (e.g., Tween 20) to facilitate efficient removal of unbound materials from the wells.

Step 4. To detect the target antigen, a second antibody (probe or "signal" antibody) that is labeled with an enzyme (horseradish peroxidase and alkaline phosphatase are most commonly used) is added and allowed to react for 15 min to 1 hr. Then the unbound labeled probe is removed by extensive washing. In the presence of target antigen in the sample, a sandwich of capture antibody/target antigen/probe antibody-enzyme is formed and immobilized in the well of the microtitration plate. If target antigen is absent from a sample, the sandwich is not formed and all of the probe antibody-enzyme conjugate is removed during washing.

Step 5. The sandwich complex is generally detected by adding a chromogenic substrate for the enzyme and incubating the reaction mixture under optimal conditions for enzyme activity; this procedure takes a few min to several hr, depending on the assay. The intensity of the soluble, colored product formed is directly proportional to the concentration of target antigen, within a certain range. The intensity of the color can be quantitated by automated instruments that are commercially available (Section 39.8). Commonly used substrates for enzymes employed in EIA include 2,2′-azino-bis(3-ethyl-benzthiazoline-6-sulfonic acid (ABTS), *o*-toluidine, 4-chloro-l-naphthol, 3,3′-diaminobenzidine, and N,N,N′N′-tetramethyl-benzidine for horseradish peroxidase and *p*-nitrophenyl phosphate for alkaline phosphatase. The reaction can be terminated by adding appropriate enzyme inactivators. Fluorogenic substrates, such as 3-(*p*-hydroxyphenyl) propionic acid for peroxidase, 4-methylumbelliferyl phosphate for alkaline phosphatase, and 4-methylumbelliferyl-*b*-D-galactopyranoside for *b*-galactosidase, may be used in place of chromogenic substrates. Some fluorogenic immunoassays are 10- to 100-fold more sensitive than their corresponding chromogenic immunoassays.[1, 26] The formation of a fluorescent reaction product from a nonfluorescent substrate can be monitored with a fluorometer adapted to scan microtitration plates (Section 39.9).

Chemiluminescence may be used as an alternative signal that an antigen/antibody reaction has occurred.[25]

39.25 Equipment and Supplies

These items are necessary or useful for performing many EIAs: microtitration plates treated by the manufacturer to bind antibody securely, automatic pipettes, plate sealer, waterbath, microplate washer (manual or automatic), purified capture antibody, carbonate buffer (0.1 M, pH 9.6), PBS (0.01 M, pH 7.2), BSA, Tween 20, probe antibody (conjugated to an enzyme, such as peroxidase or alkaline phosphatase), substrate, substrate buffer, enzyme inactivator, and microplate reader (manual or automatic).

39.26 Manufacturers of EIA Kits for Use in Food Microbiology

A partial list of commercially available immunoassay kits appears in Table 1.

39.27 General Precautions

Successful development and use of EIAs depend on several factors, notably the need for high-affinity, high-titer antibodies, such as those used in commercial kits.

Positive and negative controls must be used, either in each plate or each run with multiple plates, to ensure optimum performance of the reagents and test. Instructions of kit manufacturers must be followed explicitly. If the assay kit manufacturer recommends incubation of reactions at 37°C, plates should be sealed and incubated in a waterbath instead of an air incubator to reduce problems caused by the "edge effect."[19, 24] "Edge effect" denotes an increased adsorption of proteins by the perimeter wells compared with wells in the interior of a microtitration plate. Edge effect has been attributed to surface characteristics of plastic, thermal characteristics during manufacture, and thermal gradients created during incubation.[17]

Hydrogen peroxide, which is used as a substrate for horseradish peroxidase, is unstable. It must be stored at 4°C and diluted just before use. Many colorimetric reagents used with peroxidase, including benzidine and 3,3'-diaminobenzidine, are carcinogens or suspect carcinogens. ABTS is a mutagen. Caution for personal safety must be exercised in handling these chemicals.

The enzymatic activity of alkaline phosphatase is repressed by the presence of even very small quantities of phosphate. If phosphate buffer is used for washing, care must be taken to remove all traces of phosphate before adding the substrate.

39.28 Data Handling and Analysis

In qualitative EIAs, the most important element is setting the value that is used to discriminate between a positive test and a negative test, i.e., the "cut-off" value. The terms "positive" and "negative" are used to indicate the presence or absence of target antigen, respectively. Selection of a suitable cut-off value is crucial to reduce false responses. The cut-off value can be lowered to incur more false-positive reactions or raised to incur more false-negative reactions. In detecting foodborne pathogens, the occurrence of false-negatives is more significant than the occurrence of false-positives. Therefore, the cut-off level is usually skewed downward toward more false-positives and fewer false-negatives. One procedure frequently used to reduce the false-negative rate is to set the cut-off value at two or three times the mean of several negative control results. For more comprehensive information on data handling in qualitative and quantitative EIAs, see references 3 and 20.

39.29   References

1. Aleixo, J. A. G. and Swaminathan, B. 1988. A fluorescent enzyme immunoassay for *Salmonella* detection. J. Immunoassay 9: 83.
2. Barrell, R. A. E. and Paton, A. M. 1979. A semi-automatic method for the detection of salmonellas in food products. J. Appl. Bacteriol. 46: 153.
3. Chan, D. W. and Perlstein, M. T. 1987. "Immunoassay. A practical guide." Academic Press, Inc., Orlando, Fla.
4. Chidlow, J. W. and Smith, J. S. 1985. Microbiologic applications of fluoroimmunoassay. In "Rapid Methods and Automation in Microbiology and Immunology," ed K.-O. Habermehl, p. 422. Springer-Verlag, Berlin, Germany.
5. Coons, A. H., Creech, H. J., Jones, R. N., and Berliner, E. 1942. The demonstration of pneumococcal antigen in tissues by the use of fluorescent antibody. J. Immunol. 45: 159.
6. D'Aoust, J.-Y. and Sewell, A. M. 1988. Detection of *Salmonella* with the BioEnzabead® enzyme immunoassay technique. J. Food Prot. 51: 538.
7. D'Aoust, J.-Y. and Sewell, A. M. 1988. Reliability of the immunodiffusion 1-2 Test® system for detection of *Salmonella* in foods. J. Food Prot. 51: 853.
8. Farmer, J. J. III and Davis, B. R. 1985. H7 antiserum-sorbitol fermentation medium: A single tube screening medium for detecting *Escherichia coli* 0157:H7 associated with hemorrhagic colitis. J. Clin. Microbiol. 22: 620.
9. Finkelstein, R. A., Yang, Z., Mosley, S. L., and Moon, H. W. 1983. Rapid latex particle agglutination test for *Escherichia coli* strains of porcine origin producing heat-labile enterotoxin. J. Clin. Microbiol. 18: 1417.
10. Gribnau, T. C. J., Leuvering, J. H. W., and van Hell, H. 1986. Particle-labeled immunoassays: A review. J. Chromatogr. 376: 175.
11. Hadfield, S. G., Lane, A., and McIllmurray, M. B. 1987. A novel coloured latex test for the detection and identification of more than one antigen. J. Immunol. Meth. 97: 153.
12. Kaspar, C. W., Hartman, P. A., and Benson, A. K. 1987. Coagglutination and enzyme capture tests for detection of *Escherichia coli* b-galactosidase, b-glucuronidase, and glutamic acid decarboxylase. Appl. Environ. Microbiol. 53: 1073.
13. Kohler, G. and Milstein, G. 1974. Continuous culture of fused cells secreting antibody of predefined specificity. Nature 256: 495.
14. Metzler, J. and Nachamkin, I. 1988. Evaluation of a latex agglutination test for the detection of *Salmonella* and *Shigella* spp. by using broth enrichment. J. Clin. Microbiol. 26: 2501.
15. Munson, T. E., Schrade, J. P., and Bisciello, N. B. Jr. 1978. Automated fluorescent antibody test for *Salmonella*. In "Mechanizing Microbiology," eds. A. N. Sharpe and D. S. Clark, p. 104. Charles C. Thomas, Springfield, Ill.
16. Ngo, T. T. and Lenhoff, H. M. 1985. "Enzyme-mediated immunoassay." Plenum Press, New York, N.Y.

17. Phillips, A. P. and Martin, K. L. 1985. Identification of bacteria by flow immunofluorescence. In "Rapid Methods and Automation in Microbiology and Immunology," ed. K.-O. Habermehl, p. 408. Springer-Verlag, Berlin, Germany.
18. Rubenstein, K. E., Schneider, R. S., and Ullman, E. F. 1972. "Homogeneous" enzyme immunoassay. New immunochemical technique. Biochem. Biophys. Res. Commun. 47: 846.
19. Swaminathan, B. and Konger, R. L. 1986. Immunoassays for detecting foodborne bacteria and microbial toxins. In "Foodborne Microorganisms and Their Toxins: Developing Methodology," eds. M. D. Pierson and N. J. Stern, p. 253. Marcel Dekker, New York, N.Y.
20. Swaminathan, B. and Prakash, G. eds. 1989. "Nucleic Acid and Monoclonal Antibody Probes: Applications in Diagnostic Microbiology." Marcel Dekker, New York, N.Y.
21. Swaminathan, B., Denner, J. M., and Ayres, J. C. 1978. Rapid detection of salmonellae in foods by membrane filter-disc immunoimmobilization technique. J. Food Sci. 43: 1444.
22. Thomason, B. M. 1981. Current status of immunofluorescent methodology for salmonellae. J. Food Prot. 44: 381.
23. Tierney, B., Benson, A., and Garner, R. C. 1986. Immunoaffinity chromatography of carcinogen DNA adducts with polyclonal antibodies directed against benzo-alpha-pyrenediol epoxide DNA. J. Natl. Cancer Inst. 77: 261.
24. Tijssen, P. 1985. Practice and theory of immunoassays. Elsevier, Amsterdam, The Netherlands.
25. Weeks, I., Sturgess, M. L., and Woodhead, J. S. 1986. Chemiluminescence immunoassay: An overview. Clin. Sci. 70: 403.
26. Yolken, R. H. and Leister, F. J. 1982. Comparison of fluorescent and colorigenic substrates for enzyme immunoassays. J. Clin. Microbiol. 15: 757.

39.3   HYBRIDIZATION

39.31   Introduction

Deoxyribonucleic acid (DNA) hybridization is the process by which a single strand of DNA seeks and binds to a complementary single-stranded ribonucleic acid (RNA) or DNA molecule. DNA hybridization methods have been used to classify and identify organisms since the 1960s. In DNA/DNA hybridization, the homology or percentage of hybridization between total DNAs of two organisms is greater in closely related organisms than in distantly related organisms. The development of molecular cloning techniques in the 1970s made possible the production of DNA probes for the routine screening of samples for pathogenic microorganisms. Applications of DNA-probe techniques to food microbiology were developed in the 1980s. When compared with existing techniques,[1, 2] DNA probe-based procedures are very rapid methods for the identification of bacteria in foods.

DNA probes are 20 to 2000 nucleotide sequences of bacterial DNA that are unique to a particular group of taxonomically related organisms or organisms that share common features of interest. In some instances, probes were developed to identify specific genes, such as toxin and ribosomal ribonucleic acid (rRNA) genes. In other instances, such as the *Salmonella*-specific genomic probes, the genetic significance of the DNA is unknown; that is, the probe hybridizes to a portion of DNA common to all salmonellae, but the function encoded by that piece of DNA has not been determined.

DNA probes are available to detect pathogenic organisms that are of interest to food microbiologists. Among those that have been described or are commercially available are probes for toxigenic *E. coli*,[13, 14, 21] all *E. coli*,[16] *Listeria* spp.,[18] *Salmonella typhi*,[22] *Salmonella* spp.,[7, 10] and *Yersinia enterocolitica*.[5, 15, 17] Methods for the detection of toxigenic *E. coli*[13] and *Salmonella* spp.[9, 11, 12] in foods have undergone collaborative studies and have been approved by the Association of Official Analytical Chemists (AOAC). Methods to detect *Listeria* in dairy foods,[18] enumerate *Y. enterocolitica* in meat, poultry, dairy, seafood, and vegetable products,[17] and detect *E. coli* in foods[16] have been described, but have not been subjected to collaborative study. Other DNA probes and intentions of developing assay methods have also been described, and the future will likely bring a parade of new probes and applications to food microbiology.

Various methods of preparing DNA probes have been proposed. Many modifications exist for each of the methods described here. Synthetic or biologically prepared DNA probes may be used, each with its own advantages and disadvantages.

With the aid of a DNA synthesizer, short probe sequences of 20 to 30 bases in length are easily prepared. DNA-oligomer probes of fewer than 50 bases generally produce very low filter background "noise." Manufacture of these probes requires knowledge of the probe sequence, the determination of which is a rather straightforward application of genetic cloning techniques. Although synthetic DNA probes are expensive to synthesize, they are simple to label isotopically by using polynucleotide kinase to exchange the terminal phosphate with the phosphate isotope. Non-isotopically labeled probes are prepared by incorporating a base analog into the sequence during synthesis. Although the synthesis of oligomers is automated, batch-to-batch variations occur, necessitating rigid quality control practices. Many commercial assays use these nonbiologically synthesized DNAs.[5, 16, 18]

The most common laboratory procedure for preparing probes is to isolate the cloned fragment from a replicative plasmid by restriction endonuclease digestion. Restriction-fragment probes are economical and easy to prepare. Numerous simple methods for isotopic and non-isotopic labeling are available. A probe prepared in this manner was used in an AOAC-approved method for detection of toxigenic *E. coli*.[13] However, because the probe fragments are typically propagated in replicative plasmids, small amounts of bacterial host DNA always co-purify with the probe fragment. This is unavoidable because cells harboring the replicative plasmids must be lysed to isolate the plasmid. Contaminating fragments of host chromosomal DNA, which are labeled along with the DNA probes, may hybridize to nontarget DNA on the filter and produce background "noise." If hybridization to nontarget DNA is substantial, an increase in the incidence of false-positive identifications can result. DNA probes cloned into single-stranded DNA bacteriophage eliminate this problem because the phage can be purified free of host DNA. The phage

DNA is then used as a template for the preparation of the probe sequence. A primer DNA sequence is first hybridized to the phage DNA next to the sequence of interest. DNA polymerase and nucleotide triphosphates are added, and a copy of the template is prepared. Both isotopic and nonisotopic probes are easy to prepare by substitution with modified nucleotides. Small amounts of labeled phage DNA contaminate these preparations, but levels of non-specific hybridization of labeled phage DNA with nontarget DNA are con-siderably less than for plasmid-prepared sequences. Probes for the isotopic GENE-TRAK Systems *Salmonella* assay are prepared by *de novo* enzymatic synthesis, using DNA polymerase and template sequences cloned in a single-stranded DNA bacteriophage as described above. Methods using biological templates and enzymes are tedious, labor-intensive, and difficult to control. Consequently, most laboratories prefer to purchase DNA probes from com-mercial sources that have the resources and expertise, much of which are proprietary, to prepare and test the materials.

Solid phase and liquid phase are the two basic hybridization-assay formats. The term "phase" refers to the location of the target sequence during hybrid-ization. In solid-phase reactions, the target DNA is attached to a membrane filter or other solid support. Probes that hybridize to bound target sequences become immobilized. The toxigenic *E. coli* assay and the isotopic GENE-TRAK *Salmonella* and *Listeria* assays are examples of solid-phase assays that use filter hybridization. In solution-phase reactions, the target is suspended in liquid. After the reaction is complete, the hybrids must be separated from unhybridized DNA. The GENE-TRAK non-isotopic assays are examples of liquid-phase hybridization assay formats.

39.32   General Description of Filter Hybridization Methods

Colony-blot procedures are commonly used for hybridization. These pro-cedures were originally developed by molecular biologists to identify desired clones from among a "library" (collection) of organisms.[4, 19] Colonies on an agar surface are covered, i.e., blotted, with a solid support (see next para-graph), the solid support is lifted from the agar plate, adhering cells are lysed, and a hybridization test is performed. A colony hybridization procedure for toxigenic *E. coli*[13] differs somewhat in that the solid support (filter paper) is placed on a fresh agar plate, it is inoculated by spots of culture suspensions, and then the plate and filter are incubated to allow the cells to replicate before cell lysis and hybridization. Multiple colonies or cultures may be analyzed in batch fashion by either of these colony procedures.

The most common solid support for colony hybridization procedures is nitrocellulose. Nitrocellulose membranes can be difficult to handle and are brittle when dry. Low background noise (absorption of unhybridized probe) is the principal advantage of nitrocellulose. Neutral and negatively charged nylon filters are used less frequently. These filters are durable, but they generally produce higher background levels, compared with nitrocellulose.

Whatman filter papers have also been used successfully and are inexpensive. Resolution on filter papers is poor, and their use is restricted to plates with well-isolated colonies.

After colonies have grown on or have been absorbed to the filter support, the filters are processed to expose the bacterial DNA for hybridization. The filters are first treated with alkali to lyse the cells. Pretreatment with lysozyme or protease may be needed for bacteria that resist lysis in alkali alone. The alkali treatment also denatures duplex DNA into two single strands. The alkali is then neutralized with a buffer, and the filters are baked at 80°C for 1 to 2 hr to enhance binding of the DNA to the membrane. These preparations are stable and can be stored at room temperature for up to a month without significant deterioration. Just before hybridization, the filter is wetted with hybridization buffer and incubated for at least 30 min at the hybridization temperature. Hybridization buffer contains various molecules, such as bovine serum albumin, Ficoll, or polyvinylpyrolidone, that bind to the filter and block nonspecific binding of the DNA probe. The hybridization buffer is then replaced with fresh buffer containing the DNA probe and incubated at the required hybridization temperature. A typical hybridization solution contains filter-blocking molecules plus 1 M monovalent cation (Na^+ or K^+) to accelerate the reaction and stabilize the hybrids, a divalent cation chelator (EDTA) to inhibit DNAse activity, and a detergent (sodium dodecyl sulfate) to inhibit enzyme activity and decrease nonspecific binding. The hybridization temperature is usually set high, near 65°C, to accelerate the reaction. The preferred container for the reaction is a heat-sealable plastic pouch that minimizes the volume of solution required to wet the filter, allowing the most economical use of probe and reagents. However, the use of plastic pouches does involve much labor, tedium, and mess. Following hybridization, excess unhybridized probe and most of the nonspecifically absorbed probe are removed by washing the filters in buffers containing decreasing concentrations of salt. Isotopic or colorimetric methods are used to detect hybridized DNA probe, depending on the label on the probe.

Isotopic labels are used most frequently. The isotope is detected by autoradiography; positive hybridization reactions appear as 1- to 5-mm black spots ("dots") on the film, corresponding to the location of reactive colonies on the filter. Non-isotopic methods using enzymes that generate color responses from selected substrates are available commercially. The enzyme is conjugated to a protein that binds to specific ligands on the DNA probe to form an enzyme-binding protein-ligand-DNA complex. A commonly used ligand is biotin and a commonly used binding protein is streptavidin. Problems with sensitivity and expense are the most common limiting factors of nonisotopically labeled probes.

The isotopic filter hybridization assays developed by GENE-TRAK Systems for *Salmonella* and *Listeria* are similar in design to the colony blot procedures, but have been modified to simplify handling and reduce the time required to obtain a result. Not including the culture steps and reagent preparation time, the GENE-TRAK assays are completed within 6 hr, whereas blot assays generally require 48 hr to complete. Furthermore, the GENE-TRAK assays do not require isolation of the target organisms from enrichment culture, which would require an additional 24 to 48 hr. To save assay time, cells in mixed enrichment culture are collected on a membrane by filtration; fixation of cellular DNA and hybridization are carried out on the membrane in a test tube. A beta counter is used to quantify the amount of hybridized probe.

39.33   General Description of Liquid Hybridization Methods

In this technique, both probe and target DNA are freely suspended in solution. Following hybridization, the hybridized probe is separated from the unhybridized probe through capture of the hybrids on a solid support, leaving the unhybridized probe in solution. Hydroxylapatite chromatography can be used to capture hybrids because of high affinity of double-stranded DNA and low affinity of single-stranded DNA for hydroxylapatite in the presence of 0.15 M sodium phosphate. Alternatively, plastics coated with streptavidin can be used to capture DNA that has been labeled with biotin. Another separation method uses antibodies that specifically bind to double-stranded DNA. When these antibodies are coated on the inside walls of plastic microtitration plate wells or plastic tubes, they will capture hybrid, double-stranded DNA. In fact, plastics coated with antibodies for any antigenic molecule that can be linked to a DNA probe could be used to capture the DNA. For DNA-capture methods that do not differentiate between hybridized and unhybridized probe DNA, the unhybridized probe must be eliminated before capture. This may be accomplished by digestion with nucleases that hydrolyze only single-stranded DNA, leaving the double-stranded hybrids intact.

To capture hybrids, the non-isotopic GENE-TRAK assays use a dual probe system. One probe is called the "capture probe" and the second is the "label probe." These probes hybridize to different, but adjacent, sequences on the target nucleic acid, resulting in a linkage between the two probes. The capture probe is then nonspecifically captured by the solid support. The only labeled probe remaining on the solid support is that which is linked, through hybridization of both the capture and label probes, to the target sequence. The capture probe contains a polynucleotide tail of repeating deoxyadenosine nucleotides (poly-dA). The solid support, coated with the complementary base (poly-T), captures the probe by hybridization of complementary base pairs.

Capture of hybrids on solid supports is highly amenable to non-isotopic detection methods. However, for efficient capture of hybrids, the hybrid must be no larger than a few thousand nucleotides in length. Thus, the 4 million base pair bacterial genome must be broken into about one thousand pieces. Limited DNAse and restriction endonuclease digestions can be used to produce small fragments. A simpler alternative is to target ribosomal RNA, which is already the optimum size. An additional advantage of targeting ribosomal RNA is that it is present in the cell in many copies, up to 10,000 per cell.

39.34   Commercially Available Assay Kits

A variety of assay kits are under development. Principles behind these assays are similar; several kits currently available will be used to illustrate these principles. GENE-TRAK Systems manufactures and distributes several DNA-probe assays applicable to foods. Isotopic *Salmonella* and *Listeria* assays use a solid support and isotopic detection methods. Although the assays are similar in format, the reagents and probes used in these two assays are very different.

Nontarget cells, media constituents, and sample debris collected on filters all interfere with non-isotopic detection. Thus, non-isotopic detection methods are more suited to liquid-phase hybridization formats that utilize a capture method to purify the DNA. The non-isotopic assays for *E. coli*, *Salmonella*, and *Listeria* use a liquid phase hybridization and a non-isotopic detection method. These non-isotopic assays are similar to each other.

39.341   Isotopic GENE-TRAK Systems *Salmonella* assay

This assay was subjected to a collaborative study[11] and was adopted as official first action by the AOAC. In 1988, it became an official final action method for all foods.

The *Salmonella* Assay Manual from GENE-TRAK Systems contains a step-by-step protocol that should be referred to when performing the assay. Individuals should not attempt to prepare their own reagents because of potential batch-to-batch variations. Extensive quality control checks are required.

Culture enrichment. Food products are culturally enriched before analysis by the DNA hybridization assay. The purpose of the enrichment is to increase the number of *Salmonella* cells from an initial level that may be as low as 1 cell per 25 g or 1 cell per 375 g (composite sample) to a level that is detectable by the assay. The sensitivity of the assay is on the order of 10^6 to 10^7 *Salmonella* cells per ml of broth culture. The enrichment methods are essentially those described by AOAC[2] and in the BAM.[1] A 25-g portion of test sample is homogenized with 225 ml of appropriate pre-enrichment medium and incubated at 35°C for 24 ± 2 hr. During this pre-enrichment, *Salmonella* numbers increase to between 10^2 to 10^9 cells/ml. One-ml portions of the pre-enrichment medium are transferred to 10 ml of tetrathionate brilliant green broth and 10 ml of selenite cysteine broth and incubated 6 hr for low-moisture foods or 16 to 18 hr for high-moisture foods. One ml of each enrichment broth is then diluted with 10 ml of gram-negative broth (GNB) and incubated at 35°C for 12 to 18 hr for low-moisture foods or 6 hr for high-moisture foods. Although a full 24 hr of enrichment in the tetrathionate and selenite broths increases the *Salmonella* titer to the minimum detectable level, these cultures cannot be used directly in the assay because the media reagents and food particles may cause filtration problems and high backgrounds. Dilution with GNB eliminates both of these problems.

DNA hybridization. Assays are run in batches to minimize the amount of isotope that must be used during the hybridization step. Each batch comprises 1 to 24 test samples and 4 controls. Up to 14 samples (tests plus controls) can be processed on one GENE-TRAK 14-port vacuum manifold. With two manifolds, connected in parallel to a single vacuum pump, 24 samples and 4 controls can be processed at one time.

One filter cup is used per sample. The cup comprises two molded plastic pieces, a thick piece of filter paper, and a nylon hybridization filter membrane. The upper section of the cup is an open-ended cylinder with an inside diameter of about 23 mm and a capacity of 12 ml. Both filters are 25 mm in diameter and fit in the cup base. The cylinder attaches to the base by friction, sealing the filters in the assembly. The cup assembly is then inserted into a port on the vacuum manifold and held in place by friction.

The nylon membrane has large, 3-μm pores to facilitate filtration. All assay activity occurs on this filter. Filters with smaller pore sizes (0.45 μm) are not used because they become plugged with sample debris with some foods. Because of the large pore size in the membrane filter, some *Salmonella* cells may be lost during each filtration step. Consequently, to minimize losses, the vacuum pump should be adjusted to the lowest setting that allows most of the samples to filter within 2 min. After most of the samples have been filtered, the filtration of stubborn samples may be completed by temporarily increasing the vacuum. The lower filter, made of paper, supports the nylon membrane and ensures a seal between the cup base and cylinder.

Both positive (heat-killed *Salmonella*) and negative (heat-killed *E. coli*) controls are provided with each reagent kit. The purpose of the positive control is to ensure that sample processing and hybridization were completed properly. The negative control verifies that the washing steps were executed within specifications and determines the basis for differentiating positive and negative samples.

Samples must be processed after culture enrichment and before DNA hybridization. One ml of each GNB culture and 2 ml of the appropriate control solution are pipetted directly into individual filter cups attached to the vacuum manifold. Cells are then collected on the membrane filter by vacuum filtration. A lysis or denaturation solution is applied directly onto the filter with a squirt bottle, incubated for 2 min, and the excess removed by vacuum filtration. The lysis solution contains sodium hydroxide, which disrupts or lyses the cells and denatures duplex DNA into single-stranded DNA. The filter is treated with Tris buffer to neutralize the alkali, followed by alcohol to "fix" the single-stranded DNA to the filter. The alcohol has the added effect of drying the filter. The filters are then removed and all are placed in a single 50-ml, conical-bottom tube containing approximately 25 ml of prehybridization solution tempered at 65°C. The prehybridization solution contains various polymers that bind to the filter to block nonspecific binding of probe DNA. The recommended prehybridization time is 30 min; 15 min is usually adequate; longer incubation times, up to 24 hr, are not harmful.

Just before addition of the DNA probe, the membrane filters are transferred from prehybridization solution to 12 ml of hybridization solution. This volume of solution is the minimum amount needed to keep 28 filters wet during hybridization. The hybridization solution is composed of prehybridization solution plus a polymer, dextran sulfate. The polymer reduces the volume of liquid available for suspension of the DNA probe. The net effect is similar to increasing the concentration of DNA in solution. Because hybridization rates are directly proportional to DNA concentration, the dextran sulfate accelerates the hybridization reaction. The hybridization rate also depends on salt concentration, reaction temperature, base sequence, and length of the probe and target DNA strands. In commercial reagents, the salt concentration and DNA size and sequence are rigidly controlled. Assay instructions specify the concentration of DNA probe to be added and a reaction temperature of 65°C for 2 hr.

The *Salmonella* probe comprises approximately 4000 bases of *S. typhimurium* genomic DNA. Approximately 2000 bases each of fragments 319 and 333 are used. These are optimized subsets of the *Salmonella*-specific sequences described by Fitts.[7, 10] Bacteriophage fd is used to propagate the sequences, and the probes are prepared by using a proprietary extension reaction. The P^{32}-label is incorporated during the primer extension reaction.

Following hybridization, excess unhybridized probe and probe that has nonspecifically adsorbed to nontarget DNA on the filter must be removed. This is accomplished by a series of six wash cycles at 65°C for 5 min each. A wash cycle consists of decanting the expended liquid in the hybridization tube, adding fresh prewarmed wash solution, shaking the tube, incubating at 65°C for 5 min, and shaking the tube before starting the next wash cycle. Each successive cycle removes proportionally less of the DNA probe that had nonspecifically bound to the filter and a much smaller proportion of the specifically hybridized DNA probe. Washing is complete when the negative control filters have fewer than 500 counts per min (cpm) on each; optimally there should be 100 to 300 cpm or less on each. Typically, four or five wash cycles are sufficient, but six washes are used to ensure removal of most nonspecifically bound probe.

The wash steps are the most critical steps of the entire assay procedure. If the hybridization assay has failed to perform satisfactorily, the filter wash procedure should be reviewed carefully. Less nonspecifically bound DNA is removed if the waterbath temperature is too low and if tubes are not shaken properly. The result is a reduction in assay sensitivity and an increase in the rate of false-positive reactions. If the wash temperature is too high, the rate of false-negative reactions increases.

The radioactivity on each filter is measured with a beta-particle detector and the results are converted to cpm. A scintillation counter may be used, but the filters should be counted dry without the addition of water or scintillation cocktail. Presumptive *Salmonella*-positive samples are determined by comparing the cpm from the test filter to the cut-off value determined for each hybridization batch. The cut-off value represents the average of the three negative controls plus 500. The cut-off value for a valid assay is typically less than 1000 and usually in the 600 to 800 cpm range. The cpm of the positive control filter should be at least 5 times the cut-off value. Most of the *Salmonella*-positive samples have counts in the 2000 to 20,000 cpm range. Some positives may be close to the cut-off value; however, the majority of the samples near the cut-off value are false positives.

Positive samples are confirmed by streaking both GNBs as well as the 24-hr tetrathionate and selenite cysteine enrichments onto standard *Salmonella* selective agars for isolation, followed by standard biochemical and serological characterization (Chapter 25).

39.342   Description of GENE-TRAK Systems isotopic *Listeria* assay

This assay was designed to detect all *Listeria* species in dairy products following cultural enrichment. It is similar to the *Salmonella* assay in format and appearance, but there are several significant differences, notably that the *Listeria* assay is rRNA-dependent and the *Salmonella* assay is DNA-dependent. The GENE-TRAK Assay Manual should be consulted when performing the assay. *Listeria* materials and reagents cannot be interchanged with those for *Salmonella*. For example, the membrane filter used for *Listeria* differs from the one used for *Salmonella*; otherwise, the filter cups are handled similarly. Appropriate positive and negative control cultures are provided.

Gram-positive cells, unlike gram-negative cells, do not readily lyse when exposed to alkali. Extensive lysis is achieved by treating the cells with one or more lytic enzymes that act by weakening the cell envelope structure and then with alkali to complete lysis. In a typical procedure, 1 ml of test or control culture is placed in a test tube and 0.5 ml of enzyme powder reconstituted with buffer-chelate is added. After incubation at room temperature for 15 min, denaturation solution is added to the tube and it is incubated for an additional 15 min. The sample is poured into a filter cup and filtered to capture released ribosomal protein-rRNA complexes. No neutralization and fixation steps are needed. Because alkali hydrolyzes RNA, however, test samples on the filters are not stable and the filters should be placed in pre-hybridization solution within 30 min of treatment.

The hybridization and wash steps are identical to those for *Salmonella*, except that reagents specific for *Listeria* detection must be used. The probes for *Listeria* consist of three synthetic DNA oligomers, each about 30 nucleotides long. The probes are terminally labeled with P^{32} by enzymatic exchange of the terminal phosphate with the gamma phosphate of P^{32}-ATP in the presence of polynucleotide kinase. The probes are homologous to *Listeria* rRNA and rRNA genes. Because each cell contains approximately 10,000 copies of rRNA, the probes preferentially hybridize to the rRNA in this assay; hence, it is a DNA-RNA hybridization assay.

The hybridization results are analyzed and interpreted identically to those described for the *Salmonella* assay.

39.343 Description of GENE-TRAK Systems non-isotopic *Escherichia coli* assay

This test was designed for the qualitative detection of *E. coli* in food following culture enrichment. Hybridization of the DNA probes (a poly-dA tailed capture probe and a fluorescein-labeled detector probe) to target rRNAs occurs in the liquid phase. Hybrids are captured by hybridization of the tails to poly-T coated dipsticks. The hybrids are detected by using horseradish peroxidase covalently attached to an anti-fluorescein antibody.

Samples are enriched in lauryl tryptose broth (LTB) incubated at 35°C for 48 ± 4 hr. The quantity of sample to be analyzed depends on the level of sensitivity desired. For example, a sensitivity of less than 3/g is attained by preparing a 1:10 homogenate in LST broth and transferring 3 ml of homogenate to 30 ml of broth for incubation.

Positive (*E. coli*) and negative (*Citrobacter freundii*) controls that have been killed with formaldehyde are provided with each reagent kit.

The assay reactions occur in clean disposable 12×75 mm glass test tubes. To the tubes, add 0.45 ml of test sample, positive control solution, and negative control solution. Add 0.05 ml of lysis solution to each tube, shake, and incubate at room temperature for 5 min. Add 0.05 ml of neutralization solution, shake, and hold at 65°C for 15 min to complete the lysis. Add 0.05 ml of probe and incubate for 15 min to allow hybridization of the probes to target rRNA. To each tube add a wetted dipstick and incubate for 1 hr to capture the DNA-rRNA hybrids. Remove and rinse the dipsticks in wash buffer prewarmed to 65°C, and then place them in clean tubes containing 0.75 ml of enzyme-conjugate. Incubate for 20 min at room temperature. Rinse the dipsticks in wash buffer at room temperature and place them in tubes containing 0.75 ml of substrate-chromagen. Incubate for 10 min at room temperature before adding 0.25 ml of acid stop solution, which changes the chromogen from blue to yellow.

Read the tubes with a photometer containing a 450-nm filter. Tubes with readings that are greater than O.D. 0.2 are suspect for *E. coli* and may be confirmed with standard tests.

39.35 The Polymerase Chain Reaction

The polymerase chain reaction (PCR) is an *in vitro* method used to increase numbers of a specific DNA sequence in a sample.[9, 20, 23] The PCR provides many copies of the DNA sequence; each, in turn, can participate in a hybridization reaction. Therefore, the major advantage of PCR is that enough copies of DNA are produced that the use of high-sensitivity radioactive probes is no longer required and less sensitive nonradioactive probes can be used. As little as 50 to 100 ng of DNA can be detected using present (1989) technology. Specificity can also be increased.

Amplification is accomplished in "cycles" or "rounds" of alternating high and low temperatures. Each cycle consists of three steps. First, the double-stranded DNA in a sample (or extracted from a sample) is denatured at high temperature (70° to 100°C) to separate or unwind the strands. Then a large excess of two known synthetic oligonucleotide primers, each specific for an end portion of a target DNA region (specific DNA sequence) is added and annealed or hybridized to the DNA templates at a low temperature, usually between 37° and 55°C. Each primer is constructed so that it is complementary to a portion of one of the original DNA strands, to either the left (5′) or right (3′) end of the sequence of interest. The primers define the ends or boundaries of the segment of DNA to be duplicated. The primers are then extended by using DNA polymerase to produce two new DNA strands that are complementary to the two original strands. The use of a thermostable polymerase eliminates the need for fresh polymerase after each heating cycle. Because the primers are oriented so that the DNA polymerase proceeds across the region between the primers, the DNA extension product of one primer can serve in the next cycle as a template for the other primer. Thus, each cycle results in doubling the number of specific target DNA sequences. Typically, a 10^5 or greater amplification can be obtained within several hours (after 20 to 30 cycles). Once amplification is complete, hybridization reactions are performed to detect the amplified segment(s) of DNA.

The procedure has been automated (Cetus Corp.), and GeneAmp PCR kits are available from Cetus and United States Biochemical Corp.

The PCR is an extremely sensitive tool if nonspecific amplification of contaminant DNA is not a problem. Steffan and Atlas,[24] for example, detected one cell of a herbicide-degrading bacterium in a gram of sediment (see also Chaudhry, 1989[6]). Atlas et al.[3] detected coliform bacteria in water by using PCR and a lacZ gene probe. By using PCR gene probe detection of a lamB gene that was unique to E. coli among the coliforms, as few as one to four E. coli cells were detected in 1- to 100-ml samples of water.[3] Many applications of PCR technology may become possible in the future. Pre-enrichment or enrichment steps common to conventional microbiological procedures could be completely eliminated, and analyses could be performed directly on samples or sample extracts, if PCR technology is further simplified.

39.36   References

1. AOAC. 1984. "Bacteriological Analytical Manual," 6th ed. Assn. Off. Analyt. Chem., Arlington, Va.

2. AOAC. 1984. "Official Methods of Analysis," 14th ed. Assn. Off. Analyt. Chem., Arlington, Va.

3. Atlas, R., Bej, A., Steffan, R., Dicesare, J., and Hoff, L. 1989. Detection of coliforms in water by polymerase chain reaction (PCR) and gene probe methods. Abstr. Ann. Mtg. Amer. Soc. Microbiol., abstr. N-40, p. 291.

4. Berger, S. L. and Kimmell, A. R., eds. 1987. Cloning techniques. In "Methods in Enzymology," Vol. 152. Academic Press, Inc., New York, N.Y.

5. Chan, S., Pitman, T., Shah, J., King, W., Lane, D., and Lawrie, J. 1988. Non-radioactive DNA assay for detection and identification of foodborne *Yersinia*. Abstr. Ann. Mtg. Amer. Soc. Microbiol., abstr. P-37, p. 280.

6. Chaudhry, R. G., Toranzos, G. A., and Bhatti, A. R. 1989. Novel method for monitoring genetically engineered microorganisms in the environment. Appl. Environ. Microbiol. 55: 1301.

7. Curiale, M. S., Flowers, R. S., Mozola, M. A., and Smith, A. E. 1986. A commercial DNA probe-based diagnostic for the detection of *Salmonella* in food samples. In "DNA Probes: Applications in Genetic and Infectious Disease and Cancer," ed. L. S. Lerman, Cold Spring Harbor Lab., Cold Spring Harbor, N.Y.

8. Emswiler-Rose, B., Bennett, B., and Okrend, A. 1987. Comparison of cultural methods and the DNA hybridization test for detection of salmonellae in ground beef. J. Food. Sci. 52: 1726.

9. Erlich, H., ed. 1989. "PCR Technology: Principles and Applications for DNA Amplification." Stockton Press, New York, N.Y.

10. Fitts, R. 1985. Development of a DNA-DNA hybridization test for the presence of *Salmonella* in foods. Food Technol. 39: 95.

11. Flowers, R. S., Klatt, M. J., Mozola, M. A., Curiale, M. S., Gabis, D. A., and Silliker, J. H. 1987. DNA hybridization assay for the detection of *Salmonella* in foods: Collaborative study. J. Assn. Off. Anal. Chem. 70: 521.

12. Flowers, R. S., Mozola, M. A., Curiale, M. S., Gabis, D. A., and Silliker, J. H. 1987. Comparative study of DNA hybridization method and the conventional culture procedure for the detection of *Salmonella* in foods. J. Food Sci. 52: 781.

13. Hill, W. E. and Payne, W. L. 1984. Genetic methods for the detection of microbial pathogens. Identification of enterotoxigenic *Escherichia coli* by DNA colony hybridization: Collaborative study. J. Assn. Off. Anal. Chem. 67: 801.

14. Hill, W. E., Madden, J. M., McCardell, B. A., Shah, D. B., Jagow, J. A., Payne, W. L., and Boutin, B. K. 1983. Foodborne enterotoxigenic *Escherichia coli*: Detection and enumeration by DNA colony hybridization. Appl. Environ. Microbiol. 45: 1324.

15. Hill, W. E., Payne, W. L., and Auslisio, C.C.G. 1983. Detection and enumeration of virulent *Yersinia enterocolitica* in food by DNA colony hybridization. Appl. Environ. Microbiol. 46: 636.

16. Hsu, H.-Y., Sobell, D. I., Chan, S. W., McCarty, J., Pardos, K., Lane, D. J., and Halbert, D. N. 1989. A colorimetric DNA hybridization method for the detection of *Escherichia coli* in foods. Abstr. Ann. Mtg. Am. Soc. Microbiol., abstr. P-23, p. 322.

17. Jagow, J. and Hill, W. E. 1986. Enumeration by DNA colony hybridization of virulent *Yersinia enterocolitica* colonies in artificially contaminated food. Appl. Environ. Microbiol. 51: 441.

18. Klinger, J. D., Johnson, A. J., Croan, D., Flynn, P., Whippie, K., Kimball, M., Lawrie, J., and Curiale, M. S. 1988. Comparative studies of nucleic acid hybridization assay for *Listeria* in foods. J. Assn. Off. Anal. Chem. 71: 669.

19. Maniatis, T., Fritsch, E. F., and Sambrook, J. 1982. Molecular cloning: A laboratory manual. Cold Spring Harbor Lab., Cold Spring Harbor, N.Y.

20. Marx, J. L. 1988. Multiplying genes by leaps and bounds. Science 240: 1408.

21. Moseley, S. L., Escheverria, P., Seriwatana, J., Tirapet, C., Chaicumpa, W., Sakuldaipeara, T., and Falkow, S. 1982. Identification of enterotoxigenic *Escherichia coli* by colony hybridization using three toxigenic gene probes. J. Infect. Dis. 145: 863.

22. Rubin, F. A., Kopecko, D. J., Noon, K. F., and Baron, L. S. 1985. Development of a DNA probe to detect *Salmonella typhi*. J. Clin. Microbiol. 22: 600.
23. Schochetman, G., Ou, C.-Y., and Jones, W. K. 1988. Polymerase chain reaction. J. Infect. Dis. 158: 1154.
24. Steffan, R. J. and Atlas, R. M. 1988. DNA amplification to enhance detection of genetically engineered bacteria in environmental samples. Appl. Environ. Microbiol. 54: 2185.

39.4   IMPEDIMETRIC ASSAYS

39.41   Theory

Investigations into the association between microbial metabolism and electrochemical changes in the growth medium can be traced to the turn of the century,[7] but impedance monitoring, as performed by modern instrumentation, is a relatively new procedure.

Impedance methodology monitors microbial metabolic activity by measuring electrical impedance, which is the resistance to the flow of an alternating current through a conducting material (e.g., microbiological growth medium). These measurements are conducted by placing a pair of identical electrodes in the inoculated growth medium.

Impedance is a complex entity composed of a conductive element and a capacitive element. Changes in conductance produced during microbial growth are associated with changes in the bulk solution. The conductive element of the bulk solution is proportional to the ionic strength of the solution. The conductive element of impedance is especially important in monitoring bacterial growth in culture media that have initial low conductivity. Capacitance changes caused by microbial growth are associated with changes close to the electrodes (within several Angstroms of the electrode). A capacitor model can describe the electrode-solution interface, in which the electrode serves as one side of the capacitor and a layer of ions serves as the opposite side. Smaller ions generate a more compact and thinner layer. The conductance component was established as an important signal in the detection of microorganisms.[10, 15] Capacitance was found to be important when using high-conductivity media and in the detection of yeasts and molds.[21]

Impedance changes, and changes in the components of impedance, occur in a medium as its chemical composition changes because of the metabolic activity of microorganisms. During microbial growth, large molecules are converted into smaller, more chemically active metabolites. The appearance and accumulation of these end products of metabolism result in detectable changes in impedance.

To cause measurable changes in impedance, the microorganisms must multiply to a threshold level of 10^6–10^7 cells/ml. Once this detection level is reached, a detection time (DT) in hr is reported and recorded.

A common misunderstanding about impedance microbiology is the belief that the method will not detect low numbers of microorganisms. This confusion generally arises because the method has a detection threshold of 10^6–10^7 cells/ml. However, this observation merely means that if the initial sample contains a large number of organisms initially (e.g., 10^5 cells/ml), the detection time would be reached fairly rapidly because only four to eight cell divisions would be needed to exceed the detection threshold level. A sample containing only 1 organism/ml would take longer to detect because more cell divisions would be needed to exceed the threshold level. In commercial systems (see Section 39.42), impedance measurements are conducted on each sample every few minutes, and this information is continually analyzed by a computer. The test results can be color-coded, if desired, and are automatically displayed on a monitor as they occur. High-count samples are detected first; they can be coded to appear in red, to give the observer an early warning of poor-quality material. Borderline samples can be coded to appear in amber. Accept-able, low-count samples appear last, coded to appear in green. All results are stored on a floppy disk and can be printed out to provide a hard copy.

39.42 Commercial Systems

39.421   The Bactometer[6, 7]

The Bactometer® Microbial Monitoring System (Vitek Systems) uses com-puter-controlled impedance technology to accelerate the microbial testing of food products and raw materials by performing total microbial counts and selective estimations of yeasts and molds, coliforms, and lactic acid bacteria.

There are two models of the Bactometer. Both use a multitasking, multi-user 16-bit microcomputer, a 13-in (35-cm) color monitor, and a printer plus hard and soft disk mass storage devices. The M128 model has two incubators that can be set to operate at different temperatures (from 10° below ambient to 55°C) and can monitor up to 128 samples simultaneously. Three additional incubator units (each containing two independent sample chambers) can be added to bring the total capacity of the system to 512 samples. The Bactometer M64 has features similar to those of the M128 and can monitor 64 samples. Both models use color graphics and "pop-up window" menu displays.

The Bactometer system is menu driven, and information about the sample (test type, lot number, collection time, etc.) can be entered into the computer prior to a test run. The software allows the user to print reports, view and plot curves, and perform statistical analysis required for the creation of cal-ibration curves.

The test samples are pipetted into individual test wells of a disposable module. The instrument automatically monitors changes in conductance, capacitance, and total impedance in the module wells. Specially formulated solid agar or liquid media are used; these are listed in appropriate sections of this book.

39.422   The Malthus[1, 7]

The Malthus-AT (Malthus Instruments, Ltd.) can be used to detect a wide range of microorganisms. Up to 256 samples can be tested simultaneously for the presence of aerobic, microaerophilic, and anaerobic microorganisms. The computer-based instrument is designed for continuous automated analysis. Liquid, colloidal, and solid samples require no special preparation. The samples are analyzed by using reusable electrodes over a temperature range of 4° to 47°C. Color-coded pass/fail/suspect results are automatically displayed on an integral HP-Vectra microcomputer, and programmed checks ensure precise analysis. The Malthus Analyser has the capability for on- and off-line communications with other computers.

39.43   General Considerations and Precautions

Whereas the agar plate count method detects viable cells, the impedance method detects metabolic activity. Therefore, preparation procedures, media, and growth conditions for impedance methodology differ from those for the agar plate count. A detailed review of approaches to the development of impedance methodology is given elsewhere.[5, 7]

39.431   Media

Certain types of media are more useful than others in impedance testing. This may be because organisms use different metabolic pathways in different media and some end products produce a stronger impedance change than others. In many instances, specially formulated media produce better impedance curves than traditional media.

39.432   Time

Time to reach a certain cell density is the measured parameter. Therefore, any time elapsed after mixing the food and the medium must be accounted for. As a result, the procedure used for sample preparation must be rigidly controlled so that microbial growth does not occur before modules containing samples are placed in the incubator.

39.433   Generation times

If a correlation between DT and standard place count (SPC) is required and the sample contains a mixed population, all microorganisms under investigation must have similar generation times. Therefore, efforts must be made to minimize differences in generation times when the methodology for a particular impedance assay is developed. This is generally accomplished by using a culture medium and incubation temperature that may not be optimum for growth of some microorganisms in a sample but at which most or all multiply at about the same rate.

39.434   Inhibitors

Certain food products contain natural inhibitors or added preservatives that may prolong the lag time and thereby delay detection. Other chemicals may interfere with the production of a clear impedance signal. The effects of inhibitors and interfering substances can be minimized by neutralizing the inhibitor, diluting the sample, or using separation procedures.

39.44 Typical Applications

Most impedance procedures are simple to perform and require much less labor than is required to perform an agar plate count. This is mainly because serial dilutions are not needed; any concentration in the range of 1 to 10^7 cells/ml can be monitored. The typical procedure involves making a 1:10 dilution in an appropriate growth medium and inserting the inoculated medium into a measuring container. From that point on, impedance is monitored automatically.

Four general categories of impedance applications are given below.

39.441 Estimation of aerobic plate count

Estimation of the aerobic plate count is the most commonly used application. The usual goal is to determine if the number of microorganisms in a given sample falls above or below a predetermined level. This approach has been used in conjunction with a calibration curve (see Section 39.451) for such products as meats,[6] raw milk,[9] frozen vegetables,[14] and fish.[13, 22] A calibration curve must be generated prior to routine use of this method. In theory, impedance can be used to estimate the total bacterial population in any type of product for which the generation times of the flora can be brought close together (see Section 39.433).

39.442 Estimation of selected groups of organisms

Similar screening methods can also be used in conjunction with selective media to detect any desired group of organisms for which a selective medium can be developed. Methods have been described for coliforms in meat[8] and dairy products,[11] yeasts in yogurt[12, 24] and fruit juices,[18] gram-negative spoilers in pasteurized milk,[23] and staphylococci in meat.[16]

39.443 Shelf life

Impedance methods may be used to predict the shelf life of foods. Impedance assays to predict shelf life usually involve a preincubation step whereby the product is incubated with a diluent or medium (typically in a 1:1 ratio) at a slightly abusive temperature. This step allows the potential spoilers to multiply. The preincubation step is followed by further dilution in growth medium and impedance monitoring. The shelf life of pasteurized milk was better predicted with the impedance method than with the Moseley test.[2, 3, 17]

39.444 Sterility testing of ultra-high temperature (UHT) products

The aim of impedimetric sterility testing is to verify the absence of viable microorganisms in a given volume of product. For this purpose, it is less important to equalize microbial generation times. The first step of the assay involves preincubation of a sample (with or without added medium) at a slightly abusive temperature. This step is followed by transfer of a predetermined volume of liquid into the measuring container where impedance is monitored. Typically, the total time required for this assay is less than 48 hr. Assays have been developed for testing UHT-processed dairy products,[20] fruit juices and drinks,[19] and aseptically packaged low-acid foods.[4]

39.45   Interpretation of Results

In the quality control laboratory, there is usually a need to know only if microbial numbers in a sample are above or below a certain level. Either of two general methods can be used to analyze the data to determine whether a sample meets a predetermined specification.

39.451   Calibration curve method

Before an impedance method is adopted, a calibration curve must be generated to define the relationship between DT and a parameter of a comparison method, usually the agar plate count. Another example is days of shelf life. In order to obtain a meaningful calibration curve, one usually needs to obtain 80 to 100 samples with counts well distributed over several log_{10} cycles. These food samples should represent the natural variability in flora between different lots and include enough samples with counts above and below the specified level. The data obtained by using the impedance and comparison methods are analyzed by using a linear or quadratic regression analysis. As a result of errors inherent in both the agar plate count or other comparison method and impedance methodologies, and because the two methods measure different entities, there always will be a scatter of points around the regression line. The degree of correlation between the two methods is denoted by the correlation coefficient (r). The closer r approaches 1.0, the better is the agreement between values obtained by the two methods. However, r depends not only on the relationship between the comparison method and DTs, but also on the number of samples analyzed and the range of concentration of organisms tested. For most applications, for which the generation times of the flora can be brought close together, a correlation coefficient of $r = 0.85$ or higher can be obtained if 80 to 100 samples, with a range of 4 to 5 log_{10} cycles, are analyzed.

In creating a calibration curve, careful consideration should be given to samples containing high levels of contamination (more than 10^7 organisms/ml) and low levels of contamination (less than 10 organisms/ml). At high levels, the detection threshold is reached so rapidly that it is not possible to distinguish numbers of organisms. At low levels, sampling errors greatly increase, resulting in scatter in the data points. In addition, when few organisms are present in a sample, a tendency toward extended lag times results in long and variable detection times. It is sometimes necessary to remove extreme points from consideration. Any data point lying far outside the standard error should be checked to determine if (1) an error was made in calculating or recording the colony count, (2) an error was made in entering the data in the computer, (3) an inaccuracy of DT resulted from an abnormal curve, and (4) the data point was derived by assay of an unusual sample source.

It is often difficult to obtain samples with the range of contamination level needed to construct a calibration curve. Samples with a log or two above the specified level are the most difficult to obtain because they occur infrequently. If the choice is made to "abuse" the samples to increase the counts artificially, this should be done in a way that will closely mimic natural conditions that result in a high-count product. It is important not to alter the relative proportions of species within the natural flora. If samples used to construct the calibration curve do not contain natural flora, the curve may not be appropriate to use with naturally contaminated samples.

39.452   Sterility method

Products that usually have very low levels of contamination are often tested by using an "industrial sterility" protocol. The protocol was developed with the purpose of showing detections only if the product is contaminated above a specified level. To accomplish this, an appropriate dilution scheme is applied to dilute out the normal flora and allow the detection of higher numbers of organisms. Because dilutions were made, any detection means a contaminated product. For example, if the normal samples contain 1 to 50 cells/ml and the specified level is 1000 cells/ml, a 1:100 dilution would be used.

This method can be used for various contamination levels, depending on the dilution scheme used. It is effective for products in which a calibration cannot be generated because of lack of high- or low-count samples, inability to calibrate, etc. For the sterility method to be useful, however, a large difference in counts must exist between acceptable and unacceptable samples.

39.46   REFERENCES

1. Baynes, N. C., Comerie, J., and Prain, J. H. 1983. Detection of bacterial growth by the Malthus conductance meter. Med. Lab. Sci. 40: 149.
2. Bishop, J. R. and White, C. H. 1985. Estimation of potential shelf-life of pasteurized fluid milk utilizing bacterial numbers and metabolites. J. Food Prot. 48: 663.
3. Bishop, J. R., White, C. H., and Firstenberg-Eden, R. 1984. A rapid impedimetric method for determining the potential shelf life of pasteurized whole milk. J. Food Prot. 47: 471.
4. Coppola, K. M. and Firstenberg-Eden, R. 1988. Impedance based rapid screening of UHT low acid foods. J. Food Sci. 53: 1521.
5. Eden, G. and Firstenberg-Eden, R. 1984. Enumeration of microorganisms by their AC conductance patterns. IEEE Trans. Biomed. Eng. 31: 193.
6. Firstenberg-Eden, R. 1983. Rapid estimation of the number of microorganisms in raw meat by impedance measurements. Food Technol. 37(1): 64.
7. Firstenberg-Eden, R. and Eden, G. 1984. "Impedance Microbiology." John Wiley and Sons, Inc., New York, N.Y.

8. Firstenberg-Eden, R. and Klein, C. S. 1983. Evaluation of a rapid impedimetric procedure for the quantitative estimation of coliforms. J. Food Sci. 48: 1307.

9. Firstenberg-Eden, R. and Tricarico, M. K. 1983. Impedimetric determination of total, mesophilic, and psychrotrophic counts in raw milk. J. Food Sci. 48: 1750.

10. Firstenberg-Eden, R. and Zindulis, J. 1984. Electrochemical changes in media due to microbial growth. J. Microbiol. Meth. 2: 103.

11. Firstenberg-Eden, R., VanSise, N. L., Zindulis, J., and Kahn, P. 1984. Impedimetric coliform estimation in dairy products. J. Food Sci. 49: 1449.

12. Fleischer, M., Shampton, N., and Cooper, P. J. 1984. Estimation of yeast numbers in fruit mix for yogurt. J. Soc. Dairy Technol. 37: 63.

13. Gibson, D. M., Ogden, I. D., and Hobbs, G. 1984. Estimation of the bacteriological quality of fish by automated conductance measurements. Int. J. Food Microbiol. 1: 127.

14. Hardy, D., Kraeger, S. J., Dufour, S. W., and Cady, P. 1977. Rapid detection of microbial contamination in frozen vegetables by automated impedance measurements. Appl. Environ. Microbiol. 34: 14.

15. Hause, L. L., Komorowski, R. A., and Gayon, F. 1981. Electrode and electrolyte impedance in the detection of bacterial growth. IEEE Trans. Biomed. Eng. 28: 403.

16. Kahn, P. and Firstenberg-Eden, R. 1985. An impedimetric method for the estimation of *Staphylococcus aureus* concentration in raw ground beef. Abstr., 85th Ann. Mtg., Inst. Food Technol., abstr. 113.

17. Kahn, P. and Firstenberg-Eden, R. 1987. Prediction of shelf-life of pasteurized milk and other fluid dairy products in 48 hours. J. Dairy Sci. 70: 1544.

18. Schaertel, B. J. and Firstenberg-Eden, R. 1985. A medium for the growth and impedance measurement of lactic acid bacteria in fruit juices. Abstr., 45th Ann. Mtg., Inst. Food Technol., abstr. 450.

19. Schaertel, B. J. and Firstenberg-Eden, R. 1986. Impedimetric measurement of microbial contamination in aseptically packaged fruit juices. Abstr., 46th Ann. Mtg., Inst. Food Technol., abstr. 130.

20. Schaertel, B. J. and Firstenberg-Eden, R. 1986. Impedimetric determination of low-level microbial contamination in UHT processed dairy products. Abstr., 46th Ann. Mtg., Inst. Food Technol., abstr. 85.

21. Schaertel, B. J., Tsang, N., and Firstenberg-Eden, R. 1987. Impedimetric detection of yeast and mold. Food Microbiol. 4: 155

22. Van Spreekens, K. J. A. and Stekelenburg, F. K. 1986. Rapid estimation of the bacteriological quality of fresh fish by impedance measurements. Appl. Microbiol. Biotechnol. 24: 95.

23. Visser, I. J. R. and Groote, J. M. F. H. 1984. The Malthus microbial growth analyzer as an aid in the detection of post pasteurization contamination of pasteurized milk. Neth. Milk Dairy J. 38: 151.

24. Zindulis, J. 1984. Impedimetric detection of yeast in yogurt. Amer. Dairy Sci. Assn., 79th Ann. Mtg., June 24–27, College Station, Tex.

39.5   LUMINESCENT AND FLUORESCENT ASSAYS

39.51   Introduction

A molecule in its natural condition is generally in its "ground" or lowest energy state. When this molecule absorbs energy, it becomes "excited"; one or more of its electrons are "promoted" by this absorbed energy into one or more orbitals of higher energy. When in the excited state, the molecule is often unstable, and tends to return to the normal, ground level.

Luminescence is the process whereby a molecule in an excited state releases photons (light). The process can be entirely chemical (chemiluminescence), or it may be mediated by an enzyme or other biological material (bioluminescence). The photons emitted during return to the ground state can be detected in a luminometer or in a scintillation counter with the coincidence circuitry turned off.

Whereas luminescence involves the production of photons by chemical processes, fluorescence occurs when a fluorescent material is exposed to incident radiation and becomes excited. The excited molecule then radiates energy when one or more electrons return from a higher energy level(s) to the ground state. Generally, an electron may lose a small portion of the original energy that it absorbed, either through collision with other molecules or by transition in its energy "modes," including the funneling of some of the absorbed energy into vibration of the atoms within the parent molecule or into the rotation of the entire parent molecule. Thus, some energy has been used, and the return ("jump") to the ground state involves less energy than was originally required to excite the molecule. Because of this, the wavelength of the emitted light is longer than the wavelength of the exciting light. A fluorescing material might be excited, for example, by using invisible, ultraviolet (UV) light and be seen at longer wavelengths, in the visible range. This difference between excitation and emission wavelengths is known as the Stokes shift.

39.52   ATP

An example of a bioluminescent reaction is microbial ATP. Only living cells contain ATP, so the amount of ATP in a sample should be proportional to biomass or viable cell numbers. The most common method used to measure ATP levels is the luciferin-luciferase system. An organic compound, luciferin, when combined with firefly or cloned luciferase, Mg^{2+} ions, and ATP, undergoes a reaction wherein oxyluciferin, CO_2, AMP, inorganic PO_4^{-3}, and photons are released. If all reagents except ATP are in excess, the quantity of photons released should be proportional to the quantity of ATP present in the sample.

Theoretically, measuring the bioluminescent reaction for ATP can detect about 100 viable bacterial cells per g of food, but the practical limit is about 1000 to 10,000 bacteria or more per g. Yeast cells are larger than bacteria and contain more ATP per cell; 10 or fewer yeast cells can be detected under optimum conditions. Cells in liquids that do not contain extraneous material can be filtered to concentrate microbial cells before ATP extraction.

A typical ATP assay consists of concentrating microbial cells, destroying any intrinsic (background) ATP present (see below), extracting ATP from the microbial cells, and injecting the extract into a measurement cuvette shielded from incident light. The major advantage of the ATP assay is that it takes only 3 to 5 min to obtain results. A number of luminometers are available for ATP measurements (Analytical Luminescence Laboratory, Inc.,

Foss Food Technology Corp., Los Alamos Diagnostics, LKB, Lumac Systems, Inc., and Turner Designs).

The ATP assay has been applied to the analysis of beverages,[11] fresh beef and chicken,[6, 10, 13] fresh fish,[21] milk,[2, 3, 20] and sterility testing.[7, 14]

A number of precautions must be taken when estimating microbial numbers by ATP content.[11] The ATP content of injured or starved cells may be only 10% to 30% of that of healthy cells,[17] and resuscitation before assay may be needed. Since all living cells contain ATP, intrinsic ATP of vegetable and animal origin must be destroyed (or removed by centrifugation or filtration) before extracting and measuring microbial ATP. ATP assays on milk containing large numbers of somatic cells may give low estimates of bacterial contamination because the somatic cells produce heat-labile ATPases that hydrolyze extracted microbial ATP.[3, 19] Endogenous food colors interfere by quenching the light produced; in assays of ground beef, for example, less variation in quenching occurred in samples from the same source than in samples from different sources.[10] Extreme pH values (e.g., in juices), food particles, and inhibitory compounds that might react with ATP or with luciferase must be avoided.[11] The method of ATP extraction is important.[11, 16, 19, 22, 23] Reagents vary from manufacturer to manufacturer.[23] In some instances, an internal standard (sample but no microbial lysis) must be included with each set of assays to determine whether all nonmicrobial ATP has been inactivated. Daily calibration curves should be made. The reagents are labile, expensive, and usually packaged in multiple units. The construction of standard curves, use of internal standards, and discarding unused reagents all increase costs of the assay.

39.53   Other Bioluminescent Assays

An instrument (Microtox, Microbics Corp.) that rapidly detects toxic materials in liquid samples is based on bioluminescence.[5] In this assay, the sample is mixed with a lyophilized culture of luminescent bacteria in a luminometer cuvette. The presence of toxicity is detected by decreased luminescence resulting from injured bacteria that are no longer capable of producing ATP (or otherwise emitting photons). Liquid samples of low color intensities, such as manufacturing-plant effluents[5] and materials suspected of containing mycotoxins,[24] can be readily examined.

Lux (luminescent) genes have been cloned and inserted into bacteriophage (bacterial viruses) that attack *Salmonella*. When the genetically engineered bacteriophage encounter salmonellae in an enrichment culture, the bacteriophage attach to the salmonellae and insert a luminescent gene into the bacteria. After a short period, the salmonellae begin to express the gene by emitting light. This phenomenon may be detected in a luminometer, indicating that the culture is positive for *Salmonella*. If no salmonellae are present, no light is generated. Total assay time is about 45 min. This *Salmonella* detection system (Microbics Corp.) is being perfected.[15]

39.54   Chemiluminescent Assays

Luminol (5-amino-2,3-dihydro-1,4-phthalazinedione) and isoluminol (the 6-amino analog of luminol) emit light when oxidized by H_2O_2 in the presence of horseradish peroxidase under alkaline conditions. Thus, when horseradish peroxidase is coupled to antibodies, a positive antigen-conjugated antibody reaction can be detected by a luminol-dependent production of light. Antibodies can be labeled with luminol and a positive reaction visualized by the addition of H_2O_2 and metal ions. Light production can be enhanced,[18] resulting in highly sensitive assays.

Chemiluminescent detectors are an integral part of some automated equipment (Section 39.9).

39.55   Fluorescence and Fluorimetric Assays

Fluorimetric assays utilize the fluorescent properties of molecules. Some molecules are naturally fluorescent until they are coupled to other molecules, thereby losing their fluorescence. Should an enzyme break the bond between the two molecules, the fluorophore regains its fluorescent properties. The degree of change in fluorescence is proportional to the amount of enzyme specific to that substrate. The change is usually toward increased fluorescence when the bond separating the two components of the substrate is broken; in a few types of assays the substrate is fluorescent and fluorescence is lost when the substrate is altered by enzyme action.

Fluorimetric assays can be used to identify bacteria in foods.[1, 9] The tests are rapid, sensitive, and—if they are sufficiently specific—can be carried out on mixed cultures.[9]

Some precautions must be taken.[9] Selection of the fluorophore is important, for three reasons. First, the sensitivity of the assay depends on the "strength" (degree) of fluorescence. For example, 2-napthyl-b-D-glucuronide has a lower quantum yield than 4-methylumbelliferyl-b-D-glucuronide (MUG). Some fluorogenic substrates can be improved, however, by introducing groups that favor intramolecular quenching.[4] Second, some fluorophores may inhibit bacterial growth;[12] this is not a problem if heavy cell suspensions are used and the assay relies on preformed enzymes, but it can be a problem if bacterial growth is needed to produce a positive result. Third, the rate of hydrolysis of a fluorogenic substrate by a particular enzyme may be affected by the fluorophore;[9] enzymes from different sources have different affinities. Some fluorogenic substrates are expensive, and the price charged by different suppliers can vary fivefold. Fluorescence of the fluorophore can be pH dependent; for example, 4-methylumbelliferone is 1000 times more fluorescent at pH 9.0 than at pH 5.0.[8] pH effects can be overcome by design of the medium or by raising the pH before reactions are read.[9] Background flora may interfere with enzyme production by the target microorganism or produce an enzyme(s) that mimics the enzyme of interest. Not all bacteria within a species or group will produce the enzyme of interest.[9] Highly colored materials (such as media containing dyes) can quench fluorescence. Finally, some manufacturers add cerium oxide to glass as a quality control measure; containers should be checked for autofluorescence before use.

Advantage is taken of fluorescence in a number of assays, such as the fluorescent antibodies mentioned in Section 39.2, as well as the use of phycobiliproteins (Biomedia Corp.) as fluorescence tracers in antibody assays. Some identification kits (Section 39.7) and automated identification systems use fluorogenic substrates. Fluorescence detectors are used with many of the physical and biochemical methods described in Section 39.9.

39.56   REFERENCES

1. Bascomb, S. 1989. Feasibility of use of rapid automated enzyme tests in food microbiology. In "Rapid Methods and Automation in Microbiology and Immunology," eds. A. Balows, R. C. Tilton, and A. Turano, p. 282. Brixia Academic Press, Bresica, Italy.

2. Bossuyt, R. G. and Waes, G. M. 1983. Impedance measurements to detect postpasteurization contamination of pasteurized milk. J. Food Prot. 46: 622.

3. Botha, W. C., Luck, H., and Jooste, P. J. 1986. Determination of bacterial ATP in milk— The influence of adenosine triphosphate-hydrolyzing enzymes from somatic cells and *Pseudomonas fluorescens*. J. Food Prot. 49: 822.

4. Bratovonova, E. K. and Petkov, D. D. 1987. N-anthraniloylation converts peptide *p*-nitroanilides into fluorogenic substrates of proteases without loss of their chromogenic properties. Anal. Biochem. 162: 213.

5. Bulich, A. A. 1979. Use of luminescent bacteria for determining toxicity in aquatic environments. In "Aquatic Toxicology," eds. L. L. Marking and R. S. Kimerle, p. 98. Amer. Soc. for Testing and Materials, Philadelphia, Penn.

6. Bulte, M. and Reuter, G. 1985. The bioluminescence technique as a rapid method for the determination of the microflora of meat. Intl. J. Food Microbiol. 2: 371.

7. Bussey, D. M. and Tsuji, K. 1986. Bioluminescence for USP sterility testing of pharmaceutical suspension productions. Appl. Environ. Microbiol. 51: 349.

8. Goodwin, R. H. and Kavanagh, F. 1950. Fluorescence of coumarin derivatives as a function of pH. Arch. Biochem. Biophys. 27: 152.

9. Hartman, P. A. 1989. The MUG (glucuronidase) test for *Escherichia coli* in food and water. In "Rapid Methods and Automation in Microbiology and Immunology," eds. A. Balows, R. C. Tilton, and A. Turano, p. 290. Brixia Academic Press, Bresica, Italy.

10. Kennedy, J. E. Jr. and Oblinger, J. L. 1985. Application of bioluminescence to rapid determination of microbial levels in ground beef. J. Food Prot. 48: 334.

11. LaRocco, K. A. and Littel, K. J. 1986. The bioluminescent ATP assay for determining the microbial quality of foods. In "Foodborne Microorganisms and Their Toxins: Developing Methodology," eds. M. D. Pierson and N. J. Stern, p. 146. Marcel Dekker, Inc., New York, N.Y.

12. Littel, K. J. and Hartman, P. A. 1983. Fluorogenic selective and differential medium for isolation of fecal streptococci. Appl. Environ. Microbiol. 45: 622.

13. Littel, K. J., Pikelis, S., and Spurgash, A. 1986. Bioluminescent ATP assay for rapid estimation of microbial numbers in fresh meat. J. Food Prot. 49: 18.

14. Molin, O., Nilsson, L., and Ansehn, S. 1983. Rapid detection of bacterial growth in blood cultures by bioluminescent assay of bacterial ATP. J. Clin. Microbiol. 18: 521.

15. Schutzbank, T. E., Tevere, V., and Cupo, A. 1989. The use of "bioluminescent bacteriophages" for the detection and identification of *Salmonella* in foods. In "Rapid Methods and

Automation in Microbiology and Immunology," eds. A Balows, R. C. Tilton, and A. Turano, p. 241. Brixia Academic Press, Brescia, Italy.

16. Sheppard, E. P., Gow, J. A., and Georghiou, P. E. 1987. Luciferin-luciferase assay of adenosine triphosphate from bacteria: A comparison of dimethylsulfoxide (DMSO) and acetone with other solvents. Microbios 52: 39.

17. Theron, D. P., Prior, B. A., and Lategan, P. M. 1983. Effects of temperature and media on adenosine triphosphate cell content in *Enterobacter aerogenes*. J. Food Prot. 46: 196.

18. Thorpe, G. H. G., Kricka, L. J., Gillespie, E., Moseley, S., Amess, R., Baggett, N., and Whitehead, T. P. 1985. Enhancement of the horseradish peroxidase-catalyzed chemiluminescent oxidation of cyclic diacyl hydrazides by 6-hydroxybenzothiazoles. Anal. Biochem. 145: 96.

19. Tsai, T. S. 1986. A microwave method for the extraction of cellular ATP. J. Biochem. Biophys. Meth. 13: 343.

20. Waes, G. M. and Bossuyt, R. G. 1982. Usefulness of the benzalkon-crystal violet-ATP method for predicting the keeping quality of pasteurized milk. J. Food Prot. 45: 928.

21. Ward, D. R., LaRocco, K. A., and Hopson, D. J. 1986. Adenosine triphosphate bioluminescent assay to enumerate bacterial numbers on fresh fish. J. Food Prot. 49: 647.

22. Webster, J. J., Chang, J. C., Howard, J. L., and Leach, F. R. 1980. Some characteristics of commercially available firefly luciferase preparations. J. Appl. Biochem. 1: 471.

23. Webster, J. J., Chang, J. C., Manley, E. R., Spivey, H. O., and Leach, F. R. 1980. Buffer effects on ATP analysis by firefly luciferase. Anal. Biochem. 106: 7.

24. Yates, I. E. and Porter, J. K. 1982. Bacterial bioluminescence as a bioassay for mycotoxins. Appl. Environ. Microbiol. 44: 1072.

39.6 HYDROPHOBIC GRID MEMBRANE FILTER METHODS

39.61 Development and General Features of Hydrophobic Grid Membrane Filter Methods

Membrane filtration (MF) technology was introduced into the United States in 1951,[16] and over several decades has been adapted to a wide variety of applications.[5, 19] The hydrophobic grid membrane filter (HGMF) was described in 1974;[20, 21] in 1978 food applications were reported.[23] Details appear elsewhere regarding the development[19] and automation[24] of HGMF methodologies.[22]

The HGMF membrane is a square MF (6 × 6 cm, 0.45-μm pore size) printed on one side with a black hydrophobic grid outlining 1600 (40 × 40) small squares. Some unusual properties of the HGMF result from the confining of microbial growth within the grid-cell in which a viable cell or clump of cells was deposited; a typical appearance after incubation is of a grid carrying a random distribution of square colonies or growth units (GUs).

39.62 Advantages of Hydrophobic Grid Membrane Filtration Methods

HGMFs have four major benefits in food microbiological analyses in common with other MFs: (1) filtration removes water-soluble growth inhibitors and other undesirable substances (e.g., sugars in ice cream that can interfere with coliform determinations, or preservatives added to a food that might inhibit microbial growth); (2) filtration can often concentrate microorganisms from more than 0.1 g (1.0 ml of a 1:10 suspension) of sample to provide better limits of detection than those available from agar plates; (3) because MFs can be transferred from one agar plate to another without disturbing microbial growth, stressed cells can be enumerated by resuscitation on a nonselective medium followed by transfer undisturbed to a selective medium; and (4) colonies adhere to MFs, so membranes can be taken through complex staining procedures (e.g., for indole, or in enzyme-labeled antibody procedures) to conduct identification reactions that are not possible on agar plates.

HGMFs offer several additional advantages over conventional counting and identification procedures. One advantage is the high precision of HGMF determinations. HGMF counts conform to a most probable number (MPN) mathematic, in which each grid-cell can be likened to one tube of an MPN count done at a single dilution, thus:

$$\text{MPNGU} = 1600 \times 2.303 \times \log_{10} \frac{(1600)}{(1600 - C)} \tag{1}$$

[where C = the number of positive grid cells (see Section 39.681), and MPNGU = the most probable number of growth units filtered onto the HGMF].

Unlike tube-MPN counts, where it is feasible to use only a small number of tubes and precision is low, the large number of growth compartments on the HGMF (1600) offers better precision than plates.[22] Duplicate HGMFs are needed only for highly exacting studies.

A second advantage of HGMF determinations is range. The logarithmic form of the MPN equation (Eq. 1) allows a 1600-cell grid to accommodate a four-$\log_{10}$ range of inoculum levels, up to about 10^4GU/sample, without the usual deterioration of count caused by colony overlap; rarely are serial dilutions of the sample needed. Note that, in HGMF procedures, units are referred to as growth units (GU), rather than colony-forming units (CFU), to describe more correctly the nature of positive grid-cells (see Eq. 1). This is because the possibility that a grid-cell received more than one viable cell is accounted for in calculating microbial numbers in a sample when using GUs. A positive grid-cell GU may not necessarily be a pure culture.

A third advantage of HGMF determinations is automated counting. Manual GU counts may be made, but the HGMF was developed for automated counting. Its regular structure removes many sources of error that plague conventional electronic counters. Commercially available computer-based instruments rapidly display MPNGUs (e.g., coliforms on mFC medium) without need for calibration. They will also enumerate and/or detect a species from biochemical profiles generated on replicated HGMFs or on HGMFs taken through a series of successive growth conditions.

39.63   Disadvantages of HGMF Methods

HGMF filters are more expensive than other MFs. If only a Quebec-type colony counter is available, high numbers of positive HGMF grid-cells are tedious to enumerate. A special manual counter (Linecounter) is an inexpensive solution to this problem. An automated counter is recommended when large numbers of HGMFs are to be counted.

For some foods, it may be necessary to improve the filterability of food suspensions by enzymic digestion (see Section 39.662).

39.64 Applications

HGMF-based analyses are available for all commonly encountered foodborne microorganisms; this versatility permits a unified approach to laboratory procedures. Some HGMF techniques (aerobic plate count;[13, 15] coliform, fecal coliform, *Escherichia coli*;[9, 10, 11] and *Salmonella*[12]) have been accorded Official Action status by AOAC.[2, 3, 4] HGMF procedures have been published for fecal streptococci (enterococci),[7] *Staphylococcus aureus*,[6, 18] *Vibrio parahaemolyticus*,[8, 14] and yeasts and molds,[17] but these have not yet been subjected to collaborative validation. Consult Sharpe and Peterkin[22] for complete descriptions and critical reviews of HGMF methods, including analyses for *Clostridium perfringens*, *Pseudomonas aeruginosa*, and *Yersinia enterocolitica*.

39.65 Equipment Needed

Iso-Grid HGMFs: 1600 grid-cell, 0.45-μm pore size (QA Laboratories, Ltd.).

Filtration apparatus: Iso-Grid Filtration Unit equipped with prefilter (QA Laboratories, Ltd.) or Spreadfilter and (optional) pipette-tip prefilters (Richard Brancker Research, Ltd.).

Colworth Stomacher 400 (Tekmar Co., QA Laboratories, Ltd., and local distributors).

Membrane filter forceps (Millipore Corp.).

Vacuum manifold or flask, and vacuum pump.

Colony-counting apparatus: Linecounter (QA Laboratories, Ltd.) for manual counts, or HGMF Interpreter (Richard Brancker Research, Ltd.) for automated counts.

Waterbath at 35°C (if enzyme treatment is needed).

39.66 General HGMF Procedures

39.661 Sample preparation

Most food suspensions are filterable if the food is agitated with buffer in a Stomacher; those homogenized in a blender usually do not pass through a filter. Commonly, 1 ml of a 1:10 dilution (representing 0.1 g of food) will filter in 30 sec, and 5 ml (0.5 g of food) in 1 to 2 min. Foods that are difficult to filter can often be improved by an enzyme treatment (Section 39.662).

Mix liquid samples thoroughly with a sterile spatula or by shaking. Mix solid samples thoroughly or remove portions from several locations within the sample. Prepare a 1:10 dilution of a solid sample by aseptically weighing 10 g into a Stomacher bag; add 90 ml 0.1% peptone or peptone-tween (PT) diluent (39.67), depending on the food, and agitate for 1 min. Use a double bag for hard foods, such as pasta, or for foods that might contain hazardous organisms. Shake all dilutions before making transfers to ensure uniform distribution of the microorganisms. Filter a representative portion from the 1:10 or higher serial dilutions, as needed.

39.662   Enzyme treatment

Foods vary in the filterability of their suspensions. Resort to enzyme treatment only if essential, selecting the enzyme preparation optimal for the type of food sample being analyzed. The fact that a food is listed below does not mean that it always requires treatment.

Amylase may be suitable for cream cheese cakes, cake mixes, instant potato flakes, cocoa powder, baking chocolate, corn flakes, and nondairy coffee whitener. Cellulase may be useful for spray-dried cheese powder, cellulose-containing ice cream, and breakfast cereal. Diastase may be suitable for sour cream, cake mixes, instant potato flakes, cocoa powder, and baking chocolate. Hemicellulase may be useful for gums and gum-containing ice cream. Lecithinase is suitable for lecithin. Pectinase may be useful with citrus juice and fruit puree. Protease can be used to treat fluid dairy products, fermented cheese, sour cream, and yogurt. Trypsin is often suitable for fluid dairy products, fermented and processed cheese, ice cream, nonfat dry milk (skim milk powder), powdered breakfast drink mix, instant hot chocolate mix, pudding mix, gelatin powder, cream of chicken soup mix, curry sauce mix, pancake mix, oatmeal and raisin cookies, sausage roll, and smoked blood sausage.

Combine 5 ml of 1:10 dilution with 1 ml of required enzyme stock solution (Section 39.67). Incubate 20 min at 35°C in a waterbath. Correct for greater dilution of test sample by filtering 1.2 ml of the enzyme-treated sample (instead of 1.0 ml of original sample) for each 0.1 g of food to be examined.

39.663   Filtration

Handle HGMFs with sterile, blunt-nosed forceps. If a low count is expected, filter more than 1.0 ml of the suspension. Filter the total test volume in one operation; do not attempt to filter multiple aliquots. Record the volume filtered (vol). Instructions on the use and care of two types of filtration apparatus are given below.

Iso-Grid Filtration Unit: The manufacturer's methods manual stresses the importance of handling the Iso-Grid Filtration Unit according to instructions. Attach the unit's main vacuum tube "F" and side-tube "H" (Figure 2) to a vacuum manifold. Open the funnel and place an HGMF on filter support "A." Close the funnel and clamp with stainless steel clamp "D." Place 10 ml of sterile diluent (0.1% peptone or PT diluent, Section 39.67) in the upper

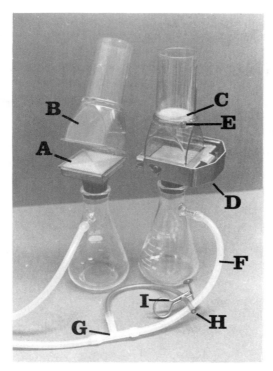

Figure 2 —Iso-Grid Filtration Apparatus (QA Laboratories, Ltd.) Shown in Both the "Open" and "Closed" Positions. A, filter support; B, upper chamber; C, stainless steel prefilter; D, toggle clamp; E, side-hole; F, main vacuum tube; G, "T" junction; H, side vacuum tube; and I, tube clamp.

chamber "B" of the funnel and add the sample. Draw the liquid through stainless steel mesh prefilter "C" by using tube "F" to apply a vacuum to the side-hole "E." Add a further 10 ml of diluent to the upper chamber and again draw it through the prefilter. Close clamp "I" on the tubing in order to draw the liquid in the chamber through the HGMF, allowing a few extra seconds for drainage. Remove the stainless steel clamp, open the funnel, and transfer the HGMF to an agar plate.

The fine mesh stainless steel prefilter tends to clog from accumulated food particles. Immediately after use, disassemble the unit and place both parts in a disinfectant solution (phenol-based disinfectants will damage the plastic). Transfer to a solution of proteolytic detergent, such as Terg-a-zyme. After soaking at least 1 hr or overnight, wash and rinse thoroughly; include 0.5% sodium thiosulfate in the rinse water if hypochlorite or an iodophor was used for disinfection. If, in spite of this care, the prefilter becomes blocked, soak the funnel overnight in proteolytic detergent followed by treatment in an ultrasonic bath. Iso-Grid filtration units can be sterilized in an autoclave at 121°C for 20 min.

The Spreadfilter (Figure 3) is convenient because it needs no sterilization after use. However, disposable pipette-tip, 110-μm prefilters (Filtertips, Richard Brancker Research, Ltd.) should be used to clarify coarse or lumpy food suspensions. The apparatus has no funnel, relying instead on the hydrophobic border of the HGMF to retain sample volumes up to 10 ml. All diluents must contain 1.0% Tween 80; otherwise, they will not spread evenly. (Note: Investigate the effects of Tween on the organism of interest in any new application.) Level the apparatus. Close valve "B" to the vacuum line. Pour sterile PT diluent (Section 39.67) on filter head "A" until liquid remains on the surface; this will help the HGMF to adhere. Lay an HGMF on the filter head. Keeping the pipette vertical, dispense a volume of sample on the filter. A sample volume of 1.0 ml is generally used, though, with care, the HGMF will hold up to 10 ml. Sample volumes of less than 1.0 ml may not spread

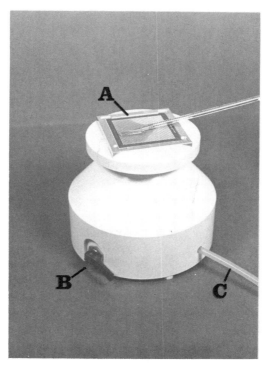

Figure 3—Spreadfilter (Richard Brancker Research, Ltd.) Showing the Delivery Pipette Being Used to Spread Inoculum Along the First HGMF Border. A, filter head; B, valve; and C, vacuum tubing.

satisfactorily. If using a pipette-tip prefilter (Section 39.65), aseptically remove it before dispensing the sample. Hold the pipette at a small angle and use it to spread the sample along one HGMF border, wetting about half the border width. Rotate the filter head 90° and make a second border spread. Repeat for the third and fourth borders, then raise the pipette vertically and let it drain. Open valve "B" to pull the liquid through. Allow a few seconds for drainage, then transfer the HGMF to an agar plate.

The apparatus requires little care and can immediately be used for another filtration. There should be no need to sterilize it because microorganisms on the filter head will not affect growth on top of HGMFs.[22] After each filtration session, however, pour 70% alcohol over the surface of the filter support and draw the alcohol by vacuum through the tubing to clean the unit and discourage microbial growth.

Seep filtration,[22] sometimes used in other MF procedures (e.g., the Anderson and Baird-Parker Direct Plate method[1]), may be applied to HGMFs if the proper equipment is unavailable or the workload is excessive. Predry 1.5% to 2.0% agar plates (at least 20-ml vol) until about 10% of the weight of agar has been lost (e.g., open, for 1 to 2 hr in a laminar flow hood or closed, overnight, in a 35°C incubator). Use pipette-tip prefilters to clarify coarse or lumpy food suspensions. Lay an HGMF on the agar surface and pipette 0.5 to 1.0 ml of food suspension into the center. With the pipette at a low angle, spread the sample over the membrane surface. Leave the plate face up on the laboratory bench until free liquid has disappeared from the filter surface or, alternatively, in an incubator at the appropriate temperature for the resuscitation period.

39.664   Plating HGMFs

Hold the HGMF by its border. Transfer to the agar surface with a rolling motion to avoid trapping air bubbles. Ensure that it is well centered in the petri dish.

39.67   Preparing Diluent and Stock Enzyme Solutions

Peptone/Tween 80 (PT) diluent: Dissolve 1.0 g peptone (Difco Laboratories # 0118) and 10.0 g Tween 80 in 1 L of distilled water. Dispense a volume into dilution bottles so that 90 ml remains after sterilization for 15 min at 121°C in an autoclave.

Tris-HCl buffer, 1.0 M: Dissolve 121.1 g tris (hydroxymethyl) amino methane in about 500 ml of distilled water. Adjust to the desired pH with concentrated HCl. Dilute to 1 L with distilled water. Store at 4°C.

Acetate buffer, 1.0M: Mix 60 ml of glacial acetic acid in about 500 ml of distilled water. Adjust solution to the desired pH with 5N NaOH and dilute to 1 L with water. Store at 4°C.

Amylase stock solution: Dissolve 10 g of alpha-amylase (Sigma Chemical

Co. A1278) in Tris-HCl buffer, pH 7.0, and dilute to 100 ml with the buffer. Warm to 35°C, if necessary, to aid dissolution. Remove insoluble material by filtering through Whatman No. 1 paper; sterilize by membrane filtration. Store up to 1 week at 4°C or 3 months at −20°C.

Cellulase stock solution: Dissolve 10 g of cellulase (Sigma C7502) in acetate buffer, pH 5.0, and dilute to 100 ml with the buffer. Continue as for amylase stock solution.

Diastase stock solution: Dissolve 10 g of diastase (Sigma A6880) in Tris-HCl buffer, pH 7.0, and dilute to 100 ml with the buffer. Continue as for amylase stock solution.

Hemicellulase stock solution: Dissolve 10 g of hemicellulase (Sigma H2125) in acetate buffer, pH 5.5, and dilute to 100 ml with the buffer. Continue as for amylase stock solution.

Lecithinase (phospholipase A2) stock solution: Dilute the commercial enzyme solution (Sigma P9139) to 25 units/ml with Tris-HCl buffer, pH 8.0. Sterilize by membrane filtration. Store up to 1 week at 4°C or 3 months at −20°C.

Pectinase stock solution: Use commercial *Aspergillus niger* pectinase containing 3 to 6 units/mg of protein (Sigma P5146). Sterilize and store as for lecithinase stock solution.

Protease stock solution: Use commercial *Bacillus subtilis* protease containing 7 to 15 units/mg of protein in aqueous solution (Sigma P8775). Sterilize and store as for lecithinase stock solution.

Trypsin stock solution: Dissolve 10 g of trypsin (Difco 0152) in Tris-HCl buffer, pH 7.6, and dilute to 100 ml with the buffer. Continue as for amylase stock solution.

39.68   Counting/Scoring HGMFs

39.681   Definitions

Positive grid-cell: A grid-cell that contains growth of the organism of interest.

Negative grid-cell: A grid-cell that does not contain any growth of the organism of interest, regardless of whether there is any other type of growth in it.

HGMF count: The number arrived at when counting either positive or negative grid-cells. Counts may be made over the entire HGMF or a central portion (eight rows) of it.

HGMF score: The total number of positive grid-cells. It may equal the HGMF count, or can be calculated from it by multiplication and/or subtraction operations, as necessary (Section 39.684).

Most probable number of growth units (MPNGU): On HGMFs, the GU is equivalent to the more familiar CFU. The MPNGU is the most probable number of growth units in the inoculum and is derived mathematically from the HGMF score (Eq. 1, Section 39.62).

39.682 Manual HGMF counts

Preferably, use a Linecounter for counting. Alternatively, use a Quebec colony counter and hand tally. Count 1 (one) for each positive grid-cell. *Do not count* the individual colonies in a grid-cell. Count all positive grid-cells, unless there are obviously more than 200.

For high densities (up to 50% occupied grid-cells), rotate the HGMF so that the center indicator lies either to the right or left. Count positive grid-cells in the 4 rows immediately above and the 4 rows immediately below the center, for a total of 8 rows. Multiply this partial HGMF count by 5 to estimate the score.

If the HGMF is so full that counting negative grid-cells appears easier, then count negative grid-cells as above. Subtract the count of negative grid-cells from 1600 or 320, as appropriate. Multiply by 5 to obtain the score if counting only the middle 8 rows (320 grid cells) of the HGMF.

Where possible, counts should be made on filters that contain 20 to 1,580 occupied grid-cells. Treat results from HGMFs that contain fewer than 20 or more than 1580 grid cells with caution. Record as too numerous to count (TNTC) any HGMF for which all the grid-cells are positive. When between 1580 and 1599 grid-cells are positive, the error term is excessive, and the count should be reported as an approximate count.

If duplicate HGMFs were prepared from a sample, record the scores of both (see Section 39.683 and Section 39.684, example 2).

39.683 Calculating the MPN of growth units

For each HGMF score, obtain the corresponding MPNGU value. Use a MPNGU table[22] or calculate using Eq. 1. If duplicate HGMFs were prepared, obtain the MPNGU value corresponding to each HGMF and calculate the average. *Do not* average scores of duplicate filters to calculate the MPNGU; calculate the average only after obtaining the MPNGU value of each HGMF.

If 1.0 ml of the 1:10 suspension was used to inoculate the HGMF, multiply the average MPNGU by 10 to obtain the number of organisms of interest per g (ml) of food. If vol ml of the 1:10 suspension was used, multiply the average MPNGU by 10/vol to calculate the number of the organisms of interest per g (ml) of food. If vol ml of a 1:C dilution was used, multiply the average MPNGU by C/vol to calculate the number of the organisms of interest per g (ml) of food.

When reporting results, round off the number of organisms per g (ml) of food to two significant figures (e.g., record 2850 as 2900).

If the lowest dilution plated shows no positive growth, the recorded value will be the lowest average obtainable with a given volume plated onto duplicate HGMFs, preceeded by a less than (<) sign. For example, for 1.0 ml inoculated on each of duplicate HGMFs (1 ml/HGMF), the value is <0.5. Multiply this figure by the dilution factor of the inoculum.

39.684   Examples of calculations

1. Count of positive grid-cells from an HGMF inoculated with 1.0 ml of a 1:10 dilution is 157:

$$MPNGU = 167$$

$$No.\ of\ organisms/g\ (ml) = 1700$$

2. Counts of positive grid-cells from 8 rows on duplicate HGMFs inoculated with 1.0 ml of a 1:10 dilution are 157 and 164, respectively:

$$Score\ for\ filter\ 1\ (157 \times 5) = 785$$

$$Score\ for\ filter\ 2\ (164 \times 5) = 820$$

$$MPNGU\ of\ filter\ 1 = 1079$$

$$MPNGU\ of\ filter\ 2 = 1149$$

$$Average\ MPNGU = 1114$$

$$No.\ of\ organisms/g\ (ml) = 11,000$$

3. Count of negative grid-cells from 8 rows on HGMF, inoculated with 1.0 ml of 1:1000 dilution is 57:

$$Score\ [1600 - (57 \times 5)] = 1315$$

$$MPNGU = 2760$$

$$No.\ of\ organisms/g\ (ml) = 2.8 \times 10^6$$

39.685   Automated HGMF counts (using the HGMF Interpreter)

Follow the manufacturer's instructions (Richard Brancker Research, Ltd.) for use of the apparatus. The instrument will calculate the MPNGU.

39.69   REFERENCES

1. Anderson, J. M. and Baird-Parker, A. C. 1975. A rapid and direct plate method for enumerating *Escherichia coli* biotype 1 in food. J. Appl. Bacteriol. 39: 111.
2. AOAC. 1985. Total coliform, fecal coliform and *Escherichia coli* in foods, hydrophobic grid membrane filter method. J. Assn. Off. Anal. Chem. 68: 404.
3. AOAC. 1986. Aerobic plate count in foods, hydrophobic grid membrane filter method. J. Assn. Off. Anal. Chem. 69: 376.
4. AOAC. 1986. *Salmonella* detection in foods, hydrophobic grid membrane filter method. J. Assn. Off. Anal. Chem. 69: 376.
5. Brock, T. D. 1983. "Membrane Filtration: A User's Guide and Reference Manual." Science Tech, Inc., Madison, Wis.
6. Brodsky, M. H., Entis, P., Sharpe, A. N., and Jarvis, G. A. 1982. Determination of aerobic plate count and yeast and mold counts in foods using an automated hydrophobic grid membrane filter technique. J. Food Prot. 45: 301.
7. Brodsky, M. H., Entis, P., Sharpe, A. N., and Jarvis, G. A., 1982. Enumeration of indicator

organisms in foods using the automated hydrophobic grid membrane filter technique. J. Food Prot. 45: 292.

8. DePaola, A., Hopkins, L. H., and McPhearson, R. L. 1988. Evaluation of four methods for enumeration of *Vibrio parahaemolyticus*. Appl. Environ. Microbiol. 54: 617.

9. Entis, P. 1983. Enumeration of total coliforms, fecal coliforms, and *Escherichia coli* in nonfat dry milk and canned custard by hydrophobic grid membrane filter method: Collaborative study. J. Assn. Off. Anal. Chem. 68: 897.

10. Entis, P. 1984. Enumeration of total coliforms, fecal coliforms and *Escherichia coli* in foods by hydrophobic grid membrane filter: Collaborative study. J. Assn. Off. Anal. Chem. 67: 812.

11. Entis, P. 1984. Enumeration of total coliforms, fecal coliforms and *Escherichia coli* in foods by hydrophobic grid membrane filter: Supplementary report. J. Assn. Off. Anal. Chem. 67: 811.

12. Entis, P. 1985. Rapid hydrophobic grid membrane filter method for *Salmonella* detection in selected foods: Collaborative study. J. Assn. Off. Anal. Chem. 68: 555.

13. Entis, P. 1986. Hydrophobic grid membrane filter method for aerobic plate count in foods: Collaborative study. J. Assn. Off. Anal. Chem. 69: 671.

14. Entis, P. and Boleszczuk, P. 1983. Overnight enumeration of *Vibrio parahaemolyticus* in seafood by hydrophobic grid membrane filtration. J. Food Prot. 46: 783.

15. Entis, P. and Boleszczuk, P. 1986. Use of Fast Green FCF with tryptic soy agar for aerobic plate count by the hydrophobic grid membrane filter. J. Food Prot. 49: 278.

16. Goetz, A., and Tsuneshi, N. 1951. Application of molecular filter membranes to the bacteriological analysis of water. J. Am. Water Works Assn. 43: 943.

17. Lin, C. C. S., Fung, D. Y. C., and Entis, P. 1984. Growth of yeast and mold on tryptan blue agar in conjunction with the Iso-Grid system. Can. J. Microbiol. 39: 1405.

18. Peterkin, P. I. and Sharpe, A. N. 1984. Rapid enumeration of *Staphylococcus aureus* in foods by direct demonstration of enterotoxigenic colonies on membrane filters by enzyme immunoassay. Appl. Environ. Microbiol. 47: 1047.

19. Sharpe, A. N. 1981. Hydrophobic grid-membrane filters: The (almost) perfect system. In "Membrane Filtration. Applications, Techniques, and Problems," ed. B. J. Dutka, p. 513. Marcel Dekker, Inc., New York, N.Y.

20. Sharpe, A. N. and Michaud, G. L. 1974. Hydrophobic grid-membrane filters: New approach to microbiological enumeration. Appl. Microbiol. 28: 223.

21. Sharpe, A. N. and Michaud, G. L. 1975. Enumeration of high numbers of bacteria using hydrophobic grid-membrane filters. Appl. Microbiol. 30: 519.

22. Sharpe, A. N. and Peterkin, P. I. 1988. "Membrane Filter Food Microbiology." Innovation in Microbiology Research Studies Series, Research Studies Press, Ltd., John Wiley & Sons, Inc., N.Y.

23. Sharpe, A. N., Diotte, M. P., Dudas, I., and Michaud, G. L. 1978. Automated food microbiology: Potential for the hydrophobic grid-membrane filter (HGMF). Appl. Environ. Microbiol. 36: 76.

24. Sharpe, A. N., Diotte, M. P., Peterkin, P. I., and Dudas, I. 1986. Towards the truly automated colony counter. Food Microbiol. 3: 247.

39.7   MINIKITS

39.71   Introduction and History

Some of the first rapid miniaturized techniques were devised in the late 1940s by Weaver,[19] who added concentrated inocula to small tubes of different bacteriological media. Results were available within hours.

Subsequently, a number of identification minikits that consisted of multi-chambered glass-tube, plastic-tube, and tray formats began to appear. Emphasis was on clinical diagnostic microbiology, but the kits also found favor with food microbiologists. Minikits were developed first to identify *Enterobacteriaceae* (*Salmonella*, *Shigella*, *Escherichia*, etc.), but now kits are available to identify a wider variety of microorganisms.

Conventional tube and plate tests presented many disadvantages, not the least of which is the time required to obtain results. Also, the number and nature of biochemical and other tests required to speciate bacteria often discouraged food microbiologists from obtaining definitive data. This situation no longer exists. Commercially available systems to identify *Enterobacteriaceae* and other microorganisms in foods now provide a rapid and convenient alternative to conventional tests.[3, 6]

The basic approaches of the miniaturized identification systems include (1) the use of small amounts of media (liquid or solid); (2) convenient vessels divided into multiple small chambers that contain dehydrated or agar media, paper strips, or discs impregnated with media; and (3) development of innovative inoculation and incubation systems. These kits possess advantages over test systems prepared by individuals in their own laboratories. They are available in convenient packages; they are usually of uniform quality; they are easy to store, use, and dispose of; and all have a numerical manual or computer-assisted system for isolate identification. Some systems are fully computerized, whereas others depend on a profile code book or a punchcard procedure. Regardless, these numerical systems are essential for the accurate identification of unusual strains. Vast amounts of research and development have been expended in developing these kits and compiling data banks that yield reliable identifications.

39.72   Kits Available

The following is a brief description of some of the commercially available miniaturized identification systems.

API-20E (Analytab Products): This kit consists of 20 miniaturized cupules containing dehydrated media and substrates. The organism to be identified is suspended in sterile physiological saline; each cupule is carefully filled with the cell suspension using a Pasteur pipette. Sterile mineral oil is added to several designated cupules, and the system is placed in a moistened plastic chamber to prevent dehydration during incubation.

API Rapid E (Analytab Products): This kit consists of 20 dehydrated substrates, each in an individual cupule attached to a paper strip. The API Rapid E and the API-20E are both 20-test systems; of the 20 tests, 13 are common to both systems and 7 are unique to each. The API Rapid E requires only 4 hr of incubation, whereas the API-20E is usually incubated for 24 hr.

Enterotube II (Roche Diagnostic Systems): This is a multichambered plastic tube with 12 compartments (each filled with a different medium) and an

inoculating needle that runs lengthwise through the tube. The system is inoculated by touching the end of the needle to an isolated colony and then pulling
the needle through the tube, thereby inoculating all 12 compartments in one
passage. Fifteen biochemical tests are incorporated in the 12 compartments.

Micro-ID (Organon Teknika): The Micro-ID consists of a white, molded
styrene tray that contains 15 reaction chambers. The first five chambers contain both a substrate and a detection disc. The remaining 10 reaction chambers
each contain a combination substrate/detection disc. The discs contain all the
reagents required to perform the tests except for the Voges-Proskauer test.
The surface of the styrene tray is covered with clear polypropylene tape that
contains the organism suspensions within the chambers during incubation but
allows complete visibility of the final reactions. A hinged cover opens to
provide access to the inoculation ports.

Minitek (Becton Dickinson Microbiology Systems): This consists of a small
plastic plate that contains 12 wells and a removable plastic top. Separate
paper discs impregnated with individual substrates (obtained from the manufacturer) are placed in each well of the plates. The organism to be identified
is inoculated into a 1.0-ml vial of Minitek Inoculum Broth. The paper discs
are inoculated with 0.05 ml of the broth suspension by using a pipettor with
a disposable tip. Following inoculation, some of the discs are overlaid with
five drops of sterile mineral oil, and the plates are put into a humidor for
incubation. This is the only system that is flexible, in that the investigator
may select any combination of tests (discs), a feature that is useful in research
or when only several discs are needed for the confirmation of a specific
foodborne organism.

R/B Enteric Differential System (Flow Laboratories): The R/B System is a
four-tube, 14-test, agar-based method that somewhat resembles conventional
tube tests. The organism to be identified is introduced into the system by
touching a special sterile needle (the last ¼ inch is bent back on itself) to an
isolated colony and consecutively inoculating all four tubes without flaming
the needle between tubes or touching another colony.

Spectrum-10 (Austin Biological Laboratories): This system consists of two
separate clear plastic trays with 10 wells (tests) per tray. The organism to be
identified is suspended in 3 ml of sterile water (pH 6.8 to 7.2), and 1 ml of
this suspension is dispensed in the back section of each of the two 10-well
trays using a sterile calibrated pipette. The trays are tilted back to a 45° angle
and gently rocked from left to right to distribute the inoculum evenly along
the back section of the tray. The trays are then gently tilted forward to allow
the inoculum to flow evenly into the test wells. Sterile mineral oil is added
to appropriate wells prior to incubation.

Other products available for the rapid presumptive identification of food
isolates include presumptive coliform/*E. coli* tubes (Hach Co.); coliform kits
(BioControl Systems, Inc.); tube and strip tests for enterococci; and various
inexpensive kits that contain only a few key tests (e.g., Austin Biological

Laboratories, Difco Laboratories, Organon Teknika, Remel, Rosco Diagnostica, etc.). Kits containing large numbers of substrates are also available (Analytab Products, Inc. and Biolog, Inc.).

39.73   Considerations and Precautions in Kit Selection and Use

Most of the published evaluations of commercial rapid multitest systems and kits have been with isolates or stock cultures obtained from clinical sources. However, some of these systems have also been evaluated for their ability to identify food isolates. Reviews have been published.[6, 7, 13] Table 2 lists some of the systems, each with manufacturer's address, number of tests, incubation time, whether or not the system has AOAC approval, percent accuracy from food studies, and references. This is not a complete list of all systems and references; only the more commonly used systems are presented to provide examples of the variety available.

Many laboratories that routinely identify *Enterobacteriaceae* isolated from raw ingredients and final food products are currently using one or more of the commercially available diagnostic kits; others are in the process of determining which kits would best fit their needs. The accuracy of identification with the various systems is similar; therefore, factors other than accuracy may predominate in the selection of a system. These factors may include AOAC approval; price; availability; time required for inoculation, incubation, and obtaining results; shelf life; ease or difficulty in determining positive and negative reactions; quality of assistance available from the manufacturer when difficulties are encountered; safety of laboratory personnel; clarity of instructions in the package insert; and costs of the computer profile code.[10] In an attempt to assist microbiologists in selecting a system, a compilation of major advantages and disadvantages of some of the systems was published.[11]

Certain precautions should be taken when using a miniaturized identification system. First, each kit should be examined before use to ensure that it was manufactured properly. For example, in the API-20E kit, the dehydrated media should be deposited only in the lower portions of the cupules, where they will be dissolved when cell suspension is added. Defective kits should be discarded or returned to the manufacturer. The systems were designed to identify pure cultures; mixed or contaminated cultures will almost invariably produce an inaccurate identification.[8] Also, some of the miniaturized systems were designed primarily, and in some instances exclusively, for identification of *Enterobacteriaceae*, and the user cannot assume that they will work satisfactorily with other organisms; Table 3 lists some systems that can be used to identify non-*Enterobacteriaceae*. Furthermore, it is not reasonable to expect that an abbreviated system can consistently be as accurate as an identification that involves an extensive battery of tests. Therefore, the user must recognize the nominal accuracy of the device that is chosen. A minikit that accommodates 96 tests in a single, microtitration-plate-type panel is now available (Biolog, Inc.; API also sells kits that contain supplementary tests).

Because each minikit yields an identification based on a limited number of tests, and the tests vary among kits, it is not unusual to encounter on occasion an isolate that might be given one name by one kit and another name by another kit. For this reason, an investigator engaged in exacting studies may wish to confirm an identification by using a different kit. In addition to biochemical results, a microbiologist should always consider colonial, morphological, and possibly serological information to make an accurate identification.

Commercially available miniaturized identification systems are easy to use, have an acceptable degree of accuracy for most purposes, and are sensible alternatives to conventional procedures in that they save a significant amount of time. However, a user should not expect to obtain reliable results unless all instructions furnished by the manufacturer are closely followed. The most critical instructions usually pertain to the preparation of inoculum, incubation conditions, and reading results. Little training is required. This was demonstrated in a study in which a group of microbiologists from a variety of places, with different training and backgrounds, were able to use these miniaturized multitest systems accurately after only a single exposure to many of the techniques in a workshop environment.[14]

Two last points should be emphasized. Identification kits are inoculated with pure cultures, usually obtained from colonies on isolation plates. This does speed up the overall identification process; however, several days may be required to reach the pure culture stage. In addition, the systems do not include appropriate tests for some important foodborne pathogens, such as *Campylobacter jejuni* and *Bacillus cereus*.

39.74   REFERENCES

1. Bailey, J. S., Cox, N. A., and Thomson, J. E. 1983. Rapid procedure for biochemical characterization and serological confirmation of suspect *Salmonella* isolates. J. Food Prot. 46: 764.

2. Cox, N. A. and Bailey, J. S. 1986. *Enterobacteriaceae* identification from stock cultures and high moisture foods with a four-hour system (API Rapid E). J. Food Prot. 49: 605.

3. Cox, N. A. and Mercuri, A. J. 1978. Comparison of two minikits (API and R-B) for identification of *Enterobacteriaceae* isolated from poultry and meat products. J. Food Prot. 41: 107.

4. Cox, N. A. and Mercuri, A. J. 1979. Rapid biochemical testing procedures for *Enterobacteriaceae* in foods. Food Technol. 33(3): 57.

5. Cox, N. A. and Mercuri, A. J. 1979. Accuracy of Micro-ID for identification of *Salmonella* and other *Enterobacteriaceae* from clinical and food sources. J. Food Prot. 42: 942.

6. Cox, N. A., McHan, F., and Fung, D. Y. C. 1977. Commercially available minikits for identification of *Enterobacteriaceae*: A review. J. Food Prot. 40: 866.

7. Cox, N. A., Mercuri, A. J., Carson, M. O., and Tanner, D. A. 1979. Comparative study of Micro-ID, Minitek and conventional methods with *Enterobacteriaceae* freshly isolated from foods. J. Food Prot. 42: 735.

8. Cox, N. A., Bailey, J. S., Thomson, J. E., Carson, M. O., Posey, D. A., and Rivera, E. 1980. Modified procedure to inoculate Micro-ID. J. Food Prot. 43: 774.

Table 2.—Characteristics of Selected Miniaturized Multitest Systems

System (manufacturer)	No. of tests	Incubation time, hr	AOAC approval	% accuracy, foods	Reference
API-20E (Analytab Products, Inc.)	20	24	yes	99	17
				97	14
				94	16
				91	10
				90	18
				82	3
				76	15
API-Rapid E (Analytab Products, Inc.)	20	4	No[a]	94	2
Enterotube II (Roche Diagnostics Systems)	15	24	?[b]	99	17
				97	14
				90	18
				84	15
				79	10

Micro-ID (Organon Teknika)	15	4	Yes	99 98 97 89	9 4 1,7,10,14 16a
Minitek (Becton Dickinson Microbiology Systems)	35[c]	24	Yes	99 97 94 92	14,17 5,16 7,10 18
R/B (Flow Laboratories)	14	24	No[a]	96 72	17 3
Spectrum 10 (Austin Biological Laboratories)	20	24	No[a]	93(82)[d] 91	12 14

[a] AOAC approval has not been denied, but the system has not yet been tested in an AOAC collaborative study.

[b] The AOAC status of Enterotube II is somewhat unclear. Enterotube received AOAC approval in 1978; however, the new, improved Enterotube II has not been subjected to collaborative study.

[c] Of the 35 available tests, 20 are suggested by the manufacturer for the routine identification of *Enterobacteriaceae*.

[d] 93% to genus level and 82% to species level.

Table 3.—Some Systems for the Identification of Selected Non-*Enterobacteriaceae*

Organism	System (manufacturer)
Anaerobes	API-20A (Analytab Products, Inc.)
	AN-Ident (Analytab Products, Inc.)
	Rapid ANA (Vitek Systems)
	Minitek (Becton Dickinson Microbiology Systems)
Lactobacillus spp.	Minitek[a] (Becton Dickinson Microbiology Systems)
	Rapid CH (Analytab Products, Inc.)
Listeria spp.	API-20S (Analytab Products, Inc.)
	API-Rapid Strept (Analytab Products, Inc.)
	Micro-ID[b] (Organon Teknika)
	Minitek[c] (Becton Dickinson Microbiology Systems)
Non-fermenters	API-20E (Analytab Products, Inc.)
	Minitek (Becton Dickinson Microbiology Systems)
	Oxi-Ferm (Roche Diagnostics Systems)
	Rapid NFT (Analytab Products, Inc.)
Staphylococcus spp.	Minitek (Becton Dickinson Microbiology Systems)
	STAPH-IDENT (Analytab Products, Inc.)
	Staph-Trac (Analytab Products, Inc.)
Yeasts	API-20C (Analytab Products, Inc.)
	Minitek (Becton Dickinson Microbiology Systems)

[a]Anaerobic system.

[b]This system can identify *Listeria* to the genus level. A Micro-ID-LIS that can identify *Listeria* to species is available now.

[c]The data base recognizes *Listeria monocytogenes* but no other *Listeria* species.

9. Cox, N. A., Bailey, J. S., and Thomson, J. E. 1981. Comparison of Micro-ID and Minitek-serology system for rapid identification of *Salmonella*. J. Food Prot. 44: 442.
10. Cox, N. A., Bailey, J. S., and Thomson, J. E. 1983. Evaluation of five miniaturized systems for identifying *Enterobacteriaceae* from stock cultures and raw foods. J. Food Prot. 46: 914.
11. Cox, N. A., Fung, D. Y. C., Goldschmidt, M. C., Bailey, J. S., and Thomson, J. E. 1984. Selecting a miniaturized system for identification of *Enterobacteriaceae*. J. Food Prot. 47: 74.
12. Cox, N. A., VanWart, M., Bailey, J. S., and Thomson, J. E. 1985. Identification of *Enterobacteriaceae* from foods with the Spectrum-10. J. Food Prot. 48: 76.
13. Fung, D. Y. C. and Cox, N. A. 1981. Rapid microbial identification systems in the food industry: Present and future. J. Food Prot. 44: 877.
14. Fung, D. Y. C., Goldschmidt, M. C., and Cox, N. A. 1984. Evaluation of bacterial diagnostic kits and systems at an instructional workshop. J. Food Prot. 47: 68.
15. Griffiths, M. W. and Phillips, J. D. 1982. Identification of bacteria of dairy origin using miniaturized test-systems. J. Appl. Bacteriol. 53: 343.
16. Guthertz, L. S. and Okoluk, R. L. 1978. Comparison of miniaturized multitest systems with conventional methodology for identification of *Enterobacteriaceae* from foods. Appl. Environ. Microbiol. 35: 109.
16a. Keelan, S. L., Flowers, R. S., and Robison, B. J. 1988. Multitest system for biochemical identification of *Salmonella*, *Escherichia coli*, and other *Enterobacteriaceae* isolated from foods: Collaborative study. J. Assn. Off. Anal. Chem. 71: 968.

17. Poelma, P. L., Romero, A., and Andrews, W. H. 1977. Rapid identification of *Salmonella* and related foodborne bacteria by five biochemical multitest systems. J. Food Sci. 42: 677.
18. Poelma, P. L., Romero, A., and Andrews, W. H. 1978. Comparative accuracy of five biochemical systems for identifying *Salmonella* and related foodborne bacteria: A collaborative study. J. Assn. Off. Anal. Chem. 61: 1043.
19. Weaver, R. H. 1954. Quicker bacteriological results. Am. J. Med. Technol. 20: 14.

39.8   REPLICATOR METHODS

39.81   Introduction

Commercial kits for culture identification (Section 39.7) are rapid and convenient, are subjected to quality control by the manufacturers, are backed by extensive data bases, and reduce laboratory-to-laboratory variation in results. However, replicator methods present another, possibly more economical, alternative to conventional methods of culture identification. Of many rapid microbiological methods proposed in the past century,[9] replicator methods are most suited to increase the efficiency of routine microbiological work in terms of (1) materials, (2) labor, (3) bench-top and incubator space, and (4) time.

In 1952, the Lederbergs[13] proposed a "velveteen" method of replicating colonies from a "master plate" to a series of additional plates containing different media. Velveteen was wrapped around a wooden block and placed in contact with the surface of a master plate. The velveteen picked up a portion of each colony; these were sequentially inoculated or replicated on about a dozen additional plates by pressing the velveteen on the surface of each plate.

About 100 replicating devices and replication formats have been described in the literature. Several are commercially available, such as RepliPlate colony transfer pads (FMC Corp.), and multiple-transfer devices with needles, pins, or pegs that pick up liquid or colonies to inoculate petri plates or other vessels containing media (Cathra Replicator,[17] MCT Medical; Whitely Replicator, Spiral System Instruments, Inc.; Mast Replicator, Mast Laboratories, Ltd.). These are entirely satisfactory, but expensive.

In 1969, Fung[2] described a functional procedure for handling large numbers of bacterial isolates. The procedure has been successfully used to identify and characterize bacteria[3, 5, 12, 14] and yeasts,[15] and to study the effects of inhibitors on bacteria[6, 8, 11] and yeasts.[15]

Costs of replica-plate methods for bacterial identification are considerably less than those of conventional, API 20E, and other methods.[1, 4, 15]

39.82   Apparatus and Procedures

The general procedure involves preparation of master plates containing pure broth cultures in wells or colonies on agar, multiple inoculation of the organisms into liquid media or onto solid media, incubation, observation of growth responses or biochemical changes, and data interpretation.

39.821   Vessels

Some replicating devices are designed for depositing broth cultures or cell suspensions on agar plates. If solid agar plates are used, the agar surface must be free of moisture. To predry plates while maintaining sterility, see seep filtration (Section 39.663).

Any vessel that can hold a small volume of medium can be used for miniaturized microbiological tests. In practice, commercially available plastic microtitration plates with 96 wells, arranged in an 8 × 12 array, have been convenient (Figure 4). Plates of other configurations are also available. The plate wells come in three shapes: "U"-shaped (round bottom), "V"-shaped (conical bottom), and flat bottomed. For biochemical tests, any shape can be used. The plates are made of lucite, vinyl, or styrene; most people prefer the styrene plates. Newer models of the Dynatech Laboratories, Inc., Microtiter plate have raised edges around each well to reduce cross-contamination between wells. Each well holds about 0.35 ml of liquid.

The plates can be obtained in either nonsterile or sterile packaging. Individually wrapped sterile plates are most convenient; however, plates can be reused after disinfection and cold sterilization. (Plates currently available are destroyed at autoclaving temperatures.) Used plates are disinfected in 500 ppm sodium hypochlorite solution for 1 hr or longer, rinsed three times with sterile distilled water, and placed under a germicidal lamp (shortwave UV light) for at least 30 min. The sterile plates can be stored in a sterile container at 4°C for up to a week. Plates may also be sterilized with a dose of 2.5 Mrad of irradiation.[10]

Plastic lids to cover the plates after inoculation are available commercially. Plastic seals, sterile aluminum foil, or sterile glass plates may also be used as covers. A piece of sterile blotting paper can be placed between the microtitration plate and lid, if necessary, to absorb condensation and prevent condensate from dropping into the plate wells during incubation.

39.822   Inoculation devices

A 96-point multiple inoculation device facilitates mass transfer of test organisms from the master plate to other plates containing liquid or solid media or to large (150-mm dia) petri dishes containing agar media. To construct a "pinhead" inoculating device (Figure 4), nail 96 rustproof pins (27 mm long, thin) into a wooden block, or fasten the pins onto a sturdy plate, in a pattern that matches the wells of a microtitration plate. All pins should protrude an equal distance from the base plate, so that when the device is pressed on a flat surface, all pinheads touch the surface simultaneously. The pinhead inoculator is used to transfer organisms to solid or liquid media. In tests using semisolid or solid agar slants, a pinpoint inoculator is used. It is constructed by affixing the pins so the sharp ends, instead of the heads, protrude from the base (Figure 4). The inoculation devices are usually operated by hand, but they can be mounted on a stand, such as a drill-press stand, for ease of operation.

39.823   Working environment

Multiple-inoculation devices can be used in an ordinary laboratory setting if the airborne contamination level is not excessive and the bench top is disinfected prior to performing the tests. A laminar flow hood or other chamber provided with a UV lamp for sterilization is preferable. An anaerobic chamber is suitable for anaerobic bacteriology.[19, 20]

39.824   Organisms and inocula

Cultures to be tested can be grown in broth in small dropping bottles (Figure 4). The lids of the dropping bottles should be loose during sterilization to keep the rubber bulbs from "exploding" when pressure is released at the end of an autoclave cycle. After inoculation and incubation of the dropping bottles, the organisms are carefully transferred to the wells of a master plate using the droppers in the dropping bottles. Three drops (about 0.1 ml) of

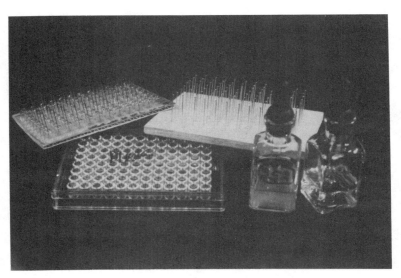

Figure 4 —Basic Materials Needed for Miniaturized Microbiological Work. Pinpoint inoculator (top left), pinhead inoculator (top right), microtitration plate with lid (center), and bottles with inoculum (left) and sterile broth (right).

inoculum per well is enough for most studies. A maximum of 96 cultures can be studied simultaneously, although it is preferable to run duplicate or triplicate determinations of the same organism (resulting in 48 or 32 cultures per plate). It is important to label the master plate accurately.

An alternative, simpler method of preparing the master plate is to transfer isolated bacterial colonies directly into the microtitration plate wells. Three drops (0.1 ml) of sterile buffer are added to each well. A colony (assumed to be a pure culture!) is touched with a sterile toothpick or wooden applicator stick. The stick is stirred 10 times in a well to suspend organisms in the buffer. Up to three wells usually can be inoculated without replenishing the inoculum on the stick. A microtitration plate can be inoculated in about 20 min. The master plate can be used immediately or covered and used within the hour.

Inocula can also be placed in commercial 8- or 12-channel troughs (Dynatech; Figure 5) that accommodate 8 or 12 different organisms. The 8-channel master plate is used to inoculate 8 series of 12 different media in a microtitration plate. The 12-channel master plate is used for 12 series of 8 different media.

39.825   Media preparation

Practically any conventional microbiological medium can be adapted for these miniaturized tests. Some companies (Mast Laboratories, Ltd.,[7] MCT Medical, Inc., and Microbact Systems[16]) sell media or prepoured plates with

Figure 5 —Eight-trough and 12-trough Disposable Reservoirs (Dynatech).

formulations adapted to replicator methodology. Except for a few media that deteriorate rapidly, plates containing sterile media and properly covered are stable for at least 2 weeks at 4°C.

The same medium can be added to all 96 wells of a plate, or different media can be placed in a single plate. Combinations of 8, 12, or multiples thereof are easiest to prepare. Multiwell dispensing devices are sold by many companies, or can be made in the laboratory.

For most purposes, great precision in dispensing liquid media is not needed; a volume variation of 10% can usually be tolerated. About 0.2 ml/well is enough for most tests, but evaporation becomes a problem when very small quantities of media are incubated for 20 hr or longer. To trap gas formed in liquid media, and to create a more microaerophilic environment, a layer of sterile mineral oil:paraffin (1:1) can be applied to the liquid media after inoculation. The mineral oil:paraffin mixture should be sterilized at 121°C for at least 1 hr, or overnight if sterilized in large quantities, because lethality is reduced in hydrophobic environments.

Semisolid and solid media must be dispensed warm (about 50°C). A semi-automatic or automatic pipettor is useful for this purpose. The Becton-Dickinson Cornwall repeating pipettor (laboratory supply houses or Popper & Sons, Inc.) has performed satisfactorily. The medium is kept warm in a waterbath or on a hot plate. To make miniaturized agar slants (such as with triple sugar iron agar), the plate is placed at a 75° angle during dispensing.

Dispensing solid media into microtitration plate wells is relatively cumbersome, as compared with pouring agar into petri dishes. However, the individual wells confine motile bacteria, such as *Proteus* spp., that may migrate across moist agar surfaces and spread into other colonies on a petri dish. In many tests, large (150-mm diameter) petri dishes are more convenient. The agar plate should be held in a laminar flow hood for an hour or placed in a 35°C incubator overnight to predry the agar surface before use. Petri plates should be marked on the bottom, so that orientation of the inocula in relation to the master plate can be easily identified. Alternatively, a dye, such as methylene blue, can be placed in one corner well of the master plate for orientation.

39.826   Multiple-inoculation procedure

About 30 min before use, place the multipoint inoculator in 95% ethanol. The level of alcohol in the container should be higher than the level of inoculum in the master plate. Remove the inoculator from the alcohol and flame to sterilize. Hold the device sideways during ignition and then point the pins upward during the final burning of the alcohol.

Allow a few seconds for the pins to cool, then lower the pins into a master plate. Transfer to either solid or liquid media. For inoculation onto solid agar, all pinheads should touch the agar simultaneously, and care should be taken not to break the agar during inoculation. The device can be recharged without resterilization and used to inoculate another plate; however, be sure the orientation of the inoculation device and master plate coincides with that used for the first inoculation. Carryover of compounds from one agar medium to the next is minimal. For transferring microorganisms into liquid media, rinse the inoculating device and resterilize the pins to avoid carryover of unwanted compounds from one liquid medium to another.

If the diameter of the pinhead is 2 mm, about 0.0006 ml of inoculum is delivered. Pinpoints deliver about 0.0002 ml. For most determinations, the exact volume of inoculum is not critical. If necessary, the volume carried by each pinhead or pinpoint can be determined by dipping the device into a solution of gram's crystal violet solution and then into individual vessels each containing 10 ml of water. The absorbancies of the water solutions can be read in a spectrophotometer at 617 nm and compared with a standard curve constructed by using known volumes of crystal violet.

39.827   Incubation

Cover the plates with sterile lids. For agar media in petri dishes, allow the liquid to be absorbed into the agar (about 30 min) before moving the plate. Incubate at the appropriate temperature. It is desirable to study on the same plate a group of organisms that have similar growth-temperature requirements. If psychrophiles are mixed with mesophiles, growth rates and metabolic activities of the test strains may differ substantially, and false-negative reactions might be obtained. Handle the plates with care to minimize cross-contamination. For many tests, results can be observed within 4 hr. Overnight incubation is enough for most other tests. Incubation of agar plates for more than 24 hr should generally be avoided because prolonged incubation may result in interference of reactions between colonies. For example, acid produced by one colony may diffuse through the agar and mask the reaction produced by the second colony. When observing the plates, take care that condensation in the lid does not contaminate any wells that might be examined later (see 39.821). If motility is a problem on agar plates, test organisms may have to be segregated.

39.828   Reading and interpretation of results

Observe broth media for turbidity (growth) and changes in color or consistency (biochemical reactions). These changes are the same as in conventional test tube methods. To facilitate reading of reactions, an inverted mirror can be used. For reading gas formation in the wells of microtitration plates, the soft plastic can be cut into strips and viewed from the side for the presence of gas bubbles. A microelectrode can be used to measure the pH, if desired.

Growth and color of colonies and media on agar in prepoured agar plates and in agar in microtitration plates are similar to those of conventional agar plate procedures. Figure 6A shows the growth patterns of test cultures plated on trypticase soy agar and incubated for 24 hr; Figure 6B shows the same

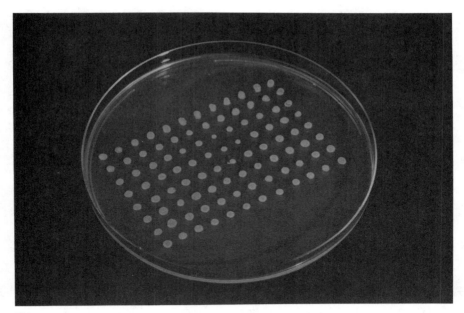

(A)

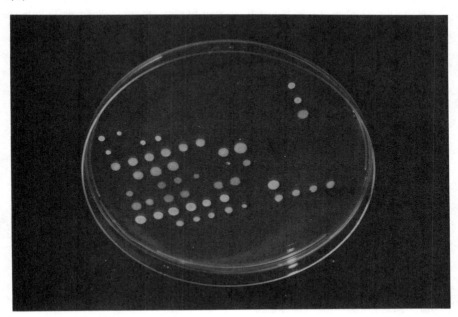

(B)

Figure 6—Growth Patterns of 96 Cultures Inoculated on Plates Containing
Trypticase Soy Agar (A) and Trypticase Soy Agar Containing a Dye
(B). The plates were incubated for 24 hr.

cultures plated on the same medium containing an inhibitor. Use of a positive and negative control colony or well will facilitate correct interpretation of results, especially when color reactions are involved. For motility tests in microtitration plates, it is essential to have motile and nonmotile controls to ensure that results are being interpreted accurately.

Existing data banks, diagnostic schemes, or designs can be used, or identification protocols can be designed to suit individual needs.[1, 14, 18] The system is flexible. Replica plating can be automated to various degrees by using multiple dispensers, etc.; complete automation is approaching reality.[19]

39.83   REFERENCES

1. Clayton, P., Feltham, R. K. A., Mitchell, C. J., and Sneath, P. H. A. 1986. Constructing a database for low cost identification of gram negative rods in clinical laboratories. J. Clin. Pathol. 39: 798.
2. Fung, D. Y. C. 1969. Rapid methods for determining staphylococcal toxins and *Salmonella* associated with poultry products. Ph.D. dissertation. Iowa State U. Parks Library, Ames, Iowa.
3. Fung, D. Y. C. 1985. Procedure and methods for one-day analysis of microbial loads in foods. In "Rapid Methods and Automation in Microbiology and Immunology," ed. K.-O. Habermehl, p. 656. Springer-Verlag, Berlin, Germany.
4. Fung, D. Y. C. and Calvo, A. 1987. Cost and time analysis of Minitek, Fung's mini-system and the conventional method in identification of *Enterobacteriaceae*. Program, Fifth International Symposium on Rapid Methods and Automation in Microbiology and Immunology, Florence, Italy, Abstr. P181, p. 448.
5. Fung, D. Y. C. and Hartman, P. A. 1975. Miniaturized microbiological techniques for rapid characterization of bacteria. In "New Approaches to the Identification of Microorganisms," eds. C.-G. Heden and T. Illeni, p. 347. John Wiley and Sons, New York, N.Y.
6. Fung, D. Y. C. and Miller, R. D. 1973. Rapid screening procedure for testing the effects of dyes on bacterial growth. Appl. Microbiol. 25: 793.
7. Funnel, G. R., Parkinson, D. L., and Bradbury, R. 1986. Biochemical identification of *Enterobacteriaceae* by multipoint inoculation using Mast ID media. Australian J. Med. Lab. Sci. 7: 75.
8. Gailani, M. and Fung, D. Y. C. 1982. Antimicrobial effects of selected antioxidants in laboratory media and in ground pork. J. Food Prot. 47: 428.
9. Hartman, P. A. 1968. "Miniaturized Microbiological Methods." Academic Press, Inc., New York, N.Y.
10. Jayne-Williams, D. J. 1975. Miniaturized methods for the characterization of bacterial isolates. J. Appl. Bacteriol. 38: 305.
11. Lahellec, C. and Colin, P. 1981. Miniaturized methods in poultry microbiology. In "Rapid Methods and Automation in Microbiology," ed. R. C. Tilton, p. 189. Amer. Soc. for Microbiol., Washington, D.C.
12. Lahellec, C. and Colin, P. 1985. Relation between serotype of *Salmonella* from hatcheries and rearing farms and those from processed poultry carcasses. Brit. Poultry Sci. 26: 179.
13. Lederberg, J. and Lederberg, E. M. 1952. Replica plating and the indirect selection of bacterial mutants. J. Bacteriol. 63: 406.
14. Lee, C. Y., Fung, D. Y. C., and Kastner, C. L. 1985. Computer-assisted identification of microflora on hot-boned and conventionally processed beef: Effect of moderate and slow initial chilling rate. J. Food Sci. 50: 553.
15. Lin, C. C. S. and Fung, D. Y. C. 1987. Comparative biochemical reactions and identification

of food yeasts by the conventional method, Fung's mini-method, Minitek and Automicrobic system. CRC Crit. Rev. 7(1): 1.

16. Ling, J. M., Hui, Y.-W., and French, G. L. 1988. Evaluation of the Microbact-24E bacterial identification system. J. Clin. Pathol. 41: 910.

17. Reiber, N. E., Kelly, M. T., Latimer, J. M., Tison, D. L., and Hysmith, R. M. 1985. Comparison of the Cathra Repliscan II, the AutoMicrobic system Gram-Negative General Susceptibility-Plus Card, and the Micro-Media system Fox Panel for dilution susceptibility testing of gram-negative bacilli. J. Clin. Microbiol. 21: 959.

18. Reuther, J. W. A. 1986. A simplified system for the identification of staphylococci by multipoint inoculation of test media. J. Med. Microbiol. 22: 179.

19. Stieglitz, B. and DeFelice, C. P. 1986. Mechanized systems for media dispensing, inoculation, and replication of microorganisms. Biotechnol. Bioeng. 28: 1310.

20. Wilkens, T. D. and Walker, C. B. 1975. Development of a micromethod for identification of anaerobic bacteria. Appl. Microbiol. 30: 825.

39.9 AUTOMATION

39.91 Introduction

About 20 or 30 years ago, the vacuum tube was replaced by the transistor. This development made possible the construction of many new and unique instruments for use in the physical and biological sciences. In recent years, computers and microprocessors have become essential components of automated instrumentation. Robotics are being perfected, automating many laborious tasks.[49] Increased precision, fewer human errors, and less worker fatigue have resulted.[25, 71]

Recent developments in automation of microbiology laboratory procedures are described in this review. Because of space limitations, the instruments mentioned here are representative examples. The list does not imply recommendation by the authors or editors of this book. A list of companies and addresses appears in Section 39.100.

39.92 Routine Laboratory Procedures

39.921 Media preparation

Solid media. Automated equipment is available to sterilize and cool media and pour and stack plates. An example is the AgarMatic automatic sterilizer AS-3 (1 to 3 L) or AS-8 (2 to 8 L) coupled to the PourMatic MP320 dish filling machine (New Brunswick Scientific Co.). The desired medium is added to the automatic sterilizer, and a microprocessor-controlled system directs the sterilization, cooling, petri-plate filling, and stacking operations. Several other automatic plate-pourers are available, such as those sold by Bellco Biotechnology, Inc., Jouan Automatic Media Preparators, Torcon Instruments, Inc., and Vista Laboratories, Ltd.

Liquid media. Some systems described in this section are "dedicated" in that the manufacturer provides hardware and reagents (Abbott Laboratories).

Others are "nondedicated" and are more flexible; they can be used with the worker's choice of containers (plates, tubes, etc.) as well as reagent kits from different companies (Hamilton Co. and Tecan US).

Several automated instruments dispense and dilute liquids. Dynatech Laboratories, Inc, markets a software-controlled, SPD 3000 automatic liquid handling system that can dispense liquids via several pumps that can either "dip and sip," "prime through," or "dispense by peristaltic action." Thus, samples can be dispensed in racks, plates, tubes, or larger containers in preprogrammed volumes. Zymark Corporation produces the Zymate laboratory robotics systems that can dispense liquids by syringe or nozzle, using robotic arms. These robots perform simple tasks, such as carrying a tube from a rack to an automatic dispenser (e.g., a Hamilton Co. precision liquid dispenser II). They can also carry out a complete complex assay procedure when coupled to a Master Laboratory Station controller. For example, the measurement of total soluble protein in bacterial lysates by the Lowry method has been completely automated.[12]

Perkin-Elmer Corporation sells a Master Lab System that automates sample-preparation procedures. A robotic sample holder is incorporated into a testing system that analyzes antibodies to a *Trichina*-specific antigen in blood samples from hogs. Over 400 analyses per hr can be run right on the slaughter line using this system.[74]

39.922   Diluting procedures

Liquid. Most of the automated liquid-handling systems, such as the Dynatech SPD 3000, Hamilton Micro Lab AT Sample Transfer System, Beckman Biomek, DuPont Summit, and Tecan Sampler, will transfer and dilute liquid specimens according to a specific program. Microwell plates, bead plates, or tubes can be used. The AOAC-approved[19, 89] Spiral Plater (Spiral System Instruments, Inc.) dilutes the sample as it is added in a spiral to an agar plate. Many of these instruments are capable of performing additional functions in automated procedures. One system can be set to sample at predetermined times, plate the samples, spread the samples, and move the plates to an incubator.[43]

Solid and semisolid materials. Spiral System Instruments, Inc., sells a gravimetric dilutor that will automatically weigh a sample (in a Stomacher bag or container) and then add the correct volume of liquid to make a desired dilution.

39.923   Counting procedures

Counting colonies on agar plates. Artek Imaging Systems markets several counters. The Autocount can count colonies in a short time. The Bio-Foss Automated Microbiology System (Foss Food Technology Corp.) also counts colonies on petri plates. Spiral Systems Instruments uses a laser beam to

sweep petri plates; further automation is obtained by adding bacterial enumeration software and a dedicated microprocessor. Users of automated counters
should take care to determine whether automated colony counts are equivalent to those obtained by manual enumeration.[15, 57]

Counting cells in liquid. The Optomax, Inc., DEFC 40-10 uses a direct
epifluorescence counting (DEFC) system. A known volume of liquid, such
as beer, milk, or water, is filtered through a microporous filter. The microorganisms are stained with a fluorescent dye, and the instrument counts the
fluorescent particles. Artek Imaging Systems Omnicon 2000 will also perform
similar DEFC analyses, as will the Bactoscan (Foss Food Technology Corp.).
Labsystems, Inc., markets a Bioscreen turbidometer that indirectly determines bacterial counts. Food samples are automatically diluted, dilutions are
dispensed into the wells of a honeycomb plate, and the wells are monitored
for bacterial growth. Counts are derived from observed growth curves in wells
containing the sample dilutions.[51]

39.924   Staining cells on slides

Several instruments will automatically stain slides. Once slides containing
smears are loaded, they are automatically dipped, washed, and dried (Tomtec,
EM Diagnostic Systems, Inc., Shandon, Inc.).[14, 17] The Fisher Code-On robotic
slide-handling system uses special "Probe on Slides" mounted in pairs. These
stain and rinse by capillary action in a narrow space between the two slides.
Although designed primarily for tissue sections and immunological reactions,
the stainer can be modified for *in situ* DNA hybridization studies or identification of pathogens in animal or plant tissues. LKB markets an automatic
stainer for electron microscopy grids.

39.93   Physical Methods of Detection

39.931   Particle counting

Particle counting can be used to enumerate microbial cells in liquids that
are relatively free of extraneous material. A suspension of microorganisms
surrounded by a laminar sheath of fluid can be passed through a column and
become electrostatically charged. The droplets containing microbial cells fall
past positively and negatively charged plates and are deflected according to
charge. The cells are electronically counted, sized, and sorted. The Coulter
Counter Corporation model JT is an example.

More sophisticated instruments, flow sorters, and flow cytometers contain
one or two laser systems or tunable lasers. When a laser beam encounters a
cell labeled with one or more fluorescent dyes, the cell fluoresces (Section
39.5). Photomultiplier tubes detect red or green fluorescence (e.g., from
fluorescein, rhodamine, or phycoerythrin dyes), as well as light scatter, and
collect these data. The instruments can be programmed to either discard the

cells or sort them into tubes or microtitration plates. EPICS CF and EPICS 750 series (EPICS Division of Coulter Counter Corp.) are two examples of cell sorters and flow cytometers. The EPICS 750 has a sort rate of 15,000 decisions per sec with a 99% purity of recovered cells. Becton Dickinson Company markets the FACS-Scan that analyzes and counts but does not sort.[72] Their FACS-Star-Plus analyzer both counts and sorts. Computerized graphics programs allow presentation of multiple analyses of the data.

Microbiological procedures that can be performed on these instruments include automated somatic cell counting,[40] sizing of yeast cells at different growth rates,[7] studying the entrance of cholera enterotoxin subunits into thymus cells,[81] determining monoclonal antibody production by hybridoma cells, and monitoring immunofluorescent reactions by using fluorescent-labeled antibodies.[1, 21, 55, 63, 85] Bacteria have been characterized by flow cytometry.[84] *Legionella* has been detected and characterized with this method;[82] *Listeria monocytogenes* was detected in raw milk by flow cytometric analysis of fluorescently labeled bacterial populations.[15b]

39.932   Image analysis systems

In their simplest form, image analysis systems consist of a video camera connected to an image-array microprocessor and host computer. The image is digitized and is converted into matrix parts called pixels. The camera can be freestanding or coupled to a microscope (including electron microscopes). The system stores, enhances, and displays images on the computer screen. The use of computers allows presentation of the data in various forms, including plotting histograms of the original grey-level images, enhancing for low-contrast images, assigning colors to various grey-level values, enumerating cells and identifying special features, measuring parameters, determining relative densities, and performing data analyses. The Zeiss IBAS system, the Optomax Video interactive display system (VIDS III), and the Bio-Foss system (image analysis and epifluorescence) are examples. The Bio-Foss system effectively automates direct epifluorescent filter techniques (DEFT)[59] to rapidly assess numbers of bacteria in milk,[60] yeasts in some unheated foods,[69] and microbial populations in foods.[34] The DEFT method also has application in poultry and meat quality assurance.[65, 73] A DEFT method for total cell counts of bacteria in water and wastewater is being proposed for the 17th edition of "Standard Methods for the Examination of Water and Wastewater."

Some equipment can monitor fluorescent reactions and even the density of spots on nitrocellulose in ELISA tests. The Richard Brancker Research, Ltd., MI-100 HGMF Interpreter system (see Section 39.685) is an image analysis system that has been used to enumerate and identify microorganisms in food, beverages, and water. Microcomputer-based image analysis systems have also been used with two-dimensional electrophoresis gels[45] and in an automated identification and antimicrobial susceptibility system (API ALA-DIN).[11, 79] The ALADIN is not currently on the market.

39.933 Chromatography

Chromatographic procedures use the physical characteristics of different components of mixtures during partition between two phases. One of these phases is stationary (usually a solid or coupled to a solid); the second phase is mobile and moves across the stationary phase. The chromatograph, in its simplest form, consists of an injector (usually a port through which the sample is injected or added), a column containing the stationary phase, and a detector that monitors the effluent and sends a signal that can be amplified and recorded. The column is usually enclosed in a heated area that can be programmed for temperature changes. The type of column packing depends on the specimens to be examined.

The substances to be examined or separated are added to the mobile ("carrier" gas or fluid) phase and interact with the stationary phase. The compounds that react least with the stationary phase are swept along and out of the column first with the carrier. Eventually, all of the substances that were added will be eluted. The last eluted will be those materials that have the greatest affinity for the stationary phase. Thus, different molecules can be separated from one another. The time of exit from the column is plotted and compared with elution times of known compounds.

The mobile phase can be a gas (gas chromatography) (GC) or liquid (liquid chromatography) (LC). The stationary phase can also be a liquid. There are infinite combinations of these phases, resulting in terms such as high-performance or high-pressure liquid chromatography (HPLC). Pressure is used in HPLC to force the compounds and the mobile phase through the column.

In partition chromatography, one liquid phase is stationary, perhaps chemically bonded to a solid support, while the other liquid phase flows down the column. Movement depends on the polarity of the solutions. The sample will be more soluble in one phase than in the other. In regular partition chromatography, the stationary phase is more polar than the mobile phase. Very polar organic compounds are usually separated by using regular partition chromatography whereas very nonpolar compounds are separated by using reverse partition chromatography. In affinity chromatography, the stationary phase includes a molecular species that specifically binds the substance to be isolated from a mixture; the bound material is subsequently eluted by changing pH, ionic strength, etc., of the mobile phase. Affinity chromatography has been used for antibody purification with protein A attached to the stationary phase. At high pH values, antibodies bind to protein A while other materials pass through the column; the bound antibody is then eluted by using a buffer of low pH.

GC is usually the choice for samples that will be volatile at temperatures up to 300°C and for samples that will form derivatives that are both stable and volatile at elevated temperatures. GC is most often used in routine microbiological analyses.

The type of detector depends on the type of sample and chromatographic system in use. For example, thermal conductivity detectors (TCDs), flame-ionization detectors (FIDs), and electron-capture detectors (ECDs) are usually used with GC, while ultraviolet/visible (UV/VIS) and chemiluminescence detectors are used with LC.

In TCDs, the carrier is usually helium gas. The effluent gas and any eluted compounds pass over a hot wire. The heat is carried to the wall of the detector, which is connected to a Wheatstone bridge. Voltage changes are recorded. As the molecular weight of the eluted compounds increases, thermal conductivity decreases.

In FIDs, hydrogen gas sweeps continually over the end of the column and is burned in air. When compounds that can be burned reach this area in the effluent carrier gas, they are ionized and attracted to a charged electrode. The voltage changes are recorded. The FID is about 10,000 times more sensitive than the TCD.

The ECD contains a radioactive element (e.g., ^{63}Ni) that gives off electrons and produces a current. If the carrier gas contains a substance that can capture the electrons, the number of free electrons is less and the current changes. A pulsed removal of the free electrons occurs in the microsecond range so the detector is renewed for the next compound appearing in the effluent. Complex chromatographic separations often require the use of two or more detectors.

Denny[13] presented a compilation of terms used in chromatography. Gas and liquid chromatographs have been automated largely by using robotic systems to deliver the samples and mobile phases into the equipment. GIRA (see list of manufacturers) employs an ISS.24 robot. Bar-coded samples are placed in the storage area of the robot; sample delivery and data accumulation and analysis are completely automated. The Zymark Corporation also offers an automated system for HPLC or GC, again based on its Zymate laboratory robotics system. The EM Science/Hitachi Model 633A-40 uses a removable, 108-sample carousel, which automates HPLC sampling. Gilson Medical Electronics also markets an autosampling injector for HPLC.

Chromatographic techniques have been used to identify microorganisms, especially anaerobes, for many years.[5, 16, 52] Gas chromatographs for the identification of microorganisms have been automated by the Hewlett-Packard Company. Their computer-controlled HP5898A Microbial Identification System is based on analysis of cellular fatty acids. The computer compares the fatty acid profile of an unknown microorganism with a data base or "library" of known profiles to identify the unknown. Subspeciation is completed within 2 min after a prepared sample (saponified, methylated, and extracted) of a pure culture is placed in the carousel.

Fatty acid methyl GC profile analyses of coagulase-positive and -negative staphylococci were used in cluster analysis to identify the cocci.[56] Diarrheal stools containing *Shigella* spp. produced distinct GC patterns.[6] Bacterial endotoxins were extracted, methylated, and analyzed by packed-column chromatography.[54] T-2 toxin production by *Fusarium acuminatum* isolated from oats and barley has been identified by GC.[66] GC and thin-layer chromatography were used to characterize 593 strains of thermophilic *Campylobacter* spp. isolated from poultry and humans.[80] HPLC has been used to identify *Clostridium* spp.[30] and anaerobic, gram-positive cocci,[29] and to detect mold[48] and mold toxins[9, 46] in processed foods and feeds. Liquid chromatography has been used with fluorescence detection to identify aflatoxins in cheese.[3]

Although identification patterns can be obtained with GC, absolute molecular identification of compounds can be achieved by combining chromatography with mass spectrometry (MS).[27] In a mass spectrograph, an electron beam or charged reagent gas ionizes the sample. The resultant fragmentation pattern of an unknown can be recorded, analyzed, and compared with fragmentation patterns characteristic of known microorganisms. Hewlett-Packard markets a custom GC/MS system combined with an infrared spectrophotometer; each component can also function separately. Kratos Analytical markets an automated inorganic and organic microprobe laser ion mass analyzer, the LIMA 3. The Finnigan MAT 90 is an automated magnetic sector mass spectrometer.

39.934 Electrophoresis

Proteins, nucleic acids, and other biological particles in a solution or suspension will migrate in an electric field. The rate of migration depends on size, shape, and net surface charge.

In a pH gradient, proteins can be separated or "focused" at the pH that corresponds to their isoelectric points (isoelectric focusing). Two-dimensional gel electrophoresis separates a mixture of proteins first according to charge and then by size. Many different support systems have been used for electrophoresis, including agarose and polyacrylamide, in the forms of gels, discs, or slabs. Constant laminar flow can provide stability to a buffer film in free-flow cell electrophoresis. Here, changes in the surface charge of the substances resulting from various interactions (e.g., antibody-antigen reactions) can be quickly ascertained. Various particles can also be separated and collected at the end of the run without decreasing biological activities. Coulter Counter Epics Division markets an ACE 710 Analytical continuous free-flow electrophoresis analytical cell. Many other companies produce various kinds of electrophoresis equipment. Using a laser beam to induce luminescence recorded by a photomultiplier tube and optics to view various gel strips allows rapid analyses and has transformed the field of microelectrophoresis.[83] The Malvern Instruments, Inc., Zetasizer II is an example of this laser "doppler" electrophoresis instrumentation. Antigen-antibody reactions, microorganism-antimicrobial agent interactions, and enterotoxin effects on target cells can be analyzed.[26, 53] Computer-directed automatic scanning densitometers,[44] such as the Helena Laboratories' Autoscanner Fluor-Vis or LKB's Ultra laser densitometer, can scan gels and plates. Bioimage, a Kodak company, markets VISAGE, an image analyzer that automates the interpretation and analysis of complex, two-dimensional electrophoresis patterns.

The AMBIS (Automated Microbiology Systems, Inc.) is a combination of a computer-controlled electrophoresis apparatus and a beta-scanning module for identifying microorganisms based on their cellular proteins. An isolate is labeled by growing it in the presence of radioactive ^{35}S-methionine; cell extracts are made and then are separated by special sodium dodecyl sulfate polyacrylamide gel electrophoresis. The gels are dried and then scanned with a two-dimensional beta-scanning system that detects and images the radioactive protein bands. A banding-pattern profile (microbial protein "fingerprint") is generated and searched against a data bank[42] of banding patterns of known bacteria. Six hr are required from isolation to identification. This technique seems useful in screening many microorganisms, including foodborne microorganisms.[36] Variations in *Clostridium botulinum*,[2] *Salmonella*,[67] and *Shigella*[22] biotypes have been reported. Multilocus enzyme electrophoresis can also be used to study genetic diversity in microorganisms.[71a]

Electrophoresis of DNA can be used to differentiate bacterial strains. For example, salmonellae isolated from food samples and from people with clinical salmonellosis may have similar physiological, serological, and antibiotic-resistance patterns. However, some strains may possess one or more plasmids. Plasmids are extrachromosomal, self-replicating, circular segments of DNA. Plasmid DNA can be extracted from lysed *Salmonella* cells and separated from cellular DNA by electrophoresis. Plasmid DNA banding patterns obtained depend on the size(s) of the plasmid(s). This information offers one more way to differentiate bacterial strains, which provides information helpful in epidemiological studies.

Because different isolates may possess different plasmids of the same size, further analyses may be warranted. The isolated plasmid DNA can be digested with restriction endonucleases and the digest subjected to electrophoresis. Restriction endonucleases cleave DNA at sites between specific pairs of bases, depending on the specific base sequence before and after that pair of bases. Each restriction endonuclease (many different enzymes are available) has an affinity for one or more specific sites. After digestion of plasmid DNA with a restriction endonuclease, the digest is subjected to electrophoresis to detect the size(s) of the fragment(s) produced. Different plasmids of the same size would most likely produce different-sized restriction endonuclease fragments if the plasmids differ in base composition.

Plasmid analysis is useful for a variety of purposes. In one study, strains of *Salmonella newport* associated with outbreaks of food infection transmitted by roast beef were detected by using plasmid analysis.[68] In other studies, strains of *Salmonella typhimurium* associated with foodborne outbreaks of salmonellosis were analyzed for epidemiological purposes,[35, 87a] and the probable source of contamination of *Staphylococcus aureus* endemic within poultry plants was determined.[15a] Some virulence factors, such as those in *Yersinia enterocolitica*, are also plasmidborne. In these instances, plasmid analysis is useful to differentiate virulent and nonvirulent strains.[32]

39.935   Calorimetry

In most chemical reactions, the heat that is produced or absorbed is proportional to the rate of the process and/or the concentration of reactants. The analysis of these thermal changes via thermocouples is termed calorimetry. Minute temperature changes can be measured in calorimeters, of which there are many different types. In flow calorimeters, temperature-equilibrated cultures from a vessel are pumped through a mixing chamber, and the production or absorbance of heat is measured by a change in voltage. In batch calorimeters, components are mixed in a chamber. In differential calorimeters, sample and reference cells are warmed at the same rate; during a reaction in the sample chamber, the temperature changes differentially. The electrical energy necessary to maintain a null temperature differential between the two cells is measured. Perkin-Elmer Corporation markets a Differential (Adiabatic) Scanning Calorimeter (DSC-4) Robotic System with a 48-position carousel and a robotic sampler arm. A computer-driven software program controls the robot and analyzes the data.

Calorimetry has been used in food research to monitor failures in food systems by measuring either the absorption or emission of heat.[4] Calorimetry can also be used to determine susceptibility or resistance to inhibitory agents, or synergistic or antagonistic effects, within a few min. A "thermogram" profile, produced by a microorganism within an hour, can be used for characterization. For example, Perry et al.[58] examined sugar utilization by many strains of *Saccharomyces* to determine which were the most rapid fermenters. Immunological reactions in calorimeters provide kinetic data in addition to indicating whether or not an antigen-antibody reaction has occurred or protein-ligand coupling has taken place.[33] Quantification of microbial populations and growth kinetics is also possible under either normal or stressed conditions.[28] Differential calorimetry has also been used to determine bacterial thermal death times.[24] An LKB microcalorimeter (Pharmacia) was used to estimate rapidly bacterial levels in ground meat.[23]

39.936   Automation of isotopic methods

Measurement of metabolism and metabolic end products during the growth of microorganisms on substrates containing radiolabels is not a new procedure for microbiologists. Substrates labeled with ^{14}C, ^{125}I, ^{3}H, ^{35}S, etc., have been used.

Depending on the label, automated gamma and beta counters are used. The BACTEC 460 system (Becton Dickinson Diagnostic Instrument Systems) monitors $^{14}CO_2$ production by sweeping headspace gas through a Geiger counter. This automated instrument can detect, identify, and perform antimicrobial susceptibility tests directly on respiratory tract specimens. It has also been used to detect microbial growth in blood cultures.[61, 88] Similar tests could be used to test the sterility of foods.[50]

Radiolabeled DNA probes and DNA hybridization are available for various procedures. Radiolabeled antigens and antibodies, e.g., containing ^{125}I, have been used to detect antigen-antibody reactions—radioimmunoassay (RIA). Packard Instrument Company manufactures automated instruments, including gamma counters, beta counters, radiochromatographs, and radioactivity flow detectors for HPLC.

39.937   Infrared detection

Infrared detectors are used in the BACTEC NR 660 and NR 730 automated instruments to monitor CO_2 production. The presence of microorganisms in a growth medium is detected by an infrared spectrometer that selectively senses changes in total carbon dioxide concentration in the headspace above a growing culture. These instruments have been used primarily to detect microorganisms such as yeasts, other fungi, and bacteria in respiratory specimens and blood cultures.[39, 47, 88] However, these infrared systems are relatively new, and food applications have not been developed, except to detect yeasts in bottled juices.[78]

39.94   Biochemical Determinations

Most of the "automated" instruments for identification and antimicrobial susceptibility testing require pure cultures, some sample preparation, and some intervention during the testing procedure. Robotic arms could probably handle much of this and no doubt will do so in the future. Several large instruments based primarily on turbidity and photometry are particularly suited to laboratories with large numbers of samples. These instruments have been well characterized and discussed.[20, 79]

39.941   AutoMicrobic System

The AutoMicrobic System (AMS) (Vitek) is based on detection of growth by measurement of turbidity. A sealed, shallow, rigid plastic "card" has wells that contain various dehydrated biochemicals or specified dilutions of antimicrobials. The card is placed in a module where it is inoculated when the inoculum reaches a preset density—absorbance. The card is then placed in an incubator, where a photometer automatically monitors each well at intervals for growth. Various cards are available for different types of microorganisms, including yeasts of clinical interest.[44] A computer records observed reactions, compares them with a data base, and provides probable identifications. Although workers agree that the Entero Pathogen Screen Card is suitable for identifying *Enterobacteriaceae*, including isolates from foods,[10, 77] there is no agreement on the system's ability to identify oxidase-positive bacteria.[62, 86]

39.942   Avantage Microbiology Center

An Abbott instrument, the Avantage Microbiology Center, identifies gram-negative bacteria[38] and clinically important yeasts[64] and performs antimicrobial susceptibility tests, based on changes in light transmission that occur during bacterial growth or assimilation of carbon sources by yeasts. The system is monitored every 5 min to give kinetic data points. The Abbott Quantum II Microbiology System, a semiautomated system, uses a small cartridge containing 20 lyophilized biochemical substrates. Colorimetric analysis occurs 4 to 5 hr after inoculation and off-line incubation. The cartridges can be read in the Abbott Quantum enzyme immunoassay instrument. Identification of *Enterobacteriaceae* is excellent.[37, 38, 62] Identification of nonfermentative or oxidase-positive gram-negative isolates from humans is satisfactory,[38, 62] but identification of isolates of veterinary origin is not.[37]

39.943   Autobac

The Autobac Series 2 instrument (Organon Teknika) senses light scattering and bases identification of enteric and nonfermentative[8, 41] microorganisms on growth inhibition by dyes and other antimicrobial substances. These include, among others, brilliant green, methylene blue, cobalt chloride, kanamycin, colistin, and cycloserine. A separate cuvette, containing selected discs of antimicrobial agents, is used for susceptibility testing. Computerized, two-stage quadratic discriminant analysis is used to interpret the data.

39.944   MicroScan Walkaway

Model W/A of the MicroScan Walkaway (Baxter) has a carousel (or tower) that holds a stack of up to 96 panels, each containing 18 substrates. The panels for identification of gram-negative bacilli are inoculated, incubated, and automatically read. A computerized data management system reports identification, antimicrobial susceptibility (MIC), and epidemiological data. Single panels are available for identification or MIC; combined panels also are available. The panels (frozen or dried) are inoculated manually or with an automated dispenser. The AutoSCAN-4 is a simpler version of this instrument.[18, 70]

39.945   Sensititre

The Sensititre Auto Identification System[75, 76] uses fluorescence technology (Section 39.5) to detect bacterial growth, metabolism, and enzyme activities.

Fermentation reactions are measured by monitoring the pH change with an indicator that fluoresces only under alkaline conditions. Specific substrates, such as phosphate or various peptides, are coupled to a compound that fluoresces when a bond is enzymatically cleaved. For antimicrobial susceptibility tests, a strip containing antimicrobial agents specified by the consumer and fluorescent substrates is inoculated. Plate incubation occurs off-line. An advantage of the Sensititre system is that visual determinations of reactions can be made if an automatic reading is not done or is questioned.[76]

39.946   Cobas-Bact

The heart of the Cobas-Bact (Roche Diagnostic Systems) for identification of *Enterobacteriaceae* is a disposable plastic ID-E rotor with a central chamber for 5 ml of inoculum with a turbidity equivalent to a 1.0 McFarland standard and 16 peripheral cuvettes containing different dehydrated substrates. The rotor is loaded into the Cobas-Bact, where it is incubated, cuvettes are inoculated by centrifugal force, and the cuvettes are monitored.[87]

39.95   Immunologic Identification Systems

Several of the instruments mentioned in Section 39.82 that automatically dispense, dilute, and wash will perform the EIAs described in Section 39.2. Some instruments (e.g., Hybritech, Inc.) can be used for EIAs or fluorescence immunoassays. A fully automated bench-top clinical analyzer (OPTIMATE, Gilford Instrument Labs) performs homogeneous fluorescence immunoassays and many routine analyses for enzymes, metabolites, drugs, etc.

The Biomek 1000 Automated Laboratory Workstation (Beckman) is a nondedicated system that will handle tubes and 96-well plates. This instrument passes a collimated light beam through the well bottoms and a series of filters, and onto a silicon photocell. The output from the photocell is amplified and sent through a high-level frequency-modulated carrier to a computer that converts the signal and performs the mathematics required to calculate the optical density of the sample. It has been used to automate a bovine brucellosis EIA for specific *Brucella* antibodies, and it has been adapted for DNA sequencing.[87b]

Baker Instruments markets an Encore System based on centrifugal force. A separate pipettor and Procore Instrument are added to this system when EIAs are conducted. Antibody-coated beads are loaded into a 28-sample transfer disc. The pipettor automatically dispenses the samples into peripheral wells and antiserum-enzyme conjugates into inner wells of the disc. The Procore Instrument then uses low-speed centrifugation to transfer the conjugates into the outer wells. During a brief incubation, the sample is bound to the antibody on the bead if homologous. At the same time, the antibody-enzyme conjugate binds to another site on the antigen. The bead is washed to remove unbound reactants, and then the pipettor adds the enzyme substrate. After another incubation period, the disc is placed in the Encore Instrument, where centrifugal force transfers the samples into quartz cuvettes. Absorbance is measured as the spinning cuvettes pass through a focused beam of light. Data are collected by a data-management system. The systems are flexible; several different EIAs and other tests can be run.

Abbott Laboratories manufactures two semiautomated instruments based on fluorescence. One involves the use of microparticles as the solid matrix binding the analyte (either antigen or antibody, depending on the test system). Alkaline phosphatase is the enzyme in the conjugate, which contains the homologous species that reacts with the analyte. The substrate is 4-methylumbelliferyl phosphate, which is cleaved by alkaline phosphatase. The instrument measures the fluorescent 4-methylumbelliferone that is released if an antigen-antibody reaction has occurred. The other instrument, the IMX, is based on the principle of fluorescence polarization. In fluorescence polarization, the analyte and a tracer (fluorescein), coupled to a known concentration of analyte, compete for antibody sites. The antigen-antibody reaction results in a molecule larger than the tracer-analyte alone, changing the degree of polarization of the fluorescent signal. The number of antibody sites available for the tracer compound and therefore the amount of polarization recorded will vary directly with the concentration of analyte in the sample.

Ciba-Corning markets the Inform 4000 Automated RIA (radioactive immunoassay) data-management system that is connected to their model 4000 gamma counter. Sample-handling systems carry out preparative procedures. Any gamma-emitting RIA can be used.

The Stratus Immunoassay system (American Dade) performs automated enzyme immunoassays. It can also use radial partition chromatography to determine the concentration of several antibiotics in biological samples. The method is based on competitive binding between an antibiotic in a sample and enzyme-labeled antibiotic to an antibody in the center of a glass fiber tab. A fluorogenic enzyme substrate is added with the wash, and the optical system monitors the reaction via front-surface fluorescence. A data-management system analyzes the results.

Many "stand alone" microtitration plate reading instruments are available for EIAs. Several of these can be interfaced with data-management systems, and robotics can be used to feed the microtitration plates into some of the instruments. Automated sampler, dispenser, diluter, and washer systems (Section 39.82) can be used to prepare the plates. Dynatech and BIORAD are among the companies that manufacture these readers. Dynatech also markets readers for luminescent reactions in microtitration plates or tubes and a fluorimetric reader for microtitration plates involving fluorescent assays; the latter can be used for kinetic measurements.[31] Perkin-Elmer recently announced the availability of an LS-50 luminescence spectrophotometer with fluorescence accessory for a variety of applications, including microtitration plate reading.

39.96   Precautions

Automated instruments should be used with caution. Some have not been tested extensively in food microbiology applications. Furthermore, an experienced microbiologist must still oversee the instruments and handle manual substitutes in case of instrument malfunction or computer downtime. Backup material and kits should be kept in reserve. Meaningful interpretation of the data also requires an experienced person, one who can recognize, for example, skewed or unusual results that might be based on the use of incorrect or deteriorated reagents rather than machine error.

Automation can be expensive. Some instruments cost $15,000 to $80,000 or more, although simple luminometers, manual microplate readers, etc., are priced under $10,000. However, several considerations, besides cost of the instrument itself, should be kept in mind when considering instrumentation. These include space constraints, daily sample load, and the cost of specialized reagents. Many of the dedicated instruments use only their own specialized plates and reagents. The reputation of the company, the ability to upgrade the instrument easily for new tests or technologies, and the service repair record of the company are also important. It is wise to visit other users of the exact model under consideration. Several companies will rent or lease complete systems or portions and will then be responsible for complete servicing, even though they might not have manufactured all portions of the systems themselves.

39.97   REFERENCES

1. Betz, J. W. 1984. Use of flow cytometry in industrial microbiology. Cytometry 5: 145.
2. Bhaduri, S., Demchick, P. H., and Huhtanen, C. N. 1986. Heterogeneity in the cellular protein profiles of *Clostridium botulinum* types A and B. J. Indust. Microbiol. 1: 165.
3. Bijl, J P., Van Peteghem, C. H., and Ekeyser, D. A. D. 1987. Fluorimetric determination of aflatoxin M1 in cheese. J. Assn. Off. Anal. Chem. 70: 472.
4. Biliaderis, C. G. 1983. Differential scanning calorimetry in food research—A review. Food Chem. 10: 239.
5. Bories, C., Rimbault, A., and Leluan, G. 1987. Simplified gas chromatographic procedure for identification and chemotaxonomy of anaerobic bacteria. Ann. Inst. Pasteur/Microbiol. 138: 587.
6. Brooks, J. B., Basta, M. T., and El Khaly, A. M. 1985. Studies of metabolites in diarrheal stool specimens containing *Shigella* species by frequency-pulsed electron capture gas-liquid chromatography. J. Clin. Microbiol. 21: 599.
7. Carter, B. L. A. and Jagadish, M. N. 1978. Control of cell division in the yeast *Saccharomyces cerevisiae* cultured at different growth rates. Exptl. Cell Res. 112: 373.
8. Costigan, W. J. and Hollick, G. E. 1984. Use of the Autobac IDX system for rapid identification of *Enterobacteriaceae* and nonfermentative gram-negative bacilli. J. Clin. Microbiol. 19: 301.
9. Coulter, J. B., Hendrickse, R. G., Lamplugh, S. M., Macfarlane, S. B., Moody, J. B., Omer, M. I., Suliman, G. I., and Williams, T. E. 1986. Aflatoxins and kwashiorkor: Clinical studies in Sudanese children. Trans. Roy. Soc. Trop. Med. Hyg. 80: 945.

10. Cox, N. A., Bailey, J. S., Thomson, J. E., and Fung, D. Y. C. 1984. Rapid identification of *Enterobacteriaceae* from food and feed. Abstr. 44th Ann. Mtg., Inst. Food Technol. 1984: Abstr. 223, p. 137.

11. D'Amato, R. F., Isenberg, H. D., McKinley, G. A., Baron, E. A., Tepper, R., and Shulman, M. 1988. Novel application of video image processing to biochemical and antimicrobial susceptibility testing. J. Clin. Microbiol. 26: 1492.

12. Del Tito, B. J. and Zabriskie, D. W. 1988. A robotics application for the measurement of total soluble protein from recombinant *Escherichia coli* by the Lowry method. Bio-Technology 6: 231.

13. Denny, R. C. 1982. "A Dictionary of Chromatography." Wiley-Interscience, New York, N.Y.

14. DePase, C. A. and Stone, L. L. 1985. The Gramstainer: A two-year evaluation. Lab. Med. 16: 241.

15. Devenish, J. A., Ciebin, B. W., and Brodksy, M. H. 1984. Automated counting of bacterial counts on spread agar plates and non-gridded membrane filters. J. Food Prot. 47: 284.

15a. Dodd, C. E. R., Chaffey, B. J., and Waites, W. M. 1988. Plasmid profiles as indicators of the source of contamination of *Staphylococcus aureus* endemic within poultry processing plants. Appl. Environ. Microbiol. 54: 1541.

15b. Donnelly, C. W. and Baigent, G. J. 1986. Method of flow cytometric detection of *Listeria monocytogenes* in milk. Appl. Environ. Microbiol. 52: 689.

16. Druker, D. B. 1981. "Microbiological Applications of Gas Chromatography." Cambridge U. Press, New York, N.Y.

17. Fung, D. Y. C. 1975. Evaluation of an automatic gram-staining machine. J. Milk Food Technol. 38: 262.

18. Gavini, F., Husson, M. O., Izard, D., Bernigaud, A., and Quiviger, B. 1988. Evaluation of Autoscan-4 for identification of members of the family *Enterobacteriaceae*. J. Clin. Microbiol. 26: 1586 and 27: 597 (1989).

19. Gilchrist, J. E., Donnelly, C. B., Peeler, J. T., and Campbell, J. E. 1977. Collaborative study comparing the spiral plate and aerobic plate count methods. J. Assn. Off. Anal. Chem. 60: 807.

20. Goldschmidt, M. C. 1980. Instrumentation, automation, and miniaturization. In "Gradwohl's Clinical Laboratory Methods and Diagnosis," 8th ed. eds. A. C. Sonnenwirth and J. Jarett, p. 1495. C. V. Mosby Co., St. Louis, Mo.

21. Goldschmidt, M. C. 1985. Coagglutination procedures and affinity chromatography in antigen and antibody detection. In "Rapid Methods and Automation in Microbiology and Immunology. ed. K.-O. Habermehl, p. 338. Springer Verlag, Berlin, Germany.

22. Goullet, P. and Picard, B. 1987. Differentiation of *Shigella* by esterase electrophoretic polymorphism. J. Gen. Microbiol. 133: 1005.

23. Gram, L. and Sogaard, H. S. 1985. Microcalorimetry as a rapid method for estimation of bacterial levels in ground meat. J. Food Prot. 48: 341.

24. Grieme, L. E. and Barbano, D. M. 1983. Method for use of a differential scanning calorimeter for determination of bacterial thermal death times. J. Food Prot. 46: 797.

25. Groover, M. P., Hughes, J. E., and Odrey, N. G. 1984. Productivity benefits of automation should offset workforce dislocation problems. Indust. Eng. 16: 50.

26. Gross, W. and Marz, W. 1988. Immunoelectrophoretic techniques in protein analysis and quantitation. Amer. Biotechnol. Lab., February: 6.

27. Gutteridge, C. S., Vallis, L., and Macfie, H. J. H. 1985. Numerical methods in the classification of microorganisms by pyrolysis mass spectrometry. In "Computer-assisted Bacterial Systematics," eds. M. Goodfellow, D. Jones, and F. G. Priest, p. 369. Academic Press, Orlando, Fla.

28. Hammerstedt, R. H. and Lovrien, R. E. 1983. Colorimetric techniques for metabolic studies of cells and organisms under normal conditions and stress. J. Exp. Zool. 228: 459.

29. Harpold, D. J. and Wasilauskas, B. L. 1987. Rapid identification of obligately anaerobic

gram-positive cocci using high-performance liquid chromatography. J. Clin. Microbiol. 25: 996.

30. Harpold, D. J., Wasilauskas, B. L., and O'Connor, M. L. 1985. Rapid identification of *Clostridium* species by high-pressure liquid chromatography. J. Clin. Microbiol. 22: 962.

31. Hessford, F., Schmitt, M., and Lazary, S. 1987. Rapid data acquisition from a microtiter plate fluorescence reader and applications in kinetic measurements. J. Immunol. Meth. 100: 269.

32. Hill, W. E., Payne, W. L., and Aulisio, C. C. G. 1983. Detection and enumeration of virulent *Yersinia enterocolitica* in food by DNA colony hybridization. Appl. Environ. Microbiol. 46: 636.

33. Hinz, J.-J. 1983. Thermodynamics of protein-ligand interactions. Ann. Rev. Biophys. Biochem. Eng. 12: 285.

34. Holah, J. T., Betts, R. P., and Thorpe, R. H. 1988. The use of direct epifluorescent microscopy (DEM) and the direct epifluorescent filter technique (DEFT) to assess microbial populations on food contact surfaces. J. Appl. Bacteriol. 65: 215.

35. Holmberg, S., Wachsmuth, I. K., Hickman-Brenner, F. W., and Cohen, M. L. 1984. Comparison of plasmid profile analysis, phage-typing, and antimicrobial susceptibility testing in characterizing *Salmonella typhimurium* isolates from outbreaks. J. Clin. Microbiol. 19: 100.

36. Hook, L. A., Bloch, P. L., Kohlenberger, R. W., and Kinningham, P. A. 1987. Automated microbial system for computer-programmed analysis of radiolabeled protein banding patterns. Dev. Indust. Microbiol. 28: 149.

37. Jones, R. L., Adney, W. S., Davis, M. A., Vonbyren, H., and Thompson, G. 1987. Evaluation of Quantum II microbiology system for identification of gram-negative bacteria of veterinary origin. J. Clin. Microbiol. 25: 2071.

38. Jorgensen, J. H., Dyke, J. W., Helgeson, N. G. P., Cooper, B. H., Redding, J. S., Crawford, S. A., Andreuszewski, M. T., and Prowant, S. A. 1984. Collaborative evaluation of the Abbott Avantage system for identification of frequently isolated nonfermentative or oxidase-positive gram-negative bacteria. J. Clin. Microbiol. 20: 899.

39. Jungkind, D., Millan, J., Allen, S., Dyke, J., and Hill, E. 1986. Clinical comparison of a new automated infrared blood culture system with the BACTEC 460 system. J. Clin. Microbiol. 23: 262.

40. Kelley, W. N. 1978. Improved automated optical somatic cell counting method for raw milk: Collaborative study. J. Assn. Off. Anal. Chem. 61: 1328.

41. Kelly, M. T., Matsen, J. M., Morello, J. A., Smith, P. B., and Tilton, R. C. 1984. Collaborative clinical evaluation of the Autobac IDX system for identification of gram-negative bacilli. J. Clin. Microbiol. 119: 529.

42. Kersters, K. 1985. Numerical methods in the classification of bacteria by protein electrophoresis. In "Computer-assisted Bacterial Systematics," eds. M. Goodfellow, D. Jones, and F. G. Priest, p. 337. Academic Press, Inc., Orlando, Fla.

43. Kvittingen, J. 1984. Pilot studies with an apparatus for automatic bacteriological testing of water. Zentralbl. Bakteriol., I, Orig. B179: 596.

44. Land, G., Stotler, R., Land, L., and Stanek, J. 1984. Update and evaluation of the AutoMicrobic yeast identification system. J. Clin. Microbiol. 20: 649.

45. Lee, C., Hu, S.-E., Lok, M. S., Chen, Y. C., and Tseng, C. C. 1988. Microcomputer-based image analysis systems for two-dimensional electrophoresis gels. BioTechniques 6: 216.

46. Leitao, J., de Saint-Blanquat, G., and Bailly, J. R. 1987. Action of phosphine on production of aflatoxins by various *Aspergillus* strains isolated from foodstuffs. Appl. Environ. Microbiol. 53: 2328.

47. Levi, M. H., Gialanella, P., Motyl, M. R., and McKitrick, J. C. 1988. Rapid detection of positive blood cultures with the BACTEC NR-6600 does not require first-day subculturing. J. Clin. Microbiol. 26: 2262.

48. Lin, H. H. and Cousin, M. A. 1985. Detection of mold in processed foods by high performance liquid chromatography. J. Food Prot. 48: 671.
49. Lochmuller, C. H. and Lung, K. R. 1985. Laboratory robotics: The advent of "soft" instrumentation. J. Chromat. Sci. 23: 429.
50. Mafart, P., Bourgeois, C., Duteurtre, B., and Moll, M. 1978. Use of (^{14}C)lysine to detect microbial contamination in liquid foods. Appl. Environ. Microbiol. 35: 1211.
51. Matilla, T. 1987. Automated turbidometry—A method for enumeration of bacteria in food samples. J. Food Prot. 50: 640.
52. Mitruka, B. M. 1975. Gas Chromatographic Applications in Microbiology and Medicine. John Wiley & Sons, New York, N.Y.
53. Montgomery, R. R., Kunicki, T. J., and Glode, L. M. 1986. Immunochemical techniques, Part I. Hybridoma technology and monoclonal antibodies. Meth. Enzymol. 121: 702.
54. Morris, N. M. and Brannan, M. A. F. 1986. Gas chromatographic determination of fatty acid composition of endotoxins from different bacteria. J. Chromatog. 374: 27.
55. Nozawa, R. T., Yokota, T., and Kuwahara, S. 1978. Assay method for *Vibrio cholerae* and *Escherichia coli* enterotoxins by automated counting of floating Chinese hamster ovary cells in culture medium. J. Clin. Microbiol. 7: 479.
56. O'Donnell, A. G., Nahaie, M. R., Goodfellow, M., Minnikin, D. E., and Hajek, V. 1985. Numerical analysis of fatty acid profiles in the identification of staphylococci. J. Gen. Microbiol. 131: 2023.
57. Peeler, J. T., Leslie, J. E., Danielson, J. W., and Messer, J. W. 1982. Replicate counting errors by analysts and bacterial colony counters. J. Food Prot. 45: 238.
58. Perry, B. F., Beezer, A. E., and Miles, R. J. 1983. Characterization of commercial yeast strains by flow microcalorimetry. J. Appl. Bacteriol. 54: 183.
59. Pettipher, G. L. 1983. "The Direct Epifluorescent Filter Technique for the Rapid Enumeration of Micro-organisms." John Wiley & Sons, Inc., New York, N.Y.
60. Pettipher, G. L., Fulford, R. J., and Mabbitt, L. A. 1983. Collaborative trial of the direct epifluorescent filter technique (DEFT), a rapid method for counting bacteria in milk. J. Appl. Bacteriol. 54: 177.
61. Pfaller, M. A. 1985. Automated instrument approaches to clinical microbiology. Diag. Microbiol. Infect. 3: 15S.
62. Pfaller, M. A., Bale, M. J., Schulte, K. R., and Koontz, F. P. 1986. Comparison of Quantum II bacterial identification system and the AutoMicrobic system for the identification of gram-negative bacilli. J. Clin. Microbiol. 23: 1.
63. Phillips, A. P. 1985. Dual parameter scatter flow immunofluorescence analysis of *Bacillus* spores. Cytometry 6: 124.
64. Qadri, S. M. H., Fluornoy, D. J., Qadri, S. G. M., and Ramirez, E. G. 1986. Rapid identification of yeasts by semi-automated and conventional methods. Med. Microbiol. Immunol. 175: 307.
65. Qvist, S. H. and Jakobsen, M. 1985. Application of the direct epifluorescent filter technique as a rapid method in microbiological quality assurance in the meat industry. Intl. J. Food Microbiol. 2: 139.
66. Rabie, C. J., Sydenham, E. W., Thiel, P. G., Lishubben, A., and Marasas, W. F. 1986. T-2 toxin production by *Fusarium acuminatum* isolated from oats and barley. Appl. Environ. Microbiol. 52: 594.
67. Reeves, M. W., Evins, G. M., Heiba, A. A., Plikaytis, B. D., and Farmer, J. J. III. 1989. Clonal nature of *Salmonella typhi* and its genetic relatedness to other salmonellae as shown by multilocus enzyme electrophoresis, and proposal of *Salmonella bongori* comb. nov. J. Clin. Microbiol. 27: 313.
68. Riley, L. W., DiFerdinando, G. T. Jr., DeMelfi, T. M., and Cohen, M. L. 1983. Evaluation of isolated cases of salmonellosis by plasmid profile analysis: Introduction and transmission of a bacterial clone by precooked roast beef. J. Infect. Dis. 148: 12.

69. Rodrigues, U. M. and Kroll, R. G. 1986. Use of the direct epifluorescent filter technique for the enumeration of yeasts. J. Appl. Bacteriol. 61: 139.

70. Rohden, D. L., Smith, P. B., Baker, C. N., and Schable, B. 1985. AutoSCAN-4 System for identification of Gram-negative bacilli. J. Clin. Microbiol. 22: 915.

71. Schmidt, G. J. and Dong, M. W. 1987. Robots: Applications in automated sample analysis. Am. Lab. 19: 62.

71a. Selander, R. K., Caugant, D. A., Ochman, H., Musser, J. M., Gilmour, M. N., and Whittam, T. S. 1986. Methods of multilocus enzyme electrophoresis for bacterial population genetics and systematics. Appl. Environ. Microbiol. 51: 873.

72. Sells, M. A. and Whiteside, T. L. 1982. Facs IV cell analyzer and sorter. J. Clin. Lab. Automat. 2: 19.

73. Shaw, B. G., Harding, C. D., Hudson, W. H., and Farr, L. 1987. Rapid estimation of microbial numbers on meat and poultry by the direct epifluorescent filter technique. J. Food Prot. 50: 652.

74. Singh, P., Oliver, D. G., Allison, D., Jang, L., and Azam, M. 1988. Immunochemical testing of pathogens in a slaughterhouse. Abstr. Ann. Mtg. Am. Soc. Microbiol., 1988: Abstr. P-51, p. 282.

75. Staneck, J. L., Vencelette, J., Lamothe, F., and Polk, E. A. 1983. Evaluation of the Sensititre system for the identification of *Enterobacteriaceae*. J. Clin. Microbiol. 17: 647.

76. Staneck, J. L., Allen, S. D., Harris, E. E., and Tilton, R. C. 1985. Automated reading of MIC microdilution trays containing fluorogenic enzyme substrates with the Sensititre Auto-reader. J. Clin. Microbiol. 22: 187.

76a. Steward, E. W., Farrell, K., and Tempelton, J. W. 1987. An automated closed loop method to obtain standard calibration curves in the brucellosis ELISA. Fed. Proc. 46: 2019.

77. Tardio, J. L., O'Brien, K., and Latt, T. 1988. Identification of *Escherichia coli* from shellfish and related environments by AutoMicrobic system. J. Assn. Off. Anal. Chem. 71: 582.

78. Threlkeld, C. H. 1982. Detection of microbial contamination utilizing an infrared CO_2 analyzer. J. Food Sci. 47: 1222.

79. Tilton, R. C. 1987. Instrumentation and rapid methods. In "Clinical and Pathogenic Microbiology," eds. B. M. Howard, J. Klaas, S. J. Rubin, A. S. Weissfeld, and R. C. Tilton, p. 157. C. V. Mosby Co., St. Louis, Mo.

80. Totten, P. A., Patton, C. M., Tenover, F. C., Barrett, T. J., Stamm, W. E., Steigerwalt, A. G., Lin, J. Y., Holmes, K. K., and Brenner, D. J. 1987. Prevalence and characterization of hippurate-negative *Campylobacter jejuni* in King County, Washington. J. Clin. Microbiol. 25: 1747.

81. Tsuru, S., Matsuguchi, M., Watanabe, M., Taniguchi, M., and Zinnaka, Y. 1984. Entrance of cholera enterotoxin subunits into thymus cells. J. Histochem. Cytochem. 32: 1275.

82. Tyndall, R. L., Hand, R. E., Mann, R. C., Evans, C., and Jernigan, R. 1985. Application of flow cytometry to detection and characterization of *Legionella* species. Appl. Environ. Microbiol. 49: 852.

83. Uzgris, E. E. 1981. Laser doppler spectroscopy: Applications to cell and particle electrophoresis. Adv. Coll. Interface. Sci. 14: 75.

84. Van Dilla, M. A., Langlois, R. G., Pinkel, D., Yajko, D., and Hadley, W. K. 1983. Bacterial characterization by flow cytometry. Science 220: 621.

85. Vanomi, M. 1984. Effects of temperature on the yeast cell cycle analyzed by flow cytometry. Cytometry 5: 530.

86. Villasante, P. A., Agulla, A., Merino, F. J., Perez, T., Landron de Guevara, C., and Velasco, A. C. 1987. Rapid automated method for screening enteric pathogens from stool specimens. J. Clin. Microbiol. 25: 584.

87. Wegner, A., Tissieres, L. J., Praplan, F. R., Kamm, W. R., and Bille, J. 1987. Cobas-Bact system for identification of members of the family *Enterobacteriaceae* in 4 h 20 min. J. Clin. Microbiol. 25: 61.

87a. Whiley, S. J., Lanser, J. A., Manning, P. A., Murray, C., and Steele, T. W. 1988. Plasmid profile analysis of a salmonellosis outbreak and identification of a restriction and modification system. Appl. Environ. Microbiol. 54: 1591.

87b. Wilson, R. K., Yuen, A. S., Clark, S. M., Spense, C., Arakelian, P., and Hood, L. E. 1988. Automation of dideoxynucleotide DNA sequencing reactions using a robotic workstation. BioTechniques 6: 776.

88. Yagupsky, P., Nolte, F. S., and Menegus, M. A. 1988. Enhanced detection of fungemia with the BACTEC 460 System by use of aerobic-hypertonic medium. Abstr. Ann. Mtg. Am. Soc. Microbiol. 1988: Abstr. C-243, p. 377.

89. Zipkes, M. R., Gilchrist, J. E., and Peeler, J. T. 1981. Comparison of yeast and mold counts by spiral, pour, and streak plate methods. J. Assn. Off. Anal. Chem. 64: 1465.

39.10 LIST OF MANUFACTURERS

Abbott Laboratories, P. O. Box 152020, Irving, TX 75015-2022

AgriTech System, Inc., Portland, ME 04101

American Dade Division, American Hospital Supply Corp., P. O. Box 520672, Miami, FL 33152

Ames Div., Miles Laboratories, Inc., Elkhart, IN 46515

Analytab Products, Inc. (API), Div. Sherwood Medical, 200 Express St., Plainview, NY 11803

Analytical Luminescence Laboratory, Inc., 11180 Roselle St., San Diego, CA 92121

API—See Analytab Products, Inc.

Artek Imaging Systems, Subsidiary of Dynatech Laboratories, 14340 Sullyfield Circle, Chantilly, VA 22021

Austin Biological Laboratories, 6620-A Manor Rd., Austin, TX 78723

Automated Microbiology Systems, Inc. (AMBIS), 939 Ruffin Rd., San Diego, CA 92123

AutoMed, 599 Cardigan Rd. Shoreview, MN 55126

BACTEC, Becton Dickinson Diagnostic Instrument Systems, 383 Hillen Rd., Towson, MD 21204

Baker Instruments, P. O. Box 2168, Allentown, PA 18001

Baxter MicroScan Div., 1584 Enterprise Blvd., West Sacramento, CA 95691

Beckman Instruments, Inc., Laboratory Automation OPRMS, 160 Hopper Ave., Waldwick, NJ 07463

Becton Dickinson Co., P. O. Box 7375, Mountain View, CA 94039

Becton Dickinson Microbiology Systems, Hunt Valley, MD 21030

Bellco Biotechnology, Inc., 340 Edrudo Rd., P. O. Box B, Vineland, NJ 08360

BioControl Systems, Inc., 19805 North Creek Parkway, Bothell, WA 98011

Bioenterprises Pty, Ltd., 28 Barcoo St., Roseville, N.S.W., Australia; distributed in U.S. by 3M.

BioImage, A Kodak Company, 1390 Eisenhower Place, Ann Arbor, MI 48104

Biolog, Inc. 3447 Investment Blvd., Suite 3, Hayward, CA 94545

Biomedia Corp., P. O. Box 8045, Foster City, CA 94404

BIORAD Instruments, 2200 Wright Ave., Richmond, CA 94804

Biotech Group, Inc., 401 E Ocean Blvd., Suite 204, Long Beach, CA 90802

Cambridge Naremco, 1820 Mt. Vernon St., Springfield, MO 65802

Cetus Corporation, 1400 Fifty-third St., Emeryville, CA 94608

Ciba-Corning, Medfield, MA 02052

Clinical Sciences, Inc., 30 Troy Rd., Whippany, NJ 07981

Coulter Counter Corp., P. O. Box 4486, Hialeah, FL 33014-0486

Difco Laboratories, P. O. Box 1058, Detroit, MI 48232

Dynatech Laboratories, Inc., 14340 Sullyfield Circle, Chantilly, VA 22021

DuPont de Nemours & Co., Special Diagnostics Div., Barley Mill Plaza, Wilmington, DE 19898

EM Diagnostic Systems, Inc., 480 Democrat Rd., Gibbstown, NJ 08027

EM Science, 111 Woodrest Rd., Cherry Hill, NJ 08034-0395

Environmental Diagnostics, Inc., 2990 Anthony Rd., Burlington, NC 27215

Finnigan MAT, 355 River Oaks Parkway, San Jose, CA 95134

Fisher Scientific Co., 711 Forbes Ave., Pittsburgh, PA 15219

Flow Laboratories, 25 Lumber Rd., Roslyn, NY 11576

FMC Corp., Marine Colloids Div., 5 Maple St., Rockland, ME 04841

Foss Food Technology Corp., 10355 W. Seventieth St., Eden Prairie, MN 55344

Genetic Systems, 3005 First Ave., Seattle, WA 98121

GENE-TRAK Systems, 31 New York Ave., Framingham, MA 01701

Gilford Instrument Laboratories, Inc., Corning Glass Works, Oberlin, OH 44074

Gilson Medical Electronics, Inc., Box 27, 3000 W. Beltline Highway, Middleton, WI 53562

GIRA, Morlaas, France

Hach Co., P. O. Box 389, Loveland, CO 80539-0389

Hamilton Co., 4970 Energy Way, P.O. Box 10030, Reno, NV 89520-0012

Helena Laboratories, 1530 Lindbergh Dr., P.O. Box 752, Beaumont, TX 77704

Hewlett-Packard Company, 3000 Hanover St., Palo Alto, CA 94304-1181

Hybritech, Inc., 11085 Torreyana Rd., San Diego, CA 92121

Idetek, Inc., 1057 Sneath Lane, San Bruno, CA 94406

IDEXX Corp., 100 Fore St., Portland, ME 04101

International Diagnostic Systems Corp., 2614 Niles Ave., St. Jospeh, MI 49085

Jouan Automatic Media Preparators, Distributed by Larry Bell & Associates, Inc., Box 217, Hopkins, MN 55343

KRATOS Analytical, 535 E Crescent Ave., Ramsey, NJ 10746

Labsystems, Inc., P. O. Box 13970, Research Triangle Park, NC 27709-3970

LKB—see Pharmacia

Los Alamos Diagnostics, P.O. Box 1221, Los Alamos, NM 87544

Lumac Systems, Inc., P.O. Box 2805, Titusville, FL 32780
Malthus Instruments, Ltd., Radiometer America, Inc., 811 Sharon Dr., Westlake, OH 44145-9990
Malvern Instruments, Inc., 200 Turnpiker Rd., Southborough, MA 01772
Mast Laboratories, Ltd., Derby Road, Bootle, Merseyside, L20 1EA, England
Microbics Corp., 2233 Faraday Ave., Ste B., Carlsbad, CA 92008
Millipore Corp., Bedford, MA 01730
Neogen Corp., 620 Lesher Place, Lansing, MI 48912
New Brunswick Scientific Co., P. O. Box 986, Edison, NJ 08818
Optomax, Inc., 109 Terrace Hall Ave., Burlington, MA 01803
Organon Teknika, 100 Akzo Ave., Durham, NC 27704
Oxoid Div. Unipath Co., 9200 Rumsey Rd., Columbia, MD 21045
Packard Instrument Co., 2200 Warrenville Rd., Downers Grove, IL 60515
Penicillin Assays, Inc., 36 Franklin St., Malden, MA 02148
Perkin-Elmer Corp., 761 Main Ave., Norwalk, CT 06859-0012
Pharmacia LKB Biotechnology, 800 Centennial Ave., P.O. Box 1327, Piscataway, NJ 08855-1327
Popper and Sons, Inc., 300 Denton Ave., New Hyde Park, NY 11040
QA Laboratories, Ltd., 135 The West Mall, Toronto, M9C 1C2, Canada
Radiometer America, Inc., 811 Sharon Dr., Westlake, OH 44145-9990
Remel, 12076 Santa Fe Dr., Lenexa, KS 66215
Rialdon Diagnostics, Denton, TX 76201
Richard Brancker Research, Ltd., 27 Monk St., Ottawa, K1S 3Y7, Canada
Roche Diagnostic Systems, Hoffman LaRoche, One Sunset Ave., Montclair, NJ 07042
Rosco Diagnostica, Taastrup, Denmark
Sensititre, 8A Industrial Way #2, Salem, NH 03079
Shandon, Inc., 171 Industry Dr., Pittsburgh, PA 15275
Sigma Chemical Co., P. O. Box 14508, St. Louis, MO 63178
SmithKline Beckman Corp., One Franklin Plaza, P. O. Box 7929, Philadelphia, PA 19101
Spectrochrom, Ltd., I.S.U. Research Park, Suite 611, 2501 No. Loop Dr., Ames, IA 50010-8283
Spiral System Instruments, Inc., 4853 Cordell Ave., Suite A-10, Bethesda, MD 20814
Stauffer Chemical Co., One Corporate Dr., Box 881, Shelton, CT 06484
Tecan US, P.O. Box 2485, Chapel Hill, NC 27515-2485
Technicon Instruments Corp., 511 Benedict Ave., Tarrytown, NY 10591
Tekmar Co., P.O. Box 371856, Cincinnati, OH 45222
3M Medical-Surgical Div., 3M Center, Bldg. 255-5S, St. Paul, MN 55144-1000
Tomtec, 707 Harborview Rd., Orange, CT 06477
Torcon Instruments, Inc., 1840 Oak St., Torrance, CA 90501

Turner Designs, 2247 Old Middlefield Way, Mountain View, CA 94043-2489

United States Biochemical Corp., P. O. Box 22400, Cleveland, OH 44122

Vicam, 29 Mystic Ave., Somerville, MA 02145

Vista Laboratories, Ltd., 8432 45th St., Edmonton, Alberta, Canada T6B 2N6

Vitek Systems, 595 Anglum Dr., Hazelwood, MO 63042

Wampole Laboratories, Div. Carter-Wallace, Inc., Cranbury, NJ 08512

Wellcome Diagnostics Div., Burroughs Wellcome Co., 3030 Cornwallis Rd., Research Triangle Park, NC 27709

Zymark Corp., Zymark Center, Hopkinton, MA 01746

Carl Zeiss, Inc., One Zeiss Dr., Thornwood, NY 10594

Chapter 40

INVESTIGATION OF FOODBORNE ILLNESS OUTBREAKS

Marilyn E. Veek, Irving Weitzman, Richard C. Swanson, and John P. Lucas

40.1   INTRODUCTION

About 400 to 600 foodborne illness outbreaks, involving 10,000 to 20,000 cases of disease, are reported annually in the United States.[4-6, 12] The real incidence, however, may be 10 to 200 times higher than these numbers because many afflicted persons do not seek medical treatment, or reports are not made to health agencies by the victims or by the medical care suppliers.[9] Thus, one estimate of the total number of cases of food- and waterborne illness in the U.S. is 1.4 to 3.4 million per year.[7] A study of diarrheal disease projects that foodborne and subsequent person-to-person transmission account for at least 24 million and possibly as many as 81 million cases per year.[2] The estimated cost of foodborne disease is between $1 and $10 billion annually, including direct medical costs, lost wages and productivity, investigational costs, and industry losses through embargo, voluntary destruction, and recall of the products involved.[14] Additionally, foodborne agents can affect organ systems other than the gastrointestinal tract. The relationship of such diverse entities as hemolytic-uremic syndrome, reactive arthritis, peri- and myocarditis, and Guillain-Barré syndrome to foodborne infections is becoming increasingly apparent.[1] Only a very large outbreak, such as the milkborne outbreak of salmonellosis centered in Chicago in 1985, which involved more than 16,000 confirmed cases,[10] or a very widespread problem, such as *Salmonella enteriditis* infections from Grade A eggs,[13] captures national attention.

Why do health agencies investigate foodborne outbreaks, and what does such an investigation involve? This chapter will address these questions.

40.2   PURPOSE OF INVESTIGATION

These are the two most important reasons for investigating foodborne outbreaks:

1. Preventing further illness by identifying the offending product and removing it from sale. This step has the most direct and immediate effect on public health. Actions involved could range from embargo of the product, to recall, to closure of the food processing facility or food service facility.
2. Obtaining information about the causative agent and its source. Knowing the agent allows the public health agency to make specific recommendations for patient treatment, as well as for preventive measures, such as providing immune globulin to persons exposed to hepatitis A. Information can also be used to prevent future outbreaks. For example, baked potatoes were not considered a hazardous food until they were involved in outbreaks of botulism; now they must be handled like any other hazardous food, with appropriate time and temperature control. Similarly, based on outbreak data, advice is given against the use of galvanized containers for storage and serving of acidic foods because of the possibility of heavy metal leaching, which may lead to zinc poisoning.

40.3   THEORY OF INVESTIGATION

The investigation of foodborne outbreaks is based on the principles of epidemiology, the study of the factors determining the occurrence of disease in populations.[8] An understanding of these factors can lead to the development of effective methods for disease prevention.

An epidemiological investigation of a foodborne outbreak involves interviews, sample collection, and sample analysis. Each of these steps can provide information vital to demonstrating the relationship between a food and a disease. Inferences can be drawn about the relationship from the following elements:

- Signs and symptoms consistent with the disease occurring in the exposed population;
- Clinical specimens to confirm the diagnosis;
- Demonstration that ill individuals were more likely to have consumed the food product than individuals who did not become ill;
- Presence of the organism or toxin in the food product in a concentration sufficient to have caused the disease; and
- Evidence of contamination and/or mishandling of the product that resulted in the presence of the organism or toxin.

Although a food product may be epidemiologically associated with a disease outbreak based solely on interviews of ill and well persons concerning their food exposures, more appropriate control and prevention measures can be taken if the causative agent is specifically identified. This identification relies on laboratory analysis of samples, including clinical specimens and leftover food products. There are published criteria for confirmation of the etiological agent responsible for outbreaks of foodborne illness and of the responsible vehicle.[11]

40.4 CONSIDERATION OF SAMPLES

Identification of the causative agent of a foodborne outbreak depends heavily on the collection of adequate samples and the appropriate handling of those samples. Although these steps are not under the direct control of the laboratory analyst, ongoing communication between the analyst and the epidemiologist or investigator can lead to a better understanding of sampling needs and, thus, a greater likelihood of identifying the causative agent. For example, it is usually helpful to collect not only implicated prepared foods, but also all remaining ingredients. The ingredient samples can provide a "baseline," or else reveal that the contamination occurred at a stage earlier than immediately before the food was consumed. Sometimes, all that remains is leftovers in the garbage, or product wrappers, but even those can be important: botulism toxin was confirmed from the wrapper of a patty melt sandwich associated with an outbreak in Peoria, Ill.[7] At the time of collection, there may not be enough information available to implicate a specific food, so numerous samples may be collected. Information that becomes available should be considered in determining whether to analyze all or only some of the samples collected.

Rapid handling and appropriate temperature control of samples are important considerations in investigating foodborne outbreaks. If samples languish on a desk or in a storage room and are not analyzed expeditiously, opportunities for controlling the outbreak may be missed, particularly if the outbreak is presumed on the basis of interviews to be caused by a particular organism or toxin, but analytical results point to a different culprit.

Another important factor is appropriate temperature control of the samples; freezing may lead to destruction of the causative organism, while refrigeration, especially if lengthy, may permit overgrowth by competing organisms. The appropriate conditions should be based on the hypothesis of the causative organism or toxin as well as the nature of the food (e.g., ice cream would normally be handled in the frozen state).

When the analyst receives the samples (or is notified that they are en route), decisions concerning the appropriate analyses to perform must be made. The epidemiologist or investigator may have developed a hypothesis as to the cause of the outbreak and thus may request a specific analysis. Alternatively, knowledge of the symptoms exhibited by persons involved in the outbreak, and/or of the nature of the suspect food, can be used in the decision process. For example, sudden onset of vomiting and diarrhea 2 to 4 hr after a meal that included ham or potato salad may indicate staphylococcal intoxication. Table 1 contains information concerning incubation periods, predominant symptoms, specimens to analyze, and the organism or toxin involved.

One aspect that is sometimes overlooked is the effect of processing on the presence or absence of an organism or toxin: many heat processes will destroy *Staphylococcus aureus* but not its toxin. Thus, if the organism had the opportunity to multiply in food that was later cooked, examination of the product for the organism may be futile, whereas the test for the presence of toxin would be appropriate.

40.5   EQUIPMENT, MATERIALS, AND SOLUTIONS

The primary tools used in investigating a foodborne illness outbreak are forms, sample containers, and inspectional equipment.

40.51   Forms

Forms are used by public health professionals to systematically record specific information about an outbreak. Relevant data are important in developing a hypothesis concerning the source of the outbreak. Because individual state and local health departments usually develop and maintain standard forms, they will not be described in detail here.

Generally, a form is used to obtain case history information from the first few individuals identified: demographic data such as address, age, and sex; signs and symptoms; other related medical information such as allergies and physician involvement; and contacts with other ill persons. Another form is used to obtain a 72-hr food history (to cover the incubation period for most foodborne illnesses; however, if an illness such as listeriosis or hepatitis A is suspected, it would be necessary to try to obtain food history information for up to 2 months before onset). As the investigation expands, and there is a need to systematically collect data concerning hypothesized exposures, the investigator may develop a questionnaire specific to the outbreak to ensure that the same questions are asked of both ill and well persons who had the same opportunity for exposure. The questionnaire will usually include a list of specific items available at the implicated meal, restaurant, etc., as well as symptoms, onset, time, demographic information, and contact identification.

The agency may also use collection reports for food and patient samples; these forms contain a description of the sample collected and a designation of the desired analysis. The laboratory may use the same or a different one to report the results of its analysis back to the health department personnel conducting the investigation.

40.52   Sample Containers

The second category of equipment for the investigation is specimen containers. For food specimens, these would include sterile plastic bags, jars, or other containers, as well as sterile sampling equipment such as swabs and spoons. Sterilizing agents, such as a propane torch, may be important if access to sterile equipment is difficult. Sufficient insulated containers and refrigerants for sample transport are also important. For patient specimens, stool collection kits, swabs, blood collection tubes, and equipment for transporting them are vital. Frequently, the laboratory will be responsible for providing specimen collection and transport equipment to the epidemiologist/investigator. Occasionally patients will collect specimens in their own containers.

40.53 Inspectional Equipment

Inspectional equipment is important for the follow-up at the location where the suspect food was prepared. In addition to sample containers and forms, the investigator may use equipment such as a thermometer for measuring the temperature of the food at various stages of preparation and serving.

40.6 INVESTIGATIVE PROCEDURES

The procedures to investigate foodborne outbreaks are described in significant detail in "Procedures to Investigate Foodborne Illness," published by the International Association of Milk, Food and Environmental Sanitarians.[11] The major steps in conducting an investigation of a foodborne outbreak are outlined below.

40.61 Receiving Notification of Illness

A public health agency may identify the possibility of a foodborne outbreak from information developed from numerous sources, such as individuals who believe their illness was caused by a particular food or meal, a physician who treated a patient for what appears to be a foodborne illness, a laboratory analysis, a school nurse, or a poison control center. The agency evaluates the information in the context of its experience with foodborne illness, and other information at hand, such as the information on a case history form or complaint log. Whether or not a complaint or possible outbreak is investigated by the agency depends on guidelines for follow-up established by the Health Officer and the local government. The definition of an outbreak (two or more cases with similar exposure and symptoms, or one case of botulism, paralytic shellfish poisoning, or other unusual case) influences the setting of the levels for investigation.

40.62 Verifying the Diagnosis

40.621 Case histories

The next step in following up a foodborne outbreak is to obtain case history information for each ill individual. The investigator will usually obtain a 72-hr

Table 1—Guide for Laboratory Tests Indicated by Certain Symptoms and Incubation Periods[a]

Incubation periods	Predominant symptoms	Specimens to analyze	Organism, toxin, or toxic substances
Upper gastrointestinal tract symptoms (nausea, vomiting) occur first or predominate			
Less than 1 hr	Nausea, vomiting, unusual taste, burning of mouth	Vomitus, urine, blood, stool	Metallic chemicals[b]
1 to 2 hr	Nausea, vomiting, cyanosis, headache, dizziness, dyspnea, trembling, weakness, loss of consciousness	Blood	Nitrites[c]
1 to 6 hr, mean 2 to 4 hr	Nausea, vomiting, retching, diarrhea, abdominal pain, prostration	Vomitus, stool	*Staphylococcus aureus* and its enterotoxins
8 to 16 hr (2 to 4 hr rarely)	Vomiting, abdominal cramps, diarrhea, nausea	Vomitus, stool	*Bacillus cereus*
6 to 24 hr	Nausea, vomiting, diarrhea, thirst, dilation of pupils, collapse, coma	Urine, blood	Amanita mushrooms[d]
Sore throat and respiratory symptoms			
12 to 72 hr	Sore throat, fever, nausea, vomiting, rhinorrhea, sometimes a rash	Throat swab	*Streptococcus pyogenes*
2 to 5 days	Inflamed throat and nose, spreading grayish exudate, fever, chills, sore throat, malaise, difficulty in swallowing, edema of cervical lymph node	Throat swabs, blood	*Corynebacterium diphtheriae*
Lower gastrointestinal tract symptoms (abdominal cramps, diarrhea) occur first or predominate			
8 to 22 hr, mean 10 to 12 hr	Abdominal cramps, diarrhea, putrefactive diarrhea associated with *C. perfringens*	Stool	*Clostridium perfringens, Bacillus cereus, Streptococcus faecalis, S. faecium*

Incubation time	Symptoms	Specimen	Agent
12 to 74 hr, mean 18 to 36 hr	Abdominal cramps, diarrhea, vomiting, fever, chills, malaise	Stool	*Salmonella* (including *S. arizonae*), *Shigella*, Enteropathogenic *Escherichia coli*, other *Enterobacteriaceae*, *Yersinia enterocolitica*, *Pseudomonas aeruginosa*(?), *Aeromonas hydrophila*, *Plesiomonas shigelloides*, *Campylobacter jejuni*, *Vibrio cholerae* (01 and non-01), *V. parahaemolyticus*
3 to 5 days	Diarrhea, fever, vomiting, abdominal pain, respiratory symptoms	Stool	Enteric viruses
1 to 6 weeks	Mucoid diarrhea (fatty stools), abdominal pain, weight loss	Stool	*Giardia lamblia*
1 to several weeks, mean 3 to 4 weeks	Abdominal pain, diarrhea, constipation, headache, drowsiness, ulcers, variable—often asymptomatic	Stool	*Entamoeba histolytica*
3 to 6 months	Nervousness, insomnia, hunger pains, anorexia, weight loss, abdominal pain, sometimes gastroenteritis	Stool	*Taenia saginata, T. solium*
Neurological symptoms (visual disturbances, vertigo, tingling, paralysis)			
Less than 1 hr	Tingling and numbness, giddiness, staggering, drowsiness, tightness of throat, incoherent speech, respiratory paralysis		Shellfish toxin
	Gastroenteritis, nervousness, blurred vision, chest pain, cyanosis, twitching, convulsions	Blood, urine, fat biopsy	Organic phosphate insecticides

Table 1—Continued

Incubation periods	Predominant symptoms	Specimens to analyze	Organism, toxin, or toxic substances
	Excessive salivation, perspiration, gastroenteritis, irregular pulse, pupils constricted, asthmatic breathing	Urine	Muscaria-type mushrooms
	Tingling and numbness, dizziness, pallor, gastroenteritis, hemorrhage, desquamation of skin, eyes fixed, loss of reflexes, twitching, paralysis		Tetraodon toxin (puffer fish poisoning)
1 to 6 hr	Tingling and numbness, gastroenteritis, dizziness, dry mouth, muscular aches, dilated eyes, blurred vision, paralysis		Ciguatera toxin
	Nausea, vomiting, tingling, dizziness, weakness, anorexia, weight loss, confusion	Blood, urine, stool, gastric washings	Chlorinated hydrocarbons (insecticides)
12 to 72 hr	Vertigo, double or blurred vision, loss of reflex to light, difficulty in swallowing, speaking, and breathing, dry mouth, weakness, respiratory paralysis	Blood, stool	*Clostridium botulinum* and its neurotoxins
More than 72 hr	Numbness, weakness of legs, spastic paralysis, impairment of vision, blindness, coma	Urine, blood, stool, hair	Organic mercury
	Gastroenteritis, leg pain, ungainly high-stepping gait, foot and wrist drop		Triorthocresyl phosphate
Allergic symptoms (facial flushing, itching)			
Less than 1 hr	Headache, dizziness, nausea, vomiting, peppery taste, burning of throat, facial swelling and flushing, stomach pain, itching of skin	Vomitus	Histamine[e]

Incubation period	Symptoms	Specimen to collect	Etiological agent
	Numbness around mouth, tingling sensation, flushing, dizziness, headache, nausea		Monosodium glutamate (Chinese restaurant syndrome)
	Flushing, sensation of warmth, itching, abdominal pain, blood, puffing of face and knees		Nicotinic acid
Generalized infection symptoms (fever, chills, malaise, prostration, aches, swollen lymph nodes)			
4 to 28 days, mean 9 days	Gastroenteritis, fever, edema about eyes, perspiration, muscular pain, chills, prostration, labored breathing	Muscle biopsy	*Trichinella spiralis*
7 to 28 days, mean 14 days	Malaise, headache, fever, cough, nausea, vomiting, constipation, abdominal pain, chills, rose spots, bloody stools	Stool, blood	*Salmonella typhi*
10 to 13 days	Fever, headache, myalgia, rash	Lymph node biopsy, blood	*Toxoplasma gondii*
10 to 50 days, mean 25 to 30 days	Fever, malaise, lassitude, anorexia, nausea, abdominal pain, jaundice	Urine, blood	Etiological agent not yet isolated, probably viral
Varying periods (depends on specific illness)	Fever, chills, head- or joint ache, prostration, malaise, swollen lymph nodes, and other specific symptoms of disease in question	Blood, stool, urine, sputum, lymph node, gastric washings (one or more, depending on organism)	*Bacillus anthracis, Brucella melitensis, B. abortus, B. suis, Coxiella burnetii, Francisella tularensis, Listeria monocytogenes, Mycobacterium tuberculosis, Mycobacterium* spp., *Pasteurella multocida, Streptobacillus moniliformis, Campylobacter jejuni*

[a]From APHA, "Compendium of Methods for the Microbiological Examination of Foods," 2nd ed. (1984).

[b]Consider chemical tests for such substances as zinc, copper, lead, cadmium, arsenic, or antimony.

[c]Test for discoloration of blood.

[d]Identify mushroom species eaten; test urine and blood for evidence of renal damage (SGOT, SGPT enzyme tests).

[e]Scrombroid poisoning should be considered. Examine foods for *Proteus* species or other organisms capable of decarboxylating histidine into histamine and for histamine.

food history but will focus especially on the time period indicated by the predominant symptoms (e.g., most recent foods eaten if the symptom is vomiting; foods eaten 6 to 20 hr before onset of cramps and diarrhea).

40.622   Clinical specimens

Additional medical information is sought from the attending physician or health professional. Clinical specimens should be obtained as soon as possible to enhance the likelihood of identifying the causative organism or toxin. The specimen collection report submitted to the laboratory should identify the onset time and nature of the symptoms as well as the collection time. The specimens should be appropriate to the disease suspected or the symptoms experienced; a blood sample would probably not be meaningful if the only symptom was diarrhea (with no fever or associated symptom).

40.623   Food sample

Leftover food samples, ingredients, and other evidence should also be collected during the initial visit to the ill person, or as soon as possible after the illness is reported.

With leftovers, the sample size will be limited by the amount available, but ingredients may be available in sufficient amounts for analysis. The investigator collecting the food samples should record the conditions under which the food was being held (such as temperature), as well as the conditions for shipment to the laboratory. It is vital that these samples be analyzed as quickly and accurately as possible so that appropriate public health measures can be taken. If analysis reveals that an ingredient is contaminated, the population at risk may be much larger than if the contamination occurred on a one-time basis in a home or at one meal.

The levels of contaminant in an ingredient may not be high enough to have directly caused the outbreak. However, the ingredient may have been the source, with mishandling of the product during or after processing resulting in the outbreak.

40.63   Epidemiologic Associations

Based on information obtained initially and through case interviews, the epidemiologist or investigator must determine whether an outbreak occurred and hypothesize the cause of it. It is frequently difficult to determine whether an illness was caused by a food, particularly if only one or two cases are involved. Common associations between people are a means of identifying outbreaks and pointing to hypotheses as to the cause.

There are three categories of associations: time, place, and person.

- Time refers to when the onset of illness occurred; in a common-source outbreak, onset times will cluster within a few hours or days (depending on the normal incubation period for the disease).

- Place refers to the source of the causative food—a common meal or product.
- Person associations refer to demographic factors such as age, sex, and ethnic or religious group.

Once identified, the association(s) can be used to develop a hypothesis concerning the illness, the food involved, and how and where the food became contaminated. Using a specific questionnaire to interview additional persons who share the association(s) helps prove or disprove the hypothesis. It is important to interview both ill and well persons who had the opportunity for the same exposures to refine the hypothesis and, for example, narrow the suspect vehicle from an entire meal to just one of the foods served. If the outbreak is large, interviews may be limited to a random sample, but generally it is helpful to interview at least 100 people. Clinical specimens may be collected from the first 10 to 20 people who appear to be associated with the outbreak to identify the causative organism or toxin and show that it is associated with the outbreak rather than a chance occurrence in one or two patients. The number of specimens needed will depend on whether the outbreak is typical, whether the suspect organism is easy to grow, or whether it is an unknown organism. Once the organism or toxin is positively identified, the information should be made available to physicians so that they can appropriately treat later cases.

40.64   Food Processing Investigation

An investigation is also made to determine how the food(s) became contaminated and/or allowed growth of pathogens after interview/questionnaire information has at least tentatively identified a specific event, such as a banquet; a specific location, such as a restaurant; or a specific food, such as milk or cheese. The investigation would start at the banquet location, restaurant, or processing plant and include a thorough review of how the product or meal in question was prepared. The source of ingredients, the times and temperatures involved in the preparation, opportunities for cross-contamination, and employee practices—including health status—would all be investigated.

Frequently, differences in the process from normal procedures can provide valuable clues as to the source of the problem. It is sometimes difficult to obtain accurate information concerning an incident, particularly if mistakes were made and punishment is feared. The nature of the food and handling problems involved in the incident may indicate the type of contamination or whether the causative organism or toxin is likely to have been present in the suspect food. For example, *Bacillus cereus* foodborne illness is generally associated with starchy foods that have been heat-shocked, such as rice or dry beans, rather than with meat and poultry. Therefore, if the causative toxin in an outbreak was *B. cereus* enterotoxin, the investigation would emphasize starchy foods and/or possible cross-contaminations to other types of food.

The investigator would look for a situation in which such a food was cooked, then either cooled too slowly, stored at temperatures in the critical range (45° to 140°F), or reheated inadequately. The possibilities of new vehicles and/or organisms should always be kept in mind, and the investigation kept broad enough to uncover these.

40.641   Major processing defects

Several major causative factors occur repeatedly in foodborne outbreaks. Cited for 656 outbreaks involving food (commercially as well as home-prepared) during 1982, in order of frequency of occurrence, were these factors:[12]

- Improper holding temperature
- Food from unsafe source
- Inadequate cooking
- Poor personal hygiene on the part of food handlers
- Contaminated equipment

Factors cited in other similar reports[3-6] include those listed above, as well as inadequate cooling, lapse of a day or more between preparing and serving foods, inadequate time or temperature or both during reheating of previously cooked foods, and cross-contamination. Because time, and particularly temperature, play a critical role in foodborne outbreaks, temperature-measuring devices are key pieces of equipment for the investigator and for the establishment preparing the food.

Yersinia enterocolitica, Listeria monocytogenes, and other bacteria that can survive and grow at refrigeration temperatures are increasingly recognized as foodborne pathogens. Thus, it is clear that refrigeration alone is not necessarily an adequate control measure for food preservation. The investigator must carefully evaluate contamination of raw materials or in-process products as factors in following up outbreaks involving refrigerated products that had not been heat-treated.

40.7   ANALYSIS AND CONCLUSION

40.71   Data Analysis

The data gathered from persons interviewed about the outbreak are analyzed to determine whether the hypothesis about the cause of the outbreak is true.

40.711   Predominant symptoms

One analysis involves determining the predominant symptoms reported by ill persons. The number of persons reporting a symptom is counted and compared to the total number of ill persons to obtain a percentage. The relative order of prevalence of symptoms is characteristic of a particular illness; for example, in an outbreak of *Clostridium perfringens* gastroenteritis, diarrhea would be the most prevalent symptom, with a few or no persons reporting vomiting or fever. If clinical specimens are unavailable or have not yet been analyzed, the predominant symptom data will suggest whether the illness is an infection or intoxication, which in turn will suggest possible food sources and laboratory tests to be run.

40.712   Epidemic curve

An epidemic curve is plotted, using data concerning the time of onset of symptoms. The time is plotted against the number of persons reporting illness. The scale of the curve is dependent on the "time span" involved in the outbreak; if all onsets occurred within a few hours, then the scale would be hours instead of days or weeks. The shape of the curve produced is dependent on whether the outbreak occurred from a "point-source" (a single meal, for example) or from person-to-person contact. A point-source outbreak curve will rise sharply to a peak, then taper off more gradually. The length of the curve will approximate the range of the incubation period of the disease. A person-to-person outbreak will show a much slower rise and a length extending over several incubation periods.

40.713   Incubation period

More useful information about the incubation period is obtained by calculating the median of onset times for the ill persons, after ingestion of the suspect meal or food, once identified. The median is used because it is not affected by unusual outlying values and thus will more closely approximate the incubation period than the mean would. This information, along with the most prevalent symptoms, helps characterize the disease involved. In general, intoxications have shorter onset times than infections.

40.714   Attack rate

In most, if not all, foodborne outbreaks, the data gathered will show that some of those who ate a particular food became ill and some did not, because of factors such as individual resistance, the amount of product consumed, and nonhomogeneity of the organism or toxin within the product. Some of those who reportedly did not eat that product will also report illness, which may be coincidental, in sympathy with those who became ill, or because the person forgot having eaten the particular food. Thus, the association of a particular food with illness usually is not 100%, and statistical methods are used to determine whether the association is significant. The starting point for this method is to determine the food-specific attack rates.

For each food served at a suspect meal, the percentage of persons who ate that food and became ill—the attack rate—is compared to the percentage of persons who did not eat the food and became ill. These two percentages are compared for each of the foods, and the food showing the largest statistically significant difference in percentages becomes the suspect food in the outbreak. For example, if 85% of those eating fried rice became ill, but only 15% of those not eating it did, the difference is 70%. If all other foods at the meal have difference figures of 5% or 10%, then clearly the fried rice is the suspect food. The statistical significance of attack rates is determined by calculating the probability of this difference having occurred by chance using 'Chi-Square' or Fisher's exact test, depending on the number of people involved. Generally, probabilities of less than 0.05% — that the difference occurred by chance — are considered statistically significant. If more than one food turns out to be statistically significant, further data analysis must be done. This problem may occur, for example, with foods commonly eaten together, such as meat and gravy. Another statistic commonly used is relative risk, the ratio of illness in the persons eating the food to those not eating it.

40.72   Conclusion

A statistically significant association of a food with an outbreak does not "prove" that that food caused the outbreak. Additional information from the laboratory is critical in determining causation. The optimum situation is one in which samples of the food are available for analysis and are found to contain sufficient numbers of organisms, or amount of toxin, to have caused illness in persons consuming the food. Additionally, appropriate specimens from ill persons would have shown the presence of the organism or toxin. The investigation at the food preparation site would have disclosed food sources and/ or handling practices that would account for the presence of the organisms or toxin. Unfortunately, in many outbreaks, one or more of these elements is lacking, usually because of unavailability of samples.

40.8   REPORTS

The final element in investigating a foodborne outbreak is to write a report. In addition to documenting the investigation, a timely report can be a valuable means of disseminating knowledge about outbreaks and their causes and thus can aid in reducing or preventing future outbreaks.

40.9   REFERENCES

1. Archer, D. L. 1988. The true impact of foodborne infections. Food Technol. 42(7): 53.
2. Archer, D. L. and Kvenberg, J. E. 1985. Incidence and cost of foodborne diarrheal disease in the United States. J. Food Prot. 48: 887.
3. Bryan, F. L. 1980. Control of foodborne diseases. In "The Safety of Foods," 2nd ed., ed. H. D. Graham, p. 55. AVI Publishing Co., Westport, Conn.
4. CDC. 1979. Foodborne disease outbreaks — Annual summary. Centers for Disease Control, Atlanta, Ga.

5. CDC. 1983. Foodborne disease surveillance—Annual summary, 1981. Centers for Disease Control, Atlanta, Ga.

6. CDC. 1983. Foodborne disease surveillance—Annual summary, 1980. Centers for Disease Control, Atlanta, Ga.

7. CDC. 1984. Foodborne botulism—Illinois. Morbid. Mortal. Weekly Rep. 33(2): 22.

8. Fox, J. P., Hall, C. E., and Elveback, L. R. 1970. "Epidemiology: Man and Disease." The MacMillan Company, London, England.

9. Hauschild, A. H. W. and Bryan, F. L. 1980. Estimate of cases of food- and water-borne illness in Canada and the United States. J. Food Prot. 43: 435.

10. Illinois Dept. of Pub. Health/FDA. 1985. Final Task Force Report. Salmonellosis outbreak, Hillfarm Dairy, Melrose Park, Ill. Food and Drug Admin., Washington, D.C.

11. International Assn. of Milk, Food and Environmental Sanitarians Inc. "Procedures to Investigate Foodborne Illness." 1987. Internat. Assn. of Milk, Food and Environ. Sanitar., Inc., Ames, IA.

12. MacDonald, K. L. and Griffin, P. M. 1986. Foodborne disease outbreaks—Annual summary, 1982. Morbid. Mortal. Weekly Rep. 35(ISS): 7SS.

13. St. Louis, M. E., Morse, D. L., Potter, M. E., Demelfi, T. M., Guzewich, J. J., Tauxe, R. V., Blake, P. A., and the *Salmonella enteriditis* Working Group. 1988. The emergence of grade A eggs as a major source of *Salmonella enteriditis* infections. J. Am. Med. Assn. 259(14): 2103.

14. Todd, E. C. D. 1984. Economic loss resulting from microbiological contamination of food. In "Proceedings of the Second National Conference for Food Protection," p. 151. Food and Drug Admin., Washington, D.C.

15. APHA. 1984. "Compendium of Methods for the Microbiological Examination of Foods," 2nd ed., ed. M. L. Speck, Amer. Pub. Health Assn., Washington, D.C.

Chapter 41

FOODBORNE VIRUSES

D. O. Cliver, R. D. Ellender, G. S. Fout, P. A. Shields, and M. D. Sobsey

41.1 INTRODUCTION

41.11 Foods as Vehicles for Human Viruses

Hepatitis A virus, Norwalk and Norwalk-like viruses, poliovirus, and echovirus cause foodborne disease in consumers of virus-contaminated foods.[7, 8, 11, 49, 54, 61, 84] Astrovirus, calicivirus, enteric adenovirus, parvovirus, and rotavirus also may cause foodborne disease.[1, 49] These enteric viruses replicate in the intestine of infected individuals and are transmitted by the fecal-oral route. They must survive the acidic environment of the stomach, the alkaline conditions and digestive enzymes of the small intestine, and the conditions encountered between hosts. Such selective pressures result in a stability that allows virtually any food to serve as a vehicle for transmission.

The most common types of foodborne viral diseases are hepatitis A (infectious hepatitis) and acute viral gastroenteritis. More than 150 foodborne outbreaks of hepatitis A have occurred since 1943.[11] Hepatitis A is usually a mild illness with an incubation period of 15 to 50 days and is characterized by fever, malaise, nausea, anorexia, and abdominal discomfort followed in several days by jaundice. Many infected children and some adults may not show symptoms at all. Occasionally, prolonged disability or death occurs, especially among the elderly.

The hepatitis A virus (HAV), which causes hepatitis A, is one of more than 70 members of the enterovirus group of the Picornaviridae family. These acid-stable viruses contain a genome of single-stranded RNA and have a particle size of about 27 nm. HAV is thought to replicate initially in the gastrointestinal tract and then spread primarily to the liver, where it infects hepatocytes and Kupffer cells. An infected individual begins to shed virus in fecal material from 7 to 10 days before onset of symptoms. Virus shedding declines rapidly after the first symptoms appear.

Enterically transmitted non-A, non-B hepatitis virus causes a hepatitis with an incubation period and symptoms similar to hepatitis A, except for women in the third trimester of pregnancy.[80] This group is reported to have a fatality rate approaching 20%. No foodborne outbreaks have been reported, but major waterborne outbreaks have occurred in Africa, Asia, and the Middle East. The first outbreaks to be reported on the American continents occurred in Mexico in late 1986.[80]

Foodborne viral gastroenteritis is usually a mild disease with various degrees of nausea, vomiting, diarrhea, malaise, abdominal pain, muscle pain, anorexia, headache, and low-grade fever. Illness develops 20 to 50 hr after contaminated foods are consumed and lasts for 1 to 8 days. Norwalk and Snow Mountain viruses, major etiological agents of this disease,[7, 54, 84] belong to the Norwalk virus group and resemble the enteroviruses in size. Their genetic makeup has not been determined, but limited molecular virology and serological studies suggest that they may be related to the caliciviruses.[27, 32]

Rotavirus, another agent of gastroenteritis, has 11 segments of double-stranded RNA and a particle size of about 70 nm. Group A, the most prevalent rotavirus group, primarily causes illness in young children and the elderly.[16] Infection in adults normally leads to mild or asymptomatic infections. Nevertheless, the New York Department of Health implicated rotavirus in seven foodborne outbreaks among adults and children from 1984 to 1986. It would be significant if the rotavirus etiology for these outbreaks could be independently confirmed. Group B rotavirus caused waterborne outbreaks with more than 20,000 cases in China in 1983[77] and a virus of the same group is associated with gastroenteritis in rats and human adults in the United States.[22] Foodborne transmission of group B viruses has not been documented, but a virus that can spread through water is likely to spread through foods as well. An additional cause for concern is that, like influenza, mixed infection of a cell with different rotavirus strains can produce new variants with altered virulence and host range.[28, 87]

Astroviruses, caliciviruses, and enteric adenoviruses normally cause gastroenteritis in young children and the elderly.[1, 49] Astroviruses and caliciviruses contain genomes of single-stranded RNA and have distinctive morphologies as seen by electron microscopy. Virus particle sizes are 28–30 nm and 30–38 nm, respectively. Enteric adenoviruses have a particle size of 70–90 nm and a genome of double-stranded DNA. Parvoviruses are the smallest animal viruses with a particle size of 18 to 26 nm and genomes of single-stranded DNA. They are observed in fecal specimens from gastroenteritis outbreaks, especially those related to shellfish consumption, but have not been shown to cause gastroenteritis in humans.[1, 24]

In addition to HAV, other enteroviruses cause foodborne disease. Echovirus 4 was identified as the agent of an outbreak in Pennsylvania in 1976.[8] At least 10 foodborne outbreaks of poliomyelitis occurred before the institution of the poliovirus vaccination programs in the United Kingdom and the United States.[11] Paralytic poliomyelitis continues to be common in developing countries where foods probably play a role in virus transmission. In surveys of foods for viral contamination, polioviruses, echoviruses, and coxsackieviruses have been the most frequent isolates.[26, 49]

Ice, ice cream, milk, pastries, salads, sandwiches, shellfish, and other foods consumed raw or subjected to additional handling after cooking are major food vehicles for virus transmission.[7, 11, 30, 49, 61, 84] The role of shellfish as a food vehicle in the United States has been changing. Infectious hepatitis associated with the consumption of shellfish has declined significantly since the 1960s, while shellfish-associated gastroenteritis has increased.[64] Foods become contaminated with viruses in several ways, including inadequate sanitary practices of infected food handlers, the use of virus-contaminated water for washing foods, and concentration of virus by shellfish growing in polluted water. Viruses cannot replicate in contaminated foods but are transmitted as small, latent particles. Thus, the number of infectious virus particles present in contaminated foods normally is low. However, the presence of only a few infectious particles in foods may be sufficient to cause disease.

Hepatitis B virus and the human immunodeficiency virus (HIV) are not known to cause foodborne disease.[4, 17] These viruses are spread through sexual contact, transfer of blood and blood products, and the perinatal routes. There is no epidemiological evidence for spread through the fecal-oral route; however, it is known that certain animal viruses can infect and be maintained in some protozoan cultures,[81] giving a potential environmental protection and a potential mechanism for entry past the stomach barrier. Studies to determine whether HIV can be transmitted by association with protozoa are in progress (FDA Contract No. 223-84-2031, Task XIV).

41.12   Significance of Virus Transmission Through Foods

The U.S. Centers for Disease Control publishes an annual summary of foodborne disease as part of the Morbidity and Mortality Weekly Report series. The latest summary describes a total of 656 outbreaks with 19,380 individual cases in 1982.[54] The etiological agent was confirmed in 220 outbreaks (34% of total outbreaks) with 11,050 cases (57% of total cases). Viruses were the confirmed agent in 21 outbreaks (3.2% of total outbreaks) with 5,325 cases (27% of total cases). Confirmed viral outbreaks accounted for 9.5% of the outbreaks and 48% of the cases of illness of known etiology.

The number of reported cases of viral illness in 1982 was much higher than in past years because of two large outbreaks of Norwalk gastroenteritis. However, more than 100 outbreaks with 1,017 cases of gastroenteritis from shellfish consumption in New York State in 1982 were grouped with outbreaks of unknown etiology.[61, 64] Since the publication of the annual summary, test specimens from seven of these outbreaks were tested and five outbreaks with 394 cases were shown to be caused by Norwalk virus. On the basis of common epidemiological features, many of the New York State outbreaks that were not tested probably were also caused by Norwalk virus. Viral outbreaks are often difficult to confirm, and thus other outbreaks of unknown etiology may be of viral origin as well.

A number of factors contribute to the failure to confirm etiological agents of viral outbreaks. Only a few laboratories have the reagents for immunoassays needed to identify outbreaks caused by Norwalk and Norwalk-related viruses. A more critical problem is often a lack of clinical and food specimens from outbreaks. In addition, some outbreaks are not associated with foodborne transmission, when low levels of virus contamination result in an insufficient number of cases to link the outbreak to specific foods. Some foodborne viruses may also produce infections in tissues remote from the intestinal tract. A clinician seeing such an illness may not suspect transmission through food when that is, in fact, the route of transmission. Certainly, poliovirus and HAV would not be a major public health concern if infections were restricted to the intestinal tract. Enteroviruses may be the etiological agents of some chronic diseases, such as postviral fatigue factor.[89] The role of foodborne viruses as a cause of chronic disease needs to be examined, especially for the very young, the elderly, and those with impaired immune systems.

41.13   Detecting Viruses in Foods

Unfortunately there is not an alternative to direct testing for viruses. The use of bacterial indicators of fecal contamination to signal the presence of virus in foods has not been successful.[5, 15, 64, 86] Instead, infectious virus particles must be separated from food components before identification. Separation is usually accomplished by liquefaction to dissolve food components, clarification to separate dissolved components from undissolved components, and concentration of virus particles from the clarified material. Particle numbers are too low after separation for direct determination by available assays and thus must be amplified in a suitable living host. This chapter discusses the proper design and execution of these procedures.

41.2   GENERAL CONSIDERATIONS

Analyzing foods for viruses is costly and often requires two or more weeks. Thus, food to be tested should be assigned a priority in accordance with the likelihood of viral contamination. Since adequate cooking inactivates virus particles, foods eaten raw or partially cooked (e.g., shellfish, salads, or frozen fruit) should have the highest priority. The next priority should be foods that require additional preparation after cooking (e.g., potato salads). Testing for viruses may be done prospectively (before an outbreak) or retrospectively (after an outbreak). Foods from outbreaks where viruses are implicated should be tested whenever available. Since maximum virus shedding from an HAV-infected individual occurs before the development of symptoms, foods handled by an infected food processor during this period are more likely to be contaminated with virus than those handled later in the course of infection. Prospective sampling is speculative and should be applied only to high-priority foods.

The isolation of any virus from a food is a matter of concern. Positive test results must be carefully authenticated, and cross-contamination of foods by laboratory equipment and personnel ruled out. The precise identification of virus isolates is an integral part of this authentication.

41.3 FOODS TO BE TESTED

41.31 Shellfish

Virus particles in sewage and surface runoff are normally associated with particulate matter. Oysters, clams, and other bivalve mollusks, while feeding, efficiently concentrate viruses and especially those associated with particulate matter from contaminated estuarine environments. Virus is trapped on the mucus of the gills and carried by ciliary action to the mouth and then to the stomach and intestinal tract. Infectious particles may become inactivated by digestive enzymes, survive by migration into the musculature, or be eliminated in the feces. Viruses may also be attached to particulate materials that are rejected as food (pseudofeces) or remain infectious in the shellfish liquor.

Shellfish samples should be collected with tongs or a hand dredge and washed in cold running water to remove external particulate matter. If shellfish are to be transported to a laboratory for immediate processing, they should be drained of water and iced. They should not be shucked until they are ready to be processed, and if possible, the ice should not come in contact with them. Shellfish and other foods described below should be processed on the day they are collected. If this is not possible, they may be refrigerated or iced for several days or stored at or below −70°C; however, freezing and thawing may decrease virus recoveries and should be avoided. Shucking knives, containers, and hands should be washed with a 1.0% solution of household bleach and rinsed in sterile water before shellfish are opened. Meats and shell liquor are collected aseptically and placed in sterile containers labeled with the sampling date, the number of shellfish in the sample, and the weight of the sample.

41.32 Vegetables and Fruits

Vegetables and fruits are usually contaminated through human contact during harvesting or processing. It is difficult to control sanitation during harvesting. Poliovirus and rotavirus survive long enough on vegetables to reach the market[3, 48] and may not be efficiently removed by washing with water alone. These foods may also become contaminated through wastewater and sludge used for irrigation and fertilization. Fortunately, no reported outbreaks in the United States have been caused by such "recycling" contamination.

Until raw fruits and vegetables are processed for salads or included in other food items, virus is present only on their outer surfaces. Thus, only the outer leaves of leafy vegetables need to be tested for virus. Nonleafy vegetables and fruit units should be sampled randomly. A composite of many smaller units is preferred over a few large units of the same weight to maximize the surface area. Prepared salads and food items to be tested for viruses should consist of randomly selected portions. A sterile drill bit can be used to obtain samples from frozen foods. Samples must be clearly identified and packaged for transport to the laboratory so that they cannot be contaminated from the environment or from other samples. Fresh foods should be held at 2°C to 4°C; freezing is not desirable because it makes fruits and vegetables harder to process. Some viruses are inactivated by drying, even at low temperatures.[42] Thus, desiccation of foods during transport and storage must be avoided.

41.33   Animal Products

No virus of animal origin is known to cause foodborne disease in humans in the United States. Like vegetables and fruits, animal food products are normally contaminated through human contact. All outbreaks associated with milk have involved unpasteurized milk. Thus, pasteurized milk need not be tested unless there are high coliform bacterial counts or some other indication of post-pasteurization contamination. Random subsamples of ground beef and fluid milk should be taken after thorough mixing. The subsamples should be handled as above to retain integrity and identity and to prevent desiccation.

41.4   EQUIPMENT, MATERIALS, AND REAGENTS

Some of the equipment for food virology research will already be available in most microbiological laboratories. Additional specialized equipment should be purchased to increase safety and decrease operating costs (including labor). Equipment should be evaluated from the standpoints of sample capacity (number of individual test samples per day and size of test portions), safety, convenience, effectiveness, and ability to maintain the integrity of each food sample. Maintenance of food sample integrity may be correlated with safety; equipment that prevents cross-contamination among all types of samples is also likely to protect worker health. Special care must always be taken to avoid accidental contamination of all samples. The use of disposable labware is recommended. Whenever possible, the equipment used for procedures to test foods for viruses should be separate from equipment used for the maintenance of laboratory virus strains.

Some common sources for equipment, materials, and reagents are given below. The list is not meant to be all-inclusive. Many of the items, especially those for which sources are not given, are carried by laboratory supply houses. Their catalogs should be consulted for economy and convenience.

41.41 Processing Food Samples

A food suspension usually is prepared by homogenization with a standard homogenizer. Homogenization also may be accomplished with an ultrasonic homogenizer or an Omni-Mixer (Omni Corporation, Waterbury, Conn.). The Omni-Mixer combines safety with efficiency during this process. Alternative methods for preparing food suspensions include grinding with a mortar and pestle, with or without chemically pure sand, and mixing with mechanical shakers, magnetic stirrers, or the Colworth Stomacher (A.J. Seward UAC House, London, England). Freon TF (trichlorotrifluoroethane, Du Pont Company, Wilmington, Del.) may be used to aid in extracting virus from food materials and clarifying food suspensions.

Food suspensions are normally clarified by centrifugation. Centrifuges used for this purpose must generate forces of at least 800 to 10,000 × g. Filtration through a roughing filter placed on a Buchner funnel or other type of filter holder also may be used for clarification. Roughing filters are prepared from glass wool,[82] cotton gauze, or cheesecloth,[78] or they are filters made from cellulose, glass fiber, or polymers. Passage of fluid through filters can be assisted with vacuum obtained with a vacuum pump or water aspirator or with pressure from an air pump or compressed, inert gas (e.g., nitrogen). Pressure usually generates faster flow rates than vacuum.

A centrifuge normally is used to concentrate virus in clarified food suspensions, but dialysis tubing, an ultrafilter apparatus, or a preparative ultra-centrifuge may be used. Ultrafilter units (62-mm, Diaflo PM-30 with 30,000 molecular weight exclusion limit or equivalent; Amicon Corp., Danvers, Maine) require a pressure source of about 3.5 atmospheres.

41.42 Virus Detection and Characterization

41.421 Production of cell cultures

Cell cultures may be obtained from animal tissue, from other laboratories, and from biological supply houses, but cultures from the latter will minimize problems with contamination and genetic variability. Any cell line used should be well characterized cytologically and routinely monitored for mycoplasma. Cell cultures often used in food virology studies may be obtained from the following organizations as indicated: American Type Culture Collection, Rockville, Md., (BS-C-1, FRhK-4, and RD); ViroMed Laboratories, Minnetonka, Minn. (PMK and RD); and Whittaker Bioproducts, Walkersville, Md., (low-passage HEK, PMK, BGM, and MA-104).

Media required to maintain cell cultures can be compounded in the laboratory or purchased in powdered or liquid forms. Purchase is highly recommended. High-quality distilled water is an essential ingredient for media prepared in the laboratory. Companies that supply tissue culture media include Difco Laboratories, Detroit, Mich.; Flow Laboratories, McLean, Va.; GIBCO Laboratories, Grand Island, N.Y.; Mediatech, Herndon, Va.; Sigma Chemical Co., St. Louis, Mo.; Sterile Systems, Logan, Utah; and Whittaker Bioproducts, Walkersville, Md.

This basic equipment is needed for cell culture: (1) biological safety cabinets or sterile cubicles, (2) liquid nitrogen storage tank, (3) low-temperature ($-70°C$ to $-135°C$) freezer, (4) inverted microscope, and (5) plasticware (sterile flasks, tubes, and pipettes).

41.422   Serological procedures

Serological procedures are used to identify viruses isolated from foods. Many enteroviruses can be identified with the Lim-Benyesh-Melnick serum pools.[53] Antisera to other viruses may be prepared in rabbits or other suitable animals by one's own laboratory or, in some instances, by purchase from immunobiological companies. In either case, reference antiserum should be used to verify the authenticity of new antisera. Small quantities of antisera and viruses for controls in serological procedures may be obtained from the following sources: American Type Culture Collection, Rockville, Md.; Research Resources Branch, National Institute of Allergy and Infectious Disease, National Institutes of Health, Bethesda, Md. (Lim-Benyesh-Melnick serum pools); and Whittaker Bioproducts, Walkersville, Md.

41.5   PRECAUTIONS

41.51   Viruses as Pathogens

Microbiological biosafety guidelines should be followed for all procedures involving viruses.[9] Personnel should receive the oral poliovirus vaccine or be screened for poliovirus neutralizing antibody before they begin work. Although viruses that are spread by the fecal-oral route are unlikely to infect by inhalation, the creation of aerosols should be avoided. Viruses and foods thought to contain viruses should be handled whenever possible in a class II biological safety cabinet or closed containers. Precautions to prevent viruses in foods from being swallowed should be stringently followed; pipetting by mouth, eating, drinking, smoking, and biting fingernails in the laboratory are not permitted.

Foods that have been implicated as vehicles of virus transmission should be treated as though they contain virulent virus. Food purchased at a market for a prospective survey is unlikely to be dangerous to personnel. These samples should be treated in the same fashion as samples from foodborne outbreaks, however, to prevent cross-contamination. Any virus derived from a food sample should be presumed virulent and treated as such. Adequate facilities for containment of the agent and decontamination of equipment, wastes, and work surfaces must be available. Laboratories that are not prepared to handle virulent viruses should avoid testing samples from outbreaks.

41.52   Virus Persistence

Laboratory, janitorial, and maintenance personnel should be protected by established decontamination procedures. Surface disinfection can be performed with a 1% solution of household bleach or with other halogen-containing compounds (e.g., Westcodyne, West Chemical Co., Princeton, N.J.). Enteric viruses are effectively removed from skin with soap and water.[13] Equipment should be autoclaved after use, if possible, and wastes autoclaved or incinerated. Viruses in aerosols are efficiently trapped by HEPA filters in biological safety cabinets and are susceptible to ultraviolet light.[63] Ultraviolet lamps must be monitored routinely to ensure their effectiveness. Personnel should be protected by established safety precautions to prevent direct or indirect skin or eye contact with ultraviolet light.

41.6   PROCEDURES

There are no officially approved, final action methods for extracting viruses from foods, and it is not possible in this chapter to describe all the available procedures for detecting viruses in all foods. Current methods for extraction are categorized into two general approaches: elution-precipitation and adsorption-elution-precipitation methods, summarized in Figures 1 and 2, respectively. Virus is first eluted from food materials in an elution-precipitation approach by liquefaction at alkaline pH. After removing undissolved food materials by clarification, viruses remaining in suspension are concentrated and assayed on cell culture. For adsorption-elution-precipitation methods, virus is first adsorbed to undissolved food components at acid pH during liquefaction. Clarification of this material results in a separation of the virus/undissolved food components from the dissolved food components, giving both an initial crude purification and concentration. Virus then is eluted from the undissolved food components by resuspension at alkaline pH. The undissolved food components are removed by clarification, and virus is concentrated and assayed. In view of the lack of approved methods, it is recommended that laboratories beginning work on the recovery of virus from foods perform pilot studies using the general approaches shown in Figures 1 and 2. The two approaches should be compared and optimized where indicated for each food/virus combination. Both approaches have a number of common elements. An overview of the major steps is presented below, followed by examples of alternative approaches and variations to the general approaches that have been used for different food groups.

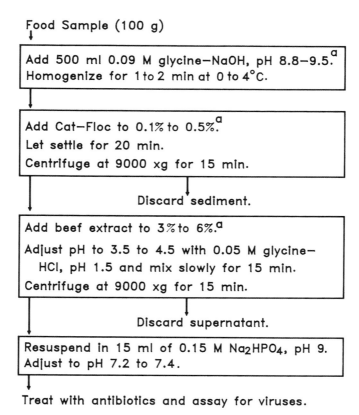

Food Sample (100 g)

Add 500 ml 0.09 M glycine−NaOH, pH 8.8−9.5.[a]
Homogenize for 1 to 2 min at 0 to 4°C.

Add Cat−Floc to 0.1% to 0.5%.[a]
Let settle for 20 min.
Centrifuge at 9000 xg for 15 min.

Discard sediment.

Add beef extract to 3% to 6%.[a]
Adjust pH to 3.5 to 4.5 with 0.05 M glycine−
    HCl, pH 1.5 and mix slowly for 15 min.
Centrifuge at 9000 xg for 15 min.

Discard supernatant.

Resuspend in 15 ml of 0.15 M Na_2HPO_4, pH 9.
Adjust to pH 7.2 to 7.4.

Treat with antibiotics and assay for viruses.

Figure 1—Elution-Precipitation Method for Extraction of Virus from Foods
    [a]Experimentally determine the optimal concentration within the
    indicated range for each food/virus combination.

41.61   Sample Processing

41.611   Sample size

A sample size of 25 to 100 g is used for most procedures. Although smaller test portions from several food types or sampling locations can be processed simultaneously, the probability of isolating virus is reduced, except in cases of high-level contamination. Test portions greater than 150 g are difficult to manipulate, and virus recovery decreases when more than 200 g is used.[58] Collaborative studies dealing with surface-contaminated foods should standardize test portion size both in terms of weight and surface area.

41.612   Liquefaction of solid food

Solid particles of food and crude food suspensions are not suitable for inoculation into cell cultures. Foods usually are suspended in 1 to 10 ml of buffer or distilled water per gram of food and liquefied by homogenization.

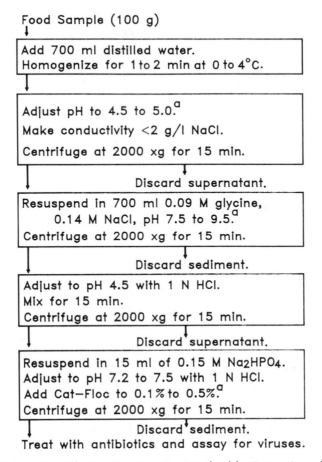

Food Sample (100 g)

Add 700 ml distilled water.
Homogenize for 1 to 2 min at 0 to 4°C.

Adjust pH to 4.5 to 5.0.[a]
Make conductivity <2 g/l NaCl.
Centrifuge at 2000 xg for 15 min.

Discard supernatant.

Resuspend in 700 ml 0.09 M glycine,
0.14 M NaCl, pH 7.5 to 9.5.[a]
Centrifuge at 2000 xg for 15 min.

Discard sediment.

Adjust to pH 4.5 with 1 N HCl.
Mix for 15 min.
Centrifuge at 2000 xg for 15 min.

Discard supernatant.

Resuspend in 15 ml of 0.15 M Na_2HPO_4.
Adjust to pH 7.2 to 7.5 with 1 N HCl.
Add Cat-Floc to 0.1% to 0.5%.[a]
Centrifuge at 2000 xg for 15 min.

Discard sediment.
Treat with antibiotics and assay for viruses.

Figure 2—Adsorption-Elution-Precipitation Method for Extraction of Virus from Foods
[a]Experimentally determine the optimal concentration within the indicated range for each food/virus combination.

Care must be taken to ensure that the food suspension is not heated during the liquefaction process. When alternative methods, such as grinding or shaking, are used to prepare liquefied food suspensions (Section 41.41), foods should be diced with sterile scissors or a knife to increase the surface area. The means of liquefaction selected should liquefy the food without producing particles so small that they cannot later be removed.

41.613   Clarification of food suspensions

Liquefaction dissolves some but not all food components. Clarification separates the dissolved components from the bulk of the undissolved components by low-speed centrifugation or filtration. An efficient clarification procedure should yield a clear fluid extract with minimal virus loss and with limited use of personnel and facilities. The polycation sewage flocculant, Cat-Floc (0.1–0.5%, final concentration; Calgon Corp., Pittsburgh, Penn.) may be used at this or other clarification steps to facilitate clarification and reduce the toxicity of food components to cell cultures.[45] Some filters used for clarification tend to adsorb virus particles.[10] Quantitative tests with experimentally inoculated virus should be performed to determine that this does not occur with the filter selected. Virus loss can be decreased by pretreating filters with 0.1% fetal bovine serum or nonionic detergents, such as 0.1% Tween 80.[73]

41.614   Concentration of food extracts

Concentration reduces the volume of the sample extract, thereby reducing the number of cell cultures required to test a sample of given size and the probability of obtaining false negative results. Concentration is conveniently accomplished by acid precipitation or organic flocculation.[41, 76] Viruses present in clarified extracts are adsorbed at acid pH to dissolved food extract proteins (acid precipitation) or to added beef extract or nonfat dry milk proteins (organic flocculation). The precipitated material is collected by low-speed centrifugation. Viruses are extracted from the precipitate with a small volume of alkaline buffer and the suspension is clarified. Some beef extract lots cannot be used for organic flocculation.[33] Each new lot received must be carefully tested for effectiveness or especially formulated for flocculation (e.g., beef extract V, BBL Microbiology Systems, Cockeysville, Md.). Alternative concentration methods of ultracentrifugation and ultrafiltration require much more time and lack capacity. Ultrafilter membranes require frequent replacement and may cause virus loss. Hydroextraction (the withdrawing of water from a food extract through a dialysis membrane by the action of a hydrophilic polymer such as polyethylene glycol) is also time-consuming and can lead to increased toxicity for cell cultures. Concentration by precipitation with polyethylene glycol, however, may be an effective alternative to organic flocculation.[52]

41.615   Removal of microbiological contaminants

Microbiological contaminants remaining at this stage may be eliminated by membrane filtration through filters with 0.2 to 0.45 μm pore size, by adding high levels of antibiotics, or by ether or chloroform treatment.[58] Membrane filtration is the most effective means of removing contaminants but may result in virus loss as described above. Ether and chloroform inactivate membrane-bound viruses, and care must be taken to remove all solvent residues before inoculating cultures. Antibiotics are usually preferred.

41.62   Cell Cultures for Food Virology

The selection of cell types for the replication of viruses from food extracts depends more upon the type of viruses present than on the type of food. Cell cultures used for food analysis should be susceptible to many types of viruses, not greatly affected by toxicity to food components, readily available, and easy to maintain in the laboratory. Primary to tertiary cultures of human embryonic kidney (HEK) or African green, cynomolgus, or rhesus monkey kidney (PMK) cells are the most sensitive cultures for growing a wide variety of enteroviruses and reoviruses. These cells offer morphological and biochemical similarity to the parent tissue but are not effective for isolating adenoviruses or group A coxsackieviruses. Continuous cell lines that may be comparable to HEK and PMK cells for enteric virus isolations include Buffalo green monkey kidney (BGM) cells, a line derived from an African green monkey;[19, 71] RD, a line of human rhabdomyosarcoma cells sensitive to a wide variety of enteroviruses, including group A coxsackieviruses;[70, 72] and MA-104, a line derived from rhesus monkey kidney cells.[62] BGM, FRhK-4 (another line from rhesus monkey kidney cells), and BS-C-1 cells (another African green monkey kidney cell line), are useful for propagation of HAV.[6, 51] HEK and PMK cell cultures have often been used preferentially, but they are too expensive for routine use in many laboratories. Two or more continuous cell lines such as BGM, RD, and MA-104 are recommended as alternatives.

Two basic procedures are used for amplifying virus isolates in cell cultures: quantal methods and enumeration methods. Cultures assayed by quantal methods are scored as negative or positive when one or more infectious particles result in the development of cytopathic effect. Compiled observations based on dilution to endpoint are usually expressed as $TCID_{50}$ (the tissue culture infectious dose that results in 50% of the cultures developing cytopathic effects). A most probable number (MPN) analysis may also be used. Because of the nature of quantal assays, the presence of more than one type of virus in the inoculum is less likely to be noted. Enumeration methods, such as the plaque and radioimmunofocus assays,[31, 51] are quantitative but more difficult to perform than quantal assays. They allow individual infectious units to be counted directly as discrete, localized areas of infection in a single culture. However, since plaque assay conditions select for some viruses and against others, more virus isolates are generally obtained from using quantal methods[72] and these are recommended except when the presence of several virus types or a noncytopathic virus is expected.

41.621   Preparation of cell cultures for virus inoculation

Cell cultures are maintained using standard tissue culture techniques.[69] Growth medium normally consists of minimum essential medium (MEM) with Earle's salts supplemented with antibiotics, 10 ml/L of 200 mM

L-glutamine, 15 ml/L of 7.5% sodium bicarbonate, and 10% fetal bovine serum (FBS). Useful antibiotics include 500 units penicillin/ml, 500 μg streptomycin/ml, 50 to 100 μg gentamicin/ml, 5 to 10 μg kanamycin/ml, and 50 units mycostatin (nystatin)/ml. Cultures can be maintained with maintenance medium (growth medium with the FBS concentration reduced to 2%) for 5 to 10 days after becoming confluent.

41.622   Inoculation of cell cultures

Virus present in food extracts usually is adsorbed to culture cells for 1 to 2 hr at 37°C. The inoculum should be redistributed over the surface of the monolayer either manually every 15 to 20 min or constantly on a rocker platform at 1 to 5 oscillations per min.[65] The size of the inoculum volume placed on cultures and the length of the adsorption period are important variables. Optimal adsorption requires an inoculum volume to monolayer surface area of ≤0.02 ml/cm², redistribution of the inoculum and an adsorption time of 2 hr.[58, 65] Larger inoculation volumes of about 1.4 ml/cm² also can be used as an effective alternative to food extract concentration when combined with an adsorption period of 16 to 20 hr.[44]

The age of the cultures at the time of inoculation is another important variable. When confluent, the replication of cells in culture ceases for many cell lines and cellular physiology is dramatically altered. Parvoviruses, which require growing cells for optimal replication, must be inoculated onto subconfluent cultures. Many viruses replicate best in newly confluent cultures, but some enteroviruses can replicate well for several days after the monolayers become confluent. Laboratories should report the cell ages used for experimentation in publications and strive for consistency.

Because cell lines differ in their susceptibility to viruses, more than one cell line should be inoculated.[56] Inoculation may be performed in parallel by dividing the inoculum among the different cell types; however, this approach results in some risk of missing a particular unit of virus by putting it on the wrong culture. Another approach is to inoculate cell lines in series by removing and pooling the inoculum after adsorption on the first cell line followed by re-adsorption onto the second cell line.[44, 58] At the end of the adsorption period the cells are overlaid with either maintenance medium for quantal assays or medium containing about 0.75% agar and 0.0015% neutral red for enumeration assays.

41.623   Maintenance and handling of cultures during virus isolation

Inoculated cultures are incubated at 37°C. Those maintained with liquid medium are examined microscopically for cytopathic effect every 2 days during the first week of incubation and twice weekly thereafter for up to 4 weeks. The culture medium is changed if the cells show signs of nonviral deterioration (i.e., portions of the cell monolayer become unattached from the culture vessel). Cultures developing cytopathic effect are scored as presumptive virus-positive and frozen at $-70°C$ when $\geq 75\%$ of the cell layer is affected. All remaining cultures are also frozen after 2 to 4 weeks of incubation. Frozen cultures are thawed and a second passage inoculum is prepared by clarifying the fluid lysate with low-speed centrifugation.

Cultures overlaid with medium that contains agar are incubated cell side up and in the dark if the overlay contains neutral red. They are observed periodically for at least 2 weeks and plaques are marked and tallied as they appear. After 2 to 4 weeks each discrete plaque and equivalent areas from negative controls are picked by transferring the cells plus the overlying agar medium into a small quantity of medium. This mixture may be frozen at $-70°C$ and thawed to release cell-associated virus. Material from discrete plaques and clarified material from all positive and negative quantal assay cultures is inoculated onto fresh cell cultures to confirm the presence or absence of viruses. At least several plaques from each positive plaque assay plate should be subcultured in this way to determine that all plaques have been caused by the same virus. Cultures that develop cytopathic effects in this second round quantal assay are stored frozen at $-70°C$. Before virus identification, frozen cultures that contain virus are thawed and clarified as above.

41.63 Controls

Adequate controls must be used when foods are tested for viruses. The interpretation of cytopathic effects observed in cell culture systems requires both experience and some subjective judgment. Each experiment must include one or more negative controls. Uncontaminated foods of the same type and quantity being tested for viruses should be analyzed in parallel with test samples when available. When uncontaminated foods are not available, cell cultures may be inoculated with a portion of a food extract that has been sufficiently heated to inactivate viruses.[60] At the very least, cell cultures should be mock-inoculated with the medium in which the final food extract is suspended and maintained with the same medium and conditions as the inoculated cultures.

Food extracts are often toxic to cell cultures despite treatments to remove the toxic components.[56] Inoculation of cell cultures with extracts from uncontaminated foods or with heated extracts can show whether food toxicity is a problem. Food toxicity causes localized cell death, resulting in false positive results or rapid cell death of the entire culture, preventing virus replication and resulting in false-negative results. Because toxicity causes these false results, all presumptive virus isolations must be verified by subculture. Toxic effects can often be minimized by reducing the volume of inoculum or the adsorption time. Removing the inoculum from the cultures after the adsorption period and rinsing the cell layer with an isotonic medium may also be helpful. If these steps are unsuccessful, alternative methods of virus extraction must be used.[14]

Extracts from unfamiliar foods may be pretested for problems with bacterial and mold contamination or cytotoxicity by preliminary inoculation of cell cultures with a relatively small portion of each extract. The remaining inoculum can be tested after several days if no problems are observed in the pretest.

A positive control is performed by extracting a known quantity of a known virus from the same quantity and type of food to be tested. This control shows whether the virus is recovered with acceptable efficiency by the method used. As always, extreme care must be taken to avoid cross-contamination.

Some viruses replicate so slowly on primary isolation that cytopathic effects are not observed in the first passage; cultures are passaged a second time to observe these viruses. Cell cultures, however, and especially primary cell cultures may harbor adventitious viruses that become cytopathic with passage. The negative cell controls must also be passaged to control for this possibility. Otherwise, the cytopathic effect caused by an adventitious virus would probably be interpreted as having been caused by a virus from the food.

41.64   Virus Identification

For virus identification the concentration of infectious particles in each test sample should be determined by an enumeration assay, if available, or by $TCID_{50}$ or MPN assays. Should the concentration of virus be low, the number of particles may have to be amplified by one or more additional rounds of infection in cell culture before identification by serological procedures. All available epidemiological data from foodborne outbreaks and physicochemical characteristics should be used to minimize the amount of serological testing needed for identification, such as disease symptoms, incubation period, duration of illness, ether and acid sensitivity, nucleic acid type, and virion size and shape.[21] Nucleic acid type can be determined by treating isolated nucleic acid with deoxyribonuclease and ribonuclease and running the treated material with untreated material on agarose gels.[55] Particle size may be estimated by electron microscopy and by use of filters of about 100, 50, and ≤ 20 nm porosity.[21] Filters with ≤ 20 nm porosity may also be used to distinguish between the presence of an infectious agent and an intoxicant.

A number of serological immunoassays are used to identify viruses and the host antibody response to viruses. The immunoassays most widely used in food virology depend on the ability of antibodies to block the infectivity of virus particles. This test is performed by reacting a battery of specific antisera, such as the Lim-Benyesh-Melnick serum pools, with unknown virus isolates and then measuring the infectivity with a quantal or enumeration assay.

Immune electron microscopy has historically been the primary method for examining fecal specimens for the presence of agents causing acute viral gastroenteritis.[40] This assay is based on the ability of low-speed centrifugation to concentrate specifically cross-linked virus-antibody complexes. Although it can be used to identify unknown viruses from food isolates, its primary use in food virology is to confirm a diagnosis of foodborne viral disease in victims of an outbreak or in a food handler. This is based on finding a four-fold increase in the amount of antibody to virus in "convalescent" serum samples taken 2 to 4 weeks after illness in contrast to "acute" serum samples taken during acute illness.

Other immunoassays depend on the ability to label antibodies with fluorescent dyes (immunofluorescence), radionuclides (radioimmunoassays and radioimmunofocus assays) or enzymes (immunoenzymatic assays). Immunofluorescence[66] and radioimmunofocus assays[51] are used to identify viruses that do not cause cytopathic effects. Like immune electron microscopy, radioimmunoassays and immunoenzymatic assays usually have been used only to identify viruses in clinical specimens from the victims of foodborne viral disease.[25, 29] These procedures, however, are sensitive enough to identify some foodborne isolates after several cycles of replication.

Some foods, such as shellfish from a polluted estuary, have a higher probability than others of having more than one type of virus. If only a single type of virus is identified in extracts from these foods, a second virus type sometimes can be isolated by using antiserum to suppress the first while retesting portions of the original food extract.

41.65   Representative Foods

41.651   Shellfish

Many methods have been developed to isolate virus from shellfish.[26, 74] Some of the shellfish species for which useful methods have been described include *Cerastoderma edule* (English cockles);[60] *Crassostrea gigas* (Pacific oyster);[47, 85] *Crassostrea virginica* (East and Gulf Coast oyster);[14, 57, 58, 75, 76, 79, 82, 83] *Mercenaria mercenaria* (hard-shell clam);[57, 58, 79, 82, 86] *Mya arenaria* (soft-shell clam);[57, 58, 82] *Mytilus edulis* (edible mussel);[88] and *Tapes japonica* (Japanese clam).[36]

Although procedures to extract viruses from shellfish have been tested more extensively than those for other foods, many problems remain unsolved. No single effective method has been found for all shellfish species or even for the same species from different locations.[14, 74] *C. virginica* oysters harvested from the Atlantic Coast of the United States differ considerably in bacterial contamination and cytotoxicity from the same species harvested on the Gulf Coast. In addition, no method gives consistent virus recovery rates. In one collaborative study the average virus recovery rate in different laboratories using a common source of shellfish and virus inoculum varied from 31% to 78%.[83] Virus-specific variability also occurs. Elution-precipitation and adsorption-elution-precipitation methods are equally effective at extracting poliovirus from *C. virginica* samples, whereas only an elution-precipitation approach resulted in efficient recovery of rotavirus.[76] In contrast, efficient recovery of HAV required an adsorption-elution-precipitation method.[74]

41.652   Vegetables and fruits

Viruses generally have been extracted from vegetables and fruits by using an elution-precipitation approach with some variations. Homogenization should be avoided, if possible. Viruses are recovered from surfaces more efficiently when the entire food substance is not incorporated into the test suspension. Figure 3 gives an example of an effective filtration procedure for lettuce and carrots.[43] The vegetables should be diced before suspension in the elution buffer. The entire test portion can be inoculated into a single 25-cm² culture dish and virus adsorbed for 16 to 20 hr. Extracts prepared with this procedure cause the formation of a residue on the cell monolayer. The residue prevents the observation of cytopathic effects but not the replication of virus. Virus replication can be confirmed by passage of the cells after 2 to 3 days of incubation. Other variations from the elution-precipitation include the use of an unusually alkaline buffer, 0.09 M glycine, pH 10.8, to recover virus from frozen strawberries;[31] a Freon TF extraction step for recovery of poliovirus from carrots, celery, mushrooms, potato salad, and radishes;[79] and 3% beef extract, pH 8.0, to recover rotavirus from whole radish bulbs or diced lettuce, celery, and carrots.[2]

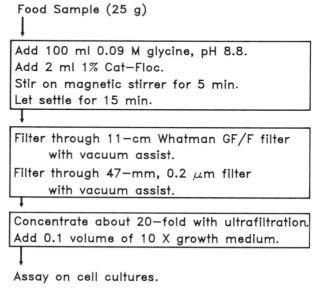

Food Sample (25 g)

Add 100 ml 0.09 M glycine, pH 8.8.
Add 2 ml 1% Cat−Floc.
Stir on magnetic stirrer for 5 min.
Let settle for 15 min.

Filter through 11−cm Whatman GF/F filter
        with vacuum assist.
Filter through 47−mm, 0.2 μm filter
        with vacuum assist.

Concentrate about 20−fold with ultrafiltration.
Add 0.1 volume of 10 X growth medium.

Assay on cell cultures.

Figure 3—Filtration Method for Extraction of Virus from Foods (43)

41.653   Animal products

Enteroviruses have been isolated successfully from ground beef by using extraction at pH 8.5–8.8 and filtration through a Whatman GF/F filter (Figure 3) or through glass wool.[50] The latter method was accepted official first action by the Association of Official Analytical Chemists but has not been widely accepted. Experimentally inoculated enteroviruses have been isolated from milk after removal of cream by refrigeration for 24 hr or by low-speed centrifugation. Curd is removed from the skim milk by precipitation at pH 4.4 and filtration through three layers of cheesecloth. After neutralization to pH 7, the whey is filtered through a GF/F filter and then through a 0.2-μm filter (Figure 3). Large volumes (0.8–1.2 ml/cm² of cell monolayer) of this extract can be inoculated into cell cultures as described above. Other variations for ground beef and milk have been described.[31, 34, 37–39, 78]

41.7   INTERPRETATION OF TEST RESULTS

41.71   Negative Results

Negative results obtained by these methods may very well be correct. The results from a prospective study in which a large proportion of the test samples are positive for viruses should be treated with skepticism. On the other hand, false-negative results can occur when samples have been taken incorrectly or processed so that the virus is discarded or inactivated. Such problems can best be identified by adding a positive control to measure recovery as described in Section 41.63. False-negative results also occur when food extracts are tested on the wrong cell cultures or when an isolated virus does not induce cytopathic effects. Inoculation of several cell types and the use of serological tests are the only solutions available for these problems.

Another factor that causes false negative results is the presence of coproantibody-neutralized virus in food extracts. Viruses neutralized with coproantibody may be reactivated by proteases present in the intestine[12] and cause human disease, but they cannot infect cell cultures without reactivation. Enteroviruses have been reactivated by Freon extraction[31] and by the addition of pancreatin to food extracts.[46] The pancreatin procedure may not be applicable to every cell type.

41.72   Positive Results

Virus isolates must be identified serologically; however, serological identification of an isolate is not sufficient to prove that the isolate is a food contaminant. Test sample contamination with virus from laboratory personnel, from other work in the laboratory, and from other foods must be ruled out. Since contamination should be extremely rare in laboratories practicing proper sterile technique, a positive result can be strengthened by reisolating the same virus from remaining portions of the original food. Portions of the original food should be saved for this purpose.

41.8   PROSPECTUS

Methods for extracting and identifying foodborne viruses have not been applied successfully to all foods or viruses. Research is needed on methods to enhance the efficiency of these viruses to infect and replicate in cell culture. Increased efficiency of infection and replication may result from compounds that reduce electrostatic interference or antiviral response, or from the development of tissue culture cell clones with desirable features, such as susceptibility to a broader range of viruses and increased resistance to toxicity.

Collaborative testing of the best available virus extraction and identification methods and refinements in methodology should be given high priority. The variables affecting virus recovery rates, microbial contamination, and tissue culture cytotoxicity need close examination. The refinement of methods will continue, but the basic approaches probably will not change drastically in the near future from those described in this chapter.

HAV from persons with hepatitis A has been adapted to growth in cell culture,[6, 18] but adaptation takes too long (4 to 6 weeks) to be useful in food virology. Unadapted virus can be detected in cell cultures much earlier by use of the radioimmunofocus assay.[51] This assay has been used successfully to monitor recovery of HAV from shellfish tissues.[74] The major disadvantage of this method is the licensing requirements and disposal problems associated with the use of radioiodine. Some human rotaviruses also have been grown in cell cultures[68] and methods have been developed to detect adapted strains in foods.[2] Whether these methods will be useful for the identification of natural isolates is not known.

Methods to detect the contamination of foods with the uncultivatable viruses in the absence of human illness have not been developed. Additional advances and improvements in cultivation and identification techniques are needed before these viruses can be identified in suspect foods. At present, the best way to establish their role in foodborne outbreaks is still by thorough epidemiological investigations. Whenever possible, fecal and serum specimens should be collected during acute illness. A second convalescent serum specimen should be collected at 3 to 4 weeks and all specimens tested by available virus-specific immunoassays.[25, 29, 30] In some cases it may also be possible to demonstrate fecal contamination of the incriminated food by measuring fecal indicator bacteria or identifying other enteric viruses.[23]

During the next few years significant improvements in methodology should occur. Hepatitis A and several rotavirus genes have been cloned and sequenced. The cloned genes have been used as hybridization probes for the identification of virus.[20, 35, 59] Several laboratories are currently cloning astroviruses and caliciviruses and attempting to clone Norwalk virus. With the recent development of the polymerase chain reaction technique (PCR),[67] a technique to amplify DNA sequences between two primers that bind to opposite strands, the potential is now available to identify a single genome copy of any virus for which genome sequence information is known (a DNA copy of an RNA virus genome initially must be prepared by reverse transcription). It is likely that the Norwalk viruses will be detected in foods with this method before they are adapted to growth in tissue culture. Theoretically, hybridization and the PCR method can speed identification for many viruses from several weeks to days.

41.9 REFERENCES

1. Appleton, H. 1987. Small round viruses: Classification and role in food-borne infections. In "Novel Diarrhoea Viruses," eds. G. Bock and J. Whelan, (Ciba Foundation Symposium 128), p. 108. John Wiley & Sons, Chichester, England.
2. Badawy, A. S., Gerba, C. P., and Kelley, L. M. 1985. Development of a method for recovery of rotavirus from the surface of vegetables. J. Food Prot. 48: 261.
3. Badawy, A. S., Gerba, C. P., and Kelley, L. M. 1985. Survival of rotavirus SA-11 on vegetables. Food Microbiol. 2: 199.
4. Benenson, A. S., ed. 1985. "Control of Communicable Disease in Man," 14th ed. p. 171. Amer. Publ. Health Assn., Washington, D.C.
5. Berg, G. 1978. "Indicators of Viruses in Water and Food." Ann Arbor Science Publishers, Inc., Ann Arbor, Mich.
6. Binn, L. N., Lemon, S. M., Marchwicki, R. H., Redfield, R. R., Gates, N. L., and Bancroft, W. H. 1984. Primary isolation and serial passage of hepatitis A virus strains in primate cell cultures. J. Clin. Microbiol. 20: 28.
7. Brondum, J., Spitalny, K. C., Vogt, R. L., Godlewski, K., Madore, H. P., and Dolin, R. 1985. Snow Mountain agent associated with an outbreak of gastroenteritis in Vermont. J. Infect. Dis. 152: 834.
8. CDC. 1978. Foodborne and waterborne disease outbreaks annual summary 1976. HEW Publ. No. (CDC) 78-8185. Dept. of Health, Ed., and Welfare, Washington, D.C.
9. CDC. 1984. Biosafety in microbiological and biomedical laboratories. HHS Publ. No. (CDC) 84-8395. Dept. of Health and Human Services, Washington, D.C.
10. Cliver, D. O. 1968. Virus interactions with membrane filters. Biotechnol. Bioeng. 10: 877.
11. Cliver, D. O. 1983. "Manual on Food Virology." VPH/83.46. World Health Org., Geneva.
12. Cliver, D. O. and Kostenbader, K. D. Jr. 1979. Antiviral effectiveness of grape juice. J. Food Prot. 42: 100.
13. Cliver, D. O. and Kostenbader, K. D. Jr. 1984. Disinfection of virus on hands for prevention of food-borne disease. Int. J. Food Microbiol. 1: 75.
14. Cole, M. T., Kilgen, M. B., and Hackney, C. R. 1986. Evaluation of methods for extraction of enteric virus from Louisiana oysters. J. Food Prot. 49: 592.
15. Cole, M. T., Kilgen, M. B., Reily, L. A., and Hackney, C. R. 1986. Detection of entero-viruses and bacterial indicators and pathogens in Louisiana oysters and their overlying waters. J. Food Prot. 49: 596.
16. Cubitt, W. D. 1982. Rotavirus infection: An unexpected hazard in units caring for the elderly. Geriat. Med. Today 1: 33.
17. Curran, J. W., Morgan, W. M., Hardy, A. M., Jaffe, H. W., Darrow, W. W., and Dowdle, W. R. 1985. The epidemiology of AIDS: Current status and future prospects. Science 229: 1352.
18. Daemer, R. J., Feinstone, S. M., Gust, I. D., and Purcell, R. H. 1981. Propagation of

human hepatitis A virus in African green monkey kidney cell culture: Primary isolation and serial passage. Infect. Immun. 32: 388.

19. Dahling, D., Berg, G., and Berman, D. 1974. BGM, a continuous cell line more sensitive than primary rhesus and African green kidney cells for the recovery of viruses from water. Health Lab. Sci. 11: 275.

20. Dimitrov, D. H., Graham, D. Y., and Estes, M. K. 1985. Detection of rotaviruses by nucleic acid hybridization with cloned DNA of simian rotavirus SA11 genes. J. Infect. Dis. 152: 293.

21. Dolin, R., Blacklow, N. R., Dupont, H., Buscho, R. F., Wyatt, R. G., Kasel, J. A., Hornick, R., and Chanock, R. M. 1972. Biological properties of Norwalk agent of acute infectious nonbacterial gastroenteritis. Proc. Soc. Exp. Biol. Med. 140: 578.

22. Eiden, J., Vonderfecht, S., and Yolken, R. H. 1985. Evidence that a novel rotavirus-like agent of rats can cause gastroenteritis in man. Lancet II: 8.

23. Eyles, M. J., Davey, G. R., and Huntley, E. J. 1981. Demonstration of viral contamination of oysters responsible for an outbreak of viral gastroenteritis. J. Food Prot. 44: 294.

24. Fout, G. S., Osborne, L. C., and Larkin, E. P. 1987. Identification of virus isolates from foodborne outbreaks. VIIIth Int. Congr. Virol. Abst. R34.9.

25. Gary, G. W. Jr., Kaplan, J. E., Stine, S. E., and Anderson, L. J. 1985. Detection of Norwalk virus antibodies and antigen with a biotin-avidin immunoassay. J. Clin. Microbiol. 22: 274.

26. Gerba, C. P. and Goyal, S. M. 1978. Detection and occurrence of enteric viruses in shellfish: a review. J. Food Prot. 41: 743.

27. Greenberg, H. B., Valdesuso, J. R., Kalica, A. R., Wyatt, R. G., McAuliffe, V. J., Kapikian, A. Z., and Chanock, R. M. 1981. Proteins of Norwalk virus. J. Virol. 37: 994.

28. Greenberg, H. B., Wyatt, R. G., Kapikian, A. Z., Kalica, A. R., Flores, J., and Jones, R. 1982. Rescue and serotypic characterization of noncultivable human rotavirus by gene reassortment. Infect. Immun. 37: 104.

29. Greenberg, H. B., Wyatt, R. G., Valdesuso, J., Kalica, A. R., London, W. T., Chanock, R. M., and Kapikian, A. Z. 1978. Solid-phase radioimmunoassay for detection of the Norwalk strain of acute nonbacterial, epidemic gastroenteritis virus and its antibodies. J. Med. Virol. 2: 97.

30. Grohmann, G. S., Greenberg, H. B., Welch, B. M., and Murphy, A. M. 1980. Oyster-associated gastroenteritis in Australia: The detection of Norwalk virus and its antibody by immune electron microscopy and radioimmunoassay. J. Med. Virol. 6: 11.

31. Herrmann, J. E. and Cliver, D. O. 1968. Methods for detecting food-borne enteroviruses. Appl. Microbiol. 16: 1564.

32. Herrmann, J. E., Kent, G. P., Nowak, N. A., Brondum, J., and Blacklow, N. R. 1986. Antigen detection in the diagnosis of Norwalk virus gastroenteritis. J. Infect. Dis. 154: 547.

33. Hurst, C. J., Dahling, D. R., Safferman, R. S., and Goyke, T. 1984. Comparison of commercial beef extracts and similar materials for recovering viruses from environmental samples. Can. J. Microbiol. 30: 1253.

34. Idziak, E. S. and Srivastava, A. N. 1975. The isolation of virus from comminuted meat. Can. Inst. Food Sci. Technol. J. 8: 219.

35. Jiang, X., Estes, M. K., Metcalf, T. G., and Melnick, J. L. 1986. Detection of hepatitis A virus in seeded estuarine samples by hybridization with cDNA probes. Appl. Environ. Microbiol. 52: 711.

36. Johnson, K. M., Cooper, R. C., and Straube, D. C. 1981. Procedure for recovery of enteroviruses from the Japanese cockle *Tapes japonica*. Appl. Environ. Microbiol. 41: 932.

37. Kalitina, T. A. 1972. Methods for recovery of enteroviruses from meat. Communication I. Preparation of meat samples for analysis. Vopr. Pitan. 31: 80.

38. Kalitina, T. A. 1975. On the method of isolating enteroviruses in meat. Vopr. Pitan. (6): 52.

39. Kalitina, T. A. 1978. A processing method for detection of poliomyelitis virus in milk. Vopr. Pitan. (6): 70.

40. Kapikian, A. Z., Wyatt, R. G., Dolin, R., Thornhill, T. S., Kalica, A. R., and Chanock, R. M. 1972. Visualization by immune electron microscopy of a 27 nm particle associated with acute infectious non-bacterial gastroenteritis. J. Virol. 10: 1075.

41. Katzenelson, E., Fattal, B., and Hostovesky, T. 1976. Organic flocculation: An efficient second-step concentration method for the detection of viruses in tap water. Appl. Environ. Microbiol. 32: 638.

42. Konowalchuk, J. and Spiers, J. I. 1975. Survival of enteric viruses on fresh vegetables. J. Milk Food Technol. 38: 469.

43. Kostenbader, K. D. Jr. and Cliver, D. O. 1973. Filtration methods for recovering enteroviruses from foods. Appl. Microbiol. 26:149.

44. Kostenbader, K. D. Jr. and Cliver, D. O. 1977. Quest for viruses associated with our food supply. J. Food Sci. 42:1253 and 1268.

45. Kostenbader, K. D. Jr. and Cliver, D. O. 1981. Flocculants for recovery of food-borne viruses. Appl. Environ. Microbiol. 41:318.

46. Kostenbader, K. D. Jr. and Cliver, D. O. 1986. Reactivation with pancreatin of coproantibody-neutralized virus in ground beef. J. Food Prot. 49: 920.

47. Landry, E. F., Vaughn, J. M., and Vicale, T. J. 1980. Modified procedure for extraction of poliovirus from naturally-infected oysters using Cat-Floc and beef extract. J. Food Prot. 43: 91.

48. Larkin, E. P. 1982. Viruses in wastewater sludges and in effluents used for irrigation. Environ. Int. 7: 29.

49. Larkin, E. P. 1986. Detection, quantitation and public health significance of foodborne viruses. In "Foodborne Microorganisms and Their Toxins," ed. M. D. Pierson and N. J. Stern, p. 439. Marcell Dekker, New York.

50. Larkin, E. P., Tierney, J. T., Sullivan, R., and Peeler, J. T. 1975. Collaborative study of the glass wool filtration method for the recovery of virus inoculated into ground beef. J. Assn. Off. Anal. Chem. 58: 576.

51. Lemon, S. M., Binn, L. N., and Marchwicki, R. H. 1983. Radioimmunofocus assay for quantitation of hepatitis A virus in cell cultures. J. Clin. Microbiol. 17: 834.

52. Lewis, G. D. and Metcalf, T. G. 1988. Polyethylene glycol precipitation for recovery of pathogenic viruses, including hepatitis A virus and human rotavirus, from oyster, water, and sediment samples. Appl. Environ. Microbiol. 54: 1983.

53. Lim, K. A. and Benyesh-Melnick, M. 1960. Typing of viruses by combinations of antiserum pools. Application to typing of enterovirus (coxsackie and echo). J. Immunol. 84: 309.

54. MacDonald, K. L. and Griffin, P. M. 1986. Foodborne disease outbreaks, annual summary, 1982. Morbid. Mortal. Weekly Rep. 35: 7SS.

55. Maniatis, T., Fritsch, E. F., and Sambrook, J. 1982. "Molecular Cloning, A Laboratory Manual." Cold Spring Harbor Laboratory, Cold Spring Harbor, N.Y.

56. Metcalf, T. G. 1978. Indicators of viruses in shellfish. In "Indicators of Viruses in Water and Food," ed. G. Berg, p. 383. Ann Arbor Science Publishers, Ann Arbor, Mich.

57. Metcalf, T. G., Eckerson, D., and Moulton, E. 1980. A method for recovery of viruses from oysters and hard and soft shell clams. J. Food Prot. 43: 89.

58. Metcalf, T. G., Moulton, E., and Eckerson, D. 1980. Improved method and test strategy for recovery of enteric viruses from shellfish. Appl. Environ. Microbiol. 39: 141.

59. Metcalf, T. G., Jiang, X., Estes, M. K., and Melnick, J. L. 1988. Nucleic acid probes and molecular hybridization for detection of viruses in environmental samples. Prog. Med. Virol. 35: 186.

60. Millard, J., Appleton, H., and Parry, J. V. 1987. Studies on heat inactivation of hepatitis A virus with special reference to shellfish. Epidemiol. Infect. 98: 397.

61. Morse, D. L., Guzewich, J. J., Hanrahan, J. P., Stricof, R., Shayegani, M., Deibel, R., Grabau, J. C., Nowak, N. A., Herrmann, J. E., Cukor, G., and Blacklow, N. R. 1986. Widespread outbreaks of clam- and oyster-associated gastroenteritis: Role of Norwalk virus. New Eng. J. Med. 314: 678.

62. Oglesbee, S. E., Wait, D. A., and Meinhold, A. F. 1981. MA104: A continuous cell line for the isolation of enteric viruses from environmental samples. Am. Soc. Microbiol. Abstr. A113.

63. Pike, R. M. and Richardson, J. H. 1979. Prevention of laboratory infections. In "Diagnostic Procedures for Viral, Rickettsial and Chlamydial Infections," 5th ed., ed. E. H. Lennette and N. J. Schmidt, p. 49. Amer. Pub. Health Assn., Washington, D.C.

64. Richards, G. P. 1985. Outbreaks of shellfish-associated enteric virus illness in the United States: Requisite for development of viral guidelines. J. Food Prot. 48: 815.

65. Richards, G. P. and Weinheimer, D. A. 1985. Influence of adsorption time, rocking, and soluble proteins on the plaque assay of monodispersed poliovirus. Appl. Environ. Microbiol. 49: 744.

66. Riggs, J. L. 1979. Immunofluorescent staining. In "Diagnostic Procedures for Viral, Rickettsial and Chlamydial Infections," 5th ed., ed. E. H. Lennette and N. J. Schmidt, p. 141. Amer. Pub. Health Assn., Washington, D.C.

67. Saiki, R. K., Scharf, S., Faloona, F., Mullis, K. B., Horn, G. T., Erlich, H. A., and Arnheim, N. 1985. Enzymatic amplification of β-globin genomic sequences and restriction site analysis for diagnosis of sickle cell anemia. Science 230: 1350.

68. Sato, K., Inaba, Y., Shinozaki, T., Fukii, R., and Matumoto, M. 1981. Isolation of human rotavirus in cell cultures. Arch. Virol. 69: 155.

69. Schmidt, N. J. 1979. Cell culture techniques for diagnostic virology. In "Diagnostic Procedures for Viral, Rickettsial and Chlamydial Infections," 5th ed., ed. E. H. Lennette and N. J. Schmidt, p. 65. Amer. Pub. Health Assn., Washington, D.C.

70. Schmidt, N. J., Ho, H. H., and Lennette, E. H. 1975. Propagation and isolation of group A coxsackieviruses in RD cells. J. Clin. Microbiol. 2: 183.

71. Schmidt, N. J., Ho, H. H., and Lennette, E. H. 1976. Comparative sensitivity of the BGM cell line for the isolation of enteric viruses. Health Lab. Sci. 13: 115.

72. Schmidt, N. J., Ho, H. H., Riggs, J. L., and Lennette, E. H. 1978. Comparative sensitivity of various cell culture systems for isolation of viruses from wastewater and fecal samples. Appl. Environ. Microbiol. 36: 480.

73. Shields, P. A. and Farrah, S. R. 1983. Influence of salts on electrostatic interactions between poliovirus and membrane filters. Appl. Environ. Microbiol. 45: 526.

74. Sobsey, M. D. 1987. Methods for recovering viruses from shellfish, seawater and sediments. In "Methods for Recovering Viruses from the Environment," ed. G. Berg, p. 77. CRC Press, Boca Raton, Fla.

75. Sobsey, M. D., Carrick, R. J., and Jensen, H. R. 1978. Improved methods for detecting enteric viruses in oysters. Appl. Environ. Microbiol. 36: 121.

76. Speirs, J. I., Pontefract, R. D., and Harwig, J. 1987. Methods for recovering poliovirus and rotavirus from oysters. Appl. Environ. Microbiol. 53: 2666.

77. Su, Chengqin, Wu, Yilun, Shen, Hong Kai, Wang, Daibao, Chen, Yunhua, Wu, Dogmin, He, Lina and Yang, Zaolun. 1986. An outbreak of epidemic diarrhoea in adults caused by a new rotavirus in Anhui province of China in the summer of 1983. J. Med. Virol. 19: 167.

78. Sullivan, R., Fassolitis, A. C., and Read, R. B. Jr. 1970. Method for isolating viruses from ground beef. J. Food Sci. 35: 624.

79. Sullivan, R., Peeler, J. T., and Larkin, E. P. 1986. A method for recovery of poliovirus 1 from a variety of foods. J. Food Prot. 49: 226.

80. Tavera, C., Velazquez, O., Avila, C., Ornelas, G., Alvarez, C., and Sepulveda, J. 1987. Enterically transmitted non-A, non-B hepatitis—Mexico. Morbid. Mortal. Weekly Rep. 36: 597.

81. Teras, J., Entzeroth, R., Scholtyseck, E., Kesa, L., and Schrauf, I. 1988. Light and electron microscope observation of virus-induced *Tetrahymena pyriformis* in newborn mice (*Mus musculus albinicus*) brain. Parasitol. Res. 74: 221.

82. Tierney, J. T., Fassolitis, A. C., Van Donsel, D., Rao, V. C., Sullivan, R., and Larkin, E. P. 1980. Glass wool-hydroextraction method for recovery of human enteroviruses from

shellfish. J. Food Prot. 43: 102.

83. Tierney, J. T., Sullivan, R., Peeler, J. T., and Larkin, E. P. 1985. Detection of low numbers of poliovirus 1 in oysters: Collaborative study. J. Assn. Off. Anal. Chem. 68: 884.

84. Truman, B. I., Makore, H. P., Menegus, M. A., Nitzkin, J. L., and Dolin, R. 1987. Snow Mountain agent gastroenteritis from clams. Am. J. Epidemiol. 126: 516.

85. Vaughn, J. M., Landry, E. F., Vicale, T. J., and Dahl, M. C. 1979. Modified procedure for the recovery of naturally accumulated poliovirus from oysters. Appl. Environ. Microbiol. 38: 594.

86. Wait, D. A., Hackney, C. R., Carrick, R. J., Lovelace, G., and Sobsey, M. D. 1983. Enteric bacterial and viral pathogens and indicator bacteria in hard shell clams. J. Food Prot. 46: 493.

87. Ward, R. L., Knowlton, D. R., and Hurst, P.-F. L. 1988. Reassortment formation and selection following coinfection of cultured cells with subgroup 2 human rotaviruses. J. Gen. Virol. 69: 149.

88. Watson, P. G., Inglis, J. M., and Anderson, K. J. 1980. Viral content of a sewage-polluted intertidal zone. J. Infect. 2: 237.

89. Yousef, G. E., Bell, E. J., Mann, G. F., Murugesan, V., Smith, D. G., McCartney, R. A., and Mowbray, J. F. 1988. Chronic enterovirus infection in patients with postviral fatigue syndrome. Lancet I(8578): 146.

Chapter 42

WATERBORNE AND FOODBORNE PARASITES

Ronald Fayer, H. Ray Gamble, J. Ralph Lichtenfels, and Jeffrey W. Bier

42.1 INTRODUCTION

Morphologic identification of protozoa and helminths can be quite difficult. Bright-field or phase-contrast microscopy and a variety of specialized stains or live specimens are used selectively to aid identification. In addition to specific references cited in the text, several atlases are recommended for such assistance.[3-5,26,31,47,49]

42.11 Parasites Involved in Foodborne and Waterborne Diseases

The prevalence of diseases caused by parasitic animals in humans is relatively low for most modern countries as a result of superior hygienic standards. Acquisition of parasites from contaminated food or drink is minimized by water-treatment systems and quality control in the production and inspection of meat from food animals. Nevertheless, many species of parasites persist in all human populations.

Among the parasites that humans acquire through ingestion of food and water are protozoa, flukes (trematodes), tapeworms (cestodes), roundworms (nematodes), and spiny-headed worms (acanthocephalids). A detailed list of the parasites, even those uncommonly or rarely found in humans, is given in Table 1. This list includes source, name of parasite, infective stage, and a reference that contains high-quality illustrations to aid in identification. Some parasites of public health importance are not listed because they are not normally considered contaminants of food or drink.

Table 1—Parasites Transmitted by Water and Food

Source	Parasite	Stage in water or food	Illustration of stage (Reference no.)
Water	Protozoa		
	Entamoeba histolytica[a]	Cysts	3
	Entamoeba coli[a]	Cysts	3
	Endolimax nana[a]	Cysts	3
	Iodamoeba buetschlii[a]	Cysts	3
	Dientamoeba fragilis[a]	Trophozoites	3
	Retortamonas intestinalis[a]	Cysts	30
	Retortamonas sinensis[a]	Cysts	30
	Chilomastix mesnili[a]	Cysts	3
	Enteromonas hominis[a]	Cysts	30
	Trichomonas hominis[a]	Trophozoites	3
	Giardia intestinalis[a]	Cysts	3
	Isospora belli[a]	Oocysts	46
	Balantidium coli[a]	Cysts	46
	Toxoplasma gondii[a]	Oocysts	46
	Cryptosporidium parvum[a]	Oocysts	25
	Nematoda		
	Capillaria hepatica[a]	Eggs	46
	Trichuris trichiura[a]	Eggs	3
	Rhabditis sp.[a]	Larvae in molluscs	44
	Mammomonogamus[a]	Eggs	4
	Enterobius vermicularis[a]	Eggs	3
	Syphacia obvelata	Eggs	NA
	Ascaris lumbricoides[a]	Eggs	3
	Toxocara cati[a]	Eggs	3
	Toxocara canis[a]	Eggs	3
	Cestoda		
	Spirometra sp.	Procercoides in *Cyclops*	44
	Taenia multiceps (larva)[a]	Eggs	4
	Taenia serialis (larva)	Eggs	4
	Echinococcus granulosus (larva)[a]	Eggs	44
	Echinococcus multilocularis (larva)[a]	Eggs	44
	Echinococcus vogeli (larva)	Eggs	NA

Table 1—Parasites Transmitted by Water and Food (*continued*)

Source	Parasite	Stage in water or food	Illustration of stage (Reference no.)
Contaminated	Trematoda		
Vegetables	*Watsonius watsoni*	Metacercariae	NA
	Gastrodiscoides hominis	Metacercariae	NA
	Fasciola hepatica	Metacercariae	44
	Fasciola gigantica	Metacercariae	44
	Fasciolopsis buski	Metacercariae	44
	Protozoa		
	Nematoda		
	Ascaris lumbricoides		
	Angiostrongylis costaricensis		44
	Angiostrongylis cantonensis		44
Molluscs	Nematoda		
Oysters	*Echinocephalus* sp.	Larvae	NA
Snails	*Angiostrongylus cantonensis*	Larvae	44
Snails, slugs	*Angiostrongylus costaricensis*	Larvae	44
	Trematoda		
Snails, oysters	*Echinostoma* sp.	Metacercariae	44
Clams	*Himasthla muehlensi*	Metacercariae	NA
Crustacea	Trematoda		
	Paragonimus westermani[a]	Metacercariae	44
Fish (F) and/ or Frog legs (FL)	Nematoda		
F	*Capillaria philippinensis*	Larvae	3
F	*Dioctophyme renale*[a]	Larvae	4
F, FL	*Gnathostoma spinigerum*	Larvae	44
F	*Pseudoterranova* spp.[a]	Larvae	44
F	*Anisakis* spp.[a]	Larvae	44
F	*Porrocaecum* spp.	Larvae	35
F	*Contracaecum* spp.	Larvae	35
	Gnathostoma spinigerum	Larvae	44
	Cestoda		

Table 1—Parasites Transmitted by Water and Food (*continued*)

Source	Parasite	Stage in water or food	Illustration of stage (Reference no.)
F	*Diphyllobothrium latum*[a]	Plerocercoids	3
F	*Diplogonoporus grandis*	Plerocercoids	44
F	*Digramma brauni*	Plerocercoids	NA
F	*Ligula intestinalis*	Plerocercoids	NA
F (probably)	*Braunia jasseyensis*	Plerocercoids	44
	Spirometra crinacci	Plerocercoids	44
Trematoda			
F	*Echinostoma* spp.	Metacercariae	44
	Echinochasmus perfoliatus	Metacercariae	44
F	*Opisthorchis felineus*	Metacercariae	3
F	*Clonorchis sinensis*	Metacercariae	3
F	*Heterophyes heterophyes*	Metacercariae	44
F	*Metagonimus yokagawai*	Metacercariae	44
F	*Metagonimus minutus*	Metacercariae	44
F	*Centrocestus armatus*	Metacercariae	NA
F, FL	*Centrocestus formosanus*	Metacercariae	NA
F	*Diorchitrema pseudocirratum*[a] and *Diorchitrema formosenum*	Metacercariae	NA
F, Shrimp	*Haplorchis yokogawai*	Metacercariae	NA
F	*Haplorchis taichui*	Metacercariae	NA
F	*Stellantchasmus amplicaecalis*	Metacercariae	NA
F	*Stellantchasmus falcatus*[a]	Metacercariae	NA
F	*Nanophyetus salmincola*[a]	Metacercariae	NA
F	*Isoparorchis hypselobagri*	Metacercariae	NA
FL	*Alaria americana*[a]	Metacercariae	NA
Acanthocephala			
F	*Corynosoma strumosum*	Juvenile	NA
F	*Bulbosoma* spp.	Juvenile	NA

Table 1—Parasites Transmitted by Water and Food (*continued*)

Source	Parasite	Stage in water or food	Illustration of stage (Reference no.)
Poultry			
	Protozoa		
	Toxoplasma gondii[a]	Tissue cysts	3, 25, 46
	Nematoda		
	Gnathostoma spinigerum	Larvae	44
Pork	Protozoa		
	Toxoplasma gondii[a]	Tissue cysts	3, 25, 46
	Nematoda		
	Trichinella spiralis[a]	Larvae	46
	Cestoda		
	Taenia solium[a]	Cysticerci	46
	Taenia spp. (Taiwan)	Cysticerci	46
Beef	Protozoa		
	Toxoplasma gondii[a]	Tissue cysts	3, 25, 46
	Cestoda		
	Taenia saginata[a]	Cysticerci	46
Goat meat	Protozoa		
	Toxoplasma gondii[a]	Tissue cysts	3, 25, 46
Lamb	Protozoa		
	Toxoplasma gondii[a]	Tissue cysts	3, 25, 46
Bear meat	Nematoda		
	Trichinella spiralis[a]	Larvae	46

[a]Indicates parasites found in North America.
NA indicates that illustrations of the infective parasite are not available.

42.12   Sources of Parasites

All waterborne parasites originate from human or animal fecal contamination of the environment. Numerous surface waters such as rivers, lakes, and ponds have recently been found to harbor encysted stages of parasites. Modern water-treatment facilities have reduced the opportunities for transmission of parasites by water; however, recent outbreaks of giardiasis (see Section 42.23) and cryptosporidiosis (see Section 42.25) following flooding or other events that result in contamination of the treated water with untreated water or debris emphasize the cosmopolitan distribution of these organisms.

Vegetables can be contaminated with numerous species of parasites through the use of fertilizers consisting of animal or human feces. Vegetables can also become contaminated during food preparation by rinsing with water containing parasites. A few species of parasites have intermediate stages, found in molluscs, that specifically encyst on vegetation (Table 1).

Shellfish, fish, poultry, beef, goat meat, lamb, pork, or game meats such as bear, deer, elk, moose, pheasant, quail, and others sometimes contain encysted, encapsulated, or free stages of parasites. These stages are not merely contaminants; they are specific developmental life-cycle stages in the animal hosts. All are temperature-sensitive and are killed by thorough cooking or by freezing. Perhaps the best known of these foodborne parasites is *Trichinella spiralis*, the roundworm (nematode) causing trichinellosis (see Section 42.332). Although the nematode is well known, fewer than 100 cases of human trichinellosis are diagnosed annually in the United States. Another foodborne parasite, *Toxoplasma gondii*, a protozoan that causes toxoplasmosis in humans (see Section 42.32), has been detected serologically in 30% or more of the population of the United States.[17,21] The major source of infection has not been unequivocally established, but cat feces and undercooked meat are the two most likely sources.

42.13   Inspection of Fish and Meat

There is currently no mandatory inspection of fish before marketing in the United States. However, the National Oceanographic and Atmospheric Administration (NOAA) of the U.S. Department of Commerce offers a voluntary seafood program on a fee-for-service basis. Any type of product, from whole fish to reconstructed products, can be inspected and certified. Labels for the various inspection procedures include "Packed Under Federal Inspection," indicating that plant sanitation and processing methods, from raw material to final product, have been inspected. The inspection can include product grading. NOAA also offers inspection of specific lots or shipments of seafood (including imported lots) for compliance with labeling requirements, wholesomeness, safety, and suitability for human consumption.

The Food and Drug Administration (FDA) of the U.S. Department of Health and Human Services periodically inspects, on an announced or unannounced basis, all interstate food processors except those that process poultry and red meats, which are inspected by the U.S. Department of Agriculture (USDA). The inspection checks for product adulteration, sanitation practices, and misbranding. FDA examines seafoods for microbial hazards, including parasites, on both a "surveillance" or a "for cause" basis when a problem is reported or suspected. A bill currently before Congress would require mandatory inspection of all seafood products in interstate commerce.[44]

There is no mandatory inspection of meat for *Toxoplasma gondii* or *Trichinella spiralis* in the United States. Voluntary inspection of pork by the pooled sample digestion method for *T. spiralis* is allowed under the Code of Federal Regulations (CFR) Title 9, Chap. 3, 318.10.[15]

Beef and pork carcasses are inspected by the USDA for the presence of tapeworm cysts of the genus *Taenia* (CFR, Title 9, Chap. 3, 311.23, 311.24).[13,14]

Cysts, also called cysticerci (plural), are small, fluid-filled, oval, white bladderworms about 7–10 × 4–6 mm. Methods of inspection are organoleptic, involving the visual examination of several regions of the carcass. The sensitivity of organoleptic inspection for cattle is relatively low; hence only some of the infected carcasses are detected. Infested regions of meat are excised from carcasses; in cases of heavy infestation carcasses might be condemned.

42.2   WATERBORNE PARASITES: PREVALENCE, DISEASE, TRANSMISSION, AND METHODS OF IDENTIFICATION

42.21   Amoebae

Of the intestinal amoebae parasitic in humans, only *Entamoeba histolytica* is consistently considered a pathogen.[32] Between 1976 and 1985 in the United States, approximately 3,000 to 7,000 cases were reported annually to the Centers for Disease Control (CDC). *E. histolytica* is transmitted without known animal reservoir hosts. The trophozoite stage, a motile form resembling a macrophage, is found in the intestine and causes acute colitis, diarrhea, or dysentery. Because the trophozoite is easily destroyed outside the body, transmission usually involves passage of the resistant cyst stage in the stool. This stage is round and surrounded by a tough outer wall. Ingestion of cysts in contaminated food or water or direct passage from person to person are the usual methods of transmission. Cysts can be transmitted from soiled fingers of infected food handlers who have poor personal hygiene. There are no drugs in the United States approved for prophylaxis against *E. histolytica*.[32]

Identification of *E. histolytica* from water is based on microscopic examination of sediment obtained either from backflushing filters through which water had passed or in the pellet of particulate matter from centrifuged water (see Section 42.27). Trophozoites are 20 to 30 μm, have a thick, clear ectoplasm and granular endoplasm; pseudopods might be visible. The nucleus, unclear in fresh specimens, is distinct when stained with hematoxylin. It has a ring of small peripheral granules and a central dark body (endosome). Cysts are 10 to 20 μm in diameter, have four nuclei, and contain rodlike bodies with rounded ends; they are distinguished from those of nonpathogenic *Entamoeba coli* by the position of the endosome in the nucleus, the number of nuclei, and the shape of the rodlike body.

42.22   *Balantidium coli*

Balantidium coli, a ciliated protozoan of medical importance, is the only species in the genus *Balantidium*. Although distributed worldwide, it is not a prevalent infection in humans. The trophozoite stage in the large intestine causes ulcerative colitis and diarrhea. The cyst is thought to be the infective stage, capable of survival in moist environments for several weeks. *B. coli* is a commensal widely distributed in pigs. Water obtained from drainage areas contaminated by human or pig feces is thought to be the major source of human infection. The treatment of choice is tetracycline, but diiodohydroxyquin or paromomycin are suitable substitutes.[46]

The *B. coli* cyst can be identified in suspect water after concentration by filtration or centrifugation (see Section 42.27). The cyst is large (45 to 65 μm) and surrounded by a distinct wall, and it contains a large nucleus that is often bean-shaped. Both cysts and trophozoites can be identified by microscopic examination of suspect stool specimens mixed with physiological saline. The freshness of the stool sample is important because trophozoites can disintegrate within a few hours after passage. Ciliated trophozoites are motile and rotate as they move. In formalin-fixed samples trophozoites often resemble debris, artifacts, or eggs.[46]

42.23   *Giardia* spp.

Giardia spp. are flagellated protozoa of the intestine.[33] Of the 40 or more so-called species from animals and humans, it is not known for certain how many can cause human infection, but it is suspected that many animals serve as sources for human infection. The life cycle of *Giardia* spp. includes a binucleated, flagellated, motile stage called (as for numerous other protozoa) a trophozoite, which is responsible for the enteritis and diarrhea, and a rounded, thick-walled cyst stage, which is responsible for survival outside the host and transmission to another host. Cysts are transmitted by the fecal-oral route. Soiled fingers, contaminated drinking water, and fecal contamination of food are the most common methods of infection. Sand filtration is needed to eliminate cysts from community drinking water because *Giardia* spp. can survive normal chlorination.

Giardia spp. cysts are identified by bright-field or phase-contrast microscopy in suspect water after concentration by filtration or centrifugation (see Section 42.27). *Giardia* spp. can be identified as trophozoites or cysts in stool specimens mixed with physiological saline. Trophozoites are motile in specimens less than a few hours old. They are 9 to 21 μm long by 5 to 15 μm wide but only about 2 μm thick. When fixed and stained with iron hematoxylin, the trophozoites look like a human face with nuclei for eyes and a median bar for the mouth. The cyst stage contains four nuclei.

An enzyme-linked immunosorbent assay is available to detect a *Giardia* sp. antigen excreted in the feces (Alexon, Santa Clara, Calif.). At least two fluorescent antibody test kits are available to detect *Giardia*: an indirect fluorescent kit for feces (Meridian Diagnostics, Cincinnati, Ohio) and a direct fluorescent antibody kit for water samples (Biovir Laboratories, Benicia, Calif.). Biovir also markets a polyclonal fluorescein-linked antibody to *Giardia* spp., of both human and animal origin, and a monoclonal fluorescein-linked antibody, which is reportedly specific for human *Giardia* sp(p). A cDNA probe 256 base pairs long has been used to detect *Giardia* sp(p). in water samples.[37]

42.24   *Isospora* (Coccidia)

The genus *Isospora* is part of a large group of protozoa collectively known as coccidia. *Isospora belli* is the only known species infectious for humans. Relatively few cases of the infection have been reported. It is thought to be transmitted from person to person because there are no other known hosts. Even the route of transmission is not known with certainty, but a fecal-oral route similar to that of other coccidia is suspected. Severe diarrhea, sometimes of long duration, produces stools that contain the oocyst, an egglike form surrounded by a tough outer wall, which can remain infectious in the environment for months under moist conditions.

Although there are no reports of *I. belli* being found in water, oocysts of other coccidia have been identified with bright-field or phase-contrast microscopy in water after concentration by centrifugation (see Section 42.27).

42.25   *Cryptosporidium* spp.

Cryptosporidium is another genus of coccidian protozoa.[22] Unrecognized as a human pathogen until the late 1970s, it is now known to be widespread, prevalent, and highly pathogenic under certain conditions. Of several recent outbreaks, one in Georgia involved about 36% of a population of nearly 36,000 persons. *Cryptosporidium parvum* is transmitted by the oocyst stage in the stool. Hand-to-mouth transmission may account for its spread in day-care centers. However, the finding of oocysts in numerous surface waters and in tapwater indicates the likelihood of spread to the general population through the water supply. Of 107 surface water samples collected in six western states, 72% were positive for the oocyst stage of a *Cryptosporidium* sp.

Identification of the oocyst stage of *Cryptosporidium* spp. is based on microscopic examination of sediment from filtered or centrifuged water (see Section 42.27). The oocyst stage is most easily identified after flotation in sucrose solution (see Section 42.27) and observation by phase-contrast microscopy. Oocysts resemble yeasts without buds but appear very light with a dark central granule. In acid-fast stained smears examined by bright-field microscopy, oocysts stained bright red. An indirect fluorescent antibody test kit for the detection of *Cryptosporidium* spp. in feces is commercially available (Meridian Diagnostics, Cincinnati, Ohio). A kit to detect *Giardia* spp. and/or *Cryptosporidium* using an indirect fluorescent antibody in water samples is also available (Meridian Diagnostics, Cincinnati, Ohio).

42.26   *Toxoplasma*

(See Section 42.32.)

42.27   Methods of Concentrating Protozoa in Suspect Water

Recovery rates of parasites from water are influenced by sample volume, number of parasites present, and water quality. Large volume, small numbers of parasites, and high turbidity decrease recovery. Other methods might be useful for recovery of a variety of protozoa, but two filtration methods found effective for recovery of *Cryptosporidium* spp. are provided as examples.[41]

The first uses 293-mm diameter polycarbonate membrane filters with a 5-μm pore size.[38] Up to 20 L of water are prefiltered under vacuum. The filtrate is collected and filtered again through a 1.0-μm pore-size filter. Oocysts retained on the 1.0-μm filter are recovered by vibrating the inverted filter in 200 ml of distilled water for 3 min at the medium setting on a Toothmaster Investment Vibrator (Whaledent International, Division of IPCO Corp.), concentrating the sediment by centrifugation, clarifying it in a potassium citrate (1.19 g/ml) density gradient, and filtering the suspension through a 1.2-μm pore-size cellulose nitrate filter. Oocysts stained with fluorescein iso-thiocyanate-labeled polyclonal antibody are detected by fluorescence micros-copy. The second method uses a Micro Wynd II 250-μm diameter polypro-pylene cartridge filter (AMF/CUNO, Meriden, Conn.) with a 1.0-μm pore size, which can be transported to a sampling site where large volumes (100 gal; 378 L) of water are to be examined.[35] When such a large volume is filtered, 6 L of 0.1% Tween 80 is needed to backflush and rinse the cut-up filter. The 6 L is concentrated by centrifugation and the pellet clarified by flotation on sucrose solution (1.24 g/ml). High recovery rates can be obtained when 0.1% Tween 80 and 1% sodium dodecyl sulfate are mixed with the sample and sonication is used to disaggregate oocysts from sediment. Oocysts recovered from the surface of the sucrose are identified on a glass slide by indirect immunofluorescence.

The oocyst stage of virtually all coccidia can be identified by microscopic examination of suspect stool samples or water contaminated with feces. Usu-ally, a differential density flotation-concentration method is used to separate fecal or other debris from oocysts. Zinc sulfate, sodium chloride, cesium chloride, Percoll® (Pharmacia, Uppsala, Sweden), sucrose (0.4–0.2 M), and other solutions with specific gravities between 1.02 and 1.12 are useful for flotation of the oocysts. They constitute the lower layer in a centrifuge tube. The upper layer consists of contaminated water or a mixture of feces and water. The tube is centrifuged for 5 min at 325–750 $\times$ *g*. A portion of the surface layer of the higher density solution is removed by aspiration and a drop is placed on a glass slide for microscopic examination.

42.3   FOODBORNE PARASITES: PREVALENCE, DISEASE, TRANSMISSION, AND METHODS OF IDENTIFICATION

42.31   Parasites of Molluscs, Crustaceans, Fish, and Frog Legs

Parasites that can be transmitted to humans by eating fish (marine and freshwater), molluscs (including clams, oysters, and snails), and crustaceans (crabs or crayfish) are helminths (worms), including nematodes, cestodes, and trematodes (Table 1). Only a few helminths (*Diphyllobothrium latum*) and the anisakids *Anisakis* spp. and *Pseudoterranova* (*Phocanema* spp.) pose important threats to humans in North America.[28] Four other helminths transmitted only rarely to humans in North America include *Eustrongylides* spp., *Paragonimus* spp., *Nanophyetus* spp., and *Alaria* spp.

42.311   Diphyllobothrium spp.

Diphyllobothrium latum, the broad fish tapeworm of humans and related species, causes diphyllobothriasis in much of the world, with greatest prevalence in northern Europe, Asia, and North America. Of an estimated total 100,000 human cases in North America, most were in the Great Lakes region. The tapeworm also infects carnivores, such as dogs, cats, bears, seals, and sea lions. The infective stage for humans and other carnivores is the worm-like, slightly flattened, flesh-colored plerocercoid (5 to 40 mm long) found in the flesh of freshwater or anadromous fish. Prevalence in fish varies greatly; 50% to 70% of pikes and walleyes are infected in some small lakes in North America. Infections result from ingestion of raw or inadequately cooked infected fish. Clinical symptoms of diphyllobothriasis include epigastric fullness, pressure, or pain, diarrhea, nausea, anorexia, vomiting, and, rarely, anemia.[9] Treatment with niclosamide is usually successful in removing the tapeworm (which can reach 10 meters in length) from the intestine.[12] Other species of *Diphyllobothrium* have been described and are known to infect humans in more restricted geographic regions. The information presented here for *D. latum* applies as well to those species.

Plerocercoids are difficult to detect in fish flesh because they are small and flesh-colored (creamy white). Plerocercoids can be recovered by shredding the tissue and inspecting it with a dissection microscope or hand lens or by artificial digestion. The latter has not been critically evaluated for efficiency. Plerocercoids are rendered uninfective by freezing ($-18°C$ for at least 24 hr) or by heating ($56°C$ for 5 min).[9]

42.312   Anisakids

Anisakiasis in humans results from ingestion of the third-stage larva of nematodes of the family Anisakidae (principally of the genera *Anisakis* and *Pseudoterranova* (*Phocanema*)) in raw, semi-raw, or pickled fish. More than 4,000 cases from Japan and 200 from Scandinavia have been reported since the disease was first recognized in 1955.[10] In the United States, only 15 cases of anisakiasis (mostly *Pseudoterranova*) have been described in detail, but many more have been documented. Larvae of *Anisakis* are found in pelagic fishes such as herring, mackerel, and salmon.[7] Principal definitive hosts are whales and porpoises. Larvae of *Pseudoterranova* are found in inshore fishes such as cod, flounder, and flukes. Principal definitive hosts are seals. Anisakid larvae are pink, and measure 15 to 37 mm long and 1 to 2 mm wide. Morphological features have been described.[36] Surveys in fish markets in the United States indicate a high prevalence of anisakidae. Clinical symptoms in humans range from a tickle in the throat before "coughing up" a larva of *Pseudoterranova* (which usually does not invade human tissues), to severe epigastric pain requiring surgery if the stomach wall is punctured. Treatment may include removal of the larva with the aid of gastroenteroscopy or more traditional surgery.

The detection of larval anisakids in fish muscle by candling has been adopted as an official procedure by the Association of Official Analytical Chemists on the basis of an intralaboratory study.[45] The candling table consists of a framework to hold a light source below a rigid acrylic plastic or other suitable work surface with 45% to 60% translucency. The surface must be large enough to accommodate an entire fillet. The light source must be "cool white" with a color temperature of 4,200 K; at least two 20-watt fluorescent bulbs are recommended. The tubes and electrical connection should be constructed to prevent overheating of the work space. The light intensity must average 1500 to 1800 lux when measured from a distance of 30 cm. Distribution of the illumination directly above the light source should be three times greater than that of the outer field. Indirect light in the vicinity of the candling table should be about 500 lux. Compression candling increases the sensitivity of this method[6] in scallops and clams.

An intralaboratory study compared recovery of nematodes from digestion of fish muscle and viscera in 2% pepsin (1:10,000) adjusted to pH 2 with HCl at $36 \pm 0.5°C$ for 24 hr with elution into saline over a 16- to 18-hr period.[29] The concentrates from both procedures were examined for parasites with the aid of a dissecting microscope. Digestion was more sensitive for recovering potentially pathogenic nematodes, whereas elution was more sensitive for recovering nonpathogens.[29] Pepsin-HCl digestion[43] may be the most complete and accurate method for collecting larvae from fish flesh, but a method using a food blender to free the larvae from the tissue of fresh and frozen fish and UV light to detect them was regarded as accurate, quick, and inexpensive.[8] Freezing ($-20°C$ for 60 hr) or cooking ($60°C$ for 5 min) kills larvae in fish.[7]

42.313   Nanophyetus

Human infection with the intestinal fluke *Nanophyetus salmincola* was first reported from the northwestern United States in 1987. The fluke is also called the salmon poisoning fluke because it transmits a rickettsia fatal to dogs that eat infected salmon. *Nanophyetus schikhobalowi* was found in up to 98% of the population in some Russian villages in eastern Siberia. The stage transmitted to humans is an ovoid metacercaria about 0.5 by 0.25 mm found on the skin or in the flesh or viscera of salmonids and to a lesser extent other species of fishes and amphibians. Symptoms include right lower quadrant abdominal discomfort, bloating, episodic diarrhea of several weeks duration, nausea, vomiting, decreased appetite, cramping, and weight loss. Anthelmintic treatment with bithionol or niclosamide has been effective in eliminating parasites.[18]

Metacercaria are detected by homogenizing the fish flesh in saline and examining the sediment after screening. In one method, the whole animal or a selected part was homogenized in 200 ml of saline and washed through a 212-μm mesh screen into a fingerbowl and allowed to settle for 1 min. The supernatant was decanted, and the sediment was diluted with saline to 1 L, transferred to a 1-L pharmaceutical flask, and allowed to settle for 1 min. The supernatant was then decanted. The previous dilution and sedimentation was repeated and the sediment was examined for cysts.[27] To our knowledge this method has not been confirmed. Cooking is recommended for killing metacercariae in fish; the effect of freezing is unknown.

42.314   Eustrongylides spp.

This rare zoonotic disease is caused by larvae of the genus *Eustrongylides*, which normally mature in fish-eating birds. Human infections result when freshwater fish harboring encysted larvae are ingested raw.[42] Eggs, from the feces of infected birds, are deposited in freshwater streams, and they are infective for segmented worms (oligochaetes) in which larvae of the parasites develop and become infective for fish. Numerous species of freshwater fish ingest the oligochaetes, and harbor fourth-stage larvae, which are infective for birds. Prevalence in small fish such as killifish may be 50% or higher in some areas. Only six human cases are known. All are from North America. Five Chesapeake Bay fishermen swallowed their bait fish raw (and whole) and experienced abdominal pain within 24 hr. Two of the symptomatic fishermen underwent surgery, and large (8 to 12 cm long) bright red nematodes were removed from the body cavity. Another man experienced symptoms resembling appendicitis one day after eating sashimi. During surgery a bright red *Eustrongylides* sp. was found. Larval nematodes are detected by examination of fish flesh. The large red nematodes, usually within a tough white oval cyst, are easily seen.

42.315   Paragonimus spp.

Paragonimiasis is caused by lung flukes of the genus *Paragonimus*, consisting of more than 30 species. Human infections are known in Asia, the South Pacific Islands, and the Americas. The species that caused the five clinical cases reported from North America are unidentified. Endemic cases in Central and South America and Africa, where the prevalence may be high, are attributable to *P. westermanni*.

Adult *Paragonimus* spp. infect cats, rats, mice, mongooses, monkeys, dogs, pigs, and cattle. Infection results from ingestion of globular metacercariae (0.3–0.5 mm in diameter) in various tissues of freshwater crustaceans (crabs, prawns, or crayfish). Metacercariae have been recovered from crayfish collected from the eastern and midwestern United States. Human cases are characterized by fever and malaise at onset, followed by dyspnea, chest pain, and eosinophilia, with accumulation of pleural fluid. Several months later a productive cough develops and operculate ova are detectable in the sputum. Anthelmintic treatment with praziquantel or niclofolan may be effective in eliminating symptoms and detectable ova.[48]

Detection in crayfish is by removal of the carapace and examination of the heart. The metacercariae are easily recognized without magnification in living specimens because the white excretory bladder contrasts sharply with the yellowish host tissue.[1]

Data are lacking on the ability of the *Paragonimus* spp. metacercaria to survive freezing. Infections can be prevented by cooking freshwater crustaceans to an internal temperature of 65°C. Care should also be exercised in preparing raw crayfish for cooking by avoiding inadvertent ingestion of uncooked cysts.

42.316   *Alaria* spp.

Alaria americana, *Alaria* spp., and a trematode identified only as a member of the subfamily Alarinae were each reported once in humans in North America. The mature adult stages of these flukes are found in the bobcat, coyote, fox, lynx, martin, skunk, and wolf throughout North America. The mesocercarial stage in muscles of the frog (second intermediate host) is infective to a variety of hosts, including humans. In the most severe human case reported, autopsy revealed thousands of larvae migrating through tissues of the lungs, liver, spleen, stomach, heart, brain, and spinal cord.[23]

Digestion of suspected infected flesh will recover the small (0.5 mm long) motile larvae (see Section 42.312). They can also be recovered by blending and sedimentation or by dissection and sedimentation alone. Extreme care should be exercised when handling the flesh of frogs.

42.317   *Angiostrongylus* spp.

Angiostrongyliasis, or eosinophilic meningoencephalitis, results when nematodes of the genus *Angiostrongylus* enter blood vesssels of the brain. The nematode is normally parasitic in rats. Humans are infected by ingesting the larvae in invertebrate intermediate hosts or by eating food contaminated with infective larvae by an invertebrate host. Molluscs such as slugs and aquatic and terrestrial snails, as well as planarians, freshwater shrimp, land crabs, and frogs serve as either intermediate or transport hosts. The disease, widespread in the South Pacific and Southeast Asia including Hawaii, has recently been reported in rats and humans in Cuba[16] and in rats in Louisiana.[11] Another form of angiostrongyliasis has been reported in Central America. It is caused by *A. costaricensis*, which resides in the mesenteric arteries of rats and humans. In Costa Rica prevalence of human infection is estimated to be 12 cases/100,000 persons.[34]

Clinical symptoms of *A. cantonensis* infections include high eosinophil counts in blood and spinal fluid and elevated lymphocytes in cerebrospinal fluid. When nematodes invade the brain, symptoms include headache, paralysis, stiff neck, coma, and death. Control or prevention of infection is difficult in endemic areas because larvae survive in drinking water and on vegetables. Heating (55°C) or boiling infected snails for 2 min or freezing at −15°C for 24 hr kills all infective larvae.

Detection is difficult because of the small size of the larvae (less than 0.5 mm long).[2] Larvae from suspected intermediate hosts are recovered by Baermann elution of minced tissue or digestion. In Baermann elution,[40] samples wrapped in gauze are placed in a funnel fitted with a short rubber hose, which is clamped shut. Lukewarm water is poured into the funnel until it wets the bottom of the sample. Under these conditions invertebrates migrate into the warm water. Once in the water, most species settle to the bottom of the funnel and can be collected by opening the clamp. Liquid collected from the funnel is examined microscopically for larvae.[2]

42.32   *Toxoplasma*

Toxoplasma gondii is a coccidian protozoa that has been studied extensively because of its economic and public health significance.[17] It is estimated that between 30% and 40% of the population of the United States have serum antibodies to *T. gondii*, indicating exposure to the organism. Members of the cat family are the only known definitive hosts (i.e., those capable of contaminating the environment with the oocyst stage in feces). All other vertebrates, including humans, are potential intermediate hosts (i.e., they can acquire the infection either by ingesting the oocysts or by eating animal tissues that contain the cyst stage). Infectious stages of *T. gondii* have been isolated from muscles and various organs such as the heart, brain, and liver of virtually all food animals including chickens, pigs, cattle, goats, and sheep. Cooking meat at 60°C or irradiation to 30 krad renders the encysted organisms uninfectious. The acquired postnatal form of the infection is often associated with mild influenza-like symptoms; however, potentially life-threatening infections are well documented in the congenital or neonatal form of the infection, especially if the mother becomes infected during the first or second trimester of pregnancy. The disease can also be serious in immunosuppressed patients undergoing therapy and often is fatal in AIDS patients. Acute toxoplasmosis can usually be treated with drugs such as pyrimethamine and sulfas or with clindamycin or spiramycin, but these drugs are relatively toxic and are not prescribed during pregnancy. Toxoplasmosis can be prevented by avoiding direct and indirect exposure to cat feces and by thoroughly cooking meat.[21]

The presence of oocysts in cat feces or water can be determined as described in Section 42.27. Because oocysts are 10 μm in diameter or slightly greater, the pore size of the filter should be adjusted accordingly. Oocysts can be detected in cat feces by mixing feces in water followed by flotation of oocysts in sucrose solution and examination by light microscopy. However, oocysts of *T. gondii* are identical in size and shape with those of two other species of coccidia and can be differentiated only by oral inoculation and testing of mice for antibodies to *T. gondii*. Cysts are not detected during routine organoleptic meat inspection.

Diagnosis of *Toxoplasma* in meat requires a biological assay as follows: a 50-g sample of meat passed through a grinder is placed in 625 ml of an acid-pepsin digestion solution (10 g pepsin with 1:10,000 activity and 10 ml of 37% HCl/L of water). The meat-digestion solution is incubated at 37°C for 90 min on a shaker. The digested sample is filtered through two layers of gauze and centrifuged at $400 \times g$ for 10 min. The sediment is resuspended in 50 ml of saline, centrifuged again, and the sediment is resuspended in 6 ml of saline containing 1,000 IU penicillin/ml and 100 µg dihydrostreptomycin/ml. Usually, 1 ml of the sample is inoculated into each of six 25-g *Toxoplasma*-free mice. After 30 days the blood serum of mice is tested for antibodies to *Toxoplasma* and brain smears are examined for cysts of *T. gondii*.

42.33   Parasites in Pork

42.331   *Toxoplasma*

(See Section 42.32)

42.332   *Trichinella*

Human trichinellosis results from eating raw or undercooked meat, most often pork, containing the infective muscle larval stage of the nematode *Trichinella spiralis*. Human trichinellosis is worldwide, but clinical cases are scarce. Fewer than 100 human cases have been diagnosed per year in the United States over the last decade, although sporadic postmortem surveys have indicated a much higher subclinical or undiagnosed rate (2.2%). Prevalence is similar in European countries. *T. spiralis* can infect virtually any warm-blooded carnivore. Pork, bear meat, and game meats containing the infective muscle larvae of *T. spiralis* are the most common source of human infection. The current infection rate of *T. spiralis* in hogs in the United States is about 1 per 1,000. Hogs acquire the infection by eating raw or undercooked garbage containing infected meat, infected rodents, or infected hog carcasses. Human infection results in many symptoms as the worms develop in the intestine and produce larvae that migrate to and encyst in striated muscles. During the larval migration and encystment, symptoms include fever, myalgia, and periorbital edema (the general trichinellosis syndrome). The diagnosis of human trichinellosis depends on a combination of factors, including a history of consumption of infected meat, symptoms, and laboratory findings of which eosinophilia is most notable. Definitive diagnosis relies on the presence of larvae in a muscle biopsy. Infections detected at the intestinal level can be treated with mebendazole or thiabendazole; mebendazole is less effective against the larvae in the muscle. Corticosteroids (e.g., prednisone) are often given during the muscle phase to reduce tissue inflammation. *T. spiralis* is detected in meat by one of two direct methods.[15,19,20,30] Serological methods for the antemortem or postmortem detection of trichinellosis are available but are currently used for epidemiologic studies only.[24,25]

1. The Compression Method

In this method, a sample of muscle tissue is obtained from a suspected animal carcass or meat. A carcass sample should be collected from one of the areas where the larvae accumulate in highest density: the tongue, diaphragm, or masseter tissues. The sample is cut into small pieces (thin slices are best) and squeezed between two glass microscope slides until the tissue becomes translucent. The sample is then examined with the aid of a compound microscope (at low magnification) or a dissecting microscope for the presence of encysted larvae. Muscle larvae in tissue are coiled within a muscle nurse cell or "cyst."

2. The Digestion Method

The level of infection of *T. spiralis* larvae in muscle tissue is often too low to be detected by the compression method; therefore, a second method involving tissue digestion is used. In this method, a larger sample of meat (one to several hundred grams) is obtained. The tissue to be examined is cleaned of adhering fat and ground in a meat grinder. (As an alternative to grinding, meat may be minced with scissors.) Ground meat is subjected to digestion in a solution of 1% pepsin (1:10,000 activity) and 1% HCl; digestion solution should be used at a ratio of 1 L for 100 g of tissue. Digestion is carried out for 3 hr at 37°C with continuous agitation, either by stirring or shaking. The digested material is then allowed to settle for 20 min, and approximately 3/4 of the supernatant fluid is decanted. The sediment is resuspended and passed through a 400-μm mesh screen to remove undigested material. The filtered digestion fluid is than allowed to settle for 20 min in a conical glass. The upper 3/4 of the supernatant is decanted and the sediment is resuspended in several volumes of tap water. This process is repeated until the supernatant is clear. The final sediment is examined under a microscope for the presence of motile larvae.

42.333   *Taenia solium*

Human taeniasis (tapeworm disease) results from ingestion of raw or undercooked pork containing the infective cysticercus larvae of *Taenia solium*. *T. solium* is distributed worldwide, with higher prevalence rates of human infection in less developed countries; it is not prevalent in the United States.

Pigs acquire larval stages by ingesting *T. solium* eggs from the environment. The eggs hatch, liberating the oncosphere that penetrates the intestine and travels via the circulation to muscle tissue. The oncosphere develops to the infective cysticercus stage in 10 to 12 weeks. Humans acquire taeniid infection by ingesting raw or undercooked pork containing cysticerci. Human taeniasis is a relatively mild disease, which can be asymptomatic or cause vague symptoms of nausea, abdominal cramps, weight loss, or headache. Human taeniasis is diagnosed by the presence of eggs or proglottids (segments) in the stool. Effective drugs are available for treatment of tapeworms; the drug of choice is praziquantel. Humans can also serve as intermediate hosts, harboring the cysticercus stage (*Cysticercus cellulosae*) of *T. solium*. Human cysticercosis caused by ingestion of eggs of *T. solium* is a widespread and serious disease involving damage primarily to the central nervous system.[39]

Hog carcasses are inspected for the presence of *C. cellulosae* at slaughter. Inspection involves palpation and incision of tongue and other muscular tissues including the masseters, esophagus, heart, and diaphragm. Because of the random distribution and low levels of infection, the presence of one cysticercus in a portion of muscle would not necessarily indicate infection in other cuts from the same carcass.

42.34   Parasites in Beef

42.341   *Toxoplasma*

(See Section 42.32.)

42.342   *Taenia saginata*

Human taeniasis (tapeworm disease) results from the ingestion of raw or undercooked beef containing the infective cysticercus (*Cysticercus bovis*) stage of *Taenia saginata*. This parasite is distributed worldwide with higher prevalence of human infection in less developed countries. The larval cysticercus stage is found in cattle. Its prevalence varies regionally but is more common than *T. solium* in the United States. The life cycle, transmission, and signs of infection are similar to those of *T. solium* (see Section 42.333), except that the larval stage of *T. saginata* does not infect humans.[39] Methods of detection are similar to those for *T. solium* (See Section 42.333). Because infection levels in beef carcasses are quite low, antemortem inspection procedures are relatively insensitive.

42.35   Parasites in Goat Meat and in Lamb

42.351   *Toxoplasma*

(See Section 42.32.)

42.4   EMERGING METHODS

Enzyme-linked immunosorbent assays to detect specific secreted parasitic antigens are currently being developed. As indirect fluorescent antibody test kits become available for more species, the level of detection in foods will increase. Gene probes and genetic tests based on the polymerase chain reaction may increase the sensitivity of parasite detection to that available for other microbial pathogens.

42.5   REFERENCES

1. Ameel, D. J. 1934. Paragonimus, its life history and distribution in North America and its taxonomy (Trematoda: Troglotrematidae). Am. J. Hyg. 19: 279.
2. Ash, L. R. 1970. Diagnostic morphology of the third-stage larvae of *Angiostrongylus cantonensis*, *Angiostrongylus vasorum*, *Aeluorostrongylus abstrusus* and *Anafilaroides rostratus* (Nematoda: Metastrongyloidae). J. Parasitol. 56: 249.
3. Ash, L. R. and Orihel, T. C. 1987. "Parasites: A Guide to Laboratory Procedures and Identification." Am. Soc. of Clinical Pathology, Chicago, Ill.
4. Beaver, P. C., Jung, R. C., and Cupp, E. W. 1984. "Clinical parasitology." Lea and Febiger, Philadelphia, Penn.
5. Bhabulaya, M. 1982. Angiostrongylosis. In "Handbook Series on Zoonoses, Section C: Parasitic Zoonoses," ed. M. G. Shultz, Vol. II, p. 25. CRC Press, Boca Raton, Fla.
6. Bier, J. W., Jackson, G. J., Sellers, R. L., and Rude, R. A. 1984. Parasitic animals in foods. In "FDA Bacteriological Analytical Manual," 6th ed., p. 21.01. Assn. Off. Anal. Chem., Arlington, Va.
7. Bier, J. W. 1988. Anisakiasis. In "Laboratory Diagnosis of Infectious Diseases—Principles and Practice," eds. W. Balows, W. J. Hausler, Jr., and E. H. Lennette, p. 768. Springer-Verlag, New York.
8. Brattey, J. 1988. A simple technique for recovering larval ascaridoid nematodes from the flesh of marine fish. J. Parasitol. 74: 735.
9. Byland, B. G. 1982. Diphyllobothrium. In "Handbook Series on Zoonoses, Section C: Parasitic Zoonoses, ed. M. G. Schultz, Vol. II, p. 217. CRC Press, Boca Raton, Fla.
10. Cheng, T. C. 1982. Anisakiasis. In "Handbook Series on Zoonoses, Section C: Parasitic Zoonoses," ed. M. G. Schultz, Vol. II, p. 37. CRC Press, Boca Raton, Fla.
11. Campbell, B. G. and Little, M. D. 1988. The finding of *Angiostrongylus cantonensis* in rats in New Orleans, Louisiana, USA. Am. J. Trop. Med. Hyg. 38: 568.
12. CDC. 1981. Diphyllobothriasis associated with salmon—United States. Morbid. Mortal. Weekly Rep. 30: 331.
13. CFR. 1987. Code of Fed. Regs., Title 9—Animals and Animal Products, Chapter III, 311.23, p. 142. U.S. Govt. Print. Office, Washington, D.C.
14. CFR. 1987. Code of Fed. Regs., Title 9—Animals and Animal Products, Chapter III, 311.24, p. 142. U.S. Govt. Print. Office, Washington, D.C.
15. CFR. 1987. Code of Fed. Regs., Title 9—Animals and Animal Products, Chapter III, 318.10, p. 207. U.S. Govt. Print. Office, Washington, D.C.
16. Dorta Contreras, A. J., Ferra Valdes, M., Plana Bouly, R., Diaz Martinez, A. G., Gonzalez Garcia, N., Escoba R. Perez, X. 1987. Eosinophilic meningoencephalitis caused by *Angiostrongylus cantonensis*. Chen, 1935; immunological study. Rev. Esp. Pediatr. 43: 379.
17. Dubey, J. P. and Beattie, C. P. 1988. "Toxoplasmosis of animals and man." CRC Press, Boca Raton, Fla.
18. Eastburn, R. L., Fritsche, T. R., and Terhune, C. A. 1987. Human intestinal infection with *Nanophyetus salmincola* from salmonid fishes. Am. J. Trop. Med. Hyg. 36: 586.
19. EEC. 1977. Commission directive 77/96/EEC. Off. J. Eur. Communities 26: 67.
20. EEC. 1984. Commission directive 84/319/EEC. Off. J. Eur. Communities 167: 34.
21. Fayer, R. and Dubey, J. P. 1985. Methods for controlling transmission of protozoan parasites from meat to man. Food Technol. 39(3): 57.

22. Fayer, R. and Ungar, B. L. P. 1986. *Cryptosporidium* and cryptosporidiosis. Microbiol. Rev. 50: 458.

23. Freeman, R. S., Stuart, P. F., Cullen, J. B., Ritchie, A. C., Mildon A., Fernandes, B. J., and Bonin, R. 1976. Fatal human infection with mesocercariae of the trematode *Alaria americana*. Am. J. Trop. Med. Hyg. 25: 803.

24. Gamble, H. R., Anderson, W. R., Graham, C. E., and Murrell, K. D. 1983. Serodiagnosis of swine trichinosis using an excretory-secretory antigen. Vet. Parasitol. 13: 349.

25. Gamble, H. R., and Murrell, K. D. 1988. *Trichinellosis*. In "Laboratory Diagnosis of Infectious Diseases—Principles and Practice," eds. W. Balows, W. J. Hausler, Jr., and E. H. Lennette. p. 1017. Springer-Verlag, New York.

26. Gardiner, C. H., Fayer, R., and Dubey, J. P. 1988. "An Atlas of Protozoan Parasites in Tissues." U.S. Govt. Print. Off., Washington, D.C.

27. Gebhart, G. A., Milleman, R. E., Knapp, S. E., and Wyberg, P. A. 1966. "Salmon poisoning" diseases second intermediate host susceptibility. J. Parasitol. 52: 54.

28. Higashi, G. I. 1985. Foodborne parasites transmitted to man from fish and aquatic foods. Food Technol. 39(3): 69.

29. Jackson, G. J., Bier, J. W., Payne, W. L., and McClure, F. D. 1981. Recovery of parasitic nematodes from fish by digestion or elution. Appl. Environ. Microbiol. 41: 912.

30. Kohler, G. and Ruitenberg, E. J. 1974. Comparison of three methods for the detection of *Trichinella spiralis* infections in pigs by five European laboratories. Bull. W. H. O. 50: 413.

31. Lee, J. J., Hutner, S. H., and Bovee, E. C. 1985. "An Illustrated Guide to the Protozoa." Soc. of Protozoologists, Lawrence, Kans.

32. Lushbaugh, W. B. and Pittman, F. E. 1982. Amebiasis. In "Handbook Series on Zoonoses, Section C: Parasitic Zoonoses," ed. L. Jacobs and P. Arambulo, Vol. II, p. 5. CRC Press, Boca Raton, Fla.

33. Meyer, E. A. and Jarroll, E. L. 1982. Giardiasis, In "Handbook Series on Zoonoses, Section C: Parasitic Zoonoses," eds. L. Jacobs and P. Arambulo, Vol. II, p. 25. CRC Press, Boca Raton, Fla.

34. Morera, P. 1973. Life history and redescription of *Angiostrongylus costaricensis* Morera and Despedes 1971. Am. J. Trop. Med. Hyg. 22: 613.

35. Musial, C. E., Arrowood, M. J., Sterling, C. R., and Gerba, C. P. 1987. Detection of *Cryptosporidium* in water by using polypropylene cartridge filters. Appl. Environ. Microbiol. 53: 687.

36. Myers, B. J. 1975. The nematodes that cause anisakiasis. J. Milk Food Technol. 38: 774.

37. Nakhforoosh, M. and Rose, J. B. 1989. Detection of *Giardia* with a gene probe. Abstracts of the 89th Annual Meeting of the Amer. Soc. for Microbiol., p. 239. Washington, D.C.

38. Ongerth, J. E. and Stibbs, H. H. 1987. Identification of *Cryptosporidium* oocysts in river water. Appl. Environ. Microbiol. 53: 672.

39. Pawlowski, Z. S. 1982. Taeniasis and cysticercosis. In "Handbook Series on Zoonoses, Section C: Parasitic Zoonoses," eds. L. Jacobs and P. Arambulo, Vol. II, p. 313. CRC Press, Boca Raton, Fla.

40. Pritchard, M. H. and Kruse, G. O. W. 1982. The collection and preservation of animal parasites. Tech. Bull. No. 1. U. of Nebraska Press, Lincoln, Neb.

41. Rose, J. B. 1988. Occurrence and significance of *Cryptosporidium* in water. J. Am. Water Works Assn. 80: 53.

42. Shirazian, D., Schiller, E. L., Glasser, C. A., and Vonderfecht, S. L. 1984. Pathology of larval *Eustrongylides* in the rabbit. J. Parasitol. 70: 803.

43. Stern, J. A., Chakravarti, D., Uzmann, J. R., and Hesselhold, M. N. 1958. Rapid counting of Nematoda in salmon by pepsin digestion. U.S. Fish and Wildlife Special Scientific Report No. 25S, p. 1.

44. Studds, G. E. and Young, D. 1989. H. R. 2511: 1–8. 101st Cong., 1st sess, Washington, D.C.

45. Valdimasson, G., Einarsson, H., and King, F. J. 1985. Detection of parasites in fish muscle by candling techniques. J. Assoc. Off. Anal. Chem. 68: 549.
46. Walzer, P. D. and Healy, G. R. 1982. Balantidiasis. In "Handbook Series on Zoonoses, Section C: Parasitic Zoonoses," eds. L. Jacobs and P. Arambulo, Vol. II, p. 15. CRC Press, Boca Raton, Fla.
47. Yamaguchi, T. 1981. "Color Atlas of Clinical Parasitology." Wolfe Medical Pub., London, England.
48. Yokogawa, S., Court, W. W., and Yokogawa, M. 1960. *Paragonimus* and paragonimiasis. Exp. Parasitol. 10: 81.
49. Zaman, V. 1980. "Atlas of Medical Parasitology." Lea and Febiger, Philadelphia, Penn.

Chapter 43

TOXIGENIC FUNGI AND FUNGAL TOXINS

Michael B. Liewen and Lloyd B. Bullerman

43.1 INTRODUCTION

The beneficial effects of molds have been known for years. Molds have not only served to synthesize antibiotics but also to produce some foods. Fermented foods such as some cheeses, soy sauce, miso, tempeh, and other Oriental delicacies are all prepared with the help of molds. However, it is also well documented that some molds produce toxic substances. Toxins produced in foods by molds have caused problems for as long as foods have been harvested and stored, but it is only since the discovery of aflatoxins in 1960 that the study of mycotoxins in general has become widespread. Since then many common molds have been shown to produce substances toxic to humans and animals, especially under laboratory conditions. After Sargeant et al.[20] first reported that aflatoxin was produced in peanuts by *Aspergillus flavus*, numerous investigators directed their interest toward finding other toxigenic molds. Stoloff[23] has summarized toxins produced by various strains of molds.

43.2 MYCOTOXICOSES

The effects of mycotoxins on human health have not been well documented. Numerous cases of poisoning from consumption of moldy bread from 1826 to 1888, an 1843 incident caused by moldy army rations in Paris, an 1878 poisoning attributed to moldy pudding, and numerous deaths in the period 1906 to 1909 from eating moldy corn meal are reported in the literature.[7, 23] Toxins produced by fungi in the genera *Claviceps* and *Fusarium* produce the human diseases ergotism and alimentary toxic aleukia, respectively. These two diseases have been well documented and described in detail because large numbers of people contracted them and their effects could be readily observed.

It has been known for centuries that ergotism results in gangrene and hallucinations and is often fatal.[3] Alimentary toxic aleukia has only recently been described in detail.[14]

Recent mycotoxin problems have come to our attention because of outbreaks of animal diseases that showed a mycotoxin as the causative agent. The classic example is "Turkey X" disease, which occurred in the early 1960s. Toxic peanut meal being used in turkey rations killed thousands of young turkeys. Sargeant et al.[20] reported the causative factor to be a toxic material produced by *A. flavus*, and they named the substance aflatoxin. Other mycotoxins found in foods or feeds with some frequency include deoxynivalenol (vomitoxin), T-2 toxin, ochratoxin, patulin, penicillic acid, and zearalenone.[7] The incidence and levels of these toxins that have been encountered in foods in the United States are very low, and most of the time are not a cause for concern. Animal feeds, on the other hand, are believed to have a higher incidence of low-level contamination. Table 1 summarizes the occurrence of potentially toxic molds and their possible toxins in various foods and agricultural commodities.

While most mycotoxins are highly toxic to many experimental animals, it is obviously impossible to experimentally determine their effects on humans. In animals there is considerable variation in the disease processes by various mycotoxins. The principal toxic effects of some mycotoxins produced by aspergilli penicillia, fusaria, and molds in several other genera are summarized by Bullerman[7] and Marth and Calanog.[16] The diseases caused by mycotoxins take various forms, although the liver and kidneys are most often damaged.

The effects of chronic exposure to mycotoxins on human health are unclear.[21, 22] Several investigators[8, 19, 25] have reported unusually frequent occurrences of primary liver carcinoma in certain African and Asiatic countries. It has been postulated that these and other liver disorders are associated with consumption of moldy grains.

Safe levels have not been established for humans or for animals. In the case of animals there is more evidence that chronic exposure to low levels of mycotoxins has detrimental effects. Broilers and turkeys exposed to low levels of mycotoxins have lower feed efficiencies and are more susceptible to infectious diseases. It is now thought, for example, that levels of aflatoxin as low as 14 ppb may have deleterious effects in poultry.[7]

43.3 MYCOTOXINS

Development and validation of the necessary chemical methods for determining the presence and level of mycotoxins is an undertaking of international scope. Coordination is achieved through a Joint Mycotoxin Committee representing the Association of Official Analytical Chemists (AOAC), the American Oil Chemists' Society (AOCS), the American Association of Cereal Chemists (AACC), and the International Union of Pure and Applied Chem-

Table 1—Summary of Selected Reports of Isolations of Potentially Toxic Molds from Various Food or Agricultural Commodities (Bullerman[7]).

Commodity	Potentially toxic genera/species found		Potential mycotoxins
Wheat, flour, bread, cornmeal, popcorn	*Aspergillus* *flavus* *ochraceus* *versicolor* *Cladosporium* *Fusarium*	*Penicillium* *citrinum,* *citreo-viride,* *cyclopium,* *martensii* *patulum,* *puberulum*	Aflatoxin, ochratoxin, sterigmatocystin, patulin, penicillic acid, deoxynivalenol, zearalenone
Peanut, in-shell pecans	*Aspergillus* *flavus* *parasiticus* *ochraceus* *versicolor* *Fusarium, Rhizopus, Chaetomium*	*Penicillium* *cyclopium* *expansum* *citrinum*	Aflatoxins, ochratoxin, patulin, sterigmatocystin
Apples and apple products	*Penicillium expansum*		Patulin
Meat pies, cooked meats, cocoa powder, hops, cheese	*Aspergillus* *flavus* *Cladosporium*	*Penicillium* *viridicatum* *roqueforti* *patulum* *commune*	Aflatoxins, ochratoxin, patulin, penicillic acid
Aged salami and sausage, country cured ham, moldy meats, cheese	*Aspergillus* *flavus* *ochraceus* *versicolor*	*Penicillium* *viridicatum* *cyclopium*	Aflatoxins, ochratoxin, patulin, penicillic acid, sterigmatocystin
Black and red pepper, macaroni	*Aspergillus* *flavus* *ochraceus*	*Pencillium* species	Aflatoxins, ochratoxin
Dry beans, soybeans, corn, sorghum, barley	*Aspergillus* *flavus* *ochraceus* *versicolor* *Alternaria,* *Cladosporium*	*Penicillium* *cyclopium* *viridicatum* *citrinum* *expansum* *islandicum* *urticae*	Aflatoxins, ochratoxin, sterigmatocystin, penicillic acid, patulin, citrinin, griseofulvin alternariol, altenuene, altertoxin

Table 1—Summary of Selected Reports of Isolations of Potentially Toxic Molds from Various Food or Agricultural Commodities (Bullerman[7]). (continued)

Commodity	Potentially toxic genera/species found		Potential mycotoxins
Refrigerated and frozen pastries	*Aspergillus flavus versicolor*	*Penicillium cyclopium citrinum martensii olivino-viride palitans puberulum roqueforti urticae viridicatum*	Aflatoxins, sterigmatocystin, ochratoxin, citrinin, patulin, penicillic acid
Moldy supermarket foods	*Penicillium cyclopium Fusarium oxysporum solani*	*Aspergillus species*	Penicillic acid, possibly other *Penicillium* toxins, T-2 toxin
Foods stored in homes, both refrigerated and non-refrigerated	*Penicillium* species	*Aspergillus species*	Aflatoxin, kojic acid, ochratoxin A, patulin, penicillic acid

istry (IUPAC). All the methods validated to date under the aegis of the Joint Mycotoxin Committee have been adopted by the AOAC and published in Chapter 26 of the "Official Methods of Analysis."[24] (Chapter 26 is also available in a separate paperback titled *Mycotoxin Methods*.) The AOCS[26] and AACC[1] have each included methods related to their specific activities in their compendia of official methods. IUPAC[26] has recommended a number of the methods, and these various adoptions are noted for each method in the separate AOAC *Mycotoxin Methods*.

43.4 MICROBIOLOGY

Mold contamination of raw farm commodities is not completely preventable. Thus it becomes desirable to determine the extent of contamination and to do so we must have methods for detecting and enumerating the molds capable of producing the various mycotoxins, i.e., the "toxigenic fungi." Further, there are situations where it may be more feasible and convenient to test for the toxigenic fungus than for the mycotoxin itself. The presence of toxigenic fungi can be used as a means of assessing the quality and acceptability of a commodity before actual toxin production has occurred. An awareness of the types of molds present in a food or feed can be an early indicator of the types of mycotoxins that could be encountered.

Unfortunately, media selective for specific fungi are not yet widely available. Compared to the development of selective media for specific spoilage and pathogenic bacteria, development of selective media for toxigenic fungi is only just beginning. However, several media are available for the detection of certain toxigenic fungi.[15] These include media for *A. flavus*, *A. parsiticus*, and *Penicillium viridicatum*.

Bell and Crawford[4] first developed a medium designed to isolate *A. flavus* from peanuts. The medium contained rose bengal, dichloran, and streptomycin. Bothast and Fennell[6] developed the next medium, called *Aspergillus* differential medium (ADM). It contained 1.0% yeast extract, 1.5% tryptone, and 0.05% ferric acid and required incubation at 28°C for 3 days. On this medium *A. flavus* and *A. parasiticus* form insoluble bright orange-yellow pigments on the colony reverse, an easily recognized phenomenon.

Hamsa and Ayres[12] modified ADM by adding streptomycin and dichloran and incubating at 28°C for 5 days. Later Assante et al.[2] showed that the orange-yellow pigment formation was due to reaction of ferric ions from the ferric citrate with aspergillic acid molecules forming a colored complex of three aspergillic acid molecules with ferric ions. Pitt et al.[18] further modified these media and developed a medium called *Aspergillus flavus-parasiticus* agar or AFPA. Incubation of AFPA is done at 30°C for 42 to 48 hr, resulting in sufficient color development to recognize *A. flavus* and *A. parasiticus* before the development of the typical olive green spores (conidia).

Pitt et al.[18] report that few other mold species produce the orange-yellow color reaction on AFPA. Occasional false positives can be obtained with some strains of *A. niger* and *A. ochraceus*. Questionable species can readily be distinguished with an additional incubation of 24 to 48 hr. *Penicillium* species apparently do not give false positives and only a few (2.9%) *A. flavus* and *A. parasiticus* isolates gave false negatives.[18] AFPA has been recommended for detection of *A. flavus* and *A. parasiticus* in spices, nuts, peanuts, oilseeds, grains, corn meal, cowpeas and livestock feeds.[5, 13]

Frisvad[9-11] has reported a selective medium for detecting nephrotoxin-producing strains of *P. viridicatum* and related species. The medium consists of yeast-extract sucrose (YES) agar, as the basal medium, supplemented with chloramphenicol (50 mg/L), chlortetracycline (50 mg/L), pentachloronitrobenzene (100 mg/L), and rose bengal (25 mg/L). This medium, referred to as PRYES agar, reportedly distinguishes between producers of ochratoxin A and citrinin and producers of xanthomegnin and viomellein. The ochratoxin A- and citrinin-producing strains of *P. viridicatum* are said to be consistently indicated by a violet brown pigment produced on the colony reverse. The xanthomegnin- and viomellein-producing strains of *P. viridicatum* and *P. aurantiogriseum* (*P. cyclopium*) are indicated by a yellow reverse and obverse.[11]

Several attempts have been made to develop selective media for the so-called field fungi such as *Fusarium*. So far these have not been successful and efforts to develop selective media for fusaria are continuing.

Other considerations for the detection of toxigenic fungi include such things as direct vs. dilution plating and adjustment of the water activity of media. For the detection of mycotoxic fungi in stored grains or seeds, direct plating of surface sanitized kernels may be preferable to grinding the sample and using dilution plating. The direct plating method permits the detection of internal mycoflora, which may be of greater concern. The direct plating method is described and has been reported to be more efficient than the dilution plating method for detecting individual mold species.[17] Combining this technique with a selective medium such as AFPA or PRYES could provide an additional technique for detecting toxigenic species. While most known toxigenic species will grow on media of unadjusted water activity (a_w), it may occasionally be desirable to reduce the a_w of a medium. The most common way of doing so is to add 7.5% NaCl to a common culture medium. The a_w can also be lowered by adding increased concentrations of sucrose (20%) or glucose (40%), or with glycerol.

43.5 EQUIPMENT, MATERIAL, AND REAGENTS

For the dilution plating technique, preparation of the sample is essentially the same as for the aerobic plate count (Chapter 4). For direct plating of foods additional equipment will be required. The direct plating technique can be applied to intact particles and whole foods such as grain kernels, seeds, dried beans, nuts, coffee beans, cocoa beans, and whole spices.[17] Before plating, samples should be held in a freezer for 72 hr ($-20°C$) to kill insects and mites and their eggs.

43.6 PRECAUTIONS

Foods containing toxigenic mold species may also contain mycotoxins. Samples should be handled accordingly. Some toxigenic mold species are also potential pathogens to humans and have spores that are allergenic. Also spores of *A. flavus* and *A. parasiticus* have been shown to contain low levels of aflatoxins. Therefore, precautions should be taken to prevent inhalation of airborne spores of aerosolized sample dusts.

43.7 MEDIA AND PROCEDURES

43.71 *Aspergillus flavus-parasiticus* agar (AFPA)

43.72 Pentachloronitrobenzene rose bengal yeast extract sucrose agar (PRYES)

43.8   REVIEWS AND COMPENDIA

In addition to references 7, 16 and 22, see also the following:

Betina, V., ed. 1984. "Mycotoxins. Production, Isolation, Separation and Purification." Elsevier Science Publishing Co., Inc., New York.

Ciegler, A. 1975. Mycotoxins: Occurrence, chemistry, biological activity. Lloydia 38: 21.

Cole, R. J. and Cox, R. H. 1981. "Handbook of Toxic Fungal Metabolites." Academic Press, New York.

Davis, N. D., Dickens, J. W., Freie, R. L., Hamilton, P. B., Shotwell, O. L., Wyllie, T. D., and Fulkerson, J. F. 1980. Protocols for surveys, sampling, post-collection handling, and analysis of grain samples involved in mycotoxin problems. J. Assoc. Off. Anal. chem. 63: 95.

Goldblatt, L. A., ed. 1969. "Aflatoxin." Academic Press, New York.

Healthcote, J. G. and Hibbert, J. R., eds. 1978. "Aflatoxins: Chemical and Biological Aspects." Elsevier Scientific Publ. Co., Amsterdam, The Netherlands.

IARC. 1976. "IARC Monographs on the Evaluation of Carcinogenic Risk of Chemicals to Man: Some naturally occurring substances," Vol. 10. Internat. Agency for Research on Cancer, Lyon, France.

IARC. 1982. "Environmental Carcinogens, Selected Methods of Analysis," Vol. 5. Analysis of Mycotoxins in Foods, IARC Sci. Publ. 44. Internat. Agency for Research on Cancer, Lyon, France.

Jemmali, M., ed. 1977. Les Mycotoxines dans l'Alimentation. Arch Inst. Pasteur Tunis (Special edition) Vol. 54(3–4).

Krogh, P., ed. 1973. "Control of Mycotoxins." Butterworths, London, England. Also in Pure Appl. Chem. 35(3).

Kurata, H. and Ueno, Y., eds. 1984. "Toxigenic Fungi. Their Toxins and Health Hazard." Developments in Food Science 7. Elsevier Science Publishing Co. Inc., New York.

Marasas, W. F. O., Nelson, P. E., and Toussoun, T. A. 1984. "Toxigenic *Fusarium* species. Identity and Mycotoxicology." The Pennsylvania State U. Press, University Park, Penn.

Marasas, W. F. O. and Nelson, P. E. 1987. "Mycotoxicology." The Pennsylvania State U. Press, University Park, Penn.

Moreau, C. 1979. "Moulds, Toxins and Food." (English trans. with additions by M. Moss). John Wiley and Sons, Chichester, England.

NRC. 1979. "Interactions of Mycotoxins in Animal Production." Nat. Res. Counc., Natl. Acad. of Sciences, Washington, D.C.

Nesheim, S. 1979. Method of aflatoxin analysis. In "Trace Organic Analysis: A New Frontier in Analytical Chemistry." National Bureau of Standards Special Pub. 519, p. 355. Natl. Bur. of Standards, Gaithersburg, Md.

Pitt, J. I. and Hocking, A. D. 1985. "Fungi and Food Spoilage." Academic Press, New York.

Pohland, A. E. and Thorpe, C. W. 1982. Mycotoxins. In "Handbook of Carcinogens and Hazardous Substances, Chemical and Trace Analysis," ed. M. C. Bowman. Marcel Dekker, Inc., New York.

Purchase, I. F. H., ed. 1971. "Mycotoxins in Human Health." Macmillan Press, London, England.

Purchase, I. F. H., ed. 1974. "Mycotoxins." Elsevier Scientific Publ. Co., Amsterdam, The Netherlands.

Rodricks, J. V., ed. 1976. "Mycotoxins and Other Fungal Related Food Problems." Advances in Chemistry Series No. 149. Amer. Chem. Soc., Washington, D.C.

Rodricks, J. V., Hesseltine, C. W., and Mehlman, M. A., eds. 1977. "Mycotoxins in Human and Animal Health." Pathotox Publishers, Inc., Park Forest South, Ill.

Schuller, P. L., Horwitz, W., and Stoloff, L. 1976. A review of sampling plans and collaboratively studied methods of analysis for aflatoxins. J. Assoc. Off. Anal. Chem. 59: 1315.

Smith, J. E. and Moss, M. O. 1985. "Mycotoxins. Formation, Analysis and Significance." John Wiley & Sons. New York.

Stoloff, L. 1979. The eras of fungal toxin research. J. Am. Oil Chem. Soc. 56: 784.

Stoloff, L. 1980. Aflatoxin control: Past and present. J. Assn. Off. Anal. Chem. 63: 1067.

Ueno, Y., ed. 1983. "Trichothecenes. Chemical, Biological and Toxicological Aspects." Developments in Food Science 4. Elsevier Science Publishing Co., Inc., New York.

Uraguchi, K. and Yamazoki, M. 1978. "Toxicology. Biochemistry and Pathology of Mycotoxins." John Wiley & Sons, New York, and Kodansha Ltd, Tokyo, Japan.

Wyllie, T. D. and Morehouse, L. G., eds. 1977. "Mycotoxic Fungi, Mycotoxins, Mycotoxicoses," Vol. 1. Mycotoxic fungi and chemistry of mycotoxins. Marcel Dekker, New York.

Wyllie, T. D. and Morehouse, L. G., eds. 1978a. "Mycotoxic Fungi, Mycotoxins, Mycotoxicoses," Vol. 2. Mycotoxicoses of domestic and laboratory animals, poultry, and aquatic invertebrates and vertebrates, Marcel Dekker, New York.

Wyllie, T. D. and Morehouse, L. G., eds. 1978b. "Mycotoxic Fungi, Mycotoxins, Mycotoxicoses," Vol. 3. Mycotoxicoses of man and plants: Mycotoxin control and regulatory aspects. Marcel Dekker, New York.

43.9 REFERENCES

1. AACC. 1983. "Approved Methods." Amer. Assn. of Cereal Chem., St. Paul, Minn.
2. Assante, G., Camarda, L., Locci, R., Merlilni, L., Nasini, G., and Papadopoulus, E. 1981. Isolation and structure of red pigments from *Aspergillus flavus* and related species grown on differential medium. J. Ag. Food Chem. 29: 785.
3. Barger, G. 1931. "Ergot and Ergotism." Gurney and Jackson, London, England.

4. Bell, D. K. and Crawford, J. L. 1967. A Botran-amended medium for isolating *Aspergillus flavus* from peanuts and soil. Phytopathology 57: 939.
5. Beuchat, L. R. 1986. Evaluation of media for simultaneously enumerating total fungi and *Aspergillus flavus* and *A. parasiticus* in peanuts, corn meal and cowpeas. In "Methods for the Mycological Examination of Food," eds. A. D. King, J. I. Pitt, L. R. Beauchat, and J. E. L. Corry, p. 129. Plenum Press, New York.
6. Bothast, R. J. and Fennell, D. I. 1974. A medium for rapid identification and enumeration of *Aspergillus flavus* and related organisms. Mycologia 66: 365.
7. Bullerman, L. B. 1979. Significance of mycotoxins to food safety and human health. J. Food Prot. 42: 65.
8. Detroy, R. W., Lillehoj, E. B., and Ciegler, A. 1971. Aflatoxin and related compounds. In "Microbial Toxins," ed. A. Ciegler, S. Kadis, and S. J. Ajl, Vol. 6, p. 3. Academic Press, New York.
9. Frisvad, J. C. 1981. Physiological criteria and mycotoxin production as aids in identification of common asymmetric penicillia. Appl. Environ. Microbiol. 41: 568.
10. Frisvad, J. C. 1983. A selective and indicative medium for groups of *Penicillium viridicatum* producing different mycotoxins in cereals. J. Appl. Bacteriol. 54: 409.
11. Frisvad, J. C. 1986. Selective medium for *Penicillium viridicatum* in cereals. In "Methods for the Mycological Examination of Food," eds. A. D. King, J. I. Pitt, L. R. Beauchat, and J. E. L. Corry, p. 132. Plenum Press, New York.
12. Hamsa, T. A. P. and Ayres, J. C. 1977. A differential medium for the isolation of *Aspergillus flavus* from cottonseed. J. Food. Sci. 42: 449.
13. Hocking, A. D. and Pitt, J. I. 1986. A selective medium for rapid detection of *Aspergillus flavus*. In "Methods for the Mycological Examination of Food," eds. A. D. King, J. I. Pitt, L. R. Beauchat, and J. E. L. Corry, p. 127. Plenum Press, New York.
14. Joffee, A. Z. 1971. Alimentary toxic aleukia. In "Microbial Toxins," Vol. 7. Algal and fungal toxins. eds. S. Kadis, A. Ciegler, and S. J. Ajl, p. 139. Academic Press, New York.
15. King, A. D., Pitt, J. I., Beuchat, L. R., and Corry, J. E. L. eds. 1986. "Methods for the Mycological Examination of Food." p. 300. Plenum Press, New York
16. Marth, E. H. and Calanog, B. G. 1976. Toxigenic Fungi. Chapter 7. In "Food Microbiology: Public Health and Spoilage Aspects," eds. M. A. DeFigueiredo and D. F. Splittstoesser, p. 210. AVI Publ. Company, Westport, Conn.
17. Mislivec, P. B. and Stack, M. E. 1984. Enumeration of yeasts and molds and production of toxins. Chapter 19. In "Food and Drug Administration. Bacteriological Analytical Manual." 6th ed. Assn. of Off. Analyt. Chem. Arlington, Va.
18. Pitt, J. I., Hocking, A. D., and Glenn, D. K. 1983. An improved medium for the detection of *Aspergillus flavus* and *A. parasiticus*. J. Appl. Bacteriol. 54: 109.
19. Purchase, I. F. H. and Vorster, L. J. 1968. Aflatoxin in commercial milk samples. S. African Med. J. 42: 219.
20. Sargeant, K., Sheridan, A., O'Kelly, J., and Carnaghan, R. B. A. 1961. Toxicology associated with certain samples of groundnuts. Nature 192: 1096.
21. Stoloff, L. 1976. Incidence, distribution and disposition of products containing aflatoxins. Proc. Am. Phytopathol. Soc. 3: 156.
22. Stoloff, L. 1983. Aflatoxin as a cause of primary liver-cell cancer in the United States: A probability study. Nutr. Cancer 5: 165.
23. Stoloff, L. 1984. Toxigenic fungi. Chapter 41. In "Compendium of Methods for the Microbiological Examination of Foods," 2nd ed., eds. M. L. Speck. Amer. Pub. Health Assn., Washington, D.C.
24. Stoloff, L. and Scott, P. M., eds. 1984. Natural Poisons. Chapter 26. In "Official Methods of Analysis," 14th ed., p. 477 Assn. Off. Analyt. Chem.
25. Taber, R. A. and Schroeder, H. W. 1967. Aflatoxin-producing potential of isolates of *A. flavus-oryzae* group from peanuts (*Arachis hypogaea*). Appl. Microbiol. 15: 140.
26. Walker, R. O., ed. 1978. "Official and Tentative Methods," 3rd ed. Amer. Oil Chem. Soc., Champaign, Ill.

Chapter 44

MEAT AND POULTRY PRODUCTS

Ralph W. Johnston and R. B. Tompkin

44.1 INTRODUCTION

Raw red meats and poultry are derived from warm-blooded animals. Their microbial flora is heterogeneous and consists of mesophilic and psychrotrophic bacteria from the animal itself, soil and water bacteria from their environment, and bacterial species introduced by man and equipment during processing.[15,17,18]

The surface flora on freshly slaughtered carcasses, usually about 10^2 to 10^4 bacteria per square inch, is primarily mesophilic, having originated from the alimentary tract and external surfaces of the live animal. Contamination from the slaughtering environment is also largely mesophilic in nature since this process occurs in rooms ambient in the summer and heated in the winter. Psychrotrophic organisms originating from soil and water are present but usually only to about 10^1 per square inch. The mesophiles are important because they indicate the degree of sanitation during the slaughtering process.

The existence of viable bacteria within the deep tissues of freshly slaughtered livestock has been a debated issue.[12,23] The development of sour rounds of beef during slow chilling and spoilage near the bone of improperly processed country hams suggest that viable bacteria can be present within the deep tissue of freshly slaughtered carcasses.

When red meats and poultry are cooked and subsequently refrigerated to deter spoilage, the bacteria on the raw tissue are greatly reduced, leaving only sporeformers and, occasionally, small numbers of thermodurics, notably the enterococci, micrococci, and some lactobacilli. Because the post-processing environment is frequently refrigerated, a low-level recontamination with psychrotrophic bacteria almost always occurs. The psychrotrophs are important because they increase in numbers even though the products are stored at proper refrigeration temperatures. They ultimately cause spoilage and thus determine the shelf life of the product. There is also growing concern about the growth of psychrotrophic pathogens, such as *Listeria monocytogenes* and *Yersinia enterocolitica* in refrigerated cooked products.

The level of coliforms has been commonly used as an indicator for hygienic conditions and the microbiological quality of meat and poultry products. For example, the presence of coliforms on the surface of properly cooked products indicates post-process contamination. However, as cooked products are subsequently held in storage, the interpretation of coliform data changes because the natural flora of meat and poultry plants includes certain psychrotrophic coliforms that can multiply at refrigeration temperatures (e.g., 2° to 5°C).[5,6,16,24,28,32] Some contamination of cooked products will occur between cooking and packaging. Since multiplication of the psychrotrophic coliforms will occur during refrigerated storage, the coliform results lose their significance as an indicator of the hygienic conditions existing during production. This is also one, among several, reasons why coliform values are not an effective indicator of the safety of refrigerated meat and poultry products.

Numerous factors influence the type of microbial spoilage occurring in fresh and processed meats and poultry products. These factors include the inherent pH of the meat; the addition of salt, nitrite, sugar, smoke (liquid or natural), or acidulants; and the state of the meat (heated, fermented, or dried). After processing, the type and rate of spoilage are influenced by the type of packaging, temperature of storage, final composition of the product, and surviving or contaminating microorganisms. The same basic principles apply equally to red meat and poultry products.

Historically, products evolved as attempts were made to prolong the quality of meat and poultry for future use and to add variety to the diet. This process has led to a wider variety of products than exists for most other commodities. In the following, meat and poultry products are categorized as to whether they are raw or ready-to-eat and then nonsalted, salted, or salted and cured. The term "cured" is used only when nitrite or nitrate is added to the products.

This chapter will address meat and poultry products commercially prepared under federal inspection and distributed to retail stores or for use in food service establishments. Products produced under state inspection or in food service establishments, retail outlets, or homes or on the farm may also be encountered by the analyst. Approximate microbial levels are mentioned throughout the text to introduce the reader to the subject. More specific information on microbial populations and microbial criteria is available[17–19,27] The normal flora, spoilage flora, and microorganisms of public health concern will be discussed within each product category.

44.2 RAW MEAT AND POULTRY PRODUCTS

44.21 Fresh Meat and Poultry

The predominant flora on freshly slaughtered carcasses is mesophilic in nature and cannot multiply at the temperatures used for carcass chilling and holding. During refrigerated holding, the carcass flora begins to shift toward psychrotrophs of the *Pseudomonas-Acinetobacter-Moraxella* group. Growth of this group of organisms eventually spoils the meat.[4] Usually, carcasses are cut into smaller portions in refrigerated work rooms. Since most bacteria on processing equipment in refrigerated rooms are psychrotrophic in nature, this fact further assures the presence of these bacteria on the meat surfaces.

Spoilage of whole cuts of meat or poultry at refrigeration temperatures is primarily a surface phenomenon resulting in formation of slime and off-odor. Spoilage of fresh meats at refrigeration temperatures is primarily a problem of aesthetics, product quality, and economics. The shelf life of raw chilled meat and poultry is prolonged by those factors affecting the growth rate of the psychrotrophs: dry surface, low initial level of psychrotrophs, the inherent pH of the meat, oxygen limitation, and temperature.[9,13] Wrapping meat in oxygen-impermeable films retards surface growth and selects for microaerophilic bacteria like *Lactobacillus* or *Brochothrix thermosphacta* at the expense of the *Pseudomonas-Acinetobacter-Moraxella* group.[11]

The microbial level of chilled meats after transportation and storage at the retail level may have little or no relationship to that at the processor's level because bacterial growth will have continued.

Coliforms, *Escherichia coli*, enterococci, *Campylobacter*, *Staphylococcus aureus*, *Clostridium perfringens*, *Listeria monocytogenes*, and *Salmonella* are often present on fresh tissues because the slaughtering process does not include a bactericidal step. The frequency and levels of these bacteria on freshly slaughtered animal carcasses will vary, depending upon climatic, farm, livestock transport, stockyard, and processing conditions. In general, all of them except *Salmonella*, *Campylobacter*, and *Listeria monocytogenes* may be present at levels of about 10^1 to 10^2. *Salmonella*, if present, usually does not exceed a level of one cell per 25 g of freshly ground meat. A summary of the U.S. and Canadian surveys performed during 1943 to 1977 reported the incidence of salmonellae to be 15% to 16% in fresh pork, 1.9% in ground beef, 0.5% in other fresh beef, and 0.5% in cooked meats.[35] The incidence of salmonellae and *Campylobacter* is higher in fresh poultry than in red meats. *Listeria* has been found in meat, poultry, and the animal environment.

The presence of pathogens in raw meat and poultry is an obvious public health concern. Although efforts are being made to reduce this contamination, none of the currently available procedures can provide pathogen-free raw meat or poultry. Thus, for the foreseeable future, proper handling of raw meat and poultry is essential to prevent foodborne illness from salmonellae, *Campylobacter*, and other indigenous pathogens. These are critical control points to preventing foodborne illness: preventing cross-contamination from the raw products to ready-to-eat foods, using adequate times and temperatures for cooking, avoiding recontamination after cooking by surfaces previously contaminated with the raw meat or poultry, and properly chilling and storing the meat or poultry after cooking.

44.22   Shelf-Stable Raw Salted and Salted-Cured Meats

This category of meat products was of necessity extremely common in the early history of the United States and continued so until home refrigeration procedures became common. Salting of beef, mutton and pork in barrels is no longer practiced in the United States; however, several raw salted products continue to be prepared and sold in large volumes, particularly in regions with predominantly agricultural histories. Salt pork, dry cured bacon, and country-cured hams continue to be produced in volume today. Innumerable variations exist in the processing and spicing of these products, but they center around two basic procedures. Salt pork, salt bacon, and salt hams are prepared by coating the meat with salt only and storing below 10°C in bins during which water is released from the product by the action of the salt. At intervals, the pieces of meat are recoated with salt. At the end of the salting period, the product contains high levels of salt and is racked and held at ambient temperatures until the surface dries. It is then rubbed with a thin coating of salt and spices (where used), netted, and sold. The salt content of these products is sufficiently high that subsequent refrigeration is not necessary. Dry cured hams and bacon frequently sold as country cured are similarly processed except that nitrite and/or nitrate is used with the salt, less salt is used, and the product is hung to dry in ambient temperature rooms for 35 to 140 days before removal and preparation for sale as shelf stable meat.

During the initial refrigerated salt treatment of the two processes, the salt and curing agents penetrate and equilibrate in the tissue. Nonsporeforming bacteria of public health concern are subjected to stress or rendered nonviable. During the subsequent drying period, salt-tolerant micrococci and enterococci grow and appear to render the products even more refractile to the growth of microorganisms of public health concern. The nitrite- or nitrate-cured products must be held in the dry room for a specified period to destroy trichinellae. Although almost all U.S. consumers cook these products before eating them, dry-cured hams have historically been consumed raw in Europe. Since it is likely that a small segment of the population will not cook these products, the trichinellae control requirement is necessary. Additional information on parasites is presented in Chapter 42.

Commercially prepared raw salted and salted-cured meats have an enviable public health record in the United States. Local health officials frequently are concerned about these products being sold at ambient temperatures. However, if the products do not bear the "Keep Refrigerated" label, it is likely that they have already been held at elevated temperatures during drying for 3 to 6 months; thus, the concern is unjustified. It is unlikely that a microbiological analysis of raw salted meats will yield bacteria of public health concern. Bone taint, a type of deep tissue spoilage occurring near the bone, is attributed to improper initial salt equalization.[25] Massive levels of micrococci and enterococci are usually encountered and have been confused with staphylococci when inappropriate methods were used. Mold may develop on these products, particularly during storage in humid conditions. The degree to which mycotoxins constitute a public health problem remains uncertain and continues to be investigated.

44.23 Perishable Raw Salted and Salted-Cured Meat

Fresh pork sausage, fresh turkey sausage, bratwurst, Polish sausage, and Italian sausage are the most commonly encountered perishable raw salted meat products. These products are also sold as perishable cooked products. The method of packaging is the major factor determining the predominant spoilage flora. Fresh sausage sold in bulk form on trays or stuffed into edible casings has a relatively short shelf life (e.g., days). The spoilage flora consists of a variety of psychrotrophs including those of the pseudomonad type. Fresh sausage sold in chub form in oxygen-impermeable films has a longer refrigerated shelf life (e.g., weeks). The restriction of oxygen leads to a predominant flora of lactic-acid-producing bacteria, which impart a tangy flavor.

Large quantities of perishable red meat and poultry products are cured with solutions of nitrite and/or nitrate salts, sodium chloride, and cure accelerators such as sodium ascorbate, sugar, and flavoring materials. More cured meats are now cooked before shipping from processing firms; however, some are sold with little or no heat treatment and must be cooked before eating. At this time there are no raw cured poultry products at the retail or food service level. Examples of some raw cured meats sold in volume include uncooked hams, bacon, and corned beef. When curing salts are applied, the initial microbial content of these products is identical to the microflora of fresh meat. During refrigerated storage, often under vacuum, the predominant normal flora of the raw meat remains constant or decreases as a consequence of the curing ingredients. Psychrotrophic lactic acid bacteria, enterococci, micrococci, and yeasts grow slowly because they are less inhibited by the salt and curing compounds. During cold storage they become the predominant microbial flora of these meats and, in time, will cause the product to spoil.

Some raw cured meats are heated or smoked to different degrees to produce dry surfaces and a smoked flavor; these procedures may extend shelf life. Heat treatments to 54.5°C with or without smoke deposition on surfaces are common for bacon. Both the heat treatment and smoking procedures cause microbial reductions. Following vacuum packaging, psychrotrophic lactic acid bacteria always seem to predominate as the cause of spoilage during cold storage. If bacon is loosely packaged in bulk quantities without vacuum or if leakers occur in vacuum packages, a more heterogeneous flora of bacteria, yeasts, and molds develops and causes spoilage.

Perishable raw salted and salted-cured meats are infrequently associated with foodborne infections or intoxications probably because consumers understand that these products require refrigeration. They are traditionally very well cooked before serving.

44.3   READY-TO-EAT MEAT AND POULTRY PRODUCTS

44.31   Perishable Cooked Uncured Meats

The microbiology of cooked meats begins with the raw materials and the cooking process. Most cooked pork and poultry products are given a thorough cooking so that only spores survive, usually less than a hundred per gram. Beef products are processed at relatively lower temperatures sufficient to destroy nonsporeforming pathogens but not necessarily some of the more thermoduric bacteria such as the enterococci. Internal microbial levels in cooked meats depend on the microbial levels and types before heating, the thermal process, and the subsequent holding-time temperatures. Freshly prepared cooked uncured meats normally have 35°C plate counts of 10^2 or less per gram. During the handling, packaging, or serving of cooked products, some low level of recontamination invariably occurs on the surface of the products from equipment and food handlers. In addition, some cooked products have their surfaces coated with spices, herbs, and other flavorings before final packaging. In recognition of the seriousness of recontamination of cooked meats with bacteria from raw meat, U.S. Department of Agriculture (USDA), state, and local regulations require that certain precautions be followed to assure the separation of cooked from raw meats. Unavoidable contamination usually will add coliforms at levels of 10^1 to 10^2 per gram to the surface of the product. The presence of *E. coli* in these products indicates unsanitary conditions and warrants investigation of the conditions of manufacture to determine the source of *E. coli* and corrective measures. Human contact with cooked food, as in slicing or deboning, invariably adds *S. aureus* at levels of 10^1 or 10^2 to many of the sample units.[33] Such levels are harmless but offer sufficient inoculum for growth to hazardous levels if subsequent conditions of time-temperature abuse occur. Thus, proper refrigeration of salads containing cooked boned meat and poultry is essential to prevent the growth of *S. aureus* and enterotoxin production.

Cooked uncured meat products offer ideal menstrua for microbial growth for they are highly nutritious, have a favorable pH, and are normally lightly salted or not salted at all. Given time and favorable temperatures, contaminants, including pathogens, will grow rapidly. Recognizing this fact, USDA and many state and local regulations require that precooked meat products shall not be held between 4° to 7°C and 60°C except during necessary periods of preparation, heating, or chilling. Many such foods are frozen for shipment and distribution. If the package does not thaw in commerce, the microbial level at retail will relate fairly well to the level shortly after the product was first frozen. Such foods, held too long above the freezing point, will be spoiled by a wide variety of organisms, including enterococci, pseudomonads, lactic acid bacteria, psychrotrophic coliforms, and yeast. The spoilage flora will be influenced by factors such as packaging and the temperature and exposure time after thawing.

Adding uncooked ingredients such as celery, spices, cheese, sauces, or gravies to a cooked meat product changes the microbial composition so that the above estimates do not apply. A full description of formulation and processing procedure is essential for proper interpretation of laboratory data.

Foods in which the level of *S. aureus* or *C. perfringens* has reached 10^6 per gram may cause illness. Cooked uncured meat and poultry products and gravy accounted for 84% of the *C. perfringens* outbreaks from 1969 through 1979 in the United States.[36] The mere presence of salmonellae is potentially hazardous. Botulism rarely has been a problem in commercially uncured precooked meats.

The hazard potential from foods precooked in commercial establishments is high,[26] but the incidence of outbreaks has been low.[39] Meat or poultry was implicated as the vehicle in 54% of all foodborne disease outbreaks in the United States from 1968 to 1977.[7] The level decreased to 33% during 1977 to 1984.[8] In the outbreaks, there was a serious departure from good practices in preparing, holding, and serving these foods in homes, restaurants, and institutions. An exception was salmonellae-contaminated rare roast beef from federally inspected establishments. Since USDA adopted new regulations in 1982, that source of salmonellosis has been corrected.

44.32   Perishable Cooked Cured Meats

Precooked cured meats include franks, bologna, ham, and a wide variety of luncheon meats made from red meats or poultry meats. The heating step in the production of these products destroys the normal raw meat flora except for spores and possibly thermoduric bacteria. During chilling, holding, and packaging, some contamination will occur to exposed surfaces. Salt and nitrite in the meat inhibit the growth of survivors and contaminants somewhat selectively. Upon prolonged refrigeration, lactic acid bacteria, micrococci, enterococci, molds, and yeasts may grow and form slime. When these products are packaged in an oxygen-impermeable package, the spoilage flora at 4.4°C and below consists primarily of lactic acid bacteria.[1,21] The formation of loose or gassy vacuum packages is often due to heterofermentative lactic acid bacteria and occasional yeasts or other psychrotrophs. Products of bacterial action sometimes react with meat pigments to form a green color.[14]

Cooked nonfermented cured meats have counts of 10^3 or less per gram; higher levels in products from retail cases reflect the time-temperature history of storage. Under proper refrigeration, such meats do not support the growth of mesophilic pathogens, so that high aerobic plate counts are unrelated to health hazard. Coliforms, present as unavoidable contaminants at low levels ($\pm 10^1$ per gram), can grow in refrigerated products if the coliforms are psychrotrophic. Human contact may sometimes introduce *E. coli* or *Staphylococcus aureus*.

Cooked cured luncheon meats seldom cause staphylococcal food poisoning because *S. aureus* does not grow as well anaerobically in the presence of salt and nitrite (luncheon meats are usually vacuum packaged). More important, *S. aureus* competes poorly with the lactic acid bacteria that dominate in vacuum-packaged cured meats and will not grow below 6.7°C (luncheon meats are usually well refrigerated).

The Centers for Disease Control reported in 1971 that 18 (45%) of 40 *Straphylococcus* outbreaks for which the vehicle could be found incriminated cured meats, mostly ham, served warm. Contamination of cooked ham during slicing followed by warm temperatures, oxygen, and the selective action of the salt favors staphylococcal growth and enterotoxin production.

Cooked cured meats seldom cause other types of foodborne illness. The heat process destroys salmonellae and other nonsporeforming pathogens. If these products become contaminated after heating, salmonellae survive very well and, if the temperature is favorable, they can multiply. The low incidence and numbers of *Clostridium botulinum* coupled with the presence of nitrite and salt, the growth of lactic acid bacteria, and the prevalence of refrigeration contribute to the control of these bacteria. Similar factors must apply to *C. perfringens*, but there has been very little research in cured meats to confirm this commonly held opinion.

44.33   Canned Cured Meats

44.331   Shelf-stable canned cured meats

Canned cured meats exist in two forms, shelf stable and perishable. Shelf-stable products include (a) canned viennas, corned beef, frankfurters, meat spreads, and chicken or turkey luncheon meat given a "botulinal cook" (F_o = 2.78) or greater; (b) 12-oz canned luncheon meat and small canned hams made from pork given less than a "botulinal cook"; (c) canned sausages that may be covered with hot oil in the final container and have a water activity $\leq$0.92, and sliced dried beef in vacuum jars and canned prefried bacon that rely upon a low water activity ($\leq$0.86) for stability; and (d) vinegar-pickled meats such as sausages and pigs feet.

Products in category (a) are similar in their microbiology to other low-acid canned foods and should be examined as in Chapters 60 or 61. The shelf-stable canned cured pork products in category (b) are limited to 3 pounds or less in size because the thermal process (F_o = 0.1–0.7) required for stability will cause an unacceptable, mushy texture in products of a larger size. Although these products are given less than a botulinal cook, they have an excellent, but not unblemished, record of safety and stability. Their stability is dependent on four interrelated factors: nitrite, salt, a low indigenous spore level in the raw materials, and a thermal process that destroys many of the spores. Those heat-injured spores that do survive are inhibited by the presence of sufficient nitrite and salt. Since it is possible to recover low levels of mesophilic sporeformers from products in category (b), "commercial sterility," as defined in the Code of Federal Regulations (21CFR Part 113.3) for low-acid foods in hermetically sealed containers, does not apply to these products, which do not spoil unless the curing process, retorting process, or can seal is faulty. Thermophilic spoilage can occur if the products are stored at abnormally high temperatures for a sufficient length of time. A faulty cure that provides insufficient levels of salt or nitrite can permit the growth of the sporeforming bacteria that survive the thermal process. Slight underprocessing can allow the survival of a higher than normal level of mesophilic spores and, thereby, increase the chance that subsequent growth will occur. Gross underprocessing results in the additional survival and growth of enterococci and other non-sporeformers. A faulty can seal can allow a variety of bacteria to enter the can and cause spoilage of the contents.

The canned sausages, sliced dried beef, and prefried bacon in category (c) do not undergo spoilage unless the water activity is higher than recommended or the vacuum seal is broken. Products that exceed a water activity level of 0.86 support the growth of more salt-tolerant bacteria such as micrococci or enterococci, particularly if the products have been sealed under a low vacuum or nitrate has been added during curing. Theoretically, it may be possible for *S. aureus* to grow in these products at water activity levels near 0.86, but such growth has not been observed in commercial practice. This fact may be due to a low level of *S. aureus*, even though the products are hand packed; the more rapid growth of the other flora; or a combination effect of pH and water activity. In addition, a report suggests that anaerobic growth of *S. aureus* is prevented below 0.90 water activity.[31] Overt spoilage does not always accompany bacterial growth in these products when the water activity is too high (e.g., 0.86 to 0.90).

Pickled pigs feet, pickled sausages, and similar products in category (d) are immersed in vinegar brine and owe their stability to low pH, acetic acid, little or no fermentable sugar remaining in the tissue, and/or an airtight package.[29] Lactic acid bacteria and spores in moderate numbers may be present. Aerobic plate counts are variable and unpredictable; coliforms and *S. aureus* are rarely present. Lactic acid bacteria in numbers exceeding 10^7 per gram may make the brine cloudy.[30] In hot weather the container may build up internal pressure. Foodborne disease organisms cannot survive, but mold can grow if the container is not properly sealed.

Hermetically sealed containers of pickled bone-in meat may develop gas and even explode from the action of the vinegar on the bone. This nonmicrobial problem should be considered by microbiologists investigating the cause of swelling.

44.332   Perishable canned cured meats

Perishable canned cured meats made from pork can be up to 22 pounds in size and must be labeled "Perishable, Keep Refrigerated." They contain levels of nitrite and salt similar to those in shelf-stable products but are heated insufficiently to control the indigenous spore population. Hence, these products require refrigerated storage for both safety and stability. These products also include ham and other cured meats that are thermal processed in hermetically sealed oxygen-impermeable films and distributed as "cook-in-bag" products.

Perishable canned cured meats can retain their acceptable quality for 1 to 3 years when properly processed and refrigerated. Spoilage of these products at refrigeration temperature usually is due to the survival and growth of psychrotrophic, thermoduric nonsporeforming bacteria (e.g., enterococci, *Lactobacillus viridescens*) that were present at abnormally high levels in the raw materials or that survived when a substandard thermal process was used. This spoilage often is characterized by sourness or off-odor and a loss of vacuum or swelling of the cans. Perishable canned cured meats normally contain low levels ($\leq 10^2$ per gram) of viable aerobic and anaerobic sporeformers that survive processing but remain dormant at refrigeration temperatures. The presence of abnormally high levels (e.g., $\geq 10^3$ per gram) of mesophilic anaerobic sporeformers that are incapable of growth below 10°C is evidence of temperature abuse and a potential botulinal hazard. An initial indication of this risk is a putrid aroma on opening the can; but the analyst must be familiar with the putrid aroma produced by putrefactive anaerobes. The presence of spores (beware of fat droplets from the product) in a wet mount preparation under phase contrast microscopy is additional, readily attainable evidence of temperature abuse.

Spoilage by psychrotrophic clostridia is rare, but about six different episodes have been observed.[20,37] Experience indicates that this form of spoilage is more common in products that have lower brine levels (e.g., $\leq 3\%$) and have been in longer term refrigerated storage (e.g., months to a year). Bacterial isolates from spoiled product (i.e., gas or loss of vacuum and a putrid aroma) have been identified as *Clostridium putrefaciens* (unpublished data of Tompkin, Shaparis, and Christiansen).

44.34   Canned Uncured Meats

These products include (a) roast beef with gravy, beef stew, chili con carne, tamales, and canned whole chicken, which are low-acid canned foods and given a botulinal cook or greater, and (b) sloppy joe and spaghetti sauce with ground meat, which can be high-acid canned foods and given a milder heat treatment. Unstable or otherwise suspect products in categories (a) and (b) should be analyzed by the procedures given in Chapter 61.

44.35   Fermented and Acidulated Sausages

Fermented products such as thuringer, summer sausage, pepperoni, cervelat, Lebanon bologna, and Genoa salami depend upon a lactic fermentation and a relatively low water activity for preservation. At the end of the fermentation period, the lactics normally exceed 10^8 per gram, members of the

Enterobacteriaceae have not increased beyond their normally low indigenous level, and *S. aureus* counts are less than 10^3 per gram. During subsequent storage, the organic acids (primarily lactic acid), salt, and drying may destroy many of the bacteria present; yet, it is not uncommon to find 10^6 per gram of lactic acid bacteria surviving in the products at the retail level. Some of these products are smoked or heated, thus greatly reducing the bacterial levels of the final product.

Proper process control will inhibit *S. aureus* growth during fermentation.[2] Fermentation acids, salt, heating, and drying control other bacteria that could cause foodborne illness. In a poorly controlled process, staphylococci can grow and produce toxin in the periphery of the sausage during the fermentation period.[3] The staphylococci gradually die during drying and storage, but the toxin remains. Thus, the level of staphylococci in the final product is not an accurate measure of the health hazard.

When testing fermented sausages for their potential in causing staphylococcal food poisoining, the outer 3 mm layer of the sausage is sampled for viable *S. aureus* at the end of the fermentation cycle before the product is heated and/or dried. Since *S. aureus* death may have occurred in products ready for consumption, it may be necessary to test the casing for thermonuclease[10] and/or the outer 3 mm of product for enterotoxin (Chapter 34).

Yeasts and molds may grow on the surface of such sausages during production and subsequent storage. Some processors cultivate a nontoxigenic surface mold to impart a characteristic flavor and appearance. Information about the formulation and processing procedure is essential for the proper interpretation of laboratory data from fermented sausages. Further information on the microbiology of fermented meat and poultry products is available.[2]

Acidulated sausages are produced by adding an acidulant (citric acid, glucono-delta-lactone, lactic acid) to the meat during formulation. These acidulants are usually added as encapsulated agents to facilitate a rapid, controlled pH drop during subsequent heating. As the product is heated, the encapsulating material breaks down, the acidulant is released, and the meat is acidulated. Since the process does not involve a microbial fermentation and higher heating temperatures may be involved than with fermented sausages, very low microbial levels are expected in these products after processing. Acidulated products can be differentiated from fermented products by reading the ingredient phrase on the label or by contacting the producer.

44.36   Dried Meats

Most commercial procedures for the preparation of dried meat (e.g., jerky, beer sticks, tosajo) include a cooking step that destroys the normal vegetative flora of the raw meat and a rapid drying procedure, which will then reduce the water activity to an inhibitory level before microorganisms of concern can grow. Molds and sometimes yeasts subsequently may grow on the surface of dried meats. Drying to a lower moisture level, using sorbic acid and vacuum packaging, and avoiding storage in a humid atmosphere will control such growth. Spoilage of dried meat by molds has no known significance for public health.[17] Occasionally, dried meats and certain perishable cured meats will develop white deposits on the surface that appear to be mold growth. A crystalline stucture on microscopic examination will exclude the possibility of mold. Deposits of this type may be due to crystallized hard fat, lactate salts, or inorganic salts such as phosphate. Consumers and analysts might confuse these crystals with broken glass.

Microbial levels on dried meats are highly variable and depend on the nature of the product, its ingredients, and the process.

Commercially dried meat products are generally free of hazard from food-borne disease bacteria, although salmonellae not destroyed by heating or resulting from recontamination of the dried product can remain viable. Dried meats improperly prepared in the home may permit the growth of pathogens during the drying process or subsequently become contaminated.

44.4   PATHOGENS

Staphylococcus aureus, *Clostridium perfringens*, *Campylobacter*, *Listeria monocytogenes*, and *Salmonella* frequently are present in low numbers on raw meat surfaces. *Clostridium botulinum* occurs infrequently. These species are most hazardous when they grow without competition in cooked products. Outbreaks attributed to *C. perfringens* appear to be limited to cooked non-cured meats, such as roast beef or turkey, as opposed to ham and other salted or cured meats. *L. monocytogenes* is of concern in cooked packaged meat and poultry products held under refrigeration for prolonged periods and particularly when the refrigeration is marginal (10°C or higher). Although *L. monocytogenes* is considered to be a pathogen, thoroughly documented outbreaks from meat or poultry products have been rare.

Other animal pathogens can cause human disease with close animal-man contact, such as among farmers and persons working in slaughtering plants. Some of these include *Brucella*, *Mycobacterium*, *Leptospira*, *Coxiella burnetti*, *Clostridium tetani*, and *Chlamydia psittaci*. Theoretically, some of these could be transmitted to consumers by contact with raw meat, but epidemiological evidence is lacking to support this possibility. The relative significance of meat and poultry as vehicles for the transmission of foodborne illness from *Campylobacter jejuni*, *Listeria monocytogenes*, *Yersinia enterocolitica*, and enteropathogenic *E. coli* continues to be investigated. The literature should be surveyed for current information on these pathogens.

44.5   RECOMMENDED METHODS

A wide variety of methods are used for sampling meat and poultry products. The sampling procedure depends on the product and the reasons for analysis.

A rinse technique can be used for poultry[34]; swabs are often used for larger carcasses. Additional suggestions for sampling meat and poultry products are available in other reference materials.[22,38]

After samples are collected and prepared for analysis, the microbiological methods can be performed as described in this book. The selection of the analyses depends on the sample and the information desired. Some of the tests that can be performed and their appropriate chapters are as follows:

Aerobic Plate Count (mesophilic)—Chapter 4

Aerobic Plate Count (psychrotrophic)—Chapter 9.

Incubate plates at 20°C for 3 days. Where lactic acid bacteria are expected, substitute APT or similar vitamin-enriched medium—Chapter 15

Coliforms, *E. coli*, and Fecal Coliforms—Chapter 24

Staphylococcus aureus—Chapter 33

Staphylococcal enterotoxins—Chapter 34

Salmonella—Chapter 25

Yeasts and Molds—Chapter 16

Enterococci—Chapter 32

Clostridium perfringens—Chapter 37

Listeria monocytogenes—Chapter 38

Yersinia—Chapter 27

Campylobacter—Chapter 29

Water Activity—Chapter 8

In certain specific investigations, other analyses may be required. Many of these are discussed elsewhere, while others, such as protein, salt, water, and fat, are not included in this book. To perform these tests, the analyst should refer to other publications.

44.6   REFERENCES

1. Allen, J. R. and Foster, E. M. 1960. Spoilage of vacuum-packaged sliced processed meats during refrigerated storage. Food Res. 25: 19.
2. Bacus, J. N. 1986. Fermented meat and poultry products. In "Advances in Meat Research," eds. A. M. Pierson and T. R. Dutson, Vol. 2, Meat and poultry microbiology, p. 123. AVI Publishing Co., Westport, Conn.
3. Barber, L. E. and Deibel, R. H. 1972. Effect of pH and oxygen tension on staphylococcal growth and enterotoxin formation in fermented sausage. Appl. Microbiol. 24: 891.
4. Barnes, E. M. 1976. Microbiological problems of poultry at refrigeration temperatures—A review. J. Sci. Fd. Agric. 27: 777.
5. Bersani, C., Cattaneo, P., Balzaretti, C., and Cantoni, C. 1984. Psychrotrophic Enterobacteriaceae occurring in refrigerated meat products. Ind. Aliment. 24: 112.
6. Beyer, K. and Sinell, H. J. 1981. Psychrotrophic microorganisms in vacuum packaged chilled beef trimmings. In "Psychrotrophic Microorganisms in Spoilage and Pathogenicity," eds. T. A. Roberts, G. Hobbs, J. H. B. Christian, and N. Skovgaard, p. 191. Academic Press, New York.
7. Bryan, F. L. 1980. Foodborne diseases in the United States associated with meat and poultry. J. Food Prot. 43: 140.
8. Bryan, F. L. 1988. Risks associated with vehicles of foodborne pathogens and toxins. J. Food Prot. 51: 498.

9. Dainty, R. H., Shaw, B. G., and Roberts, T. A. 1983. Microbial and chemical changes in chill-stored red meats. In "Food Microbiology: Advances and Prospects," eds. T. A. Roberts and F. A. Skinner, p. 151. Academic Press, New York.

10. Emswiler-Rose, B. S., Johnston, R. W., Harris, M. E., and Lee, W. H. 1980. Rapid detection of staphylococcal thermonuclease on casings of naturally contaminated fermented sausages. Appl. Environ. Microbiol. 40: 13.

11. Gardner, G. A. 1981. *Brochothrix thermosphacta* (*Microbacterium thermosphactum*) in the spoilage of meats—A review. In "Psychrotrophic Microorganisms in Spoilage and Pathogenicity, eds. T. A. Roberts, G. Hobbs, J. H. B. Christian, and N. Skovgaard, p. 139. Academic Press, New York.

12. Gill, C. O. 1979. A review. Intrinsic bacteria in meat. J. Appl. Bacteriol. 47: 367.

13. Gill, C. O. 1986. The control of microbial spoilage in fresh meats. In "Advances in Meat Research," eds. A. M. Pierson and T. R. Dutson, Vol. 2, Meat and poultry microbiology, p. 49. AVI Publishing Co., Westport, Conn.

14. Grant, G. L., McCurdy, A. R., and Osborne, A. D. 1988. Bacterial greening in cured meats: A review. Can. Inst. Food Sci. Technol. J. 21: 50.

15. Grau, F. H. 1986. Microbial ecology of meat and poultry. In "Advances in Meat Research," eds. A. M. Pierson and T. R. Dutson, Vol. 2, Meat and poultry microbiology, p. 1. AVI Publishing Co., Westport, Conn.

16. Hechelmann, H., Bem, Z., Uchida, K., and Leistner, L. 1974. Occurrence of the tribe Klebsielleae in refrigerated meats and meat products. Fleischwirtschaft 54: 1515.

17. Intern. Comm. on Microbiol. Spec. for Foods. 1980. Meats and meat products. In "Microbial Ecology of Foods," Vol. 2, Food commodities, p. 333. Academic Press, New York.

18. Intern. Comm. on Microbiol. Spec. for Foods. 1980. Poultry and poultry meat products. In "Microbial Ecology of Foods," Vol. 2, Food commodities, p. 410. Academic Press, New York.

19. Intern. Comm. on Microbiol. Spec. for Foods. 1986. "Microorganisms in Foods." Vol. 2. Sampling for microbiological analysis: Principles and specific applications. U. of Toronto Press, Toronto, Ontario.

20. Johnston, R. W. and Krumm, G. W. 1980. The microbiological safety of canned, cured perishable meat products. In "Proceedings of the 26th European Meeting of Meat Research Workers," Vol. 2, p. 295. Colorado Springs, Colo.

21. Kempton, A. G. and Bobier, S. R. 1970. Bacterial growth in refrigerated, vacuum-packed luncheon meats. Can. J. Microbiol. 16: 287.

22. Kotula, A. W., Ayres, J. C., Huhtanen, C. N., Stern, N. J., Stringer, W. C., and Tompkin, R. B. 1980. Guidelines for microbiological examination of meat. In "Proc. 33rd Ann. Recip. Meat Conf.," p. 65. Amer. Meat Sci. Assn. West Lafayette, Ind.

23. Mackey, B. M. and Derrick, C. M. 1979. Contamination of the deep tissues of carcasses by bacteria present on the slaughter instruments or in the gut. J. Appl. Bacteriol. 46: 355.

24. Mossel, D. A. A. and Zwart, H. 1961. The rapid tentative recognition of psychrotrophic types among Enterobacteriaceae isolated from foods. J. Appl. Bacteriol. 23: 185.

25. Mundt, J. O. and Kitchen, H. M. 1951. Taint in southern country-style hams. Food Res. 16: 233.

26. NRC. 1964. An evaluation of public health hazards from microbiological contamination of foods. Publication No. 1195. Natl. Acad. of Sciences, Natl. Res. Council, Washington, D.C.

27. NRC. 1985. An evaluaton of the role of microbiological criteria for foods and food ingredients. Natl. Res. Council, National Academy Press, Washington, D.C.

28. Newton, K. G. 1979. Value of coliform tests for assessing meat quality. J. Appl. Bacteriol. 47: 303.

29. Niven, C. F. 1952. Significance of the lactic acid bacteria in the meat industry. In "Proc. Fourth Res. Conf.," p. 31. Am. Meat Inst., Chicago, Ill.

30. Niven, C. F. 1956. Vinegar pickled meats. A discussion of bacterial and curing problems encountered in processing. Bull. No. 27, Am. Meat Found., Chicago, Ill.

31. Scott, W. J. 1953. Water relations of *Staphylococcus aureus* at 30°C. Australian J. Biol. Sci. 6: 549.
32. Stiles, M. E., and Ng, L. K. 1981. Enterobacteriaceae associated with meats and meat handling. Appl. Environ. Microbiol. 41: 867.
33. Surkiewicz, B. F., Harris, M. E. and Johnston, R. W. 1973. Bacteriological survey of frozen meat and gravy produced at establishments under federal inspection. Appl. Microbiol. 26: 574.
34. Surkiewicz, B. F., Johnston, R. W., Moran, A. B., and Krumm, G. W. 1969. A bacteriological survey of chicken eviscerating plants. Food Technol. 23: 80.
35. Tompkin, R. B. 1978. The red meat processor's role in salmonellosis prevention. In "Proceedings: National Salmonellosis Seminar, January 10–11," U.S. Dept. of Agr., Washington, D.C.
36. Tompkin, R. B. 1983. Indicator organisms in meat and poultry products. Food Technol. 37(6): 107.
37. Tompkin, R. B. 1986. Microbiology of ready-to-eat meat and poultry products. In "Advances in Meat Research," eds. A. M. Pierson and T. R. Dutson, Vol. 2, Meat and poultry microbiology, p. 89. AVI Publishing Co., Westport, Conn.
38. USDA Microbiology Laboratory Guidebook. 1975. Food Safety Inspection Service, U.S. Dept. of Agr., Washington, D.C.
39. USHEW/PHS/CDC. 1973. Foodborne Outbreaks, Annual Sum. 1972. U.S. Dept. of Health, Ed. and Welfare. U.S. Pub. H. Serv., Washington, D.C.

Chapter 45

MILK AND MILK PRODUCTS

R. L. Richter, R. A. Ledford, and S. C. Murphy

45.1 INTRODUCTION

The microbiological quality of milk and milk products is influenced by the initial flora of the raw milk, the processing conditions, and post-pasteurization contamination. High moisture products such as fluid milks, cottage cheese, condensed milk, ice cream mixes, and cultured milks have a maximum shelf life of 2 to 3 weeks because of microbial growth even under good processing and refrigerated storage conditions. The shelf life of cultured milk products is somewhat longer than that of unfermented products because of their high acidity. Other dairy products such as ultrapasteurized milk products, sweetened condensed and evaporated milk, ripened cheeses, and butter have an extended shelf life because of reduced water activity, pH, temperature of storage, and/or heat treatment applied during processing.

Recognition by public health authorities and the dairy industry in the early 1900s that raw milk was a major public health concern resulted in the development of regulations that defined proper conditions for the production and handling of milk. These recommendations evolved into the Milk Ordinance of 1924 and an interpretation of these recommendations in the Code in 1927.[19] The current document is known as the Pasteurized Milk Ordinance, 1985 Revision,[20] and defines the conditions under which Grade A milk products must be produced and processed. Methods to evaluate milk and milk products for quality and safety have been standardized and are published by the American Public Health Association as the *Standard Methods for the Examination of Dairy Products* (SMEDP).[37]

The Food and Drug Administration (FDA) and the U.S. Department of Agriculture (USDA) both define the microbiological limits for products they regulate (Tables 1 and 2). These microbiological criteria can be met consis-

Table 1—Microbial Standards for Raw Milk and Fluid Products.

Product	Standard	Reference
Grade A raw milk for pasteurization		20
Individual producer samples	100,000/ml	
Commingled samples	300,000/ml	
USDA raw milk for manufacturing		48
Grade no. 1	500,000/ml	
Grade no. 2	1,000,000/ml	
Undergrade	>1,000,000/ml	
Grade A pasteurized fluid products		20
Bacteria	20,000/ml	
Coliforms		
Packaged	10/ml	
Bulk for transport	100/ml	
Grade A aseptically processed		20
Bacteria No growth by tests specified in Section 6 of the Grade A Pasteurized Ordinance.		

tently provided good manufacturing practices are employed, but they do not necessarily provide guidelines that ensure maximum shelf life or stability of product quality. The dairy industry has accepted the responsibility for processing safe, wholesome products that retain desirable qualities throughout the shelf life of the product. Acknowledgment of this responsibility has resulted in the establishment of quality criteria that are more demanding than those established by regulatory agencies.

45.2   RAW MILK

Raw milk as it leaves the udders of healthy animals normally contains very low numbers of microorganisms. Total counts usually are less than a thousand per ml. *Micrococcus*, *Staphylococcus*, *Streptococcus*, and *Corynebacterium* spp. are the most common bacteria usually present.[12, 23, 25, 35] If lactating cows have mastitis, large numbers of the infectious organisms may be shed into the milk and contribute to higher total counts of bulk milk if milk from infected cows is not kept separate.[4, 21] *Staphylococcus aureus* and *Streptococcus agalactiae* are commonly associated with contagious mastitis while coliforms, *Pseudomonas*, and other *Streptococcus* spp. are more related to environmental mastitis.[33] Mastitic infections are generally accompanied by a rise in the somatic cell count of milk. Most bacteria in milk as it leaves the cow generally do not grow well under refrigeration, thus their numbers in bulk milk usually do not increase significantly.

After it leaves the udder, milk may become contaminated with microorganisms from the surfaces of the cow, the environment, and unclean milking systems.[35, 42–45] Contamination is generally bacterial; yeasts and molds occur

Table 2—Microbiological Standards for Manufactured Milk Products.

Product	Standard		Reference
Dry whole milk			
U.S. extra	50,000/g	SPC	63
	10/g	Coliform	63
U.S. standard	100,000/g	SPC	63
	10/g	Coliform	63
U.S. grade not assigned	>100 × 10⁶/g	DMC	64
Nonfat dry milk (roller and spray process)			
U.S. extra	50,000/g	SPC	57, 59
U.S. standard	100,000/g	SPC	57, 59
U.S. grade not assigned	>100 × 10⁶/g	DMC	58, 60
Instant nonfat dry milk			
U.S. extra	30,000/g	SPC	65
	10/g	Coliform	65
U.S. grade not assigned	75 × 10⁶/g	DMC	66
Dry buttermilk			
U.S.	50,000/g	SPC	62
U.S. standard	200,000/g	SPC	62
Dry whey			
U.S. extra	50,000/g	SPC	61
	10/g	Coliform	61
Edible dry casein			
U.S. extra	30,000/g	SPC	67
	0/0.1g	Coliform	67
U.S. standard	100,000/g	SPC	68
	≤2/0.1/g	Coliform	68
	0/100g	Salmonella[a]	69
	0/g	Coagulase[a]-Staphylococcus	69
	5,000/g	Thermophiles[a]	69
	5/0.1/g	Yeasts and molds[a]	69
Plastic and frozen cream	30,000/ml	SPC	51, 52
	20/ml	Yeasts and molds	51, 52
	10/ml	Coliform	51, 52
Ice cream			
Plain	50,000/g	SPC	54
	10/g	Coliform	54
Sherbet	50,000/g	SPC	55
	10/g	Coliform	55
Sweetened condensed milk	1,000/g	SPC	56
	10/g	Coliform	56
	5/g	Yeasts	56
	5/g	Molds	56
Butter and whipped butter	100/g	Proteolytic	49, 50
	20/g	Yeasts and molds	49, 50
	10/g	Coliform	49, 50
	10/g	Enterococci[b]	49, 50
Cottage cheese	10/g	Coliform	53
	100/g	Psychrotrophic	53
	10/g	Yeasts and molds	53

[a]Optional
[b]Optional except when required or requested

rarely or in low numbers. Unclean udders and teats can contribute organisms from a variety of sources (e.g., manure, soil, feed, and water). They include lactic acid bacteria, coliform and other gram-negative bacteria, *Bacillus*, and *Clostridium* spp., as well as the normal surface flora (e.g. *Micrococcus* and *Staphylococcus* spp.). Improperly cleaned milk contact surfaces can add substantial numbers of microorganisms to subsequent milkings by providing conditions (nutrients) for growth of contaminating microorganisms. Large numbers of thermoduric bacteria (*Micrococcus, Microbacterium, Streptococcus, Lactobacillus, Bacillus* spp.) are associated with persistent poor cleaning of milking machines, pipelines, bulk storage tanks, and transfer hoses while higher numbers of gram-negative bacteria or lactic streptococci may occur from occasional neglect.[35] Thermoduric bacteria have a direct influence on the total bacterial counts of freshly pasteurized milk, but their growth in the farm bulk tank is minimal. In summary, the types of organisms that prevail in raw milk depend on the initial microbial population, the extent of cleaning and sanitizing of milking equipment and utensils, and the time and temperature of storage.

Because raw milk is cooled immediately and held at refrigeration temperatures, increases in the microbial load of milk in the bulk tank are usually psychrotrophic in nature. *Pseudomonas, Flavobacterium*, and *Alcaligenes* spp. as well as some of the coliform bacteria tend to be the predominant psychrotrophic bacteria of raw milk in storage.[2, 8, 41, 43, 44] These bacteria if allowed to grow to large numbers can cause bitter, fruity, rancid, and unclean flavors that persist throughout further processing. Some gram-negative psychrotrophic bacteria, particularly *Pseudomonas* species, are also capable of producing heat-stable enzymes (proteases and lipases) in raw milk that can cause defects in the final product.[2, 8, 40] Some gram-positive organisms capable of growth in refrigerated milk are species of *Bacillus, Micrococcus*, and *Arthrobacter*.[8] They are usually of less significance as defect producers than are the gram-negative bacteria. The lactic streptococci (proposed change in genus nomenclature to *Lactococcus*[39]) grow and produce acid in poorly refrigerated raw milk. A malty flavor defect may also occur under these conditions. However, the use of refrigerated bulk tanks has reduced the frequency of milk spoilage by lactic streptococci. Other flavor defects of raw milk that are non-microbial in nature must be considered in evaluating raw milk quality. These include such flavors as rancid, oxidized, feed flavors, and defects associated with high somatic cell count milk (mastitic milk).

Microorganisms associated with foodborne illness may enter the raw milk supply through infected animals, milking personnel, or the environment. Recently, the consumption of raw milk (on the farm or as certified raw milk) has been implicated in outbreaks of foodborne illness involving *Salmonella* species, *Campylobacter jejuni*, and *Yersinia enterocolitica*.[5, 6] The contamination of pasteurized product with raw milk containing *Listeria monocytogenes* and *Salmonella* species has been implicated in recent major outbreaks.[22, 38]

Efforts should be made to minimize microbial numbers in raw milk supplies because processing does not eliminate quality defects. Standard Plate Counts (SPC) are routinely obtained to assess the overall sanitation and storage conditions of dairy farms. Counts of less than 10,000 CFU/ml are easily maintained. Some believe the Preliminary Incubation method for raw milk to be a more reliable indicator of farm sanitation than the SPC because it enumerates those organisms that may occur through poor dairy hygiene.[37] Thermoduric counts are useful in determining the number of microorganisms that will survive pasteurization. Raw milk received by a dairy plant is generally processed before results of the plating methods are available. The Direct Microscopic Clump Count (DMC) and Direct Microscopic Somatic Cell Count (DMSC) methods can be used for rapid estimates of total numbers of microorganisms and somatic cells before the raw milk is further processed. However, these counts are most successful when bacteria counts are high and are of limited value for milk with low bacteria counts.

45.21   Recommended Methods

Standard Plate Count—Chapter 4, SMEDP[37]
Thermoduric—Chapter 10, SMEDP[37]
Direct Microscopic Clump Count—Chapter 5, SMEDP[37]
Direct Microscopic Somatic Cell Count—SMEDP[37]
Electronic Somatic Cell Count—SMEDP[37]
Other Methods for Specific Determinations
Psychrotrophic Plate Count—Chapter 9, SMEDP[37]
Coliform Count—Chapter 24, SMEDP[37]
Preliminary Incubation—SMEDP[37]
For individual pathogens such as *Salmonella*, *Campylobacter*, *Listeria*, and *Yersinia* consult appropriate chapters of this book.
Mastitis Pathogens—Laboratory and Field Handbook on Bovine Mastitis; National Mastitis Council.[33]
Consult Chapter 39, for rapid methods.

45.3   PASTEURIZED MILK

The initial microflora of freshly pasteurized milk consists primarily of thermoduric bacteria and spores. The types and numbers of thermoduric bacteria are dependent on the microbial population of the raw milk before pasteurization. Gram-positive *Bacillus*, *Micrococcus*, *Lactobacillus*, *Microbacterium*, *Corynebacterium*, *Streptococcus*, and *Arthrobacter* spp. are among the more common thermoduric organisms.[8] Large numbers of these bacteria in the raw milk supply can contribute significantly to the Standard Plate Count of pasteurized products and in some cases cause the Standard Plate Count to exceed regulatory standards. Most thermoduric bacteria grow slowly in refrigerated milk and are generally outgrown by gram-negative psychrotrophic species that gain entry primarily as post-pasteurization contaminants.[8, 70] However, in the absence of psychrotrophic bacteria or if large numbers of thermoduric bacteria survive pasteurization, certain thermodurics, particularly psychrotrophic sporeforming *Bacillus* spp., can grow and cause spoilage (e.g., sweet-curdling).[3, 36]

The predominant gram-negative psychrotrophic bacteria in pasteurized milk are species of *Pseudomonas*, *Flavobacterium*, and *Alcaligenes*, as well as some members of the coliform group.[8, 35] Spoilage of pasteurized milk by gram-negative psychrotrophic bacteria results in fruity, rancid, bitter, and unclean flavors. Generally, populations in excess of 10^6 per ml are required before flavor defects are detectable organoleptically. The rate of microbial growth and quality deterioration of the product is influenced by the numbers and types of bacteria in the freshly pasteurized product and the storage temperature. For optimum shelf life, refrigerated storage should be below 4°C. Under ideal processing and handling conditions, the shelf life of pasteurized milk should well exceed 14 days. Spoilage caused by organisms other than gram-negative bacteria will occur in the absence of these organisms, although at a much slower rate.

Microbiological tests most commonly used to evaluate freshly pasteurized milk are the Standard Plate Count and the coliform count. Although these methods are used routinely to determine compliance with regulatory standards, they are of limited value in predicting the keeping quality (shelf life) of milk, which is considered to be a function of the extent of post-pasteurization contamination. The presence of coliforms in freshly pasteurized milk is normally an indication of post-pasteurization contamination. However, the levels of coliforms and other post-pasteurization contaminants in freshly processed milk may be below detection levels by conventional methods. The Moseley Keeping Quality test has been used as an indication of the shelf life of the product by determining the extent of microbial growth under typical storage conditions. The primary disadvantage of the test is that 7 to 9 days are required to obtain results. Other methods designed to determine within a shorter time period the presence of low levels of coliforms and other gram-negative psychrotrophic bacteria that presumably do not survive pasteurization have been suggested.[2] Most involve preliminary incubation of the samples at temperatures selective for psychrotrophic bacteria, with or without reagents inhibitory to gram-positive bacteria followed by selective plating procedures and/or the detection of microbial metabolites.[2] The usefulness of these methods in detecting post-pasteurization contamination and predicting shelf life has not been fully determined. However, the reader should be aware that there are procedures that may be useful in a given situation.[2]

Bacteria related to foodborne illness are destroyed by proper pasteurization.[5, 13, 22, 35] Recent outbreaks of salmonellosis and listeriosis in pasteurized milk have been linked to post-pasteurization contamination. Contamination of pasteurized milk through the addition of ingredients was implicated in an outbreak caused by *Y. enterocolitica* in chocolate milk.[5] Post-pasteurization contamination with *L. monocytogenes* and *Y. enterocolitica* is of major concern to the dairy industry since these organisms grow at refrigeration temperatures.

45.31   RECOMMENDED METHODS

Standard Plate Count—Chapter 4, SMEDP[37]
Coliform Count—Chapter 24, SMEDP[37]
Other Methods for Specific Determinations
   Psychrotrophic Count—Chapter 9, SMEDP[37]
   Moseley Keeping Quality Test—SMEDP[37]
For individual pathogens such as *Salmonella*, *Campylobacter*, *Listeria*, and
   Yersinia consult appropriate chapters of this book.
Consult Chapter 39 for rapid methods.

45.4   DRIED PRODUCTS

Dairy products that are dried include milk, skimmed milk (nonfat dry milk), buttermilk, whey, cheese, and some fermented milk products. The manufacture of these products usually involves the preparation of a concentrate before drying by spray, roller, or foam processess. Milk is separated or standardized, pasteurized, and preheated at selected time and temperature combinations to produce low-heat, medium-heat, or high-heat products. Preheated milk is concentrated in an evaporator with the temperature of the concentration process selected to produce the desired characteristics in the product. Increasing concentration temperatures are used to produce low-heat, medium-heat, and high-heat products. Concentrated milk is briefly exposed to high temperatures during drying with the amount of heat applied depending on the type of product being manufactured and the method of drying. The microflora of dried milks is affected by the time and temperature combinations used during preheating, concentration, and drying. Failure to achieve satisfactory bacteria counts in dried milk products is usually due to the use of poor-quality raw milk. Psychrotrophic bacteria, coliform bacteria, and yeasts and molds are reduced to very low levels during preheating[26] and their presence in dried milk products indicates contamination from equipment or the environment during or after manufacture. The typical microflora of dried milk consists of thermoduric micrococci, thermoduric streptococci, corynebacteria, and aerobic sporeformers.[15]

Most dried dairy products are often used as ingredients of other foods and are subject to further processing. Yet, dried milks must be considered sensitive products from a public health aspect because they are often consumed after reconstitution without additional heating. It is well established that dried milk can be a source of foodborne illness because of contamination with *Salmonella* and *Staphylococcus*.[17, 28] Food poisoning caused by *S. aureus* is not currently a serious problem. However, poor temperature control during storage of raw milk before processing or following heat treatments during processing can lead to growth of *S. aureus* and the production of enterotoxin that can survive subsequent manufacturing processes. Growth of *S. aureus* in milk after pre-heat treatment and before drying has been identified as the probable cause of several outbreaks of *Staphylococcus* intoxication.[28] Proper storage temperatures and process controls will eliminate the hazard of food poisoning from *S. aureus* in dried milk products. Environmental contamination of dried milk products with *Salmonella* is a major concern for manufacturers of dried milk products. The history of foodborne illness in dried milk caused by *Salmonella* has been reviewed by Marth.[28] The seriousness of *Salmonella* as a pathogen and the probability that dried milk might be consumed without futher processing caused the institution of process control measures and an extensive monitoring program that has significantly reduced the incidence of *Salmonella* in dried milk products.[35] The strengths and weaknesses of the regulatory *Salmonella* surveillance program used in the United States to routinely monitor dried milk products for *Salmonella* have been identified in a recent study by the National Research Council.[34]

Because of their low water activity, dried products rarely spoil or deteriorate because of microbial growth. Standards specifying Standard Plate Counts, coliform counts, and yeast and mold counts of dried milk products reflecting quality grades and product processes have been established by the USDA and the American Dry Milk Institute (Tables 1 and 2).[1, 47] The sanitary quality of the processing conditions and environment can be monitored by evaluating the dried milk products for post-pasteurization contamination through indicator organisms such as yeasts, molds, and coliforms. These microorganisms are destroyed by the heat treatments used during the manufacture of dried milk products and their presence in these products reflects contamination from unsanitary equipment or the environment following manufacture. Total counts, thermoduric counts, and aerobic mesophilic spore counts, in increasing order of sensitivity, reflect the effect of changing conditions during the manufacture of dried milk.[26] These counts can be used as indicators of the quality of the raw milk used to manufacture the dried product. The Direct Microscopic Count, which measures both viable and dead bacteria, can also be used to provide information relative to the original bacterial population of the raw milk. When there is reason to suspect possible public health concerns because of *Staphylococcus*, it would be advisable to test for staphylococcal toxin. The *Salmonella* surveillance program is not a substitute for microbiological control by the manufacturer, and manufacturers should test products for *Salmonella* in accordance with the sampling plans recommended in the NAS/NRC *Salmonella* report.[31]

45.41   Recommended Methods

Standard Plate Count—Chapter 4, SMEDP[37]
Coliform Count—Chapter 24, SMEDP[37]
Yeast and Mold Count—Chapter 16, SMEDP[37]
Direct Microscopic Clump Count—Chapter 5, SMEDP[37]
Thermoduric Count—Chapter 10, SMEDP[37]
Psychrotrophic Count—Chapter 9, SMEDP[37]
Salmonella—Chapter 25
Staphylococcal Enterotoxins—Chapter 34
Mesophilic Spore Count—Chapter 18, SMEDP[37]

45.5   BUTTER

Butter, one of the few foods defined by law, must contain at least 80% milkfat.[19] It can be salted or unsalted, and it may or may not contain added starter cultures consisting of *Streptococcus lactis*, *Streptococcus cremoris*, or *Leuconostoc* spp. for additional flavor. The composition of butter is approximately 80.5% fat, 16% to 16.5% moisture, 1.0% to 1.5% curd, and 1.75% to 2.0% salt. Butter is manufactured by creating a water-in-oil emulsion by churning cream, causing a phase inversion of cream in a continuous process or in a conventional churn. During the churning process, moisture from the buttermilk or from water added to adjust the moisture content of the butter is worked into the lipid structure. The moisture is dispersed as fine droplets throughout butter. In properly worked butter, the droplets are uniform and of small size. This composition is critical to stability because poorly worked butter will have an uneven distribution of moisture; areas of high moisture will permit microbial growth if the butter is contaminated during or after manufacture. Additional storage stability is provided by the addition of salt, which can result in a salt-in-water concentration as high as 16%.

The microflora of butter reflects the quality of the cream, the sanitary conditions of the equipment used to manufacture the butter, and the environmental and sanitary conditions during packaging and handling. Pasteurization of cream causes a significant reduction in the number of all but the most heat-resistant bacteria. Palatability problems caused by bacteria include rancid, putrid, malty, and fishy tastes. The development of yeasts and molds on the surface of butter can cause surface discoloration and flavor problems.[14] These flavor and surface growth problems are usually caused by species of *Pseudomonas*, *Streptococcus*, *Geotrichum*, and *Candida*. Butter has been implicated in an outbreak of food poisoning caused by staphylococci.[32] Minor and Marth[30] studied the growth and survival of *S. aureus* in butter and cream. Survival and growth of this organism in butter were affected by storage temperature of the cream and salt content of the butter. Poor-quality cream could be a source of food poisoning if conditions were sufficient to permit growth and enterotoxin production by *Staphylococcus*.

Various tests can be used to determine the quality and safety of butter or to determine sources of contamination during the manufacturing process. Standard Plate Counts, coliform counts, and yeast and mold counts can be useful to detect sources of contamination and to assess the degree of processing sanitation. Lipolytic and proteolytic counts are useful for evaluating the keeping quality of butter since lipolysis and proteolysis are directly related to the development of specific flavor defects. In cases where potential public health problems related to staphylococcal growth and enterotoxin production are suspected, staphylococcal counts might be desirable. However, these determinations would be of limited value if growth of *S. aureus* and enterotoxin production preceded pasteurization.

45.51   Recommended Methods

Standard Plate Count—Chapter 4, SMEDP[37]
Coliform Count—Chapter 24, SMEDP[37]
Lipolytic Count—Chapter 11, SMEDP[37]
Proteolytic Count—Chapter 12, SMEDP[37]
Yeast and Mold Count—Chapter 16, SMEDP[37]
Psychrotrophic Count—Chapter 9, SMEDP[37]
Staphylococcus aureus Count—Chapter 33

45.6   FROZEN DAIRY PRODUCTS

Frozen dairy products include ice cream, ice milk, sherbet, novelties, and frozen yogurt. The microbial content of frozen products largely reflects the quality of the ingredients used for their manufacture: milk, cream, nonfat milk solids, sugar, chocolate, fruits and nuts, egg products, emulsifiers, and stabilizers. Milk, cream, and the soluble components are normally blended and pasteurized. Therefore, microbial counts of the pasteurized mix are generally low (<100 per ml). Sporeformers (*Bacillus* spp.) and some of the hardier thermoduric bacteria originating from the fluid or dry components are usually the only survivors. Addition of flavors, coloring agents, and ingredients such as fruits, nuts, and chocolate chips to the mix after pasteurization can be a source of contaminants. In addition, post-pasteurization contamination can occur from poorly cleaned equipment, air incorporation, poor use of product rerun, and personnel.[18] The presence of coliforms in pasteurized mixes and frozen products is an indication of post-pasteurization contamination, although false positives are possible because of the ability of certain noncoliforms to ferment sucrose.[27]

The quality of soft-serve mixes (ice cream, ice milk, and frozen yogurt) suffers when these products are stored for extended periods, particularly at the upper range of refrigeration temperatures, before freezing. The numbers and types of spoilage organisms will depend on the extent of post-pasteurization contamination and the time-temperature exposure.

Although there is no growth in frozen dairy products, many types of bacteria (including pathogens if present) can survive in frozen products.[6] *Listeria monocytogenes* has been isolated from ice cream and novelties.[38] Ice cream has also been implicated as a vehicle for *Salmonella* infection, although most of the outbreaks associated with this organism occurred as a result of using raw eggs in the manufacture of homemade ice cream.[5] Staphylococcal intoxications involving soft-serve ice creams have been reported.[5]

Normally, Standard Plate Counts and coliform counts of the finished product are used as indicators of microbial contamination usually caused by poor-quality ingredients or inadequate plant sanitation.[37] Products and ingredients may be tested at various stages during processing to determine the source of microbial contamination; Standard Plate Counts, coliform counts, yeast and mold counts, and thermoduric counts are useful. All bulk ingredients should be evaluated before use in the manufacture of frozen dairy foods.

45.61   Recommended Methods

Standard Plate Count—Chapter 4, SMEDP[37]
Coliform Count—Chapter 24, SMEDP[37]
Thermoduric Count—Chapter 10, SMEDP[37]
Yeast and Mold Counts—Chapter 16, SMEDP[37]
Dried Dairy Products—SMEDP[37]
For the microbial evaluation of a non-dairy ingredient (fruits, nuts, cocoa, sugars, and egg and egg products) consult the appropriate chapter in this book. For individual pathogens such as *Salmonella*, *Campylobacter*, *Listeria*, and *Yersinia* consult the appropriate chapters of this book.

45.7   CONCENTRATED PRODUCTS

Concentrated milk products include evaporated milk, condensed milk, sweetened condensed milk, and, to a limited extent, condensed sour products. They are manufactured by the removal of moisture by heat and differ in the amount of heat treatment given during processing, the degree of concentration, and in the ingredients added to increase shelf stability or to influence the final characteristics of the product. The procedure for manufacturing condensed milk, condensed skim milk, and condensed sour products consists of pasteurization, preheating, evaporation, and cooling. Concentration of milk for the preparation of low-heat products can be in single or multiple effect evaporators that operate at temperatures from 37° to 52°C under reduced pressure.[7] The reduced temperatures employed in multiple effect evaporators can provide an opportunity for the growth of thermoduric and thermophilic bacteria. Plain condensed milk products are usually concentrated 3:1, contain no added ingredients to inhibit bacterial growth, and will support microbial growth. They are susceptible to microbial spoilage and must be stored under refrigerated conditions. The microflora of plain condensed milk products will consist of gram-positive thermoduric bacteria that survive pasteurization and the heat treatment applied during concentration, and bacteria associated with unsanitary equipment or environmental contamination. *Bacillus*, *Micrococcus*, *Lactobacillus*, *Microbacterium*, Coryneform bacteria, *Streptococcus*, and *Arthrobacter* spp. are common thermoduric bacteria that survive these heat treatments.[14] The number and types of these bacteria in condensed milk reflect the quality of the milk used to manufacture the condensed milk. The presence of psychrotrophic bacteria, coliform bacteria, and yeasts and molds in condensed milk indicates contamination of the product during or after manufacture. If milk is concentrated at temperatures below 60°C, growth of thermophilic bacteria might occur and reduce the quality of the product. Standard Plate Counts can be used to evaluate the quality of the raw milk used to manufacture condensed milk and will provide some indication of the sanitary conditions of the manufacturing environment. However, if more specific information regarding the quality of the raw milk is desired, thermophilic counts or spore counts might be useful.

The sanitary condition of the processing equipment and the environment can be evaluated by coliform and psychrotrophic counts of plain condensed milk. Condensed fermented products are preserved by the concentration of acid and low pH of the products. Spoilage may occur if sufficient air is available for mold growth. Growth of mold on these products can cause the pH to increase near the mold growth permitting the growth of other bacteria that can lead to rapid spoilage of the product.[35]

Sweetened condensed milk must contain a minimum of 8.5% milkfat and 28% total milk solids. The minimum concentration of sugar is not specified other than to be of sufficient quantity to prevent spoilage.[46] A sucrose concentration of 42% to 43% is usually sufficient to produce a sucrose/water ratio of 60% to 66%. Sugar concentrations at the higher limit are necessary for maximum shelf life. The major differences between condensed milk and sweetened condensed milk are that the latter is usually sold in cans and has sugar added; lactose is also crystallized in sweetened condensed milk to prevent the formation of large lactose crystals that would cause the product to be "grainy" or "sandy."[7] However, the type of spoilage that might occur is considerably different.

The main types of spoilage in sweetened condensed milk are osmophilic, sucrose-fermenting yeasts such as *Torula* spp. and molds. Species of *Aspergillus* and *Penicillium* have been implicated in the production of mold on the surface of sweetened condensed milk when sufficient air is available for their growth.[15] This problem can be eliminated by filling cans to a level that eliminates air for growth, by using practices that reduce the probability of yeast and mold contamination after processing, and by using sucrose with low yeast and mold counts. Spoilage by other types of microorganisms is rare and indicates a problem related to the composition of the product, especially the concentration of sugar. Coliform counts and yeast and mold counts are useful to evaluate sanitary conditions during processing and afterward. High yeast and mold counts can also indicate contamination from sucrose. Consequently, sucrose should be checked for these organisms. Standard Plate Counts, thermoduric counts, thermophilic counts, and spore counts can provide information about the quality of the raw milk used to produce these products.

Evaporated milk production differs from the production of plain condensed milk in these ways: a more intensive preheat treatment is given to evaporated milk to provide storage stability; a stabilizing mineral mixture may be added to reduce gelation during storage; and the product is sterilized in a can by batch or continuous retort procedures. Consequently, the product can be considered a commercially sterile, low-acid food. Federal regulations specify a minimum fat and total milk solids content of 7.5% and 25%, respectively.[47] Spoilage results from inadequate heat treatment or from leakage of the cans after packaging. Spoilage by *Bacillus stearothermophilus* may occur if the product is stored at abnormally high ambient temperatures.[36] Methods for determining commercial sterility and for identifying causes for the absence of sterility in low-acid foods can be found in Chapters 60 and 61.

45.71   Recommended Methods

Standard Plate Count—Chapter 4, SMEDP[37]
Coliform Count—Chapter 24, SMEDP[37]
Yeast and Mold Count—Chapter 16, SMEDP[37]
Thermoduric Count—Chapter 10, SMEDP[37]
Thermophilic Count—SMEDP[37]

45.8   FERMENTED DAIRY PRODUCTS

Cheeses, yogurts, and fermented milks represent a diverse class of dairy products derived from the alterations of milk by microbial and enzymatic activities. A typical dairy fermentation is initiated by the growth of lactic acid bacteria [*Streptococcus* spp. (see proposed change in genus nomenclature to *Lactococcus*[39]), *Lactobacillus* spp.] responsible for the production of lactic acid from lactose. The compositional, structural, and flavor characteristics of the fermented product are determined by the processing conditions, such as type of starter culture used, type of enzyme addition, incubation and ripening temperature, milk composition and handling, salt addition, processing and aging conditions, and ripening microflora. These parameters also determine the types of microorganisms capable of survival and/or growth in the product.

45.81   Cheeses

Cheeses are fresh or unripened (cottage cheese, cream cheese, mozzarella, or Neufchatel) or ripened (aged). Ripened cheeses can be further categorized by moisture content as soft surface-ripened (Camembert, Brie), semisoft (Muenster, Gouda, Edam, Roquefort, or Blue), hard (Cheddar, Swiss, Emmentaler, or Gruyère), or hard-grating cheese (Romano or Parmesan).[35] In cheese production, the initial microflora of the raw or heated milk (subpasteurized to pasteurized) is rapidly overshadowed by the active starter organism(s). Subnormal activity of the starter culture may allow growth of undesirable microorganisms. The primary functions of starter cultures (Table 3) include production of lactic acid, which promotes curd formation in conjunction with coagulating enzymes such as rennet, lowering of the redox potential, and destruction or prevention of the growth of pathogens and spoilage organisms. They also contribute to the flavor characteristics of the product. Starter populations in excess of 10^9 per gram of milk or curd are common in the initial stage of the fermentation.

Table 3—Lactic Starter Cultures and Related Products.

Culture	Product
Streptococcus lactis subsp. *lactis*[1]	Cottage cheese, buttermilk, sour cream, Cheddar,
S. lactis subsp. *cremoris*	soft and semisoft cheeses, Gouda, blue-vein cheese, other cheeses
S. lactis subsp. *diacetylactis*	Cottage cheese, buttermilk,
Leuconostoc cremoris	sour cream, semisoft cheese, Cheddar
Streptococcus thermophilus	Yogurt, mozzarella, Emmentaler, Gruyère, Swiss, hard Italian cheese
Lactobacillus helveticus	Yogurt, mozzarella,
Lactobacillus bulgaricus	Emmentaler, Gruyère,
Lactobacillus lactis	Swiss, hard Italian cheese, kefir, koumis
Lactobacillus acidophilus	Acidophilus milk, yogurt
Propionibacterium shermanii	Emmentaler, Gruyère, Swiss, Gouda

Adapted from Kosikowski,[24] Law,[27] and Olson and Mocquot,[35]
[1]The division of *S. lactis* into three subspecies (*S. lactis* subsp. *lactis*, *S. lactis* subsp. *diacetylactis*, and *S. lactis* subsp. *cremoris*) as proposed by Garvie and Farrow[16] is used because these correspond to the traditional nomenclature of the dairy industry. A change in genus nomenclature of the lactic streptococci to *Lactococcus* has been proposed by Schleifer[39]

Ripening of cheeses under controlled conditions of temperature and humidity determines the final flavor and body characteristics of the product. The development of these characteristics involves enzymes of the starter organism, inherent milk enzymes, and the activity of the secondary flora (Table 4). During ripening of Cheddar cheese, the number of the starter organisms generally declines as the secondary flora increases ($>10^8$ per gram). Gram-negative rods, micrococci, and other non-lactic gram-positive bacteria also tend to decrease[41] during the ripening of cheese.

Microbial spoilage in cheese is generally limited because of the combined effect of acid and salt and is less likely in the lower moisture cheeses. Spores of *Clostridium tyrobutyricum* in the milk used for the manufacture of Emmentaler, Edam, and Gouda can survive the heat treatment used for cheese milk and cause late gas formation (blowing defect) and related off-flavors during ripening. Thermoduric *Streptococcus thermophilus* can cause flavor defects in Gouda cheese.[27] The presence of heat-stable enzymes (from psychrotrophic bacteria) can be detrimental to the quality of both fresh and ripened cheese[9, 10, 27] by causing bitter or rancid flavors and by impairing the coagulation properties of the milk. Fresh cheeses, such as cottage cheese and other high-moisture cheeses, may be subject to spoilage by gram-negative psychrotrophic bacteria (*Pseudomonas*, *Flavobacterium*, or *Alcaligenes*), coliforms, and yeast and molds that enter as post-pasteurization contaminants.[8] Most hard-ripened cheeses are not subject to gram-negative spoilage though coliform contami-

Table 4—Secondary Flora of Ripened Cheese.

Cheese	Secondary flora
Soft (surface ripened)	
Camembert	Yeasts
Brie	*Penicillium caseicolum*
Semisoft	
Caerphilly	Lactobacilli
Limburger (surface ripened)	Yeasts, *Brevibacterium linens*
Blue-vein	
Roquefort	*Penicillium roqueforti*,
Gorgonzola	yeasts, micrococci
Stilton	
Hard	
Cheddar	Lactobacilli, pediococci
Emmentaler	*Propionibacterium shermanii*,
	group D streptococci
Gruyère	*Propionibacterium shermanii*,
	group D streptococci,
	yeasts, coryneforms, *B. linens*

Adapted from Law[27]

nation has been associated with the gassy defect in cheese making (for example, Cheddar).[24] Ripened cheese is more prone to surface growth of yeast and molds particularly if exposed to atmospheric oxygen. Defects in cheese have also been attributed to the starter cultures, culture failure, and undesirable as well as the secondary flora.[27]

Microbial competition, reduced water activity, organic acids, and a low pH generally limit the growth of pathogens in cheese. A slow starter culture (due to bacteriophage, antibiotics, etc.) can allow growth of bacteria related to foodborne illnesses such as *Staphylococcus*, *Salmonella*, and enteropathogenic *E. coli*,[5, 22, 29] which enter with raw milk or as post-pasteurization contaminants. *S. aureus* will normally decline during the ripening stage, but if sufficient numbers ($>10^7$ per ml) are reached during cheese making, enterotoxin may persist in the cheese. *Salmonella* spp. survive beyond the ripening period[5] with the potential to cause infection at relatively low doses.[11] Most enteropathogenic strains of *E. coli* are inactivated at pH$<$ 5.0[29] although in low-acid, semisoft, surface-ripened cheese, fecal coliforms are commonly found.[5, 35] Post-heating contamination or the use of contaminated raw milk can be a source of *L. monocytogenes*, as was implicated in an outbreak involving a low-acid Mexican-style cheese.[13] *Listeria* is capable of surviving in Cheddar, Camembert, and cottage cheese[38] although growth is limited because of the low pH of most cheeses.

45.82   Yogurt and Fermented Milks

Yogurt and fermented milks (buttermilk) and cream (sour cream) are unripened cultured dairy products. They are generally ready for consumption with minimum processing after development of the desired acidity through a lactic acid fermentation. Yogurt fermentation involves a mixed culture of *S. thermophilus* and *Lactobacillus bulgaricus*, which are thermophilic in nature, while lactic *Streptococcus* and *Leuconostoc* spp. are normally used in cultured milks and sour cream. The more exotic cultured milks (e.g., kefir, koumis) are derived from mixed fermentations involving yeasts, *Lactobacillus* spp., lactic streptococci, and *Leuconostoc* spp. *Lactobacillus acidophilus* may be used in the production of both yogurts and fermented milks.[24]

In a normal fermentation, a final pH of $<$4.5 is developed in cultured milk products. This low pH generally prevents the growth of most spoilage and pathogenic organisms, although interference with acid development may allow growth of undesirable microorganisms. Yeasts and molds, which tolerate the lower pH, are the more predominant organisms involved in the spoilage of cultured milks. *Bacillus subtilus* and *Bacillus cereus* can cause bitter flavors if large numbers survive pasteurization. Coliforms, if present, decline rapidly after manufacture of yogurt, although they may survive in cultured buttermilk and sour cream.[29]

Fermented dairy products normally contain high numbers of starter microorganisms or secondary ripening flora, making total counts insignificant except in products that are heated to inactivate added cultures. Yeast and mold counts and coliform counts may be used as indicators of processing sanitation with some fermented products. Counts of psychrotrophic bacteria are useful for cottage cheese and similar products that are subject to spoilage by psychrotrophic bacteria.

45.83 Recommended Methods

Yeast and Mold Counts—Chapter 16, SMEDP[37]
Coliform Counts—Chapter 24, SMEDP[37]
Psychrotrophic Counts—Chapter 9, SMEDP[37]
(Cottage cheese)—Chapter 9, SMEDP[37]
Other Methods for Specific Determinations
Staphylococcus Enterotoxin/Thermonuclease—Chapter 34
For individual pathogens such as *Salmonella*, *Campylobacter*, *Listeria*, and *Yersinia* consult appropriate chapters of this book.
Consult Chapter 39 for rapid methods.

45.9 REFERENCES

1. ADPI. 1965. "Standards for Grades of Dry Milks, Including Methods of Analysis." Am. Dairy Prod. Inst. Chicago, Ill.
2. Bishop, J. R. and White, C. H. 1986. Assessment of dairy product quality and potential shelf-life—a review. J. Food. Prot. 49: 739.
3. Bodyfelt, F. 1980. Quality assurance: Heat resistant psychrotrophs affect quality of fluid milk. Dairy Record. March 1980: 97.
4. Bramley, A. J., McKinnon, C. H., Staker, R. T., and Simpkin, D. L. 1984. The effect of udder infection on the bacterial flora of the bulk milk of ten dairy herds. J. Appl. Bacteriol. 57: 317.
5. Bryan, F. L. 1983. Epidemiology of milk-borne diseases. J. Food. Prot. 46: 637.
6. Bryan, F. L. 1988. Risks associated with vehicles of foodborne pathogens and toxins. J. Food Prot. 51: 498.
7. Campbell, J. R. and Marshall, R. T. 1975. "The Science of Providing Milk for Man." McGraw-Hill Book Co., New York.
8. Cousin, M. A. 1982. Presence and activity of psychrotrophic microorganisms in milk and dairy products: A review. J. Food. Prot. 45: 172.
9. Cousin, M. A. and Marth, E. H. 1977. Cheddar cheese made from milk that was precultured with psychrotrophic bacteria. J. Dairy Sci. 60: 1048.
10. Cousins, C. M., Sharpe, M. E., and Law, B. A. 1977. The bacteriological quality of milk for Cheddar cheese making. Dairy Ind. Int. 42(7): 12.
11. D'Aoust, J. -Y., Warburton, D. W., and Sewell, A. M. 1985. *Salmonella typhimurium* phage-type 10 from Cheddar cheese implicated in a major Canadian foodborne outbreak. J. Food Prot. 48: 1062.
12. de Vries, T. 1975. Primary infection of milk. 1. Bacterial infection inside the udder and its relation with the cell count in milk. Neth. Milk Dairy J. 29: 127.
13. Donnelly, C. W. 1988. Listeria and U.S. dairy products: The issues in perspective. Dairy and Food Sanita. 8: 297.
14. Foster, E. M., Nelson, F. E., Speck, M. L., Doetsch, R. N., and Olson, J. C. Jr. 1957. "Dairy Microbiology." Prentice-Hall, Inc., Englewood Cliffs, N. J.
15. Frazier, W. C. 1958. "Food Microbiology." McGraw-Hill Book Co., New York, N. Y.

16. Garvie, E. I. and Farrow, J. A. E. 1982. *Streptococcus lactis* subsp. *cremoris* comb. nov. and *Streptococcus lactis* subsp. *diacetilactis* nom. rev., comb. nov. Int. J. Syst. Bacteriol. 32: 453.

17. George, E. Jr., Olson, J. C. Jr., Jezeski, J. J., and Coulter, S. T. 1959. The growth of staphylococci in condensed skim milk. J. Dairy Sci. 42: 816.

18. Goff, H. D. 1988. Hazard analysis and critical control point identification in ice cream plants. Dairy and Food Sanita. 8: 131.

19. Gunderson, F. L., Gunderson, H. W., and Ferguson, E. R. Jr. 1963. "Food Standards and Definitions in the United States—A Guide Book." Academic Press, New York.

20. HHS/PHS/FDA. 1985. Grade A pasteurized milk ordinance, 1985 revision. U.S. Dept. of Health and Human Serv. Pub. Health Serv./Food and Drug Admin. Pub. No. 229.

21. Jeffrey, D.C. and Wilson, J. 1987. Effect of mastitis related bacteria on total bacterial count of bulk milk supplies. J. Soc. Dairy Tech. 40(2): 23.

22. Jervis, D. I. 1988. Behaviour of pathogens in dairy products. Dairy Ind. Int. 53(3): 15.

23. Kleter, G. 1974. The bacterial flora in aseptically drawn milk. Neth. Milk Dairy J. 28: 220.

24. Kosikowski, F. W. 1982. "Cheese and Fermented Milk Foods," 2nd ed. F. V. Kosikowski and Assoc., Brooktondale, N. Y.

25. Kurweil, R. and Busse, M. 1973. Total count and microflora of freshly drawn milk. Milchwissenschaft 28: 427.

26. Kwee, W. S., Dommett, T. W., Giles, J. E., Roberts, R., and Smith, R. A. D. 1986. Microbiological parameters during powdered milk manufacture. Aust. J. Dairy Tech. 41: 3.

27. Law, B. A. 1984. Microorganisms and their enzymes in the maturation of cheeses. In "Progress in Industrial Microbiology," Vol. 19. Modern applications of traditional biotechnologies, p. 245. Elsevier Sci. Pub. Co. Inc., New York.

28. Marth, E. H. 1985. Pathogens in milk and milk products. In "Standard Methods for the Examination of Dairy Products," 15th ed., ed. G. H. Richardson. Amer. Pub. Health Assn. Washington, D.C.

29. Mikolajcik, E. M. 1980. Psychrotrophic bacteria and dairy product quality. 3. Organisms of public health importance in fermented dairy foods. Cult. Dairy Prod. J. 15(2): 14.

30. Minor, T. E. and Marth, E. H. 1972. *Staphylococcus aureus* and enterotoxin A in cream and butter. J. Dairy Sci. 55: 1410.

31. NAS/NRC. 1969. An evaluation of the *Salmonella* problem. Committee on *Salmonella*. Nat. Res. Council, Nat. Acad. of Sci. Washington, D.C.

32. Nat. CDC. 1970. Staphylococcal food poisoning traced to butter—Alabama. Morbid. Mortal. Weekly Rep. 19: 271.

33. National Mastitis Council, Inc. 1987. "Laboratory and Field Handbook on Bovine Mastitis." W. D. Hoard and Sons Co. Fort Atkinson, Wis.

34. NRC. 1985. Application of microbiological criteria to foods and food ingredients. In "An Evaluation of the Role of Microbiological Criteria for Foods and Food Ingredients," p. 184. Nat. Res. Coun. Nat. Acad. Press, Washington, D.C.

35. Olson, J. C. Jr. and Mocquot, G. 1980. Milk and Milk Products. In "Microbial Ecology of Foods," eds. J. H. Silliker, R. P. Elliott, A. C. Baird-Parker, F. L. Bryan, J. H. B. Christian, D. S. Clark, J. C. Olson Jr., and T. A. Roberts, Vol. II, p. 470. Academic Press, New York.

36. Overcast, W. W. and Atmaram, K. 1974. The role of *Bacillus cereus* in sweet curdling of fluid milk. J. Milk Food Technol. 37: 233.

37. Richardson, G. H. 1985. "Standard Methods for the Examination of Dairy Products." 15th ed. Am. Pub. Health Assn., Washington, D.C.

38. Rosenow, E. M. and Marth, E. H. 1987. *Listeria*, listeriosis and dairy foods: A review. Cult. Dairy Prod. J. 22(4): 13.

39. Schleifer, K. H. 1987. Recent changes in the taxonomy of lactic acid bacteria. FEMS Microbiol. Rev. 46: 201.

40. Speck, M. L. and Adams, D. M. 1976. Symposium: Impact of heat stable microbial enzymes

in food processing. Heat resistant proteolytic enzymes from bacterial sources. J. Dairy Sci. 59: 786.

41. Stadhouders, J. 1975. Microbes in milk and dairy products. An ecological approach. Neth. Milk Dairy J. 29: 104.

42. Thomas, S. B. 1972. The significance of thermoduric bacteria in refrigerated bulk collected milk. Dairy Ind. Int. 37(9): 475.

43. Thomas, S. B. 1974. The microflora of bulk collected milk—Part 1. Dairy Ind. Int. 39(8): 237.

44. Thomas, S. B. 1974. The microflora of bulk collected milk—Part 2. Dairy Ind. Int. 39(8): 279.

45. Thomas, S. B. and Druce, R. G. 1972. The incidence and significance of coli-aerogenes bacteria in refrigerated bulk collected milk. Dairy Ind. Int. 37: 593.

46. USDA. 1977. Federal and state standards for the composition of milk products (and certain non-milkfat products). Agr. Handbook No. 51. U.S. Dept. Agr., Washington, D.C.

47. USDA. 1988a. Grading and inspection, general specifications for approved plants and standards for grades of dairy products. 7CFR58 Off. of the Fed. Reg., Nat. Arch. and Rec. Admin., Washington, D.C.

48. USDA. 1988b. Subpart B—General specifications for dairy plants approved for USDA inspection grading service. 7CFR58.135. Off. of the Fed. Reg., Nat. Arch. and Rec. Admin., Washington, D.C.

49. USDA. 1988c. Subpart B—General specifications for dairy plants approved for USDA inspection grading service. 7CFR58.345. Off. of the Fed. Reg., Nat. Arch. and Rec. Admin., Washington, D.C.

50. USDA. 1988d. Subpart B—General specifications for dairy plants approved for USDA inspection grading service. 7CFR58.346. Off. of the Fed. Reg., Nat. Arch. and Rec. Admin., Washington, D.C.

51. USDA. 1988e. Subpart B—General specifications for dairy plants approved for USDA inspection grading service. 7CFR58.348. Off. of the Fed. Reg., Nat. Arch. and Rec. Admin., Washington, D.C.

52. USDA. 1988f. Subpart B—General specifications for dairy plants approved for USDA inspection grading service. 7CFR58.349. Off. of the Fed. Reg., Nat. Arch. and Rec. Admin., Washington, D.C.

53. USDA. 1988g. Subpart B—General specifications for dairy plants approved for USDA inspection grading service. 7CFR58.528. Off. of the Fed. Reg., Nat. Arch. and Rec. Admin., Washington, D.C.

54. USDA. 1988h. Subpart B—General specifications for dairy plants approved for USDA inspection grading service. 7CFR58.648. Off. of the Fed. Reg., Nat. Arch. and Rec. Admin., Washington, D.C.

55. USDA. 1988i. Subpart B—General specifications for dairy plants approved for USDA inspection grading service. 7CFR58.653. Off. of the Fed. Reg., Nat. Arch. and Rec. Admin., Washington, D.C.

56. USDA. 1988j. Subpart B—General specifications for dairy plants approved for USDA inspection grading service. 7CFR58.938. Off. of the Fed. Reg., Nat. Arch. and Rec. Admin., Washington, D.C.

57. USDA. 1988k. Subpart L—United States standards for grades of nonfat dry milk (spray process). 7CFR58.2528. Off. of the Fed. Reg., Nat. Arch. and Rec. Admin., Washington, D.C.

58. USDA. 1988l. Subpart L—United States standards for grades of nonfat dry milk (spray process). 7CFR58.2529. Off. of the Fed. Reg., Nat. Arch. and Rec. Admin., Washington, D.C.

59. USDA. 1988m. Subpart M—United States standards for grades of nonfat dry milk (roller process). 7CFR58.2553. Off. of the Fed. Reg., Nat. Arch. and Rec. Admin., Washington, D.C.

60. USDA. 1988n. Subpart M—United States standards for grades of nonfat dry milk (roller process). 7CFR58.2554. Off. of the Fed. Reg., Nat. Arch. and Rec. Admin., Washington, D.C.

61. USDA. 1988o. Subpart O—United States standards for dry whey. 7CFR58.2605. Off. of the Fed. Reg., Nat. Arch. and Rec. Admin., Washington, D.C.

62. USDA. 1988p. Subpart Q—United States standards for grades of sweetcream buttermilk. 7CFR58.2654. Off. of the Fed. Reg., Nat. Arch. and Rec. Admin., Washington, D.C.

63. USDA. 1988q. Subpart S—United States standards for grades of dry whole milk. 7CFR58.2705. Off. of the Fed. Reg., Nat. Arch. and Rec. Admin., Washington, D.C.

64. USDA. 1988r. Subpart S—United States standards for grades of dry whole milk. 7CFR58.2708. Off. of the Fed. Reg., Nat. Arch. and Rec. Admin., Washington, D.C.

65. USDA. 1988s. Subpart U—United States standards for instant nonfat dry milk. 7CFR58.2753. Off. of the Fed. Reg., Nat. Arch. and Rec. Admin., Washington, D.C.

66. USDA. 1988t. Subpart U—United States standards for instant nonfat dry milk. 7CFR58.2754. Off. of the Fed. Reg., Nat. Arch. and Rec. Admin., Washington, D.C.

67. USDA. 1988u. Subpart V—United States standards for grades of edible dry casein (acid). 7CFR58.2803. Off. of the Fed. Reg., Nat. Arch. and Rec. Admin., Washington, D.C.

68. USDA. 1988v. Subpart V—United States standards for grades of edible dry casein (acid). 7CFR58.2804. Off. of the Fed. Reg., Nat. Arch. and Rec. Admin., Washington, D.C.

69. USDA. 1988w. Subpart V—United States standards for grades of edible dry casein (acid). 7CFR58.2805. Off. of the Fed. Reg., Nat. Arch. and Rec. Admin., Washington, D.C.

70. Washam, C. J., Olson, H. C., and Vedamuthu, E. R. 1977. Heat-resistant psychrotrophic bacteria isolated from pasteurized milk. J. Food Prot. 40: 101.

Chapter 46

EGGS AND EGG PRODUCTS

Glenn Froning, Amy Izat, Greg Riley, and Howard Magwire

46.1 INTRODUCTION

In 1987, the number of eggs consumed in the United States was 250 per person. Of this, 83% were consumed as shell eggs and 17% as egg products in the form of liquid, frozen, and dried products, as well as specialties such as frozen precooked omelettes. The 17% represents about three-fourths billion pounds per year and an increasing proportion of shell eggs consumed as egg products. In 1980, 13% of all eggs consumed in the United States were consumed as egg products.

Shell eggs have many uses in the home, in restaurants, and in institutions, either alone or as ingredients in other foods. Egg products generally are used in the food industry in mixes, bakery foods, noodles, mayonnaise and salad dressings, candies, ice cream, and so on to provide desirable functional properties. There are also several other uses, such as pet foods. The widespread use of eggs as ingredients of other foods makes them prime suspects in foodborne disease outbreaks because of their excellent nutritional environment for supporting bacterial growth. This potential hazard requires careful microbiological control in production and usage.

The production of shell eggs has undergone considerable change during the past 40 years. In the 1940s, most eggs were produced on family farms by small flocks of a few hundred birds or less. Today, most eggs are produced by flocks of 30,000 or more, with some commercial operations reaching millions of birds. Many of these operations are automated with mechanical feeding, watering, egg collection, and cartoning systems. Over the years, shell egg quality has been improved by genetic selection of birds, better production practices, refrigeration of the eggs, and more rapid marketing systems.

Shell eggs are graded according to exterior and interior quality factors and sized according to weight. The standards, grades, and weight classes are established by the U.S. Department of Agriculture (USDA). USDA operates a voluntary grading program. Before marketing, shell eggs go through a mechanized process of sorting, washing, drying, candling (grading), weighing, and packaging. Undergrade eggs (with poor shell condition or poor interior quality) are usually sent to an egg breaking firm for the production of egg products. Graded, as well as nest-run eggs (not sized or graded), are also commonly used in producing egg products. Federal law prohibits the use of "leakers" (with shell and shell membranes broken) and eggs showing evidence of spoilage for producing products for human consumption.

The quality of egg products has greatly improved in recent years. USDA is responsible for mandatory inspection of egg products plants. On July 1, 1971, federal legislation went into effect requiring mandatory USDA inspection of egg products operations (Egg Products Inspection Act, Public Law 91-5971). Regulations established under this law specify minimum standards for breaking stock, the sanitary conditions of facilities and equipment, pasteurization conditions, holding conditions, and other parts of the operations. This law also provides that egg products shall be *Salmonella* negative, using a specified sampling and testing program. Over the years the industry has applied new technologies to improve the quality of egg products, and companies purchasing egg products have specified tight production and microbiological requirements.

Current regulations and quality-control procedures have continued to evolve from work performed in the 1950s and 1960s as a cooperative effort between industry, the Food and Drug Administration (FDA), and USDA. Before implementation of continuous USDA inspection in 1971, numerous outbreaks of salmonellosis in humans were attributed to egg products. As a result of industry-government cooperation, new processes and control procedures were developed, and thus since 1971, commercially produced egg products have not been a major source of human salmonellosis.

46.2 GENERAL CONSIDERATIONS

46.21 Composition

As in other foods, the composition of the egg influences the types of organisms that will develop. Since the parts of the egg differ considerably in composition, susceptibility to spoilage or the growth of pathogens differs considerably in each part.

Shell eggs consist of approximately 9.5% shell, 63% white, and 27.5% yolk.[16] The shell is relatively porous, containing mostly calcium carbonate crystals; a keratin-type protein coats the shell and fills the pores. Two membranes separate the egg white from the shell, and as the egg cools, an air cell forms generally at the large end of the egg where the two membranes separate. During storage, this air cell increases in size as water evaporates through the shell. A membrane also surrounds the yolk. The thick portion of the egg white, known as the chalazae, holds the yolk near the center of the egg.

Egg white contains approximately 10.5% to 11.5% solids, of which 86.0% is protein, 9.0% total reducing sugars (3.2% free glucose), and 5.0% ash. Only a trace of lipids is present. Several of the egg white proteins have biological activity that retards bacterial growth either through lyses of bacteria or by tying up certain nutrients: lysozyme lyses many gram-positive microorganisms; conalbumin binds iron and other metals, retarding growth of certain bacteria; ovomucoid inhibits trypsin activity; avidin binds biotin; and riboflavin is bound to protein. The pH of egg white is less than 8.0 at oviposition but increases rapidly to pH 9.0 during holding in air, then slowly levels off at about pH 9.3. The increase in pH is due to the loss of CO_2 from the egg white.

Egg yolk contains 52% solids, of which 31.0% is protein, 64.0% is lipids (41.9% triglycerides, 18.8% phospholipids, and 3.3% cholesterol), 2.0% is total carbohydrates (0.4% free glucose), and 3.0% is ash. The pH of the yolk in freshly laid eggs is 6.0 and changes very little during holding. The pH of the blended yolk and white varies between pH 7.0 and pH 7.6.

46.22   Functional Properties

Egg yolk and egg white have some unique functional properties that make them useful, not only when prepared by themselves, but also when used as ingredients in other foods. Coagulation, emulsifying power, and foaming power are the most important of these functional properties. In the manufacture of egg products, the processing and holding conditions must not damage these properties. For example, pasteurization times and temperatures have been established to destroy pathogens while not substantially damaging functional properties.

46.23   Pasteurization

USDA prescribes minimum conditions of pasteurization for egg products sufficient to destroy harmful viable microorganisms. Liquid whole eggs are required to be held at 60°C for 3.5 min. Recently, research has been conducted on the combined use of increased thermal treatment and aseptic packaging to produce extended shelf-life liquid whole egg.[6,28,29]

Many factors affect the thermal resistance of *Salmonella* in eggs. Salt, pH, sugar, type of acid used to adjust the pH, and total solids are all important. In liquid whole egg, *Salmonella* species have maximum heat resistance at about pH 5.5. The actual pasteurizing condition required is determined experimentally for each product. Cotterill et al.[17] constructed thermal destruction curves for several egg products. These curves are useful in estimating pasteurization time and temperatures.

USDA permits dried egg whites to be pasteurized in the dry state (hot-room method) at a minimum temperature of 54.4°C for not less than 7 days in lieu of pasteurization of the liquid egg white before drying.[18] Spray-dried whites having approximately 6% moisture should be filled into bulk packages as they discharge from the dryer and the packages are moved immediately to the "hot room." Otherwise, it may take 3 or 4 days to heat the center of the package to the hot-room temperature.[62]

46.3   NORMAL FLORA

46.31   Shell Eggs

The shell and the contents of the egg at the time of oviposition are generally sterile or harbor very few microorganisms.[13,30,58] Contamination of the shell occurs afterwards from nesting material, floor litter, and avian fecal matter. Due to the presence of pores, the shell is a poor barrier to microorganisms, whereas the shell membrane appears to act as a fair barrier.[58] The contaminating flora is mainly gram-positive cocci, but gram-negative rods are also present in low numbers;[9] however, the gram-negative organisms generally cause spoilage of shell eggs. The egg contents may become contaminated by improper washing and storage methods. The physical and chemical barrier provided by the egg shell, shell membranes,[31,35] and antimicrobial substances in the albumen favor the penetration and multiplication of the gram-negative bacteria.[8] The egg yolk offers an excellent medium for growth of microorganisms.[58]

46.32   Egg Products

The number of bacteria in liquid egg products before pasteurization depends on several factors, including the condition and quality of the shell eggs used for breaking, the method of washing and sanitizing the shell eggs, the sanitation of the equipment, and the time and temperature at which the liquid is held. The most common types of bacteria found in liquid eggs before pasteurizing are gram-negative rods.

The total aerobic plate count of commercial egg products is usually relatively low, less than 25,000 per gram, because of pasteurization or other heat treatment.[15,52] Yolk containing 10% salt need not be pasteurized if used in mayonnaise or salad dressing having a pH of 4.1 or less in accordance with the FDA requirement. Bacteria that survive pasteurization are usually heat-resistant *Bacillus*, enterococci, and micrococci.[50] After pasteurization, care must be taken to avoid recontamination.

46.4   FLORA CHANGES IN SPOILAGE

46.41   Shell Eggs for Breaking

As discussed in Section 46.21, eggs possess several natural barriers that prevent bacterial invasion, i.e., the shell, membranes, and antibacterial factors present in the egg white. Almost all eggs in the United States are washed before they are packed. Bacterial contamination can occur through improper washing.[48] For example, if the wash solution temperature is less than the temperature of the egg, bacteria can be drawn into the egg through shell pores when the contents contract. Also, eggs washed with water contaminated with iron are more susceptible to spoilage, apparently because excessive iron overcomes the ability of conalbumin to inhibit bacterial growth. Egg washers that are not properly designed, maintained, and cleaned can increase contamination of the shell.[47] Cracks in the shell also present an avenue of contamination.

The most common spoilage organisms of shell eggs are gram-negative types, such as *Pseudomonas, Serratia, Proteus, Alcaligenes*, and *Citrobacter*. For example, *Pseudomonas* spoilage is commonly found in eggs that have been improperly cleaned and stored for extended periods. They usually show a green fluorescence of the whites under ultraviolet light or other discolorations and off-odors.[27] If sufficiently advanced, spoilage is evident by odor and liquefaction of the yolk as well as by a thinning of the whites.

46.42   Egg Products

The manufacture of egg products begins with egg-breaking and separating operations. An automated system consists of a loader, a washer, and a breaker-separator unit. Three persons are required to operate this system. The person who places the shell eggs on the automatic loader also removes eggs not suitable for use in edible products. Another person checks the eggs coming from the washer and removes eggs that are not clean, as well as eggs that have become leakers or are otherwise unsuitable. The operator of the egg-breaking machine controls its speed to permit proper inspection of the contents. This person removes cracker heads and separating cups when an egg is found unsuitable (contents showing off-odor or liquefaction must be removed and not allowed to contaminate other eggs). With such a system, the liquid egg products should have relatively good microbiological quality. Any bacteria in the products will come from the exterior of the shell, or from the interior where insufficient growth of the organisms had not been detected by the operator. Since the contents of individual eggs must be examined, centrifugal egg separators are not allowed for edible eggs in breaking plants. Centrifugal separators have been used recently by the food service industry. Many states have banned their use in restaurants because of microbiological concerns.

These devices also are routinely used for separating inedible eggs in many breaking plants.

USDA has specified the maximum temperatures and times for holding liquid egg products after preparation to minimize bacterial growth.

46.43   New Egg Products

Several new convenience egg products have been marketed in recent years, such as frozen egg sandwiches, frozen egg breakfast meals, low-cholesterol frozen egg products (yolk-reduced or yolkless), pickled eggs, and diced hard-cooked eggs for salad bars. Special precautions are necessary to ensure that end-point cooking temperatures and handling procedures maintain low bacterial counts as well as pathogen-free products. Hard-cooked eggs have become particularly popular in salad bars and in various pickled products. Commercial hard-cooked eggs are packed in containers with an organic acid and mold inhibitors such as 0.1% sodium benzoate or potassium sorbate.[33] To maintain low bacterial loads, hard-cooked eggs must be cooled rapidly after cooking, and strict sanitation must be maintained during peeling, handling, and packaging.[57] It has been recommended that hard-cooked eggs packed in an acid-benzoate solution be given a final heat treatment in the package.[58] Eggs packed in a citric acid-sodium benzoate solution should be stored at $-1.0°C$ for maximum shelf life.

46.5   PATHOGENS OF CONCERN

46.51   *Salmonella*

Salmonellae are of most concern in egg products. Other pathogens have been isolated, but they have not been found to be as important in foodborne disease outbreaks. Toxigenic staphylococci usually are not found in either unpasteurized or pasteurized egg products, although they present a potential problem in salt yolks since salt selectively favors their growth. Cases of salmonellosis traceable to eggs and egg products have been reported in the past. However, these have greatly diminished since the initiation of pasteurization and other requirements of mandatory USDA inspection.

The number of *Salmonella* species isolated from unpasteurized liquid egg products is usually fewer than 1 per gram. The specified pasteurization procedures produce a 6 to 8 log reduction of *Salmonella* in liquid egg products.[15,52,55] Thus, the likelihood of finding *Salmonella* in a pasteurized product is low. If found, its presence may well be due to recontamination. If so, all processing procedures will require very careful inspection to eliminate the source of the contamination.

Recently, *Salmonella enteritidis* has become a major concern. There have been increasing outbreaks in the Northeast United States, and this infection has been reported to be due to transovarian contamination.[56] *Salmonella enteritidis* infections have been of particular concern in England. New control measures for breeding and laying flocks are being developed by USDA and FDA in the United States.

46.52 Other Egg Pathogens

Pathogenic organisms of emerging concern in eggs and egg products include *Campylobacter jejuni*, *Listeria monocytogenes*, and *Yersinia enterocolitica*. All three are resistant to lysozyme.[37] *Campylobacter* can survive (under anaerobic conditions) or grow (under aerobic conditions) in inoculated yolk, in albumen and yolk mixtures, in liquid whole egg, on the surface of the shell, and in the inner shell and shell membranes.[14,21,34,38,49] The organism is not sensitive to the high pH of the albumen but is sensitive to conalbumin.[14] Therefore, *Campylobacter* cannot survive for extended time periods ($>$ 48 hr) in albumen.[14,34,38] The killing effect in albumen is temperature dependent, with the longest survival time at 4°C.[14,38] *Campylobacter* could not be recovered from commercially pasteurized yolk, albumen, liquid whole egg, or scrambled egg mix, or from chopped whole eggs or egg and cheese omelets.[38] It has been reported that 8.1% of laying hens are chronic shedders (positive $>$ 30% of sampling times) of the organism, but the organism has not been recovered from the contents of eggs produced by infected hens.[5, 21, 53] Identical serotypes were recovered from infected hens' feces and human patients in an outbreak in which eggs were uncooked.[23]

Listeria monocytogenes and *Y. enterocolitica* both grow at refrigeration temperatures.[7,10,46] It has been estimated that 10% to 30% of personnel who work in egg product plants and slaughterhouses harbor *L. monocytogenes*.[40] Listeriosis occurs frequently in the hen, producing lesions in the oviduct; however, there is no indication of transovarian transmission.[32,39,51] *Listeria* can grow rapidly in liquid egg or reconstituted dried egg at room or refrigerated temperatures.[43,61] The organism was recovered from the yolk of an inoculated fried egg in which the albumen had congealed but the yolk was still soft.[61] The organism has also been recovered from pasteurized milk (61.7°C for 3.5 min, and 72.2°C for 16.4 sec) when pre-pasteurization levels were greater than 5 $\times$ 10⁴/ml, and 1 $\times$ 10⁵, respectively.[7,11] Present egg product pasteurization requirements[18] may not be adequate for destruction of the organism if high levels are present. *Y. enterocolitica* has been isolated from domestic fowl, game birds, wild birds, processed poultry, and egg products.[19,20,36,46] The organism is capable of survival under extremely alkaline conditions.[3,42,59] Certain strains of *Y. enterocolitica* can survive in egg washwater under simulated commercial conditions of pH 10 and 38°C.[54] Southam et al.[54] recommended that washwater temperatures be maintained at pH $\geqslant$ 10 and a temperature $\geqslant$40°C.[54] On peeled hard-cooked eggs, the organism can survive for 8 to 9 weeks at $-$20°C[41] and can grow at 4°C in a 0.5% citric acid solution.[4]

46.6   INDICATORS OF LACK OF SANITATION

Coliform, as well as yeast and mold counts, are generally used as indicators of unsanitary conditions. *E. coli* counts may be a more important indicator than coliform counts.

Chemical methods also indicate poor egg quality or poor storage conditions. For example, the amount of lactic acid formed during bacterial growth has been used to show improper handling and poor sanitation.[45]

46.7   RECOMMENDED METHODS[1,2]

46.71   Sampling and Preparation of the Sample

1. Shell eggs

Select shell eggs at random from cases or cartons representative of the lot. Transfer the eggs to clean cartons or cases for transport to the laboratory, and maintain the eggs at temperatures below 10°C until analyzed. Avoid the sweating of the eggs that results from transferring shell eggs from cold storage temperatures of around 4.4°C to room temperature without a tempering period, particularly when humidity is high. Returning sweating eggs to cold storage enhances the penetration of bacteria through the shell. Also, moisture on the shell surface greatly increases the chances of contamination during the removal of the egg contents. Therefore, the eggs should not be handled until they have been warmed to room temperature.

If the interior of the shell eggs is to be examined, use the following steps:

a. Wash each egg with a brush using soap and water 11 degrees warmer than that of the egg, at least a temperature of 32.2°C.
b. Drain off excess moisture and immerse the egg in 70% alcohol for 10 min.
c. Remove from alcohol, drain, and flame.
d. Handle the alcohol-flamed eggs using sterile gloves, and aseptically remove the egg meat by cracking the egg with a sterile breaking knife. Sterile sample containers should be used; for example, sterilized blender jars or mason jars for use with Osterizer blenders are satisfactory containers. Otherwise, shake the contents of the sample container with glass beads, or beat with a sterile spoon, or with a sterile electric mixer until the sample is homogeneous. For separate examination of egg white and egg yolk, use a sterile commercial separator or a sterile spoon. Free the yolk of excess egg white by rolling it on a sterile towel.
e. Weigh 11 g of the homogenous sample into a 99 ml saline, phosphate, or peptone water dilution blank containing glass beads.
f. Shake 25 times by hand through a 1 ft arc for 7 sec.
g. Prepare appropriate serial dilutions using similar dilution blanks.

Several methods can be used to make microbiological counts of the shell surface, e.g., giving a broth surface rinse, or removing the white and yolk and then blending the shells and shell membranes with sterile water, broth, or an isotonic salt solution.

In the United States, sampling procedures are usually those specified by USDA for testing *Salmonella*.[60,63] The samples may be used for other microbiological analyses. Basically three types of samples are taken for *Salmonella* determination: surveillance, confirmation, and certification. Surveillance samples, the routine samples taken to determine the presence or absence of *Salmonella*, are collected and analyzed by the processor. Confirmation samples are taken by USDA inspectors for verification of the surveillance sampling and testing programs and are analyzed by a USDA laboratory. Certificates are issued by USDA for *Salmonella*-negative products usually when requested by a customer of the processor. For example, some customers in foreign countries request USDA certification. Certificates are issued only if a certified sample has been drawn by USDA, analyzed by its laboratory, and found to be negative for *Salmonella*.

Where egg products are to be used in Category I products, more intensive sampling and testing are usually required. Some customers, for example, require using the sampling plan described by Foster[31] and the testing of 1,500 g per lot.

2. Liquid and frozen egg products

Obtain samples of liquid eggs from vats or tanks at the plant or from containers. Make sure that the product has been thoroughly mixed. Use a sterilized dipper or sampling tube to withdraw the sample. Sterile pint mason jars or friction top cans are satisfactory for holding the samples. Obtain about three-fourths of a pint of sample and hold it below 4.4°C for no more than 4 hr if possible. Avoid freezing, which will destroy many of the bacteria present. If there is doubt as to the homogeneity of the liquid in a vat, take several three-fourths-pint samples and composite them in a 2-quart jar to give a more representative sample.

Record the temperature of the containers from which the samples were taken. Often temperature may be the key to abnormal bacterial populations because temperatures above 7.2°C indicate improper handling.

Select cans of frozen egg representative of the lot. Open the cans, and with a sterile spoon remove any ice or frost on the frozen egg. The area selected for drilling should not be humped or peaked. With a high-speed electric drill, puncture the egg about 1 inch from the edge of the can using the following steps:

a. Slant the bit so it will go through the center of the frozen egg to within an inch or two of the opposite lower edge of the can.
b. Transfer the shavings to a sample container with a sterile spoon. Keep the shavings frozen at all times.
c. Pack in an insulated box with dry ice for transport to the laboratory.

Frequency of sampling of liquid and frozen egg products is based on the performance and history of a plant's capability to produce a *Salmonella*-negative product. Frequency of sampling is increased or decreased according to a flow chart (Figure 1) issued by USDA.[63,64] One 4-oz sample is collected per lot (one lot may represent a day's production) and from this amount 100 g are used for *Salmonella* analysis. For a plant without a history of *Salmonella*-negative product, all lots must be sampled until 83 consecutive lots show negative *Salmonella* results. Sampling then is decreased to 1 in every 2 lots. If 83 consecutive lots are negative, sampling is decreased to 1 in every 4 lots. After this period, if 83 more consecutive lots are negative, sampling is decreased to 1 in every 8 lots. If *Salmonella*-positive lots occur at any time, sampling must then be increased according to the flow chart.

3. Dried egg products

Sample dried egg products with a sterilized spoon or trier. Transfer sample to a sterile jar or plastic bag. Do not fill the container more than two-thirds full to leave room for mixing.

If the product is in small packages, select several unopened packages. Open them at the laboratory under aseptic conditions and transfer a liberal quantity to a sterile can or beaker. Thoroughly mix with a sterile spoon to obtain a homogeneous mixture.

As required by USDA, each lot of dried egg product must be sampled and tested for *Salmonella*.[64] Usually a lot is considered to be a day's production of each product from each dryer.

For surveillance sampling, the company is required to have analyzed 3 samples drawn from each lot of each product produced from each dryer. Alternatively they may elect to have surveillance samples drawn and analyzed at the same level as that prescribed for certification. For certification, the number of samples drawn and the amount of product tested from each lot are given as follows:

Number of containers in lot	Number of individual samples to be drawn	Number of analyses and amount of sample to be analyzed per analysis
50 or less	4	(1) 100 g
51 to 150	8	(2) 100 g
151 to 500	12	(3) 100 g
501 to 1500	16	(4) 100 g
Over 1500	20	(5) 100 g

Twenty-five gram of each sample are removed, and 4 of these samples are combined to make the 100 g composite used for the *Salmonella* test.

4. Tests to be done on each lot:

    Aerobic Plate Count 35°C—Chapter 4

    Aerobic Plate Count 32°C—Chapter 4

    Coliform Group—Chapters 4 and 24

    Enterobacteriaceae—Chapters 4 and 24

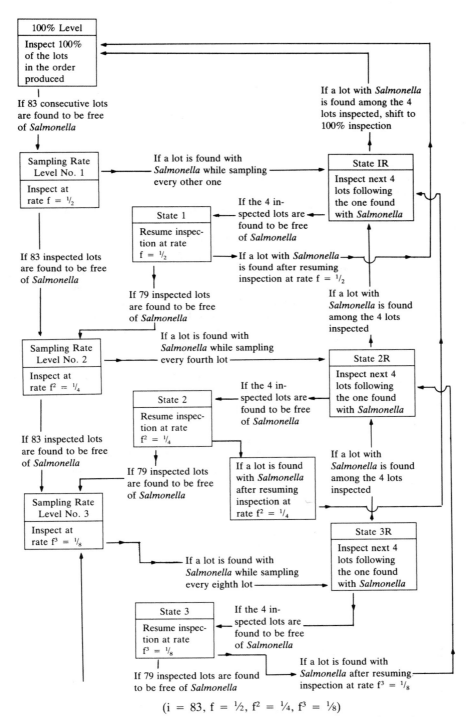

$(i = 83, f = \frac{1}{2}, f^2 = \frac{1}{4}, f^3 = \frac{1}{8})$

Figure 1—Flow Process Chart for Multilevel Continuous Sampling Plans

E. coli—Chapters 4 and 24
Yeast and Mold Count—Chapters 4 and 16
Direct Microscopic Count—Chapter 5[12]
Salmonella—Chapters 4 and 25

In addition to the culture method for *Salmonella*,[22] 3 new rapid *Salmonella* methods that give negative results in 48 hr have been introduced. All have received official first action approval from the Association of Official Analytical Chemists (AOAC) and are in the process of obtaining USDA approval for the detection of *Salmonella* in eggs and egg products.

Gene-Trak® (produced by Integrated Genetics, Inc., Framingham, Mass.) is a DNA hybridization procedure.[25] Following pre- and selective-enrichment steps, 3 filtration steps are followed that trap the bacteria present on a filter matrix, lyse the cells and separate the DNA into single strands, and fix the DNA to the matrix. A radioisotope-labeled DNA probe, specific for *Salmonella*, is added and allowed to hybridize with any *Salmonella* DNA that may be bound to the filter matrix. The amount of radioisotope bound is then measured and used to determine positive or negative results.

The Bio-Enzabead™ Screen Kit (produced by Organon Teknika Corp., Charleston, S.C.) is an enzyme immunoassay procedure.[24] A slightly modified procedure exists for low-moisture products.[26] Following pre- and selective-enrichment steps, a solid-phase immunoassay is performed. Monoclonal antibodies specific for *Salmonella* antigen are coated on metal beads, which are placed in the sample, and any *Salmonella* antigen present binds to the antibodies. A reaction mixture is added and positives are indicated by a color reaction.

The *Salmonella* 1-2 Test (produced by Biocontrol, Inc., Kent, Wash.) is also an antibody-antigen test. Following pre-enrichment, one arm of an L-shaped tube, containing tetrathionate broth supplemented with brilliant green and L-serine, is inoculated. The other arm, containing a motility medium, is inoculated with *Salmonella* flagellar antibodies. During incubation the antibodies diffuse into the motility medium while the *Salmonella* grow into it. Where they meet, the *Salmonella* are immobilized forming a white "U"-shaped band indicating a positive test.

All three tests are rapid *Salmonella* screening procedures. Positive results are confirmed by plating, biochemical testing, and serotyping according to the BAM culture method.[22] Additional information on rapid methods is presented in Chapter 39.

46.8 INTERPRETATION OF DATA

The aerobic plate count of the interior contents of shell eggs should be less than 10 microorganisms per gram. A count of more than 100 microorganisms per gram usually indicates bacterial invasion through the shell, possibly due to improper washing and sanitizing of the shell surface, followed by a period of storage or excessive handling of "sweated" eggs. The storing of eggs in a cooler at a relative humidity above 85% encourages mold growth on the surface of shell eggs.

Aerobic plate counts of unpasteurized liquid egg from commercial egg-breaking operations are generally in the range of 10^3 to 10^6 per gram. Aerobic plate counts exceeding 10^7 per gram usually indicate the use of poor-quality eggs for breaking but may also be due to poor sanitation or improper storage of the liquid eggs. Coliform counts in raw liquid eggs can be expected to be from 10^2 to 10^5 per gram, yeast and mold less than 10 per gram, and *Salmonella* less than 1 per gram.

All egg products, liquid, frozen, or dried, should meet the following specifications:

Aerobic Plate Count	<25,000 per g
Coliform Group	<10 per g
Yeast and Mold	<10 per g
Salmonella	Negative by prescribed sampling and testing procedures

The reasons that egg products do not meet the above specifications include poor microbiological quality of the unpasteurized liquid eggs, improper pasteurization, and recontamination after pasteurization. Liquid or frozen eggs subject to temperature abuse also will be of poor microbiological quality.[44]

46.81   Potential Hazards

Generally egg products are used in foods that are cooked or baked in such a way that *Salmonella* and other pathogens are destroyed, or used in foods such as mayonnaise and salad dressing, where the pH is sufficiently low to inhibit bacterial growth. However, if a contaminated egg product is brought into a food plant, there is always the possibility of contamination of other foods. Egg products are also used in some foods where pathogens, such as *Salmonella*, can survive, such as in meringue for pies. In any case, it is important that egg products be microbiologically safe.

46.82   Action Taken When Egg Products Are Below Specification

If *Salmonella*-positive samples of egg products are found, USDA allows the following procedures:

1. If *Salmonella*-positive results are obtained in either liquid or frozen egg products, the egg processor must test the next 4 consecutive lots and go through the frequency of sampling outlined in the USDA-specified flow diagram.
2. For frozen egg products, containers are divided into sublots of 100 or less and the number of samples taken is the square root of the number

in the sublot. The samples from each sublot are composited, and a 100-g aliquot is analyzed from each composite sample.

3. For dried egg whites the entire lot must be heat-treated again, resampled, and tested. Alternately, the product may be resampled and tested as prescribed for yellow products below.

4. For dried yellow products (made from whole egg and/or yolk), the entire lot must be reconstituted, repasteurized, and redried. Alternatively, yellow products may be resampled and tested as follows:

   a. For containers of 100 lbs (net) or over, containers must be divided into sublot groups of 4 consecutively produced containers and samples drawn from each container in the sublot.

   b. For containers of 50 lbs to 99 lbs (net), containers must be divided into sublot groups of 8 consecutively produced containers and samples taken from every other container in the sublot.

   c. For containers of less than 50 lbs (net), containers must be divided into sublot groups of 12 consecutively produced containers and samples drawn from every third container in the sublot.

   d. Twenty-five gram from each of the 4 consecutively numbered samples are combined into a 100-g composite for testing.

If the sublots of frozen or dried egg products are still found to be *Salmonella*-positive, they must be reprocessed and repasteurized.

46.9   REFERENCES

1. APHA. 1976. "Compendium of Methods for the Microbiological Examination of Foods," ed. M. L. Speck. Amer. Pub. Health Assn., Washington, D.C.
2. AOAC. 1975. "Official Methods of Analysis of the AOAC," 12th ed. Assn. of Off. Anal. Chem., Washington, D.C.
3. Aulisio, C. C. G., Mehlman, I. J., and Sanders, A. C. 1980. Alkali method for rapid recovery of *Yersinia enterocolitica* and *Yersinia pseudotuberculosis* from foods. Appl. Environ. Microbiol. 39: 135.
4. Bailey, J. S., Fletcher, D. L., and Cox, N. A. 1987. The influence of added egg yolk on the microbiological quality of hard-cooked eggs stored in a citric acid/sodium benzoate solution. Poultry Sci. 66: 861.
5. Baker, R. C., Paredes, M. D., and Qureshi, R. A. 1987. Prevalence of *Campylobacter jejuni* in eggs and poultry meat in New York State. Poultry Sci. 66: 1766.
6. Ball, H. R. Jr., Hamid-Samimi, M., Foegeding, P. M., and Swartzel, K. R. 1987. Functionality and microbial stability of ultrapasteurized aseptically packaged refrigerated whole egg. J. Food Sci. 52(5): 1212.
7. Bearns, R. E. and Girard, K. F. 1958. The effect of pasteurization on *Listeria monocytogenes*. Can. J. Microbiol. 4: 55.
8. Board, R. G. 1964. The growth of gram-negative bacteria in the hen's egg. J. Appl. Bacteriol. 27: 350.
9. Board, R. G. and Tranter, H. S. 1986. The microbiology of eggs. In "Egg Science and Technology," eds. W. J. Stadelman and O. J. Cotterill, p. 75. AVI Publishing Co., Westport, Conn.
10. Bojsen-Moeller, J. 1972. Human listeriosis. Diagnostic, epidemiological, and clinical studies. Acta Path. et Microbiol. Scand., Section B. Supp. 229: 1.

11. Bradshaw, J. G., Peeler, J. T., Corwin, J. J., Hunt, J. M., and Twedt, R. M. 1987. Thermal resistance of *Listeria monocytogenes* in dairy products. J. Food Prot. 50: 543.

12. Breed, R. S. 1911. The determination of the number of bacteria by direct microscopic examination. Zentralbl. Bakteriol. II. Abt. 30: 337.

13. Brooks, J. and Taylor, D. J. 1955. Eggs and egg products. Rep. Fd. Invest., Bd. 60, H. M. S. O. London, England.

14. Clark, A. G. and Bueschkens, D. H. 1986. Survival and growth of *Campylobacter jejuni* in egg yolk and albumen. J. Food Prot. 49: 135.

15. Cotterill, O. J. 1968. Equivalent pasteurization temperatures to kill salmonellae in liquid egg white at various pH levels. Poultry Sci. 47: 354.

16. Cotterill, O. J. and Glauert, J. L. 1979. Nutrient values for shell, liquid/frozen, and dehydrated eggs derived by linear regression analysis and conversion factors. Poultry Sci. 58: 131.

17. Cotterill, O. J., Glauert, J. L., and Krause, G. F. 1973. Thermal destruction curves for *Salmonella oranienburg* in egg products. Poultry Sci. 52: 568.

18. Cunningham, F. E. 1986. Egg-product pasteurization. In "Egg Science and Technology," eds. W. J. Stadelman and O. J. Cotterill, p. 260. AVI Publishing Co., Westport, Conn.

19. DeBoer, E., Hartog, B. J., and Oosterom, J. 1982. Occurrence of *Yersinia enterocolitica* in poultry products. J. Food Prot. 45: 322.

20. DeBoer, E., Seldam, W. M., and Oosterom, J. 1986. Characterization of *Yersinia enterocolitica* and related species isolated from foods and porcine tonsils in the Netherlands. Int. J. Food Microbiol. 3: 217.

21. Doyle, M. P. 1984. Association of *Campylobacter jejuni* with laying hens and eggs. Appl. Environ. Microbiol. 47: 533.

22. FDA. 1984. "Bacteriological Analytical Manual," 6th ed. Chapter 7. U.S. Food and Drug Admin., Washington, D.C.

23. Finch, M. J. and Blake, P. A. 1985. Foodborne outbreaks of campylobacteriosis: The United States experience, 1980–1982. Amer. J. Epidemiol. 122: 262.

24. Flowers, R. S., Eckner, K., Robison, B. J., Gabis, D. A., Mattingly, J. A., and Silliker, J. H. 1986. Enzyme immunoassay for detection of *Salmonella* in foods: Collaborative study. J. Assn. Off. Anal. Chem. 69(5): 786.

25. Flowers, R. S., Klatt, M. J., Mozola, M. A., Curiale, M. S., Gabis, D. A., and Silliker, J. H. 1987. DNA hybridization assay for detection of *Salmonella* in foods: Collaborative study. J. Assn. Off. Anal. Chem. 70(3): 521.

26. Flowers, R. S., Klatt, M. J., Robison, B. J., Mattingly, J. A., Gabis, D. A., and Silliker, J. H. 1987. Enzyme immunoassay for detection of *Salmonella* in low-moisture foods: Collaborative study. J. Assn. Off. Anal. Chem. 70(3): 530.

27. Florian, M. L. E. and Trussell, P. C. 1957. Bacterial spoilage of shell eggs. IV. Identification of spoilage organisms. Food Technol. 11: 56.

28. Foegeding, P. M. and Stanley, N. W. 1987. Growth and inactivation of microorganisms isolated from ultrapasteurized egg. J. Food Sci. 52: 1219.

29. Foegeding, P. M. and Swartzel, K. R. 1985. Pasteurization design criteria for production of extended shelf-life refrigerated liquid whole egg. J. Food Proc. and Preserv. 8 (1984): 219.

30. Forsythe, R. H., Ayres, J. C., and Radlo, J. L. 1953. Factors affecting the microbiological populations of shell eggs. Food Technol. 7: 49.

31. Foster, E. M. 1971. The control of *Salmonella* in processed foods: A classification system and sampling plan. J. Assn. Off. Agr. Chemists 54(2): 259.

32. Gray, M. L. 1958. Listeriosis in fowls—A review. Avian Dis. 2: 296.

33. Hale, K. K., Potter, L. M., and Martin, R. B. 1981. Firmness and microbial quality of hard cooked eggs stored in citric acid. Poultry Sci. 60: 1664.

34. Hänninen, M. L., Korkeala, H., and Pakkala, P. 1984. Growth and survival characteristics of *Campylobacter jejuni* in liquid egg. J. Hyg. 92: 53.

35. Hartung, T. E. and Stadelman, W. J. 1962. The influence of metallic cations on the penetration of the egg shell membranes by *Pseudomonas fluorescens*. Poultry Sci. 41: 1590.
36. Heddleson, K. L. 1972. Fowl cholera. In "Diseases of Poultry," 6th ed., eds. M. S. Hufstad, B. W. Calnek, C. F. Hemboldt, W. M. Reid, and H. W. Yoder Jr., p. 219. Iowa State Univ. Press, Ames, Iowa.
37. Hughey, V. L. and Johnson, E. A. 1987. Antimicrobial activity of lysozyme against bacteria involved in food spoilage and foodborne disease. Appl. Environ. Microbiol. 53: 2165.
38. Izat, A. L. and Gardner, F. A. 1988. The incidence of *Campylobacter jejuni* in processed egg products. Poultry Sci. 67: 1431.
39. Kampelmacher, E. H. 1962. In "Listeric Infection," ed. M. L. Gray, p. 145. Montana State College, Bozeman, Mont.
40. Kampelmacher, E. H. and van Noorle Jansen, L. M. 1969. Isolation of *Listeria monocytogenes* from faeces of clinically healthy humans and animals. Zentralbl. Bakteriol., Parasitenkd., Infektionskr. Hyg., Abt. 1:Orig., Reine A 211: 353.
41. Kendall, M. R. and Gilbert, J. 1980. Survival and growth of *Yersinia enterocolitica* in broth media and in food. Technical Series, Soc. Appl. Bacteriol. 15: 215.
42. Kinner, J. A. and Moats, W. A. 1981. Effect of temperature, pH, and detergent on survival of bacteria associated with shell eggs. Poultry Sci. 60: 761.
43. Khan, M. A., Newton, I. A., Seaman, A., and Woodbine, M. 1975. The survival of *Listeria monocytogenes* inside and outside its host. In "Problems of Listeriosis." Lecture: Microbiol. Unit, Dept. Appl. Biochem. & Nutr., Univ. of Nottingham, Nottingham, U. K.
44. Kraft, A. A., Elliott, L. E., and Brant, A. W. 1958. The shell membrane as a barrier to bacterial penetration of eggs. Poultry Sci. 37: 238.
45. Kraft, A. A., Torrey, G. S., Ayres, J. C., and Forsythe, R. H. 1967. Factors influencing bacterial contamination of commercially produced liquid egg. Poultry Sci. 46: 1204.
46. Leistner, L., Heckelmann, H., Kashiuazaki, M., and Albertz, R. 1975. Nachweis von *Yersinia enterocolitica* in Faeces und Fleisch von Schweinen, Rinden und Geflügel. Fleischwirtschaft 55: 1599.
47. Lepper, H. A., Bartram, M. T., and Hillig, F. 1944. Detection of decomposition in liquid, frozen, and dried eggs. J. Off. Agr. Chem. 27: 204.
48. Moats, W. A. 1981. Factors affecting bacterial loads on shells of commercially washed eggs. Poultry Sci. 60: 2084.
49. Morishige, M., Kinjo, T., and Minamoto, N. 1984. Growth and survival of *Campylobacter jejuni* in yolk. Res. Bull. Faculty of Agr., Gifu Univ., Gifu-ken, Japan.
50. Rosser, F. T. 1942. Preservation of eggs. II. Surface contamination on egg shell in relation to spoilage. Canad. J. Res. 200D: 291.
51. Seeliger, H. P. R. 1961. "Listeriosis." Hafner Publishing Co., New York.
52. Shafi, R., Cotterill, O. J., and Nichols, M. L. 1970. Microbial flora of commercially pasteurized egg products. Poultry Sci. 49: 578.
53. Shane, S. M., Gifford, D. H., and Yogasundram, K. 1986. *Campylobacter jejuni* contamination of eggs. Vet. Res. Comm. 10: 487.
54. Southam, G., Pearson, J., and Holley, R. A. 1987. Survival and growth of *Yersinia enterocolitica* in egg washwater. J. Food Prot. 50: 103.
55. Speck, M. L. and Tarver, F. R. 1967. Microbiological populations in blended eggs before and after commercial pasteurization. Poultry Sci. 46: 1321.
56. St. Louis, M. E., Morse, D. L., Potter, M. E., DeMelfi, T. M., Guzewich, J. J., Tauxe, R. V., and Blake, P. A. The emergence of grade A eggs as a major source of *Salmonella enteritidis* infections. JAMA 259(14): 2103.
57. Stadelman, W. J. and Cotterill, O. J. 1986. "Egg Science and Technology." AVI Publishing Co., Westport, Conn.
58. Stadelman, W. J., Ikeme, A. I., Roop, R. A., and Simmons, S. E. 1982. Thermally processed hard-cooked eggs. Poultry Sci. 61: 388.

59. Stern, N. J., Pierson, M. D., and Kotula, A. W. 1980. Effects of pH and sodium chloride on *Yersinia enterocolitica* growth at room and refrigeration temperatures. J. Food Sci. 45: 64.
60. Stuart, L. S. and McNally, E. H. 1943. Bacteriological studies on the egg shell. U.S. Egg Poultry Mag. 49: 28.
61. Urbach, H. and Schabinski, G. 1955. Zur Listeriose des Menschen. Zeit. Hyg. 141: 239.
62. USDA. 1969. Egg pasteurization manual. ARS 74–48. U.S. Dept. of Agr., Agr. Res. Serv. Washington, D.C.
63. USDA. 1972. Egg products inspection handbook. Dried egg products instructions. AMS-PY Instruc. 910 (Egg Products)-5. Revision 2. U.S. Dept. of Agr., Washington, D.C.
64. USDA. 1975. Egg products inspection handbook. Section 8—Sampling for bacteriological, chemical, and physical testing. AMS-PY Instruc. 910 (Egg Products)-1. U.S. Dept. of Agr., Washington, D.C.
65. USDA. 1985. Laboratory methods for egg products. Agr. Marketing Serv., Poult. Div., U.S. Dept. of Agr., Washington, D.C.

Chapter 47

FISH, CRUSTACEANS, AND PRECOOKED SEAFOODS

Ranzell Nickelson II and Gunnar Finne

47.1 INTRODUCTION

Seafoods are more perishable than other high-protein foods. In seafood products, changes in flavor, odor, texture, and color reflect the level of freshness vs. decomposition caused primarily by microbial activity. The rate of decomposition is influenced by the initial number and types of bacteria and storage conditions, such as temperature, humidity, and gaseous atmosphere. Certain seafoods contain high levels of osmoregulators in the form of nonprotein nitrogen (e.g., amino acids, trimethylamine oxide, or urea) that are readily available to bacteria. Large quantities of many fish and crustaceans are harvested from cold water; therefore, the microflora is not inhibited as effectively by refrigeration as is the normal microflora of warm-blooded animals. The place and method of processing seafood species and warm-blooded animals (i.e., aboard ship vs. a slaughter plant) also affect perishability.

Safety in seafood products with reference to bacterial contamination is usually concerned with the potential for food poisoning. In a simplified overview, poor-quality products, spoiled or decomposed, are rarely responsible for food poisoning because they usually are discarded before consumption. Food poisoning in seafood products, as with other foods, except in instances such as scombroid or histamine poisoning, normally is the result of mishandling during or after preparation.

This chapter, devoted to fish, crustaceans, and precooked seafood, focuses on many different seafood species and products. Within the limits of this text, it would be difficult to describe the bacteriology of all seafood species because they are harvested from many different areas of the world, at different times of the year, for various product forms, and under numerous testing procedures and conditions. The information presented here should permit a practical approach for the microbiological analysis of products and for the interpretation of test results.

47.2   FRESH AND FROZEN FISH AND CRUSTACEANS

47.21   Natural Flora

The subsurface flesh of live, healthy fish is considered bacteriologically sterile. The largest concentrations of microorganisms are found in the intestine, gills, and surface slime. The numbers and types of microorganisms found on freshly caught fish are influenced by the geographical location of the catch and the season and method of harvest.[47] The microflora of fish is related to the environment from which the fish is harvested.[48]

Differences to be expected include variations in salinity, temperature, organic matter, and water quality found in each harvest area. For example, the average number of bacteria found on freshly caught Gulf of Mexico shrimp is reported to range from 10^3 to 10^4/g, while freshly caught inshore bay shrimp have counts from 10^4 to 10^5/g.[23, 58] The area of catch also can influence the types of microorganisms found on fish. The incidence of *Salmonella* has been shown to be higher in fish from polluted waters than in those from the open ocean.[24]

The microflora of water, sediments, and marine organisms of the South Atlantic Ocean and the Gulf of Mexico can change considerably from summer to winter, particularly for organisms such as *Vibrio parahaemolyticus*, which have been shown to cycle with zooplankton blooms.[13] When water temperatures increase, both plankton production and the incidence of *V. parahaemolyticus* increase. The vibrios cannot be detected in the water during the winter months, but they may be found in the sediment. Results of an investigation of the microbial flora of pond-reared brown shrimp (*Penaeus aztecus*) show the changes that can occur in shallow waters along the western Gulf Coast.[60] The flora of shrimp and pond water were monitored from June through October. During the initial months of the experimental period, coryneform bacteria were predominant. Lowest counts occurred in August when water temperatures and salinities were highest. Coryneform bacteria and species of *Vibrio*, *Flavobacterium*, *Moraxella*, and *Bacillus* were common isolates. At harvest, a decrease in coryneform bacteria and subsequent increases in *Vibrio*, *Flavobacterium*, and *Moraxella* species were noted.

The microflora of shrimp harvested from the Gulf of Mexico consisted predominantly of coryneform bacteria, *Pseudomonas*, *Moraxella*, and *Micrococcus*. *Pseudomonas*, the most common spoilage organism, was not isolated from pond water or from shrimp, possibly indicating a difference in the harvesting and handling techniques.[58] The harvest method has been shown to influence the number of bacteria on fish also.[47] Trawled fish usually exhibit higher numbers of bacteria than do line-caught fish because the trawled fish are dragged along the bottom and exposed to mud, and the contents of their guts may be forced out as the trawl is hauled in.

Before any conclusions can be drawn about the natural microflora of seafood, certain nonintrinsic factors, such as type of organism, initial isolation media used, and incubation temperatures, must be considered.

The gram-negative, nonfermentative rods that compose a major portion of the natural microflora, and also of the spoilage microflora, have been in a state of taxonomic confusion for the past 20 years. *Achromobacter* of the *Pseudomonas-Achromobacter* group, as described in many research summaries, is not included as a genus in the 8th edition of "Bergey's Manual of Determinative Bacteriology." [8] The relatively biochemically inert organisms previously classified as *Achromobacter* now are distributed throughout the coryneform group, as well as species of *Moraxella, Acinetobacter,* and *Alcaligenes.*

Plating medium can affect the number and the types of bacteria isolated because of differences in nutrient and salt requirements of the various microorganisms. Differences in types of microflora reported for shrimp[9, 25, 58, 65] may have been influenced by the types of media used. Many of the coryneform bacteria appear as small colonies only after 2 to 3 days incubation and fail to multiply after initial transfer.[59] The nutrient requirements for some of these organisms are quite strict. Salinity of the medium also can affect the numbers and types, especially if halophilic organisms are present. *V. parahaemolyticus* can best be isolated on appropriate media prepared with added salt.[57]

It is now generally accepted that a plate incubation temperature of 25°C will produce significantly higher numbers than incubation at 35°C, which was the accepted standard for many years. Vanderzant et al.[61] found counts on breaded shrimp ranging from 11,000 to 6,800,000/g at 35°C. In contrast, the same samples yielded 60,000 to 27,000,000/g when plates were incubated at 25°C.

A survey of fresh retail products from Seattle showed the overall quality of seafoods to be high.[1] Most probable number (MPN) coliforms averaged 199/g, MPN *Escherichia coli* 21/g, MPN *Staphylococcus aureus* 66/g, enterococci 9121/g, *Clostridium perfringens* 18/g, *Bacillus cereus* 100/g, and *V. parahaemolyticus* 3.7/g. *Vibrio cholerae, Clostridium botulinum, Salmonella* spp., and *Shigella* spp. were not detected. Aerobic plate counts exhibited a mean of 2.0×10^5/g at 22°C, which indicates a historical improvement in quality. Foster et al.[21] reported only 39% of products surveyed to meet the ICMFS[28] criteria ($n = 5$, $c = 3$, $m = 10^6$/g, $M = 10^7$/g), whereas the more recent survey shows that 98% met these criteria.

47.22 Spoilage Microflora

The shelf life, the time of storage before microbial spoilage of a fish is evident, is determined by the number and types of bacteria and the storage temperature. The numbers and types of microorganisms are determined by the natural microflora and the manner in which the fish was handled between harvesting and storage. The true storage temperature includes not only the final market box temperature, but the ambient temperature at harvest, delays in refrigerated storage, and fluctuations in storage temperature.

It is recognized generally that the predominant spoilage organisms belong to the genus *Pseudomonas*. These organisms are capable of causing spoilage because of two important characteristics. First, they are psychrotrophic, and thus multiply at refrigeration temperatures. Secondly, they attack various substances in the fish tissue to produce compounds associated with off-flavors and off-odors. These compounds are reported to be methyl mercaptan, dimethyl disulfide, dimethyl trisulfide, 3-methyl-1-butanal, trimethylamine, and ethyl esters of acetate, butyrate and hexanoate.[37, 38]

As noted in the previous section, the natural microflora of tropical-subtropical products can be expected to contain *Pseudomonas* as an insignificant proportion of the total population. There are several possible reasons for subsequent spoilage by *Pseudomonas*, involving one or more of the following: (1) shorter generation time than other organisms, (2) antagonistic or synergistic reactions, (3) the ability to attack large protein molecules, and (4) overall biochemical activity. Regardless of the mode of action, the time from catch to spoilage is based to a great extent on the storage temperature and on the initial numbers of *Pseudomonas* and related organisms present. Since few are present in the natural microflora, it may be assumed that extensive numbers and subsequent spoilage are due to abuses in handling practices and/or storage.

47.23   Health-Related Bacteria

Of 1,586 outbreaks of foodborne illness reported between 1977 and 1984 for which a vehicle could be identified, seafoods were responsible for 24.8%.[7] Fish were responsible for 59% of the seafood total with scombroid (histamine poisoning) and ciguatera (reef fish toxin) contributing to the majority of the cases. Shellfish were responsible for one-third of the seafood cases with Norwalk or "Norwalk-like" viruses being the probable cause of a majority of cases. Reported and confirmed outbreaks frequently involved small numbers of people.

Seafoods are susceptible to all of the common food poisoning organisms as well as to some that are unique to marine products such as *C. botulinum* type *E*, *Vibrio* spp., ciguatera, scombroid poisoning, and Norwalk. Organisms of public health concern common to all food products include *Salmonella*, *S. aureus*, and *C. perfringens*.

47.231   *Salmonella*

Although not normally isolated from fish and shellfish from open seas, these organisms can be isolated from seafoods harvested from contaminated inland waters. *Salmonella* presents no direct health hazard in raw products expected to be cooked before consumption because normal cooking destroys them. They are of concern, however, in products consumed raw and in products ready for consumption without further heat processing. The presence of *Salmonella* also is of concern because it can be transmitted to other foods via cross-contamination, from raw to cooked foods. *Salmonella* is a normal inhabitant of the intestinal tract of reptiles and amphibians and has been of concern in imported processed frog legs. It has not been a problem in other properly handled, prepared, and stored seafood products. Its presence indicates direct or indirect fecal contamination from man or animal.

47.232   *S. aureus*

Although seldom isolated from freshly harvested seafood products, *S. aureus* can be found in products that involve extensive human handling, like picked crab meat.

47.233   *C. perfringens*

C. perfringens is normally found in the intestinal tract of man and in soil and is usually not associated with freshly harvested seafood products. It has the potential for causing problems in sauces or soups, such as gumbo. Although it may contribute to histamine production in scombroid fish held at high temperatures ($>30°C$), it is not a problem in properly prepared and stored seafood products.

Seafoods are also a source of *V. parahaemolyticus*, *C. botulinum* type E, and *Proteus* spp., food poisoning organisms unique to seafood products.

47.234   *V. parahaemolyticus*

This organism can be isolated from a variety of seafood products and marine environments. It has been reported to be responsible for up to 60% of the food poisoning incidents in Japan, where large quantities of seafoods are consumed raw. The organism, when isolated from fresh seafoods, usually is found in low numbers ($<100/g$) and is sensitive to refrigeration and heat. Therefore, a seafood product must be grossly abused during storage and preparation (undercooking, cross-contamination between raw and cooked products, temperature abuse) before *V. parahaemolyticus* becomes a problem.

47.235   *C. botulinum* type E

Isolated almost exclusively from marine environments, *C. botulinum* type E is of special concern because it is more psychrotrophic than other types within the species, is capable of producing toxin during refrigeration, and is non-proteolytic. There has been concern in the past about smoked seafood products. Class II, non-proteolytic, types E and B are capable of growth in a water phase salt concentration of 5% to 7% at storage temperatures as low as 3.3°C.[17] Since the spoilage flora is destroyed by smoking, *C. botulinum* would have extra time to produce its toxin in an abused product. Recent concerns center around the use of modified- or controlled-atmosphere packaging during which oxygen levels are decreased or other gases are increased to reduce the normal spoilage microflora and extend the shelf life of the product. This raises the question, can a package of seafood contain botulinal toxin and still be organoleptically acceptable to the consumer?

47.236   *Proteus/Hafnia/Klebsiella/Enterobacter*

Proteus is found in low numbers and may be a part of the normal microflora. *Proteus* and similar organisms have presented a problem in scombroid fishes such as tuna and mackerel by converting histidine to histamine. The organism is not psychrotrophic, so the production of histamine indicates high-temperature storage abuse. Although certain psychrotrophic bacteria possess a histidine decarboxylase capability, it is at an insignificant level.[46] Other amines such as putrescine from lysine and cadaverine from ornithine may also contribute to scombroid poisoning.[36] The problem, in any case, can be solved through proper handling and refrigeration aboard the vessel.

Organisms of more recent concern include *Yersinia enterocolitica*, *E. coli*, *V. cholerae*, *Vibrio vulnificus*, *Aeromonas hydrophila*, *Plesiomonas shigelloides*, and *Listeria monocytogenes*.

47.237   *Y. enterocolitica*

Y. enterocolitica has been isolated from raw seafood products and can grow at refrigeration temperatures. Pathogenic strains have been isolated from crabs harvested from cold waters.[20] There are no documented outbreaks from consumption of seafood products caused by this organism.

47.238   *E. coli*

E. coli has been used traditionally as an indicator of fecal contamination and for the potential presence of *Salmonella*. *E. coli* is not considered a good indicator of fecal pollution for seafood from cold water because of a rapid decline of *E. coli* in seawater of low temperatures.[20] It has been established, however, that the isolation of *E. coli* from blue crab meat, in conjunction with inspections that show a source of fecal material, does constitute "filth" in the form of fecal material.

47.239   *V. cholerae*

Several cases of food poisoning have been traced to the consumption of seafoods contaminated with *V. cholerae*. There is some indication that the organism may be a part of the normal marine microflora.[14] There is little relationship between the incidence of vibrios and fecal coliforms in that *V. cholerae* was isolated from over 50% of water samples taken from approved shellfish harvesting estuaries of the U.S. West Coast.[29] Outbreaks in many reported cases could be attributed to gross mishandling of the seafood product. A note of caution on the heat sensitivity of *V. cholerae* is raised by Makukutu and Guthrie.[34] Since the organism is not often isolated from foods implicated in cholerae-like diarrhea outbreaks, hot foods are not usually suspected. They showed that *V. cholerae* 01 and non-01 could survive in hot foods for 1 hr at 60°C but may not be easily recovered because of heat injury.

47.240   *V. vulnificus*

V. vulnificus is a marine, halophilic, lactose-positive bacterium that has been isolated from numerous marine environments. It produces a general septicemia, wound infections, and less frequently diarrhea. In the former manifestation, mortality rates as high as 50% have resulted in those individuals with high levels of serum iron or immune impairment. The original source of these infections seems to be the consumption of raw oysters. Unlike *V. cholerae* and *V. parahaemolyticus*, the environmental and clinical isolates of *V. vulnificus* appear to be identical.[55] Isolations of *V. vulnificus* from marine samples are highest when temperatures exceed 20°C and water salinities are between 5‰ and 20‰.[50]

Advisories have been published cooperatively between industry, universities, and regulatory agencies in an attempt to initiate a consumer education program on *V. vulnificus*.[56]

47.241   *A. hydrophila*

Aquatic environments are a common source of *A. hydrophila*. It is reported as the cause of "red leg" disease in frogs and the most frequent isolate from their intestinal tract—46%.[26] *A. hydrophila* has also been implicated as a foodborne illness related to the consumption of raw oysters.[2]

47.242   *P. shigelloides*

As in the case with *V. vulnificus*, *P. shigelloides* seems to be an opportunistic pathogen found in people with diarrhea as well as those without. It has been implicated as the causative agent of foodborne disease from water, oysters, crab, and fish.[39] At greater risk from the consumption of raw or improperly cooked seafood products are the very young, elderly, and immuno-compromised.

47.243   *L. monocytogenes*

The literature contains information on *Listeria* isolations from soil, animals, birds, sewage, silage, stream water, mud, trout, and crustaceans. Public health concerns have rapidly expanded from dairy products to processed meats and seafood products. A survey conducted on frozen seafood products in the United States[63] showed some samples of shrimp (raw and cooked), cooked crab meat, lobster tail, finfish, and surimi to be positive for *L. monocytogenes*. In another survey,[4] *Listeria* spp. were isolated from 48 of 124 raw seafood samples and 24 of the 48 were *L. monocytogenes*. The highest incidence was found in freshwater catfish, in which 15 out of 20 samples were positive for *L. monocytogenes*. Listeriosis has been implied from raw shellfish or raw finfish in an outbreak in New Zealand.[32]

The close association of *Listeria* with soil and water probably explains the incidence of *Listeria* in seafood products, especially those from fresh water and brackish environments. Organisms previously reported as "coryneforms" in freshly harvested seafood products may have been members of the genus *Listeria*.[42, 59]

Cooked, ready-to-eat products such as crab meat, cooked shrimp, heat-and-serve surimi, stuffed shrimp, stuffed finfish, and those products consumed raw such as shellfish and cold-smoked fish are considered to be high-risk products for which a *Listeria* control program should be established. Environmental samples from processing plants must be evaluated carefully. Positive environmental samples may be from the normal microflora of the raw product and not the source of problems as identified in dairy plants. Management of *Listeria* through good manufacturing practices and the identification of critical control points will allow seafood processors to control but not eliminate *Listeria*.

The psychrotrophic nature of *Listeria* must be a primary consideration in any attempt to prolong the refrigerated storage of a seafood product. In a study of the bacteria from pasteurized oyster meat held under refrigeration, *Listeria* was not isolated until after storage for 5 months at 0.5°C.[42]

For the role of viruses and parasites in seafoods, please consult Chapters 41 and 42 of this book.

47.3 COOKED CRUSTACEAN PRODUCTS

Crab, shrimp, lobster, and langostino products are precooked to extend shelf life, to impart a desirable characteristic flavor, or to facilitate picking or peeling. In addition, crab meat and langostino may be pasteurized at 85°C for 1 min after picking and peeling to enhance refrigerated storage life.

Blue crabs are steamed under pressure or boiled before picking to produce what is termed fresh-picked crab meat. Survival of the natural microflora, multiplication of organisms during storage before picking, and post-cooking contamination contribute collectively to the number and types of bacteria found in crab meat. One survey indicated that 93% of the plants operating under good sanitary conditions produced crab meat with MPN coliforms of less than 20/g, MPN *E. coli* <3g, MPN coagulase-positive staphylococci less than 30/g, and aerobic plate counts (at 35°C) of less than 10^5/g.[44] A survey of retail samples of blue crab meat complicates the issue of microbiological standards and where they should be applied. Blue crab meat with an APC (geometric mean) of 5.2 × 10^5 at 30°C had counts of 3.6 × 10^9 in the upper 10% of samples examined.[64] These large differences in count may reflect a wide range of sanitary practices, but differences in time and temperature profiles during distribution are most likely involved.

Dungeness, snow, and king crab (cooked whole or cooked portions) and cooked lobsters fall into a unique category because little edible flesh actually is exposed to recontamination after cooking.

Exposed areas, flesh and shell, are useful in determining post-cooking contamination, whereas meat extracted from beneath the shell is a better indication of cooking effectiveness. Aerobic plate counts for cooked frozen products should be conducted at 35°C and 25°C for public health and shelf-life indicators, respectively. Distribution patterns of the microbial flora in Dungeness crab meat revealed the presence of three classes of microorganisms.[31] *Moraxella, Pseudomonas, Acinetobacter*, and *Flavobacterium-Cytophaga* spp. originated from the raw crab and became dominant during refrigerated storage. *Arthrobacter* and *Bacillus* spp. also originated from the raw crab but did not grow in the meat. *Micrococcus, Staphylococcus*, and *Proteus* were introduced during processing and did not grow. A high incidence of false-positive fecal coliforms as detected in EC broth has been reported.[45] Fecal coliforms were detected in only 10% of the samples and the most common level MPN for that 10% was 40/100g.

Geometric means for aerobic plate counts incubated at 35°C for cooked peeled shrimp and raw peeled shrimp have been reported at 7.3 × 10^3/g and 3.0 × 10^6/g, respectively.[53]

Pasteurization of shrimp, crab meat, and langostinos is intended to extend refrigerated shelf life and is not intended to render the product commercially sterile. Since *C. botulinum* is normally found in the marine environment and in marine food animals, its presence raises important public health questions concerning pasteurized products. Heat resistance studies have shown that spores of nonproteolytic type E strains are destroyed by commercial pasteurization of crab meat. Spores of types B and F survived, but they did not appear to be a public health hazard.[49] The microflora of crab meat is reported to be reduced from 10^4 to 10^1/g during pasteurization.[62] Types of isolates after pasteurization included species of *Bacillus, Corynebacterium, Lactobacillus, Flavobacterium, Acinetobacter, Pseudomonas*, and *Brevibacterium*.

Pasteurization (83°C for 1 min) for blanched, peeled langostinos caused the following changes in microbial counts: Before pasteurization APC 1.3 × 10^5/g (25°C); MPN coliforms 9.1/g; MPN *E. coli* <3/g; and MPN coagulase-positive staphylococci >1100/g; and after pasteurization APC <10^3 − 1.2 × 10^4/g; coliforms <3/g; *E. coli* <3/g; and MPN coagulase-positive staphylococci <3−23/g.[54]

47.4   BREADED AND PREPARED SEAFOOD PRODUCTS

Breaded and prepared seafood products can vary greatly in numbers and types of microorganisms because of the addition of nonmarine ingredients. The weight of breaded products may include 25% to 65% flour, seasonings, nonfat dry milk, and dried eggs. Prepared products such as fish cakes and crab cakes contain spices, onions, and celery. The degree of cooking employed (i.e., raw, partial, or complete) further affects the number and types of organisms.

Surveys of frozen raw breaded shrimp processing plants have indicated that plants with good quality control can consistently produce a finished product with bacterial loads lower than the original incoming raw shrimp.[51] Aerobic plate counts on finished product samples from plants operating under good sanitary conditions ranged from 1.1×10^4 to 6.8×10^6/g at 35°C and 6.0×10^4 to 2.7×10^7/g at 25°C.[61] The initial flora consisted primarily of *Pseudomonas*, *Achromobacter*, *Aeromonas*, *Bacillus*, *Moraxella*, *Microbacterium*, *Micrococcus*, or coryneform bacteria. *Bacillus*, *Microbacterium*, *Micrococcus*, and coryneform bacteria were predominant in retail samples. The bacterial flora of batter and breading, which consisted primarily of *Bacillus* and *Microbacterium* species, probably contributed to this condition.

In a survey of fish breading operations, it was demonstrated that raw fish from plants operating under good conditions had average APC values of less than 10^5/g, MPN coliform less than 100/g, and no more than 20% of the units positive for *E. coli* or staphylococci. Fried breaded fish had APC values of less than 2.5×10^4/g, MPN coliform was less than 10/g, and no more than 10% of the units were positive for *E. coli* or staphylococci.[52]

In a survey of plants by Duran et al.[15] in which all were operating under good manufacturing practices, aerobic plate counts ranged from 3.3×10^5 to 2.1×10^6 at 35°C and 7.6×10^5 to 7.8×10^6 at 30°C. Coliforms ranged from 148–160/g; MPN *E. coli* was <3/g; *S. aureus* was <10/g; and *Salmonella* was isolated from only 1 of 188 samples and was traced back to the dry batter containing egg products. Again the peeling, batter, and breading operations produced a finished product of lower aerobic plate counts than the incoming raw shrimp.

Products such as crab stuffing or crab cakes contain fresh or dehydrated vegetables and normally have higher coliform counts than other products. This fact was reflected in a proposed guideline MPN for frozen fish sticks, frozen fish cakes, and frozen crab cakes of 230, 1500, and 4300/g, respectively.[11, 12]

47.5   SALTED AND SMOKED PRODUCTS

The main feature of salting fish involves the removal of some of the water from the fish tissue and its partial replacement by salt. Salting or brining may be done either as a hard cure, by stacking fish with layers of dry salt, or as a light dry cure, where limited dry salt is used, or in a brine solution—pickling. Depending upon the method used and the time of treatment, salted fish or seafood products may range from 1% salt to a fully salted dry fish containing in excess of 20% salt. The heavy or hard-cured fish is most commonly dried and stored as a stable product under dry storage conditions. The less salted fish may be used for smoking or consumed as a salted or pickled product.

Smoking fish and fishery products serves a number of different functions. Although traditionally used as a method of preservation, fish is smoked to give it a distinct flavor. In addition, smoking contributes to an increase in the shelf life of the product because of microbial destruction and lowering of the water activity. Several types of smoked fishery products are available. These can be classified according to the temperature maintained during smoking, cold or hot smoked, the salt content, and the duration of smoking and/or drying. For cold smoked fish, the smoke is applied at a low temperature. Cold smoking may continue for a short period to produce lightly smoked fish, such as lox, or over long periods to produce kippered products. Hot smoking is conducted at much higher temperatures and results in a barbecued or cooked product. Smoked products are dried to varying degrees, depending on the smoking procedures, which result in a wide range of free water content. The result is a great variety in the microbial distribution. For hard-smoked products with high heat input, the more heat-stable organisms such as *Bacillus*, *Micrococcus*, and yeasts will be predominant. For milder smoked fish, a number of gram-negative organisms will survive; *Pseudomonas* and *Moraxella-Acinetobacter* are common in the microflora of such products.

Smoked seafood products are perishable and should be treated as such. Storage stability will be dependent primarily on the water activity, salt content, total heat input during smoking, and storage conditions. For lightly brined and lightly smoked products, the refrigerated spoilage pattern will be similar to that of fresh refrigerated fish; *Pseudomonas* will be the dominant organism. For heavier smoked and more salted products, gram-positive organisms, together with halophiles, will prevail and molds will be seen more frequently. Hard-smoked products with a low water activity are spoiled primarily by molds.

The potential for growth and toxin production by *C. botulinum* type E is the concern related to the safety of smoked seafood products. This organism can be a part of the normal microflora of fish and marine sediments, and can grow and produce toxin at a temperature as low as 3.3°C. In products where the heat input during smoking is limited, the spores may survive and, since surface areas of smoked fish tissue have an oxidation-reduction potential sufficiently low to permit sporulation and growth, *C. botulinum* may present a health hazard. The elimination of the heat-sensitive spoilage microflora and temperature abuse of the final product encourage toxin production. Eklund et al.[17] reported that a hot-smoked fish process coupled with a vacuum-packaged, post-processing, heat-pasteurization step is capable of inactivating the Class II, non-proteolytic, type E and B spores, but not the more heat-resistant proteolytic *C. botulinum* spores. Their recommendation is that such a product be labeled "Keep refrigerated. Store below 38°F (3.3°C)."

47.6   OTHER SEAFOOD PRODUCTS

47.61   Minced Fish Flesh, Surimi, and Seafood Analogs

The mechanical separation (deboning) of fish flesh from dressed fish, filleting waste, frames, or V-cuts, has become an established practice in larger filleting and freezing plants. Minced fish flesh, the resulting product, can be processed directly into consumer products, frozen in blocks or prepared into surimi, which is a food-processing intermediate material.

The deboning process is an added concern relative to microbial contamination as compared to whole or filleted fresh or frozen fish. In addition to the increased number of possible contamination points during the deboning process, the nature of the product gives ample opportunity for an increased microbial population to develop. During deboning, tissue masceration not only increases the surface area, but it also allows for the release of cellular fluids rich in free amino acids and other substrates ideal for microbial growth. It is essential, therefore, that equipment be kept scrupulously clean and that the minced flesh be kept as cold as possible during processing. Blackwood[6] demonstrated the importance of good sanitary practices during deboning of fish flesh. When comparing two plants using similar raw materials, facilities, and processing equipment, one plant produced minced fish flesh with an average aerobic plate count of $6.7 \times 10^5/g$ with 1 out of 56 samples positive for fecal coliforms. The average plate count for minced flesh produced in the second plant was $1.5 \times 10^7/g$ with 60% being positive for fecal coliforms.

The types of organisms present in minced flesh were shown by Nickelson et al.[41] to be very similar to the types of organisms present on the raw material. Ten processing lots representing six species of fish showed *Moraxella-Acinetobacter* spp. to be the most prevalent microbial type in the fish before, during, and after processing into minced fish flesh. Increases of up to one log during the production of minced flesh from whole fish were also reported. During freezing, marked decreases in the total microbial counts of the minced flesh were noted. Licciardello and Hill[33] examined 208 imported frozen minced fish samples and found all to be in compliance with the proposed standards of the International Commission on Microbiological Specification for Foods (ICMSF).[27]

Surimi is a food-processing intermediate material made from heavily washed minced fish flesh normally produced from pollock-type species. To the washed minced flesh are added cryoprotectants such as sorbitol, other sugars, and polyphosphates. The cryoprotectants allow surimi to be frozen for long periods of time without any substantial loss in the gel-forming capacity of the myofibrillar proteins. Because washing and addition of cryoprotectants dramatically alter the composition of the minced flesh, Ingham and Potter[28] compared the microbiological properties of minced flesh and surimi produced from Atlantic pollock. The aerobic plate count and psychrotrophic count of the minced flesh and surimi samples stored at 5°C and 13°C were initially similar, but reached higher levels in surimi with time. They also pointed out that careful handling and storage are equally important for both products to maintain microbiological quality.

Because of its gel-forming ability, surimi can be processed into a variety of different seafood analogs. These analogs are prepared from chopped surimi with added salt, starch, and polyphosphates, together with flavor and aroma components. The final product can be flavored and shaped into imitation crab, shrimp, lobster, scallops, or fish portions. Amano[3] reported that the initial load of bacteria on the raw fish plays an insignificant role in relation to the storage life of the final product. The number of organisms associated with the raw fish are dramatically reduced during the extensive washing of the mince and because of their heat sensitivity they are also destroyed during heat setting of the gel. This fact was also demonstrated by Yoon et al.,[67] who investigated the microbiological and chemical changes in imitation crab during storage. They showed that because of the heat processing and added ingredients, crab analogs contain lower microbial numbers and a different microflora from uncooked fish. During storage at 0°C and 5°C, psychrotrophic gram-negative organisms that survived the heat processing and initially were present in low numbers became the major spoilage organisms. At higher storage temperatures, *Bacillus* spp. dominated the spoilage population. The source of *Bacillus* spores was shown to be the starch and other ingredients added to the surimi during processing.

In general, fresh fish are seldom the cause of foodborne illness because fish spoils before pathogenic microorganisms proliferate and form toxin. However, heat used in the production of analogs reduces competing organisms. If these products are subsequently contaminated with pathogens and subjected to conditions where these pathogens can grow, they may become a health hazard. Yoon and Matches[66] inoculated samples of imitation crab legs and flaked crab meat with *S. aureus*, *Salmonella*, *Y. enterocolitica*, and *A. hydrophila* and stored them at 0°C, 5°C, 10°C, and 15°C. *S. aureus*, *Salmonella*, and *Aeromonas* grew at 10°C and 15°C, but not at the two lower temperatures. *Yersinia* grew at all four temperatures tested. The rapid growth at these temperatures indicates the potential hazard if seafood analogs should become contaminated and subjected to temperature abuse during distribution.

47.62   Fish Protein Concentrate

During the production of fish protein concentrate (FPC), the combination of heat and isopropyl alcohol extraction will remove most lipid material and also lower the water activity to an extent that microorganisms will not be able to multiply. Heat, together with the organic solvent, will destroy most of the nonsporeforming microorganisms present on the raw material.[22, 43] Postprocessing contamination is the major source of bacteria in FPC. According to FDA regulations,[10] fish protein concentrate shall be free of *E. coli* and pathogenic organisms, including *Salmonella*, and have a maximum total bacterial plate count of 10,000 organisms/g. The organisms most frequently found in FPC are *Bacillus*, *Micrococcus*, and molds.

47.63   Pickled Products

Pickle-curing uses salt, vinegar, and spices to preserve and enhance the flavor of herring or similar fish. Pickled fish are presalted, washed to remove excess salt, and then repacked into smaller containers. A hot pickle solution consisting of vinegar, sugar, and spices is added. During the presalting, the most common microflora are *Micrococcus* and *Bacillus* spp. The same types of organisms are found most frequently in freshly pickled products as well. Secondary microbial contamination from handling may occur during repacking, and additional organisms can be added with the pickling ingredients. During the storage of pickled products, the microflora undergoes changes with a selective proliferation of halotolerant microaerophiles.

Erichsen[18] reported that three to four types of microorganisms were found to dominate successively in pickled seafood during storage. Initially, most strains belonged to *Micrococcus* spp. with a lower level of *Staphylococcus* spp.; both are found commonly in the raw material used. No coagulase-positive staphylococci could be isolated, either in the raw material or in the pickled product. The next group of organisms to appear during the storage of pickled fish belonged to the genus *Pediococcus*. The contribution of these organisms to the flavor and quality of the final product is not known. They are homo-fermentative and known to lower the pH of the product. The last group of organisms predominating in pickled fish at the time of visual gas production belonged to the genera *Lactobacillus* and *Leuconostoc*. These organisms were hetero-fermentative and haloduric, and they preferred the lower pH for carbohydrate fermentation. The organisms that ultimately cause product deterioration were atypical for fresh fish. During prolonged storage, pickled fish display some softening of the tissue and cloudiness of the pickling solution, indicating proteolysis of the product.

47.64   Fermented Fish

Fermentation of fish is a common type of preservation used in southeast Asia. Many fish sauces and pastes are produced through natural fermentation. The process is quite simple: the fish are heavily salted and allowed to stand at natural atmospheric conditions for several months. Since the high salt content retards microbial growth, hydrolysis of the fish protein is thought to occur by naturally occurring tissue enzymes, cathepsins.

For low salt products, halophilic or halotolerant populations consisting of gram-positive organisms will prevail. One of these products, "i-sushi," which is fermented by various strains of *Lactobacillus*, has been associated with food poisoning outbreaks from toxin production by *C. botulinum* type E.

47.7   MODIFIED-ATMOSPHERE PACKAGING AND STORAGE

In general, there are three different ways in which modification of the atmosphere surrounding a fresh food material can be utilized as a method of preservation: (1) atmospheric modification through a packaging technique such as vacuum packaging; (2) atmospheric pressure reduction within the container to accomplish a hypobaric condition; and (3) atmospheric modification through enrichment of the container atmosphere by addition of different gas blends. Although no commercial feasibility for the use of hypobaric preservation of fishery products has been demonstrated, the interest in both vacuum and modified-atmosphere packaging of seafood products has increased greatly over the last years.

To prevent growth of aerobic spoilage organisms, fresh seafoods can be packaged under vacuum in gas-impermeable packages or containers. Under such conditions, residual oxygen is used by the resident microflora and tissue enzymes to produce carbon dioxide, resulting in a lowering of the surface oxidation-reduction potential. These conditions will suppress the growth of common aerobic spoilage organisms and favor the growth of facultative anaerobic organisms including lactic acid bacteria. The delay in spoilage is achieved due to the slower growth rates and the less extensive organoleptic changes that are characteristic of these organisms.

The mechanism of shelf-life extension for products packaged in modified atmospheres is similar to that under vacuum. High levels of carbon dioxide during storage at refrigeration temperatures will selectively inhibit the growth of gram-negative pseudomonads and other gram-negative psychrotrophs, which normally grow rapidly and are responsible for the characteristic off-odors and off-flavors of seafood products. The gram-positive micrococci, streptococci, and lactobacilli are more tolerant to high concentrations of carbon dioxide and often become the dominant microflora.

Temperature abuse of vacuum- and controlled-atmosphere-packaged fresh foods may result in rapid growth of both spoilage and pathogenic bacteria. With respect to fishery products preserved short of sterilization, a large amount of research has centered around the significance of *C. botulinum*. Two factors contribute to a higher risk of *C. botulinum* toxigenesis in seafoods than other foods: (1) *C. botulinum* types E and non-proteolytic types B and F are able to grow at temperatures of 3.3°C and 5°C, respectively, and (2) the prevalence of *C. botulinum* spores in fresh and salt water fish is relatively high. Eyles and Warth[19] have reported spore loads of 17 spores/100g fish in haddock fillets.

With existing refrigeration equipment and distribution practices, there is no guarantee that temperatures of vacuum- and modified-atmosphere-packaged seafood products never exceed 3°C. An important question is thus whether or not organoleptic spoilage will precede toxin production and thus warn the consumer. A few studies have addressed this question with conflicting results. However, there is a general indication that as the storage temperature is increased from 0°C to 10°C, the time interval between unacceptable spoilage and detectable toxin production in fish stored under modified atmospheres shortens and the safety margin thus decreases. Studies by Eklund[16] and Lee and Solberg[30] have demonstrated toxin production in controlled-atmosphere-packaged fish stored at 10°C or below before perceptible spoilage. The conflicting data relative to rate of spoilage versus rate of toxigenesis can best be explained by the large number of variable factors that will affect both of these rates. Some of these factors are initial numbers and types of organisms present, species of fish used, number and quality of spores used as inoculum, packaging methodology, and criteria to evaluate spoilage. Even though raw fish are normally adequately cooked before consumption, which normally assures destruction of any botulinum toxin, modified atmosphere technology has not been widely adopted by the seafood industry because of the potential for botulinum toxicity.

47.8   RECOMMENDED METHODS

47.81   Sample Shipment

All fish and crustacean samples should be collected and transported in such a manner as to represent closely the original product. They should be collected in the original package and shipped at a temperature near that of the product at the time of collection. Severe changes in temperature, either higher (thawing) or lower (direct contact with dry ice), can greatly influence the results of a bacteriological analysis.

Frozen seafood products can be packaged with dry ice in an insulated container for 24 to 30 hr with no significant change in aerobic plate count. The coliform population can be reduced by the extreme cold ($-30°C$ within 1 hr); therefore, prolonged frozen storage should be avoided. After 30 hr, 10 to 12 pounds of dry ice will vaporize and result in subsequent increases in temperature and aerobic plate counts.

Packaged chemical gels are gaining popularity and, if previously frozen for at least 36 hr, will maintain an insulated container for 24 to 30 hr. Once melting begins, however, the temperature rises rapidly, and the microbial population increases at the rate of one log/24 hr. Coliform counts do not appear to be reduced by the cold of the ice gel; these tend to increase with rising temperature.

Wet ice is effective for 24 hr, but the "washing" action of the melting ice can produce inaccurate bacterial counts or destroy the product if it has not been properly wrapped.

A frozen product may be shipped in an insulated container without additional cooling, but the temperature will increase gradually after 6 hr. Bacterial counts are relatively stable after 12 hr, but they show a dramatic increase after 24 hr.

When freezing a fresh product is unavoidable because of delays in shipping or analysis, destruction or injury of microorganisms can be expected. Special precautions should be taken with products to be examined for *V. parahaemolyticus* or *C. perfringens* because both are sensitive to refrigeration.

47.82   Sample Method

47.821   Rinse samples

Since most contamination is surface related, the rinse technique offers a rapid, reliable, and nondestructive means of sampling. The product is placed into a sterile plastic bag and weighed. An appropriate volume of sterile diluent, 0.1% peptone, phosphate buffer, or 0.5% NaCl is added, and the bag is massaged by hand for 1 to 2 min. Examples of products best suited for this technique include green headless (shell-on tails) shrimp, small dressed fish, fillets, peeled and deveined shrimp, frog legs, and shell-on crab legs.

47.822   Swab Samples

The usefulness of swab samples is limited generally to comparing surface areas of large fish, such as belly cavity vs. head, or to sampling food contact surfaces. (See Chapter 2.)

47.823   Tissue samples

Tissue samples in this context refers to the blending or "stomaching" of a product or part of a product. Seafoods best suited for this technique include crab meat, fillets, breaded portions, breaded shrimp, squid, crab cakes, and minced flesh. Frozen samples can be taken with a sterile drill bit. (See Chapter 2.)

47.824   Skin samples

Removal of a known area of skin by template or bore is applicable to larger fish. After incisions are made, the skin is removed from the muscle with sterile forceps and scalpel. With packaged fish, there is a need to include microorganisms on the inside of the packaging film. After treatment of the exterior of the film with a suitable bactericidal solution, sampling of film and fish can be carried out as described above.

47.83   Microbiological Procedures

47.831   Aerobic plate count

Use the method described in Chapter 4, modified by the incorporation of 0.5% sodium chloride in the medium (some nonselective media already contain 0.5%, e.g., trypticase soy agar). For routine assessment of quality, plate incubations at 25°C for fresh and frozen, and 35°C for cooked products are recommended. Occasionally, both temperatures are used to assess the quality as well as the safety of a product.

47.832   Coliform group

Use the method described in Chapter 24. The MPN technique for breaded products should be used with some caution because materials from the breading-batter may contribute to false counts in lower dilutions.

E. coli (See Chapter 24.)

S. aureus

The MPN technique has limited value in the examination of fresh and fresh frozen seafood products because of the high number of halotolerant organisms exhibiting growth in media containing 10% NaCl. It is recommended that the enumeration of *S. aureus* from fresh and fresh frozen seafoods be made by direct plating onto Baird-Parker agar plates. Cooked products can be examined according to the MNP technique. Both procedures are described in Chapter 33.

Additional tests

V. parahaemolyticus and *V. cholerae* (See Chapter 28.)

C. botulinum (See Chapter 36.)

L. monocytogenes (See Chapter 38.)

Y. enterocolitica (See Chapter 27.)

Salmonella (See Chapter 25.)

Direct microscopic count (See Chapter 5.)

This is not a substitute for an aerobic plate count but may be used as a rapid, simple means of assessing the quality of seafood products that are subject to surface contamination. Counts normally will be 1 to 2 logs higher.

47.9   INTERPRETATION OF RESULTS

The wide variety of seafood products makes it impossible to establish arbitrary guidelines defining the quality or safety of a product. It was generally accepted for years that an aerobic plate count of 10^6/g indicated spoiled seafood. Reports in the literature now list counts as high as 10^8/g without objectionable quality changes. These differences occur because of normal and spoilage flora compositions, plate incubation temperatures, and product history. *Salmonella* has public health significance in certain seafood products. Questions have been raised concerning products like raw frog legs where *Salmonella* is a part of the normal flora of healthy frogs.

No uniform guidelines can be used to interpret the result of bacteriological testing of seafood products. Instead, each product must be evaluated on the basis of its own characteristics, and guidelines must be established to practical good manufacturing procedures. Several studies[5, 11, 12, 21, 27, 35, 40, 44, 51, 52, 53, 61] may be helpful in evaluating the acceptability of seafood and seafood products.

47.10   REFERENCES

1. Abeyta, C. 1983. Bacteriological quality of fresh seafood products from Seattle retail markets. J. Food Prot. 46: 901.
2. Abeyta, C., Kaysner, C. A., Wekell, M. M., Sullivan, J. J., and Stelma, G. N. 1986. Recovery of *Aeromonas hydrophila* from oysters implicated in an outbreak of foodborne illness. J. Food Prot. 49: 643.
3. Amano, K. 1961. The influence of fermentation on the nutritive value of fish with special reference to fermented fish products of southeast Asia. In "Fish in Nutrition," eds. R. Kreuzer and E. Heen, p. 180. Fishing News Ltd., London, England.
4. AMSI. 1988. Isolation and identification procedure for *Listeria* in seafood products. Research Report to Gulf and South Atlantic Fisheries Development Foundation, Tampa, Fla.
5. Baer, E. F., Duran, A. P., Leininger, H. V., Read, R. B. Jr., Schwab, A. H., and Swartzentruber, A. 1976. Microbiological quality of frozen breaded fish and shellfish products. Appl. Environ. Microbiol. 31(3): 337.
6. Blackwood, C. M. 1974. Utilization of mechanically separated fish flesh—Canadian experience. In "Fishery Products," ed. R. Kreuzer, p. 325. Fishing News Ltd., London, England.
7. Bryan, F. L. 1988. Risks associated with vehicles of foodborne pathogens and toxins. J. Food Prot. 51: 498.
8. Buchanan, R. E. and Gibbons, N. E. 1974. "Bergey's Manual of Determinative Bacteriology," 8th ed. Williams and Wilkins Co., Baltimore, Md.
9. Campbell, L. L. Jr. and Williams, O. B. 1952. The bacteriology of Gulf Coast shrimp. IV. Bacteriological, chemical and organoleptic changes with ice storage. Food Technol. 6: 125.
10. CFR. 1967. Food additives. Whole fish protein concentrates. Code of Fed. Regs. 32: 1173–1175. Off. of Fed. Reg. Nat. Arch. and Rec. Admin., Washington, D.C.
11. CFR. 1980. Frozen fish sticks, frozen fish cakes, and frozen crab cakes: Recommended microbiological quality standards. Code of Fed. Regs. 45(108): 37524–37526. Off. of Fed. Reg. Nat. Arch. and Rec. Admin., Washington, D.C.
12. CFR. 1981. Frozen fish sticks, frozen fish cakes, and frozen crab cakes: Recommended microbiological quality standards. Code of Fed. Reg. 46(113): 31067–31068. Off. of Fed. Reg. Nat. Arch. and Rec. Admin., Washington, D.C.
13. Colwell, R. R. 1974. *Vibrio parahaemolyticus*—Taxonomy, ecology and pathogenicity. In "Proc. of the 2nd U.S.-Japan Conference of Toxic Microorganisms. International Symposium of *Vibrio parahaemolyticus*." Saikon Publ. Co., Tokyo, Japan.
14. DePaola, A. 1981. *Vibrio cholerae* in marine foods and environmental waters: A literature review. J. Food Sci. 46: 66.
15. Duran, A. P., Wentz, B. A., Lanier, J. M., McClure, F. D., Schwab, A. B., Swartzentruber, A., Barnard, R. J., and Read, R. B. 1983. Microbiological quality of breaded shrimp during processing. J. Food Prot. 46: 974.
16. Eklund, M. W. 1982. Significance of *Clostridium botulinum* in fishery products preserved short of sterilization. Food Technol. 36(12): 107.
17. Eklund, M. W., Peterson, M. E., Paranjpye, R., and Pelroy, G. A. 1988. Feasibility of a heat-pasteurization process for the inactivation of nonproteolytic *Clostridium botulinum* types B and E in vacuum-packaged, hot process (smoked) fish. J. Food Prot. 51: 720.
18. Erichsen, I. 1967. The microflora of semi-preserved fish products. III. Principal groups of bacteria occurring in tidbits. Antonie van Leeuwenhoek. J. Microbiol. Ser. 33: 107.
19. Eyles, M. J. and Warth, A. D. 1981. Assessment of the risk of botulism from vacuum-packaged raw fish: A review. Food Technol. Aust. 33: 574.
20. Faghri, M. A., Pennington, C. L., Cronholm, L. S., and Atlas, R. M. 1984. Bacteria associated with crabs from cold waters with emphasis on the occurrence of potential human pathogens. Appl. Environ. Microbiol. 47: 1054.
21. Foster, J. F., Fowler, J. L., and Dacey, J. 1977. A microbial survey of various fresh and frozen seafood products. J. Food Prot. 40(5): 300.

22. Goldmintz, D. and Hull, J. C. 1970. Bacteriological aspects of fish protein concentrate production. Develop. Ind. Microbiol. 11: 335.
23. Green, M. 1949. Bacteriology of shrimp. II. Quantitative studies on freshly caught and iced shrimp. Food Res. 14: 372.
24. Gulasekharam, J., Velaudapillai, T., and Niles, G. R. 1956. The isolation of *Salmonella* organisms from fresh fish sold in a Colombo fish market. J. Hyg. 54: 581.
25. Harrison, J. M. and Lee, J. S. 1968. Microbiological evaluation of Pacific shrimp processing. Appl. Microbiol. 18: 188.
26. Hird, D. W., Diesch, S. L., McKinnell, R. G., Gorham, E., Martin, F. B., Meadows, C. A., and Gasiorowski, M. 1983. *Enterobacteriaceae* and *Aeromonas hydrophila* in Minnesota frogs and tadpoles, (*Rana pipiens*). Appl. Environ. Microbiol. 46: 1423.
27. ICMSF. 1974. "Microorganisms in Foods." 2. Sampling for microbiological analysis: Principles and specific applications. Inter. Comm. on Microbiol. Specif. for Foods. U. of Toronto Press, Canada.
28. Ingham, S. C. and Potter, N. N. 1987. Microbial growth in surimi and mince made from Atlantic pollock. J. Food Prot. 50: 312.
29. Kaysner, C. A., Abeyta, C., Wekell, M. M., DePaola, A., Stott, R. F., and Leitch, J. M. 1987. Incidence of *Vibrio cholerae* from estuaries of the United States West Coast. Appl. Environ. Microbiol. 53: 1344.
30. Lee, D. A. and Solberg, M. 1983. Time to toxin detection and organoleptic determination in *Clostridium botulinum* incubated fresh fish fillets during modified atmosphere storage. Abstr. 43rd Annu. Inst. Food Technol. Meet. Abstr. No. 483.
31. Lee, J. S. and Pfeifer, D. K. 1975. Microbiological characteristics of Dungeness Crab (*Cancer magister*). Appl. Microbiol. 30: 72.
32. Lennon, D., Lewis, B., Mantell, C., Becroft, D., Farmer, K., Tonkin, S., Yeates, N., Stamp, R., and Mickleson, K. 1984. Epidemic perinatal Listeriosis. Pediatr. Inf. Dis. 3: 30.
33. Licciardello, J. J. and Hill, W. S. 1978. Microbiological quality of commercial frozen minced fish blocks. J. Food Prot. 41: 948.
34. Makukutu, C. A. and Guthrie, R. K. 1986. Behavior of *Vibrio cholerae* in hot foods. Appl. Environ. Microbiol. 52: 824.
35. Martin, R. E. and Pitts, G. T. 1981. "Handbook of State and Federal Microbiological Standards and Guidelines." National Fisheries Institute, Inc., Washington, D.C.
36. Middlebrooks, B. L., Toom, P. M., Douglas, W. L., Harrison, R. E., and McDowell, S. 1988. Effects of storage time and temperature on the microflora and amine development in Spanish Mackerel (*Scomberomorus maculatus*). J. Food Sci. 53: 1024.
37. Miller, A. III, Scanlan, R. A., Lee, J. S., and Libbey, L. M. 1973a. Identification of the volatile compounds produced in sterile fish muscle (*Sebastes melonops*) by *Pseudomonas fragi*. Appl. Microbiol. 25: 952.
38. Miller, A. III, Scanlan, R. A., Lee, J. S., and Libbey, L. M. 1973b. Volatile compounds produced in sterile fish muscle (*Sebastes melonops*) by *Pseudomonas putrefaciens*, *Pseudomonas fluorescens*, and an *Achromobacter* species. Appl. Microbiol. 26: 18.
39. Miller, M. L. and Koburger, J. A. 1986. Tolerance of *Plesiomonas shigelloides* to pH, sodium chloride and temperature. J. Food Prot. 49: 877.
40. Nickelson, R., Hosch, J., and Wyatt, L. W. 1975. A direct microscopic count procedure for the rapid estimation of bacterial numbers on green-headless shrimp. J. Milk Food Technol. 38: 76.
41. Nickelson, R., Finne, G., Hanna, M. O., and Vanderzant, C. 1980. Minced fish flesh from nontraditional Gulf of Mexico finfish species: Bacteriology. J. Food Sci. 45: 1321.
42. Pace, J., Wu, C. Y., and Chai, T. 1988. Bacterial flora in pasteurized oysters after refrigerated storage. J. Food Sci. 53: 325.
43. Paskell, S. L. and Goldmintz, D. 1973. Bacteriological aspects of fish protein concentrate production from a large-scale experiment and demonstration plant. Develop. Ind. Microbiol. 14: 302.

44. Phillips, F. A. and Peeler, J. T., 1972. Bacteriological survey of the blue crab industry. Appl. Microbiol. 24: 958.
45. Powell, J. C., Moore, A. R., and Gow, J. A. 1979. Comparison of EC broth and medium A-1 for the recovery of *Escherichia coli* from frozen shucked snow crab. Appl. Environ. Microbiol. 37: 836.
46. Ryser, E. T., Marth, E. H., and Taylor, S. L. 1984. Histamine production by psychrotrophic pseudomonads isolated from tuna fish. J. Food Prot. 47: 378.
47. Shewan, J. M. 1961. The microbiology of sea-water fish. In "Fish as Food," ed. George Borgstrom, Vol. 1, p. 487. Academic Press, New York.
48. Shewan, J. M. 1971. The microbiology of fish and fishery products: A progress report. J. Appl. Bacteriol. 34: 299.
49. Solomon, H. M., Lynt, R. K., Lilly, T. Jr., and Kautter, D. A. 1977. Effect of low temperatures on growth of *Clostridium botulinum* spores in meat of the blue crab. J. Food Prot. 40: 5.
50. Stelma, G. N., Spaulding, P. L., Reyes, A. L., and Johnson, C. H. 1988. Production of enterotoxin by *Vibrio vulnificus* isolates. J. Food Prot. 51: 192.
51. Surkiewicz, B. F., Hyndman, J. B., and Yancey, M. V. 1967. Bacteriological survey of the frozen prepared foods industry. II. Frozen breaded raw shrimp. Appl. Microbiol. 15: 1.
52. Surkiewicz, B. F., Groomes, R. J., and Shelton, L. R. 1968. Bacteriological survey of the frozen prepared foods industry. IV. Frozen breaded fish. Appl. Microbiol. 16: 147.
53. Swartzentruber, A., Schwab, A. H., Duran, A. P., Wentz, B. A., and Read, R. B. Jr. 1980. Microbiological quality of frozen shrimp and lobster tail in the retail market. Appl. Environ. Microbiol. 40: 765.
54. Tillman, R. E., Nickelson, R., and Finne, G. 1981. The bacteriological quality and safety of pasteurized langostino tails. In "Proc. Sixth Trop. and Subtrop. Fish. Tech. Conf. of the Americas," p. 161. Sea Grant College Program, Texas A & M U., College Station, Tex.
55. Tison, D. L. and Kelly, M. T. 1986. Virulence of *Vibrio vulnificus* strains from marine environments. Appl. Environ. Microbiol. 51: 1004.
56. U. of Florida. 1988. *Vibrio vulnificus*—An advisory note. Food Sci. and Human Nutr. Dept., U. of Fla., Gainesville, Fla.
57. Vanderzant, C., Nickelson, R., and Parker, J. C. 1970a. Isolation of *Vibro parahaemolyticus* from Gulf Coast shrimp. J. Milk Food Technol. 33: 161.
58. Vanderzant, C., Mroz, E. and Nickelson, R. 1970b. Microbial flora of Gulf of Mexico and pond shrimp. J. Milk Food Technol. 33: 346.
59. Vanderzant, C., Nickelson, R., and Judkins, P. W. 1971. Microbial flora of pond-reared brown shrimp (*Penaeus aztecus*). Appl. Microbiol. 21: 916.
60. Vanderzant, C., Judkins, P. W., Nickelson, R., and Fitzhugh, H. A. 1972. Numerical taxonomy of coryneform bacteria isolated from pond-reared shrimp (*Penaeus aztecus*) and pond water. Appl. Microbiol. 23: 38.
61. Vanderzant, C., Matthys, A. W., and Cobb, B. F. 1973. Microbiological, chemical, and organoleptic characteristics of frozen breaded raw shrimp. J. Milk Food Technol. 36: 253.
62. Ward, D. R., Pierson, M. D., and Van Tassell, K. R. 1977. The microflora of unpasteurized and pasteurized crab meat. J. Food Sci. 42: 597.
63. Weagant, S. D., Sado, P. N., Colburn, K. G., Torkelson, J. D. Stanley, F. A., Krane, M. H., Shields, S. C., and Thayer, C. F. 1988. The incidence of *Listeria* species in frozen seafood products. J. Food Prot. 51: 655.
64. Wentz, B. A., Duran, A. P., Swartzentruber, A., Schwab, A. H., and Read, R. B. 1983. Microbiological quality of fresh blue crab meat, clams and oysters. J. Food Prot. 46: 978.
65. Williams, O. B., Campbell, L. L. Jr., and Rees, H. B. Jr. 1952. The bacteriology of Gulf Coast shrimp. II. Qualitative observations on the external flora. Tex. J. Sci. 4: 53.
66. Yoon, I. H. and Matches, J. R. 1988. Growth of pathogenic bacteria on imitation crab. J. Food Sci. 53: 688. Erratum J. Food Sci. 53: 1582.
67. Yoon, I. H., Matches, J. R., and Rasco, B. 1988. Microbiological and chemical changes of surimi-based imitation crab during storage. J. Food Sci. 53: 1343.

Chapter 48

MOLLUSCAN SHELLFISH: OYSTERS, MUSSELS, AND CLAMS

John J. Miescier, Daniel A. Hunt, James Redman,
Arnold Salinger, and John P. Lucas

48.1 INTRODUCTION

Bivalved molluscs such as oysters, mussels, and clams are economically important marine food species found in abundance in estuarine and marine waters. These organisms are filter feeders and commonly are eaten whole in the living state. While feeding on plankton and other microflora, shellfish may concentrate pathogenic bacteria and viruses from polluted waters.

Historically, *Salmonella typhi* has been the most significant microbial contaminant from the point of view of shellfish-borne epidemics.[52] Based on the number of outbreaks and cases during the last decade, hepatitis A is now the major public health problem associated with the consumption of raw shellfish in the United States. In 1973, consumption of raw oysters harvested in Louisiana growing waters resulted in two outbreaks of hepatitis, one in Houston, Tex., with 263 cases and one in Calhoun, Ga., involving 15 cases.[59]

Worldwide, the largest shellfish-associated epidemic of viral etiology occurred in Australia in 1978.[57] More than 2,000 cases of gastroenteritis were reported. The epidemic was caused by the consumption of raw oysters contaminated by Norwalk agent.

Vibrio cholerae and *Vibrio parahaemolyticus* have been incriminated to a lesser degree. Outbreaks of *V. parahaemolyticus* gastroenteritis in the United States have been primarily associated with the consumption of shrimp and crabs.[16, 21, 30] Two shellfish-associated outbreaks of cholera occurred in Western Europe during the first half of the decade, one in Portugal in 1974[11] and the other in Italy in 1973.[8] During that period, there was little public health concern for shellfish-borne cholera in the U.S. However, there has been an upsurge in interest in *V. cholerae* since publication of the first edition of this book in 1976.

Eight cases of cholera epidemiologically associated with the consumption of home-cooked crabs occurred in Louisiana in 1978.[14] Group 1 *V. cholerae* El Tor Inaba was isolated from the eight cases and from an additional three asymptomatic individuals during the outbreak. This was the first outbreak of cholera in the United States involving more than one case since 1911.

Non-O group 1 *V. cholerae* has been isolated from individuals with cholera-like gastroenteritis following consumption of oysters.[50] Non-toxigenic O group 1 and non-O group 1 *V. cholerae* have also been isolated from environmental samples.[47]

Vibrio vulnificus, a lactose-fermenting non-cholera vibrio, has caused primary septicemia and death following the consumption of raw oysters in individuals with therapeutically induced or naturally low gastric acid, diabetes, cirrhosis, leukemia, acquired immunodeficiency syndrome (AIDS), AIDS-related complex, hemochromatosis, thalassemia major or alcoholism.[10, 17, 27, 54] In persons with pre-existing liver disease, a 50% mortality rate has been reported.[25] Individuals with such underlying illnesses should not consume raw or lightly cooked shellfish.[25, 27, 54] Healthy individuals can develop gastroenteritis as a result of ingesting shellfish contaminated with *V. vulnificus*.[27, 54]

Listeria monocytogenes, a gram-positive coccoid rod is widely distributed in nature and is resistant to salt, alkali, and desiccation.[29, 49, 68] It has been isolated from sewage, soil, animals, birds, insects, green plants, silage, water, and food products including milk, cheese, meat products, fruits, vegetables, raw shrimp, cooked and peeled shrimp, cooked crabmeat, raw lobster tails, fin fish, and surimi-based imitation seafoods.[26, 29, 49, 67, 68] Its occurrence in oysters, clams, and mussels has not been previously reported in the United States. Also, there is no published information on the occurrence and survival of *L. monocytogenes* in marine and estuarine waters.[67] Infection with *L. monocytogenes* is usually characterized as septicemia, meningitis, or abortion, and occurs most commonly in neonates and immunosuppressed individuals.[29, 49] Listeriosis may be either sporadic or epidemic.[29] Recent outbreaks of human listeriosis have been attributed to the consumption of coleslaw, milk, and soft cheese.[67] A 1980 epidemic of perinatal listeriosis involving 22 individuals in New Zealand may have been associated with the consumption of shellfish and raw fish.[49]

Campylobacter jejuni is currently recognized as one of the principal bacterial causes of human gastroenteritis, and raw clams have been implicated in an outbreak of campylobacteriosis.[12]

Colwell and Liston[19] have reported that gram-negative, asporogenous rods of *Pseudomonas*, *Vibrio*, and *Flavobacterium* predominate the normal flora of the Pacific oyster, *Crassostrea gigas*, in Washington waters, and that gram-positive organisms constitute less than 20% of isolates. They further reported that the coliform count as calculated from the total viable count and most probable number (MPN) values never constituted more than 0.5% of the total viable count in their samples of Pacific oysters. A similar pattern was demonstrated by Vanderzant et al.[66] in studies of the eastern oyster, *Crassostrea virginica*, from Galveston Bay. Lovelace et al.[51] reported *Vibrio, Pseudomonas, Achromobacter*, and *Cytophaga/Flavobacterium* as the predominant organisms found in eastern oysters from two natural harvesting sites in Chesapeake Bay. At one site 7% of the isolates were either *Enterobacter* or *Proteus* species, but neither of these two species, were reported in oysters from the second site. This finding supports the Colwell and Liston report of low coliform population in oysters from the West Coast and indicates that the presence of an elevated number of coliforms, including "fecal" types in shellfish immediately after harvesting, may be indicative of the presence of a potential public health problem, although the presence of nonfecal coliforms can confuse the issue.

In the United States, sanitary control of the shellfish industry is based primarily on the classification and control of the harvest areas through comprehensive sanitary surveys of the shoreline, bacteriological monitoring of growing area waters, and prohibition of harvesting from areas not meeting "approved" growing area criteria. Routine control procedures are based on guidelines in the National Shellfish Sanitation Program (NSSP) Manual of Operations.[39]

Historically, it appears that strict adherence to NSSP guidelines for the classification and control of shellfish growing areas has resulted in the production of safe shellfish where the hazard has been directly associated with sewer outfalls. With the possible exception of *Vibrio* gastroenteritis, shellfish-borne outbreaks have been usually associated with a breakdown in growing area control procedures resulting in the harvesting of contaminated shellfish. However, the question of the effectiveness of NSSP guidelines in preventing shellfish-borne illness caused by *Vibrio*, which may be able to colonize and survive in estuarine waters long distances from sewer outfalls, remains to be resolved.[23] Historically, contaminated wet storage areas have long been incriminated in shellfish-associated epidemics. More recently, imported clams that had been harvested from polluted waters and relayed and processed in shellfish purification plants have caused outbreaks of gastroenteritis of undetermined origin in the United States.[56]

The safety of shellfish has been predicated on the levels of indicator organisms, primarily the coliform group, present in the growing waters and on the direct relationship of these organisms to known sources of pollution. In 1964, the National Workshop adopted the fecal coliform criterion for the wholesale market standard for shucked oysters,[33, 48] and in 1968, for all species of fresh and fresh frozen shellfish.[34] The validity of the NSSP shellfish meat and growing water bacteriological standards has been challenged throughout the history of the program.[42] Recently, research has been proposed and implemented to verify or supplant the current standards with new or adjunct criteria.[24, 37, 69] There were no official NSSP procedures for the isolation of pathogenic bacteria from shellfish before 1971. In 1971, the National Workshop adopted the Bacteriological Analytical Manual of the Food and Drug Administration[38] as the official reference for the detection and enumeration of *V. parahaemolyticus* in shellfish.[35] The procedure for the isolation of *V. cholerae* may also be the current procedure of choice (see Chapter 28).

Bacteriological quality of shellfish meats may be determined at several marketing levels: as harvested, by in-plant sampling, in storage, upon receipt at the wholesale market, and at the retail market level. The only microbiological standard for the shellfish meats developed by the NSSP is for product quality at the time of receipt at the wholesale market. Fresh or fresh frozen shellfish are generally considered to be satisfactory at the wholesale market if the fecal coliform MPN does not exceed 230/100 g, and the 35°C plate count is not more than 500,000/g of sample. It is recognized, however, that the level of accumulation of indicator organisms under a given set of environmental conditions may vary according to type of shellfish and individual species.[41]

Bacteriological quality of shellfish meats may also be determined in association with a process known as microbial depuration. According to the NSSP, depuration or controlled purification is intended to reduce the number of pathogenic microorganisms that may be present in shellfish harvested from moderately polluted (restricted) waters to such levels that the shellfish will be acceptable for human consumption without further processing.[40] Depuration is not intended for shellfish from heavily polluted (prohibited) waters nor is it intended to reduce the levels of poisonous or deleterious substances that the shellfish may have accumulated from their environment. The acceptability of the depuration process is contingent on the state shellfish control authority exercising very stringent supervision over all phases of the process.

Certain critical factors, such as water chemistry, turbidity, temperature, salinity, dissolved oxygen, processing tank dimensions, rate of flow, tank loading, and clearance between shellfish containers and walls, must be controlled if the shellfish are to pump effectively and eliminate pathogenic organisms that may be present. The source of process water and the water treatment system must be such that an adequate volume and quality of water can be provided to accomplish effective purification.

Currently, all depuration plants in the United States use ultraviolet (UV) light to disinfect process water. UV treatment is highly effective for inactivating bacteria and viruses, provided the units are kept clean to prevent buildup of materials that reduce radiation intensity.

Controlled purification studies have shown that the minimum processing time is 48 hr under optimum conditions, but that under certain conditions longer depuration periods may be required for adequate shellfish purification. Depuration periods of less than 48 hr are not acceptable. The efficacy of the process is measured on the basis of end-point fecal coliform densities (per

100 g) of the depurated shellfish species, using standard geometric mean and upper 10% levels.

48.2   EXAMINATION OF SHELLFISH

48.21   Collection and Transportation of Samples

Samples of shell stock and shucked unfrozen shellfish should be examined within 6 hr after collection, and in no case should they be examined if they have been held more than 24 hr after collection. The report of the examination should include a record of the time elapsed between collection and examination.

Individual containers of shellfish samples should be marked for identification, and the same mark should be put in its proper place on the descriptive form that accompanies the sample.

A history and description of the shellfish should accompany the sample to the laboratory, including (1) date, time, and place of collection, (2) the area from which the shellfish were harvested, (3) the date and time of harvesting, and (4) the conditions of storage between harvesting and collection.

Not all of this information may be obtainable for shellfish samples collected in market areas. In such a case, the identification of the shipper, the date of shipment, and the harvesting area should be determined, as well as the date, time, and place of collection.

48.22   Shell Stock (Shellfish in the Shell)

Samples of shellfish should be collected in clean containers. The containers should be waterproof and durable enough to withstand the cutting action of the shellfish and abrasion during transportation. Waterproof paper bags, paraffined cardboard cups, and plastic bags are suitable types of containers. A tin can with a tight lid is also suitable.

Shell stock samples should be kept in dry storage at a temperature above freezing but lower than 10°C until examined. Shell stock must not be allowed to come in contact with ice.

An adequate number of shellfish must be collected to obtain a representative sample to allow for the selection of sound animals suitable for shucking. With most species, 10 to 12 shellfish should be examined, regardless of their individual size or weight.

Because of their large size, 10 to 12 shellfish of certain species such as the Pacific oyster, *Crassostrea gigas*, the surf clam, *Spisula solidissima*, and certain larger sizes of the hard clam, *Mercenaria mercenaria*, may require using blender jars of a larger size than usual. Certain blenders will accept ordinary mason jars and thus, a 2- or 4-quart container may be used for blending these species.

Where 2-quart containers are not available, the 10 to 12 shellfish should be ground for 30 sec. Then 200 g of this meat homogenate should be blended with 200 g sterile buffered phosphate water or 0.5% sterile peptone water for 60 sec.

On the other hand, 10 or 12 shellfish of certain other species, such as the Olympia oyster, *Ostrea lurida*, and small sizes of the Pacific little neck clams, *Protothaca staminea* and *Tapes japonica*, may produce much less than 100 g of shell liquor and meats. Blender containers of smaller size are indicated, but even when pint or half-pint jars are used, as many as 20 to 30 of these species will be required to produce an adequate volume for proper blending.

48.23   Shucked Shellfish

A sterile widemouthed jar of a suitable capacity with a watertight closure is an acceptable container for samples of shucked shellfish taken in shucking houses, repacking establishments, or bulk shipments in the market. The shellfish may be transferred to the jar with sterile forceps or spoon. Samples of the final product of shucking houses or repacking establishments may be taken in the final packing cans or containers. The comments pertaining to species of various sizes in the section on shell stock apply to shucked shellfish. Consumer-size packages are acceptable for examination provided that they contain an adequate number of animals.

Samples of shucked shellfish should be refrigerated immediately after collection by packing in crushed ice, and they should be so kept until examined.

48.24   Frozen Shucked Shellfish

If the package contains an adequate number of animals (10 to 12), one or two packages may be taken as a sample. Samples from larger blocks may be taken by coring with a suitable instrument, or by quartering, using sterile technique. Cores or quartered samples should be transferred to sterile widemouthed jars for transportation to the laboratory.

It is desirable to keep samples of frozen shucked shellfish in the frozen state at temperatures close to those at which the commercial stock was maintained. When such storage is not possible, samples of frozen shucked shellfish should be packed in crushed ice and kept so until examined.

48.3   PREPARATION OF SAMPLE FOR EXAMINATION. SHELLFISH IN THE SHELL

48.31   Cleaning the Shells

The hands of the examiner must be scrubbed thoroughly with soap and water and rinsed with 70% ethanol.

Scrape off all growth and loose material from the shell, and scrub the shell stock with a sterile stiff brush under running water of drinking quality, paying particular attention to the crevices at the junctions of the shells. Place the cleaned shell stock in clean containers or on clean towels and allow to drain in the air.

48.32 Removal of Shell Contents

Before starting the removal of shell contents, the hands of the examiner must be thoroughly scrubbed with soap and water and rinsed with 70% ethanol. Open the shellfish as directed below, collecting the appropriate quantities of shell liquor and meats in a sterile blender or other suitable sterile container.

48.321   Oysters

Hold the oyster in the hand or on a fresh clean paper towel on the bench with the deep shell on the bottom. Using a sterile oyster knife, insert the point between the shells on the ventral side (at the right when the hinge is pointed away from the examiner), about one-fourth the distance from the hinge to the bill. Entry also may be made at the bill after making a small opening with a sterile instrument similar to bonecutting forceps.

Cut the adductor muscle from the upper flat shell and pry the shell wide enough to drain the shell liquor into a sterile tared beaker, widemouthed jar, or blender jar. The upper shell then may be pried loose at the hinge and discarded, and the meats transferred to the beaker or jar after severing the muscle attachment to the lower shell.

Figure 1—Scrubbing Shellfish with Sterile Brush after Washing Hands and Rinsing with 70% Ethanol

48.322   Hard clams

Entry into the hard clam, *Mercenaria mercenaria*, or the Pacific little neck clam, *Protothaca* sp., is best done with a sterile, thin-bladed knife similar to a paring knife. To open the clam, hold it in the hand, place the edge of the knife at the junction of the bills, and force it between the shells with a squeezing motion. An alternative method is to nibble a small hole in the bill with sterile bonecutting forceps and sever the two adductor muscles with the knife. Drain the shell liquor into the sample container. Cut the adductor muscles from the shells and transfer the body of the animal to the sample container.

48.323   Other clams

The soft clam, *Mya arenaria*, the Pacific butter clam, *Saxidomus giganteus*, the surf clam, *Spisula solidissima*, and similar species may be shucked with a sterile paring knife, entering at the siphon end and cutting the adductor muscles first from the top valve and then from the bottom valve.

Mussels, *Modiolus*, and *Mytilus* species may be entered at the byssal opening. The byssal threads should be removed during the cleansing of the shell. The knife may be inserted and the shells spread apart with a twisting motion, allowing the draining of the shell liquor. Cut away the many attachments from the shell. (See Figures 2 and 3.)

48.324   Shucked shellfish

Transfer a suitable quantity from a sample jar to a sterile tared blender jar or other container, using a sterile spoon.

48.33   Dilution and Grinding

Weigh the sample to the nearest gram. Transfer the weighed sample to a sterile blender jar and add an equal amount, by weight, of sterile phosphate buffered dilution water or 0.5% sterile peptone water. Grind for 60 to 120 sec in a laboratory blender operating at approximately 14,000 RPM. Two ml of this mixture contain 1 g of shellfish meat. The optimum grinding time will vary with make of machine, condition of machine, species of shellfish, and, probably, the physical state of the meats. In general, a grinding time of 60 to 90 sec will be optimum for all species. Excessive grinding in small containers should be avoided to prevent overheating. (See Chapter 2 on Sampling and Sample Preparation.)

A dilution of equal amounts by weight of shucked packs of certain species of shellfish results, after grinding, in a mixture that is of too heavy a consistency for pipetting and transferring to culture tubes. Meats of the hard shell clam, surf clam, and butter clam are often in this category. In these cases, using a greater proportion of dilution water is permissible. Addition

a. Oyster

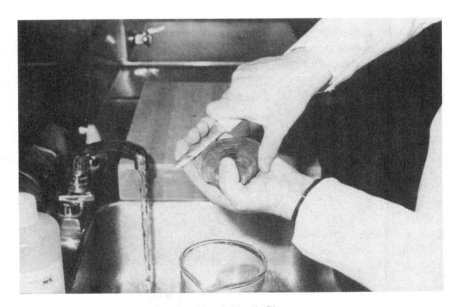

b. Hard Shell Clam

Figure 2—Shucking with Sterile Knife into Sterile Beaker

Figure 2—(*Continued*)

c. Sea Clam

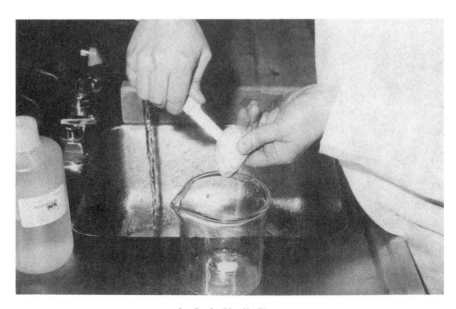

d. Soft Shell Clam

Figure 3—Using Bone Cutters to Break Shell of Hard Shell Clam

of 3 parts by weight of dilution water to 1 part of the weighed sample is suggested. With such dilutions, 4 ml of the ground sample will be equal to a 1 g portion of shellfish. If the 1:4 dilution method is used, adjustment in the concentration of presumptive broth in the tubes receiving the 1 g portions should be made accordingly.

48.4 MICROBIOLOGICAL PROCEDURES

48.41 Tests for Members of Coliform Group

The recommended procedures for the microbiological examination of shellfish are described in "Recommended Procedures for the Examination of Seawater and Shellfish."[1] They include methods for coliforms, fecal coliforms, and the Standard Plate Count (aerobic plate count). For methods in conformance with these recommendations, refer to Chapter 4 (Aerobic Plate Count) and Chapter 24 (Coliforms and Fecal Coliforms).

48.42 Salmonella

In 1950, Bidwell and Kelly[9] reported the isolation of *Salmonella typhimurium* from New York oysters. Duck farm wastes were judged to be the source of the organism. Brezenski and Russomanno[15] successfully isolated 12 *Salmonella* serotypes from hard clams harvested from Raritan Bay. Six ser-

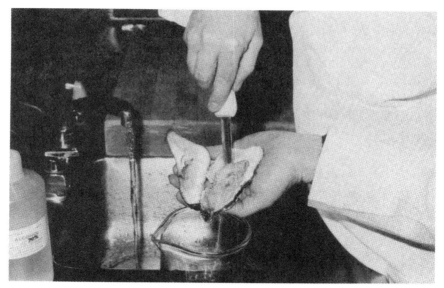

Figure 4—Removing Meat from Shell (Note Shell Liquor Also Is Drained into Beaker)

Figure 5—Weighing Shucked Meat and Shell Liquor

Figure 6—Pouring Shucked Meats and Shell Liquor into Blender Jar

otypes were isolated from oysters taken from New Hampshire waters by Slanetz, Bartley, and Stanley.[64] During the Eighth National Shellfish Sanitation Workshop, Andrews et al.[4] reported the isolation of 5 *Salmonella* serotypes in hard clams and 11 serotypes in oysters from Northeast and Gulf Coast waters. For detection of *Salmonella* in food, see Chapter 25 and the FDA Bacteriological Analytical Manual.

48.43 *Vibrio parahaemolyticus*

Vibrio parahaemolyticus is a marine-occurring organism that is reported to be the cause of "summer diarrhea" in Japan and of gastrointestinal outbreaks from the consumption of blue crabs in Maryland and shrimp in Texas. The organism was listed as the probable cause of an oyster-borne, gastrointestinal outbreak in the State of Washington in 1969.[32] An unidentified *Vibrio* has been associated with a gastrointestinal outbreak in England from the consumption of depurated oysters. In consideration of the volume of oysters, mussels, and clams eaten raw in the United States and the low incidence of disease, it would appear that the potential hazard to consumers of raw molluscan shellfish from *V. parahaemolyticus* is minor. The organism has been recovered from numerous marine food species from the Atlantic, Gulf, and Pacific Coasts and is reported to be distributed in the marine environment.[32]

Because of the potential hazard from this organism, the Seventh National Shellfish Sanitation Workshop[35] recommended that the Food and Drug

Figure 7—Adding Equal Weight of Sterile Buffered Distilled Water

Administration's Bacteriological Analytical Manual (BAM)[38] procedure be accepted as the official reference of the NSSP for the examination of shellfish for *V. parahaemolyticus*. It was recommended further that state laboratories conduct the test for this organism when routine tests of marine foods suspected in foodborne outbreaks fail to demonstrate other enteric pathogens or bacterial toxins. For the detection of *V. parahaemolyticus*, refer to the current edition of the BAM and to Chapter 28 of this book.

48.44   *Vibrio cholerae*

There are no official NSSP procedures for the analysis of shellfish for this bacterium. Refer to the methodology listed in Chapter 28 and the BAM chapter for *V. cholerae*.[38]

48.45   *Vibrio vulnificus*

Vibrio vulnificus is a free-living, lactose-fermenting, gram-negative, halophilic, toxin-producing, opportunistic bacterial pathogen endemic to the marine and estuarine environments.[7, 17, 58] It has been recovered from seawater, estuarine sediments, and a variety of marine foods from nearly all coastal waters in the United States and abroad.[46, 55, 58, 67] The densities of this organism are highest during the relatively warm months of April to October, especially along the Gulf Coast.[13] Oysters, clams, and mussels are filter feeders and can concentrate this bacterium from the surrounding water. There

Figure 8—Blending

are no official NSSP procedures for analyzing shellfish for *V. vulnificus*. Refer to the methodology in Chapter 28 of this book and the BAM.

48.46   *Listeria monocytogenes*

There are no official NSSP procedures for analyzing shellfish for *L. monocytogenes*. Refer to the methodology in Chapter 38 of this book and the BAM.

48.5   INTERPRETATION OF DATA

The NSSP microbiological quality standard for fresh and fresh frozen oysters, mussels, and clams was developed as a guideline of acceptable quality for shellfish harvested, processed, and shipped according to recommended practices, and sampled upon receipt at the wholesale market, retail markets, or restaurants, if shipped directly to the receiver. The standard, a maximum fecal coliform MPN of 230/100 g of sample and a Standard Plate Count not exceeding 500,000/g for shellfish, can be used by control receiver agency programs to determine product quality as delivered by the shipper, or, in case of excessive counts, forwarded to the producer state control agency for investigative and corrective purposes.

Because the bacteriological quality may reflect growing area water quality, the bacteriological water-quality standards should be mentioned briefly. The coliform standard for approved growing areas, a median MPN value of 70, with not more than 10% of samples exceeding an MPN of 230 for a 5 tube,

3 dilution method, or an MPN of 330 for a 3 tube, 3 dilution method, has been unchanged essentially since 1946. To develop a growing area standard more indicative of fecal pollution, the Food and Drug Administration proposed a fecal coliform standard at the 1974 National Workshop.[36] The proposal stated, "The median fecal coliform MPN value for a sampling station shall not exceed 14 per 100 ml of sample and not more than 10 percent of the samples shall exceed 43 for a 5 tube, 3 dilution test, or 49 for a 3 tube, 3 dilution test." The methodology is the same as for meats, except that 10 ml, 1 ml, and 0.1 ml volumes of sample usually are used for routine samples. The fecal coliform criterion and standard are being used by state, federal, and Canadian agencies to classify shellfish waters.

Shelf life and bacteriological quality will vary according to species, salinity, and bacteriological quality of growing area waters, climate, processing controls, refrigeration, and other conditions. For example, the northern quahog (*Mercenaria mercenaria*) harvested from New England waters normally will have a lower bacteriological count and longer shelf life than a soft shell clam (*Mya arenaria*) harvested from the warmer, less saline waters of the Mid-Atlantic States. Therefore, the proper interpretation of wholesale market data requires knowledge of the sanitary control conditions of the product from growing area to market.

Experience with the shellfish product is valuable when interpreting results, and since this is not always easily attainable, the analyst is advised to consult with the appropriate agency of the state or country in which the product originated.

48.6 RAPID METHODS (See also Chapter 39)

There has been considerable interest in recent years in rapid methods, particularly to monitor controlled purification (depuration) systems for shellfish harvested from marginally polluted waters and for inland state shellfish monitoring programs.

Heffernan and Cabelli[31] developed a 24-hr plate method for the determination of elevated temperature coliforms using a modified MacConkey medium incubated at 45.5°C in an air incubator for 24 hr. The method was recommended as an official procedure for monitoring depuration processing of the soft shell clam (*Mya arenaria*) at the Eighth National Shellfish Sanitation Workshop in 1974.[36] This procedure was tested against the standard method using a 12 tube, 3 dilution MPN system. It works well with the soft shell clam and the hard shell clam (*Mercenaria mercenaria*) but has not proven to be effective with oysters.

Using a variety of frozen foods including seafoods, Fishbein et al.[28] effectively recovered *Escherichia coli* using LST broth incubated at 44°C in a waterbath for 24 hr. Andrews et al.[5] and Andrews and Presnell[3] evaluated a multiple tube test for the recovery of *E. coli* from shellfish and shellfish waters using A-1 medium incubated at 44.5°C for 24 hr. The APHA MPN method was compared to the A-1 and a modification of the A-1 method (A-1-M) for recovery of fecal coliforms and *E. coli* from sea water by Hunt and Springer.[43] In a more recent study involving 16 state, federal, and Canadian provincial laboratories, Hunt et al. compared the modified A-1 method with the APHA MPN method for recovery of fecal coliforms and *E. coli* in shellfish meats.[44]

Qadri et al.[60] have developed two rapid methods for determining fecal contamination in oysters, which are reported as sensitive and accurate as the standard APHA method. One involves incubating MacConkey broth for 2 hr at 37°C, then for 22 to 24 hr at 44° C. The second method uses the same incubation system but includes the inoculation of peptone broth as well as MacConkey broth.

The Anderson and Baird-Parker direct plate method (DP) is a 24-hr test for enumerating type 1 *E. coli* in food.[2] It was based upon the *E. coli* test for water developed at the Lawrence Experiment Station in Lawrence, Mass., by Delaney, McCarthy, and Grasso.[22] In a study conducted by the International Commission on Microbiological Specifications for Foods (ICMSF), the method compared favorably with the MPN procedure of the APHA in enumerating *E. coli* type 1 from raw meat.[63] No international study has been done on the DP method for shellfish meats. However, Anthony Rowse, microbiologist in the Food Laboratory, Health Commission of New South Wales, informed the second author in a private communication that the DP method ". . . was compared with various MPN techniques for *E. coli* enumeration in the Sidney Rock oyster (*Crassostrea commercialis*) and was found to produce accurate results in 24 hr." Rowse further reported that the DP method is being used by the Division of Analytical Laboratories, Health Commission of New South Wales.[62]

The roll tube method used in the United Kingdom is referred to later in this chapter. Rippey et al.[61] have developed a fluorometric method for enumerating *E. coli* in molluscan shellfish. The method, a modification of the traditional APHA MPN method for fecal coliform bacteria, incorporates a fluorogenic molecule, 4-methylumbelliferyl-β-D-glucuronide (MUG), into the confirmatory medium (EC) at a concentration of 50 μg/ml. After incubation, inoculated tubes are examined for fluorescence under long-wave ultraviolet light. The presence of *E. coli* is indicated by fluorescence. The MUG method, which requires only 48 hr for enumerating *E. coli* in shellfish, represents a considerable saving in time and labor over the standard *E. coli* APHA MPN procedure, which takes up to 10 days to complete. With increases in cost for analytical services and greater demand on laboratory personnel, the search for acceptable rapid test procedures should be continued.

48.7   INTERNATIONAL MICROBIOLOGICAL STANDARDS

Foreign countries use various microbiological criteria, standards, and methods to assess the sanitary quality of molluscan shellfish. The microbiological methods are used to enumerate criteria such as the total coliform group, the fecal coliform group, *E. coli*, or a total aerobic plate count (Standard Plate Count). In addition, some countries require that shellfish be tested for the presence of bacterial enteric pathogens.

The Federal Republic of Germany assesses the sanitary quality of shellfish by determining the total number of bacteria, the coliform score, and the presence of pathogenic enteric bacteria by serological methods.[20]

In Canada, Japan, New Zealand, Mexico, and the Republic of Korea, both the fecal coliform MPN test (EC Medium, 24 hr at 44.5° ± 0.2°C) and the 2-day, 35°C Standard Plate Count are used to assess the sanitary quality of shellfish to be exported to the United States.[1, 71] New South Wales, Australia, requires that shellfish be submitted to both the fecal coliform MPN test and a plate count.[6]

The use of *E. coli* as an indicator of fecal contamination in shellfish has been common in Europe for many years. In the United Kingdom, estimates of *E. coli* levels in shellfish are made by using a roll tube colony count method that employs modified MacConkey agar incubated at 44° ± 0.2°C for 18 hr.[71] Preincubation for 2 hr at 37°C has been shown to improve the yield and specificity of the method.[70] The methods for examining shellfish in Holland and Belgium are identical to the method used in the United Kingdom.[71]

The enumeration of *E. coli* in shellfish is accomplished by the use of an MPN method in France.[72] The method involves a presumptive test that requires the inoculation of portions of macerated shellfish into tubes of brilliant green lactose bile broth. The tubes are then incubated at 30°C for 24 to 48 hr. The identification of *E. coli* is made according to the method of Mackenzie, Taylor, and Gilbert for each presumptive culture fermenting lactose with the production of gas.[53]

In Denmark, *E. coli* type I densities in shellfish are determined by plating on violet red bile agar followed by incubation at 45°C for 48 hr. In addition, shellfish samples are submitted to a 5-day, 20°C plate count and a *Salmonella* test.[72]

E. coli densities in shellfish are determined by the use of an MPN method in Italy. The method utilizes a 3 tube, 3 dilution test in lactose broth incubated at 37°C for 48 hr. This is followed by confirmation in brilliant green lactose bile broth and tryptone broth (indole) incubated at 44°C for 48 hr.[18]

Shellfish for export from Sweden must meet the requirements of the importing countries.[20]

Microbiological criteria for shellfish are also presented by the International Commission on Microbiological Specifications for Foods (ICMSF).[45]

48.8   REFERENCES

1. APHA. 1970. "Recommended Procedures for the Examination of Sea Water and Shellfish," 4th ed. Amer. Pub. Health Assn. 1970, Washington, D.C.

2. Anderson, J. M. and Baird-Parker, A. C. 1975. A rapid and direct plate method for enumerating *Escherichia coli* biotype I in food. J. Appl. Bacteriol. 39: 111.
3. Andrews, W. H. and Presnell, M. W. 1972. Rapid recovery of *Escherichia coli* from estuarine water. Appl. Microbiol. 23: 521.
4. Andrews, W. H., Diggs, C. D., Presnell, M. W., Miescier, J. J., Wilson, C. R., Goodwin, C. P., Adams, W. N., Furfari, S. A., and Musselman, J. F. 1975. Comparative validity of members of the total coliform and fecal coliform groups for indicating presence of *Salmonella* in the Eastern oyster, *Crassostrea virginica*. J. Milk Food Technol. 38: 453.
5. Andrews, W. H., Diggs, C. D., and Wilson, C. R. 1975. Evaluation of a medium for the rapid recovery of *Escherichia coli* from shellfish. Appl. Microbiol. 29: 130.
6. Australian Pure Food Act—Standards for Shellfish. 1908. Health Comm. of New South Wales. Sydney, N.S.W. Govt. Printer, Sydney, Australia.
7. Bachman, B., Boyd, W. P. Jr., Lieb, S., and Rodrick, G. E. 1983. Marine noncholera *Vibrio* infections in Florida. South. Med. J. 76: 296.
8. Baine, W. B., Mazzotti, M., Greco, D., Izzo, E., Zampieri, A., Angioni, G., Di Gioia, M., Gangarosa, E. J., and Pocchiari, F. 1974. Epidemiology of cholera in Italy in 1973. Lancet 2: 1370.
9. Bidwell, M. H. and Kelly, C. B. Jr. 1950. Ducks and shellfish sanitation. J. Amer. Pub. Health Assn. 40: 923.
10. Blake, P. A., Merson, M. H., Weaver, R. E., Hollis, D. G., and Heublein, P. C. 1979. Disease caused by a marine vibrio. Clinical characteristics and epidemiology. N. Eng. J. Med. 300: 1.
11. Blake, P. A., Rosenberg, M. L., Costa, J. B., Ferreira, P. S., Guimaraes, C. L., and Gangarosa, E. J. 1977. Cholera in Portugal. 1974. I. Modes of transmission. Am. J. Epidemiol. 105: 337.
12. Blaser, M. J., Taylor, D. N., and Feldman, R. A. 1983. Epidemiology of *Campylobacter jejuni* infections. Epidem. Rev. 5: 157.
13. Bonner, J. R., Coker, A. S., Berryman, C. R., and Pollock, H. M. 1983. Spectrum of vibrio infections in a Gulf Coast community. Ann. Intern. Med. 99: 464.
14. Bradford, H. B. and Caraway, C. T. 1978. Follow-up on *Vibrio cholerae* serotype Inaba infection—Louisiana. Morbid. Mortal. Weekly Rep. 27: 388.
15. Brezenski, F. T. and Russomanno, R. 1969. The detection and use of Salmonellae in studying polluted tidal estuaries. J. Water Pollut. Control Fed. 41: 725.
16. Caraway, C. T., Gregg, J., and McFarland, L. 1978. *Vibrio parahaemolyticus* foodborne outbreak—Louisiana. Morbid. Mortal. Weekly Rep. 27: 345.
17. Chin, K. P., Lowe, M. A., Tong, M. J., and Koehler, A. L. 1987. *Vibrio vulnificus* infection after raw oyster ingestion in a patient with liver disease and acquired immunodeficiency syndrome-related complex. Gastroenterology. 92: 796.
18. Codex Alimentarius Commission, 1973. Codex Committee on Food Hygiene. Italian Delegation Proposal to the Molluscan Shellfish Codex. Washington, D.C.
19. Colwell, R. R. and Liston J. 1960. Microbiology of shellfish. Bacteriological study of the natural flora of Pacific oysters (*Crassostrea gigas*). Appl. Microbiol. 8: 104.
20. Coppini, R. 1965. Sanitary regulations for molluscs. General Fisheries Council for the Mediterranean Studies and Reviews. 29: 1.
21. Dadisman, T. A. Jr., Nelson, R., Molenda, J. R., and Garber, H. J. 1972. *Vibrio parahaemolyticus* gastroenteritis in Maryland. I. Clinical and epidemiologic aspects. Am. J. Epidemiol. 96: 414.
22. Delaney, J. E., McCarthy, J. A., and Grasso, R. J. 1962. Measurement of *E. coli* type I by the membrane filter. Water Sewage Works. 109: 289.
23. DePaola, A. 1981. *Vibrio cholerae* in marine foods and environmental waters: A literature review. J. Food Sci. 46(1): 66.
24. Dufour, A. P. 1985. Annual report—First year. Health effects associated with shellfish consumption. NOAA/EPA IAG RW13931029.

25. FDA. 1985. *Vibrio vulnificus* and patients with liver disease. Food and Drug Admin. Drug Bulletin. 15: 5.

26. FDA. 1987. Research on *Listeria monocytogenes*. Food and Drug Admin. Drug Bulletin. 17: 28.

27. FDA. 1988. Concern continues about *Vibrio vulnificus*. Food and Drug Admin. Drug Bulletin 18: 3.

28. Fishbein, M., Surkiewicz, B. F., Brown, E. F., Oxley, H. M., Padron, A. P., and Groomes, R. J. 1967. Coliform behavior in frozen food. I. Rapid test for the recovery of *Escherichia coli* from frozen foods. Appl. Microbiol. 15: 233.

29. Fleming, D. W., Cochi, S. L., MacDonald, K. L., Brondum, J., Hayes, P. S., Plikaytis, B. D., Holmes, M. B., Audurier, A., Broome, C. V., and Reingold, A. L. 1985. Pasteurized milk as a vehicle of infection in an outbreak of listeriosis. N. Eng. J. Med. 312: 404.

30. Gregory, R. L., Felsenfeld, O., Cannon, H. E., Calmes, H. W., Caraway, C. T., Hauser, G. H., D'Alfonso, J. A., Fishbein, M., and Gunera, N. 1972. *Vibrio parahaemolyticus*—Louisiana. Morbid. Mortal. Weekly Rep. 21: 341.

31. Heffernan, W. P. and Cabelli, V. J. 1970. Elimination of bacteria by the northern quahog, (*Mercenaria mercenaria*): Environmental parameters significant to the process. J. Fish. Res. Bd. Can. 27: 1569.

32. HEW/PHS/CDC. 1973. Surveillance Summary. *Vibrio parahaemolyticus* gastroenteritis. United States 1969–1972. Morbid. and Mortal. Weekly Rep. 22: 231.

33. HEW/PHS/FDA. 1964. "Proceedings, Fifth National Shellfish Sanitation Workshop." U.S. Dept. Health, Ed., and Welfare, Pub. Health Serv., Food and Drug Admin., Washington, D.C.

34. HEW/PHS/FDA. 1968. "Proceedings, Sixth National Shellfish Sanitation Workshop." U.S. Dept. Health, Ed., and Welfare, Pub. Health Serv., Food and Drug Admin., Washington, D.C.

35. HEW/PHS/FDA. 1971. "Proceedings, Seventh National Shellfish Sanitation Workshop." U.S. Dept. Health, Ed., and Welfare, Pub. Health Serv., Food and Drug Admin., Washington, D.C.

36. HEW/PHS/FDA. 1974. "Proceedings, Eighth National Shellfish Sanitation Workshop." U.S. Dept. Health, Ed., and Welfare, Pub. Health Serv., Food and Drug Admin., Washington, D.C.

37. HEW/PHS/FDA. 1977. "Proceedings, Tenth National Shellfish Sanitation Workshop." U.S. Dept. Health, Ed., and Welfare, Pub. Health Serv., Food and Drug Admin., Washington, D.C.

38. HHS/PHS/FDA. 1984. "Bacteriological Analytical Manual." U.S. Dept. Health, Human Serv. and Food and Drug Admin., Div. of Microbiol., Washington, D.C.

39. HHS/PHS/FDA. 1989. "Manual of Operations, National Shellfish Sanitation Program," Part I, Sanitation of shellfish growing areas. Revision. U.S. Dept. of Health and Human Serv., Pub. Health Serv., Food and Drug Admin., Washington, D.C.

40. HHS/PHS/FDA. 1989. "Manual of Operations, National Shellfish Sanitation Program," Part II, Sanitation of the harvesting, processing and distribution of shellfish. Revision. U.S. Dept. of Health and Human Serv., Pub. Health Serv., Food and Drug Admin. Washington, D.C.

41. Hunt, D. A. 1977. Indicators of quality for shellfish waters. In "Bacterial Indicators/Health Hazards Associated with Water," ed. A. W. Hoadley and B. J. Dutka, p. 337. Amer. Soc. for Testing and Materials. Philadelphia, PA.

42. Hunt, D. A. 1979. Microbiological standards for shellfish growing waters—Past, present and future utilization. Proc. Nat. Shellfish Assn. 69: 142.

43. Hunt, D. A. and Springer, J. 1978. Comparison of two rapid test procedures with the standard EC test for recovery of fecal coliform bacteria from shellfish-growing waters. J. Assn. Off. Anal. Chem. 61: 1317.

44. Hunt, D. A., Lucas, J. P., McClure, F. D., Springer, J., and Newell, R. 1981. Comparison of modified A-1 method with standard EC test for recovery of fecal coliform bacteria for shellfish. J. Assn. Off. Anal. Chem. 64: 607.

45. ICMSF. 1986. "Microorganisms in Foods. 2" Sampling for microbiological analysis: Principles and Specific Applications. Univ. of Toronto Press.

46. Joseph, S. W., Colwell, R. R., and Kaper, J. B. 1982. *Vibrio parahaemolyticus* and related halophilic vibrios. CRC Crit. Rev. Microbiol. 10: 77.

47. Kaper, J., Lockman, H., Colwell, R. R., and Joseph, S. W. 1979. Ecology, serology, and enterotoxin production of *Vibrio cholerae* in Chesapeake Bay. Appl. Environ. Microbiol. 37: 91.

48. Kelly, C. B. Results of a cooperative study to evaluate bacteriological criteria of market oysters. In "Proceedings, Shellfish Sanitation Workshop," p. 16. U.S. Dept. Health, Ed., and Welfare. Pub. Health Serv., Food and Drug Admin. Washington, D.C.

49. Lennon, D., Lewis, B., Mantell, C., Becroft, D., Dove, B., Farmer, K., Tonkin, S., Yeates, N., Stamp, R., and Mickleson, K. 1984. Epidemic perinatal listeriosis. Pediatric Infect. Dis. 3: 30.

50. Lewis, C., Harris, J., Hausfeld, K., Prather, E. C., Roberts, A. E., Gunn, R. A., Janowoski, H., Lieb, S., and Gissendanner, E. 1979. Non-01 *Vibrio cholerae* Infections—Florida. Morbid. Mortal. Weekly Rep. 28: 571.

51. Lovelace, T. F., Tubiash, H., and Colwell, R. R. 1968. Quantitative and qualitative commensal bacterial flora of *Crassostrea virginica* in Chesapeake Bay. Proc. Nat. Shellfish Assn. 58: 82.

52. Lumsden, L. L., Hasseltine, H. E., Leake, J. P., and Veldee, M. V. 1925. A typhoid fever epidemic caused by oyster-borne infection (1924–25). Suppl. No. 50, Public Health Reports, U.S. Pub. Health Service, Washington, D.C.

53. Mackenzie, E. F. W., Taylor, E. W., and Gilbert, W. E. 1948. Recent experiences in the rapid identification of *Bacterium coli* type I. J. Gen. Microbiol. 2: 197.

54. Madden, J. M. 1986. Fact sheet on foodborne pathogenic microorganism—*Vibrio vulnificus*. In "Foodborne Pathogenic Microorganisms," p. X-1. Division of Microbiology, Center for Food Safety and Applied Nutrition, Food and Drug Admin., Washington, D.C.

55. Morris, J. G. Jr. and Black, R. E. 1985. Cholera and other vibrioses in the United States. N. Eng. J. Med. 312: 343.

56. Mulnick J. 1983. Suspected Warren Township, N.Y., shellfish outbreaks. EMS memo to several offices. U.S. Dept. of Health and Human Serv. Pub. Health Serv. Food and Drug Admin. Region II, Washington, D.C.

57. Murphy, A. M., Grohmann, G. S., Christopher, P. J., Lopez, W. A., Davey, G. R., and Melsom, R. H. 1969. An Australia-wide outbreak of gastroenteritis from oysters caused by Norwalk virus. Med. J. Austra. 2: 329.

58. Oliver, J. D., Warner, R. A., and Cleland, D. R. 1983. Distribution of *Vibrio vulnificus* and other lactose-fermenting vibrios in the marine environment. Appl. Environ. Microbiol. 45: 985.

59. Portnoy, B. L., Mackowiak, P. A., Caraway, C. T., Walker, J. A., McKinley, T. W., and Klein, C. A. Jr. 1975. Oyster associated hepatitis. Failure of shellfish certification programs to prevent outbreaks. J. Am. Med. Assoc. 233: 1065.

60. Qadri, R. B., Buckle, K. A., and Edwards, R. A. 1974. Rapid methods for the determination of faecal contamination in oysters. J. Appl. Bacteriol. 37: 7.

61. Rippey, S. R., Chandler, L. A., and Watkins, W. D. 1987. Fluorometric method for enumeration of *Escherichia coli* in molluscan shellfish. J. Food Prot. 50: 685.

62. Rowse, A. Personal communication. Food Laboratory, Health Commission of New South Wales, Australia.

63. Silliker, J. H., Gabis, D. A., and May, A. 1979. ICMSF methods studies. XI. Collaborative/comparative studies on determination of coliforms using the most probable number procedure. J. Food Prot. J. Food Prot. 42: 638.

64. Slanetz, L. W., Bartley, C. H., and Stanley, K. W. 1968. Coliforms, fecal streptococci, and *Salmonella* in seawater and shellfish. Health Lab. Sci. 5: 66.

65. Tilton, R. C. and Ryan, R. W. 1987. Clinical and ecological characteristics of *Vibrio vulnificus* in the Northeastern United States. Diagn. Microbiol. Infect. Dis. 6: 109.

66. Vanderzant, C., Thompson, C. A. Jr., and Ray, S. M. 1973. Microbial flora and level of *Vibrio parahaemolyticus* of oysters (*Crassostrea virginica*), water, and sediment from Galveston Bay. J. Milk Food Technol. 36: 447.
67. Weagant, S. D., Sado, P. N., Colburn, K. G., Torkelson, J. D., Stanley, F. A., Krane, M. H., Shields, S. C., and Thayer, C. F. 1988. The incidence of *Listeria* species in frozen seafood products. J. Food Prot. 51: 655.
68. Wehr, H. M. 1987. *Listeria monocytogenes*—Current dilemma. J. Assn. Off. Anal. Chem. 70: 769.
69. White, H. H. 1987. Cooperative national research project on the relationship between shellfish growing water indicators and human health risks. A history and prospectus of the project, p. 136. Proceedings of the 1987 Interstate Seafood Seminar, Virginia Beach, Va.
70. Wood, P. C. 1963. The sanitary control of molluscan shellfish. Some observations on existing methods and their possible improvement. Intern. Counc. for Exploration of the Sea. Shellfish Commitee. No. 24. C. M. Fisheries Lab. Burnham-on-Crouch, Essex, England.
71. Wood, P. C. 1970. The principles and methods employed for the sanitary control of molluscan shellfish. Technical Conference on Marine Pollution and Its Effects on Living Resources and Fishing. FIR:MP/70/R-12, World Health Org. Food and Agriculture Org., Rome, Italy.
72. WHO. 1978. Recommended International Code of Hygienic Practice for Molluscan Shellfish. Food Standards Programme, CAC/RCP 18–1978. World Health Org., Food and Agr. Org., Rome, Italy.

Chapter 49

FRUITS AND VEGETABLES

R. E. Brackett and D. F. Splittstoesser

49.1 INTRODUCTION

This chapter concerns fresh produce and nonsterile-processed fruits and vegetables. Examples of the latter are products preserved by freezing or dehydration. Some of these foods will be cooked before consumption, and others will be eaten raw.

Products that might be classed with both fresh and processed vegetables are the chopped salad ingredients, e.g., lettuce and carrots that are sold in grocery stores and to institutions. Contamination during processing and changes in microbial growth patterns during storage of the minimally processed products may alter the microflora of these foods quantitatively and qualitatively.[31, 48]

49.2 FRESH PRODUCE

49.21 Normal Flora

1. Sources

There is great variation in the number of microorganisms on fruits and vegetables received from orchards, vineyards, and growing fields. All green plants possess a resident microflora that normally subsists on the slight traces of carbohydrates, protein, and inorganic salts that dissolve in the water exuding from, or condensing on, the epidermis of the host.[49] Other important factors include contamination from soil, water, dust, and other natural sources and the extent of contact during harvest with the soiled surfaces of harvesters and containers. Other factors include intrinsic properties of the fruit or vegetable, such as a thick skin that could protect against surface damage and subsequent growth of saprophytic organisms.

2. Numbers

Populations of microorganisms on vegetables vary widely and often depend on the type of vegetable.[35] The actual population of microorganisms on vegetables will also depend on environmental conditions during production and harvest. Aerobic plate counts can be as high as 10^7 per g on tubers[52] and other vegetables[9] that are in contact with the soil. Vegetables grown above ground, such as lettuce,[25] fennel,[8] parsley,[17] southern peas,[30] and others[27] can have similar populations of bacteria. However, the population of microorganisms that may occur on any given vegetable varies greatly. Cabbage, for example, may have as few as 10^4 or as many as 10^9 bacteria per g.[10, 24] Microorganisms are typically found on the outer surfaces of vegetables, although healthy internal tissues may also harbor low populations of microorganisms.[15]

Fruits may also harbor large numbers of microorganisms; for example, typical counts on strawberries and grapes range from 10^5 to 10^6 per g.[33, 35] In contrast, tomatoes may contain only 10^1 to 10^3.[4, 29] As with vegetables, numbers of microorganisms will vary depending on environmental conditions.

3. Predominant organisms

An important factor is whether the population resulted primarily from growth on the produce or on product-contaminated surfaces, or originated from an unrelated source. A soil-contaminated fruit or vegetable will possess a bacterial flora composed primarily of sporeformers, coryneforms, and other soil microorganisms, while one that had supported microbial growth will yield the microorganisms that compete best on that particular substrate. The high acid and sugar content of fruits often permits yeasts and molds to predominate. In contrast, the high carbohydrate and low acid content of many vegetables favors the lactic acid bacteria. Some low-saccharine vegetables have predominantly an aerobic, gram-negative flora, both hyaline and yellow-pigmented.[3, 32, 35]

Mold counts of fresh vegetables seldom exceed 10^5 per g. Dematiaceous fungi dominate as the preharvest flora,[54] while nondematiaceous fungi dominate after harvest.[51] Fruits such as the strawberry may bear a variety of fungi.[1]

4. Indicator bacteria

Certain coliform bacteria and enterococci are part of the naturally occurring microflora of plants.[20, 25, 29, 30, 35] Some species, *Klebsiella* in particular, give a positive fecal coliform test.[18] The presence of *Escherichia coli* can be related to the use of polluted water for irrigation[12] or washing, the presence of animal feces, unclean hands, or contaminated surfaces of harvesters and containers.

49.22   Floral Changes and Spoilage

Populations of microorganisms will normally increase dramatically during storage. The degree and rate of this increase will depend on the form of the product and storage conditions. For example, microbes will usually grow faster on cut vegetables than on whole vegetables.[3, 24] Temperature, humidity, and the use of packaging or a modified atmosphere will also influence the microflora.[3, 16] Ultimate populations of bacteria often reach 10^6–10^7 cells per g before the product appears spoiled.[4, 24] Gram-negative bacteria will usually predominate on stored fresh vegetables, although storage and packaging conditions may result in changes in types of microorganisms that develop.[4]

Market or storage diseases are the terms given the rots produced in fresh fruits and vegetables. Many of the diseases are named after their appearance, e.g., grey, brown, cottony, and stem-end rots. Molds are generally responsible for spoilage, particularly in fruits. More than 20 mold genera, including *Alternaria, Botrytis, Penicillium*, and *Phytophthora*, have been recognized as causes of spoilage. Some of these molds are opportunistic pathogens, whereas others are true plant pathogens that can invade healthy plant tissue.[2, 36]

Certain bacteria can also cause fruit and vegetable spoilage. The bacterium of greatest concern is *Erwinia carotovora*, the cause of bacterial soft rot in a great variety of vegetables. However, some members of *Pseudomonas, Bacillus*, and *Clostridium* are also important spoilage organisms.[19]

49.23   Human Disease Microorganisms

Although the presence of pathogenic microorganisms on raw fruits and vegetables does not appear to be a serious problem in developed countries, studies have shown that lettuce, cucumbers, radishes, and other produce that are widely used in salads may harbor salmonellae, *Listeria, Aeromonas* spp., and viruses as well as various amoebae and nematodes.[5, 6, 26, 28, 34, 46] A serious outbreak of listeriosis resulted from eating coleslaw prepared from contaminated cabbage,[28] and a large outbreak of shigellosis was traced to commercially distributed shredded lettuce.[6]

Enteric pathogens are common contaminants of vegetables that are grown in countries where polluted water is used for irrigation[8, 47] or where sewage sludge is used as a fertilizer.

49.3   PROCESSED FRUITS AND VEGETABLES

49.31   Normal Flora

As discussed previously, fruits and vegetables may harbor large numbers of microorganisms at the time of harvest. In the preparation of these foods for freezing, fermentation, or drying, various procedures remove or destroy many of the organisms.

1. Washing

Water sprays remove many of the surface microorganisms, i.e., those that are not protected by the native mucilaginous material of the plant surface. On peas, for example, more than 90% of the microorganisms picked up at the viner may be removed by the first washing.[41]

2. Heat

Blanching is an early processing step for most vegetables and a few fruits.

The temperatures employed, 86° to 96°C, destroy all but the most heat-resistant microorganisms; only bacterial spores usually survive. Examples of other processes that employ a lethal temperature are the heating of Concord grapes to about 60°C prior to pressing to extract pigment, and the lye or steam peeling of various fruits and vegetables in a hot lye bath to facilitate skin removal.

3. Germicides

Chlorine in flume and spray water reduces the number of viable contaminants. The relatively high concentrations of sulfur dioxide used to treat apple slices before freezing and various fruits and vegetables prior to dehydration destroy most vegetative microorganisms. In winemaking, the addition of 100 ppm sulfur dioxide reduces the number of wild yeasts by 99.9% or more.

4. Freezing and dehydration

Although many organisms are destroyed by these processes, large numbers, including many vegetative forms, manage to survive. A further decrease in viable numbers occurs during the storage of frozen or dried fruits and vegetables. The rate of this decrease is influenced by many factors, such as storage conditions, the food type, and the predominant microflora.

49.32   Floral Changes—Frozen Vegetables

1. Sources of Contamination

Blanching is the critical control step in the processing of frozen vegetables. Since it destroys most of the contaminating organisms, the microflora of the packaged product reflect mainly recontamination after the blanch.

The major source of organisms on frozen vegetables is contaminated equipment.[41] Units that have been especially troublesome are choppers, slicers, conveyor and inspection belts, and filling machines. The surfaces of some of these units are difficult to reach for proper cleaning. Belts, which generally are quite accessible, may present problems because of the tenacity with which microorganisms adhere to certain surfaces. In addition, some fabrics absorb liquids and thus permit microbial biofilms to accumulate within the belt interior. These biofilms later become a source of contamination when fractures develop in the belt surface.

The degree of difficulty in controlling post-blanch contamination is related to vegetable type. With corn, large amounts of starch are released onto equipment surfaces and into flume water, whereas minimal quantities of soluble solids are leached from the vegetable during the processing of green beans and peas. Chopped leafy vegetables usually have higher microbial counts than the nonchopped products.[37]

2. Predominant flora

A wide variety of saprophytic bacteria can be isolated from frozen vegetables. The predominant flora is influenced by vegetable type and perhaps even geographic location. Gram-negative rods predominate on certain vegetables such as greens; on others, *Streptococcus* and *Leuconostoc* species are most numerous. The proportion of lactic acid bacteria on frozen blanched vegetables has been found to increase as the processing season progresses; with corn, for example, the percentage increased from 30% of the aerobic count on the first day of processing to more than 90% by the 15th day.[38] This is due to development of a characteristic microflora on processing lines. Many of the streptococci isolated from vegetables differ in some characteristics from described species.[22, 23, 43]

Low numbers of *Geotrichum candidum* filaments can be recovered on vegetables at various processing stages, but most are removed by blanching and subsequent hydrocooling.[45] As a result, frozen vegetables often are negative for this mold. Other molds also may be present in low numbers.

3. Indicator organisms

Coliforms and enterococci are common contaminants of frozen vegetables and may be present in relatively large numbers, sometimes thousands per g.[40] Their presence usually does not indicate fecal contamination. It appears that they are introduced onto equipment surfaces, perhaps via the air, and become a part of the microflora of the processing line, along with the more numerous contaminants such as lactic acid-producing cocci. *Escherichia coli* is a relatively rare contaminant of blanched vegetables, and thus its recovery may indicate fecal contamination. A majority of frozen vegetables that yield positive tests for fecal coliforms are negative for *E. coli*.[44] Enterococci resembling *Streptococcus faecalis* (see Chapter 32) differ from strains of human origin.[11, 21]

49.33   Floral Changes—Frozen Fruits

1. Sources of contamination

Although fruits generally are not blanched, much of the microflora acquired in the orchard and during the harvest is removed by various steps in the washing and peeling. Thus, as with vegetables, many of the contaminants on processed fruits originate from equipment within the plant.

2. Predominant flora

Because of the low pH of most fruits, aciduric yeasts and molds predominate, with yeasts usually the more numerous. *Geotrichum candidum* has been termed "machinery mold" because it may accumulate on fruit-processing equipment.[7] Of the acid-tolerant bacteria, the lactic acid group is most common, although species of *Acetobacter*, *Gluconobacter*, and *Zymomonas* may also develop in the acid environment of fruit-processing lines.

3. Indicator organisms

Coliforms can be recovered from various fruits even though the pH may be too low to support growth of these organisms. As with vegetables, the presence of indicator bacteria on frozen fruits and fruit products usually does not indicate a public health problem.[53]

49.34   Human Disease Microorganisms

Frozen blanched vegetables appear to present few problems with respect to organisms that cause foodborne illnesses. Although coagulase-positive staphylococci can be recovered, their numbers are usually very low, under 10 per g.[42] Attempts to isolate salmonellae from certain frozen vegetables have been unsuccessful,[39] while data regarding the incidence of anaerobic pathogens such as *Clostridium perfringens* seem to be lacking.

The fact that vegetables are often in contact with soil means that they commonly harbor spores of *Clostridium botulinum*. Unexpected outbreaks of botulism have occurred in vegetables that had been processed in a nontraditional manner. An outbreak of botulism resulting from the consumption of potato salad was believed to have been caused by toxin formation in foil-wrapped baked potatoes that had been held at room temperature for a number of days. Experimentally, as few as 10 spores per potato resulted in toxin formation within 5 days.[46] As another example, chopped garlic in soybean oil, a product responsible for 37 cases of botulism, was shown to support growth and toxin production without showing obvious evidence of spoilage.[34]

Fruits are generally too acidic for growth of the more common foodborne pathogens. Many organisms do not survive in a low-pH environment, e.g., *Salmonella* and *Shigella* die off rapidly in citrus juices.[13] In contrast, *L. monocytogenes* can survive well on both chopped and whole tomatoes. Toxigenic fungi are a potential problem. Patulin, a mycotoxin produced by *Penicillium expansum* and a number of other molds, has been found in apple juice. It appears that the most effective control is to exclude moldy fruit from the product.[14]

49.4   RECOMMENDED METHODS

49.41   Standard Plate Count (Chapter 4)

49.42   *Geotrichum* Count (Chapter 5)

49.43   Yeasts and Molds (Chapter 16)

49.44   Coliform Bacteria (Chapter 24)

49.45   *Listeria Monocytogenes* (Chapter 38)

49.5   INTERPRETATION OF DATA

The microbiology of fresh fruits and vegetables often has little relationship to their quality or safety. Sound vegetables, for example, may yield extremely high aerobic plate counts because of high resident populations, or because of contamination from soil and other natural sources. The routine microbiological examination of most fresh fruits and vegetables, therefore, is not recommended. However, it might be prudent to do routine microbiological examination of fruits and vegetables destined for chronically ill or immunocompromised persons. Some pathogens, such as *L. monocytogenes*, can be particularly hazardous for such people.

Because most of the organisms on frozen and other processed fruits and vegetables originate from equipment surfaces, aerobic plate counts provide a means of assessing sanitation of the processing line. Problems in controlling contamination may differ with the type of fruit or vegetable. For example, a given population of bacteria on green beans may signify poor sanitation, while the same count on chopped broccoli may indicate excellent conditions.[37] Many frozen fruits and vegetables have aerobic plate counts below 50×10^3 per g.

Coliforms and enterococci are part of the normal vegetable processing line flora, and populations of 10^2 or 10^3 per g of processed product are not uncommon.

Coagulase-positive *Staphylococcus aureus* may be present on vegetables, but usually in low numbers, under 10 per g. The routine culturing of fruits and vegetables for staphylococci is not justified.

49.6 REFERENCES

1. Beneke, E. S., White, L. S., and Fabian, F. W. 1954. The incidence and pectolytic activity of fungi isolated from Michigan strawberry fields. Appl. Microbiol. 2: 253.
2. Brackett, R. E. 1986. Vegetables and related products. In "Food and Beverage Mycology," 2nd ed., ed. L. R. Beuchat, p. 129. Van Norstead, New York.
3. Brackett, R. E. 1987. Microbiological consequences of minimally processed fruits and vegetables. J. Food Qual. 10: 195.
4. Brackett, R. E. 1988. Changes in the microflora of packaged tomatoes. J. Food Qual. 11: 89.
5. Callister, S. M. and Agger, W. A. 1987. Enumeration and characterization of *Aeromonas hydrophila* and *Aeromonas caviae* isolated from grocery store produce. Appl. Environ. Microbiol. 53: 249.
6. Davis, H., Taylor, J. P., Perdue, J. N., Stelma, G. N. Jr., Humphreys, J. M. Jr., Rowntree, R. III, and Greene, K. D. 1988. A shigellosis outbreak traced to commercially distributed shredded lettuce. Am. J. Epidemiol. 128: 1312.
7. Eisenberg, W. V. and Cichowicz, S. M. 1977. Machinery mold—Indicator organisms in food. Food Technol. 31: 52.
8. Ercolani, G. L. 1976. Bacteriological quality assessment of fresh marketed lettuce and fennel. Appl. Environ. Microbiol. 31: 847.
9. Etchells, J. L., Costilow, R. N., Bell, T. A., and Rutherford, H. A. 1961. Influence of gamma radiation on the microflora of cucumber fruit and blossoms. Appl. Microbiol. 9: 145.
10. Geeson, J. D. 1979. The fungal and bacterial flora of stored white cabbage. J. Appl. Bacteriol. 46: 189.
11. Geldreich, E. E. and Kenner, B. A. 1969. Concepts of fecal streptococci in stream pollution. J. Water Pollution Fed. 41: 336.
12. Geldreich, E. E. and Bordner, R. H. 1971. Fecal contamination of fruits and vegetables during cultivation and processing for market. A review. J. Milk and Food Technol. 34: 184.

13. Hahn, S. S. and Appleman, M. D. 1952. Microbiology of frozen orange concentrate. I. Survival of enteric organisms in frozen orange concentrate. Food Technol. 6: 156.

14. Harwig, J., Chen, Y.-K., Kennedy, B. P. C., and Scott, P. M. 1973. Occurrence of patulin and patulin-producing strains of *Penicillium expansum* in natural rots of apple in Canada. Can. Inst. Food Sci. J. 6: 22.

15. Hayward, A. C. 1974. Latent infections by bacteria. Ann. Rev. Phytopath. 12: 87.

16. Hobbs, G. 1986. Ecology of food microorganisms. Microb. Ecol. 12: 15.

17. Kaferstein, F. K. 1976. The microflora of parsley. J. Milk Food Technol. 39: 837.

18. Knittel, M. D., Seidler, R. J., Eby, C., and Cabe, L. M. 1977. Colonization of the botanical environment by *Klebsiella* isolates of pathogenic origin. Appl. Environ. Microbiol. 34: 557.

19. Lund, B. M. 1983. Bacterial spoilage. In "Postharvest Pathology of Fruits and Vegetables," ed. C. Dennis, p. 219. Academic Press, New York.

20. Meneley, J. C. and Stanghellini, M. E. 1974. Detection of enteric bacteria within locular tissue of healthy cucumbers. J. Food Sci. 39: 1267.

21. Mundt, J. O. 1973. Litmus milk reaction as a distinguishing feature between *Streptococcus faecalis* of human and nonhuman origins. J. Milk Food Technol. 36: 364.

22. Mundt, J. O. 1975. Unidentified streptococci from plants. Int. J. Syst. Bacteriol. 25: 281.

23. Mundt, J. O., Graham, W. F., and McCarty, I. E. 1967. Spherical lactic acid-producing bacteria of southern-grown raw and processed vegetables. Appl. Microbiol. 15: 1303.

24. Priepke, P. E., Wei, L. S., and Nelson, A. I. 1976. Refrigerated storage of prepackaged salad vegetables. J. Food Sci. 41: 379.

25. Riser, E. C., Grabowski, J., and Glenn, E. P. 1984. Microbiology of hydroponically-grown lettuce. J. Food Prot. 47: 765.

26. Rude, R. A., Jackson, G. J., Bier, J. W., Sawyer, T. K., and Risty, N. G. 1984. Survey of fresh vegetables for nematodes, amoebae, and *Salmonella*. J. Assn. Off. Anal. Chem. 47: 613.

27. Ruiz, B. Garcia-Villanova, Galvez Vargas, R., and Garcia-Villanova, R. 1987. Contamination on fresh vegetables during cultivation and marketing. Int. J. Food Microbiol. 4: 285.

28. Schlech, W. F., Lavigne, P. M., Bortolussi, R. A., Allen, A. C., Haldane, E. V., Wort, A. J., Hightower, A. W., Johnson, S. E., King, S. H., Nicholls, E. S., and Broome, C. V. 1983. Epidemic listeriosis–evidence for transmission by food. New Engl. J. Med. 308: 203.

29. Senter, S. D., Cox, N. A., Bailey, J. S., and Forbus, W. R. Jr. 1985. Microbiological changes in fresh market tomatoes during packing operations. J. Food Sci. 50: 254.

30. Senter, S. D., Cox, N. A., Bailey, J. S., and Meredith, F. I. 1984. Effects of harvesting, transportation, and cryogenic processing on the microflora of southern peas. J. Food Sci. 49: 1410.

31. Shapiro, J. E. and Holder, I. A. 1960. Effect of antibiotic and chemical dips on the microflora of packaged salad mix. Appl. Microbiol. 8: 341.

32. Skovgaard, N. 1984. Vegetables as an ecological environment for microbes. In "Microbial Associations and Interactions in Food." ed. I. Kiss, T. Deak, K. Incze, p. 27. Akademia Kiado, Budapest.

33. Smart, H. F. 1934. Microorganisms surviving the storage period of frozen pack fruits and vegetables. Phytopath. 24: 1319.

34. Solomon, H. M. and Kautter, D. A. 1988. Outgrowth and toxin production by *Clostridium botulinum* in bottled chopped garlic. J. Food Prot. 51: 862.

35. Splittstoesser, D. F. 1970. Predominant microorganisms on raw plant foods. J. Milk Food Technol. 33: 500.

36. Splittstoesser, D. F. 1986. Fruits and fruit products. In "Food and Beverage Mycology," 2nd ed., ed, L. R. Beuchat, p. 101. Van Norstead, New York.

37. Splittstoesser, D. F. and Corlett, D. A. Jr. 1980. Aerobic plate counts of frozen blanched vegetables processed in the United States. J. Food Prot. 43: 717.

38. Splittstoesser, D. F. and Gadjo, I. 1966. The groups of microorganisms composing the "total" count population in frozen vegetables. J. Food Sci. 31: 234.

39. Splittstoesser, D. F. and Segen, B. 1970. Examination of frozen vegetables for salmonellae. J. Milk Food Technol. 33: 111.
40. Splittstoesser, D. F. and Wettergreen, W. P. 1964. The significance of coliforms in frozen vegetables. Food Technol. 18: 134.
41. Splittstoesser, D. F., Wettergreen, W. P., and Pederson, C. S. 1961. Control of microorganisms during preparation of vegetables for freezing. II. Peas and corn. Food Technol. 15: 332.
42. Splittstoesser, D. F., Hervey, G. E. R. II, and Wettergreen, W. P. 1965. Contamination of frozen vegetables by coagulase-positive staphylococci. J. Milk Food Technol. 28: 148.
43. Splittstoesser, D. F., Mautz, J., and Colwell, R. R. 1968. Numerical taxonomy of catalase negative cocci isolated from frozen vegetables. Appl. Microbiol. 16: 1024.
44. Splittstoesser, D. F., Queale, D. T., Bowers, J. L., and Wilkison, M. 1980a. Coliform content of frozen blanched vegetables packed in the United States. J. Food Safety 2: 1.
45. Splittstoesser, D. F., Bowers, J., Kerschner, L., and Wilkison, M. 1980b. Detection and incidence of *Geotrichum candidum* in frozen blanched vegetables. J. Food Sci. 45: 511.
46. Sugiyama, H., Woodburn, M., Yang, K. H., and Movroydis, C. 1981. Production of botulinum toxin in inoculated pack studies of foil-wrapped baked potatoes. J. Food Prot. 44: 896.
47. Tamminga, S. K., Beumer, R. R., and Kampelmacher, E. H. 1978. The hygienic quality of vegetables grown in or imported into the Netherlands: A tentative survey. J. Hyg. Camb. 80: 143.
48. Terry, R. C. and Overcast, W. W. 1976. A microbiological profile of commercially prepared salads. J. Food Sci. 41: 211.
49. Thaysen, A. C. and Galloway, L. D. 1930. "The Microbiology of Starch and Sugars," p. 191. Oxford Univ. Press, New York.
50. Tierney, J. T., Sullivan, R., and Larkin, E. P. 1977. Persistence of poliovirus 1 in soil and on vegetables grown in soil previously flooded with inoculated sewage sludge or effluent. Appl. Environ. Microbiol. 33: 109.
51. Torrey, G. S. and Marth, E. H. 1977. Isolation and toxicity of molds from foods stored in homes. J. Food Prot. 40: 187.
52. Vaughn, R. H. 1951. The microbiology of dehydrated vegetables. Food Res. 16: 429.
53. Vaughn, R. H. and Murdock, D. I. 1956. Sanitary significance of microorganisms in frozen citrus products. Am. J. Public Health 46: 886.
54. Webb, T. A. and Mundt, J. O. 1978. Molds on vegetables at the time of harvest. Appl. Environ. Microbiol. 35: 655.

Chapter 50

FERMENTED AND ACIDIFIED VEGETABLES

H. P. Fleming, R. F. McFeeters, and M. A. Daeschel

50.1 INTRODUCTION

Vegetables may be preserved by fermentation, direct acidification, or a combination of these along with other processing conditions and additives to yield products that are referred to as pickles. Pasteurization and refrigeration are used to assure stability of certain of these products. Organic acids and salt (sodium chloride) are primary preservatives for most types of pickles. Lactic acid is produced naturally in fermented products. Acetic acid (or vinegar) is the usual acid added to pasteurized, unfermented (fresh-pack) pickles. Acetic acid also is added to many products made from fermented (saltstock) cucumbers. Other preservatives such as sodium benzoate, potassium sorbate, and sulfur dioxide may be added to finished products. Although the term "pickles" in the United States generally refers to pickled cucumbers, the term is used herein in a broader sense to refer to all vegetables that are preserved by fermentation or direct acidification. Cucumbers, cabbage, olives, and peppers account for the largest volume of vegetables and fruits commercially pickled. Lesser quantities of onions, tomatoes, cauliflower, carrots, melon rinds, okra, artichokes, beans, and other produce also are pickled.

The fermentation of vegetables is due primarily to the lactic acid bacteria, although yeasts and other microorganisms may be involved, depending on the salt concentration and other factors. Salt serves two primary roles in the preservation of fermented vegetables: It influences the type and extent of

---

Revised from earlier editions, includes some information previously provided by J. L. Etchells (deceased) and T. A. Bell (retired).

microbial activity, and it helps prevent softening of the vegetable tissue. Some vegetables are brined at such high salt concentrations as to greatly retard or preclude fermentation. Salt may be added in the dry form, as with cabbage, or as a brine solution, as with most other vegetables. The concentration of salt used varies widely among vegetables, depending on tendency of the vegetable to soften during brine storage. Softening of brined cucumbers can be reduced or prevented by adjusting the level of salt to inhibit pectinolytic enzymes.[2,3] Fermentation is an economical means for temporary preservation of produce such as cucumbers, cabbage, and olives. The produce is fermented and stored in large tanks until it is needed for further processing. After removal from brine storage, brined cucumbers may be desalted if needed before being finished into various products such as dills, sweets, sours, hamburger dill chips, mixed vegetables, and relishes.[42] Finished saltstock dill cucumber pickles contain a minimum of 0.6% lactic acid, according to USDA grade standards.[106] The products may or may not be pasteurized, depending on the addition of sugar and other preservatives. Extensive reviews are available on the brining and fermentation of cabbage,[92, 101] cucumbers,[40, 45] and olives.[44, 108, 109, 110].

Direct acidification with acetic acid (without pasteurization) has been a primary method for many years of preserving various pickles and sauces in the United Kingdom, where the products are referred to as acetic acid preserves. British researchers have determined that the minimum acetic acid concentration necessary to achieve satisfactory preservation of all pickles and sauces is 3.6%, calculated as a percentage of the volatile constituents of the product.[7] The high concentration of acid needed for preservation results in such a strong acid flavor, however, that the relative importance of this method of preservation has diminished. Milder acidic flavors are more in demand today, and use of acidification in combination with pasteurization has become more important. Nevertheless, some specialty products such as hot pepper sauce and sliced peppers still are preserved principally by high concentrations of acetic acid without pasteurization.

Fresh-pack cucumber pickles are preserved by mild acidification (0.5% to 1.1% acetic acid[106]) of fresh cucumbers, followed by heating to an internal product temperature of 74°C and holding for 15 min, according to the original recommendations of Etchells et al.[24, 30, 85] Such products are effectively pasteurized, since they are heated enough to inactivate microbial vegetative cells, and sufficient acid has been added to prevent outgrowth of bacterial spores. Although some packers still use this heat process, others now vary the times and temperatures, depending on product type and risk factors (not health-related spoilage) acceptable to the packer. Fermented pickles, such as whole genuine dills and hamburger dill chips, may or may not be heated. If pasteurized, these products may be given a milder heat treatment than fresh-pack pickles, such as an internal product temperature of 71°C with no holding time. The fresh-pack process has been applied to peppers and other vegetables. Fresh-pack pickles are considered acidified foods for regulatory purposes. According to the U.S. Food and Drug Administration (FDA), " 'Acidified foods' means low-acid foods to which acid(s) or acid food(s) are added; these foods include, but are not limited to beans, cucumbers, cabbage, artichokes, cauliflower, puddings, peppers, tropical fruits, and fish, singly or in any combination. They have a water activity (α_w) greater than 0.85 and have a finished equilibrium pH of 4.6 or below. These foods may be called, or may purport to be, 'pickles' or 'pickled . . .' "[107]

Refrigerated pickles may or may not be fermented before refrigeration. Also, they may or may not be acidified, although mild acidification is highly recommended.[41] Most commercially prepared and distributed refrigerated pickles sold today are not fermented, but are acidified and contain a preservative such as sodium benzoate.

Increasing environmental concerns related to waste disposal are influencing methods for preservation of pickled vegetables, particularly those involving use of salt for bulk storage. The U.S. Environmental Protection Agency (EPA) has proposed a maximum of 230 ppm of chloride in fresh waters,[23] a limit that may not be readily achievable by many vegetable briners who discharge chloride wastes into freshwater streams. Organic acids (lactic and acetic) in combination with calcium chloride and preservatives (e.g., sodium benzoate) are now used instead of sodium chloride for bulk storage of olives for "green-ripe" processing into canned black olives in California.[111] Salt is still used, however, for fermented olives. The use of calcium salts (chloride or acetate) has led to reduced levels of sodium chloride for bulk fermentation and storage of cucumbers. Calcium salts have been found to enhance firmness retention of cucumbers at reduced concentrations of sodium chloride.[10, 53, 56, 69, 105] Recent studies have revealed, however, that spoilage microorganisms may present a serious problem in fermented cucumbers if the salt concentration is too low.[59]

50.2 NORMAL FLORA

Fresh produce contains a varied epiphytic microflora (Chapter 49). Pickling cucumbers were found to contain as high as 5.3×10^7 total aerobes, 1.9×10^4 aerobic spores, 9.8×10^5 total anaerobes, 5.4×10^2 anaerobic spores, 6.1×10^6 coliforms, 5.1×10^4 total acid formers, 4.6×10^3 molds, and 6.6×10^3 yeasts per g of fresh cucumber.[38] The numbers increased during storage at higher temperatures (21°C) and humidity (> 70% relative humidity). Although some investigators have held that the interior of sound, fresh cucumbers is sterile, others have found microorganisms, mostly gram-negative rods, within the healthy fruit.[82, 97] In cucumbers, bacteria were more often near the skin and less often in the central core; in tomatoes, their frequency was highest near the stem-scar and central core and decreased toward the skin.[97] Cabbage contains the greatest number of bacteria on the outer leaves and lower numbers toward the center of the head.[92]

The floral changes during natural fermentation of brined vegetables may be characterized into four stages: initiation, primary fermentation, secondary fermentation, and post-fermentation.[45] During initiation, the various gram-positive and gram-negative bacteria that were on the fresh vegetable compete for predominance. *Enterobacteriaceae*, aerobic spore-formers, lactic acid bacteria, and other bacteria may be active. Eventually, the lactic acid bacteria gain predominance by lowering the pH, and primary lactic fermentation occurs. During primary fermentation, five species of lactic acid-producing bacteria are active, listed in approximate order of their occurrence: *Streptococcus faecalis*, *Leuconostoc mesenteroides*, *Pediococcus cerevisiae* (probably *P. pentosaceous* and/or *P. acidilactici*, according to recent classification[100]), *Lactobacillus brevis*, and *Lactobacillus plantarum*. Although all five species are active during fermentation of sauerkraut,[92] which contains relatively low concentrations of salt (c. 2.25%), only the latter three species predominate in fermentation of cucumbers, which contain higher concentrations of salt (c. 5% to 8%).[40] *Lactobacillus plantarum* characteristically terminates the lactic fermentation, apparently because of its greater acid tolerance.[91]

During fermentation of brined cucumbers, lactic acid bacteria may grow within the cucumber tissue as well as the brine.[16] Gas composition of the cucumbers at the time of brining greatly influences the ratio of bacterial growth in the cucumbers and the brine.[19] Yeasts were found not to grow within the cucumber tissue, presumably because of their larger size, which prevented their entry through stomata of the cucumber skin.

Green olives contain inhibitors of lactic acid bacteria,[47, 49, 71] which are thought to influence fermentation of Spanish-type green olives.[36, 72] Yeasts are not inhibited and predominate in the fermentation when the olives are neither properly lye treated nor heat shocked before brining.[36]

Various species of fermentative yeasts also are active during primary fermentation. If fermentable sugars remain after primary fermentation, these sugars may give rise to secondary fermentation dominated essentially by yeasts. Fermentative yeasts grow as long as fermentable sugars are available; this may result in severe gaseous spoilage (bloater formation).[26, 33, 32] During post-fermentation, growth of oxidative yeasts, molds, and bacteria may occur on brine surfaces of open tanks that are not exposed to ultraviolet radiation of sunlight.[27, 88] Vegetable brining tanks are typically uncovered and are held outdoors to allow sunlight to reduce or prevent surface growth. Surface growth does not occur in fermented and anaerobically stored green olives.[109] Attempts are being made to develop a suitable anaerobic tank for the cucumber-brining industry.

Attempts have been made to use lactic starter cultures in sauerkraut, olives, cucumbers, and other products.[46] *Pediococcus cerevisiae* and *L. plantarum* have been used in pure culture or controlled fermentations of cucumbers[35, 39] and olives.[36] Although starter cultures have been used on a limited commercial scale for fermenting cucumbers over the past 10 years, they are not widely used.

50.3   FLORA CHANGES IN SPOILAGE

50.31   Saltstock Vegetables and Genuine Dill Pickles

Vigorous activity in the cover brine by coliform bacteria, obligate halophiles, heterofermentative lactic acid bacteria, and fermentative species of yeasts is associated with gaseous fermentation and resulting bloater spoilage. Even homofermentative lactic acid bacteria such as *L. plantarum* and *P. cerevisiae* produce sufficient CO_2, when combined with CO_2 from cucumber tissue, to cause bloater formation in brined cucumbers.[48] Recent studies have shown that the major source of CO_2 production by homofermentative lactic acid bacteria is decarboxylation of malic acid, a natural constituent of pickling cucumbers.[79] It has been demonstrated that cultures that do not degrade malic acid ferment cucumbers with reduced bloater damage.[80] Procedures have been developed to produce and isolate nonmalate-decarboxylating mutants of *L. plantarum*.[18, 20] Purging fermenting cucumber brines with nitrogen has been shown to be effective in preventing bloater formation.[14, 39, 48, 52] Purging is now widely used by the pickle industry. Air purging also is effective in preventing bloater formation,[14, 52] but can result in cucumber softening due to mold growth,[15, 52, 62] reduced brine acidity due to yeast growth,[94] and off-colors and -flavors unless the purging regimen is carefully controlled. Bloater formation has been attributed to growth of gas-forming microorganisms in the brine surrounding the cucumbers[37] or within the cucumber.[16, 96]

Softening of brined vegetables is caused by pectinolytic enzymes of plant or microbial origin. Growth of film yeasts on brine surfaces may occur and result in loss of brine acidity. Accompanying mold growth on the brine surface can cause softening of sauerkraut, cucumbers, or olives. Heavy scum yeast and/or mold growth is usually the result of neglecting brined material during the curing and storage period. Softening of brined cucumbers may result from mold polygalacturonases that accompany the cucumbers, especially cucumbers with flowers attached,[5, 34] into the brine tank. This problem may be reduced by draining and rebrining of the tank c. 36 hr after initial brining. Recycled brine may be treated to inactivate softening enzymes.[63, 78] Adding calcium chloride can slow down the rate of enzymatic softening of fermenting cucumbers.[11] However, this should not be relied upon to eliminate enzymatic softening problems. Care must be taken to minimize contamination of cucumbers, particularly the small fruit, with flowers and plant debris, which can be a source of contamination by pectinolytic molds.

Butyric acid spoilage of brined olives has been attributed to two distinct types of microbial action. In one type, *Clostridium butyricum* and a closely related group of clostridia produce butyric acid from sugars during the primary stage of fermentation.[65] In a second type of malodorous olive fermentation, "zapatera" spoilage results from decomposition of organic acids at a time when little or no sugar is present and the lactic acid fermentation stops before the pH has decreased below pH 4.5.[73] Propionibacteria were isolated from brined olives with indications of "zapatera" spoilage and were hypothesized to grow and cause a rise in pH because of degradation of lactic acid, thus permitting subsequent growth by *Clostridium* species.[8, 67, 93]

Recently, butyric acid spoilage of brined cucumbers was found to occur after an apparently normal primary fermentation by lactic acid bacteria.[59] *Clostridium tertium* was identified as contributing to the spoilage. Evidence from end products indicated that unidentified bacteria, possibly propionibacteria species, degraded lactic acid, causing a rise in pH that allowed *C. tertium* to grow.

50.32   Finished Pickle Products from Saltstock Vegetables (Not Pasteurized)

Fully cured saltstock vegetables are made into various types of finished pickle products by a series of operations involving leaching out most of the salt, souring with vinegar, and then sweetening with sugar if desired. Preservation of these products depends on sufficient amounts of vinegar alone (for sour pickles), or a combination of vinegar and sugar with or without sodium benzoate (for sweet pickles).[1] If the concentration of these ingredients is inadequate and the product is not pasteurized, fermentation usually takes place. Osmotolerant yeasts are the principal spoilage organisms in such products.[1] Molds and film yeasts may grow on the surface of the liquid chiefly as the result of faulty jar closure. Lactic acid bacteria, propionibacteria and butyric acid bacteria also may cause spoilage in unpasteurized fermented vegetables that do not contain adequate concentrations of acetic acid or other preservatives.

50.33   Acetic Acid Preserves

The 3.6% acetic acid (as a percentage of volatile constituents) required for preservation of pickles and sauces[7] is similar to, but slightly lower than the concentration found necessary by Bell and Etchells[1] to prevent yeast spoilage in finished pickles from saltstock cucumbers. Microbial spoilage apparently occurs in acetic acid preserves when the concentration of acid is marginal. Spoilage microorganisms include yeasts[21] and lactobacilli, particularly the heterofermentative *Lactobacillus fructivorans*.[22]

50.34   Pasteurized Pickle Products

Spoilage usually occurs in these products when they are improperly pasteurized or improperly acidified so that an equilibrated brine product of pH 3.8 to 4.0 is not achieved. Spoilage is due chiefly to acid-forming bacteria and, to a lesser extent, yeasts that survive faulty heat treatment, or butyric acid bacteria when the product is not acidified adequately at the outset. Molds and film yeasts are factors in cases of poor jar closure.

50.35   Refrigerated Pickle Products

1. Fermented

A wide array of fermented, refrigerated cucumber pickle products are prepared as specialty products.[41] Examples of such products include overnight dills, half-sour dills, genuine kosher dills, kosher new dills, sour garlic pickles, half-sour new pickles, fresh-packed half-sour pickles, new half-sours, home-style new pickles, half-sour kosher new dills, and the like. The cover brine may or may not be acidified. The products are held in barrels for a few days or longer at room temperature and then refrigerated at 2° to 5°C. They may be distributed in bulk or in consumer-size glass containers. In some cases, they may be initially brined, held, and distributed in consumer-size containers. Under such conditions and at equilibrated brine strengths of 10 to 12 salometer (1 salometer = 0.264% salt by weight), microbial growth (chiefly coliforms, gas-forming and nongas-forming lactics, and fermentative yeasts) and enzymatic activity (pectinolytic and cellulolytic) together with the curing process continue at a slow rate.[37] Gaseous spoilage of the product is caused chiefly by the gas-forming microbial groups mentioned earlier. Gas production may be sufficient to reach 15 lb pressure within the container.

Softening problems may be even greater than for saltstock cucumbers since these products are held at much lower concentrations of salt. Fresh, whole garlic cloves and other spices are normally added to such products. These spices may contain high activities of softening enzymes that increase softening problems. In a few months, the stored pickles may have lost much of their characteristic flavor, texture, and color and also may be bloated because of gaseous fermentation by the principal gas-forming microbial groups present.

Whether these pickles are made in bulk or in the retail jar, the very nature of the product makes it difficult to maintain good quality for any reasonable length of time. The barreled product reaches the good manufacturing practices (GMP)-recommended brine pH of 4.6 or below for acidified foods, usually before refrigeration or shortly thereafter, and then slowly continues acid development. This recommended condition for brine-product pH cannot be assured for the product made in the retail jar because there is no uniform process accepted by packers wherein the product is acidified at the outset or where it is deliberately incubated for development of natural lactic acid fermentation.

Sauerkraut marketed in plastic bags in refrigerated display cases is preserved by the addition of sodium benzoate and bisulfite.[103] The shelf life of such products is influenced by chemical changes that may result in discoloration (browning) and objectionable flavor formation.

2. Not fermented

Most of these products for national distribution are acidified with vinegar to an equilibrium pH well below 4.6, contain 2% to 3% NaCl, and are immediately refrigerated upon packing.[41] They may contain sodium benzoate or other preservatives. Like the fermented refrigerated product, the cucumbers are not heated either before or after packing. If properly acidified, refrigerated, and preserved, the products will maintain acceptable quality for several months and do not present a public health concern. Recipes that do not contain vinegar or other acid in the initial cover liquor, however, should be viewed with great caution.

50.4   PATHOGENIC MICROORGANISMS

We know of no authenticated reports of pathogenic microorganisms associated with standard commercial pickle products prepared under "good manufacturing practices" of acid, salt, and sugar content (and combinations thereof) from brined, salted, and pickled vegetable brine-stock, including cucumbers. The Commissioner of the FDA stated that "No instances of illness as the result of contamination of commercially processed fermented foods with *Clostridium botulinum* have been reported in the United States."[107] Even so, certain types of microorganisms that may cause spoilage of the product may, at times, be encountered, such as molds, yeasts, and acid-tolerant lactic acid bacteria. These organisms, usually under conditions associated with neglect, may reduce the quality of the texture and flavor of the product—whether prepared in bulk or retail container—and render it unusable. However, these organisms are not considered human pathogens.

Essentially the same pattern of consumer safety applies to fresh-pack (pasteurized) pickle products. These products have continued to increase in popularity until they now use over 40% of the annual cucumber crop in the United States. These pickles usually are prepared from raw cucumbers, but may include other vegetables in a mixture; also, vegetables other than cucumbers may be packed, such as various types of peppers, okra, carrots, green beans, and tomatoes. The process calls for the packed product to be acidified at the outset with a sufficient amount of food-grade organic acid, e. g., vinegar, acetic acid, or lactic acid, to result in an equilibrated brine product pH of 4.0 or below (preferably 3.8). Vinegar (acetic acid) is usually the acidulant of industry choice for cucumber pickle products. The basic pasteurization procedure, with product heated to an internal temperature of 74°C and held for 15 min, has been used successfully by industry since c. 1940.[24, 28, 30] Insufficient acidification of pasteurized pickles can result in butyric acid-type spoilage, possibly involving public health concerns.

Listeria monocytogenes, a foodborne pathogen, in recent years has become a major concern to the food industry. The bacterium is commonly found in the environment and has been isolated from various plant materials, including silage,[43] soybeans, corn,[113, 114] and cabbage.[98] Beuchat et al.[6] showed that *L. monocytogenes* was able to grow on raw cabbage and in cabbage juice. Conner et al.[13] found death of *L. monocytogenes* (one strain tested, LCDC 81-861, is a pathogen isolated from coleslaw) to occur in cabbage juice adjusted to pH $\leq$ 4.6 with lactic acid and incubated at 30°C; at 5°C, the death rate was slower than at 30°C. However, two strains tested grew well at pH values of 5.0 to 6.1. In a nutrient medium acidified with hydrochloric acid, the minimum pH values at which growth of *L. monocytogenes* was detected at 30°, 20°, 10°, 7°, and 4°C were, respectively, 4.39, 4.39, 4.62, 4.62, and 5.23.[64] Johnson et al.[70] demonstrated that *Listeria* could be recovered from fermented sausage made with beef intentionally contaminated with the bacterium. To our knowledge, *Listeria* has not been reported in fermented vegetables. However, the observation that *Listeria* can be isolated from fermented materials (silage and sausage), coupled with the bacterium's ability to tolerate moderately low pH[13, 43, 64, 70] and high salt concentrations (growth in complex media at 10% salt[99]) suggests that *Listeria* may pose a concern for mildly acidified or fermented vegetables.

50.5 RECOMMENDED METHODS

50.51 Collection and Storage of Brine Samples

In examination of pickle products, brine or pickle liquor covering the vegetable material is required. The size of container to be sampled may range from a small jar of pickles to a 1,000-bu tank of fermented brine stock. Brine samples from containers such as tanks and barrels should be taken for bacteriological analysis as follows:

Insert a suitable length of 3/16-in stainless steel tubing, sealed at one end with lead or solder and perforated with several 1/16-in holes for a distance of 6 to 8 in from the sealed end, through an opening between the wooden boards composing the false head down into the brine toward the mid-depth of the vegetable material. Withdraw brine through a sanitized, attached piece of rubber tubing into a 12-oz bottle. Fit the receiving bottle with a two-hole rubber stopper and two short lengths of glass tubing, one for the rubber tubing leading from the stainless steel sampling tube and the other for a suction bulb to start siphoning action. The length of the steel sampling tube is governed by the depth of the container to be sampled. Withdraw and discard approximately 24 oz of brine before taking the final sample, about 10 mL, into a sterile test tube. Sterile vacuum tubes with rubber stoppers are suitable. If microbial changes during the fermentation are to be followed, start sampling at the time the material is salted or brined and continue at regular intervals of 1 to 2 days during active fermentation. After sampling, wash the whole assembly thoroughly.

For tightly headed barrels such as those used for genuine dills and salted vegetables for nonpickle use, take the sample through the top or side bung. For smaller containers, such as jars or cans of pickle products, shake thoroughly and take the sample from the center of the material by means of a sterile pipette. Wash the tops of the metal cans with alcohol, flame, and puncture. A beer can opener is useful for puncturing metal tops. If the containers show evidence of gas pressure, carefully release gas by puncturing the sanitized top with a flamed ice pick. Containers under heavy gas pressure may be refrigerated overnight to reduce the gas pressure prior to sampling.

Brine samples from actively fermented material should be examined as promptly as possible after collection to prevent changes in the microbial flora. The same is true for samples of packaged pickle products. If it is necessary to ship or store samples, this should be done under the best of refrigerated conditions; the elapsed time from collection to examination should not exceed 24 hr. When shipment by air is required, samples are collected in sterile, 16- × 105-mm tubes fitted with plastic screw caps having rubber liners. Pulp and oil liners, or plastic liners such as teflon, may leak because of changes in air pressure.

Brine samples may be preserved for subsequent chemical determinations by the addition of one to two drops of toluene or Merthiolate (1% aqueous solution) per 10 mL of sample. Samples preserved with the above chemicals are unfit for human consumption and should be so marked.

Many techniques have been developed for sample preparation and storage of ascorbic acid samples. For fermented and acidified vegetables, quickly mixing a sample with at least four volumes of 3% wt/vol metaphosphoric acid is a good sample preparation procedure. Little or no ascorbic acid is lost after 24 hr of storage in the refrigerator. Metaphosphoric acid stabilizes ascorbic acid much better than sulfuric acid or oxalic acid does. To reduce dehydro-ascorbic acid to obtain the total ascorbic acid, 0.1% BAL (2,3-dimercapto 1-propanol) can be added to the metaphosphoric acid solution.[60] A recent review of ascorbic acid analysis of plant tissues is given by Helsper.[68]

50.52 Microscopic Examination

Microscopic examination of brine and vegetable samples for bacteria and yeasts is helpful at times, particularly when carried out in conjunction with plate count observations.

1. Bacteria

Make direct counts for bacteria according to the following procedures:

Place 0.01 mL amounts of liquid on slides using a calibrated pipette or loop and spread evenly over a 1 cm^2 area; fix with heat.

Stain according to the Kopeloff and Cohen modification of the gram stain.[74] Count according to the Wang[112] modification of the Breed[9] technique.

Report results as "numbers of different morphological types of gram-positive and gram-negative bacterial cells per mL of brine."

To determine the number of bacteria within brined vegetable tissue, blend the tissue to a homogeneous slurry and filter through coarse filter paper (Reeve Angel 202, Whatman Laboratory Products, Inc., Clifton, N.J.). Bacteria within the filtrate are then enumerated with a Petroff-Hauser counting chamber at a magnification of about 500×.[19]

2. Yeasts

Use the microscopic technique for determining yeast populations in fermenting vegetable brines and various types of finished pickle products undergoing gaseous spoilage by the organisms, particularly where populations are in excess of 10^4 cells per mL of sample and where yeast colonies are not required for isolation and study. The use of a vital stain permits differentiation of yeast population into viable and nonviable cells and increases the usefulness of the direct counting technique.

The counting procedure is essentially the method of Mills[84] as modified by Bell and Etchells[1] for counting yeasts in high salt content brines and in high sugar content liquors:

Add 1 mL of brine or pickle liquor sample to 1 mL of 1:5,000 (0.02%) erythrosin stain.

Shake the sample stain mixture to obtain an even suspension.

Using a 3-mm diameter platinum loop, transfer enough of the mixture to the area under the cover glass of an improved Neubauer double-ruled hemacytometer to fill the chamber in one operation.

Allow cells to settle for approximately 5 min, and count the yeast cells using a microscope equipped with a 4-mm objective and $15\times$ oculars.

Record cells stained pink as "dead yeast cells" and unstained cells as "live yeast cells."

The number of yeast cells per mL of brine or pickle liquor may be calculated thus:

$$\frac{\text{Number of yeast cells counted} \times \text{dilutions} \times 250,000}{\text{Number of large squares counted}} = \text{Numbers per mL}$$

If only one side of the hemacytometer counting chamber is used (25 large squares), the lowest yeast count obtainable is 20,000 per mL, while if both sides are counted (50 large squares), a population as low as 10,000 per mL can be counted.

Report yeast count as "total yeast cells," "live yeast cells," and "dead yeast cells per mL of sample."

50.53 Titratable Acidity and pH

Determine titratable acidity of a 10-mL sample of the fermentation brine or finished pickle liquor (liquid of the final product) by diluting the sample with 30 to 50 mL of distilled water; titrate with 0.1 N NaOH using phenolphthalein as the indicator. Alternatively, samples may be titrated to pH 8.2 with a pH meter. Report values for fermented, brined samples as g of lactic acid per 100 mL of sample, and for finished pickle liquor samples as g of acetic acid per 100 mL of sample.

For a 10-mL sample, use the following calculations:

a. mL of 0.1 N alkali used $\times$ 0.090 = g of lactic acid per 100 mL.
b. mL of 0.1 N alkali used $\times$ 0.060 = g of acetic acid per 100 mL.

When only a small amount of the original sample is available, use a 2-mL amount for titration purposes. Such small samples are not recommended. For the 2-mL sample, multiply the mL of 0.1 N alkali by 5, then by the above number for lactic or acetic acid.

Carry out pH determinations of the samples with a pH meter, checking the instrument frequently with a standard buffer in the pH range of the sample under test.

50.54   Determining Chloride and Calcium Contents of Brine

It is often helpful to know the approximate salt content in performing microbiological examinations of brines. Use a salometer, and test about 200 mL of brine. A chemical test for salt is required for small amounts of sample or when a higher degree of accuracy is desired than that obtainable with the salometer.

The following method is recommended. Transfer 1 mL of sample to a flask, and dilute with 15 to 20 mL of distilled water. Titrate with 0.171 N silver nitrate solution, 29.063 g per liter, using 3 to 5 drops of 0.5% dichlorofluorescein as the indicator. Agitate to keep the precipitate broken up until a light salmon pink color develops. Report as "g of sodium chloride per 100 mL of the sample." When 1 mL of sample is titrated, each mL of silver nitrate solution is equal to 1 g of sodium chloride per 100 mL.

A rapid colorimetric procedure based upon calcium binding by methylthymol blue can be used to measure the calcium content of brines or blended tissue.[66] Samples are mixed with an equal volume of 4% wt/vol trichloroacetic acid solution. Acidified solution, containing 50 to 600 µg calcium, is added to a test tube, and reagent solution is added. An immediate absorbance change at 612 nm occurs. The relationship between calcium concentration and absorbance is hyperbolic. A standard curve can be constructed by hand, or the data may be fitted to a hyperbola using nonlinear regression.

50.55   Determining Fermentation Substrates and Products

To determine whether the intended fermentation occurred or to determine the nature of an off-fermentation, it is important to measure both the substrates and products of a fermentation process. High-performance liquid chromatography (HPLC) procedures to measure all major substrates and products of both heterolactic acid and homolactic acid fermentations have been developed using refractive index detection.[81] Alternative HPLC columns can be used, depending on particular analytical goals and problems. We now use a calcium- rather than a lead-modified resin column for sugar determinations because the analysis time is shorter and fructose and ethanol coelute on the lead column. However, sucrose is stable during chromatography on the lead column, but unstable on the calcium column. Therefore, if sucrose is an important sugar in the samples of interest, the lead column is preferred. For the analysis of organic acids, reversed-phase columns gradually lose resolution and need to be replaced periodically. Also, not all C_{18} columns adequately separate malic acid, lactic acid, acetic acid, and ethanol. Resin columns in the H+ form are extremely stable and reproducible for organic acid analysis using 0.02 N sulfuric acid as the eluent. We have used a single column (Bio-Rad HPX-87H) for more than 3 years without loss of performance. One problem with this procedure for cucumber pickle analysis is that fructose and malic acid coelute. The coelution problem has been solved in two ways using the same column as cited above. Lázaro et al.[75] developed equations to quantify fructose and malic acid differentially based on peak heights obtained from ultraviolet and refractive index detectors connected in series. Frayne[61] actually resolved malic acid and fructose by connecting two of the HPLC columns in series.

Though HPLC is today the method of choice for analysis of fermentations, it has the disadvantage that an expensive instrument is required. An alternative approach for analysis of many fermentation substrates and products is enzymatic analysis using commercially available kits. The analysis can be done manually with an inexpensive visible colorimeter or spectrophotometer. The main disadvantage is that only a single compound can be analyzed at a time. Compounds for which kits are available include glucose, fructose, malic acid, L-lactic acid, acetic acid, ethanol, and CO_2. Commercial sources for such kits include Boehringer Mannheim Biochemicals and Sigma Chemical Company. Enzymatic analysis is the only routine way to measure the L-isomer of lactic acid specifically.

It is important for the stability of fermented vegetables that all fermentable sugars be metabolized by the end of the fermentation process. For products like cucumbers that have little or no sucrose, colorimetric measurement of reducing sugars is a simple, rapid quality control procedure to assess the completion of sugar utilization. The dinitrosalicylic acid (DNS) procedure[83, 104] is recommended. The reagent is stable at room temperature for many months. The assay can be reliably performed with an inexpensive colorimeter. A fermentation can be considered complete if the brine contains less than 0.05% reducing sugar and acid shows no increase for several days.

50.56   Determining Softening Enzyme Activity

Softening enzymes in brines of fermenting cucumbers and other vegetables may be determined by the highly sensitive viscometric method of Bell et al.[4] The procedure, which has been widely used in the pickle industry for many years, is based on viscosity loss of a buffered polypectate solution. Brine samples, 25 mL, are dialyzed in running water for 3 hr and distilled water for 1 hr. One mL of the dialyzed sample is added to 5 mL of 1.2% sodium polypectate, which is dissolved in 0.018 M, pH 5.0 citrate buffer in an Ostwald-Fenske no. 300 viscometer. A drop of toluene is added to the sample to prevent microbial growth during incubation. The flow time of the pectate solution is measured after sample addition and at 20 hr. The viscosity loss is calculated according to the following equation:

$$\text{Percent loss in viscosity} = \frac{A - B}{A - W} \times 100, \tag{1}$$

where A is the initial flow time in seconds, B is the flow time at 20 hr, and W is the flow time for water. Bell et al.[4] provide a table that relates loss in viscosity to the units of pectate depolymerizing activity. A less than 9% loss of viscosity in 20 hr is considered to represent weak to negative activity in brine samples.

Refer to Chapter 14 for isolation of pectinolytic organisms and characterization of pectinolytic enzymes.

50.57   Determining Dissolved Carbon Dioxide

The advent of purging to remove CO_2 from fermenting cucumber brines and thus prevent bloater formation has created a need to determine the concentration of dissolved CO_2 in the brine. For the highly accurate determinations that may be required for research purposes, dissolved CO_2 is determined by the micro distillation procedure.[51] A 10-mL brine sample is injected by syringe into a capped jar containing an acid solution. A small vial of standardized NaOH placed inside the jar traps the CO_2 as it distills from the acidified solution. After 24 hr at 37°C, the vial is removed, $BaCl_2$ is added, and the remaining base is titrated to the phenolphthalein end-point with HCl. Values are expressed as mg CO_2 per 100 mL brine.

For quick estimates that may be required for quality control tank monitoring, dissolved CO_2 is determined with a micro CO_2 apparatus. Adaptation of this instrument for the determination of CO_2 in fermenting cucumber brines has been described.[50] This is a gasometric method based on the classical Van Slyke procedure. A 1-mL brine sample is placed in the instrument vial, a volumetric syringe is clamped into place, an acid solution is added, the apparatus and sample vial are shaken, and the gas volume displacement is read on the calibrated syringe scale. Carbon dioxide in the brine sample is calculated from scale readings of the brine compared to a CO_2 solution of known concentration and is expressed as mg CO_2 per 100 mL brine. It is suggested that brine samples be taken from brine tanks through a siphon tube (see Section 50.51) and 8.5 mL syringed through a needle into a Vacutainer tube (10 mL draw, Becton-Dickinson, containing 0.5 mL of c. 3 N NaOH) to minimize CO_2 loss. The samples are then equilibrated to the same temperature as the known solution before analysis.

In both methods, the total CO_2 content of the solution is determined and is expressed as mg CO_2 per 100 mL brine, or as percent saturation.[54]

50.58 Microbiological Analyses

1. Aerobic plate count

Use plate count agar or nutrient agar and incubate for 3 days at 32°C. Overlay the solidified, plated samples with about 8 to 10 mL of the same medium to prevent or minimize spreaders.

2. Lactic acid bacteria

Lactic acid bacteria associated with pickled vegetables of the genera *Lactobacillus* and *Pediococcus* are selectively enumerated with *Lactobacillus* selection medium (LBS), appropriately modified as noted below. Overlay the plated samples with the same medium to permit earlier enumeration of colonies. Incubate at 32°C for about 4 days or until suitable colony enlargement occurs. The incubator should be humidified to retard desiccation of the medium during incubation. Fructose, 1%, may be added to the medium to ensure greater enumeration of certain lactobacilli.[102] Bromcresol green (or brilliant green, as in Chapter 62), 0.0075%, may be added to aid in colony counting, but may further retard growth of lactic acid bacteria in an already inhibitory medium. Cycloheximide, 200 ppm, should be added as needed to inhibit yeasts.

Total lactic acid bacteria may be estimated by plating samples in MRS agar containing 0.02% sodium azide and incubating for 1 to 4 days at 30°C.[17]

To enumerate differentially all species of lactic acid bacteria associated with vegetable fermentations, plate fermenting samples in a noninhibitory medium such as tryptone-glucose-yeast extract agar.[90] After incubation at 32°C for 48 hr, isolate colonies for later identification on the basis of acid and gas production, cell morphology, and mucoid growth;[89] other reactions may be used.

The decarboxylation of malic acid to lactic acid and CO_2 is an undesirable reaction in cucumber fermentations because of the CO_2 produced. Most lactic acid bacteria can decarboxylate the malic acid in cucumbers. Specific strains of *L. plantarum* have been developed that no longer can decarboxylate malic acid.[18] To distinguish between malate-decarboxylating (MDC^+) and malate-nondecarboxylating (MDC^-) lactic acid bacteria, a differential medium has been formulated (MD medium, see Chapter 62 for composition), which is suitable as either a broth or a plating medium. The differential reaction is based upon pH changes in the medium caused by malate decarboxylation. A pH decline (MDC^-) is shown by a color change from blue to green, whereas there is no color change for the MDC^+ reaction. This medium is not selective for lactic acid bacteria.

HHD medium (see Chapter 62 for composition) is used for the differential enumeration of homofermentative and heterofermentative lactic acid bacteria.[76] This medium incorporates fructose, which is reduced to mannitol by heterofermentative but not homofermentative lactic acid bacteria. In agar medium, homofermentative colonies of lactic acid bacteria are blue to green, while heterofermentative are white. HHD medium is not selective for lactic acid bacteria.

3. Total *Enterobacteriaceae*

Add 1% glucose to violet red bile agar, which is referred to as MacConkey glucose agar.[86] Incubate for 24 to 48 hr at 32°C.

4. Coliform bacteria

Use violet red bile agar, incubate plates at 32° or 35°C for 24 hr, and count all purplish red colonies surrounded by a reddish zone of precipitated bile, 0.5 mm in diameter or larger.

5. Yeasts and molds

Acidify sterile, tempered, 45°C dextrose agar with 10% tartaric acid (usually 5% by volume) to achieve a final pH 3.5 ± 0.1. Potato dextrose or malt agar may be used when acidified to pH 3.5 as above. Incubate for 3 to 5 days at 30°C.

Alternatively, the antibiotic method described in Chapter 16 may be used. Small colonies of lactic acid bacteria may appear on the acidified medium above, but are suppressed in the antibiotic medium. We use plate count agar (Chapter 62), supplemented with a solution containing 500 mg each of chlortetracycline HCl and chloramphenicol in 100 mL of sterile, distilled water and added aseptically to the tempered agar (45°C) at a rate of 2 mL of antibiotic solution per 100 mL medium, as recommended in Chapter 16.

Mold colonies are filamentous and, thus, are distinguished readily from yeasts on acidified dextrose agar. Differentiation of subsurface yeasts and film yeasts presents more difficulty. Surface colonies of the common film-forming yeasts associated with pickle products and vegetable brines, i.e., species of *Debaryomyces, Endomycopsis, Candida*, and *Pichia*,[27, 87] are generally dull and very rough, as contrasted to the usual round, raised, white, glistening colonies of the fermentative, subsurface yeasts, i.e., species of *Torulopsis, Brettanomyces, Hansenula, Saccharomyces*, and *Torulaspora*.[29, 32, 33] However, even when distinguishing colony characteristics of the two yeast groups exist, they are not considered sufficiently clear-cut for separation. Because of this, the procedure outlined under Section 50.58.6 should be used. Film yeasts rapidly form a heavy wrinkled surface film at one or both salt concentrations. Certain species, such as *Saccharomyces halomembranis*, form heavier films at 10% salt than at 5%.[25, 27, 31, 87]

6. Film yeasts

For an estimate, pick representative filamentous colonies from the yeast plates into tubes of dextrose broth containing 5% and 10% salt. Incubate 3 to 5 days at 32°C and observe for heavy surface film. Two salt concentrations are suggested because some species develop heavier films at the lower salt strength (5%), whereas, with other species, the reverse is true.

7. Obligate halophiles

Use tubes of liver broth plus salt (Chapter 62). Prepare decimal dilutions, seal with sterilized, melted petroleum jelly, and incubate 7 days at 32°C. Record positive tubes daily by noting the raising of the petroleum seal caused by gas production and the absence of any distinctive odor.

This medium has proved satisfactory for detecting obligate halophiles sometimes found in brined and dry-salted vegetables. The salt content of the medium should approximate that of the sample. No growth of coliforms or yeasts has been encountered in this medium. This is probably due to the inability of either group to initiate satisfactory early growth in laboratory media even at moderately high salt concentrations in competition with the very fast-growing obligate halophiles.

8. Butyric acid-forming bacteria

Neutralize the brine sample with an excess of sterile calcium carbonate. Heat a 50- to 100-mL sample in a waterbath for 20 min at 80°C to kill vegetative cells. Prepare decimal dilutions and inoculate previously heated and cooled tubes of liver broth medium. Seal with melted petroleum jelly and incubate 7 days at 32°C. Examine tubes daily for production of gas and a strong butyric acid odor.

50.6 INTERPRETATION OF DATA

50.61 Saltstock Vegetables and Genuine Dill Pickles

Proper record-keeping of salting procedures and chemical and microbiological data can greatly aid the commercial briner in assessing causes for success or failure in preserving the quality of brined vegetables. Records of chemical determinations of salt, titratable acidity, pH, fermentable sugars, dissolved CO_2, and softening enzyme activity are very useful in such assessments, depending on the particular commodity.

In fermented vegetables, it is important that the lactic acid fermentation become established early to preclude growth by spoilage bacteria. Acidity and pH data provide this information. Salt concentrations above 8% for cucumbers and olives or above 2.5% for cabbage may prevent or retard a desirable lactic fermentation. Unusually low salt concentrations may result in softening of the brined vegetables.

If the dissolved CO_2 concentration in the brine of fermenting cucumbers is allowed to exceed about 50% saturation (equals 54 mg per 100 mL at 21°C and 6.6% NaCl) at any time during brine storage, bloater damage may result. Maintaining the brine CO_2 concentration below 50% saturation will greatly aid in reducing bloater damage.[54] Sporadic bloater damage may occur even in effectively purged brine-stock cucumbers. Such damage may be due to growth of bacteria within the brined fruit.[16] Since brines must be purged as long as fermentation occurs, it is important to monitor the level of fermentable sugars in the brine. When fermentable sugars are not detected and acid development has ceased, the fermentation is considered to be complete, and purging can be safely discontinued.

Microbial softening enzyme activity of brines may indicate the cause of soft brine-stock pickles, especially if the cucumbers are held at relatively low brine strengths (5% to 8% NaCl). Higher salt concentrations will prevent softening by these enzymes,[2] but high salt levels present disposal problems in addition to affecting the lactic fermentation adversely. Recent studies have indicated that calcium chloride, c. 0.2% to 0.4%, and other salts of calcium may inhibit the action of softening enzymes.[10] Calcium chloride is now being added to commercial cucumber brines. The extent of protection against softening offered by calcium has not been fully assessed.

The absence of softening enzyme activity in older brine-stock pickles does not necessarily mean that such activity did not cause the softening. Softening enzymes that accompany the cucumbers and attached flowers into the brine tank may exert their influence early in brine storage and then be dissipated or inactivated so as not to be detectable later.

Softening in the seed area of large cucumbers, commonly termed "soft centers," is thought to be due to natural polygalacturonase of overly mature cucumbers,[95] not to microorganisms.

The advent of reliable HPLC procedures to measure changes in substrates and products of fermentations has made it practical to assess the balance between substrate utilization and product formation in complex food fermentations. Carbon recovery of <100% indicates that some fermentation products have been missed in the analysis, while recovery of >100% suggests that unknown substrates have been fermented. Examples of fermentation balances done on complex fermentations have been published.[12, 55, 57, 58, 77] The determination of fermentation end products was extremely useful in recent efforts to determine microorganisms responsible for spoilage of fermented cucumbers.[59]

50.62 Finished Pickle Products from Saltstock Vegetables

These products normally contain a few thousand microorganisms per mL. These counts may be composed chiefly of spores of aerobic bacteria that remain inactive in the acid medium and tend to decrease during storage. Fermentative yeasts and lactic acid bacteria may cause vigorous gas production, which causes the pickle liquor to become highly charged with gas and to possess a tang when tasted. Viable microorganisms, normally latent in properly fermented and preserved products, may cause gaseous spoilage in improperly finished products. Gaseous spoilage and cloudy cover brine may be the result in hamburger dill chips, genuine dill pickles, Spanish-style green olives, and similar products, if residual sugar remains.

50.63 Pasteurized Pickle Products

Properly acidified, packaged, and pasteurized pickle products are not subject to microbial spoilage. When spoilage occurs, it is usually due to under-pasteurization. Some commercial packers minimize heat processing in order to maintain greater product quality. Minimal processing is done at the risk of spoilage. Spoilage results in recall of the product at the packer's expense. No public health problem exists in pasteurized pickle products that have been properly acidified. After spoilage occurs, however, as evidenced by gas pressure and brine turbidity, there is no way to ensure that the product was properly acidified initially. Lactic acid bacteria are normally found in such products. The spoiled product usually contains acid, but it is not known at that point if the original product, particularly if it was fresh produce, was sufficiently acidified to prevent growth of *Clostridium* before growth of the lactic acid bacteria.

Improper acidification can also be a source of spoilage with potential public health significance, as discussed in Section 50.4. Improper closure can result in growth of aerobic microorganisms on the surface of the brine and a reduction in acidity.

50.7 REFERENCES

1. Bell, T. A. and Etchells, J. L. 1952. Sugar and acid tolerance of spoilage yeasts from sweet-cucumber pickles. Food Technol. 6: 468.
2. Bell, T. A. and Etchells, J. L. 1961. Influence of salt (NaCl) on pectinolytic softening of cucumbers. J Food Sci. 26: 84.
3. Bell, T. A., Etchells, J. L., and Jones, I. D. 1950. Softening of commercial cucumber salt-stock in relation to polygalacturonase activity. Food Technol. 4: 157.
4. Bell, T. A., Etchells, J. L., and Jones, I. D. 1955. A method for testing cucumber salt-stock brine for softening activity. USDA-ARS Pub. 72-5, 18 pp.
5. Bell, T. A., Etchells, J. L., and Costilow, R. N. 1958. Softening enzyme activity of cucumber flowers from northern production areas. Food Res. 23: 198.
6. Beuchat, L. R., Brackett, R. E., Hao, D. Y., and Conner, D. E. 1986. Growth and thermal inactivation of *Listeria monocytogenes* in cabbage and cabbage juice. Can. J. Microbiol. 32: 791.
7. Binsted, R., Devey, J. D., and Dakin, J. C. 1971. "Pickle and Sauce Making," 3rd ed. Food Trade Press Ltd., London, England.
8. Borbolla y Alcala, J. M. R. and Rejano Navarro, L. 1981. On the preparation of Sevillian style olives. The fermentation. II. Grasas y Aceites 32: 103.
9. Breed, R. S. 1911. The determination of the number of bacteria in milk by direct microscopic examination. Zentralblatt fur Bakteriologie und Parasitenkunde. II. Abt. 30: 337.
10. Buescher, R. W., Hudson, J. M., and Adams, J. R. 1979. Inhibition of polygalacturonase softening of cucumber pickles by calcium chloride. J. Food Sci. 44: 1786.
11. Buescher, R. W., Hudson, J. M., and Adams, J. R. 1981. Utilization of calcium to reduce pectinolytic softening of cucumber pickles in low salt conditions. Lebensm. Wiss. Technol. 14: 65.
12. Chen, K. H., McFeeters, R. F., and Fleming, H. P. 1983. Fermentation characteristics of heterolactic acid bacteria in green bean juice. J. Food Sci. 48: 962.
13. Conner, D. E., Brackett, R. E., and Beuchat, L. R. 1986. Effect of temperature, sodium

chloride and pH on growth of *Listeria monocytogenes* in cabbage juice. Appl. Environ. Microbiol. 52: 59.

14. Costilow, R. N., Bedford, C. L., Mingus, D., and Black, D. 1977. Purging of natural salt-stock pickle fermentations to reduce bloater damage. J. Food Sci. 42: 234.

15. Costilow, R. N., Gates, K., and Lacy, M. L. 1980. Molds in brined cucumbers: Cause of softening during air purging of fermentations. Appl. Environ. Microbiol. 40: 417.

16. Daeschel, M. A. and Fleming, H. P. 1981. Entrance and growth of lactic acid bacteria in gas-exchanged, brined cucumbers. Appl. Environ. Microbiol. 42: 1111.

17. Daeschel, M. A., Mundt, J. O., and McCarty, I. E. 1981. Microbial changes in sweet sorghum (*Sorghum bicolor*) juices. Appl. Environ. Microbiol. 42: 381.

18. Daeschel, M. A., McFeeters, R. F., Fleming, H. P., Klaenhammer, T. R., and Sanozky, R. B. 1984. Mutation and selection of *Lactobacillus plantarum* strains that do not produce carbon dioxide from malate. Appl. Environ. Microbiol. 47: 419.

19. Daeschel, M. A., Fleming, H. P., and Potts, E. A. 1985. Compartmentalization of lactic acid bacteria and yeasts in the fermentation of brined cucumbers. Food Microbiol. 2: 77.

20. Daeschel, M. A., McFeeters, R. F., Fleming, H. P., Klaenhammer, T. R., and Sanozky, R. B. 1987. Lactic acid bacteria which do not decarboxylate malic acid and fermentation therewith. U.S. Patent No. 4,666,849.

21. Dakin, J. C. and Day, P. M. 1958. Yeasts causing spoilage in acetic acid preserves. J. Appl. Bact. 21: 94.

22. Dakin, J. C. and Radwell, J. Y. 1971. Lactobacilli causing spoilage of acetic acid preserves. J. Appl. Bact. 34: 541.

23. EPA. 1987. Water quality criteria; availability of document. Fed. Reg. 52: 37655-37656. Environ. Prot. Agency, Washington, D.C.

24. Etchells, J. L. 1938. Rate of heat penetration during the pasteurization of cucumber pickles. Fruit Products J. 18: 68.

25. Etchells, J. L. 1941. Incidence of yeasts in cucumber fermentations. Food Res. 6: 95.

26. Etchells, J. L. and Bell, T. A. 1950a. Classification of yeasts from the fermentation of commercially brined cucumbers. Farlowia 4: 87.

27. Etchells, J. L. and Bell, T. A. 1950b. Film yeasts on commercial cucumber brines. Food Technol. 4: 77.

28. Etchells, J. L. and Jones, I. D. 1942. Pasteurization of pickle products. Fruit Products J. 21: 330.

29. Etchells, J. L. and Jones, I. D. 1943. Bacteriological changes in cucumber fermentation. Food Indus. 15: 54.

30. Etchells, J. L. and Jones, I. D. 1944. Procedure for pasteurizing pickle products. The Glass Packer 23: 519.

31. Etchells, J. L., Fabian, F. W., and Jones, I. D. 1945. The *Aerobacter* fermentation of cucumbers during salting. Michigan Agric. Expt. Sta. Tech. Bull. No. 200.

32. Etchells, J. L., Costilow, R. N., and Bell, T. A. 1952. Identification of yeasts from commercial fermentations in northerm brining areas. Farlowia 4: 249.

33. Etchells, J. L., Bell, T. A., and Jones, I. D. 1953. Morphology and pigmentation of certain yeasts from brines and the cucumber plant. Farlowia 4: 265.

34. Etchells, J. L., Bell, T. A., Monroe, R. J., Masley, P. M., and Demain, A. L. 1958. Populations and softening enzyme activity of filamentous fungi on flowers, ovaries and fruit of pickling cucumbers. Appl. Microbiol. 6: 427.

35. Etchells, J. L., Costilow, R. N., Anderson, T. E., and Bell, T. A. 1964. Pure culture fermentation of brined cucumbers. Appl. Microbiol. 12: 523.

36. Etchells, J. L., Borg, A. F., Kittel, I. D., Bell, T. A., and Fleming, H. P. 1966. Pure culture fermentation of green olives. Appl. Microbiol. 14: 1027.

37. Etchells, J. L., Borg, A. F., and Bell, T. A. 1968. Bloater formation by gas-forming lactic acid bacteria in cucumber fermentations. Appl. Microbiol. 16: 1029.

38. Etchells, J. L., Bell, T. A., Costilow, R. N., Hood, C. E., and Anderson, T. E. 1973a.

Influence of temperature and humidity on microbial, enzymatic and physical changes of stored, pickled cucumbers. Appl. Microbiol. 26: 943.

39. Etchells, J. L., Bell, T. A., Fleming, H. P., Kelling, R. E., and Thompson, R. L. 1973b. Suggested procedure for the controlled fermentation of commercially brined pickling cucumbers—The use of starter cultures and reduction of carbon dioxide accumulation. Pickle Pak Sci. 3: 4.

40. Etchells, J. L., Fleming, H. P., and Bell, T. A. 1975. Factors influencing the growth of lactic acid bacteria during brine fermentation of cucumbers. In "Lactic Acid Bacteria in Beverages and Food," p. 281. Academic Press, New York.

41. Etchells, J. L., Bell, T. A., and Moore, W. R. Jr. 1976. Refrigerated dill pickles—Questions and answers. Pickle Pak Sci. 5: 1.

42. Fabian, F. W. and Switzer, R. G. 1941. Classification of pickles. Fruit Products J. 20: 136.

43. Fenlon, D. R. 1985. Wild birds and silage as reservoirs of listeria in the agricultural environment. J. Appl. Bacteriol. 59: 537.

44. Fernandez-Diez, M. J. 1971. The olive. In "The Biochemistry of Fruits and Their Products," Vol. 2, ed. A. C. Hulme, p. 255. Academic Press, New York.

45. Fleming, H. P. 1982. Fermented vegetables. In "Economic Microbiology. Fermented Foods," Vol. 7, ed. A. H. Rose, p. 227. Academic Press, New York.

46. Fleming, H. P. and McFeeters, R. F. 1981. Use of microbial cultures: Vegetable products. Food Technol. 35: 84.

47. Fleming, H. P., Walter, W. M. Jr., and Etchells, J. L. 1969. Isolation of a bacterial inhibitor from green olives. Appl. Microbiol. 18: 856.

48. Fleming, H. P., Thompson, R. L., Etchells, J. L., Kelling, R. E., and Bell, T. A. 1973a. Bloater formation in brined cucumbers fermented by *Lactobacillus plantarum*. J. Food Sci. 38: 499.

49. Fleming, H. P., Walter, W. M. Jr., and Etchells, J. L. 1973b. Antimicrobial properties of oleuropein and products of its hydrolysis from green olives. Appl. Microbiol. 26: 777.

50. Fleming, H. P., Thompson, R. L., and Bell, T. A. 1974a. Quick method for estimating CO_2 in cucumber brines. Advisory statement publ. and distr. by Pickle Packers Internl., Inc., St. Charles, Ill.

51. Fleming, H. P., Thompson, R. L., and Etchells, J. L. 1974b. Determination of carbon dioxide in cucumber brines. J. Assn. Off. Analyt. Chem. 57: 130.

52. Fleming, H. P., Etchells, J. L., Thompson, R. L., and Bell, T. A. 1975. Purging of CO_2 from cucumber brines to reduce bloater damage. J. Food Sci. 40: 1304.

53. Fleming, H. P., Thompson, R. L., Bell, T. A., and Hontz, L. H. 1978a. Controlled fermentation of sliced cucumbers. J. Food Sci. 43: 888.

54. Fleming, H. P., Thompson, R. L., and Monroe, R. J. 1978b. Susceptibility of pickling cucumbers to bloater damage by carbonation. J. Food Sci. 43: 892.

55. Fleming, H. P., McFeeters, R. F., Thompson, R. L., and Sanders, D.C. 1983. Storage stability of vegetables fermented with pH control. J. Food Sci. 48: 975.

56. Fleming, H. P., McFeeters, R. F., and Thompson, R. L. 1987. Effects of sodium chloride concentration on firmness retention of cucumbers fermented and stored with calcium chloride. J. Food Sci. 52: 653.

57. Fleming, H. P., McFeeters, R. F., Daeschel, M. A., Humphries, E. G., and Thompson, R. L. 1988a. Fermentation of cucumbers in anaerobic tanks. J. Food Sci. 53: 127.

58. Fleming, H. P., McFeeters, R. F., and Humphries, E. G. 1988b. A fermentor for study of sauerkraut fermentation. Biotech. Bioeng. 31: 189.

59. Fleming, H. P., Daeschel, M. A., McFeeters, R. F., and Pierson, M. D. 1989. Butyric acid spoilage of fermented cucumbers. J. Food Sci. 54: 636.

60. Floridi, A., Coli, R., Fidanza, A. A., Bourgeois, D. F., and Wiggins, R. A. 1982. High performance liquid chromatographic determination of ascorbic acid in food: Comparison with other methods. Int. J. Vit. Nutr. Res. 52: 193.

61. Frayne, R. F. 1986. Direct analysis of the major organic components in grape must and wine using high performance liquid chromatography. Am. J. Enol. Vitic. 37: 281.

62. Gates, K. and Costilow, R. N. 1981. Factors influencing softening of salt-stock pickles in air-purged fermentations. J. Food Sci. 46: 274.

63. Geisman, J. R. and Henne, R. E. 1973. Recycling food brine eliminates pollution. Food Eng. 45: 119.

64. George, S. M., Lund, B. M., and Brocklehurst, T. F. 1988. The effect of pH and temperature on initiation of growth of *Listeria monocytogenes*. Let. Appl. Microbiol. 6: 153.

65. Gililland, J. R. and Vaughn, R. H. 1943. Characteristics of butyric acid bacteria from olives. J. Bacteriol. 46: 315.

66. Gindler, E. M. and King, J. D. 1972. Rapid colorimetric determination of calcium in biologic fluids with methylthymol blue. Amer. J. Clin. Path. 58: 376.

67. Gonzalez Cancho, F., Rejano Navarro, L., and Borbolla y Alcala, J. M. R. 1980. Formation of propionic acid during the conservation of table green olives. III. Responsible microorganisms. Grasas y Aceites 31: 245.

68. Helsper, J. P. F. G. 1987. High performance liquid chromatography of ascorbic acid. In "High Performance Liquid Chromatography in Plant Sciences," ed. H. F. Linskens and J. F. Jackson, p. 114. Springer-Verlag, Berlin.

69. Hudson, J. M. and Buescher, R. W. 1985. Pectic substances and firmness of cucumber pickles as influenced by $CaCl_2$, NaCl and brine storage. J. Food Biochem. 9: 211.

70. Johnson, J. L., Doyle, M. D., Cassens, R. G., and Schoeni, J. L. 1988. Fate of *Listeria monocytogenes* in tissues of experimentally infected cattle and hard salami. Appl. Environ. Microbiol. 54: 497.

71. Juven, B. and Henis, Y. 1970. Studies on the antimicrobial activity of olive phenolic compounds. J. Appl. Bacteriol. 33: 721.

72. Juven, B., Samish, Z., Henis, Y., and Jacoby, B. 1968. Mechanism of enhancement of lactic acid fermentation of green olives by alkali and heat treatments. J. Appl. Bacteriol. 31: 200.

73. Kawatomari, T. and Vaughn, R. H. 1956. Species of *Clostridium* associated with zapatera spoilage of olives. Food Res. 21: 481.

74. Kopeloff, N. and Cohen, P. 1928. Further studies on a modification of the Gram stain. Stain Technol. 3: 64.

75. Lázaro, M. J., Carbonell, E., Aristoy, M. C., Safón, J., and Rodrigo, M. 1989. Liquid chromatographic determination of acids and sugars in homolactic cucumber fermentations. J. Assn. Off. Anal. Chem. 72: 52.

76. McDonald, L. C., McFeeters, R. F., Daeschel, M. A., and Fleming, H. P. 1987. A differential medium for the enumeration of homofermentative and heterofermentative lactic acid bacteria. Appl. Environ. Microbiol. 53: 1382.

77. McFeeters, R. F. and Chen, K.-H. 1986. Utilization of electron acceptors for anaerobic mannitol metabolism by *Lactobacillus plantarum*. Compounds which serve as electron acceptors. Food Microbiol. 3: 73.

78. McFeeters, R. F., Coon, W., Palnitkar, M. P., Velting, M., and Fehringer, N. 1978. Reuse of fermentation brines in the cucumber pickling industry. EPA 600/2-78-207.

79. McFeeters, R. F., Fleming, H. P., and Thompson, R. L. 1982. Malic acid as a source of carbon dioxide in cucumber juice fermentations. J. Food Sci. 47: 1862.

80. McFeeters, R. F., Fleming, H. P., and Daeschel, M. A. 1984. Malic acid degradation and brined cucumber bloating. J. Food Sci. 49: 999.

81. McFeeters, R. F., Thompson, R. L., and Fleming, H. P. 1984. Liquid chromatographic analysis of sugars, acids, and ethanol in lactic acid vegetable fermentations. J. Assn. Off. Anal. Chem. 67: 710.

82. Meneley, J. C. and Stanghellini, M. E. 1974. Detection of enteric bacteria within locular tissue of healthy cucumbers. J. Food Sci. 39: 1267.

83. Miller, G. L. 1959. Use of dinitrosalicylic acid reagent for determination of reducing sugar. Anal. Chem. 31: 426.
84. Mills, D. R. 1941. Differential staining of living and dead yeast cells. Food Res. 6: 361.
85. Monroe, R. J., Etchells, J. L., Pacilio, J. C., Borg, A. F., Wallace, D. H., Rogers, M. P., Turney, L. J., and Schoene, E. S. 1969. Influence of various acidities and pasteurizing temperatures on the keeping quality of fresh-pack dill pickles. Food Technol. 23: 71.
86. Mossel, D. A. A., Mengerink, W. H. J., and Scholts, H. H. 1962. Use of a modified MacConkey agar medium for the selective growth and enumeration of *Enterobacteriaceae*. J. Bacteriol. 34: 381.
87. Mrak, E. M. and Bonar, L. 1939. Film yeasts from pickle brines. Zentralblatt fur Bakteriologie und Parasitenkunde. II. Abt. 100: 289.
88. Mrak, E. M., Vaughn, R. H., Miller, M. W., and Phaff, H. J. 1956. Yeasts occurring in brines during the fermentation and storage of green olives. Food Technol. 10: 416.
89. Pederson, C. S. and Albury, M. N. 1950. Effect of temperature upon bacteriological and chemical changes in fermenting cucumbers. N.Y. Agric. Expt. Sta. Bull. 744.
90. Pederson, C. S. and Albury, M. N. 1954. The influence of salt and temperature on the microflora of sauerkraut fermentation. Food Technol. 8: 1.
91. Pederson, C. S. and Albury, M. N. 1961. The effect of pure culture inoculation on fermentation of cucumbers. Food Technol. 15: 351.
92. Pederson, C. S. and Albury, M. N. 1969. The sauerkraut fermentation. N.Y. Agric. Expt. Sta. Bull. 824.
93. Plastourgos, S. and Vaughn, R. H. 1957. Species of *Propionibacterium* associated with zapatera spoilage of olives. Appl. Microbiol. 5: 267.
94. Potts, E. A. and Fleming, H. P. 1979. Changes in dissolved oxygen and microflora during fermentation of aerated, brined cucumbers. J. Food Sci. 44: 429.
95. Saltveit, M. E. Jr. and McFeeters, R. F. 1980. Polygalacturonase activity and ethylene synthesis during cucumber fruit development and maturation. Plant Physiol. 66: 1019.
96. Samish, Z., Dimant, D., and Marani, T. 1957. Hollowness in cucumber pickles. Food Manuf. 32: 501.
97. Samish, Z., Etinger-Tulczynska, R., and Bick, M. 1963. The microflora within the tissue of fruits and vegetables. J. Food Sci. 28: 259.
98. Schlech, W. F. III, Lavigne, P. M., Bortolussi, R. A., Allen, A. C., Haldane, E. V., Wort, A. J., Hightower, A. W., Johnson, S. E., King, S. H., Nicholls, E. S., and Broome, C. V. 1983. Epidemic listeriosis—Evidence for transmission by food. N. England J. Med. 308: 203.
99. Seelinger, H. P. R. and Jones, D. 1986. Genus *Listeria*. In "Bergey's Manual of Systematic Bacteriology," Vol. 2, ed. P. H. A. Sneath, N. S. Mair, M. E. Sharpe, and J. G. Holt, p. 1235. Williams and Wilkins, Baltimore, Md.
100. Sneath, P. H. A., Mair, N. S., Sharpe, M. E., and Holt, J. G., eds. 1986. "Bergey's Manual of Systematic Bacteriology," Vol. 2. Williams and Wilkins, Baltimore, Md.
101. Stamer, J. R. 1975. Recent developments in the fermentation of sauerkraut. In "Lactic Acid Bacteria in Beverages and Food," ed. J. G. Carr, C. V. Cutting, and C. G. Whiting, p. 267. Academic Press, New York.
102. Stamer, J. R. and Stoyla, B. O. 1967. Growth response of *Lactobacillus brevis* to aeration and organic catalysts. Appl. Microbiol. 15: 1025.
103. Stamer, J. R. and Stoyla, B. O. 1978. Stability of sauerkraut packaged in plastic bags. J. Food Protec. 41: 525.
104. Sumner, J. B. and Sisler, E. B. 1944. A simple method for blood sugar. Arch. Biochem. 4: 333.
105. Tang, H.-C. L. and McFeeters, R. F. 1983. Relationships among cell wall constituents, calcium, and texture during cucumber fermentation and storage. J. Food Sci. 48: 66.
106. USDA. 1966. U.S. standards for grades of pickles. U.S. Dept. of Agric. Fed. Reg. 31:

10231-10305, Off. Fed. Reg. Natl. Arch. and Records Serv., Gen. Serv. Admin., Washington, D.C.

107. US HEW/PHS. 1979. Acidified foods and low-acid canned foods in hermetically sealed containers. Pub. Health Serv., Food and Drug Admin. Fed. Reg. 44: 16204-16238. Off. Fed. Reg. Natl. Arch. and Records Serv., Gen. Serv. Admin., Washington, D.C.

108. Vaughn, R. H. 1954. Lactic acid fermentation of cucumbers, sauerkraut, and olives. In "Industrial Fermentations," Vol. 2, ed. L. A. Underkofler and R. J. Hickey, p. 417. Chem. Publ., New York.

109. Vaughn, R.H. 1975. Lactic acid fermentation of olives with special reference to California conditions. In "Lactic Acid Bacteria in Beverages and Food," ed. J. G. Carr, C. V. Cutting, and G. C. Whiting, p. 307. Academic Press, New York.

110. Vaughn, R. H. 1981. Lactic acid fermentation of cabbage, cucumbers, olives, and other products. In "Prescott and Dunn's Industrial Microbiology," 4th ed., ed. G. Reed, p. 185. Avi Publ., Westport, Conn.

111. Vaughn, R. H., Martin, M. H., Stevenson, K. E., Johnson, M. G., and Crampton, V. M. 1969. Salt-free storage of olives and other produce for future processing. Food Technol. 23: 124.

112. Wang, S. H. 1941. A direct smear method for counting microscopic particles in fluid suspension. J. Bacteriol. 42: 297.

113. Welshimer, H. J. 1968. Isolation of *Listeria monocytogenes* from vegetation. J. Bacteriol. 95: 300.

114. Welshimer, H. J. and Donker-Voet, J. 1971. *Listeria monocytogenes* in nature. Appl. Microbiol. 21: 516.

Chapter 51

FRUIT BEVERAGES

W. S. Hatcher, Jr.,
J. L. Weihe, D. F. Splittstoesser,
E. C. Hill, and M. E. Parish

51.1 INTRODUCTION

Fruit juices may be squeezed directly from the fruit as in citrus processing, or they may be prepared from macerated or crushed material as in the processing of grapes, cherries, berries, and apples. Juices may be highly clarified, or they may contain considerable amounts of suspended solids. They may be marketed at their natural strength or as concentrates prepared by freezing or evaporation. Preservation can be accomplished by thermal processing including aseptic packaging, refrigeration, freezing, ultra-filtration, or the addition of microbial inhibitors.

Federal standards of identity have been established for some fruit juices, but not for most drinks called ades, nectars, cocktails, and other terms. These names do not signify absolute values as to the percentage of fruit or fruit juice in the beverage. Fruit juices are the unconcentrated liquid extracted from pure mature fruit. Fruit juice drinks may contain 5% to 20% or more of juice, often combined with acids, natural or artificial colors and flavors, and other additives.

51.2 NORMAL MICROFLORA

51.21 Grove, Orchard, and Vineyard

The microorganisms found on sound fruit surfaces, especially those with a thick rind or skin, may be any of the various genera associated with soil, air, irrigation water, and insect pests in fruit-growing areas. Populations may be

953

relatively low, e.g., 10^3 per apple.[15] Succulent fruits with thin skins such as concord grapes, on the other hand, commonly possess yeast populations of 10^5 to 10^6 per g.[32]

Unsound, rotten fruits are heavily contaminated, and a small percentage of unwholesome fruit can "seed" operating equipment with spoilage microorganisms.[10, 21]

51.22   Processing Effects

Certain processing operations reduce the number of viable microorganisms, while others may serve as significant sources of contamination.[14] Washing fruits may reduce counts by more than 90%. Other procedures that remove or destroy microorganisms are hot pressing, lye peeling, fining, centrifuging, and pasteurizing.

Equipment used in the preparation of fruit juices is frequently a significant source of contamination. Unit operations such as presses, extractors, finishers, mills, pipelines, and conveyors are areas where microbial buildup may occur.[29] Growth may take place in the juice itself when it is held too long at ambient temperature.

51.23   Predominant Organisms

Fruit juices are generally acidic, with pH values ranging from approximately 2.4 for lemon juice to 4.2 for tomato juice. All contain sugars with amounts varying from 2% in lemon to more than 20% in some varieties of grape.[31] The low pH of these foods selects for yeasts, molds, and a few groups of aciduric bacteria.

The microorganisms of greatest significance in processing citrus juices are the lactic acid bacteria, primarily species of *Lactobacillus* and *Leuconostoc*, yeasts, and molds. In single-strength juice the lactic acid bacteria generally outgrow the fungi; however, multiplication of these bacteria is inhibited by the high sugar content of products concentrated above 30° Brix.[12] Refrigerated temperatures (≤ 5°C) also select for the fungi, even in single-strength juices.

After concentration and freezing, the microbial population is greatly reduced. Most of the surviving organisms are yeasts that may grow if temperatures are elevated above freezing. The most frequently found yeasts in commercial orange concentrate are *Candida*, *Saccharomyces*, and *Rhodotorula*.[35]

Yeasts are usually the most important group in apple and grape juices. Mills and presses can be significant sources of contamination. The yeasts most commonly isolated from these products and from carbonated fruit-containing beverages belong to the genera *Saccharomyces*, *Candida*, and *Torulopsis*. Psychrotrophic species may grow in Concord grape juice during the period that it is stored at -2°C to precipitate tartrates.[30]

High levels of mold contamination are generally attributed to unsound fruit entering the processing facility. Machinery mold, *Geotrichum candidum*, may be introduced into fruit products from unsanitary equipment. Low numbers of heat-resistant molds such as *Byssochlamys* spp. and *Neosartorya fisheri* often are present on the raw fruit[33] and may survive the processing steps (Chapter 17). Other fungi frequently associated with fruit products include *Alternaria, Botrytis, Colletotrichum, Diplodia, Fusarium, Penicillium,* and *Phomopsis*.[24, 31]

51.24   Indicator Bacteria

Coliforms as well as enterococci are frequently isolated from citrus and other fruit products,[26, 27, 28] but neither their presence nor their absence is indicative of sanitary conditions during harvesting, processing, or packaging.[2] They may become part of the normal processing plant flora; however, their presence does not indicate fecal contamination. When examining juice concentrates for coliforms, some yeasts may give false-positive presumptive tests.[16]

51.3   PATHOGENS

Pathogenic bacteria are usually not a problem in fruit juice beverages; most are killed by a heat treatment given the product at some stage in the process, the pH is generally too low to support their growth, and most die off rapidly in a high-acid environment. However, nonpasteurized apple cider, sold at a roadside stand, was responsible for more than 200 cases of salmonellosis.[1] Subsequent studies showed that *Salmonella typhimurium* could survive at least 30 days in pH 3.6 apple juice.[5] Toxigenic molds may grow on fruits that are processed into beverages. Traces of patulin have been found in apple juice.[13] Clinically significant yeasts were found in commercial orange concentrate,[35] and hepatitis was probably spread among hospital employees by a worker who may have contaminated orange juice during its preparation.[3] Cancer patients undergoing chemotherapy or radiation treatment and others with immunosuppressive diseases may be at risk from opportunistic bacteria and yeasts such as *Klebsiella, Enterobacter, Escherichia, Candida, Torulopsis,* and related organisms normally found in small numbers in orange juice.

At this writing there have been no reports of *Listeria* in concentrated or single-strength fruit juices or drinks. Preliminary juice plant surveys have not resulted in detection of this organism.[25] However, many single-strength juice and drink products are packaged under contract in dairies where *Listeria* contamination could occur. Current data suggest that when inoculated into a beverage system at the 10^6 colony-forming unit (CFU) per ml level, *Listeria* can survive at this level for less than 21 days at pH 4.0, less than 7 days at pH 3.8, and less than 4 days at pH 3.6 when incubated at refrigeration temperatures.[23] Death is much more rapid at higher temperatures.

51.4   SPOILAGE

In the processing of citrus concentrates, single-strength juice may be held in stainless steel tanks for 30 to 120 min prior to high-temperature evaporation. During this period the product is most susceptible to microbial degradation. Growth of lactic acid bacteria may result in the production of acetylmethyl-carbinol and diacetyl, which gives an off-flavor similar to buttermilk.[8, 9] Above 30° Brix, fruit juice concentrates are subject to spoilage by osmophilic yeasts.[34] Citrus juice concentrates are generally stored at −10° to 0°C, temperatures that minimize the growth of yeasts and molds.[18, 20]

Heat-resistant molds (Chapter 17) may survive the thermal process given canned juice beverages. Some evidence indicates that juice drinks are more susceptible to this type of spoilage than are single-strength fruit juices.

The successful use of benzoic and sorbic acids to preserve juice drinks depends on the elimination of most yeasts and aciduric bacteria from the various ingredients.

Improved flavor parameters associated with nonthermally treated juices have created a growing market for "fresh," unpasteurized fruit juices. The increased microbial instability of these products requires greater industrial attention to sanitation and storage conditions. Microbial spoilage of unpasteurized fruit juices is most commonly due to aciduric microbes such as lactic acid bacteria and yeasts. A qualitative survey of the bacterial flora from unpasteurized orange juice indicated the presence of *Lactobacillus fermentum*, *L. plantarum*, *Leuconostoc mesenteroides* subsp. *dextranicum*, *L. mesenteroides* ssp. *mesenteroides*, and *L. paramesenteroides*.[22]

51.5   RECOMMENDED METHODS

51.51   Aerobic Plate Count (Chapter 4)

51.52   Aciduric Bacteria

Plate on orange serum agar. Incubate 48 hr at 30°C.

51.53   Geotrichum Count (Chapter 5)

51.54   Yeasts and Molds (Chapter 16)

51.55   Heat-Resistant Molds (Chapter 17)

51.56   Direct Microscopic Count (Chapter 5)

For citrus products, stain 5 ml of 12° Brix juice with an equal volume of 0.075% aqueous crystal violet, color index 681. After mixing thoroughly, distribute 0.01 ml over 1 cm² of a clean slide. Dry under a heat lamp.[12]

51.57   Diacetyl Test[4, 11, 12]

1. Preparation of reagents

a. Alpha-naphthol

Dissolve 5 g of fresh alpha-naphthol (Eastman 170 or C.P.) in 100 ml of 99% isopropyl alcohol. Store in brown bottles under refrigeration.

b. Potassium hydroxide with creatine

Dissolve 40 g of KOH pellets in distilled water to make 100 ml of solution. When cool, add 0.3 g creatine. Store in brown bottles under refrigeration (reagents may be stored for several weeks).

c. Antifoam solution

Mix 1 g of Dow-Corning Antifoam AF emulsion to 10 ml of distilled water.

2. Procedure

Add 300 ml of reconstituted juice (12° Brix) to a 1-L boiling flask with 24/40 ground glass joint.

Add 2 drops of antifoam.

Connect to 300-mm Graham condenser with 24/40 ground glass joint at top. Connect flask and condenser with a connecting tube containing 24/40 ground glass inner joints at each end.

Place 25-ml graduated cylinder at effluent end of condenser. Tip cylinder so that oil condensate will float on top and not be mixed. Many laboratories separate oil by filtering condenser effluent through Whatman No. 1 filter paper and collecting filtrate in a graduated cylinder.

Place 750-watt flask heater under flask containing juice and heat at high temperature.

Collect 25 ml of distillate.

Remove full graduate. Replace with another and collect next 25-ml fraction. Repeat. Collect the first three 25-ml fractions.

Discard second fraction.

Pipette 10 ml of distillate from first fraction. Avoid disturbing oil layer if distillate is not filtered. Transfer to a clean 25-mm x 200-mm test tube.

Add 5 ml of 5% alpha-naphthol solution using an automatic pipette.

Add 2 ml KOH-creatine solution.

Allow 10 min for full color development. Prepare a reagent blank at the same time using distilled water in place of juice distillate; add reagents in the same way.

Measure optical density (OD) at 530 nm and read ppm diacetyl from a calibration curve obtained by applying this procedure to standards of known amounts of diacetyl (Eastman 1591 in distilled water). Note that many processors use a variation of this procedure, measuring OD after a 1-min reaction time.[17] This modification is satisfactory for detecting diacetyl when acetyl-methylcarbinol is present in concentrations of less than 2 ppm.

If differentiation between diacetyl and acetylmethylcarbinol is desired, the test is run on the third fraction. Acetylmethylcarbinol is azeotropic with water and will be present in the third fraction at approximately the same concentration as in the first fraction. Since diacetyl comes off in the first fraction, color produced in the third fraction will be due to acetylmethylcarbinol only. If the third fraction value is subtracted from the first, the difference represents diacetyl. The second fraction is collected only as a rinse, removing any residual diacetyl from the condenser.

Some varieties of oranges, such as mature Valencias, contain acetylmethylcarbinol as a normal constituent. By determining the diacetyl and acetylmethylcarbinol content of juice prepared in the laboratory from sound fruit, one can estimate the quantities generated by microbial growth in the processed product.

51.58   Experimental Procedures

Recently a number of rapid methods for detection of microorganisms have been applied to citrus juices. They include radiometry,[7] impedance,[36] adenosine triphosphate measurements,[6] and the plate loop method.[19] Additionally, a gas chromatographic method for the detection of diacetyl and acetoin in citrus juice is being investigated.[37] This method can separately quantify diacetyl and acetoin down to 0.05 and 10 ppm, respectively. Other GC methods for diacetyl detection are less sensitive.

51.6   INTERPRETATION OF DATA

The microbiology of fruit beverages will vary greatly depending on the nature of the fruit, the methods of processing, and the means of preservation. High microbial populations often indicate poor fruit quality, unsanitary equipment, or the opportunity for growth in the food at some stage in the process. However, since each product and process is different, one cannot apply the criteria developed for one to another.

Heat-processed beverages can be free of viable aciduric microorganisms but yield low numbers of viable sporeforming bacteria when cultured on nonselective media. These organisms cannot grow in the high-acid environment of most fruit products, and thus their presence has no bearing on shelf stability. Direct microscopic counts for yeasts, bacteria, or molds may provide a clue to conditions of sanitation during processing; however, most of these organisms will have been removed in the process of creating a highly clarified beverage.

Frozen concentrated juices generally contain microbial populations of 10^2 to 10^5 CFU per ml of reconstituted product. Although high temperature evaporators, operated above 90°C, destroy most microorganisms, opportunity exists for recontamination of the concentrated product. Furthermore, retail orange juice concentrates are generally prepared by diluting 60° to 65° Brix concentrate to 40° to 45° Brix using water or freshly extracted, single-strength juice. This juice may serve as a source of contamination if processors fail to pasteurize it in the belief that nonpasteurized juice provides a concentrate with the freshest, most natural flavor.

Heat-resistant mold spores may be present in low numbers in fruit juice concentrates. They can present a problem if the juice is to be used as a constituent of a beverage that will be preserved with a heat process.

Nonsterile fruit beverages may contain low numbers of coliforms and enterococci, but their presence is not an indication of fecal contamination.

The low pH of most fruit beverages prevents the growth of enteric pathogens. Products that have received a heat treatment at some stage of the process should be free of these organisms. In rare instances salmonellae have been introduced into nonpasteurized apple juice and have survived for an extended time period.

51.7   REFERENCES

1. Anon. 1975. *Salmonella typhimurium* outbreak traced to a commercial apple cider. Morbid. and Mortal. Weekly Rpt. 24: 87.
2. Dack, G. M. 1955. Significance of enteric bacteria in foods. Am. J. Pub. Health 45: 1151.
3. Eisenstein, A. B., Aach, R. D., Jacobson, W., and Goldman, A. 1963. An epidemic of infectious hepatitis in a general hospital—Probable transmission by contaminated orange juice. J.A.M.A. 185: 101.
4. Fields, M. L. 1964. Acetylmethylcarbinol and diacetyl as chemical indexes of microbial quality of apple juice. Food Technol. 18: 114.
5. Goverd, K. A., Beech, F. W. Hobbs, R. P., and Shannon, R. 1979. The occurrence and survival of coliforms and salmonellae in apple juice and cider. J. Appl. Bacteriol. 46: 521.
6. Graumlich, T. R. 1985. Estimation of microbial populations in orange juice by bioluminescence. J. Food Sci. 50: 116.
7. Hatcher, W. S., DiBenedetto, S., Taylor, L. E., and Murdock, D. I. 1977. Radiometric analysis of frozen concentrated orange juice for total viable microorganisms. J. Food Sci. 42: 636.
8. Hays, G. L. 1951. The isolation, cultivation and identification of organisms which have caused spoilage in frozen orange juice. Proc. Fla. State Hort. Soc. 64: 135.
9. Hays, G. L. and Riester, D. W. 1952. The control of "off-odor" spoilage in frozen concentrated orange juice. Food Technol. 6: 386.
10. Hill, E. C. and Faville, L. W. 1951. Studies on the artificial infection of oranges with acid tolerant bacteria. Proc. Fla. State Hort. Soc. 64: 174.
11. Hill, E. C. and Wenzel, F. W. 1957. The diacetyl test as an aid for quality control of citrus products. 1. Detection of bacterial growth in orange juice during concentration. Food Technol. 11: 240.
12. Hill, E. C., Wenzel, F. W., and Barreto, A. 1954. Colorimetric method for detection of microbiological spoilage in citrus juices. Food Technol. 8: 168.
13. Lindroth, S. and Niskanen, A. 1978. Comparison of potential patulin hazard in homemade and commercial apple products. J. Food Sci. 43: 446.
14. Luthi, H. 1959. Microorganisms in noncitrus juices. Advan. Food Res. 9: 221.
15. Marshall, C. R. and Walkley, V. T. 1951. Some aspects of microbiology applicable to commercial apple juice production. I. Distribution of microorganisms on fruit. Food Res. 16: 448.
16. Martinez, N. B. and Appleman, M. D. 1949. Certain inaccuracies in the determination of coliforms in frozen orange juice. Food Technol. 3: 392.

17. Murdock, D. I. 1976. Fruit drinks, juices, and concentrates. In "Compendium of Methods for the Microbiological Examination of Foods," ed., M. L. Speck. Am. Pub. Health Assn., Washington, D.C.

18. Murdock, D. I. and Hatcher, W. S. Jr. 1975. Growth of microorganisms in chilled orange juice. J. Milk Food Technol. 38: 470.

19. Murdock, D. I. and Hatcher, W. S. Jr. 1976. Plate loop method for determining total viable count of orange juice. J. Milk Food Technol. 39: 470.

20. Murdock, D. I. and Hatcher, W. S. Jr. 1978. Effect of temperature on survival of yeast in 45 and 65 brix orange concentrate. J. Food Protect. 41: 689.

21. Murdock, D. I., Folinazzo, J. F., and Brokaw, C. H. 1953. Some observations of gumforming organisms found on fruit surfaces. Proc. Fla. State Hort. Soc., 66: 278.

22. Parish, M. E. and Higgins, D. P. 1988. Isolation and identification of lactic acid bacteria from samples of citrus molasses and unpasteurized orange juice. J. Food Sci. 53: 645.

23. Parish, M. E. and Higgins, D. P. 1989a. Survival of *Listeria monocytogenes* in low pH model broth systems. J. Food Prot. 52: 144.

24. Parish, M. E. and Higgins, D. P. 1989b. Yeasts and molds isolated from spoiling citrus products and by-products. J. Food Prot. 52: 261.

25. Parish, M. E. and Higgins, D. P. 1989c. Extinction of *Listeria monocytogenes* in single-strength orange juice: Comparison of methods for detection in mixed populations. J. Food Safety 9: 267.

26. Patrick, R. 1951. Sources of coliform bacteria in citrus juice for concentrates. Proc. Fla. State Hort. Soc. 64: 178.

27. Patrick, R. 1953. Coliform bacteria from orange concentrate and damaged oranges. Food Technol. 7: 157.

28. Patrick, R. and Hill, E. C. 1958. Enterococcus-like organisms in citrus concentrates. Food Technol. 12: 337.

29. Patrick, R. and Hill, E. C. 1959. Research Bull. 618. Univ. Florida Agric. Expt. Sta., Gainesville, Fla.

30. Pederson, C. S., Albury, M. N., Wilson, D. C., and Lawrence, N. L. 1959. The growth of yeasts in grape juice stored at low temperatures. I. Control of yeast growth in commercial operation. Appl. Microbiol. 7: 1.

31. Splittstoesser, D. F. 1978. Fruits and fruit products. In "Food and Beverage Mycology," ed. L. R. Beuchat, AVI Pub. Co., Westport, Conn.

32. Splittstoesser, D. F. and Mattick, L. R. 1981. The storage life of refrigerated grape juice containing various levels of sulfur dioxide. Am. J. Enol. Viticult. 32: 171.

33. Splittstoesser, D. F., Kuss, F. R., Harrison, W., and Prest, D. B. 1971. Incidence of heat resistant molds in eastern orchards and vineyards. Appl. Microbiol. 21: 335.

34. Troller, J. A. and Christian, J. H. B. 1978. "Water Activity and Food." Academic Press, New York.

35. Weihe, J. L. 1986. Citrus and beverage microbiology. In "Proceedings of the 26th Annual Short Course for the Food Industry," ed. R. F. Matthews, Univ. of Florida, Inst. of Food and Agricultural Sciences, Gainesville, Fla.

36. Weihe, J. L., Seibt, S. L., and Hatcher, W. S. Jr. 1984. Estimation of microbial populations in frozen concentrated orange juice using automated impedance measurements. J. Food Sci. 49: 243.

37. Wicker, L., Parish, M. E., and Braddock, R. J. 1988. Analysis of diacetyl and acetylmethylcarbinol by GLC and application to citrus concentrate quality control. Presented at 85th Ann. Mtg. of the South. Assn. of Agric. Scient., New Orleans, La.

Chapter 52

SPICES AND GUMS

Philip A. Guarino and Rodney J. H. Gray

52.1 INTRODUCTION

52.11 Spices

Spices are dried plants or parts of plants that, alone or as mixtures, in whole or ground form, are used primarily for flavoring or seasoning and to impart aroma or color to foods and beverages. Condiments are spices and blends of spices that may be formulated with other flavor accentuators and potentiators to enhance the flavor of foods. "Spices and condiments" is the official nomenclature adopted by the International Organization for Standardization (ISO). This group, based in Budapest, represents associations in various countries involved in producing, exporting, and importing spices. It has defined more than 70 species and herbs.[41] Pruthi[63, 64] has reviewed the nomenclature and characteristics of all recognized spices and condiments. As a commodity group, spices also include certain dehydrated vegetables (bell peppers, celery, garlic, onion) and seeds (poppy, sesame). Various publications of governments[51, 55, 65, 84] and trade associations[6] cover definitions and specifications of domestic and imported raw and processed spices.

Spice-bearing plants are chiefly indigenous to the Asian tropics, roughly within 25 degrees of the equator.[58, 59, 60, 55] Herbs, the aromatic leaves and flowers of certain plants, are grown in the more temperate climates of the Mediterranean, Middle East, North Africa, and North America. India, one of the major spice producers and exporters,[63, 64] accounts for more than 50% of the international spice trade. Major suppliers to the United States are Canada (mustard seed), Mexico (sesame, oregano, capsicums), Indonesia, and India.[80] Within the United States, California provides a significant contribution.[34] The spice map of the world continues to change as natural or political disasters revitalize old sources and give opportunities and importance to new areas of spice production.

Spices are obtained from various parts of aromatic and herbaceous plants; for example, bark (cassia, cinnamon), berries (allspice, black pepper), bulbs (garlic, onion), floral parts (cloves, saffron), fruits (caper, capsicums, caraway), leafy parts (bay, oregano, parsley, sage), roots or rhizomes (ginger, turmeric), and seeds (cumin, mustard, poppy, sesame).

The chemical composition of spices is well documented.[31, 32, 51, 59, 64]

52.12   Gums

The terms gums, hydrophilic colloids, hydrocolloids, and water-soluble polymers have been used interchangeably to refer to a wide range of useful plant and microbial polysaccharides, or their derivatives, that hydrate in cold or hot water to form viscous solutions or dispersions.[19, 88] Those of plant origin include acacia (gum arabic), gum tragacanth, karaya, and ghatti. In addition to these exudates, natural gums include seaweed extracts (agar, alginates, carrageenan), gums from seed (locust bean or carob, guar), microbial gums (xanthan),[12, 43] and fruit extracts (pectins).[26] Modified gums include amidated pectins, propylene glycol alginate, and cellulose derivatives such as sodium carboxymethyl cellulose, hydroxypropyl cellulose, and methyl cellulose.[3, 19, 25, 44, 89]

Industrial importance stems from the functional properties of aqueous solutions or dispersions of these hydrocolloids. Stabilization, dispersion, or suspension are the functional properties usually exhibited. In addition, hydrocolloids may function as gelling agents or serve as emulsifiers, binders, flocculating agents, film formers, foam stabilizers, mold release agents, or lubricants.[2, 3, 19, 26]

52.2   GENERAL CONSIDERATIONS

52.21   Spices

The physical and chemical diversity of spice materials presents problems for their analysis by chemists and microbiologists. Under normal dry storage conditions, spices are nonperishable items. Some spices in the ground form, however, may diminish in color (paprika,[17] turmeric, saffron[64]), flavor (dill[60]), or pungency (black pepper[31, 32]). Some spices stimulate microbial activity,[24, 60, 88, 90, 91, 92] others exhibit antibacterial action (cloves, mustard seed, garlic, onion, oregano).[1, 13, 14, 29, 33, 37, 47, 50, 69, 79, 90] The preservation effects of several spices are enhanced by their content of antioxidants. Cloves, cinnamon, sage, rosemary, mace, oregano, allspice, and nutmeg are highly antioxidant.[11, 27, 60, 69, 91] In some countries microbiocidal treatments of processed spices are permitted.[28, 52, 64] The relative effects of ethylene oxide,[29, 36, 81, 82, 85, 86, 87] propylene oxide,[66, 83] gamma irradiation,[85, 93] and microwave treatments[85] have been reported.

In general, processed spices are examined with standard procedures for aerobic plate count, molds, yeasts, and coliform bacteria.[5, 7] If coliforms are present, the presence and content of *E. coli* is determined. When unsanitary storage of spices is indicated, the presence of *Salmonella* and *Shigella* must be determined.[23] Additional analyses may be requested by certain food processors and seasoning formulators. These include testing for coagulase-positive staphylococci, anaerobic sporeformers, enterococci, lactobacilli, and *Bacillus cereus*.

52.22 Gums

A wide range of functional properties make gums useful in practically all formulated foods. Among these are dairy products, sauces, pie fillings, salad dressing, whips, soups, emulsions, puddings, and jellies. Gums in dehydrated form are microbiologically stable. Most, however, will support microbiological growth in the presence of sufficient moisture. Rehydrated gums should therefore be used promptly following preparation. Enzymes excreted by bacteria, primarily *Bacillus* species,[16, 75] can degrade unused gel or gum solutions. Most susceptible to bacterial action are the gums tragacanth, acacia, karaya, guar, locust bean (carob), carrageenan, and sodium alginates.[74, 75] Kappa carrageenan has been suggested as a low-cost substitute for agar in media intended for the culture of yeasts and molds.[49]

Most gums produce high-viscosity solutions when dissolved in water at very low concentrations, usually less than 1%. This properly confounds the classical analytical procedures used in microbiology that center around the use of decimal dilutions.

In the preparation of gums for microbiological analysis, a 1:10 dilution is so viscous as to be unworkable and often a 1:50 dilution will be marginal. Hence, the detection limit of the normal aerobic plate count on these materials may be relegated to ~2000 per g (i.e., where a minimum of 20 colony-forming units per plate of a 10^{-2} dilution is required). Multiple plating, depositing larger volumes per plate, and use of large Petri plates are all approaches to consider in addressing this viscosity-based problem.

With the exception of the viscosity property of gums, their microbiological analysis may follow the standard procedures used in the microbiological examination of foods.

52.3   NORMAL FLORA

52.31   Spices

Like many raw agricultural commodities, spices accumulate mixed populations of bacteria and molds. These vary in concentration with different production regions, harvest methods, and post-harvest treatments. Aerobic plate counts typical of different untreated spices are compared in Table 1. Plate counts in the millions per g are usually obtained from black and white pepper, celery seed, ginger, and paprika.[29, 46, 86, 88] The predominant organisms in randomly selected spice samples were aerobic sporeformers, which accounted for between 50% and 95% of all organisms found in the materials examined. Among the aerobic sporeformers in black pepper, white pepper, paprika, marjoram, coriander, allspice, and onion powder, proteolytic organ-

Table 1—Aerobic Plate Count of Untreated Spices and Spices Treated with Ethylene Oxide.[86]

	Colony-forming units/g			
	Untreated		Treated	
Spices	Minimum	Maximum	Minimum	Maximum
Ground				
Allspice	150,000	3,400,000	300	4,700
Basil	13,00	3,900,000	1,200	28,900
Caraway	1,000	930,000	<10	300
Celery Seed	1,200	7,200,000	<10	38,000
Cinnamon	. . .	45,900	<10	2,000
Cloves	<10	2,800	<10	2,700
Coriander	13,000	3,700,000	<10	17,600
Cumin	1,700	10,000,000	<10	9,000
Dill Seed	5,500	340,000	50	4,400
Fennel	8,200	88,000	<10	5,800
Fenugreek	22,000	380,00	<10	9,500
Ginger	120,000	18,000,000	<10	14,600
Marjoram	26,000	2,400,000	50	1,200
Mace	5,100	10,000	. . .	. . .
Paprika	180,000	22,900,000	300	8,200
Whole				
Bay Leaves	7,500	20,000	600	5,900
Oregano	7,300	1,300,000	<10	4,900
Black Pepper	58,000	53,000,000	200	26,000
Cayenne Pepper	. . .	13,000,000	<10	1,900
Red Pepper	73,000	600,000	<10	3,200
White Pepper	93,000	6,600,000	<10	150
Rosemary	15,000	920,000	<10	770
Sage	2,900	70,000	. . .	. . .
Thyme	92,000	3,200,000	<10	7,200
Turmeric	660,000	7,900,000	<10	12,000
Savory	49,000	71,000	<10	320

isms dominated. Amyolytic organisms also occurred in significant numbers in black and white pepper as well as in allspice, onion powder, and cinnamon.[8] Moderately low bacterial counts, a few hundred thousand or less per g, have been found in cassia, mace, and nutmeg.[29, 46] Lowest populations occur in those spices whose essential oils exhibit antimicrobial effects.[13, 60, 64, 69, 88, 90]

The antibacterial action of cloves, for example, is due to their eugenol content. In mustard seed it is allyl isothiocyanate,[33] and in onion and garlic it is sulfur compounds that are the antibacterial agents.[33, 79] Oregano, sage, and rosemary are also bactericidal.[69] At low concentrations, oregano is stimulatory to lactic acid bacteria.[16, 91, 92] These and other toxicants, e.g., myristicin in mace and nutmeg, occur naturally in spices.[33]

In one test 2% of weight per volume extracts in water and ethanol of 26 spices were used to challenge *Bacillus* spp., *Sarcina lutea*, *E. coli*, and *Saccharomyces* in agar diffusions. *E. coli* and *Saccharomyces cerevisiae* were not inhibited, but inhibitory activity occurred against one or more of the other test organisms when rosemary, horseradish, basil, ginger, sage, onion, allspice, and cloves were used to challenge. On the other hand, growth of some test organisms was enhanced by the spice extracts.[20]

During cleaning and processing of spices, progressive reductions in the numbers and types of microorganisms take place.[64] Organisms remaining after physical treatments are generally mixtures of aerobic sporeforming bacteria and common molds.[29, 42, 60, 67] Other organisms found occasionally, usually in small numbers, are thermophiles, streptococci, coliform bacteria, anaerobic sporeformers, and yeasts.[29, 46, 60, 61, 64] High counts of psychrotrophic bacteria, *Enterobacteriaceae*, and yeasts may be found in herbal spices grown in areas with moderate climate.[20] In processed spices, spores of *Clostridium perfringens* are present, but seldom more than a few hundred per g.[35, 61] *Salmonella*, *Shigella*, and coagulase-positive staphylococci are rarely detected in spices.[23, 29, 42, 46] Other than *Bacillus cereus*, bacteria of public health significance have not been found in processed spices.[45, 62]

In the *Bacillus* genus, *Bacillus cereus* is occasionally found within spices, but usually in low numbers. *Bacillus cereus* has been recognized as the etiological agent in food poisoning outbreaks in Europe as far back as 1906. In Hungary, it was ranked as the third most common cause of food poisoning during the period 1906 to 1966. This high incidence of *Bacillus cereus* food poisoning in meat has in the past been attributed to the Hungarian custom of highly seasoning meats with spices that often contain large numbers of aerobic sporeformers.[27]

While *Staphylococcus aureus* continues to be conspicuous by its absence in spices, cytochrome oxidase-positive *Pseudomonadaceae* are generally present; however, quantitative tests to determine their numbers are not usually performed.

Spices carry a variety of molds, ranging in numbers from insignificant levels to many millions per g. The most frequently isolated molds include *Asper-

gillus, Penicillium, and *Absidia* spp.[20] Aspergilli are usually abundant in black and white pepper.[18, 42, 46] *Aspergillus flavus* and *A. niger* are generally the most prominent species.[18, 22] While isolates of *A. flavus* obtained from spices have been shown to produce aflatoxins during growth on laboratory media,[10, 22, 37, 68] the levels of aflatoxins detected in processed spices are very low.[68] Aflatoxin was not detected in 20 samples of various spices containing *Aspergillus flavus.*[20] Inoculation of moistened ground spices and herbs with toxigenic strains of aspergilli resulted in aflatoxin production in the media prepared with ginger, rosemary, sesame seed, caraway seed, and celery seed.[37, 50] Certain spices, especially cinnamon and cloves and to some extent mustard and oregano, inhibit mold growth and toxin formation.[37, 50]

52.32   Gums

The microbiology of the major botanical gums is the subject of very few articles in the scientific literature. Some work in the 1970s provides one of the few sources of published information on this topic.[71, 72, 73, 74, 75] These authors reported high numbers of organisms on gums (10^8 per g), but the data referred primarily to the raw agricultural product or unprocessed starting materials. Much lower counts were found in the finished products (alginate, carrageenan, locust bean gum, and guar flour). Aerobic sporeformers, primarily *Bacillus* sp., predominated.

Streptococcus faecalis occurred in some of the gum tragacanth, carrageenan, and guar samples.[71] *Staphylococcus aureus* (coagulase-positive strains) were also detected in some of the gum tragacanth and locust bean flour samples at levels up to 3×10^5 per g. The latter findings, however, have not been confirmed by laboratories in the United States on routine analysis of gums. *Clostridium perfringens* is found occasionally in tragacanth, acacia, and locust bean flour,[72] but not in gum karaya and guar flour. Anaerobic sporeformers were not detected in alginates and carrageenan. *Escherichia coli* was not found in any of the samples representing the 1970 study;[73] however, laboratories in the United States have found this organism occasionally in raw samples.

52.4   POST-HARVEST CHANGES

52.41   Spices

Post-harvest treatment of spices ranges from primitive sun-drying and sifting to extensive methods of air-scrubbing, milling, fumigation, and encapsulation of soluble extracts.[15, 29, 38, 64] Pneumatic separators remove dust and foreign materials. During milling, the temperature increase, as much as 10° to 45°C, markedly reduces the microbial loads on cumin, coriander, chillies, and black pepper.[63, 64] Newer technology employs vacuum milling systems for low-temperature grinding to preserve the delicate flavors and essences of spices.[34] Extremely low counts of microorganisms and better retention of volatile oils can be attained commercially by controlled heat treatment of raw spices, such as allspice and ginger, during extrusion, redrying, and milling.[9]

Fumigation of spices with ethylene oxide or with propylene oxide effectively reduces microbial populations as much as 99 + % (Table 1), including some organisms considered to be public health hazards.[25, 30, 62, 81, 82, 83] Only a few sporeforming bacteria remain after treatment. Vegetative cells, including coliforms and *E. coli*, have consistently been absent after fumigation.[57] Current U.S. Food and Drug Administration (FDA) regulations limit the ethylene oxide residue to 50 ppm, and to 300 ppm propylene oxide in spices.[81]

Irradiation of spices with gamma rays has been shown to reduce the microbial population.[28, 85, 93] One study suggested that irradiation is by far the safest and most effective method of treatment, yielding no toxic products, and this method has been studied with hope for application in developing countries.[21, 85]

Soluble extracts of spices and seasonings may be plated onto polysaccharide carriers or encapsulated. Volatile flavors of black pepper, cinnamon, celery, cumin, onion, oregano, and garlic are retained, and the color of paprika and turmeric are protected against oxidation.[15, 36] These products exhibit very low aerobic plate counts and exceptionally long shelf life.

52.42 Gums

Although processing methods for many gums are proprietary, patents and other literature provide some insight. In general, tree gums secreted at wounds and incisions are colorless, but they darken on drying and aging. In acacia exudates, bacteria accumulate and grow and even contribute to the gum's thickening properties. Most tree gums are collected by hand, sorted, graded, packed, and shipped from the growing area. The processor further grades, cleans, mills, and blends the gum. Tragacanth gum is sold as ribbons, flakes, granules, or powder. Gum ghatti exudates are sun-dried and pulverized.

Carrageenan is extracted from red algae with hot water, filtered and concentrated, precipitated with alcohol, dried, and milled. A similar process is used to derive pectin from citrus peels. Gums such as carrageenan and pectin are then commonly standardized to provide the user with constant gelling and thickening properties. Standardization is often achieved by addition of sugar. The contribution of standardizing agents to the microbial status of gums should not be ignored.

Standard specifications for most gums are published, in the form of monographs, in Food Chemicals Codex, The National Formulary, and the U.S. Pharmacopoeia. Several of the latter monographs contain microbial limits, e.g., the alginates and carrageenan contain requirements that read, "The total bacterial count does not exceed 200 per g, and the tests for *Salmonella* species and *Escherichia coli* are negative." The negative test for *Salmonella* is a requirement common also to agar, pectin, and xanthan gums. The requirements for the latter also include the specification of a negative test for *Escherichia coli*.

52.5 SAMPLING AND PREPARATION FOR ANALYSIS

To undertake analysis of spices or gums, take 200-g samples from a minimum of five containers representing the shipment or lot to be examined, or use another suitable sampling plan.[39, 48] (Chapter 2). Aseptic technique is mandatory. Sterilize the sampling equipment after use. Many spice and gum materials may be sampled with a "trier" or "thief." Clean spoons, scoops, or similar implements may be used to sample whole nutmeg, whole ginger, and other root items, as well as cassia bark, which cannot be conveniently sampled by means of a trier or thief. Sampling of all ground spices is done most readily by means of a clean tablespoon. Place samples in individual sterile plastic bags, label clearly, and forward to the microbiological laboratory without delay. The laboratory should examine all five sample units separately, if possible, and composite only as a last resort when limited facilities or time prevent the recommended amount of testing. The laboratory should retain the individual samples for possible additional testing.

52.51 Procedures for Spices

Sample preparations and their initial dilution, as outlined below, are applicable to most of the routine microbiological examinations. Exceptions are those certain procedures that are not done routinely and methods used to detect *Salmonella* and *Shigella*.

1. Whole spice analysis
   a. Berries, seeds, herbs

Aseptically weigh an 11-g sample into a 4- or 8-oz widemouth polypropylene or glass bottle containing 99 mL sterile phosphate buffer.

Shake 5 min at 200 strokes per min with a mechanical shaker, such as Burrell wrist-action shaker.

Inoculate appropriate media within 15 min, mustard seed samples within 3 min.

   b. Roots or bark

Weigh 100 g of representative sample into a sterile, dry blender jar; blend the sample at the lowest setting for 30 sec or until a moderately fine particle size is attained.

Aseptically weigh 11-g sample into a 4- or 8-oz widemouth polypropylene or glass bottle containing 99 mL of sterile phosphate buffer.

Shake at least 25 times in a 1-ft arc.

Inoculate appropriate media within 15 min.

2. Analysis of ground spices, blends, or seasonings

Aseptically weigh 11 g of sample into a 4- or 8-oz widemouth polypropylene or glass bottle containing 99 mL of sterile phosphate buffer.

Shake at least 25 times in a 1-ft arc.

Inoculate appropriate media within 15 min.

52.52   Procedures for Gums

Weigh 5 to 12.5 g of sample (according to thickening power of gum) into a stomacher bag or other appropriate sterile container with 495 mL sterile phosphate buffered diluent or 0.1% peptone.

Stomach 2 min.

Dilute and inoculate standard media for aerobic plate count, staphylococci, enterococci (*S. faecalis*), *E. coli*, *Salmonella*, anaerobic sporeformers, yeasts, and molds.

52.6   METHODS

52.61   Spices

Since many spices contain essential oils and some of these are inhibitory to bacteria,[32, 33, 65] it is necessary to prepare decimal dilutions that are high enough to overcome the effect of the active compounds. Low dilutions may result in erroneous low counts when examining naturally inhibitory spices, especially ground mustard seed, cinnamon, cloves, onion powder, and garlic powder.

Essential oils produced by spices require initial dilutions for *Salmonella* to be increased over those suggested by recommended procedures. Toxicity tests in regard to *Salmonella* demonstrated that spice to pre-enrichment ratios of 1:1000 are necessary for cloves, pimiento, cinnamon, oregano, and mustard seed in order to test confidently for this organism of public health concern.[57]

52.62   Gums

In general, analysis of gums follows the standard procedures used in the microbiological examination of spices.[72, 73, 74]

52.63   Other Methods

    a. Aerobic plate count (Chapter 4)
    b. Molds and yeasts[7] (Chapter 16)
    c. Coliform bacteria[7, 70, 78, 79] (Chapter 24)
    d. MPN method (Chapter 6)
    e. Violet red bile agar coliform count
    f. *Escherichia coli* [7, 78, 79] (Chapter 24)
    g. *Salmonella* and *Shigella*[4, 7, 24, 78] (Chapters 25 and 26)

h. Aerobic sporeformers[7, 70] (Chapter 18)
i. Mesophiles (Chapter 19)
j. Thermophiles, including flat sours (Chapter 21)
k. Anaerobic sporeformers[7, 70] (Chapter 19)
l. Mesophiles (Chapter 20)
m. Thermophiles, including H^2S formers (Chapter 23)
n. Clostridium perfringens[72] (Chapter 37)
o. Supplementary tests[7, 70, 76]
p. Coagulase-positive staphylococci[7] (Chapter 33)
q. Enterococci[7] (Chapter 32)
r. Lactobacilli[7] (Chapter 15)

52.7 INTERPRETATION OF DATA

Spices and gums are exposed to mixed populations of microorganisms during their biological development, harvest, processing, and delivery to the marketplace. Organisms of public health significance are encountered occasionally in processed spices and gums. Large numbers of aerobic sporeforming microorganisms are found. These may be potential spoilage agents, or their activity may contribute to quality loss in foods in which they are used. Generally the microbial load of *Bacillus* spp. is high, and some common molds may be present. Toxigenic fungi can be isolated from some spices, but the occurrence of aflatoxins in processed spices is sporadic, and mycotoxin concentrations are very low.

Current recommendations from governmental, academic, and industrial microbiologists advocate the establishment of in-process controls to assure product integrity, rather than reliance on end-product testing for compliance with specifications.

The recent National Academy of Sciences Subcommittee on Microbiological Criteria for Foods and Food Ingredients extends the rationale for these recommendations.[76] The International Commission on Microbiological Specifications for Foods[40] has also endorsed this approach, recognizing the nature of gums and spices and the inappropriateness of arbitrary specifications.

While fumigation with ethylene oxide is permitted for spices in many countries, it is not permitted for gums. If needed, fumigation and microbial destruction can, however, be effectively achieved using propylene oxide for both gums and spices. The use of this agent is regulated by the FDA. Any particular lot can be exposed only once to the agent, with exposure time and temperature maxima of 24 hr and 125°F, respectively. Residues are limited to a maximum of 300 ppm propylene oxide.

Fumigation, where permitted, and selective heat treatments of spices and gums are extremely effective in the reduction of microbial populations, often achieving near-sterilization of the products.

52.8   REFERENCES

1. Anderson, E. C., Esselen, W. B. Jr., and Handleman, A. R. 1953. The effect of essential oils on the inhibition and thermal resistance of microorganisms in acid food products. Food Res. 14: 499.
2. Andres, C. 1975. Stabilizers 1. Gums. Food Proc. 36 (12): 31.
3. Andres, C. 1976. Stabilizers 2. Gums. Food Proc. 37(1): 83.
4. Andrews, W. H., Wagner, D., and Roetting, M. J. 1979. Detection of *Salmonella* in Onion and Garlic Powders: Collaborative Study. J. Assn. Offic. Anal. Chem. 62: 499.
5. AOAC. 1980. "Official Methods of Analysis," 13th ed., p. 836. Assn. Offic. Anal. Chem., Washington, D.C.
6. ASTA. 1971. Cleanliness Specifications for Unprocessed Spices, Seeds and Herbs. Amer. Spice Trade Assn., Inc., Englewood Cliffs, N.J.
7. ASTA. 1976. Official Microbiological Methods, 1st ed., ed. P. A. Guarino, P. C. Verrioli, and J. J. Peppler. Amer. Spice Trade Assn., Inc., Englewood Cliffs, N.J.
8. Baxter, R. and Holzapfel, W. H. 1982. A Microbial Investigation of Selected Spices, Herbs, and Additives in South Africa. J. Food. Sci. 47: 570.
9. Bayusik, M. J. and Chen, P. H. 1980. Method of Sterilizing Spices. U.S. Patent 4,210,678.
10. Beljaars, P. R., Schumans, J. C. H. M., and Koken, P. J. 1975. Quantitative fluorodensitometric determination and survey of aflatoxins in nutmeg. J. Assn. Offic. Anal. Chem. 58: 263.
11. Bishov, S. J., Masouka, Y., and Kapsalis, J. G. 1977. Antioxidant effect of spices, herbs and protein hydrolyzates in freeze-dried model systems: Synergistic action with synthetic phenolic antioxidants. J. Food Proc. Preserv. 1: 153.
12. Blanshard, J. M. V. and Mitchell, J. R. 1979. "Polysaccharides in Food." Butterworth, Inc., Woburn, Mass.
13. Blum, H. B. and Fabian, F. W. 1943. Spice oils and their components for controlling microbial surface growth. Food Prod. J. 22: 326.
14. Bullerman, L. B., Lieu, F. Y., and Seier, S. A. 1977. Inhibition of growth and aflatoxin production by cinnamon and clove oils. J. Food Sci. 42: 1107.
15. Burns, T. F. 1980. Spice quality control. Meat Processing. 19: 16.
16. Cadmus, M. C., Jackson, L. K., Burton, K. A., Plattner, R. D., and Slodki, M. E. 1982. Biodegradation of xanthan gum by Bacillus sp. Appl. Environ. Microbiol. 44: 5.
17. Carnevale, J., Cole, E. R., and Crank, G. 1980. Photocatalyzed oxidation of paprika pigments. J. Agric. Food Chem. 28: 953.
18. Christensen, C. M., Fanse, H. A., Nelson, G. H., Bates, F., and Mirochia, C. J. 1967. Microflora of black and red pepper. Appl. Microbiol. 15: 622.
19. Cottrell, I. W. and Baird, J. K. 1980. Gums. In "Kirk-Othmer Encyclopedia of Chemical Technology," 3rd ed. Vol. 12, p. 45. John Wiley & Sons, Inc., New York.
20. de Boer, E., Spiegelenberg, W., and Janssen, F. 1985. Microbiology of Spices and Herbs. Antonie van Leeuwenhoek J. Microbiol. Serol. 51: 435.
21. FAO/IAEA Div. of Atomic Energy in Food & Agr. 1973. "Aspects of the Introduction of Food Irradiation in Developing Countries." UN Food and Agri. Org./Internl. Atom. Energy Agency, Vienna, Austria.
22. Flannigan, B. and Hui, S. C. 1976. Occurrence of aflatoxin-producing strains of *Aspergillus flavus* in the mold floras of ground spices. J. Appl. Bacteriol. 41: 411.
23. Foster, E. M. 1971. The control of salmonellae in processed foods: A classification system and sampling plan. J. Assn. Offic. Anal. Chem. 54(2): 259.
24. Frazier, W. C. and Westhoff, D. C. 1978. "Food Microbiology, 3rd ed. McGraw-Hill, New York.
25. Glicksman, M. 1969. "Gum Technology in the Food Industries." Academic Press, New York.

26. Glicksman, M. 1982. "Food Hydrocolloids." CRC Press, Boca Raton, Fla.

27. Goepfert, J. M., Spira, W. M., and Kim, H. U. 1972. Bacillus cereus: Food poisoning organism. A review. J. Milk Food Technol. 35: 213.

28. Gottschalk, H. M. 1977. A review on spices. In "Food Irradiation Information," ed. W. T. Potter, P. S. Elias, and H. M. Gottschalk. Inter. Project Field Food Irradiat. No. 7, p. 7. Institute Strahlentechnologie, Karlsruhe, West Germany.

29. Guarino, P. A. 1973. Microbiology of Spices, Herbs and Related Materials. Spec. Rep. No. 13, Proc. 7th Annual Symposium, Fungi and Foods, p. 16. N.Y. State Agri. Experiment Stat., Geneva, N.Y.

30. Guarino, P. A. and Peppler, H. J. 1976. Spices and Condiments. In "Compendium of Methods for the Microbiological Examination of Foods," ed. M. L. Speck, Am. Pub. Health Assn., Washington, D.C.

31. Guenther, E. 1949. "The Essential Oils," Vol. 2. Van Nostrand, New York.

32. Guenther, E. 1950. "The Essential Oils," Vol. 4. Van Nostrand, New York.

33. Hall, R. L. 1974. Toxicants occurring naturally in spices and flavors. In "Toxicants Occurring Naturally in Foods." Committee on Food Prot. Nat. Res. Coun., Nat. Acad. of Sciences, Washington, D.C.

34. Hannigan, K. J. 1980. Spices: Changes ahead. Food Eng. 52(6): 47.

35. Hauschild, A. H. W. 1973. Food poisoning by Clostridium perfringens. Can. Inst. Food Sci. Technol. J. 6(2): 106.

36. Havighorst, C. R. 1980. Spice "secrets." Food Eng. 52(6): 52.

37. Hitokoto, H., Morozumi, S., Wauka, T., Sakai, S., and Kurata, H. 1980. Inhibitory effects of spices on growth and toxin production in toxigenic fungi. Appl. Environ. Microbiol. 39: 818.

38. Huth, H. 1972. Method for Manufacturing Practically Sterile, Concentrated Aromas of Spices, Vegetables and Mushrooms. U.S. Patent 3,681,090.

39. ICMSF. 1974. "Microorganisms in Foods 2," ed. F. S. Thatcher and D. S. Clark 2. Sampling for Microbiological Analysis: Principles and Specific Applications. Intern. Comm. on Microbiol. Spec. for Foods., Univ. Toronto Press, Toronto, Ont., Can.

40. ICMSF. 1986. "Micro-organisms in Foods 2," 2nd ed.: Sampling for Microbiological Analysis: Principles and Specific Applications. Univ. Toronto Press, Toronto, Ont., Can.

41. IOS. 1972. Spices and Condiments. Nomenclature Finalized Draft Proposal. TC-34/SC-7 (Secretariat 107) 252E, Second List, Internl. Org. for Standardization, Budapest, Hungary.

42. Julseth, R. M. and Deibel, R. H. 1974. Microbial profile of selected spices and herbs at import. J. Milk Food Technol. 37: 414.

43. Kang, K. S. and Cottrell, I. W. 1979. Polysaccharides. In "Microbial Technology," 2nd ed., ed. H.J. Peppler and D. Perlman, Vol. 1, p. 417. Academic Press, New York.

44. Kennedy, J. F., Phillips, G. O., Wedlock, D. J., and Williams, P. A. 1985. Cellulose and Its Derivatives, John Wiley & Sons, New York.

45. Kim, H. U. and Goepfert, J. M. 1971. Occurrence of Bacillus cereus in selected dry food products. J. Milk Food Technol. 34: 12.

46. Kirshnaswamy, M. A., Patel, J. D., and Parthasarathy, N. 1971. Enumeration of micro-organisms in spices and spice mixtures. J. Food Sci. Technol. 8(4): 191.

47. Koedam, A. 1977. Animikobielle Wirksamkeit aetherischer Oelle. Riechst. Aromen, Kosmet. 27(1): 6; 27(2): 36.

48. Kramer, A. and Twigg, B. 1973. "Quality Control for the Food Industry," 3rd ed. Vols. 1 and 2. AVI Publ. Co., Westport, Conn.

49. Laserna, E. C., Uyenco, F., Epifanio, E., Veroy, R. L., and Cajipe, G. J. B. 1981. Carrageenan from Eucheuma striatum (Schmitz) in media for fungal and yeast culture. Appl. Environ. Microbiol. 42: 174.

50. Llewellyn, G. C., Burkett, M. L., and Eadie, T. 1981. Potential mold growth, aflatoxin and antimycotic activity of selected natural spices and herbs. J. Assn. Offic. Anal. Chem. 64: 955.

51. Marsh, A. C., Moss, M. K., and Murphy, E. W. 1977. "Composition of Foods, Spices, and Herbs. Raw, Processed, Prepared." Agriculture Handbook No. 8-2. Agric. Research Serv., U.S. Dept. of Agric., U.S. Govt. Print. Off., Washington, D.C.

52. McCormick, R. D. 1981. U.S. must be allowed to catch up with foreign lead in irradiation. Food Develop. 15(6): 7.

53. Morozumi, S. 1978. Isolation, purification and antibiotic activity of o-methoxycinnamalde-hyde from cinnamon. Appl. Environ. Microbiol. 36: 577.

54. Nes, I. F. and Skjelvale, R. 1982. Effect of natural spices and oleoresins on *Lactobacillus plantarum* in the fermentation of dry sausage. J. Food Sci. 47: 1618.

55. NHW (Canada). 1977. Proposed Amends. to the Food and Drug Act and Regs., Natl. Health and Welfare, Ottawa, Ont., Can.

56. NHW (Canada). 1978. Ethylene Oxide. Item E. 1 in Division 16, Table 8, p. 57. Food and Drug Act and Regs., Natl. Health and Welfare, Ottawa, Ont., Can.

57. Pafumi, J. 1986. Assessment of the Microbiological Quality of Spices and Herbs. J. Food Prot. 49: 958.

58. Parry, J. W. 1969a. "Spices," Vol. 1. Chem. Publ. Co., New York.

59. Parry, J. W. 1969b. "Spices," Vol. 2, 2nd ed. Chem. Publ. Co., New York.

60. Pivnick, H. 1980. Spices. In "Microbial Ecology of Foods," Vol. 2, p. 731. Academic Press, New York.

61. Powers, E. M., Lawyer, R., and Masuoka, Y. 1975. Microbiology of processed spices. J. Milk Food Technol. 38: 683.

62. Powers, E. M., Latt, T. G., and Brown, T. 1976. Incidence and levels of *Bacillus cereus* in processed spices. J. Milk Food Technol. 39: 668.

63. Pruthi, J. W. 1976. "Spices and Condiments," 1st ed. Natl. Book Trust, New Delhi, India.

64. Pruthi, J. S. 1980. "Spices and Condiments: Chemistry, Microbiology, Technology." Adv. Food Research Suppl. No. 4. Academic Press, New York.

65. Rhodes, M. E. 1979. "Food Mycology." G. K. Hall & Co., Boston, Mass.

66. Sair, L. 1972. Ground Spice Product. U.S. Patent 3,647,487.

67. Schwab, A. H., et al. (1982). Microbiological quality of some spices and herbs in retail markets. Appl. Environ. Microbiol. 44: 627.

68. Scott, P. M. and Kennedy, B. P. C. 1975. Analysis of spices and herbs for aflatoxins. Can. Inst. Food Sci. Technol. J. 8(2): 124.

69. Shelef, L. A., Naglik, O. A., and Bogen, D. W. 1980. Sensitivity of some common food-borne bacteria to the spices sage, rosemary and allspice. J. Food Sci. 45: 1042.

70. Skinner, F. A. and Lovelock, D. W. eds., 1979. "Identification Methods for Microbiologists," 2nd ed. Academic Press, London, England.

71. Souw, P. and Rehm, H. J. 1973. Investigations on microorganisms in thickening agents. I. Cell counts of aerobic microorganisms. Chem. Mikrobiol. Technol. Lebensm. 2(6): 187.

72. Souw, P. and Rehm, H. J. 1975a. II. Cell counts of anaerobic sporeformers. Chem. Mikrobiol. Technol. Lebensm. 4(3): 71.

73. Souw, P. and Rehm, H. J. 1975b. III. Survival of *Escherichia coli, Streptococcus faecalis*, and *Staphylococcus aureus* in dried thickening agents. Chem. Microbiol. Technol. Lebensm. 4: 97.

74. Souw, P. and Rehm, H. J. 1975c. IV. Microbial degradation of three plant exudates and two seaweed extracts. Z. Lebensm. Unters.-Forsch. 159(5): 297.

75. Souw, P. and Rehm, H. J. 1976. V. Degradation of the galactomannans guar gum and locust bean gum by different bacilli. European J. Appl. Microbiol. 2: 47.

76. Subcom. of Microbiol. Criteria. 1985. "An Evaluation of the Role of Microbiological Criteria for Foods and Food Ingredients." National Academy of Sciences. National Acad. Press, Washington, D.C.

77. Swientek, R. J. 1981. Rapid bacteria identification kits gaining food industry acceptance. Food Proc. 43(4): 160.

78. Thatcher, F. S. and Clark, D. S., eds., 1968. "Microorganisms in Foods: I. Their significance and methods of enumeration." Univ. of Toronto Press, Toronto, Ont., Can.
79. Tynecka, Z. and Gos, Z. 1973. Inhibitory action of garlic (*Allium sativum*) on growth and respiration of some microorganisms. Acta Microbiol. Pol. Ser. B. 5: 51.
80. USDA. 1987. Teas, Spices, and Essential Oils. Foreign Agriculture Circular. U.S. Dept. of Agric., Washington, D.C.
81. USHEW. 1977. Ethylene Oxide. Tolerances for Residues. 40 CFR 180.151. U.S. Food and Drug. Admin., Dept. Health, Ed., and Welfare, Washington, D.C.
82. USHEW. 1978a. Ethylene Oxide. 21 CFR 193.200. U.S. Food and Drug Admin., Dept. Health, Ed., and Welfare, Washington, D.C.
83. USHEW. 1978b. Propylene Oxide. 21 CFR 193.380. U.S. Food and Drug Admin., Dept. Health, Ed., and Welfare, Washington, D.C.
84. USHEW. 1978c. Spices and Other Natural Seasonings. 21 CFR 182.10, U.S. Food and Drug Admin., Dept. Health, Ed., and Welfare, Washington, D.C.
85. Vajdi, M. and Pepeira, R. R. 1978. Comparative effects of ethylene oxide, gamma irradiation and microwave treatments on selected spices. J. Food Sci. 38: 393.
86. Weber, F. E. 1980a. Controlling microorganisms in spices. Cereal Foods World 25: 319.
87. Weber, F. E. 1980b. Ethylene oxide still most effective spice sterilant. Food. Eng. 52(5): 171.
88. Weiser, H. H., Mountney, G. J., and Gould, W. A. 1971. "Practical Food Microbiology and Technology," 2nd ed. AVI Publ. Co., Westport, Conn.
89. Whistler, R. L. and Zysk, J. R. 1978. Carbohydrates. In "Kirk-Othmer Encyclopedia of Chemical Technology," 3rd ed. Vol. 4, p. 535. John Wiley & Sons, New York.
90. Wright, W. J., Bice, C. W., and Fogelberg, J. M. 1954. The effect of spices on yeast fermentation. Cereal Chem. 31: 100.
91. Zaika, L. L. and Kissinger, J. C. 1981. Inhibitory and stimulatory effects of oregano on *Lactobacillus plantarum* and *Pediococcus cerevisiae*. J. Food Sci. 46: 1205.
92. Zaika, L. L., Zell, T. E., Palumbo, S. A., and Smith, J. L. 1978. Effect of spices and salt on fermentation of Lebanon bologna-type sausage. J. Food Sci. 43: 186.
93. Zehnder, H. J., Ettel, W., and Jokob, M. 1979. Zur Keimverminderung bei Gewuerzen mit Hilfe ionisierender Strahlen. Alimenta 18: 43.

Chapter 53

SALAD DRESSINGS

R. B. Smittle and M. C. Cirigliano

53.1 INTRODUCTION

Commercially manufactured salad dressings began to appear on the American market around 1912.[41] Mayonnaise, cooked starch-based dressings resembling mayonnaise, and pourable dressings are the types of salad dressings most commonly marketed. Sufficient cooking to sterilize would destroy the physical integrity of these products; thus, preservation usually depends on the vinegar (acetic acid) or lemon juice present. Acetic acid concentration in excess of 1.5% makes a product unpalatable, but a concentration much below this level may permit spoilage. Worrell[41] suggests that the shelf life of properly prepared mayonnaise is between 3 and 6 months. However, it is common in the salad dressing and mayonnaise industry to have a 9- to 12-month shelf life. The shelf life of commercial mayonnaise and salad dressing is largely dictated by the physical and chemical characteristics of the product as opposed to the microbiological stability.

53.2 GENERAL CONSIDERATIONS

Mayonnaise is a creamy, pale yellow food with a mild to tangy flavor. The pH range is usually from 3.6 to 4.0, which is mainly due to the product's containing 0.5% to 1.2% acetic acid. Acetic acid, and occasionally other organic acids, are important for flavoring and are also the primary preservative agents. However, sodium benzoate and potassium sorbate are also frequently included as preservatives. The oil content (U.S.A.) ranges from 65% to 80%.[31, 32] In the aqueous phase, the salt (NaCl) content is about 9.0% to 11.0%, and sugar usually represents 7.0% to 10.1%. The water activity (a_w) of a typical dressing with 12% salt is around 0.925. Traditionally, mayonnaise

975

and salad dressings have been manufactured with oil, vinegar, water, and various flavor ingredients such as tomato, spices, sugar, and vegetable pieces. Today, salad dressings range from the traditional Italian type (two-phase high acetic acid and high oil levels) to the refrigerated spoonable type containing fresh dairy ingredients. In the 1980s, a trend has developed toward the manufacture of less tart (reduced vinegar), low calorie (reduced oil) products. Two significant microbiological consequences occur with both of these reductions. First, as the acetic acid content decreases, the pH of the product is raised. Higher pH levels create a more microbiologically unstable product. Second, as the oil content decreases, the water phase is increased, which in turn decreases the salt and the organic acid concentration in the water phase. This water phase is the critical microbiological concern.

53.3   NORMAL FLORA

The microorganisms in salad dressings come from the ingredients, from manufacturing equipment, and from the air. Few species are able to survive the low pH of salad dressings, and these few generally appear in low numbers.[7, 19] Bachmann[2] isolated *Bacillus subtilis*, *B. mesentericus* (*B. pumilis* and *B. subtilis*),[9] micrococci, a diplococcus, and a mold from several types of unspoiled dressings. Fabian and Wethington[7] found no thermophiles, coliforms, or lipolytic bacteria, and only a few yeasts in 103 samples of unspoiled dressings. Some dressings contained a few molds. Of 10 unspoiled dressings examined by Kurtzman et al.,[19] nine appeared sterile, and one contained *B. subtilis* and *B. licheniformis*, but with fewer than 50 organisms per g.

53.4   FLORAL CHANGE IN SPOILAGE

The microflora causing salad dressings to spoil seems quite restricted and ordinarily consists of a few species of *Lactobacillus*, *Saccharomyces*, and *Zygosaccharomyces*. Typically, the spoilage organisms of mayonnaise have been a few species of *Hansenula*, *Pichia*, *Geotrichium*, *Saccharomyces*, and *Lactobacillus*.[27] The source of spoilage organisms generally can be traced to unsanitary equipment such as infrequently cleaned mixing, pumping, and filling machines. Perhaps such equipment is contaminated initially by low levels of spoilage organisms from ingredients and, rarely, from aerosols created during cleaning. Surface spoilage of dressings may also result from airborne contaminants. Mold and film yeasts have on occasion been encountered on dressings with large headspaces or improperly torqued caps, where increased amounts of air were available for their growth.[27]

Mayonnaise and other salad dressings spoil for a variety of reasons: separation of emulsion, oxidation, and hydrolysis of the oils by strictly chemical processes and from the growth of microorganisms.[8, 12, 37]

Microbiological spoilage is frequently manifested by gas formation that forces out the dressing when the container is opened. Other indicators of spoilage, such as off-flavor and change in color, odor, or texture, may occur. Iszard,[13, 14, 15] one of the first to report microbiological spoilage of mayonnaise, demonstrated *B. petasites* (*B. megaterium*)[9] as the cause. Spoilage of a Thousand Island dressing was caused by *B. vulgatus* (*B. subtilis*),[22] and the source of contamination was found to be the pepper and paprika used in the formulation. Mayonnaise and dressings, as they are now produced, would probably not be spoiled by Bacillus spp. because of their generally low pH and high acetic acid contents.

Lactobacillus fructivorans was first isolated from spoiled salad dressing,[4] and later proved to be a common spoilage organism[19] that required special isolation media. Cirigliano[5] and Smittle[27] have reported that salad dressings are frequently spoiled by *L. plantarum*, *L. buchneri*, *L. fermentum*, *L. brevis*, *L. fructivorans*, and on occasion by *L. cellobiosus*.

Yeasts frequently cause spoilage in a variety of dressings. Fabian and Wethington[6] found a species of *Saccharomyces* in spoiled French dressing and mayonnaise, and Williams and Mrak[40] showed that a yeast similar to *Saccharomyces globiformis* (*S. bailii?*) caused spoilage of a starch-base dressing. Two-thirds of the spoiled dressing samples examined by Kurtzman et al.[19] contained *S. bailii* (*Zygosaccharomyces bailii*). Since the samples came from widely separated areas of the United States, this suggests *S. bailii* to be the yeast primarily responsible for dressing spoilage. Appleman et al.[1] found a mixture of *B. subtilis* and *Saccharomyces* sp. responsible in one instance of mayonnaise spoilage. *S. bailii* and *L. plantarum* were present in high numbers in a blue cheese dressing.[19]

53.5   HUMAN DISEASE MICROORGANISMS

The survival of pathogenic microorganisms in salad dressings and mayonnaise has been investigated by numerous workers. When Wethington and Fabian[38] inoculated salad dressing with *Salmonella* and *Staphylococcus*, they found that survival time depended on product pH. At pH 5.0, one strain of *Staphylococcus* survived 168 hr, but at pH 3.2 survival was limited to 30 hr. The longest survival time for *Salmonella* in dressing was 144 hr at pH 5.0, and 6 hr at pH 3.2. Similar data have been reported by other investigators.[11, 17, 26] Vladimirov and Nefedieva[36] reported *Escherichia coli* was able to survive one day in mayonnaise, and the data of Bachmann[2] suggested survival of no more than 10 days. Smittle[26] reviewed the literature concerning the microbiology of these products and concluded that mayonnaise and salad dressing prepared according to the U.S. Food and Drug Administration (FDA) Standard of Identity[31, 32] are bactericidal to the vegetative cells of *Salmonella*, *Staphylococcus aureus*, *Clostridium botulinum*, *Clostridium perfringens*, *Streptococcus viridans*, *Shigella flexneri*, and *Bacillus cereus*. Furthermore, he concluded that mayonnaise of pH 4.1 or less (0.25% acetic acid) ensures a bacteriologically safe product.[26] Recent FDA regulatory activity has reflected a concern for *Candida krusei* and *Candida pseudotropicalis*, two opportunistic yeast pathogens in pourable dressings.[33, 34]

53.6   MICROBIAL INDICATORS OF POOR SANITATION

Microorganisms tolerant of the conditions existing in salad dressings are used as indicators of poor sanitation. Not only are a few selected organisms capable of growing in the undiluted product, but some can grow to large populations in the diluted product as encountered in improperly cleaned and sanitized equipment. Three groups of organisms are commonly used as microbial indicators. They are the yeasts and molds, lactobacilli, and aerobic bacilli. High numbers of these groups are indicative of poor sanitation and potential spoilage problems. Specifically, the presence of any spoilage organism at any level is unacceptable. Since most yeasts and molds, and lactobacilli introduced in low numbers, die quickly, salad dressings and mayonnaise usually contain <10 per g of these organisms. Any persistence or increase in numbers to > 10 per g should be a warning of a sanitation problem.

When salad dressings become diluted, bacteria can grow. However, when diluted material containing bacteria is mixed with undiluted product, the vegetative cells of most bacteria usually die quickly unless acid or preservative adaptation has taken place. Usually, only bacterial spores survive, and these are detected using standard plating procedures. These spores remain viable almost indefinitely. The presence of aerobic bacilli in excess of 50 per g should be considered indicative of a sanitation problem. The exception to this discussion is salad dressings containing unprocessed (unheated) cheese or other cultured dairy products (e.g., cream and buttermilk). Cheeses and other fermented dairy products containing live molds and cultured bacteria must have their own set of standards, which need to be individually determined. All of these indicators are minimized by using microbiologically acceptable ingredients and by cleaning and sanitizing equipment properly. Areas of particular concern are pumps, mixing and filling equipment, and product transfer lines. The implementation of frequent CIP and CPD cleaning regimens, as well as the periodic breakdown of all equipment and replacement of worn gaskets and O-rings, is recommended, particularly where the manufacture of sensitive low-acid salad dressings is involved.

53.7   EQUIPMENT, MATERIALS, AND SOLUTIONS

53.71   Equipment

Balance
Glass slides and coverglasses
Incubator, 22° to 28°C

Incubator, 35°C
Lab stomacher bags
Metal spatulas
Microscope
Petri dishes
Pipettes
Quebec Colony Counter

53.72   Materials and Solutions (Chapter 62)

Butterfield's buffered phosphate diluent
Carbon dioxide
Crystal violet, 0.5%
Fructose (for MRS agar)
Gram stain reagents
Lactobacillus heterofermentative screen broth
MRS agar
0.1% peptone water
Plate count agar (PCA)
Potato dextrose agar (PDA), pH 3.5
PDA with antibiotics

53.8   RECOMMENDED METHODS

53.81   Sample Preparation

Stir sample with a sterile glass rod or a sterile metal spatula; place 50 g into a sterile stomacher bag. Add enough diluent to prepare a 1:10 dilution using sterile phosphate buffer or 0.1% peptone water and treat for 2 min. Make subsequent dilutions to 10^6 with phosphate buffer or peptone water.[19, 30]

53.82   Yeasts and Molds

For isolation, use PDA agar (Chapter 62) with 100 mg/L of chlortetracycline HCl and chloramphenicol to inhibit bacteria. Incubate plates at 25° ± 5°C and examine at 3 and 5 days. As an alternative, use PDA (Chapter 62) acidified with 10% tartaric acid to at least pH 3.5.

53.83   Aerobic Bacteria

For isolation, use PCA containing 100 μg/ml of cycloheximide for inhibition of fungi. Some yeasts, not likely to be found in salad dressings, are resistant to this level of cycloheximide. Incubate plates at 28° to 35°C, and examine at 2 and 5 days.[19]

53.84   Lactobacilli

Fastidious lactobacilli such as *Lactobacillus fructivorans L. brevis* cannot be detected easily on PCA, but they are readily isolated on *Lactobacillus*-selective MRS agar.[3, 20, 23] Incubate plates of MRS agar supplemented with 0.5% fructose at 20° to 28°C in a carbon dioxide-enriched atmosphere and examine at 3, 5, and 14 days.[29] The use of a carbon dioxide-enriched atmosphere generally shortens the incubation time.[28] The CO_2 necessary for incubation can be obtained by flushing the incubation container with CO_2 from a gas cylinder or generating CO_2 with commercially available devices. Alternatively, overlay and incubate MRS agar plates at 20° to 28°C, and examine at 5, 7, and 14 days.

53.85   Heterofermentative Screen

To screen salad dressings and ingredients for acetophilic bacteria, pipette 1 ml of 1:10 dilution into each of 3 *Lactobacillus* heterofermentative screen broth tubes. Incubate tubes at 32°C for 72 hr ± 2 hr. Positive tubes have trapped CO_2 in the Durham tube or bubbles of CO_2 clinging to the inside of the tube and a color change from green to yellow indicating acid production.

Perform a gram stain or wet mount to verify the presence or absence of yeasts. This procedure can also be used as a yeast screen by omitting the actidione from the formula followed by staining and isolation on PDA for confirmation.

53.86   Coliforms, fecal coliforms, *E. coli, Salmonella* , and *Staphylococcus aureus, Listeria monocytogenes,* and *Yersinia enterocolitica*

If mayonnaise and salad dressings are suspected of causing illness, they should be examined for coliforms, including *E. coli* (Chapter 24), *Salmonella* spp. (Chapter 25), *Staphylococcus aureus* (Chapter 33), *Listeria monocytogenes* (Chapter 38), and *Yersinia enterocolitica* (Chapter 27). Because of their acidity, the products should first be neutralized. Product pH and total acidity should also be measured.

53.87   Microscopic Observation of Dressings

Yeasts and bacteria are readily stained for microscopic observation by using crystal violet. A small drop of 0.5% crystal violet may be mixed directly with the product on a microscope slide or mixed with a drop of the product diluted 1:10 with distilled water.

53.88   Identification of Spoilage Microorganisms

Yeasts can be identified by the culture techniques of Wickerham[39] and the classification systems found in "The Yeasts."[18] Criteria for identification of Lactobacillus can be found in "Bergey's Manual"[16] and in papers by Rogosa and Sharpe,[25] Charlton et al.,[4] Vaughn et al.,[35] Kurtzman et al.,[19] and Smittle and Flowers.[28] Species of *Bacillus* can be identified on the basis of the scheme presented by Gordon et al.[9]

53.9 INTERPRETATION OF DATA

Sometimes obviously spoiled dressings contain few viable microorganisms (fewer than 10^2 per g) or none at all. In these instances, the microorganisms had probably died after the nutrients were exhausted or after the accumulation of metabolic byproducts. A direct microscopic examination will usually reveal the dead cells. If even a few cells are seen per field, this sighting indicates that large populations of viable organisms were present in the dressing at one time and were probably responsible for the spoilage observed.

Gaseous fermentation may not be evident in spoiled dressings until several weeks after manufacture. *Lactobacillus fructivorans* and other lactobacilli grow slowly, and considerable time is needed for microbial population increase and visible gas buildup. Some spoilage may be observed only by an increase in acid or a flavor change, especially spoilage from the homofermentative lactobacilli, such as *L. casei* and *L. plantarum*. This slow growth is particularly evident on isolation plates; 10 to 14 days may elapse before colonies are observed.[19] It seems likely that this slow growth, as well as failure to use the proper isolation medium, may account for the relatively few reports of *L. fructivorans* in spoiled salad dressings.

Zygosaccharomyces bailii and certain other haploid species of *Zygosaccharomyces* ferment fructose and glucose quickly, but may give a delayed fermentation of sucrose.[19, 21] This explains the long delay between manufacture and spoilage of products contaminated with these yeasts when sucrose is the sweetener. Kurtzman et al.[19] showed that 9 out of 13 strains of *S. bailii* (*Z. bailii*)[18] from spoiled dressings fermented sucrose vigorously, but fermentation did not begin until 12 to 56 days after inoculation.

Salad dressings average approximately pH 4 (3.0 to 4.6)[7, 19] because of their acetic content, and this acidity accounts for the absence of food poisoning microorganisms. Dressings formulated at a significantly higher pH should be examined for the presence of food poisoning microorganisms. Mixing of dressings into meat, potato, and similar salads dilutes the acetic acid so that its inhibitory properties may be diminished.[10] Nevertheless, mayonnaise and salad dressings frequently retain much of their inhibitory characteristic when mixed with meat and vegetables,[10, 24, 26] and Smittle[26] recommended that when these ingredients are to be used in salads, they should be mixed with the salads as soon as possible to retard microbial growth.

53.10 REFERENCES

1. Appleman, M. D., Hess, E. P., and Rittenberg, S. C. 1949. An investigation of a mayonnaise spoilage. Food Technol. 3: 201.

2. Bachmann, F. M. 1928. A bacteriological study of salad dressings. Wisc. Acad. Sci. Arts Lett., Trans 23: 529.

3. Carr, J. G. 1975. VI.3 Lactics of the world unite. In "Lactic Acid Beverages and Food," ed. J. G. Carr, C. V. Cutting, and G. C. Whiting, p. 369. Academic Press, New York.

4. Charlton, D. B., Nelson, M. E., and Werkman, C. H. 1934. Physiology of *Lactobacillus fructivorans* sp. nov. isolated from spoiled salad dressings. Iowa State J. Sci. 9: 1.

5. Cirigliano, M. C. 1985. Microbiological hazards to processing. Presented at Sanitation Seminar, Sept. 1985. Assn. for Dressings and Sauces, Atlanta, Ga.

6. Fabian, F. W. and Wethington, M. C. 1950a. Spoilage in salad and French dressing due to yeasts. Food Res. 15: 135.

7. Fabian, F. W. and Wethington, M. C. 1950b. Bacterial and chemical analyses of mayonnaise, salad dressing, and related products. Food Res. 15: 138.

8. Frazier, W. C. 1967. "Food Microbiology," p. 537. McGraw-Hill, New York.

9. Gordon, R. E., Haynes, W. C., and Pang, C. H-N. 1973. The Genus *Bacillus*. Agric. Handbook No. 427. U.S. Dept. Agric., Washington, D.C.

10. Gould, S., Woolford, A., Rappaport, H., and Goepfert, J. M. 1976. Factors affecting the behavior of *Salmonella* and *Staphylococci* in meat salad. Annual Report 1976. Food Res. Inst., Madison, Wisc.

11. Gram, H. G. 1957. Abtotung von *Salmonellen*, *Staphylococcus aureus*, *B. proteus*, und *B. alkaligenes* durch mayonnaise. Fleischwirtsch 9: 111.

12. Gray, H. G. 1927. Bacterial spoilage in mayonnaise, relishes, and spreads. Canning Age 8: 643.

13. Iszard, M. S. 1927a. The value of lactic acid in the preservation of mayonnaise dressing and other dressings. Canning Age 8: 434.

14. Iszard, M. S. 1927b. The value of lactic acid in the preservation of mayonnaise dressing and other products. J. Bacteriol. 13: 57.

15. Iszard, M. S. 1927c. Supplementary report on the use of lactic acid as a preservative in mayonnaise and allied products. Spice Mill 50: 2426.

16. Kandler, O. and Weiss, N. 1986. Regular, nonsporing gram-positive rods. In "Bergey's Manual of Systemic Bacteriology," ed. J. G. Holt, Vol. 2, p. 1208. Williams and Wilkins, Baltimore, Md.

17. Kintner, T. C. and Mangel, M. 1953. Survival of staphylococci and salmonellae experimentally inoculated into salad dressing prepared with dried eggs. Food Res. 18: 6.

18. Kreger-van Rij, N. J. W. "The Yeasts, a Taxonomic Study," 3rd ed. North-Holland Publishing Co., Amsterdam, Holland.

19. Kurtzman, C. P., Rogers, R., and Hesseltine, C. W. 1971. Microbiological spoilage of mayonnaise and salad dressings. Appl. Microbiol. 21: 870.

20. Lawrence, D. R. and Leedham, P. A. 1979. Detection of lactic acid bacteria. J. Inst. Brew. 85: 119.

21. Pappagianis, D. and Phaff, H. J. 1956. Delayed fermentation of sucrose by certain haploid species of *Saccharomyces*. Antonie van Leeuwenhoek J. Microbiol. Serol. 22: 353.

22. Pederson, C. S. 1930. Bacterial spoilage of a Thousand Island dressing. J. Bacteriol. 20: 99.

23. Peladan, F., Erbs, D., and Moll, M. 1986. Practical aspects of detection of lactic bacteria in beer. Food Microbiol. 3: 281.

24. Rappaport, H. and Goepfert, J. M. 1975. Behavior of *Salmonella* and *Staphylococcus aureus*. Annual Report 1975. Food Res. Inst., Madison, Wisc.

25. Rogosa, M. and Sharpe, M. E. 1959. An approach to the classification of the lactobacilli. J. Appl. Bacteriol. 22: 329.

26. Smittle, R. B. 1977. Microbiology of mayonnaise and salad dressing: A review. J. Food Protection. 40: 415.

27. Smittle, R. B. 1987. The microbiology of dressings and sauces. Presented at Microbiology Quality Assurance Seminar, Sept. 1987. Assn. for Dressings and Sauces, Atlanta, Ga.

28. Smittle, R. B. and Flowers, R. M. 1982. Acid tolerant microorganisms involved in the spoilage of salad dressings. J. Food Protection. 45: 977.

29. Splittstoesser, D. F., Lienk, L. L., Wilkinson, M., and Stamer, J. R. 1975. Influence of wine composition on the heat resistance of potential spoilage organisms. Appl. Microbiol. 30: 369.

30. Straka, R. P. and Stokes, J. L. 1957. Rapid destruction of bacteria in commonly used diluents and its elimination. Appl. Microbiol. 5: 21.

31. U.S. FDA. 1975a. 21 CFR 25.1, Food and Drug Admin. Govt. Print. Off., Washington, D.C.

32. U.S. FDA. 1975b. 21 CFR 25.3, Food and Drug Admin. Govt. Print. Off., Washington, D.C.

33. U.S. FDA. 1984. FDA Enforcement Report, Nov. 11, 1984, F-263-5. Press Off. Food and Drug Admin., Washington, D.C.

34. U.S. FDA. 1986. FDA Enforcement Report, April 30, 1986, F-802-6. Press Off. Food and Drug Admin., Washington, D.C.

35. Vaughn, R. H., Douglas, H. C., and Fornachon, J. C. M. 1949. The taxonomy of *Lactobacillus hilgardii* and related heterofermentative lactobacilli. Hilgardia 19: 133.

36. Vladimirov, B. D. and Nefedieva, N. P. 1937. Mayonnaise as a culture medium for microorganisms. Vop. Pitan. 6: 85.

37. Walker, H. W. and Ayres, J. C. 1970. Yeasts as Spoilage Organisms. In "The Yeasts," Vol. 3, ed. A. H. Rose and J. S. Harrison, p. 463. Academic Press, New York.

38. Wethington, M. C. and Fabian, F. W. 1950. Viability of food-poisoning staphylococci and salmonellae in salad dressing and mayonnaise. Food Res. 15: 125.

39. Wickerham, L. J. 1951. Taxonomy of yeasts. U.S. Dept. Agric. Tech. Bull. No. 1029: 1.

40. Williams, O. B. and Mrak, E. M. 1949. An interesting outbreak of yeast spoilage in salad dressing. Fruit Prod. J. 28: 141.

41. Worrell, L. 1951. Flavors, spices, condiments. In "The Chemistry and Technology of Food and Food Products," Vol. 2. ed. M. B. Jacobs, p. 1706. Interscience Publ. New York.

Chapter 54

SWEETENERS AND STARCHES

Richard B. Smittle, Edward P. Krysinski, and Edward R. Richter

54.1 INTRODUCTION

Natural sweeteners are derived from plant material and are processed to an extent that their physical appearance is completely unlike the source material. They come in a variety of sugar compositions, depending on their origin and processing steps, and are sold as liquid syrups or in dry crystalline or powder forms. In many cases, the source material is highly vulnerable to microbial spoilage during harvesting and processing. However, the final products are usually microbiologically stable, depending on the water activity (a_w).[17]

The most commonly used sweetener, sucrose, is extracted and purified from cane, *Saccharum officinarum*, and beets, *Beta vulgaris*.[17, 24] Other sweeteners are derived from the enzymatic and acid hydrolysis of corn starch to yield corn syrups with various concentrations of reducing sugars. The glucose resulting from hydrolysis can be converted to fructose using isomerase to form a glucose-fructose mixture called high-fructose corn syrup. Maple syrup, honey, and molasses are other natural sweeteners used in many foods as flavoring agents.

Next to cellulose, starch is the most prevalent naturally occurring biological substance on earth.[32] Of the 18 million tons of starch purified annually, half is used primarily for food.[2] Corn is the most common source of starch in the United States; potatoes and manioc are common sources of starch in Europe and Asia.

Starch molecules are comprised of polymers of D-anhydroglucose occurring in linear or branched forms. Amylose, the linear form of starch, is the primary component responsible for the swelling action (viscosity increase) when the starch granules are hydrated.[20] Amylopectin, the other polymer in starch, is a highly branched structure that resists gelatinization and is characterized by good clarity and stability. With the advent of modern processing techniques and genetic control of the corn plant resulting in chemical and physical modifications of starch, its use has increased dramatically in modern food product development. Examples of products that routinely contain starch or modified starch include thermally processed low-acid foods such as pork and beans, puddings, and gravies; acid foods such as salad dressings, barbecue sauces, and other condiments; baked goods and snack foods; dry blended food such as instant puddings, seasoning mixes, and soups; and dry coatings on candies and chewing gums.[32] Recently, starch-based polymers have been developed for use as biodegradable plastics in which the starch is the substrate for microbial action that helps to degrade the synthetic polymer.

In the United States, starch production and its use in the food industry are regulated by the Food and Drug Administration (FDA). Chemical modification of starch is defined in 21 CFR (Code of Federal Regulations) 172.892[10] and in the Food Chemicals Codex.[25] The process and chemicals used to modify starch vary but usually fall into one of four classes: bleached, converted, crossed linked, and stabilized.[11, 31, 32]

54.2 GENERAL CONSIDERATIONS

Low water activity is largely responsible for the microbial stability of starches and natural sweeteners.[34] Crystalline or powdered starches and sugars will remain microbially stable if they are kept dry.[17] On the other hand, liquid syrups, which are solutions of sweeteners and water, may spoil because of their higher water content.[17, 29, 34, 36] Maple syrup, honey, molasses, mixtures of sucrose and invert, glucose, and fructose or glucose with fructose are in this category. Industrially prepared syrups range from 67° to 86° Brix, depending on the sweetener. In general, small sugar molecules exert greater osmotic pressure than large molecules. The preservatives sodium benzoate and potassium sorbate may be added to syrups to prevent spoilage, but their efficacy may be limited if the pH is not low enough. In addition, these preservatives cannot be added to some consumer products because of undesirable organoleptic changes.

The general steps of corn starch processing involve steeping, wet milling, washing and purification, and modification and drying.[28, 31] Steeping is a controlled enzymatic degradation in which corn is soaked in 45° to 50°C water containing 0.1% to 0.2% sulfur dioxide[28] for 24 to 48 hr at a pH of *ca.* 4.0.[37] These conditions are critical since the high moisture state of the product makes it vulnerable to microbial attack, which can result in alcoholic or butyric acid byproducts.[31] After steeping, the kernels are cracked open by liquid cyclone, releasing the germ. The germ is pressed to remove oil, and the remaining aqueous starch-gluten mixture is separated, washed, chemically and/or physically modified, and dried to 10% to 17% moisture using flash, belt, or drum dryers.[37]

Tapioca is starch produced from the roots of the manioc plant, which grows in equatorial regions.[37] After harvest, the roots are washed prior to starch separation. Sulfur dioxide and low pH are used as described for corn starch to help control microbial contamination during the steeping process. After drying, the raw starch is often exported to processing plants where it is further processed and modified to meet specific needs of the food industry.

54.3   NORMAL AND INDICATOR FLORA

Microorganisms in starches and sweeteners come from the raw source materials or from the manufacturing processes.[18] High processing temperatures and/or low water activity of starches and natural sweeteners afford little opportunity for microbial survival and growth, but recontamination may occur after heat treatment.

The steeping process is a critical control point in the manufacture of corn starch. Here, the starch grain is subjected to high moisture during the enzymatic degradation of the corn. Sulfur dioxide and low pH are used to inhibit gram-negative bacteria, but lactic acid bacteria and flat sour sporeformers have been reported to proliferate during the steeping process.[16, 19] Although aflatoxin can be present on corn used to produce starch, there is little if any carryover of aflatoxin to the edible product of the wet milling process (starch). However, the residuals (steepwater, gluten, germ) may contain the toxin.[4]

Raw tapioca starch is produced in areas such as Thailand, Brazil, and some African countries. Since the manioc roots are harvested from the soil, various soil microorganisms are initially present on the product and often proliferate during storage of the root prior to processing. Sodium hypochlorite and hydrogen peroxide are frequently used to reduce the microbial load of starch slurries,[31] and propylene oxide has been used as a package fumigant for bulk quantities of starch.[3]

Plant and equipment sanitation as well as water quality have been identified as factors affecting microbial contamination.[37] As a rule, there are usually $<10^2$ microorganisms per gram of sweetener.[30] There is usually <1 yeast per gram.[34] Organisms that are likely to survive are sporeforming aerobic mesophiles and anaerobic bacilli. Further, after heating, especially in syrups, aerobic mesophilic bacteria, yeasts, and molds from the environment may contaminate the product.

Microorganisms such as *Bacillus stearothermophilus, B. coagulans, Clostridium thermosaccharolyticum, C. nigrificans*, certain mesophilic bacteria, yeasts, and molds[7, 9] may be present, but not grow in starches, sugars, and syrups. However, these organisms can cause spoilage of products when they are present in starches and sweeteners used as ingredients for other foods.[17, 34]

The following is a summary of standards for these organisms for application of starches and sweeteners in food canning and beverage manufacturing.

1. National Food Processors Association's Bacterial Standards for Sugar:[14, 26] Five samples are examined after heating.
   a. Total thermophilic spore counts—average of not more than 125 spores/10 g of sugar.
   b. Flat sour spores—average of not more than 50 spores/10 g of sugar.
   c. Thermophilic anaerobic (TA) spores—may be present in up to three of the five samples, but in any one sample, not more than four of six tubes inoculated by the standard procedure should contain TA spores.
   d. Sulfide spoilage spores—may be present in up to two of the five samples.
2. Bottlers' Standards for Dry, Granulated Sugar.[27]
   a. <200 mesophilic bacteria/10 g; <10 yeasts/10 g; <10 molds/10 g.
3. Bottlers' Standards for Liquid Sugar (Sugar Syrup) in 10 g of Dry Sugar Equivalent (DSE).[27]
   a. <100 mesophiles; <10 yeasts; <10 molds.

Food processors typically set microbiological specifications for starch according to the risk of spoilage that the starch may pose for the product and also according to the industry's ability to produce the ingredient with a certain microbial load. In general, starch contains <50,000 SPC/g; <0.3 MPN coliform/g; <0.3 MPN *E. coli*/g; <100 yeasts and molds/g; and is negative for *Salmonella* and *Staphylococcus aureus*. Liquid sweeteners select for microorganisms that tolerate low a_w, and contamination by osmotolerant organisms, especially yeasts, presents the greater risk of spoilage. Because of their importance as spoilage organisms, yeasts capable of growth at <0.85 a_w have been investigated thoroughly and found to be part of the normal flora in the raw intermediate products of honey, maple syrup, molasses, corn syrup, and cane and beet sugar.[34, 36] The most prominent osmotolerant yeasts appear to be in the genus *Zygosaccharomyces (Saccharomyces)*.[36] Some other yeasts that appear as part of the normal flora belong to the genera *Pichia, Candida, Torula*, and *Schizosaccharomyces*.[36]

54.4 SPOILAGE ORGANISMS

The most common agents of undesirable fermentation in liquid syrups such as honey, maple syrup, and corn syrups are osmophilic yeasts, especially *Zygosaccharomyces rouxii*.[17, 35, 36] In addition to *Z. rouxii, Saccharomyces cerevisiae* and *S. mellis* may grow in liquid sucrose. It has been reported that honey is particularly prone to spoilage by *Z. japonicus, Z. barkeri, Z. mellis, Z. prioriano, Z. nussbaumeri*, and *Z. richteri*, all of which have been found in normal and fermented honeys.[36] The hygroscopicity and viscosity of honey may allow the development of a water-sugar gradient where yeasts can grow in sectors of the gradient with sufficiently high a_w.[35] *Torulopsis apicola* has spoiled white crystalline sucrose that had become contaminated with moisture.[34] Raw sugar that was stored in the country of origin has been shown to be spoiled by *S. rouxii* and *T. candida*.[34] Molasses has been spoiled by *S. heterogenicus* and *T. holnii*.[34] Brown and white sugar syrups have been spoiled by *Z. rouxii*, *Z. bailii* var. *osmophilus*, *Saccharomyces* spp., *Candida valida*, *Hansenula anomola* var. *anomola*, *Kloeckera apiculata*, *Candida* spp., *Torulopsis* spp., and *S. cerevisiae*.[34]

Saccharomyces aceris-sacchari, *S. behrensianus*, *S. monocensis*, *Z. mellis*, *Z. barkeri*, *Z. japonicus*, and *Z. nussbaumeri* have been isolated from spoiled maple syrup. *Z. bailii* and *Z. rouxii* have been routinely isolated from corn syrup (R. B. Smittle, personal communication). *S. zsopfi* has been isolated from canned fermented cane syrup.[36]

Microbial spoilage of liquid sugars and corn syrups may be prevented by destruction or removal of contaminating microorganisms, use of sanitizing agents on processing and syrup storage equipment, and prevention of water vapor condensates in storage vessels. To prevent condensation, filtered air treated by ultraviolet irradiation is forced over the surface of the liquid. Prompt use of syrups also helps to reduce the incidence of spoilage.

Under aerobic conditions, molds can grow and cause visible spoilage of syrups.[36] For example, in table syrups, especially maple syrup without an added preservative, molds may grow on the surface of the syrup, particularly after the consumer opens the container. Syrups preserved by potassium sorbate may be spoiled by sorbate-resistant molds, which produce a solvent-like odor.[35]

The presence of thermophilic spores is the most important issue in the microbiology of starch. Since starch is a product of soil-grown crops, it is not uncommon to find various soilborne *Bacillus* species in the finished product. In addition to the presence of microorganisms themselves, the presence of heat-stable amylases, which can remain after the cells have been killed, may also cause spoilage of products made with enzyme-contaminated starches. Often the microbial load may be reduced during the manufacturing process only to leave active enzymes that may continue to degrade the product post production or when the raw ingredient is incorporated into a finished product. For this reason, not only should the number of microbial contaminants be determined during routine quality testing, but the types of organisms should also be identified.

54.5 PATHOGENS

The refining processes of crystalline sweeteners and liquid syrups derived directly from plant material destroy vegetative cells of pathogens. With the exception of honey, commercially produced starches and sweeteners are not involved in outbreaks of foodborne illness. Honey has been implicated as the source of botulinal spores in cases of infant botulism. Spores of *Clostridium botulinum* can grow and produce toxin in the intestines of infants, but preformed botulinal toxins have not been found in honey.[1, 6, 8, 21, 22] In the United States, surveys of honey not related to illness suggest the presence of about 1 to 10 spores/kg[15, 23, 33]; in Europe, surveys of honey not associated with infant botulism indicate the absence of spores of *C. botulinum*.[12, 13]

The gram-positive pathogen *Bacillus cereus* and related aerobic sporeformers may be present in starches used as food ingredients. These organisms have the potential to grow in such foods as puddings and sauces that have been prepared to a high a_w with contaminated ingredients and then temperature abused.[18] Foodborne illness could then result from consumption of such temperature-abused foods.

54.6   RECOMMENDED METHODS

The following chapters in this compendium discuss specific procedures required for sample preparation and analyses for particular microorganisms.

54.61   Methods for Osmophilic/Xerotolerant Yeasts and Molds

Halophilic and osmophilic organisms: Chapter 13
Yeasts and molds: Chapter 16
Confectionery products: Chapter 56

54.62   Methods for Nonosmophilic/Xerotolerant Microorganisms

Sample preparation: Chapter 2
Aerobic plate count: Chapter 4
Yeasts and molds: Chapter 16
Coliforms, *E. coli*: Chapter 24
Salmonella: Chapter 25
Staphylococcus aureus: Chapter 33
Bacillus cereus: Chapter 35
Microscopic examination: Chapter 5
Mesophilic aerobic sporeformers: Chapter 18
Thermophilic flat sour sporeformers: Chapter 21
Aciduric flat sour sporeformers: Chapter 20
Thermophilic anaerobic sporeformers: Chapter 22
Sulfide spoilage sporeformers: Chapter 23
Clostridium botulinum spores in honey: References 12, 15, 22, 23, 33

The standard heat-shocking procedures, i.e., heating for 10 min under 5 pounds per square inch of steam pressure, used in the enumeration of thermophilic spores in starches and sweeteners, must be followed strictly to minimize the inaccuracy and unreliability of the method. For example, substitute heat-shocking treatments of samples in a hot water bath for longer times assumes a z-value that may be a source of error relative to the standard heat-shock procedure.[5]

54.63   Special Procedures

Water activity: Chapter 8

54.9   INTERPRETATION OF DATA

Water activity is the most important ecological factor for controlling microbial growth in starches and sweeteners.[34] Dry starch, crystalline, granulated, and powdered sweeteners are microbiologically stable and need only be kept dry to prevent microbial degradation. However, syrups with an a_w range of 0.65 to 0.70 are subject to spoilage by yeasts.[35] The presence of only a few viable osmophilic yeasts is a more important spoilage risk for syrups than is the presence of large numbers of other microorganisms that cannot grow at the low a_w of these products. Thus, in conducting tests, evaluating analytical data, and making decisions for possible remedial actions, it is important to identify the types of organisms that can grow in the product. The amount of sugar in solution, storage temperature, available oxygen, pH, added preservatives, and storage time will select for the type of organisms, if any, that can cause spoilage.[34]

Normally, syrups and dry sweeteners contain few microorganisms; most contain <100/g[30] and few yeasts.[34] Any syrup or granulated sugar in excess of these guidelines or those set by various trade associations must be treated with care, depending on the use of the product, e.g., in confectionery manufacturing, canning, or bottling.[14, 26, 27]

54.10   REFERENCES

1. Arnon, S. S., Midura, T. F., Damus, K., Thompson, B., Wood, R. M., and Chin, J. 1979. Honey and other environmental risk factors for infant botulism. J. Pediatr. 94:331–336.
2. Aspinall, G. O. 1985. "The Polysaccharides." Vol. 3, p. 210. Academic Press, Orlando, Fla.
3. Banwart, G. J. 1989. "Basic Food Microbiology," 2nd ed., pp. 305–306. Van Nostrand Reinhold, New York.
4. Bennett, G. A. and Anderson, R. A. 1978. Distribution of aflatoxin and/or zearalenone in wet-milled corn products: A review. J. Agr. Food Chem. 26:1055–1060.
5. Bernard, D. 1980. NFPA position in regards to changes in the thermophile enumeration procedure as it applies to the use of NFPA standards for thermophiles in starches. NFPA Laboratory Memorandum. May 28, 1980.
6. Brown, L. W. 1979. Commentary: Infant botulism and the honey connection. J. Pediatr. 94:337–338.
7. Cameron, E. J. and Williams, C. C. 1928. The thermophilic flora of sugar in its relation to canning. Zentralbl. Bakteriol., Parasitenkd. Infektionskr., Abt. 1 76:28–37.
8. Chin, J., Arnon, S. S., and Midura, T. F. 1979. Food and environmental aspects of infant botulism in California. Rev. Infect. Dis. 1:693–696.
9. Clark, F. M. and Tanner, F. W. 1937. Thermophilic canned food spoilage organisms in sugar and starch. Food Res. 2:27–39.

10. CFR. 1986. Modified starches. Code of Fed. Regs., Title 21, Sect. 172.892. U.S. Govt. Print. Office, Washington, D.C.

11. Corn Refiners Association. 1986. "Corn Starch," 7th ed. Corn Refiners Assoc., Washington, D.C.

12. Fleming, R. and Stojanowic, V. 1980. Examination of honeys for spores of *Clostridium botulinum*. Arch. Lebensmittelhyg. 31:179–180.

13. Hartgen, Von H. 1980. Examination of honeys for botulinum toxin. Arch. Lebensmittelhyg. 31:177–178.

14. Horwitz, W., ed. 1975. Thermophilic bacterial spores in sugars: Official first action. In "Official Methods of Analysis of the Association of Official Analytical Chemists," pp. 920–921. AOAC, Washington, D.C.

15. Huhtanen, C. N., Knox, D., and Shimanuki, H. 1981. Incidence and origin of *Clostridium botulinum* spores in honey. J. Food Prot. 44:812–814.

16. International Commission on Microbiological Specifications for Foods. 1980. "Microbial Ecology of Foods, Vol. I. Factors Affecting Life and Death of Microorganisms." pp. 24–28. Academic Press, New York.

17. International Commission on Microbiological Specifications for Foods. 1980. "Microbial Ecology of Foods, Vol. II. Food Commodities. Sugar, Cocoa, Chocolate, and Confectioneries." Academic Press, New York.

18. Kramer, J. M. and Gilbert, R. J. 1989. *Bacillus cereus* and other *Bacillus* species. In "Foodborne bacterial pathogens," ed. M. P. Doyle. Marcel Dekker, New York.

19. Liggett, R. W. and Koffler, H. 1948. Corn steep liquor in microbiology. Bacteriol. Rev. 12:297–311.

20. Luallen, T. E. 1985. Starch as a functional ingredient. Food Technol. 39:59–63.

21. Marx, J. L. 1978. Botulism in infants: A cause of sudden death? Science 201:799–801.

22. Midura, T. F., Snowden, S., Wood, R. M., and Arnon, S. S. 1979. Isolation of *Clostridium botulinum* from honey. J. Clin. Microbiol. 9:282–283.

23. Mitamura, H., Kameyama, K., and Amdo, Y. 1979. The contamination of spore-forming bacteria in honey. Report of the Hokkaido Institute of Public Health. 29:16–19.

24. Muller, E. G. 1986. The sugar industry. In "Quality Control in the Food Industry," Vol. 3, 2nd ed., ed. S. M. Herschdoerfer. Academic Press, London.

25. NAS. "Food Chemical Codex," 3rd ed. 1981. National Academy Press, Washington, D.C.

26. National Food Processors Association. 1972. "Bacterial Standards for Sugar," rev. National Food Processors Assoc., Washington, D.C.

27. National Soft Drink Association. 1975. "Quality Specifications and Test Procedures for Bottlers' Granulated and Liquid Sugar." National Soft Drink Assoc., Washington, D.C.

28. Petersen, N. B. 1975. "Edible Starches and Starch Derived Syrups." Noyes Data Corp. Park Ridge, N.J.

29. Pitt, J. I. 1975. Xerophilic fungi and the spoilage of foods of plant origin. In "Water Relations of Foods," ed. R. B. Duckworth. Academic Press, London.

30. Scarr, M. P. 1968. Symposium on growth of microorganisms at extremes of temperature: Thermophiles in sugar. J. Appl. Bacteriol. 31:66–74.

31. Smith, R. 1981. Quality control in corn refining. In "Corn Annual," pp. 24–28. Corn Refiners Assoc., Washington, D.C.

32. Smith, P. S., 1983. Food starches and their uses. In "Gum and Starch Technology Eighteenth Annual Symposium," Vol. 17, pp. 34–42, ed. D. L. Downing. Cornell University Cooperative Extension.

33. Sugiyama, H., Mills, D. C., and Cathy Kvo, L. J. 1978. Number of *Clostridium botulinum* spores in honey. J. Food Prot. 41:848–850.

34. Tilbury, R. H. 1976. The microbial stability of intermediate moisture foods with respect to yeasts. In "Intermediate Moisture Foods," eds. R. Davies, G. G. Birch, and K. J. Parker. Applied Science Publishers, London.

35. Troller, J. A. 1979. Food spoilage by microorganisms tolerating low a_w environments. Food Technol. 33:72–75.
36. Walker, H. W. and Ayres, J. C. 1970. Yeasts as spoilage organisms. In "The Yeasts," Vol. 3, eds. A. H. Rose and J. S. Harrison. Yeast Technology. Academic Press, New York.
37. Whistler, R. L. and Paschall, E. F. 1967. "Starch: Chemistry and Technology," Vol. II. Academic Press, New York.

Chapter 55

CEREAL AND CEREAL PRODUCTS

Joseph Mayou and Lloyd Moberg

55.1 INTRODUCTION

Cereal and cereal products constitute a significant food resource for people throughout the world. Cereal grains include wheat, oats, corn, rye, barley, millet, sorghum, and rice. Soybeans, which are pulses, not grains, are included in this chapter because numerous soy products are similar to those produced from cereals. Cereal products include flour(s), breakfast cereals, snack foods, corn meal, doughs, pasta, and dry mixes for cakes, pastry, and breads. Many cereal products are used in the formulation and manufacturing of other products, e.g., sausages, cold cuts, confectionaries, and baby food.

Public health, ingredient or product spoilage, and good manufacturing practices (GMP) are of primary concern to the cereal microbiologist. Microorganisms of public health significance may present a potential threat if cereal grains and products are improperly stored, processed, or handled. These microorganisms include *Staphylococcus aureus, Salmonella* spp., *Clostridium perfringens, Escherichia coli, Clostridium botulinum, Bacillus cereus,* and various toxigenic molds.[12, 14, 18, 29, 30, 34, 36, 40, 45] Other pathogenic microorganisms such as *Listeria monocytogenes, Yersinia* spp., and *Aeromonas* spp. may be considered, depending on the ultimate use of the ingredient or product.

Various spoilage microorganisms can proliferate on cereal grains and finished products held under improper storage conditions. Such spoilage may manifest itself as visually undesirable grains or organoleptically unpalatable products. The majority of these spoilage microorganisms represent the normal flora of cereal grains. They include yeasts, molds, psychrotrophic, thermophilic and thermoduric bacteria, lactic acid bacteria, and the "rope bacteria."

Good manufacturing practices can serve to control, and even reduce, the levels of pathogenic and spoilage microorganisms in cereal grains during processing and storage. The aerobic plate count, coliform count, and yeast and mold count are important indices of good sanitation, handling, processing, and storage practices. For details that are beyond the scope of this chapter, see the reviews and published studies on the microbiology of cereal and cereal products[6, 7, 17, 19, 21, 24, 37, 39] and Chapter 43, which addresses toxigenic molds and mycotoxins.

55.2 FACTORS AFFECTING BIOLOAD

Cereal and cereal products may be arbitrarily divided into the eight general categories described in Table 1. The "bioload," as defined here, represents the total microflora of the agricultural commodity or product. The data presented in Table 1 are based on routine quality control tests performed on various items of the specified categories. The microbiological procedures used for these tests are described in this compendium. They represent industry-wide experience and are presented for illustrative purposes; they are not intended to denote microbiological acceptance criteria.

55.21 Cereal Grains

The microflora of cereal grains are generally representative of the environment in which they are grown.[42] A multitude of environmental factors influences the composition of these microflora. The rainfall, sunlight, temperature, and soil conditions during the growing season and at harvest are all important in determining the number and type of microorganisms that are present. Agricultural practices (e.g., "organic" farming, types of chemicals used, and harvesting equipment and methods) also influence the cereal grain microflora. Bird, insect, and rodent activity in the field additionally contribute to the heterogeneity of the microflora.

The diversity of the microflora found on cereal grains at harvest is compounded by further contamination during transport and storage.[15] Abusive conditions during either of these periods may permit water uptake with subsequent microbial growth.

Different varieties of grains often do not differ markedly from each other with respect to microbial populations. Mold, yeasts, and most of the aerobic mesophiles present on cereal grains are indigenous to the plants themselves. Some grains are routinely contaminated with *Cladosporium* molds, while others contain *Aspergillus, Fusarium, Alternaria,* and other types.[2, 10, 11] As noted, external contaminants (coliforms, *E. coli,* and enterococci) may be contributed by birds, insects, and rodents, all of which are ecologically associated with cereal grains. Storage conditions such as the moisture content of the grain, the temperature, and the time of storage are critical factors in controlling the growth of microorganisms.[11, 22, 23, 27, 31, 35, 38, 44]

Bacterial populations in grains normally reach levels of 10^6 per g. The wide variety of species present may include aerobic mesophilic sporeformers, lactic acid bacteria, coliforms, and pseudomonads.[21] Low numbers of pathogenic organisms have also been recovered from cereal grains. These include *B. cereus, C. perfringens, C. botulinum,* and *Salmonella* spp; however, cereal grains and their milled products have seldom been implicated in foodborne disease.[33] Generally, the low water activity (a_w) of cereal grains prevents bacterial growth. These microorganisms can survive the milling process and thus contaminate flours and the resultant products.

Yeasts and molds may contaminate cereal grains to levels of 10^4 per g.[21] Field fungi will slowly die off in grains properly dried to less than 13% moisture. Inadequate drying or improper storage in wet conditions will allow some molds to grow and spoil the grains. *Aspergillus flavus* and *A. parasiticus* are common contaminants of certain cereal grains.[8] These molds, like others, can produce mycotoxins, thereby presenting a potential health hazard to consumers. Fluorescence detection methods are available as a screening test to identify potential mycotoxigenic grains. However, rigid application of Hazard Analysis Critical Control Point (HACCP) principles to control moisture during harvest, shipment, and storage would be a prudent measure to prevent the spoilage of grain.

55.22   Flour(s), Corn Meal, Corn Grits, Semolina

Most of the microorganisms found in flour and other milled products originate on the raw materials from which they are milled.[13, 28] Other sources of potential contamination are transportation facilities, mill unloading devices, conveyors, processing equipment, the milling sequence, and exposure to moisture during the milling process. Grains (e.g., wheat, rye, and barley) are tempered by spraying with water and holding in bins for varying periods of time. This procedure may permit microorganisms to proliferate. The use of chlorine in the spray water is a proven means to reduce the microbiological bioload on the grain. Bleaching of flour can also reduce the microbial population, although spores are unaffected.[41] Corn meal, corn grits, and some corn flours are traditionally produced by a "dry milling" process that avoids the tempering steps.

Soy flour is manufactured by a different process. The soy beans are moistened, dehulled, flaked, extracted with organic solvent to remove the oil, then "caked" and ground into flour. *Salmonella* spp. have been detected often in soy flour. Salmonellosis and yersiniosis in humans and animals have been traced to soybeans and soy products.[24]

The microbial levels in properly handled and processed flours will be no greater than the levels in raw grains. Bacterial populations may reach a level near 10^6 per g. Yeasts and molds may be recovered at 10^4 per g. The presence of psychrotrophs, flat-sour organisms, and thermophilic sporeformers may be of particular interest to processors of canned or chilled foods. The presence of "rope bacteria" is of interest to manufacturers of baked goods.

Table 1—Normal Microbiological Profile of Cereal Grains and Cereal Products

Product category	Normal microflora	Quantitative range	Remarks
I. Cereal grains	Molds	10^2–10^4/g	a) Counts represent "normal" grains in commercial channels; "mildewed" or "musty" or "spoiled" grain would be beyond these ranges.
	Yeasts and yeast-like fungi	10^2–10^4/g	
	Bacteria		
	Aerobic plate count	10^2–10^6/g	
	Coliform group	10^2–10^4/g	
	E. coli	$<10^2$–10^3/g	
	Actinomycetes	10^3–10^6/g	
II. Flour(s), Corn meal, Corn grits, Semolina	Molds	$<10^2$–10^4/g	a) Microbial counts in flour can vary from one storage period to another depending on moisture content and storage conditions.
	Yeasts and yeast-like fungi	<10–10^2/g	
	Bacteria		b) Soy flours sometimes contain salmonellae.
	Aerobic plate count	10^2–10^6/g	
	Coliform group	<1–10/g	
	"Rope" spores	<1–10^2/g	
III. Breakfast cereals and snack foods	Molds	<1–10^3/g	a) Cereals are additionally tested for E. coli and salmonellae.
	Yeasts and yeast-like fungi	<1–10^2/g	
	Bacteria		b) Snacks are routinely tested for salmonellae and coagulase-positive staphylococci.
	Aerobic plate count	<1–10^2/g	
	Coliform group	<1–10^2/g	
IV. Frozen and refrigerated (chemically leavened)	Molds	<10–10^4/g	a) Refrigerated (chemically leavened) doughs have <10 yeast per g. Yeast counts represent inoculum intentionally added to frozen doughs as part of the formulation.
	Yeasts and yeast-like fungi	10^5–10^6/g	
	Bacteria		b) Routinely tested for salmonellae, E. coli, and coagulase-positive staphylococci.
	Aerobic plate count	10^2–10^7/g	
	Coliform group	<10–10^2/g	
	Psychrotrophs	<10–10^3/g	
V. Baked goods	Molds	<10–10^3/g	
	Yeast and yeast-like fungi	<10–10^3/g	

	Bacteria		
	Aerobic plate count	$<10^2$–10^3/g	
	Coliform group	<10–10^2/g	
VI. Soy protein	Bacteria		a) Quantitative ranges reflect both original contamination and growth during storage of intermediate moisture products.
	Aerobic plate count	10^2–10^5/g	
	Coliform group	10^2–10^3/g	
	E. coli	<10–10^2/g	b) Molds, yeast, salmonellae, and staphylococci routinely tested for.
	Psychrotrophs	10^2–10^4/g	
	C. perfringens	<1–10^2/g	c) Soy protein products intended for anaerobic storage (e.g., canning) should be routinely tested for thermophilic sporeformers, flat sour organisms, putrefactive sporeformers, and sulfide spoilage organisms.
VII. Pasta products	Bacteria		a) Wide ranges in bioloads in these products reflect the difference between egg-based & macaroni-type products.
	Aerobic plate count	10^3–10^5/g	
	Coliform group	<10–10^3/g	
	Molds and yeasts	10^2–10^5/g	b) Routinely tested for salmonellae and staphylococci.
VIII. Dry mixes	Molds	10^2–10^5/g	a) Routinely tested for salmonellae and E. coli.
	Yeasts and yeast-like fungi	10^2–10^5/g	
	Bacteria		
	Aerobic plate count	10^2–10^6/g	
	Coliform group	<1–10^4/g	

Table based on "routine" quality control tests normally performed on various items of specified category; data represent industry-wide experience; data presented as "orders of magnitude" for illustrative purposes only. Milled rice produced commercially in the southern area of the United States in 1954 was virtually free from internal infection by fungi, and free from internal infection by bacteria, yeast, and actinomycetes.[37] Results from investigations of 1968,[11] relative to the conditions that determine the prevalence of individual kinds of fungi in stored rice, were similar to those observed in the 1954 study.

55.23   Breakfast Cereals and Snack Foods

The three basic breakfast cereal manufacturing processes are "flaking," "puffing," and "extrusion." In each case, moisture is introduced into the formulation, thus providing an opportunity for microbial growth. Controlling the time that the formulation is held at this moisture level will limit the amount of microbial growth. The heat applied during the cooking process when the product is moist will reduce the microbial levels. A potential for post-heat contamination may appear during an enrichment application or "enrobing" operation, to add vitamins, minerals, sweeteners, or colorings to the cereals. If the additives are contaminated, or the process or equipment is unsanitary, the finished product may be contaminated. However, the low moisture levels of breakfast cereals and snack foods will prevent any further microbial growth.

55.24   Refrigerated and Frozen Doughs

The ingredients used in the formulation of doughs provide the primary source of their indigenous microflora. These include flour, dry milk, eggs, sugar, spices, flavorings, and water. The equipment and environment of manufacture also play an important role in the microbiology of the finished product. These commodities are dispatched in an unbaked state by the manufacturer. The final heat treatment is provided by the consumer.

In frozen doughs, no microbial growth will occur during distribution and storage if the products are held at the prescribed temperature. Microbial counts in refrigerated doughs will increase during storage. However, the rate of increase will depend on the types and numbers of microorganisms initially present and the storage temperature. Most refrigerated doughs are formulated with low a_w and pH in an attempt to retard bacterial growth. All refrigerated doughs are chemically leavened rather than formulated to contain a yeast starter culture; slow yeast growth during refrigerated storage would eventually burst the container. Wild-type yeasts may be present in low numbers in refrigerated doughs. Lactic acid bacteria are of special concern in the spoilage of refrigerated doughs.[9, 22, 39] Heterofermentative lactics are regarded as the primary spoilage agent of refrigerated doughs. Gas production by these organisms will burst the container.

55.25   Baked Goods

"Baked goods" refers to breads, cakes, pie shells, and pastries. The baking process destroys most of the microorganisms in baked goods.[26] Post-baking contamination can result in the spoilage of certain baked goods if they are stored at ambient temperatures for prolonged periods. Mold is one of the most common forms of spoilage for breads and other baked goods. Preservatives are commonly added to reduce the potential for mold spoilage.[25]

Sporeformers that survive the baking process may also cause spoilage of baked products. Breads and other baked goods are subject to spoilage by the "rope bacteria," mucoid variants of *Bacillus subtilus*.[5] This bacterium causes a condition known as "rope" in these products, so called because of the ropy and stringy texture of the product interior.

The microbiology of filled baked goods varies considerably, based primarily on the microbiology of the filling rather than that of the cereal portion. Many fillings will not support the growth of pathogenic microorganisms; they are formulated with a pH < 4.0, or an a_w < 0.85. However, some custard and cream fillings are outside this range and thus support the growth of certain pathogens. These must be considered potentially hazardous and treated as perishable foods, i.e., kept refrigerated.

55.26   Soy Protein Products

The ingredients of these products are essentially soy flour and a variety of additives (color, flavoring, and vitamins). Each additive may contribute to the microbial population of the finished commodity. Some steps in the process may also add to the contamination. Finished soy protein products range in moisture content from 2% to 64%. The higher moisture content along with the nutritional quality of some of these products may be conducive to microbiological growth. The range of counts and the variety of microbiological types encountered (see Table 1) suggest that the problems may be those of storage and sanitation.

The microorganisms of concern in soy protein are somewhat dependent on its end use. If used as an ingredient in a retorted, canned product, then thermophilic sporeformers, flat sour organisms, putrefactive sporeformers, and sulfide spoilage organisms would be of high importance. If used in a shelf stable or perishable product which has received minimal heat during processing, then *Salmonella* spp. would be of importance. Because of the frequent isolation of *Salmonella* from soy flour, it should be treated as a sensitive ingredient of such products.[45]

55.27   Pasta Products

Pasta products (usually manufactured from durum wheat flour) essentially fall into two categories: egg-based pasta such as noodles and macaroni-type pasta such as macaroni, spaghetti, and vermicelli. The former, as its name implies, contains flour, water enrichment nutrients, and pasteurized dried, frozen, or fresh eggs. The latter contains only flour, water, and enrichment nutrients. Both products are manufactured in much the same fashion: mixed, extruded, shaped, cut, and dried. The initial microbiological profile of the mixed dough is directly related to the quality of the ingredients. During its manufacture, the product is a semisoft, unheated dough of approximately 30% moisture that can support microbial growth. Microorganisms can also grow during the slow, low-temperature drying process. Not until the moisture drops below 13% during the drying process (several hours) would the micro-biological activity be inhibited.

Microbiological counts in freshly dried pasta may be as high as 10^7 per g, but will decrease during storage because of its low moisture content. Improper drying of the pasta may allow the growth of some molds.[24] *S. aureus* has been a problem in the manufacture of pasta products.[29, 34] Enterotoxin production is a potential hazard because of the ideal growth conditions during mixing and initial drying. Proper equipment cleaning and sanitation can minimize this threat. *Salmonella* spp. may also occur in pasta if contaminated eggs have been used as an ingredient. The conditions that permit staphylococci to grow also permit salmonellae to grow. Boiling the pasta will kill vegetative cells during normal preparation, but staphylococcal enterotoxin will remain.[16, 29]

55.28   Dry Mixes

The manufacture of dry mixes is a dry blending of such ingredients as flour, dried eggs, flavorings, sugar, and dried dairy products. The finished product will reflect the microbiological profile of the individual ingredients and the cleanliness of the mixing equipment. Usually the microbial load is not reduced in the dry mix process. Microbiological control can be affected by quality control of the ingredients, use of clean equipment, and maintenance of low, microbiologically inhibitory moisture levels in the finished product.

Sanitation of equipment in dry mix manufacturing is of primary importance. Wet cleaning should be avoided whenever possible since this usually causes more problems than it solves.

55.3   METHODS

The following summary suggests routine and special analyses that are employed to determine the microbiological condition of the eight product categories discussed above.[1, 3, 4, 32, 43]

55.31   Routine Analyses

1. Mold and yeast determinations (Chapters 4 and 16)
The mold and yeast count is an indication of the sanitary history of the product as well as a prediction of potential future spoilage during storage. Recommended sample size is 50 g diluted 1:10 in 450 ml of diluent.

2. Aerobic plate count (Chapter 4)
Sample size: 50 g in 450 ml diluent

3. Coliform organisms and *Escherichia coli* (Chapters 6 and 24)
The finding of coliform bacteria in cereal grains and flour is common and does not necessarily imply mishandling, but *E. coli* in a finished ready-to-eat product may be of public health concern. It may imply recontamination from fecal sources after the product has been processed.

4. Staphylococci (Chapters 33 and 34)

Enterotoxin-producing staphylococci represent a potential hazard to pasta manufacturers. Generally, staphylococci contaminate the mix during processing rather than entering with the flour. Therefore, testing of the raw mix or the finished product is a better determination of a potential problem.

5. Salmonella (Chapter 25)

55.32 Special Analyses

Special analyses are to be performed on certain products under specified circumstances.

1. "Rope" spores (Chapter 18)

Analysis for rope spores should be performed on cereal grains and flours where the prospect of "ropy" dough, from the action of *B. subtilus*, is of concern.

2. Mycotoxins (Chapter 43)

Mycotoxins are toxins elaborated by certain fungi that may grow on moist grains. Epidemiological evidence[28] suggests that humans can be affected by ingestion of these toxins. Table 2 lists the toxins of fungal origin whose natural occurrence has been demonstrated.

Table 2—Mycotoxins of Demonstrated Natural Occurrence

Toxin	Mold	Occurrence
Aflatoxins	*Aspergillus flavus* *Aspergillus parasiticus*	Corn, grains, nuts
Citrinin	*Penicillium* spp. *Asperigillus* spp.	Rice
Ergot alkaloids	*Claviceps purpurea*	Cereal grains, various forage grasses
Ochratoxins	*Aspergillus* spp. *Penicillium viridicatum*	Corn, wheat, oats, barley
Penicillic acid	*Penicillium* spp. *Aspergillus* spp.	Corn
Sterigmatocystins	*Aspergillus* spp. *Penicillium luteum* *Bipolaris* sp.	Wheat
Trichothecenes vomitoxin	*Fusarium* spp. *Myrothecium* spp. *Trichothecium* spp. *Stachybotrys atra*	Corn, various cereals
Zearalenone, related macrolides	*Gibberella zeae*	Corn

3. Staphylococcal enterotoxins (Chapter 34)

In addition to assaying a cereal product for the presence of coagulase-positive staphylococci, assaying for thermonuclease or enterotoxin is also sometimes advisable, as when the viable *S. aureus* count suggests the presence of some hazard. If the history of the product reveals that growth of staphylococci could have taken place, as with temperature abuse, it is useful to assay the product for toxin.

4. *Clostridium perfringens* (Chapter 37)

Clostridium perfringens food poisoning is often associated with meat and poultry. Soy protein products are often designed as substitutes for meats, and their physicochemical properties may be conducive to the growth of *C. perfringens*. Such products should be analyzed for the presence of this organism.

5. *Bacillus cereus* (Chapter 35)

Rice has repeatedly been incriminated in foodborne disease outbreaks because of *B. cereus*.[20] In food poisonings where rice is the suspected vehicle, analyses should be done for *B. cereus*.

55.33   Other Special Tests (Chapters 9 to 23)

Cereal products may be tested for psychrotrophs, thermophiles, anaerobes, flat sour spores, hydrogen sulfide producers, lactic acid producers, nitrate-utilizing gas producers, and sulfide spoilage spores.

55.4   REFERENCES

1. AACC. 1983. "Approved Methods of the American Association of Cereal Chemists," 8th ed. Am. Assn. of Cereal Chem., St. Paul, Minn.
2. Abramson, D., Sinha, R. N., and Mills, J. T. 1984. Quality changes in granary-stored wheat at 15 and 19% moisture content. Mycopathologia 87: 115.
3. AOAC. 1984. "Official Methods of Analyses of the Association of Official Analytical Chemists." 14th ed. Assn. of Off. Analyt. Chem., Washington, D.C.
4. APHA. 1966. "Recommended Methods for the Microbiological Examination of Foods," 2nd ed. Am. Pub. Health Assn., New York.
5. Barrett, F. 1970. Extending the keeping quality of bakery products. The Bakers Digest, Aug., p. 48.
6. Bothast, R. J., Rogers, R. F., and Hesseltine, C. W. 1973. Microbial survey of corn in 1970–71. Cereal Science Today. 18: 18.
7. Bothast, R. J., Rogers, F. R., and Hesseltine, C. W. 1973. "Microbiology of Corn and Milled Corn Products." North. Reg. Res. Lab., Peoria, Ill.
8. Busby, W. F. and Wogan, G. N. 1979. Foodborne mycotoxins and alimentary mycotoxicoses. In "Food-borne Infections and Intoxications," 2nd ed., ed. H. Reimann and F. L. Bryan, Academic Press, New York.
9. Chen, R. W. 1979. Refrigerated doughs. Cereal Foods World 24: 46.
10. Christensen, C. M. 1946. The quantitative determination of molds in flour. Cereal Chemistry 23: 322.
11. Christensen, C.M. 1968. Influence of moisture content, temperature, and time of storage upon invasion of rough rice by storage fungi. Phytopathology 59: 145.
12. Cohen, H. and M. LaPointe. 1986. Determination of ochratoxin A in animal feed and cereal grains by liquid chromatography. J. Assn. Off. Anal. Chem. 69: 957.

13. Dack, G. M. 1961. Flour microbiology. Cereal Science Today 6: 9.
14. Davis, N. D., Dickens, J. W., Free, R. L., Hamilton, P. B., Shotwell, O. L., and Wyllie, T. D. 1980. Protocols for surveys, sampling, post-collection handling, and analysis of grain samples involved in mycotoxin problems. J. Assn. Off. Anal. Chem. 63: 95.
15. DeHoff, T. W., Stroshine, R., Tuite, J., and Baker, K. 1984. Corn quality during barge shipment. Transactions of the ASAE, p. 259.
16. Denny, C. B., Tan, P. L., and Bohrer, C. W. 1966. Heat inactivation of staphylococcal enterotoxin A. J. Food Sci. 31: 762.
17. Doty, J. 1961. Bacteria control in the flour milling operation. American Milling Process 89: 20.
18. Flannigan, B. 1986. *Aspergillus clavatus*—An allergenic, toxigenic deteriogen of cereals and cereal products. Internat. Biodeteriorat. 22: 79.
19. Frazier, W. C. 1967. Chap. 13, Contamination, preservation, and spoilage of cereals and cereal products. In "Food Microbiology." 2nd ed., p. 179. McGraw Hill, New York.
20. Goepfert, J. M., Spira, W. M., and Kim, H. U. 1972. *Bacillus cereus*: Food poisoning organism. A review. J. Milk Food Technol. 35: 213.
21. Hesseltine, C. W. and Graves, R. R. 1966. Microbiological research on wheat and flour. Econ. Bot. 20: 156.
22. Hesseltine, C. W., Graves, R. R., Rogers, R., and Burmeister, H. R. 1969. Aerobic and facultative microflora of fresh and spoiled refrigerated dough products. Appl. Microbiol. 18: 848.
23. Hill, R. A. and Lacey, J. 1983. Factors determining the microflora of stored barley grain. Ann. Appl. Biol. 102: 467.
24. ICMSF. 1980. Chap. 23. Cereal and cereal products. In "Microbial Ecology of Foods," 1st ed., p. 669. Intern. Comm. Microbiolog. Specs. for Foods. Academic Press, New York.
25. Jackel, S. 1980. Natural breads may cause microbiological problems. Bakery Production and Marketing 15: 138.
26. Knight, R. A. and Menlove, E. M. 1961. Effect of the bread-baking process on destruction of certain mold spores. J. Sci. Food Agr. 12: 653.
27. Kuiper, J. and Murray, G. M. 1978. Spoilage of grain by fungi. Agricult. Gazette of New South Wales. Oct., p. 39.
28. Kurata, H., Ogasawara, K., and Frampton, V. L. 1957. Microflora of milled rice. Cereal Chem. 34: 47.
29. Lee, W. H., Staples, C. L., and Olson, J. C. Jr. 1975. *Staphylococcus aureus* growth and survival in macaroni dough and the persistence of enterotoxins in the dried products. J. Food Sci. 40: 119.
30. Marth, E. M. 1967. Aflatoxins and other mycotoxins in agricultural products. J. Milk Food Technol. 30: 192.
31. McMahon, M. E., Hartman, P. A., Saul, R. A., and Tiffany, L.H. 1975. Deterioration of high-moisture corn. Appl. Microbiol. 30: 103.
32. NCA. 1968. "Laboratory Manual for Food Canners and Processors." Vol. 1. p. 105. Natl. Canners Assn. AVI Publ. Co., Westport, Conn.
33. NRC. 1985. "An Evaluation of the Role of Microbiological Criteria for Food and Food Ingredients," p. 272. Natl. Res. Council. Natl. Acad. Press, Washington, D.C.
34. Ostovar, K. and Ward, K. 1976. Detection of *Staphylococcus aureus* from frozen and thawed convenience pasta products. Lebensm-Wiss. U. Technol. 9: 218.
35. Prasad, D. C., Muir, W. E., and Wallace, H. A. H. 1978. Characteristics of freshly harvested wheat and rapeseed. Transactions of the ASAE. 21: 782.
36. Sadek, M. A., El-Zayet, F. M. M., ABD El-Fadel, M. G., and Taha, R. A. 1985. Isolation and enumeration of *B. cereus* and some other microorganisms from balady bread. Zeitschrift für die Gesamte Hygiene und Ihre Grenzgebiete 31: 623.
37. Semeniuk, G. 1954. Microflora, Chap. 111. In "Storage of Cereal Grains and Their Products," AACC Monograph Series 11, p. 77.

38. Sinha, R. N., Muir, W. E., and Sanderson, D. B. 1985. Quality assessment of stored wheat during drying with near-ambient temperature air. Can J. Plant Sci. 65: 849.
39. Slocum, G. G. 1963. Let's look at some microbiological problems associated with cereal foods. Cereal Science Today 8: 313.
40. Stoloff, L., Trucksess, M., Anderson, P. W., Glabe, E. F., and Aldridge, J. G. 1978. Determination of the potential for mycotoxin contamination of pasta products. J. Food Sci. 43: 228.
41. Thatcher, F. S., Coutu, C., and Stevens, F. 1953. The sanitation of Canadian flour mills and its relationship to the microbial content of flour. Cereal Chem. 30: 71.
42. Thomas, P. M. 1971. Role of microflora in the deterioration of agricultural commodities in warehouses. Allahabad Farmer 45: 463.
43. U.S. FDA. 1984. "Bacteriological Analytical Manual for Foods." Food Drug Admin. Gov. Print. Off., Washington, D.C.
44. Wallace, H. A. H., Sinha, R. N., and Mills, J. T. 1976. Fungi associated with small wheat bulks during prolonged storage in Manitoba. Can. J. Botany 54: 1332.
45. Wilson, C. R., Andrews, W. H., Poelma, P. L., and Wagner, D. E. 1985. Recovery of *Salmonella* species from dried foods rehydrated by the soak method. J. Food Prot. 48: 505.

Chapter 56

CONFECTIONERY PRODUCTS

Lawrence M. Lenovich and Patrick J. Konkel

56.1 INTRODUCTION

Confectionery goods comprise a broad spectrum of products that share sweetness as a common characteristic. This class of products can be subdivided into several types. Sugar confectionery includes boiled sweets, toffees, fudge, caramel, nougat, marzipan, jellies, creams, and others. Chocolate confectionery includes many of the sugar confections covered in chocolate as well as solid pieces and bars. Some novel products, which have been developed in recent years, deserve mention. Numerous granola, wafer, and biscuit products enrobed with chocolate and layered with flavored creams, nuts, and caramel fall within this category.

The majority of these products are not susceptible to microbial spoilage, primarily because of their high percentage of solids, which results in a water activity (a_w) of less than 0.85. However, spoilage of some confections by osmotolerant yeasts and molds can occur and the low-a_w environment of confectionery products can result in the survival of pathogenic microorganisms that may have entered the product through raw materials or environmental contamination. Other product characteristics such as pH and preservatives act as antimicrobial barriers to provide stability.

Government agencies and commercial associations contribute to standards for these products. In the United States, confectionery manufacturing and standards of identity are regulated by the Food and Drug Administration (FDA).[8, 9] The recommendations of the Codex Alimentarius Commission (Codex), if accepted by a national government, become the laws of the accepting country.[5] The International Office of Cocoa and Chocolate and the International Sugar Confectionery Manufacturers' Association set guidelines that reflect the concerns of producers, but these are not legal requirements.[29]

56.2   GENERAL CONSIDERATIONS

Water activity is probably the single product characteristic that most influences the microbial ecology of confections (Table 1). High sugar concentrations can provide a_w of less than 0.50, which prevents microbial spoilage. Growth of spoilage-causing yeasts and molds is unlikely at a_w levels of 0.62 and 0.72, respectively.

56.21.   Sugar Confections

Sugar confections fall into two main classes: (a) hard candies, toffee, and caramel; and (b) fondants, creams, and pastes. Hard candies and toffee are not subject to microbial degradation and are usually of little concern to the food microbiologist. On occasion, improperly formulated caramel used as centers for chocolate will undergo yeast spoilage. Only fondants, creams, and pastes have a significant history of microbial spoilage.

Many confections contain both sucrose and invert sugars whereas others are formulated with sucrose, invert sugar, or corn syrup to yield the desired organoleptic qualities. Formulations with a dissolved solids concentration in the syrup phase of 75% wt/wt may be near the minimum to prevent fermentation by yeasts.[37] The use of sucrose alone is not satisfactory because a saturated solution of sucrose has an a_w (0.84) suitable for yeast and mold growth. The correct ratio of sucrose, glucose, and invert sugar generally prevents fermentation.

Fondants, creams, and pastes are often used as base materials to formulate other confections. Other components such as colors, flavors, fruits, and nuts can be added for variety. If properly formulated, these products should withstand microbial spoilage.

Additional stability can be obtained through the incorporation of acidulants and preservatives.

Table 1.—Water Activity of Some Confections[a]

Product	Water Activity
Fondant cream	0.75–0.84
Marzipan	0.65–0.70
Marshmallow	0.63–0.73
Turkish delight	0.60–0.70
Fruit jellies	0.59–0.76
Licorice	0.53–0.66
Gums and pastilles	0.51–0.64
Chocolate	0.37–0.50
Toffee	<0.48
Boiled sweets	<0.30

[a]Adapted from Hilker[24]

56.22.   Chocolate Confectionery

Products manufactured with cocoa and chocolate make up a large segment of the confectionery industry. Chocolate confectionery often includes sugar confectionery as a base material with a coating of chocolate. Chocolate-coated centers may include fondants, creams, and fruits. Invertase is often added to invert sucrose to obtain a liquid center having an a_w sufficiently low to prevent fermentation.

Chocolate-coated centers have a continuous coating of chocolate, which serves as a moisture barrier against the absorption of atmospheric moisture. If moisture is taken up through cracks or discontinuities in the coating, weeping (formation of syrup on the chocolate) may occur because absorbed water dilutes the sugar in the center.[30] This physical defect can be mistakenly attributed to yeast spoilage.

56.3   SPOILAGE OF CONFECTIONERY

56.31.   Bacteria

Early studies attributed the spoilage of chocolate-coated fondant creams[25, 50] to nonpathogenic *Clostridium* spp. from egg albumen and sugar. This would appear highly improbable with current manufacturing practices because most fondant creams contain at least 70% dissolved solids, and clostridia are unlikely to grow below a_w 0.94, which is equivalent to 48% wt/wt sucrose or even less glucose. It is also improbable that members of the genera *Bacillus, Clostridium, Leuconostoc,* and *Lactobacillus* are capable of directly causing spoilage of confections[13] because they are unlikely to grow at an a_w of <0.90.[48]

56.32.   Yeasts

Yeasts are the principal causes of spoilage in confectioneries,[3, 4, 13, 35, 47, 53] but molds may cause spoilage when moisture, packaging, and temperature conditions are favorable.

Spoilage of confectionery by fermentative yeasts must be studied with considerable care because the causative organisms may lyse, resulting in auto-sterilization, or may not be detected if inappropriate methods are used (see MS1559Q). Direct microscopic observation of a spoiled product is often a valuable diagnostic tool; however, organisms found in high numbers may not be the cause of spoilage. In order for microbial spoilage to occur, the water activity must be ≥0.60, the product must contain organisms capable of growth in that product, and factors such as temperature and pH must permit growth.

The limiting a_w for growth of osmotolerant yeasts in confectionery is about 0.60, but there appears to be an interaction between available nutrients and the limiting a_w. For example, the limiting a_w for osmotolerant yeasts in nutrient rich confectioneries such as pralines and caramel is 0.60,[48] but in a less nutrient-rich confectionery the a_w required to limit osmotolerant yeasts is about 0.75.[39] Further, growth of most osmotolerant yeasts in sugar-rich materials will not occur unless some B vitamins are present.[31]

Zygosaccharomyces rouxii and, less frequently, *Brettanomyces bruxellensis* have been identified as causes of spoilage, but in many literature reports of spoilage the osmotolerant yeasts were not identified. *Z. rouxii* can grow over a wide range of pH,[14] and has an increased resistance to sorbate with decreasing a_w.[41] *Torulopsis etchellsii, Torulopsis versatilis*, and *Candida pelliculosa* have caused gassy spoilage of chocolate syrup with 75° Brix.[47]

Marzipan is spoiled by yeasts when the population reaches 10^5 to 10^7.[52] *Z. rouxii* is the common spoilage yeast and causes gassy bursting of the marzipan, accompanied by the development of weak aromatic, yeasty, or yeasty-bitter odors. The growth of osmotolerant yeasts may be so slow in marzipan and coated fondants that evidence of spoilage may not be seen for several months.[32] The doubling times for *Z. rouxii* in persipan and marzipan raw masses are about 1 and 0.5 days, respectively.[3] Initial levels of the spoilage organism also control the time required for spoilage to be evident.

Yeast spoilage of chocolate-covered creams and marzipan is evidenced by cracking of the coating and leaking of the fondant and syrup. Drying of the syrup as a result of cracking may decrease the a_w and thereby stop growth.

56.33. Molds

Molds may spoil confectionery through development of visible mold mycelia on the surfaces of products or packaging materials. Their growth may produce a musty odor and taste. A soapy taste may develop in high fat-content products because of enzymatic hydrolysis of lipids.[32] Molds of the genera *Aspergillus, Verticillium, Penicillium, Mucor, Rhizopus,* and *Tricothecium*[26, 51] are among the many different molds isolated from confectionery products. Visible molds usually occur on the surface, but development may also occur in the interior.[32, 51] Proper control of water content in the formula is essential to prevent mold spoilage. As an example, marzipan made with 20% moisture (higher than normal) was individually wrapped in foil and then packed in polyethylene bags to prevent loss of moisture; this led to mold spoilage.[22] Syneresis in pectin jellies provides water for mold growth.

Spoilage of raw ingredients such as nuts, dairy products, cocoa, and cocoa beans by molds may occur as a result of storage under moist conditions. Some ingredients should be packaged in moisture-proof packaging. Packaging of ingredients while hot may lead to moisture condensation and localized mold growth[7] on the interior of moisture-proof containers; thus, packaging of certain ingredients should permit the escape of a limited amount of moisture.[6] Migration of moisture can take place within a product in a moisture-proof package, especially if there is a temperature differential.[23]

56.34. Miscellaneous Defects

Fat blooms and sugar blooms on chocolate are physical defects that are misdiagnosed frequently as mold growth. Fat bloom makes chocolate appear gray-white. Fat bloom has a greasy appearance and under the microscope minute fat crystals are seen. Fat bloom is associated with improper temperature control at one or more stages in processing or storage.[34] Sugar bloom is similar to fat bloom but is not greasy. In severe cases sugar bloom has a crystalline appearance, is rough to the touch, and has small sugar crystals that can be seen under the microscope. Sugar bloom is associated with storage of chocolate products exposed to temperature changes sufficient to cause condensation of moisture on the surface. It is also caused by storage under conditions of high (78% or higher) relative humidity.[34]

Lipases from microorganisms can cause hydrolytic rancidity in chocolate products.[34, 44] Hydrolytic rancidity occurs when cocoa butter replacers such as palm kernel oil are used. As an example, hydrogenated palm kernel oil contains about 47% lauric acid and is especially useful as a cocoa butter replacer. Active lipases separate lauric acid from the fat as a free fatty acid and this results in a distinctly soapy taste.[42] Capric and myristic acids also have a soapy taste.

Residual lipases remaining after processes have destroyed or otherwise removed microorganisms from ingredients may cause hydrolytic rancidity. For example, a soapy taste in "white chocolate" was attributed to lipolyzed milk in which a *Bacillus* had grown prior to drying.[54]

Free fatty acids may be oxidatively metabolized to ketones; this results in a defect known as perfume rancidity.[36] Esterified fatty acids in hydrogenated liquid oils and nuts in some confections may be oxidized.

Off-flavors, other than from lipolytic and oxidative rancidity, may occur in confectionery and be mistaken for microbiological or lipolytic spoilage. Absorption of odors from plastic wrappers, from inks used in printing,[34] and from storage near detergents, disinfectants, oils, or tobacco may impact off-odors to confectionery products.

56.4 PATHOGENS

Confectionery products by the nature of their composition, processing, and physical and chemical characteristics rarely are associated with foodborne diseases.

Pathogenic microorganisms such as *Salmonella* or other *Enterobacteriaceae* may be introduced into the confection processing environment through raw materials, including commodities like cocoa beans and raw milk. Several incidents have been reported of salmonellosis caused by consuming contaminated chocolate products.[11, 19, 21, 57] Other foodborne microbial infections are possible but infrequently encountered. The potential of *Listeria monocyto-*

genes as a contaminant in chocolate and confectionery products has not been fully established. Further research is needed to determine the incidence and significance of *L. monocytogenes* in these products. Cocoa bean roasting and milk pasteurization and cooking operations are generally believed adequate to destroy most vegetative microorganisms in these materials.[27] Pathogens may also enter the environment or product through ingredients like eggs, gelatin, cereal grain products, nuts, coconut, and spices[38] or via pests or personnel. Effective traffic, air, pest, and especially water control systems can prevent such pathogenic contaminants from establishing residences, reproduction pockets, and subsequent cross-contamination within the processing environment.[12]

Because confectionery products usually do not support the growth of bacteria, these products have not been associated with bacteriologically induced intoxications, e.g., by *Staphylococcus aureus*, *Bacillus cereus*, or *Clostridium perfringens*. Mycotoxicoses from this product group also have not been reported, although occasionally product spoilage by molds has been observed, and the introduction of mycotoxins from ingredients, e.g., nuts, has been of concern.[27]

Except for sporeforming bacteria, the presence of significant levels of pathogenic microorganisms in confectionery products usually is avoidable through raw materials and environmental (post-process) contamination controls.

Bacilli are the usually predominant microorganisms in many confectionery products, with *B. cereus* probably often present.[18] However, these products have not been associated with illnesses caused by that organism.

Although bacteria do not grow in most confections, the water activity and/or fat contents generally afford marked microbial survival.[20] When a confectionery product contains a pathogenic organism, it is likely to survive in the product for several months after manufacturing.[46]

56.5   MICROBIAL CONTROL PROCEDURES

The prevention of spoilage and microbial contamination of chocolate and confectionery products is accomplished in several ways.

56.51.   Raw Materials

Sensitive raw ingredients may serve as a means of entry for pathogenic microorganisms into the plant environment. Ingredients used in the manufacture of confectionery that may be considered sensitive materials are processed eggs, gelatin, coconut, dairy products, cocoa beans, nuts, and colors.[38] If contamination is present, the level is usually low. Therefore it is essential to use sampling plans adequate for the detection of small numbers of microorganisms, e.g. salmonellae.[28] Also, refer to Chapter 2 of this book and the Bacteriological Analytical Manual.[49]

Segregation of raw materials and unit operations that process these ingredients is important in preventing cross-contamination between raw and finished goods. For the manufacture of chocolate products, it is absolutely necessary to handle cocoa beans as a contaminated raw material. Therefore operations that clean, roast, and winnow beans should be physically separated from subsequent downstream processing.

56.52. Thermal Processing

The manufacture of chocolate and confectionery products offers limited but real opportunities for microbial destruction. Roasting of cocoa beans at temperatures of 210° to 250°F should destroy non-sporeforming pathogenic bacteria such as salmonellae. The same roasting procedure substantially reduces the microbial content of beans. Heat-resistant sporeforming bacteria such as *Bacillus cereus, Bacillus licheniformis*, and *Bacillus subtilis* survive roasting and will carry over into finished goods.

Recent advances in chocolate processing offer a variety of cocoa bean treatments prior to or in lieu of roasting to reduce microbial contamination. Micronizing is an infrared treatment to which whole beans are subjected before shelling. Micronizing improves removal of shell from the nib, thereby reducing microflora on the nib surface. Treatment of unroasted nibs with moist heat followed by convection heating has been shown to be more effective for microbial control than dry heat.[2] Another alternative has been "liquor roasting," where a low percentage of moisture is added to cocoa liquor prior to heating.[33] Removal of added moisture completes the process resulting in microbial counts in the order of 10^1 to 10^2 per g.

The use of a thermal process during certain confectionery operations presents an opportunity to control spoilage fungi. The amount of heat applied for destruction of these microorganisms varies somewhat depending on the a_w of the product. But on a practical basis, yeasts in fondants, for example, are normally destroyed within 20 min at 60°C[20] or in syrups by 15 to 20 min at 80°C.[45]

56.53. Product Formulation

Appropriate control of a_w during product formulation will prevent yeast and mold spoilage. Control of a_w in the formulation of sugar confectionaries is achieved through increasing osmotic pressure by adding glucose syrup, corn syrup with high dextrose equivalent, high fructose syrup, or invert sugar with sucrose. Sucrose syrup alone does not provide a sufficiently low a_w. Addition of 2% to 4% glycerol or sorbitol retards crystallization. Inhibition of yeasts is enhanced by the addition of a small amount of lactic or acetic acid. Where legally permitted, the addition of combinations of acidulants and preservatives, e.g., citric acid and sorbic acid, offers protection against yeast growth.[40]

56.54. Plant Environment

The processing environment of a chocolate or confectionery plant should be treated like any other food manufacturing facility with respect to good manufacturing practices. Certain areas, however, deserve special attention to enhance the control of microbial contamination.

Air, dust, and moisture provide means of microbial transmission in these plant environments. Dust generated by raw material handling can be conveyed throughout a plant if air handling systems are not properly installed. This may lead to cross-contamination of in-process or finished goods. Uncontrolled moisture may provide opportunities for microbes to proliferate and establish themselves permanently in a plant that produces low a_w products. Sources of uncontrolled moisture may be water and steam line leaks, condensation, leaking roofs, and improper "wet cleaning" methods.

Proper cleaning and sanitation procedures should be selected based upon type of equipment, material composition, and location of moisture sensitive processes within the plant. Judicious use of water for cleaning should be established and complement the plant's moisture control plan.

Special care should be given to the control of osmotolerant yeasts in processing equipment. Confectionery residues in equipment are naturally selective for osmotolerant yeasts. Process equipment in which water is used for production should be washed well with aqueous cleaning solutions and disinfected with chemical sanitizers or steam. Removal of food residues from difficult-to-clean equipment is also necessary to prevent the establishment of preservative-resistant yeast populations.[40]

An effective environmental sampling program should be established to monitor the above areas of concern. Implementation of a Hazard Analysis Critical Control Point (HACCP) program[55] is recommended to control the quality and safety of confectionery manufacture.[56]

56.6 RECOMMENDED METHODS

56.61. Routine Methods

Aerobic plate count—Chapter 4
Coliform organisms and *Escherichia coli*—Chapter 24
Salmonella—Chapter 25
Yeasts and molds—Chapter 16

56.62. Supplemental Recommendations

Bacillus cereus—Chapter 35
Listeria—Chapter 38
Mycotoxins—Chapter 43
Osmophilic yeasts—Chapter 13

Staphylococcus aureus—Chapter 33
Water activity—Chapter 8

56.63. Rapid Alternatives

For various specific applications, some of the more "rapid" methods occasionally are useful. However, they are not broadly applicable to monitoring all raw materials, environmental control, in-process and finished product testing, or for all product types. Careful thought is necessary to identify the exact purpose of an evaluation, its urgency, the required precision, and often the correlation between the rapid test results and those from another more conventional or standard test procedure. Some of the alternative systems are listed below:

Enzyme immunoassays for *Salmonella*[16] (Chapters 25, 39). *Listeria* (Chapter 38), and aflatoxin[43]

Nucleic acid hybridization assays for *Salmonella*[16, 17] (Chapter 39) and *Listeria* Chapters 38, 39)

Impedance (conductance/capacitance) determinations[15] for aerobic plate count, yeasts, and coliforms (Chapter 39)

Coliform direct plating (VRB) procedure (Chapter 24)

E. coli MUG assay[1] (Chapter 39).

For cocoa and chocolate products, the *Salmonella* test pre-enrichment medium should be formulated to attenuate the naturally occurring microbial inhibitors in these products.

56.7 INTERPRETATION OF DATA

Aerobic plate counts generally are less than 10^4 per g for sugar confections and 10^3 per g to 10^6 per g (often dependent upon the nature of the cocoa bean roasting) for cocoa and chocolate products.[10]

Coliform organisms frequently are undetectable and rarely are present at levels above 100 per g in confectionery products. *E. coli* usually is not found— <1 per g by direct plating on VRB; <3 per g by most probable number (MPN).

Molds rarely are present at levels above 100 per g in sugar confections and occasionally may be found in the range 10^2 per g to 10^3 per g in cocoa and chocolate products.

Yeast counts usually do not exceed 100 per g. The absence of osmotolerant yeasts is critical for some products with a_w values above 0.62 (see Chapter 13, Halophilic and Osmophilic Microorganisms).

Occasionally low levels, below 10^3 per g, of *Staphylococcus aureus* or *Bacillus cereus* may be present; they do not seem to indicate any health hazard at these levels in confectionery products.

Any level of *Salmonella* is unacceptable in chocolate and confectionery products.

56.8   REFERENCES

1. Andrews, W. H., Wilson, C. R., and Poelma, P. L. 1987. Glucuronidase assay in a rapid MPN determination for recovery of *Escherichia coli* from selected foods. J. Assn. Off. Anal. Chem. 70(1): 31.

2. Anon. 1979. Cocoa preparation by Barth's newly developed NARS short dwell process. Confect. Prod. 45: 546.

3. Blaschke-Hellmessen, R. and Teuschel, G. 1970. *Saccharomyces rouxii* Boutroux als Ursache von Garungserscheinungen in geformten Marzipan- und Persipanartikeln und deren Verhutung in Herstellerbetrieb. Die Nahrung 14(4): 249.

4. Bocklet, G. 1980. Marzipan, seine Herstellung und Verarbeitung. Brot und Backwaren 28(7/8): 19.

5. CAC. 1981. Codex Alimentarius Comm. Standards for Cocoa Products and Chocolate. CAC/ Vol. VII, ed. 1. World Health Organization.

6. Cakebread, S. H. 1969. Chemistry of candy. Shelf-life of candy. Manufacturing Confectioner 49(2): 38.

7. Cakebread, S. H. 1971. Chemistry of candy: Factors in microbiological deterioration. Manufacturing Confectioner 51(4): 45.

8. CFR. 1987a. Part 110—Current Good Manufacturing Practice in Manufacturing, Packing, or Holding Human Food. In Title 21, parts 100 to 169. Code of Fed. Reg. U.S. Govt. Print. Office, Washington, D.C.

9. CFR. 1987b. Part 163—Cacao products. In Title 21, parts 100 to 169. Code of Fed. Reg. U.S. Govt. Print. Office, Washington, D.C.

10. Collins-Thompson, D. L., Weiss, K. F., Riedel, G. W., and Cushing, C. B. 1981. Survey of and microbiological guidelines for chocolate products in Canada. Can. Inst. Food Sci. Technol. J. 14(3): 203.

11. Craven, P. C., Baine, W. B., Mackel, D. C., Barker, W. H., Gangarosa, E. J., Goldfield, M., Rosenfeld, H., Altman, R., Lachapelle, G., Davies, J. W., and Swanson, R. C. 1975. International outbreak of *Salmonella eastbourne* infection traced to contaminated chocolate. Lancet 1: 788.

12. D'Aoust, J. Y. 1977. *Salmonella* and the chocolate industry. A Review. J. Food Prot. 40(10): 718.

13. Defigueiredo, M. P. 1979. Confectionery products. In "Controlling Microorganisms in Food Processing." Spec. Rep. No. 31, April 1979, p. 20. New York State Agric. Exper. Sta., Geneva, N.Y.

14. English, M. P. 1953. The fermentation of malt extract by an osmophilic yeast. J. Gen. Microbiol. 9: 15.

15. Firstenberg-Eden, R. 1986. Electrical impedance for determining microbial quality of foods. In "Foodborne Microorganisms and Their Toxins: Developing Methodology," ed. M.D. Pierson and N.J. Stern, p. 129. Marcel Dekker, Inc., New York.

16. Flowers, R. S., Klatt, M. J., Mozola, M. A., Curiale, M. S., Gabis, D. A., and Silliker, J. H. 1987a. DNA hybridization assay for detection of *Salmonella* in foods: Collaborative study. J. Assn. Off. Anal. Chem. 70(3): 521.

17. Flowers, R. S., Klatt, M. J., Robison, B. A., Mattingly, J. A., Gabis, D. A., and Silliker, J. H. 1987b. Enzyme immunoassay for detection of *Salmonella* in low-moisture foods: Collaborative study. J. Assn. Off. Anal. Chem. 70(3): 530.

18. Gabis, D. A., Langlois, B. E., and Rudnick, A. W. 1970. Microbiological examination of cocoa powder. Appl. Microbiol. 27: 66.

19. Gastrin, B., Kampe, A., Nystrom, K., Oden-Johanson, B., Wessel, G., and Zetterberg, B. 1972. An epidemic of *Salmonella durham* caused by contaminated cocoa. Lakartidningen 69(46): 5335. (Original in Swedish).

20. Gibson, B. 1973. The effect of high sugar concentrations on the heat resistance of vegetative microorganisms. J. Appl. Bacteriol. 36: 365.

21. Gill, O. N., Bartlett, C., Sockett, P., Vaile, M., Rowe, B., Gilbert, R., Dulake, C., Murrell, H., and Salmosa, S. 1983. Outbreak of *Salmonella napoli* infection caused by contaminated chocolate bars. Lancet 1: 574.

22. Gondar, I. 1980. Marzipan production in the Duna chocolate factory. Edesipar 31(2): 44. (Original in Hungarian). Food Sci. and Tech. Abstr. 13(05) 5K31, 1981.

23. Hazeu, W. and Heuck, H. J. 1966. Changes of humidity inside packages due to environmental conditions. Society of Chemical Industries, Monograph Series. London, 23: 224.

24. Hilker, J. S. 1976. Confectionery products. In "Compendium of Methods for the Microbiological Examination of Foods," 1st ed., ed. M. L. Speck, p. 608. Am. Pub. Health Assn., Washington, D.C.

25. Hill, G. 1925. *Clostridium multifermentans* in chocolate cream candies. J. Bacteriol. 10: 413.

26. Hopko, I. 1979. Food hygienic aspects of the confectionery industry. Edesipar 30(1): 8. (Original in Hungarian).

27. ICMSF. 1980. "Microbial Ecology of Foods." Vol. 2. "Food Commodities." Internl. Comm. on Microbiol. Spec. for Foods. Academic Press, New York.

28. ICMSF. 1986. "Microorganisms in Foods." Vol. 2. "Sampling for Microbiological Analysis; Principles and Specific Applications." 2nd ed. Internl. Comm. on Microbiol. Spec. for Foods. Univ. of Toronto Press, Toronto, Can.

29. IOCC. 1977. "Microbiological Examination of Chocolates and Other Cocoa Products." International Office of Cocoa and Chocolate and International Sugar Confectionery Manufacturers' Assn. 1972, Ave. de Cortenbergh, B-1040, Bruxelles, Belg.

30. Lindley, P. 1972. Chocolates and sugar confectionery, jams, and jellies. In "Quality Control in the Food Industry," Vol. 3, ed. S. M. Herschodoerfer. p. 259. Academic Press, New York.

31. Lochhead, A. G. and Landerkin, G. B. 1942. Nutrilite requirements of osmophilic yeasts. J. Bacteriol. 44: 343.

32. Mansvelt, J. W. 1964. Microbiological spoilage in the confectionery industry. Confectionery Production 30(1): 33.

33. Martin, R. A. Jr. 1987. Chocolate. In "Advances in Food Research," ed. C. D. Chichester, p. 211. Academic Press, New York.

34. Minifie, B. 1980. "Chocolate, Cocoa, and Confectionery: Science and Technology," 2nd ed. Avi Publ., Westport, Conn.

35. Mohs, H. J. 1979. Hygiene defects. The potential for whole batches to be spoiled. Susswaren 23(11): 27.

36. Mossel, D. A. A. and Sand, F. E. M. J. 1968. Occurrence and prevention of microbial deterioration of confectionery products. Conserva 17(2): 23.

37. Pitt, J. I. 1975. Xerophilic fungi and the spoilage of foods of plant origin. In "Water Relations of Foods," ed. R. B. Duckworth, p. 273. Academic Press, London.

38. Pivnick, H. and Gabis, D. A. 1984. Confectionery products. In "Compendium of Methods for the Microbiological Examination of Foods," 2nd ed., ed. M. L. Speck, p. 700. Am. Pub. Health Assn., Washington, D.C.

39. Pouncy, A. E. and Summers, B. C. L. 1939. The micromeasurement of relative humidity for the control of osmophilic yeasts in confectionery products. J. Soc. of Chem. Indus. England. Transactions and Communication 58: 162.

40. Restaino, L., Lenovich, L. M., and Bills, S. 1982. Effect of acids and sorbate combinations on the growth of four osmophilic yeasts. J. Food Protect. 45: 1138.

41. Restaino, L., Bills, S., Tscherneff, K., and Lenovich, L. M. 1983. Growth characteristics of *Saccharomyces rouxii* isolated from chocolate syrup. Appl. Environ. Microbiol. 45(5): 1614.

42. Rossell, J. B. 1983. Measurements of rancidity. In "Rancidity in Foods," eds. J. Allen and R. J. Hamilton, p. 259. Proc. of an SCI Symposium. Applied Science Publ. Ltd., London, England.

43. Scott, P. M. 1988. Mycotoxins. J. Assn. Off. Anal. Chem. 71(1): 70.

44. Shahani, K. M. 1975. Lipases and esterases. In "Enzymes in Food Processing," 2nd ed., ed. G. Reed, p. 184. Academic Press, New York.

45. Silliker, J. H. 1977. Bacterial Contaminants in Confections. Presented to the 94th Annual Conv. of the Natl. Confectioners Assn., Chicago, Ill., June 25.

46. Tamminga, S. K. 1979. The longevity of *Salmonella* in chocolate. Antonie van Leeuwenhoek J. Microbiol. Serol. 45(1): 153.

47. Tilbury, R. H. 1976. The stability of intermediate moisture foods with respect to yeasts. In "Intermediate Moisture Foods," eds. R. Davies, G. G. Birch, and K. J. Parker, p. 138. Applied Science Publ., London.

48. Troller, J. 1979. Food spoilage by microorganisms tolerating low-a$_w$ environments. Food Technol. 33(1): 72.

49. U.S. FDA. 1984. "Bacteriological Analytical Manual," 6th ed., Food Drug Admin. Assn. of Off. Anal. Chem., Arlington, Va.

50. Weinzirl, J. 1922. The cause of explosion in chocolate candies. J. Bacteriol. 7: 599.

51. Windisch, S. and Neumann, I. 1965a. Uber die "Wasserflecken" des Marzipans und ihre Entstehung. Zeitschrift fur Lebensmittel-Untersuchung und -Forschung 129: 9.

52. Windisch, S. and Neumann, I. 1965b. Zur mikrobiologischen Untersuchung von Marzipan. 3. Mitteilung: Erfahrungen aus der Betriebskontrolle bei der Marzipanherstellung. Susswaren 9(10): 540.

53. Windisch, S., Kowalski, S., and Zander, I. 1978. Demonstration of osmotolerant yeasts in almonds. CCB Review for Chocolate, Confectionery and Bakery. 3(2): 28.

54. Witlin, B. and Smyth, R. D. 1957. "Soapiness" in "white" chocolate candies. Amer. J. Pharmacy. 129: 135.

Chapter 57

NUT MEATS

A. Douglas King, Jr. and L. Duane Lindsay

57.1 INTRODUCTION

Nut meats are derived from processed nuts harvested from trees, shrubs, or plants. They are consumed salted, dry or oil roasted, or raw. Nut meats are sold primarily to the food processing industry and are used in baked goods, cake mixes, candy, cereals, ice cream, etc. Nut meats are also sold shelled or in-shell for direct consumer use.

The nut meat industry has shown a steady growth over the past few decades. The largest nut meat production worldwide and in the United States is peanuts. The U.S. value of peanut production approached $950 million in 1985.[22] Almonds, pecans, and walnuts are the three largest U.S. tree nut crops. Worldwide, filbert production is second to peanuts. The U.S. production of tree nuts has more than doubled from 1971 to 1985, as has the U.S. export of tree nuts. About one-third of the U.S. tree nut and one-fifth of the shelled peanut production is exported. Half of shelled peanut production goes into peanut butter.

United States Standards for grades of the various nut meats are published by the United States Department of Agriculture (USDA) Marketing Service. Frequently buyers specify quality parameters for lots of nut meats for purchase. Specification covenants are made between customer and vendor.

57.2 GENERAL CONSIDERATIONS

Nut meat processing is normally a dry process. Nut meats with field dust deposited on them during growth and harvesting bring contaminating microorganisms into the processing plant. This is especially true of nuts with soft shells like almonds or peanuts and nuts with broken shells. Air lift (aspiration) sorting to remove lightweight pieces, such as shell and shriveled nut meats, also removes some field dirt.

Peanuts (ground nuts) are dried in the field after digging but before storage. Peanuts are usually dry roasted before grinding into peanut butter. Thus, peanut butter has a low water activity and microbial growth is prevented. Peanut butter has been recalled because of the presence of *Salmonella*. The presence of such pathogens in peanut butter is usually a result of mishandling after dry roasting. Aflatoxin is a concern because of the chance of mold growth and mycotoxin formation in the field or during storage.

The shells of pecans and certain other nuts are softened by humidifying to avoid breaking the nut meats during cracking.[2,7] Pistachio processing includes a flotation step to remove immature fruits. Pecan shell fragments are separated from nut pieces by flotation. Blanching in water or steam loosens the pellicle from almonds and peanuts. A salt water dip salts some nut meats. These water treatments can cause microbial contamination of the nut meat. Water treatments can also moisten the nut meats and increase their water activity. Good sanitation and frequent changes of water are needed to control microbial buildup.

Nuts that are not dry enough following harvest must be dried to prevent mold growth during storage. Heat is sometimes used to dry nut meats and to reduce microbial counts, but darkening of the nut meats may occur. Nut meats removed from refrigeration, particularly during periods of humid conditions, can have condensate formed on them. The condensate will cause the water activity to rise, encouraging growth of mold. Tempering the product to avoid radical temperature change, therefore, is a good practice. The moisture content of normal tree nuts ranges from 3.8% to 6.7%, which gives a water activity of 0.7 or lower, values where microbial growth is prevented[3] (Chapter 8).

The microbial flora on nut meats dies off during storage. Survival depends on temperature, nut meat water activity, composition of the nut meat, and time. Moisture contents that are higher, but below the level where growth can occur, and higher storage temperature accelerate the death rate.[11,12]

Gas sterilization of nut meats with propylene oxide reduces the microbial population.[1] Use of propylene oxide is permitted on tree nut meats but not on peanuts.[24] Regulations limit residual content of the agent in the nut meat to 300 ppm. Propylene oxide should only be applied once, in retorts, for a maximum of 4 hr exposure, at a temperature no higher than 125°F.

For further discussion of the microbiology of nut meats see ICMSF.[9]

57.3 MICROFLORA

Under normal conditions, bacteria that contaminate nut meats do not present a spoilage problem because they will not grow at the low water activity of these foods. Molds are of somewhat greater concern because of their ability to grow in relatively dry environments.

The number and types of microorganisms present on nut meats will depend primarily on conditions of harvest, processing, and storage. Genera of bacteria isolated from almonds and pecans (tree nuts) include *Enterobacter*, *Escherichia*, *Bacillus*, *Xanthomonas*, *Clostridium*, *Pseudomonas*, *Leuconostoc*, *Streptococcus*, *Micrococcus*, and certain members of the coryneform group (i.e., *Brevibacterium* and *Corynebacterium*). Nut meats are frequently contaminated with the molds *Penicillium*, *Aspergillus*, and *Fusarium*.[5,6,10,13,18] Nut meats from hard-shelled varieties have lower microbial counts than those from soft-shelled varieties. The nut meats of almonds in intact shells have lower counts than those from soft-shelled varieties. The nut meats of almonds in intact shells have lower counts than shelled nuts, and almonds harvested onto canvas have lower counts than those knocked to the ground. Nuts with the least foreign material have the lowest counts. Insect-damaged nut meats are more heavily contaminated than those that have not been infested.[13] The microbial counts on nut meats are often several thousand per g or less. Coliforms are not uncommon, but *Escherichia coli* is present on 4% or less of the samples.

The U.S. Food and Drug Administration (FDA) considers nuts to be adulterated when moldy or when positive for *E. coli*.[23] *E. coli* has not been found in pecans with unbroken shells.[8,19] Also, meats of whole pecans with no visible breaks or cracks did not become contaminated when soaked 24 hr in lactose broth containing *E. coli*. Longer soaking of pecans, e.g., 48 hr in water, resulted in the opening of 24% of the shell sutures; most failed to close completely when the nuts were redried. Similar findings have been made with walnuts.[15] Nuts harvested from orchards where farm animals have grazed are more likely to be contaminated with *E. coli* than those from orchards where grazing has not occurred.[16,17] Since *E. coli* may be present on nut meats before processing, its presence on processed nuts does not necessarily indicate poor processing plant practices.[13,17,19,20] Microorganisms present on almonds, Brazil nuts, filberts, peanuts, pecans, and walnuts are the result of contamination with orchard soil combined with (a) damaged or cracked nuts, (b) insect infestation, (c) diseased nuts, (d) contamination within the processing environment,[17] and (e) time in contact with the soil.[18]

57.4 PATHOGENS

Although tree nuts and ground nuts often are subject to microbial contamination, they are seldom vehicles in food poisoning outbreaks. Rarely they may contain *Salmonella*.[17] Usual thermal treatments that have been applied to in-shell pecans and pecan halves heavily contaminated with *Salmonella senftenberg*, *Salmonella anatum*, and *Salmonella typhimurium* did not destroy the salmonellae consistently.[4,13]

57.5 MOLDS AND MYCOTOXINS

Molds are common on nut meats. If the water activity of nut meats is high enough, mold spores will germinate. After germination, the hyphae can penetrate pecan tissue.[6] Nut meats are sometimes added to other foods, resulting in an environment where molds on the nut meats can grow, causing spoilage. Propylene oxide is sometimes used to reduce mold counts. Contamination, especially of peanuts, with aflatoxin produced by the mold *Aspergillus flavus* is particularly a health concern. For further discussion of mycotoxins see Chapter 43. Current FDA guidelines permit only 20 ppb aflatoxin in nut meats.

57.6 LABORATORY TESTS

Chapters 4, 24, and 16 describe the detection and enumeration of aerobic bacteria (APC), coliforms and *E. coli*, and molds and yeasts, respectively. Samples are rinsed to remove microorganisms from the nut meat surface. Twenty-five grams of nut meats are shaken 25 times in 0.1% peptone water or Butterfield's buffered phosphate initially and again 25 times 3 to 5 min later. Nut meats with a pellicle that does not come off easily are placed in a flask with the rinse solution on a rotary shaker for 10 min before removing the aliquot for microbial analysis. Avoid undue exposure to the inhibiting and destructive effects of tannins from the nuts by making serial dilutions promptly. No more than 15 min should elapse from adding diluent until completing the dilutions and inoculations.

Several media are available to count molds and yeasts on nut meats. If mucoraceous fungi such as *Mucor* or *Rhizopus* cause overgrowth on fungal petri plates, than dichloran rose bengal chloramphenicol agar (DRBC) or rose bengal chlortetracycline agar (RBC) is recommended for surface plating. Otherwise oxytetracycline glucose yeast extract agar (OGY) or potato dextrose agar (PDA) are suitable media.[14,21] Aspergillus flavus and parasiticus agar (AFPA) is a good medium to detect and enumerate these two molds.[14,21] Plates are examined after 42 to 48 hr incubation at 30°C for a characteristic bright orange-yellow reverse color.

FDA has specified that if an *E. coli* most probable number (MPN) of at least 0.36 per g, IMVIC confirmed, is found in two or more subsamples when less than 10 subsamples are examined, or in 20% or more of the subsamples where more than 10 are examined, the product is in noncompliance.[23]

Methods for detection of *Salmonella* are in Chapter 25. Compositing of analytical sample units is a time-saving measure. The presence of *Salmonella* in nut meats not intended for further processing is unacceptable.

Reference to appropriate methods for the determination of aflatoxins and other mycotoxins are given in Chapter 43.

57.7   REFERENCES

1. Beuchat, L. R. 1973. *Escherichia coli* on pecans: Survival under various storage conditions and disinfection with propylene oxide. J. Food Sci. 38: 1063.
2. Beuchat, L. R. 1975. Incidence of mold on pecan nuts at different points during harvesting. Appl. Microbiol. 29: 852.
3. Beuchat, L. R. 1978. Relationship of water activity to moisture content in tree nuts. J. Food Sci. 43: 754.
4. Beuchat, L. R. and Heaton, E. K. 1975. *Salmonella* survival on pecans as influenced by processing and storage conditions. Appl. microbiol. 29: 795.
5. Beuchat, L. R. and Heaton, E. K. 1980. Factors influencing fungal quality of pecans stored at refrigeration temperatures. J. Food Sci. 45: 251.
6. Chipley, J. R. and Heaton, E. K. 1971. Microbial flora of pecan meat. Appl. Microbiol. 22: 252.
7. Forbus, W. R. Jr., Tyson, B. L., and Ayers, J. L. 1979. Commercial feasibility of an in-line steam process for conditioning pecans to improve shelling efficiency and maintain product (nut meat) quality. J. Food. Sci. 44: 988.
8. Hall, H. E. 1971. The significance of *Escherichia coli* associated with nut meats. Food Technol. 25: 230.
9. ICMSF. 1980. Chapter 21 In "Microbial Ecology of Foods," Vol. 2, p. 635. Academic Press, New York.
10. Joffe, A. Z. 1969. The mycoflora of fresh and stored ground nut kernels in Israel. Mycopathol. Mycol. Appl. 39: 255.
11. King, A. D. Jr. and Schade, J. E. 1986. Influence of almond harvesting, processing, and storage on fungal population and flora. J. Food Sci. 51: 202.
12. King, A. D. Jr., Halbrook, W. U., Fuller, G., and Whitehand, L. C. 1983. Almond nut meat moisture and water activity and its influence on fungal flora and seed composition. J. Food Sci. 48: 615.
13. King, A. D. Jr., Miller, M. J., and Eldridge, L. C. 1970. Almond harvesting, processing and microbial flora. Appl. Microbiol. 20: 208.
14. King, A. D. Jr., Pitt, J. I., Beuchat, L. R., and Corry, J. E. L. 1986. "Methods for the Mycological Examination of Food." Plenum Press, New York.
15. Kokal, D. 1965. Viability of *Escherichia coli* on English walnut meats (*Juglans regia*). J. Food Sci. 30: 325.
16. Kokal, D. and Thorpe, D. W. 1969. Occurrence of *Escherichia coli* in almonds of Nonpareil variety. Food Technol. 23: 227.
17. Marcus, K. A. and Amling, H. J. 1973. *Escherichia coli* field contamination of pecan nuts. Applied Microbiology 26: 279.
18. McDonald, D. 1970. Fungal infection of ground nut fruit after maturity and during drying. Trans. Br. Mycoli. Soc. 54: 461.
19. Ostrolenk, M. and Hunter, A. C. 1939. Bacteria of the colon-aerogenes group on nut meats. Food Research 4: 453.
20. Ostrolenk, M. and Welch, H. 1941. Incidence and significance of the colon-aerogenes group on pecan meats. Food Research 6: 117.
21. Pitt, J. I. and Hocking, A. D. 1985. "Fungi and Food Spoilage." Academic Press, Sydney, Australia.
22. USDA. 1985. Agricultural Statistics, Dept. of Agric., Govt. Print. Off., Washington, D.C.
23. USHEW. 1973. "Guideline Manual 7412.06" Pub. Health Serv. Food and Drug Admin., Bureau of Foods. U.S. Dept. Health, Ed., and Welfare, Washington, D.C.
24. USHEW. 1978. Propylene Oxide. 21 CFR 193.380. Pub. Health Serv. Food and Drug Admin. U.S. Dept. Health, Ed., and Welfare, Washington, D.C.

Chapter 58

SOFT DRINKS

Don F. Splittstoesser and David P. Ransom

58.1 INTRODUCTION

Soft drinks are a class of nonalcoholic beverages that contain water, nutritive or nonnutritive sweeteners, acids, flavors, colors, emulsifiers, preservatives, and various other compounds that are added for their functional properties. Some contain fruit juices such as citrus, apple, pear, and grape. Most of the soft drinks consumed in the United States are carbonated with 1.5 to 4 volumes of carbon dioxide.

The pH range of soft drinks is from 2.5 to 4.0. Colas and ginger ales generally have the lowest pH while root beers and cream sodas have some of the highest values. Citric acid is the most widely used acidulant. Colas, which commonly have a pH of 2.5 to 2.8, generally are acidified with phosphoric acid.

58.2 MICROBIOLOGY

58.21 Types of Organisms

While a variety of microorganisms may be found in soft drinks, only a few aciduric groups are of significance. Most bacteria, including pathogenic species, rapidly die off in the acidic environment of these beverages.[3] Bacterial spores would be expected to survive for extended periods of time, but would not be able to germinate and grow at the low pH of most soft drinks. Yeasts are the most important group of spoilage microorganisms because they tolerate the acidity and can multiply under anaerobic conditions. Certain lactic acid bacteria can also grow under these conditions when sufficient nutrients are present for this fastidious group of microorganisms. Although acetic acid bacteria and molds are also aciduric, they will grow only when dissolved oxygen is present, as may be the situation in certain noncarbonated soft drinks.[5]

Growth results in the production of haze, sediment, off-flavors, and gas. When yeasts are responsible for spoilage, sufficient carbon dioxide may be produced to burst the bottle or can.

58.22   Sources of Contamination

The flavor concentrates, sweeteners, and other ingredients of soft drinks are rarely the source of the yeasts and lactic acid bacteria that can cause spoilage. During preparation, the concentrates have been processed to give a commercially sterile product, and sugar for the soft drink industry has long had a specification that prescribes no more than 10 yeasts, 10 molds, and 200 bacteria per 10 g.

Buildup of microorganisms in the bottling plant is the major cause of beverage contamination. Osmophilic yeasts can grow in liquid sugar during storage in tanks, especially in areas where condensate forms and thus reduces the Brix. Spoilage organisms can multiply in equipment that is difficult to clean, such as proportioning pumps, pipelines, carbonators, and filling machines.[1, 9] Cans and bottles can also be a source of contamination if not adequately washed before filling.

58.23   Principles of Preservation

Successful preservation of soft drinks depends on controlling contamination and applying various synergistic factors, described below, that prevent microbial growth.[2, 4, 6, 10]

Careful cleaning and sanitizing during shutdown periods will prevent excessive contamination. All areas downstream from the blending operations are especially vulnerable to microbial buildup.[1] The traditional method has been to use a germicide such as chlorine to sanitize the lines after cleaning. The current trend, however, is to kill the spoilage organisms by circulating hot water, about 185°F, through the lines for at least 20 min. This procedure has been found to be more effective than the use of cold sanitizers. Such treatment should be conducted within 24 hr before the line is operated.

The low pH and high levels of carbonation in colas generally make them resistant to the growth of spoilage microorganisms. Other carbonated soft drinks often contain benzoic acid, sorbic acid, or a combination of the two to prevent the growth of yeasts. However, certain species, in particular *Zygosaccharomyces bailii*, are able to tolerate high concentrations of these preservatives,[7] as well as moderately high carbonation. Soft drinks that contain fruit juices are also susceptible to spoilage by lactic acid bacteria, primarily species of *Lactobacillus* and *Leuconostoc*. In general, these organisms are resistant to benzoic and sorbic acids, and therefore controlling contamination is the most effective preventive measure.

In some countries a heat treatment is used for the preservation of soft drinks.[8] However, such pasteurization is not currently practiced in the United States.

58.3   RECOMMENDED METHODS

58.31   Sampling Procedures

Sampling must be designed to identify specific sites of contamination in a bottling plant. When testing for filler bowl contamination, the sample size should be a complete turn of the filler because frequently only one or two filler valves contribute to spoilage risk. Rinse water (chlorinated or dechlorinated water rinsed through filler valves) or finished beverage may be collected by normal filling procedures using standard beverage containers. When sampling product from the warehouse or trade, a sample size equal to three times the number of valves in the filler is necessary to guarantee that one complete turn of the filler is tested. Because high-speed equipment can fill 2,000 containers per min, it is important to collect a sample size statistically valid for detecting one or two contaminated valves.

Samples should also be collected at appropriate locations on the line from the syrup room to the filler. To accomplish this, sample petcocks must be plumbed into the system at key locations and samples properly collected. Care must be taken to avoid contamination or lethality (from flaming) during sampling. Additionally, swab samples should be collected to detect concentrations of spoilage organisms in key locations.

Examples of locations for petcock sampling are—
    Water and syrup sides of proportioner
    Blending pump after proportioner
    Sight glasses on saturator, carbo cooler, and batch tanks
    Syrup lines
    Water lines
    Sugar lines
Swab samples are frequently collected from—
    Sight glasses
    Snifts
    Gaskets
    Syrup manifolds
    Transfer hoses and couplings
    Syrup stainers
    Portable pumps

58.32   Aciduric Bacteria (Chapter 15)

58.33   Yeasts and Molds (Chapter 16)

58.34   Membrane Filtration (Chapter 4)

Membrane filtration is normally used when culturing microorganisms from soft drinks or rinse water samples because concentration is necessary to detect low levels of contamination. These methods are rapid, are easily learned by personnel with little training in microbiology, and, unlike procedures employing pipetting, foaming is not a problem when vacuum filtering large volumes of beverage. Sterile media are added to filter pads from premeasured ampoules, which are commercially available. The filters are incubated 5 days at 25°C for the detection of yeasts and molds and 2 to 5 days at 35°C for bacteria. Traditional plating methods are not used in beverage plants because of a lack of equipment for working with agar and because sample sizes would be inadequate. Selective enrichment methods for various spoilage organisms are available and can be employed in bottling plants provided a source of sterile liquid media is available.

58.4   INTERPRETATION OF DATA

Data generated in soft drink bottling plants are useful in assessing either sanitation or spoilage risk. When general media are used and fresh (less than 1 hr old) samples are tested, total count data can indicate sanitation effectiveness. Sanitation cannot be assessed by testing old rinse water samples, because of frequent growth of organisms, or by testing old beverage samples, because of frequent death of organisms. When selective media are used, spoilage organisms can be quantified and an estimate of spoilage risk can be made for specific beverages that have been challenged with similar organisms in a research laboratory. Data from swab sampling and selective enrichment tests can be used to indicate the presence or absence of spoilage organisms in key locations of a bottling plant.

Interpretation of data is dependent upon the type of beverage, formulation, and company specifications. Following is a hypothetical table indicating how data might be interpreted for beverage X in company Y.

Sample	Microorganism	Results	Interpretation
Beverage or rinse water	Spoilage yeast[a]	≥50 cfu[b]/100 ml	Extreme risk; shut line down and sanitize until counts are below 10 cfu/ml. Hold product 21 days and retest.

		10 to 50 cfu/100 ml	High risk; improve sanitation. Hold product 21 days and retest.
		1 to 10 cfu/100 ml	Moderate risk; improve sanitation.
		<10 cfu/100 ml	Low risk.
Finished beverage	Lactic acid bacteria	>10 cfu/100 ml	Moderate risk; improve sanitation.
Swab from sugar tank	Spoilage yeast	Positive enrichment test in 48 hr	High risk of contamination spreading to line; sanitize tank and retest.
Rinse water	All organisms (TPC)^c	≥200 cfu/100 ml	High risk; improve sanitation. Hold product 21 days and retest.
		50 to 200 cfu/100 ml	Moderate risk; improve sanitation.
		<50 cfu/100 ml	Low risk.
Beverage or rinse water	All yeasts	≥200 cfu/100 ml	Extreme risk; shut line down and sanitize until counts are below 10 cfu/ml. Hold product 21 days and retest.
		50 to 200 cfu/100 ml	High risk; improve sanitation. Hold product 21 days and retest.
		10 to 50 cfu/100 ml	Moderate risk; improve sanitation.
		<10 cfu/100 ml	Low risk.

^{a}*Zygosaccharomyces bailii*, *Z. rouxii*, *Z. bisporus*, and atypical *Saccharomyces cerevisiae*, which are preservative resistant.
^{b}Colony forming units.
^{c}Total plate count.

58.5 REFERENCES

1. Berry, J. M. 1979. Yeast problems in the food and beverage industry. In "Food Mycology," ed. M. E. Rhodes. G. K. Hall, Boston.
2. Cole, M. B., Franklin, J. G., and Keenan, M. H. J. 1987. Probability of growth of the spoilage yeasts *Zygosaccharomyces bailii* in a model fruit juice system. Food Microbiol. 4: 115.
3. Eagon, R. G. and Green, C. R. 1973. Effect of carbonated beverages on bacteria. Food Res. 22: 687.

4. Insalata, N. F. 1952. Carbon dioxide versus beverage bacteria. Food Engineering 24: 84.
5. Juven, B. J. and Shomer, I. 1985. Spoilage of soft drinks caused by bacterial flocculation. J. Food Protect. 48: 52.
6. Perigo, J. A., Gimbert, B. L., and Bashford, T. E. 1964. The effect of carbonation, benzoic acid and pH on the growth rate of a soft drink spoilage yeast as determined by a turbidostatic continuous culture apparatus. J. Appl. Bacteriol. 27: 315.
7. Pitt, J. I. 1974. Resistance of some food spoilage yeasts to preservatives. Food Technol. Australia 26: 238.
8. Put, H. M. C. and De Jong, J. 1980. The heat resistance of selected yeasts causing spoilage of canned soft drinks and fruit products. In "Biology and Activities of Yeasts," eds. F. A. Skinner, S. M. Passmore, and R. R. Davenport. Academic Press, London, England.
9. Sand, F. E. M. J., Kolfschoten, G. A., and Van Grinsven, A. M. 1976. Yeasts isolated from proportioning pumps employed in soft drink plants. Brauwissenschaft 29: 294.
10. Witter, L. D., Berry, J. M., and Folinazzo, J. F. 1958. The viability of *Escherichia coli* and a spoilage yeast in carbonated beverages. Food Res. 23: 133.

Chapter 59

BOTTLED WATER

Sarah Cowman and Robert Kelsey

59.1 INTRODUCTION

Bottled water has been defined by the Food and Drug Administration (FDA) as water that is sealed in bottles or other containers and is intended for human consumption.

There are four basic types of water offered to the consumer as follows:

Spring or Well Water, taken directly from a spring or well and bottled with minimum treatment.

Specifically Prepared Drinking Water, where the mineral content has been adjusted and controlled. The source may be a public water supply or a private source.

Purified Water, conforming to the United States Pharmacopeia (U.S.P.) standard[6] for purified water with minerals removed to less than 10 mg/l. Water can be "purified" by distillation, ion exchange, or reverse osmosis. Methods of preparation must be indicated. Only water prepared by distillation can be called "Distilled Water."

Fluoridated Water, where fluoride has been added to drinking water, at the optimum concentration as set forth in the FDA Quality Standards.[2]

No definition or quality for "mineral" water has yet been established by the FDA.

Standards[2] for bottled water products set forth by the FDA include a requirement for microbiological quality that is based on coliform detection levels. Not more than one coliform organism is allowed per 100 ml of water using an arithmetic mean when tested by the membrane filter method. Additionally with this method, not more than 1 analytical unit in a sampling of 10 shall have 4.0 or more coliforms per 100 ml. Using the multiple-tube fermentation method, not more than 1 unit in a sampling of 10 shall have a most probable number (MPN) of 2.2 or more coliform organisms per 100 ml. By this latter method, no unit shall have a MPN of 9.2 or more coliforms per 100 ml.

No heterotrophic plate count limit is specified in the standards.

The FDA Good Manufacturing Practice (GMP) for Bottled Water, as revised,[3] requires weekly coliform analyses for each type of bottled water produced in a plant, and, additionally, requires that any source water obtained from other than a public water system be analyzed for coliforms once a week as a minimum.

Microbiological tests on containers and closures are required in the GMP regulation for bottled water. At least four containers and closures are selected just before filling and sealing every 3 months as a minimum. Heterotrophic plate counts and coliform determinations are made. All samples should be free of coliforms. Also, no more than one of the four samples may exceed the following total heterotrophic plate count requirements: one colony per milliliter capacity of the container, or one colony per square centimeter of surface area of the closure.

59.2   TYPES OF MICROORGANISMS

Ozone is typically used as a disinfectant in the bottled water industry. It is applied just before bottling. As a result of this practice, bottled water products are typically coliform-free with very low heterotrophic plate counts (less than 100/ml) at the time of bottling. A few hardy organisms natural to water can survive even though strict adherence to Good Manufacturing Practice is followed. The bacteria multiply during storage after the ozone has dissipated. The organisms follow a cyclic pattern of growth before dying off. However, no microbial spoilage occurs.

59.21   Predominant Flora

The predominant organisms found in bottled water are gram-negative rods, which can grow in distilled or other mineral-free water as well as in the more mineralized waters. Included in the group are organisms of the genera *Pseudomonas*, *Flavobacterium*, *and Moraxella-Acinetobacter.*

59.22   Indicator Organisms

Although coliform organisms are rarely found in bottled water, routine testing for the organisms is carried out since they serve as an indicator of possible contamination. Non-fecal coliforms, which occur naturally in soil, water, and vegetation, indicate contamination from airborne sources or product contact surfaces. Fecal coliforms, on the other hand, indicate a possibility of sewage contamination, with the associated possibility of pathogenic contamination. Most coliforms are not themselves pathogens, and only a few species can cause gastrointestinal illness. However, if Good Manufacturing Practice is followed, no coliform organisms should be found in bottled water.

59.3 EQUIPMENT, MEDIA, AND REAGENTS

59.31 Equipment

Incubator 35°C, 44.5°C

59.32 Culture Media (Chapter 62)

Brilliant green lactose bile broth (BGB)
Eosin methylene blue (EMB) agar (Levine)
Lauryl tryptose broth
LES Endo agar
M-Endo Medium (broth or agar)
M-FC (agar or broth)
m-HPC agar
R2A agar
Tryptone glucose extract agar (TGEA)
Tryptone glucose yeast agar (Plate count agar)
Nutrient agar

59.33 Reagents (Chapter 62)

Gram stain (Hucker)
Phosphate buffer (Butterfield)

59.4 RECOMMENDED METHODS

59.41 Sampling (Chapter 2)

Whenever possible, sample directly from the original sealed container. Original sealed containers need not be refrigerated.

When it is necessary to use a secondary container, collect sample aseptically in a suitable, presterilized bottle and process as soon as possible. If testing of samples cannot be completed within 8 hr of collection, refrigerate the sample for transport. Under no circumstances should the time between collection and processing exceed 24 hr. Record time and temperature of storage of all samples.[1]

59.42   Heterotrophic Plate Count (Chapter 4)

Use the pour plate, spread plate, or membrane filtration method described in Chapter 4. Suitable media for pour or spread plate methods include tryptone glucose extract agar (TGEA), plate count agar (tryptone glucose yeast agar), or R2A agar. For membrane filtration method, use R2A agar or m-HPC agar.

For most samples, plates suitable for counting will be obtained by plating 1 ml or 0.1 ml of undiluted sample. The membrane filtration method allows use of 100 ml (or more) samples and, therefore, is much more sensitive for samples with very low counts.

Incubate all samples, except samples on R2A agar, at 35°C ± 0.5°C for at least 72 hr. Because bacteria found in bottled water demonstrate a prolonged lag phase during adaptation to growth on tryptone glucose extract agar or plate count agar, such bacteria may not form colonies that can be counted after 48 hr incubation; thus an additional 24-hr incubation is required for a reliable result.[1] Incubate samples on R2A agar at 35°C for 5 to 7 days, or at 20°C to 28°C for 7 days.

59.43   MPN for Members of the Coliform Group (Chapters 6 and 24)

See 24.52 and 24.53 with the following exception:

For routine examination of bottled water, use 10 fermentation tubes, each containing 10 ml of undiluted sample. For more precision, use 5 tubes each of 10 ml, 1.0 ml, and 0.1 ml of undiluted sample. (See Chapter 6.)

Based on the number of positive, confirmed tubes, use the following chart to determine the most probable number (MPN) of coliforms.

MPN Index and 95% Confidence Limits for Various Combinations of Positive and Negative Results When Ten 10-mL Portions Are Used

Number of tubes giving positive reaction out of 10 of 10 mL each	MPN index/ 100 mL	95% confidence limits (approximate) Lower	Upper
0	< 1.1	0	3.0
1	1.1	0.03	5.9
2	2.2	0.26	8.1
3	3.6	0.69	10.6
4	5.1	1.3	13.4
5	6.9	2.1	16.8
6	9.2	3.1	21.1
7	12.0	4.3	27.1
8	16.1	5.9	36.8
9	23.0	8.1	59.5
10	>23.0	13.5	Infinite

59.44   Completed Test for Coliforms

Submit at least 10% of all positive, confirmed samples to the completed test to establish definitely the presence of coliform bacteria and to provide quality-control data.[1,5]

Streak an eosin methylene blue (EMB) agar (Levine) plate, using an inoculating needle curved at the tip, from a brilliant green lactose bile broth (BGB) tube showing gas, as soon as possible after gas formation. Incubate the plate inverted for 24 ± 2 hr at $35° \pm 0.5°C$. Be careful not to disturb the surface integrity of the EMB when streaking the agar. This makes picking of the individual colonies difficult.

Transfer a typical (nucleated, with or without metallic sheen) colony from the surface of the EMB agar plate using a transferring needle and inoculate a nutrient agar slant and then a lauryl tryptose broth tube with the colony. Use a well-isolated colony with no colonies within 0.5 cm of the colony to be transferred.

Incubate nutrient agar slants and lauryl tryptose broth tubes at $35° \pm 0.5°C$ for 24 ± 2 hours or 48 ± 3 hr if no gas is produced in 24 hr.

Prepare gram-stained (Hucker Modification) slides from nutrient agar slants whose corresponding lauryl tryptose broth tubes show gas. Demonstration of gram-negative nonspore-forming rod-shaped bacteria in the agar culture is a positive completed test showing a member of the coliform group to be present in the sample. The Gram stain may be omitted from the completed test for potable water samples such as bottled water.

59.45   Membrane Filter Method for Coliforms (Chapter 4)

Use 100 ml of sample for coliforms and transfer filter pad to LES Endo agar or M-Endo medium (broth or agar) for incubation at $35° \pm 0.5°C$ for 22 to 24 hr. Count colonies that are pink to dark red with a green metallic surface sheen. The sheen may vary from a small pinhead to complete coverage of the colony. Report results as coliform colonies[1,5] per 100 ml.

Verify each positive plate by transferring growth from sheen colonies to parallel tubes of lauryl tryptose broth and brilliant green bile. Verify all sheen colonies, regardless of the amount of sheen, when the number of sheen colonies is 5 to and including 10/100 ml. When the number of sheen colonies exceeds 10/100 ml, randomly select and verify 10 colonies that are representative of all sheen colonies. Gas formed in the brilliant green bile in 48 hr verifies the colony as a coliform. If only the lauryl tryptose tube shows gas, transfer a sample from this tube to a second brilliant green bile tube. Verification at this stage again requires gas production in 48 hr.

For fecal coliforms, use 100 ml of sample. Incubate on M-FC agar or nutrient pad with M-FC agar broth. Incubate at $44.5° \pm 0.2°C$ for 24 hr and count typical blue (or blue-green) colonies. Report counts less than 20 as estimated count per 100 ml.

59.46   Other Rapid Methods for Coliforms and E. coli

Several rapid test procedures are available to detect coliforms and *E. coli* in water samples (see also Chapter 39 on Rapid Methods). The AC (Autoanalysis Colilert) test is one of these.[4]

59.47   Test Method for Containers and Closures

Containers (Chapter 3)—Pour 100 ml sterile phosphate buffer into the container to be tested. Swirl to contact the entire inside surface area. Make a heterotrophic plate count and coliform test on the exposed buffer solution. Report heterotrophic plate count per ml of capacity of the container and any coliforms present.

Closures—Wet a swab in sterile phosphate buffer solution, and swab the entire inside surface of the closure twice. Insert the swab in a tube of 10 ml sterile phosphate buffer and break off stick below the area touched by the fingers. Mix well. Use 1 ml of suspension and do an aerobic plate count and a coliform test. Multiply the count by 10 to give the number per closure or calculate the count per square centimeter of surface area of the closure.

59.5   INTERPRETATION OF DATA

The usual organisms that grow in bottled water measured by the heterotrophic plate count are not of sanitary significance and do not result in microbial spoilage or flavor impairment of the products. Low plate counts (less than 100/ml) at the time of bottling serve as indicators of Good Manufacturing Practice. The presence of coliform organisms serves as an indicator of lack of Good Manufacturing Practice and potential health problems.

59.6   REFERENCES

1. APHA/AWWA/WPCF. 1985. "Standard Methods for the Examination of Water and Wastewater," 16th ed. Part 900, Amer. Pub. Health Assn., Amer. Water Works Assn., Water Pollut. Contr. Fedn., Washington, D.C.
2. CFR. 1988a. Quality Standards for Foods with No Identity Standards, Bottled Water. Code of Federal Regulations, Title 21, Part 103. U.S. Govt. Printg. Off., Washington, D.C.
3. CFR. 1988b. Processing and Bottling of Bottled Drinking Water, Code of Federal Regulations, Title 21, Part 129. U.S. Govt. Printg. Off., Washington, D.C.
4. Edberg, S. C., Allen, M. J., Smith, D. B., and The National Collaborative Study. 1988. National field evaluation of a defined substrate method for the simultaneous enumeration of total coliforms and *Escherichia coli* from drinking water: Comparison with the standard multiple tube fermentation method. Appl. Environ. Microbiol. 54: 1595.
5. U.S. EPA. 1978. "Microbiological Methods for Monitoring the Environment, Water and Wastes," Environ. Monitor. and Support Lab., Off. of Research and Dev., U.S. Environ. Protec. Agency, Washington, D.C.
6. U.S. Pharmacopeia, 21st Rev. 1985. Purified Water, P. 1124, U.S. Pharmacopeial Convention, Inc. Mack Publ. Co., Easton, Penn.

Chapter 60

CANNED FOODS—TESTS FOR COMMERCIAL STERILITY

John M. Dryer and Kurt E. Deibel

60.1 INTRODUCTION

When spoilage occurs in a closed container of canned foods, it manifests itself by obvious gas production, swelling the lid of the container, by a change in the consistency, odor, or pH of the product, and/or by an increase in the number of microorganisms seen in the microscopic examination of the food. The commercial sterility test is not designed for detailed diagnosis of spoilage, and, therefore, when any of the above spoilage criteria are met, the analyst should go directly to Chapter 61 for procedures to determine the exact cause of spoilage.

Canned foods in the context of this chapter are those that have been preserved by heat in hermetically sealed containers. Several definitions have been used for the term "hermetically sealed," but they usually imply a container that excludes the passage of gas or microorganisms. For the ensuing discussions, a hermetically sealed container is one that prevents the entry of microbes, thereby preventing spoilage from external sources after the container has been sealed. The canned food should remain unspoiled indefinitely if properly heat processed and if the seal remains intact. With the exception of canned cured meats, canned foods do not rely on preservatives or inhibitory agents other than acids to ensure stability. The heat treatment given canned foods is enough to produce commercial sterility, not complete sterility. Complete sterility is defined here as a state completely free of all viable microorganisms. The heat process required to achieve complete sterility would destroy the product consistency and nutritional values that currently exist in commercially canned foods. The highly heat-resistant and nontoxic thermophilic sporeformers (Chapters 20, 21, 22, and 23), under proper handling and storage conditions, remain dormant in commercially canned foods and present no problems; therefore, canned foods are called "commercially sterile."

Commercial sterility of thermally processed food is defined in Title 21 of the Code of Federal Regulations, Part 113.3(e)[4] as the condition achieved (1) by the application of heat, which renders the food free of (a) microorganisms capable of reproducing in the food under normal nonrefrigerated conditions of storage and distribution and (b) viable microorganisms (including spores) of public health significance; or (2) by the control of water activity and the application of heat, which renders the food free of any microorganisms capable of reproducing in the food under normal nonrefrigerated conditions of storage and distribution.

Under this definition, for a commercially sterile, heat-processed food to contain viable microorganisms is permissible. The microorganisms, however, do not increase in numbers and consequently do not cause physical changes in the food product. Likewise, pathogens either are not present or are incapable of reproducing in the product.

Viable microorganisms normally may be recovered from commercially sterile, heat-processed foods under three general conditions: (1) The microorganism is an obligate thermophilic, sporeforming bacterium, and the normal storage temperature is below the thermophilic range. (2) The heat-processed food is within the high-acid (<3.7) to acid range pH (3.7 to 4.6). Acid-intolerant microorganisms may be present, but are incapable of growth because of the acidic conditions. (3) Mesophilic or thermophilic sporeformers may be recovered from canned foods that use a combined process of heat and water activity to prevent outgrowth and spoilage. Finding microorganisms in these three instances is normal, and the product is considered commercially sterile.

Food processors are able to heat-process food to achieve absolute sterility, but this is not done for several reasons. Overcooking (excessive time or temperature) encourages the development of off-flavors, color and consistency changes, and nutrient losses. "Commercial sterility heat processing" enables the manufacturer to pack a microbiologically safe, shelf-stable food without undue impairment of flavor, color, consistency, or nutrient content. Kautter and Lynt[10] in 1973 estimated that in the United States alone, 775 billion containers of food had been produced in the prior 45 years, and, of these, only 4 were associated with botulism leading to death of the consumer. Foods that are packed in hermetically sealed containers have a remarkable and enviable record of public health safety and consumer satisfaction.

Food canners have a history of cooperatively sharing technical advances for the improvement of the entire industry. In addition, numerous safeguards are employed (both voluntarily and as enforced by regulatory agencies) to ensure the adequacy of commercial sterilization cooking procedures. Requirements for processing low-acid foods and acidified foods, and appropriate records to be kept, are found in parts 108, 113, and 114 of Title 21 of the Code of Federal Regulations.[4]

Commercial sterility testing of canned foods should be conducted on normal-appearing canned food by visually examining the incubated container and the product, measuring the vacuum, odor, and pH, and, if necessary, making a microscopic examination to detect large numbers of bacteria. Subculturing rarely is done on a routine basis because it is time-consuming and expensive and has a high risk of laboratory contamination or of faulty interpretation.[6, 7] Situations sometimes arise, such as the running of preliminary test packs using a new processing method, when subculturing may be desired or even necessary; therefore, procedures for this purpose will be described in this chapter.

"Sterility (Commercial) of Foods (Canned Low-Acid)" has "final action" status in *AOAC Methods* (1984).[1] That method should be used if only low-acid foods, those other than alcoholic beverages with a finished equilibrium pH greater than 4.6 and a water activity greater than 0.85, are being tested. The methods listed in this chapter follow closely the Association of Official Analytical Chemists (AOAC) procedure for low-acid foods; in addition, methods designed for acidified and acid foods (those with a pH of 4.6 or below) are given.

60.2   GENERAL CONSIDERATIONS

60.21   Treatment of Sample

The food manufacturer selects test samples representing the production lot and incubates them for 10 days at 30° to 35°C to determine if a certain segment of production meets commercial sterility criteria. If conventional retorts are used for sterilization, each retort load is examined with at least one sample. If sterilization is accomplished by continuous means, samples are drawn at periodic intervals during the time of pack. Products to be stored in vending machines above about 40°C would require that extra samples be drawn for 5 to 7 days of incubation at 55°C.

After incubation, record the product identity and the manufacturer's code. The container should be examined critically for abnormal conditions such as leakage, swells, flippers, prior opening, etc. (See Chapter 61 for a thorough explanation of container appearances.) If spoilage is evident, use the procedures described in Chapter 61. If the container is defective or damaged, the sample is not suitable for commercial sterility testing.

60.22   Sources of Error

Sources of error in tests for commercial sterility derive in large measure from misinterpretation of findings; therefore, it is recommended that the reader refer to sections dealing with confirmation and interpretation of data where bases of judgment are fully expanded. Misinterpretations can derive from laboratory contamination, insufficient numbers of containers sampled, and the presence of heat-resistant enzymes that may digest food components, thereby giving the impression of microbial spoilage.

60.23   Special Equipment and Supplies

1. Work areas: Preferred method

A laminar flow work station meeting ultra-clean environment specifications, Class 100, is preferred[8] in sterility evaluations of hermetically sealed containers. This equipment will provide a work environment free of particles 0.3 microns or larger at an efficiency of 99.99% with an air flow of 100 feet per min. Primary disinfection of the unit can be obtained by a thorough washing of the interior surfaces (being careful to avoid contact with filtration media) with a bactericidal solution. After chemical disinfection, the blower should be operated for at least 1 hr prior to performing analyses within the unit.

2 Work areas: Alternate method

If the equipment described in the preferred method is not available, the samples may be opened in a room secure from drafts. The counter surface should be scrubbed thoroughly with soap and water and then disinfected with an appropriate bactericidal agent such as 100-ppm chlorine solution.

3. Bacteriological can opener

A special can opener designed for the aseptic opening of metal containers for bacteriological sampling without distorting the can seams is the Bacti-Disc Cutter (Wilkens-Anderson Company, 425 West Division St., Chicago, Ill. 60651). Under no circumstances should a common kitchen-type can opener be employed because sample contamination and distoration of the double seam will occur.

60.24   Recommended Controls

1. Glassware

All glassware should be autoclaved for a minimum of 20 min at 121°C. Equipment, wrapped in kraft paper, should be placed in a sterilizing oven at 170° to 180°C for 2 hr. Heat-sensitive sterilization indicators may be affixed to each autoclave load to identify readily the status of a given unit of equipment. If equipment is to be sterilized well in advance of use, double-layer aluminum foil dust covers should be placed over flasks, dilution bottles, etc.

2. Laminar flow work station

Efficiency of the unit should be monitored through the use of open, uninoculated control media exposed to the work station environment during the entire transfer period. Three controls should be used, one placed to the right and one to the left of the samples undergoing analysis, and one in front of the samples roughly in the middle of the work area.

3. Media

Media sterility checks should be performed on common liquid media by incubating for 48 hr at appropriate temperatures and then examining for the absence of growth. Uninoculated control plates should be prepared and incubated for every lot of solid media employed in routine test studies.

4. Personnel requirements

Prior to working with samples, the hands and face of personnel should be scrubbed thoroughly with an appropriate germicidal hand soap.[7] Personnel should wear clean lab coats, and items of personal clothing such as neckties should be removed or contained. Persons known to have colds, boils, or similar health problems should not perform these evaluations. Personnel with shoulder-length hair, sideburns below ear lobe, mustaches or beards must wear sterile protective snoods and sterile full-head coverings.[3] Completely cover the hair with a clean, disposable operating room cap.

60.3   EQUIPMENT, MATERIALS, AND REAGENTS

1. Pipettes

Straight-wall, 200- to 250-mm long, 7-mm ID, 9-mm OD pipettes should be used. Either glass or disposable plastic is acceptable. All pipettes should be cotton-plugged before sterilization to prevent contamination from the user. Nondisposable pipettes used in sterility test work should not be stored in pipette cans but rather should be wrapped not more than five to a package in heavy kraft paper. This package should be steam-sterilized at 121°C for 20 min, then dried in vacuo. Alternatively, the packages may be placed in a sterilizing drying oven at 170° to 180°C for 2 hr.

2. pH meter

Electronic pH meters should be used to determine pH of the product in question. Accuracy must be within 0.1 pH unit of a known buffer solution. A pH indicator paper with a suitable range may be used for pH determinations on a large number of homogeneous samples. However, any sample showing variation from the normal should be checked on an electronic meter (Chapter 8).

3. Forceps

Nonserrated forceps,[5] at least 8 in in length, should be available to handle large particles and other nonpipettable products.

4. Microscope

A suitable bacteriological microscope fitted with an oil immersion lens or a phase system is needed. Microscopic examination of a food product for bacterial contamination should be made at magnifications of not less than 930X.

5. Culture tubes

All tubes should have a screw cap closure and be manufactured of borosilicate or Pyrex™ glass or suitable plastic. If plastic is used, it must be nontoxic and capable of withstanding normal glassware sterilization temperatures. Cotton plugs are not acceptable as closures on either type of tube.

6. Petri dishes

Sterile dishes should be 100 × 20- or 100 × 15-mm plastic or glass. Only new, sealed sleeves of disposable plastic dishes should be used in sterility test work. If glass is used, standard petri storage cans should be employed for storage of the glassware. Only freshly sterilized containers should be used in sterility test work.

7. Culture media and reagents

When media are commercially available in the dehydrated form, they should be used in preference to media formulated in individual laboratories. See Chapter 62.

Dextrose tryptone broth (DTB) (for cultivation of aerobes)
PE-2 medium (for cultivation of anaerobes)
Potato dextrose agar (PDA) (for cultivation of yeasts and molds)
Orange serum broth (OSB) (for cultivation of acid-tolerant microorganisms)
Sabouraud dextrose agar (SDA) (for cultivation of yeasts and molds)
All-purpose medium with Tween (APT) broth (for cultivation of *Lactobacillus*)
Acid products test broth
Ziehl-Neelsen's carbol fuchsin stain
Crystal violet stain (0.5% to 1% solution)

60.4 PRECAUTIONS

60.41 Safety Procedures

Never taste the contents of any low-acid food container that are suspected of having undergone spoilage because of the potential presence of botulism toxin!

When opening swollen containers for examination, use caution and wear personal protective equipment (goggles, protective face masks, etc.).

60.42 Disposal of Spoiled Containers

Refer to Chapter 61 for details of the disposal of contaminated material.

60.5 PROCEDURE

The most reliable test for determining commercial sterility of a container of product is to incubate that container at an appropriate temperature long enough to allow any significant microorganisms contained therein to grow and to manifest their presence.[9] If microorganisms proliferate under the proper storage conditions imposed, the product is not commercially sterile and should be examined as described in Chapter 61.

60.51   Incubation

Incubation conditions are governed partly by the purpose of the commercial sterility test:

1. Routine production monitoring

For low-acid products destined for storage at temperatures above about 40°C (hot vending), containers from each sampling period or retort load should be incubated at 55°C for 5 to 7 days. For all other low-acid products, incubate at 30° to 35°C for 10 days, except certain meat products packed under continuous regulatory agency inspection;[12] where facilities are limited to 35°C, incubation for 10 days may be used. For acid or acidified foods, incubate at 25° to 30°C for 10 days.

2. Examination of a production lot or lots because of suspected noncommercial sterility

If possible, incubate the entire lot or lots; otherwise, incubate a statistically randomized sample of the lot or of each lot. Use incubation temperatures as in No. 1, but increase the time to 30 days in the case of mesophiles.

60.52   Examination

Containers may be removed from the incubator whenever outward manifestations of microbial growth appear (e.g., swells, or with transparent containers, noticeable product change). At the end of the incubation period, some containers should be opened to detect possible flat sour spoilage.

Weigh each suspect container to the nearest gram and record the weight on the data sheet. Subtract the average tare weight of the empty container from each unit weight to determine the approximate net weight of each sample; this information will be of value in diagnostic tests mentioned in Chapter 61.

If the only purpose of the test procedure is to determine commercial sterility of the product (and provided the analyst is thoroughly familiar with the particular product and with potential types of microbial spoilage of that product), containers may be examined without employing aseptic techniques. Open the containers carefully; note abnormal odors, consistency changes, and frothiness; measure pH electrometrically or colorimetrically; if results are not conclusive at this point, prepare a smear for microscopic examination. If the product is controlled by water activity (a_w), perform an a_w examination (Chapter 8). The observation of abnormalities compared to containers of normal control product means that the containers of the products are not commercially sterile. In that case, follow the procedures in Chapter 61 on the remaining unopened abnormal product.

If the analyst is unfamiliar with the particular product and its potential spoilage characteristics, it is necessary to use aseptic procedures in opening and examining each container.

60.53   Opening Container Aseptically[1, 7, 9, 11]

The container must be clean. If obvious soil, oil, etc., are present, wash with detergent and water, rinse, and wipe dry with clean paper towels.

1. Cans

Hold the clean, uncoded end of the can over a large Meker burner, just above the blue portion of the flame, continuing until the visible moisture film evaporates. (If the can swells, keep side seam directed away from analyst and flame cautiously.) Flame a clean Bacti-Disc Cutter, then aseptically cut and remove a disc of metal from the end. (With cans having an "easy-open" feature on one end, open the opposite end. Do not disturb the "easy-open" end in the event that it is subsequently necessary to examine the score.) Subculture immediately.

2. Glass jars

Clean and flame the closure as described for cans. An index line should be scribed or otherwise permanently marked on both the cap and the glass. This procedure will allow for the quantitative measurement of the closure security by a qualified container examiner if such an examination is deemed necessary. Open with a clean, flamed Bacti-Disc Cutter (avoid unseating or moving the closure with respect to the jar; subsquent seal examination may be desirable). Subculture immediately.

If complete removal of the jar closure is necessary, the jar should be cleaned as above, then inverted in a disinfecting solution for an appropriate period of time (e.g., 100 ppm chlorine for 10 min). A sterile cotton pad then is placed on the closure. A flame-sterilized Bacti-Disc Cutter point is used to puncture the closure and thus relieve the vacuum. The closure then may be removed with less danger of admitting microbial contaminants over the glass-sealing surface.

3. Nonrigid containers (e.g., pouches)

Clean and sanitize the container surface with a detergent sanitizing agent. Dry with a sterile, fresh towel. If the product is maneuverable, push it away from one end. With clean, lightly flamed scissors, cut the end off just under the container seal. (On large containers, a 2- to 3-in opening may be made by cutting off the corner of the container with a diagonal cut.) Open the container without touching the cut ends. Subculture immediately.

60.54   Subculture Media—Selection

The best subculture medium for use in examining spoiled canned foods is a portion of the normal product that has been tubed and sterilized. Its use eliminates a question sometimes raised with the use of artificial laboratory medium as to whether or not organisms recovered by the laboratory medium actually grow in the product. Liquid products may be tubed without modification. Products consisting of solids and liquids should be blended mechanically, retaining the normal ratio of solids to liquids. Products lacking free moisture should be blended mechanically, with sterile water added as necessary to make a slurry capable of being tubed. Low-acid product tubed media should be sterilized in the autoclave for 15 min at 121°C; acid product tubed media should be sterilized by steaming 30 min at 100°C.

Laboratory media (see Chapter 62) suitable for canned food examination include the following:

For low-acid foods:
    Tryptone broth (for the growth of aerobes)
    PE-2 medium in screw-cap tubes (for the growth of anaerobes)
For acid foods:
    Orange serum broth (for bacteria and yeasts encountered in this category of foods).
Some lactobacilli do not grow well; therefore, if these organisms are suspected as being present, use APT broth also.
    Acid products test broth (a culture broth for acid-tolerant microorganisms)
    Potato dextrose agar—acidified (a plating medium used when heat-resistant yeasts and molds may be present)
    Sabouraud dextrose agar (a plating medium for molds and yeasts)
    APT broth (for growth of *Lactobacillus*)

60.55   Subculture Product Samples, Observe Product Characteristics

Transer c. 2 g of product from each container with a straight-walled pipette to duplicate tubes of subculture media. For low-acid products, inoculate two tubes of sterile PE-2 medium. Since these tubes are intended to allow the outgrowth of anaerobes, they should be exhausted in flowing steam for an exposure of 20 min and cooled to 55°C *prior* to inoculation if not freshly prepared and autoclaved. Be sure to inoculate the lower portion of the tube and tighten the caps after inoculation. Then inoculate duplicate tubes of the aerobic medium (tryptone broth). Incubate at 30° to 35°C. If normal temperature for storage or handling of the product is higher than 40°C, also inoculate duplicate tubes of any medium used for incubation at 55°C; otherwise, do not incubate at 55°C. For acid products, inoculate two tubes of sterile product, or of the acid medium or media of choice, and incubate at 25° to 30°C. If molds are suspected, prepare potato dextrose agar pour plates and incubate at 30°C. Incubate all subcultures for at least 5 days before declaring them negative. At the time subcultures are prepared, transfer an additional 10 g of product to a sterile culture tube and refrigerate; this will serve as a reference sample for repeat subcultures if necessary. Measure pH of the product, and observe product odor and appearance relative to a control sample.

60.56   Mass Culture Technique for Aseptically Packed Tomato or Fruit Concentrates

Acid product test broth has been developed as a culture medium for the selective cultivation of *Lactobacillus*, *Leuconostoc*, and yeasts capable of causing spoilage in acid product concentrates such as tomato paste and fruit pastes. It is an excellent medium for the recovery of minimal contamination, and, therefore, the utmost care must be taken by workers to ensure that the medium is not contaminated during handling. Since the broth is intended primarily as a mass culture medium for detecting low-level contaminants or localized contaminants in aseptically packed acid products, approximately 100 g of product under tests should be inoculated aseptically into 300 ml of sterile medium contained in 500-ml screw-cap flasks. Care must be taken to disperse the product adequately through the broth; a sterile stirring rod should be used.

A minimum of three flasks per sample should be inoculated. An extra aseptic sample retained from each container should be incubated with the flasks. In addition, a retained sample should be held at refrigeration temperatures for use in microscopic comparisons with the incubated product or for repeating the test. Incubation of the cultures should be at 30°C for 5 days with visual examination for fermentation or biological surface growth daily. The extra retained incubation samples should be incubated for 10 days. At the end of the incubation period, all samples should be examined microscopically for evidence of bacterial or yeast contamination.

60.57   Microscopic Examination of Product

Prepare a wet mount of product liquid (or of surface scrapings of product not having excess free liquid) for examination with a phase contrast-equipped microscope, or make a smear for simple staining and examination. Crystal violet or Ziehl-Neelsen carbol fuchsin stains are recommended (see Chapter 62). Products having a high solids content in the liquid portion often resist adhering to a slide, and they may be diluted advantageously with approximately equal volumes of sterile distilled water on the slide. A flamed bacteriological loop may be used for making smears. Examine both the product being tested and a normal control product to enable judgment regarding the presence of abnormal levels of microorganisms in the former.

60.58   Confirmation of Positive Laboratory Medium Subcultures

Inherent characteristics of acid, acidified, and water activity-controlled food products preclude the germination and outgrowth of some viable bacterial spores present. Laboratory media may not exhibit similar bacteriostatic properties, resulting in positive subcultures, which may lead to the erroneous conclusion that the product in question is not commercially sterile. When the true significance of such positive subcultures is in doubt, use them to inoculate the sterile product, either tubed or canned, followed by incubation. Organisms of significance will grow and manifest their presence in the product. Again, use of the sterile product as the primary subculture medium, together with direct microscopic examination and assessment of product abnormalities compared to normal control, usually will obviate a confirmatory procedure.

Laboratory contamination is indicated when an organism producing gas in an anaerobic medium at 35°C is isolated from low-acid canned foods having an obvious vacuum. Aseptically inoculate growing organisms into another normal can, close the hole with solder, and incubate 14 days at 35°C. Swelling of the container indicates that the organism was not in the original sample and is due to laboratory contamination.[1]

60.6   INTERPRETATION OF DATA

Serious consequences can result if commercial sterility testing information is based on faulty laboratory techniques or if errors are made in evaluating data. Strict observance of the preceding methods will lessen the chances of designating a product contaminated when, in actuality, it is commercially sterile. Likewise, the instances of incorrectly claiming a product to be commercially sterile will be decreased. A similar test has been adopted by the AOAC as "final action."[1]

The development of swelled containers (any degree) may indicate microbial activity. The presence of a swell condition by itself, particularly at the flipper, springer, or soft swell level, however, does not indicate positively that the product is not commercially sterile. Growth must be confirmed by demonstrating excessive microorganisms by direct smear, or an abnormal product (pH, consistency, odor, etc.) as compared to the normal product. Some causes of low-degree swells, which cannot be confirmed microbiologically in a commercial sterility test, are overfilling, low filling temperatures, improper vacuum closing procedures, inadequate vacuum mixing (certain comminuted products), incipient spoilage, and chemical swells ("hydrogen springers").[2] At a high elevation in such areas as Denver, Colorado, cans that would appear normal at sea level often show swells.

Nonsterility of flat containers is shown if direct smears reveal excessive microorganisms and if one or more product characteristics are abnormal. Subculture may be necessary to support these conclusions.

Duplicate cultures should show comparable biochemical reactions and microbial flora. These, in turn, should be similar to those in the original product (e.g., predominating flora in direct smears of product will usually appear in subcultures, and biochemical reactions will be comparable).

If only one tube of a duplicate set is positive, adventitious (laboratory) contamination should be suspected. Comparison of the positive culture with the original product, especially in direct smears, often will clarify the situation. If not, new subcultures should be prepared from the retained sample.

A stained smear or a wet mount examined by phase microscopy that shows only an occasional cell in some fields usually does not suggest a spoiled product. Representative coverage of a smear is necessary to form an accurate evaluation; examination of 10 to 20 fields is necessary to avoid being misled. Comparison with the normal product is mandatory.

It is sometimes difficult to differentiate bacterial cells from food particles when microscopically examining a food product. On occasion, food-grade yeast is an ingredient of the processed food. Check the list of ingredients on the label for yeast. Caution must be taken not to assume that these yeast cells are contaminating microorganisms. Fermented products (e.g., sauerkraut) will show a high normal microbial population by direct smear.

If a recovery medium has a near-neutral pH and the food being tested is an acid food, microbial growth will probably take place. This is normal and expected and does not indicate the lack of commercial sterility. When testing an acid food, an acid pH recovery medium should be used.

60.61   Confirmation Program

If, when using proper commercial sterility testing procedures, microbial growth is recovered from a container of food that displays no evidence of spoilage, the following program should be carried out:

The bacterial isolate, or isolates, should be grown in pure culture.

An unopened container of food exhibiting the same manufacturer's code as the one previously tested should be selected.

By aseptic techniques, a small puncture hole should be made through the can end or jar closure.

The product should be inoculated (under the surface) with the microbial isolate.

The puncture hole should be flamed to create a vacuum in the headspace and aseptically sealed with solder or similar material. (It is sometimes necessary to warm the closed container to 40° to 45°C before puncturing to ensure that the seal will be under vacuum.)

The inoculated container should be incubated at 30° to 35°C for 10 days.

The container should be opened and the product examined.

If the previously tested container did contain microorganisms (i.e., was not commercially sterile), spoilage indications (or lack thereof) should be identical for both containers. If the first container exhibited a normal-appearing product but the analyst recovers growth upon subculture and if, after inoculating the second container with the microbial isolate, the analyst observes spoilage (gas, liquefaction, etc.), it should be concluded that the first container was commercially sterile; growth was the result of contamination due to faulty technique.

Open containers should be emptied, washed, and dried. Keep them properly identified in the event subsequent container examination is deemed desirable (see Chapter 61).

60.62   Defects Caused by Heat-Resistant Enzymes

The enzymatic liquefaction of starch-based products, such as high temperature-short time (HTST)-processed puddings and sauces, is caused by heat-stable microbial enzymes such as alpha-amylase. A severe thinning of the product consistency occurs, sometimes coupled with the formation of a clear, gel-like substance. Extremely small amounts of active enzyme can cause this phenomenon and can be present in ingredient material that, by either chemical or microbiological analysis, would be considered suitable for use. This defect does not result in a physical distortion of the container and is evident only after opening the container.

Direct microscopic smear of the product may now show unusual numbers of microorganisms. Bacteriological culturing of the suspect sample, assuming proper handling techniques are used, will be negative for viable microorganisms normally associated with either microleakage or underprocessing.

When interpreting direct microscopic smears, be careful to examine a normal control in order to arrive at a proper judgment regarding levels of microorganisms in the suspect product.

Product that has undergone enzymatic deterioration will usually have a slightly reduced pH as measured against a normal sample. No off-odor will be apparent, but, because of the severe consistency change and possible gel formation, the product will be obviously unfit for consumption.

Enzymatic liquefaction is an economic problem for the packer and has no public health significance with regard to safety of the product.

60.7   REFERENCES

1. AOAC. 1984. "Official Methods of Analysis of the Association of Official Analytical Chemists," 14th ed. Sections 46:063–46:070, p. 827. Assn. of Off. Anal. Chem., Arlington, Va.
2. APHA. 1966. "Recommended Methods for the Microbiological Examination of Foods," 2nd ed., ed. J. M. Scharf, p. 35. Am. Pub. Health Assn., New York.
3. Barbeito, M. S., Mathews, C. T., and Taylor, L. A. 1967. Microbiological laboratory hazard of bearded men. Appl. Microbiol. 15: 899.
4. CFR. 1987. Parts 108, 113, and 114, Title 21 of the Code of Fed. Reg., U.S. Govt. Print. Off., Washington, D.C.
5. Corson, L. M., Evancho, G. M., and Ashton, D. H. 1973. Use of forceps in sterility testing: A possible source of contamination. J. Food Sci. 38: 1267.
6. Denny, C. B. 1970. Collaborative study of procedure for determining commercial sterility for low-acid canned foods. J. Assn. Off. Anal. Chem. 53: 713.
7. Denny, C. B. 1972. Collaborative study of a method for determining commercial sterility of low-acid canned foods. J. Assn. Off. Anal. Chem. 55: 613.
8. Fed. Std. 209a. 1967. No. 252-522/280. U.S. Govt. Print. Off., Washington, D.C.
9. Hersom, A. C. and Hulland, E. D. 1981. "Canned Foods, Thermal Processing, and Microbiology," 7th ed., p. 259. Chemical Publ. Co., New York.
10. Kautter, D. A. and Lynt, R. K. 1973. Botulism. Nutr. Rev. 31: 265.
11. Schmitt, H. P. 1966. Commercial sterility in canned foods, its meaning and determination. Quart. Bull. Assn. of Food and Drug Offic. of the U.S. 30: 141.
12. Speck, M. L. and Adams, D. M. 1976. Heat-resistant proteolytic enzymes from bacterial sources. J. Dairy Sci. 59: 786.

Chapter 61

CANNED FOODS—TESTS FOR CAUSE OF SPOILAGE

Cleve B. Denny and D. A. Corlett, Jr.

61.1 INTRODUCTION

The major objective of spoilage diagnosis is to distinguish between the post-process contamination (leakage) and insufficient thermal processing (failure of the scheduled thermal process). Postprocess contamination usually results in a mixed microbiological flora of vegetative cells and occasionally spore-formers, that may have little or no heat resistance. Insufficient processing is characterized by pure cultures of heat-resistant sporeformers, and may have serious public health implications because of the potential presence of *Clostridium botulinum* and its toxins. For this reason, heat treatment of the appropriate subculture inocula is a key part of the diagnosis.

These methods are intended for thermally processed foods packaged in hermetically sealed containers. Containers include metal and plastic cans; glass; metal and plastic retort trays, cups, and bowls; and flexible pouches. Spoilage diagnosis is essentially the same for all containers. The chief difference is that flexible packages, trays, and pouches may have little or no vacuum.

A comprehensive examination procedure is required for expedient and accurate diagnosis of spoilage. It must include the history of the defective product, the structural integrity of the containers, the physical and chemical state of the food, and other factors that may be related to the presence of viable microorganisms. This information is used in conjunction with the microbiological examination. Failure to include all information may lead to an inaccurate diagnosis having obvious serious public health and economic implications. The methods for spoilage diagnosis are not recommended for tests of commercial sterility of canned foods. Commercial sterility determination methods are different, and they are described in Chapter 60. In addition, the spoilage diagnosis procedures for conventional thermally processed canned foods may not be suitable for examination of perishable, "pasteurized" canned cured meats, such as refrigerated canned hams. Methods for examining these products are given in Chapter 44.

Canned foods are defined as any thermally processed food product packed in a hermetically sealed container. Packages of this type may include metal or plastic cans, trays, drums, pouches, glass, and newer innovative containers.

61.2   MICROBIOLOGY OF CANNED FOODS

Thermal processing of canned foods depends on many factors associated with the type of product, its normal pH, its consistency, the size of the container, and the type of cooker.[5, 19] The pH is the most important factor that determines the degree of thermal processing needed to achieve product stability because of the inhibitory effect of acidity on survival and outgrowth of indigenous microorganisms. For this reason commercially processed foods are divided into two major pH categories: low-acid foods, having a pH above 4.6, and acid foods, having a pH of 4.6 or lower.[8, 9, 32]

61.21   Processing of Low-Acid Foods (pH Above 4.6)

Low-acid foods are thermally processed to produce a condition known as commercial sterility. Commercial sterility is defined as the condition in which all *Clostridium botulinum* spores and all other pathogenic bacteria have been destroyed as well as the more heat-resistant organisms, which, if present, could produce spoilage under normal conditions of storage and distribution.[29]

Commercially sterile foods, however, are not necessarily sterile in the classical sense. Occasionally, canned low-acid foods may contain low numbers of certain thermophilic spores that will not cause spoilage unless the food is stored at temperatures above 43°C. To sterilize a canned product completely usually would degrade product quality.

61.22   Processing of Acid Foods (pH 4.6 or Below)

An acidity of pH 4.6 or less is sufficient to inhibit the growth of *C. botulinum* in foods and to permit the application of a less severe thermal process to the food.

Since there is a significant advantage in quality retention to using acid foods, some low-acid foods are acidified to pH 4.6 or less.[32] When "controlled acidification" is used, the control of the product pH is critical to insure against possible outgrowth of *C. botulinum* in the product. Acid foods, in the higher pH ranges, may contain low numbers of thermophilic sporeformers that do not become a problem unless the food is stored at temperatures above 43°C. Acid foods also may contain dormant mesophilic spores that are inhibited from growth by the acid.

61.23   Factors Responsible for Spoilage in Canned Foods in General

Microbiological spoilage in canned foods usually is indicated by a swelling of the container. When no abnormal external signs are present, spoilage may still be indicated by an abnormal odor or appearance. The causes of these general conditions usually are related to one of the following factors:

Insufficient processing, permitting survival of mesophilic microorganisms.

Inadequate cooling after processing, or high-temperature storage and distribution conditions, permitting growth of various thermophilic microorganisms.

Leakage, permitting microorganisms to contaminate the product after processing.

Other conditions may occur in low-acid and acid canned foods that result in a swelling of the container and abnormal product appearance and thus confuse the investigator. The conditions are:

"Incipient spoilage" that occurs before the product or ingredient(s) are processed and may be caused by microbial or enzymatic action. Incipient microbial action may result in CO_2 production and the presence of excessive numbers of dead microbial cells in the product. Enzymatic action also may result in CO_2 evolution as well as off-odors (particularly in vegetables).

"Hydrogen swells" that result from chemical action of the food on the container, producing hydrogen gas.[23] When advanced corrosion has occurred, "pinholes" in cans and lids of glass jars may be present. Hydrogen swells are most common in overage merchandise.

Nonenzymatic browning (Maillard reaction) that sometimes occurs in canned products having high levels of sugar, amino acids, and acid. Carbon dioxide may be produced in sufficient amounts to bulge the container, particularly during storage of the product at elevated temperatures. This problem is occasionally encountered in canned fruit concentrates.

Product formulation errors and/or mishandling (e.g., freezing of the canned food).

Enzymatic changes such as liquification, off-flavors, curdling, and discoloration sometimes occur in foods packed by the ultra-high temperature (UHT) or high-temperature/short-time (HTST) heat processes such as those used in aseptic-type systems. Whether regeneration or extreme heat resistance of the enzyme is the cause, the result is the same. Containers appear normal, and high numbers of microbial cells are not seen by direct microscopic observation. Enzymatic activity creates an economic problem for the packer, but has no significance in regard to safety of the product.

61.24   Microbiological Groups Associated with Spoilage in Low-Acid Foods

61.241   Insufficient processing

Insufficient processing is indicated chiefly by the survival of bacterial spores, particularly those of the *Clostridium* species, and sometimes of the *Bacillus* species, which subsequently spoil the product. From the public health standpoint, this is a most serious situation because of the potential development of *C. botulinum* and its toxin.

Generally, anaerobic mesophilic spoilage is associated with putrid odors and the presence of rod-shaped microorganisms in pure culture with or without typical clostridial sporangia or spores. If putrid odors and clostridial-type spores are found during examination, the product should be tested for botulinum toxin by the mouse inoculation procedure, regardless of the percentage of the pack exhibiting spoilage[21] (Chapter 36). If there is no odor and clostridial-type spores are found, trypsin treatment may be needed to activate the toxin. If a low-acid canned food misses retorting completely, it may or may not produce a swell, but will normally have a reduced pH and the product will have a noncooked texture.

61.242   High-temperature spoilage (thermophilic spoilage)

Low-acid foods may spoil during storage above 43°C because of growth of extremely heat-resistant sporeforming thermophilic microorganisms. Most of these bacteria grow at 55°C, some as high as 70°C. Some are facultative thermophiles and may also grow at 35°C or lower. Thermophilic bacteria are not pathogenic.

Thermophiles occur naturally in agricultural soils, and their spores frequently are present in low numbers in commercially sterile products. Certain ingredients (sugar and starch) used in the product may be contaminated with excessive numbers of these organisms, or growth of thermophiles may occur in warm preprocessing equipment. Spoilage of this type is more common when the canned product is inadequately cooled or subsequently stored at high temperatures.

It is very important during microbiological examination of low-acid foods to avoid confusing thermophilic and mesophilic sporeforming bacterial isolates. They may be confused because in the vegetative state the cells will grow over a much wider temperature range than when they germinate and grow out from the spore state. For this reason it is essential to produce spores at the temperature of isolation (30° to 35°C or 55°C), heat-shock the suspension to destroy vegetative cell forms, and subculture at both 30° to 35°C and 55°C. The temperature of outgrowth from the spore state indicates whether the isolate is an obligate thermophile (growth only at 55°C), facultative thermophile (growth at both 30° to 35°C and at 55°C), or a true mesophile (optimum growth at 30° to 35°C).

It should be emphasized that heat-shocking for the above purposes must be conducted on subcultures. Heat-shock of the microorganisms in the food sample may unintentionally destroy sporeformers if they are all in the vegetative cell form or when acidic conditions prevail in the food caused by acid-producing spoilage organisms.

In low-acid foods the most common forms of thermophilic spoilage and the causative microorganisms are categorized as follows:

1. "Flat sour" spoilage is indicated when the container is not swollen and when the pH of the product is significantly lowered. The causative microorganisms are sporeformers, such as *Bacillus stearothermophilus*, a facultative anaerobe. Spore germination occurs at thermophilic temperatures only, but vegetative cell growth may occur at mesophilic temperatures as well (Chapter 21).

2. "Thermophilic anaerobe" (TA) spoilage is indicated by swelling, and commonly by the bursting of the container. The condition is caused by obligately thermophilic, sporeforming anaerobes such as *Clostridium thermosaccharolyticum* that produce large quantities of hydrogen and carbon dioxide. The product usually has a "cheesy" odor. Vegetative cells of TAs may grow at temperatures below the thermophilic growth range (Chapter 22).

3. "Sulfide stinker" spoilage is characterized by a flat container in which the contents are darkened and have the odor of rotten eggs. This type of spoilage is caused by the sporeforming anaerobic, obligately thermophilic microorganism *Desulfotomaculum nigrificans*, which produces hydrogen sulfide. No swelling of the container is produced because the hydrogen sulfide is very soluble in the food; however, it does react with any iron present to form black iron sulfide (Chapter 23).

61.243   Container leakage

Environmental sources such as air, water, or dirty contact surfaces may contribute to microbial contamination of processed foods through rough handling of filled containers, or because of defective or damaged containers and closures.[20] Subsequent spoilage often results in swelling of the containers when the pathway of the original leak becomes blocked, preventing the escape of gas. If the opening is large enough, leakage of the product may occur. Spoilage in flat containers, with or without vacuum, may result from contamination of the product with microorganisms that produce little or no gas.

Numerous groups of microorganisms may be found in instances of container leakage, including the following: cocci, short and long rods (lactic acid bacteria), yeasts and molds, aerobic sporeformers, and mixtures (very common). Generally, leaker spoilage is characterized by the presence of mixed cultures of cocci, coccal-bacilli, and rods. All of these organisms exhibit little or no heat resistance.

Aerobic sporeformers are sometimes present in pure or mixed culture as a result of leakage. The predominance of sporeformers is becoming more common because of the widespread chlorination (0.5 ppm or more of free residual chlorine) of cannery cooling water, which destroys most vegetative microorganisms.

In addition, postprocessing can-handling equipment may be a source of seam or closure contamination before the seam compound has had a chance to "set up" and seal the closure. This may occur immediately following thermal processing when containers contact wet, dirty roll tracks or receive rough handling in the presence of contaminated surfaces. Rough handling sufficient to cause leakage does not necessarily result in permanent dents in the can, and permanent dents do not necessarily result in leakage.

The possibility of occurrence of anaerobic sporeforming organisms including *C. botulinum* must be considered. If, during microbiological examination of the product, large club-shaped rods with subterminal spores are found, particularly in combination with a putrid odor, the product should be tested for botulinum toxin by the mouse inoculation procedure (Chapter 36). If not toxic, the sporeformers are the more common putrefactive anaerobes.

It is essential to conduct thorough leakage tests and detailed structural examinations of all containers, although failure to demonstrate leakage sites does not rule out leaker spoilage. This fact cannot be overemphasized when a decision must be made to differentiate spoilage that is due to leakage from spoilage that is caused by insufficient processing, especially when the microbial flora found in the product do not necessarily indicate either situation. The original container closure records are required under Sections 113.60 and 113.100(c) of Title 21 of the Code of Federal Regulations and should particularly be examined if container leakage is suspected.

61.25 Microbiological Groups Associated with Spoilage of Acid Foods

Microbiological spoilage in acid foods is caused by microorganisms capable of growing at pH 4.6 or lower. *Clostridium botulinum* does not grow in these products (unless abnormal conditions raise the pH above 4.6).[32]

Generally it is considered necessary to use acidified media to recover acid-tolerant microorganisms selectively from acid foods. This encourages the growth of the acid-tolerant spoilage organisms and inhibits the outgrowth of acid-sensitive organisms that may have survived the thermal process but were inhibited by the normal acidity of the product. The acid-sensitive, sporeforming, heat-resistant bacteria that can be recovered occasionally from acid foods using media with a neutral pH have no significance. Neutral media, therefore, should not be used when examining acid foods.

After isolation in acid media, it is often convenient to grow acid-producing and/or fastidious bacteria on a neutral medium when they are suspected of causing spoilage of acid foods. These microorganisms are usually lactic acid bacteria (lactobacilli, streptococci, or pediococci), and they can be differentiated from aerobic sporeformers by their negative catalase test (Chapter 15).

Groups of microorganisms that may be associated with spoilage in acid foods are described as follows:

61.251   With insufficient processing

A variety of acid-tolerant sporeforming microorganisms may survive processing. Their survival usually is a result of excessive preprocessing contamination or a mild heat process given to preserve texture (particularly in fruit products). These microorganisms fall into the following groups:

1. "Butyric anaerobes" such as the mesophilic, sporeforming anaerobe *Clostridium pasteurianum*, which produces butyric acid as well as carbon dioxide and hydrogen (Chapter 19).
2. Aciduric "flat sours," particularly *Bacillus coagulans*,[31] in tomato products. This acid-tolerant facultative anaerobic sporeformer grows both at 30° to 35°C and at 61°C (Chapter 20).
3. Heat-resistant molds, often contaminants of juice concentrates and fruits prior to processing. The causative microorganisms are usually *Byssochlamys fulva, Neosartorya fischeri*, or *Talaromyces flavus*, fungi that produce very heat-resistant ascospores. Spoilage is evidenced by a moldy taste and odor, color fading, the presence of mold mycelia in the product, and sometimes by slight swelling of the container lid (Chapter 17).
4. Yeasts and asporogenous bacteria, especially in cases of gross underprocessing. This type of spoilage may be indistinguishable from leaker spoilage unless the containers are thoroughly examined for leakage and structural defects and postprocessing handling conditions are known to be satisfactory (Chapter 16).

61.252   With high-temperature spoilage (thermophilic spoilage)

Thermophilic spoilage may occur in acid foods, particularly in tomato products. Cultural tests should include "cross temperature" incubation of isolates at 30° to 35°C and at 55°C to differentiate mesophiles from thermophiles.

61.253   With leakage

Pure or mixed cultures of acid-tolerant bacteria, yeasts, and molds are commonly found in leaker spoilage of acid products. The containers may be swollen or flat.

Gas and swelling of the can are commonly produced by bacteria or yeasts and sometimes by molds. Spoilage in flat cans is caused by bacteria (rods and cocci) that do not produce gas. The contents usually show a slight lowering of pH (generally less than 0.2 pH unit), with or without obvious organoleptic changes in the product. Mold spoilage usually is evidenced by the presence of mycelia and fungal spores in flat containers having a leak large enough to permit entrance of oxygen. Sometimes a mat of mycelial growth is present on the surface of the product. A heavily etched ring on the sidewall at the product surface level inside the freshly opened can often indicates that oxygen has leaked into the can.

61.3   EXAMINATION METHODS FOR DIAGNOSING SPOILAGE CONDITIONS IN CANNED FOODS

The following methods are designed to guide the investigator in conducting a thorough and carefully documented examination. Results obtained by these methods may be recorded on the sample data collection forms and compared to the "Keys to Probable Cause of Spoilage" in Section 61.4.

The diagnosis of spoilage in canned foods should be conducted by trained microbiologists or trained technicians under supervision. If difficulties are encountered in the examination of samples or in the interpretation of results, assistance is available from recognized authorities in the field, such as the National Food Processors Association; the container supplier; the Food Microbiology Methods Development Branch, CFSAN, U.S. Food and Drug Administration; or the Microbiology Division, Meat and Poultry Inspection Program, Food Safety and Inspection Service, U.S. Department of Agriculture.

61.31   Gathering and Interpreting Background Information

Information regarding the circumstances of production and storage and the incidence of defects in canned foods suspected of spoilage is invaluable for diagnosis.[25] Frequently the cause and nature of spoilage will be evident after a thorough review of background information.

To illustrate this point, aseptically canned foods (those where the container and product are sterilized separately and then filled and closed) such as juices, puddings, and milk do not lend themselves to the procedures listed in this chapter. Contamination may occur in the container before filling, in the cooling of the liquid product, in a diversion valve area, or in the filling or closing area. Microorganisms resulting from this cold recontamination before closing may resemble leakage types. Therefore, subculturing usually does not help in the diagnosis. Instead, a history of the spoilage often will pinpoint the cause. For instance, spoilage that starts early in the day and builds up to 100% by the end of the day usually indicates recontamination of the product in the cooling, diversion, or filling equipment areas. Low numbers of spoiled food containers scattered throughout a day or period usually indicate contamination of container or lid, filter housing, filtered air, or sealing machine.

For other canned foods not using aseptic packaging procedures, terminal heat processing is used, and the guide for interpretation is suggested below.

A suggested "Request for Analysis" form is provided (Figure 1) for gathering this information. The best way to use the form is to request persons submitting samples to fill out the questionnaire at the time the collected samples are submitted for examination. Some detailed information may not be available initially and may need to be obtained later.

To aid in the use of background information, Figure 2 below is provided:

Request for Analysis Form

No. _____   Date _____

Type of Product and Style Pack: _____

A. Information from Point of Collection of Sample(s): _____
   1. Source _____
   2. Number of samples _____
      Sampling Instructions: Please submit 12 suspect units, if available, and 12
      units of sound product from a similar code as controls. Submit *all* suspect
      containers (and an equal number of controls of similar code) if *less* than 12
      suspect units are available.
   3. Date of collection _____
   4. Code(s) _____
   5. Container size _____
B. Information Concerning Code Lot of Submitted Sample(s):
   1. Location of spoiled goods _____
   2. Temperature of storage—Plant: _____ Warehouse: _____ Retail: _____
   3. Number of spoiled and normal containers of each size involved _____
      _____
   4. Percent spoilage (number spoiled divided by number in lot × 100) _____
   5. Packing dates, periods, and lines involved _____
      _____
   6. Date when spoilage first appeared or noted _____
   7. Are any cans burst, hard swells, soft swells, flippers, or low vacuum, and
      are any flat cans spoiled (complaints of spoilage in flat cans)? _____
   8. Were any irregularities noted during production of product in _____
      a. Preparation _____
      b. Thermal processing _____
      c. Cooling temperature _____
      d. Chlorination of cooling water _____
      e. Sanitation of post-process handling (can lines, labeling area, etc.) _____
         _____
      f. Container integrity _____
         _____
      g. Other (damage, mishandling) _____
         _____
   9. Type of cooker or processor _____
  10. Process Used—I.T. _____ Time _____ Temp. _____

Please submit appropriate records for any items noted in B.

C. Alleged Illness Complaint Information:
   1. Number of persons involved _____
   2. Symptoms _____
      _____
      _____
   3. Time before onset of symptoms _____
   4. What other foods and beverages also were ingested _____
      _____
      _____

Figure 1—Request for Analysis Form

Information	Interpretations
1. Number of spoiled containers	i. An isolated container is usually a random leaker, although insufficient processing must be considered. ii. More than one container, especially one or more than one per case, may indicate defective containers, rough handling, or insufficient processing.
2. Age of product and storage condition	i. Excessive age and/or excessive high-temperature of storage may produce detinning and hydrogen swells in metal cans. ii. Perforation because of corrosion or damage of the container may produce leaking and/or mixed culture leakage spoilage, with swells in some cases where the perforations are blocked. iii. Thermophilic spoilage may result from high-temperature storage, in excess of 43°C.
3. Location of spoilage in stacks: temperature of the warehouse	i. Spoilage in center of stacks or near ceiling may indicate failure to cool product sufficiently, resulting in thermophilic spoilage. ii. Scattered spoilage may indicate insufficient processing or leakage. iii. Excessive spoilage usually indicates insufficient processing.
4. Processing records, including retort charts, "cook check tags," or other thermal process records	i. Irregular "cooks" may be correlated with spoilage from insufficient processing.

Figure 2—Guide for Interpretation of Background Information

61.32   Procedures for Examination of Containers and Contents

Conduct all steps in sequence. Record data on the "Spoilage Examination Data" sheet included for this procedure (Figure 3).

61.321   Sampling

The number of units available for analysis will vary with the circumstances. When the item has been in distribution for a long time, few sample units may

Date: _____

Identification: _____

Source: _____

Analyst: _____

Lab Nos: _____

61.321	61.322	61.323		61.324	61.328	61.329	61.330	61.333	
		Gross Wt.						Container Exam and Microleak Testing	Container Condition Interior
Sample No.	Container Condition Exterior	Gms.	Ozs.	Vacuum or Gas	Odor, Appearance	Microscopic Examination	pH		
Code Size									

Figure 3—Form for Spoilage Examination Data

be available. Items with recent codes or those in plant or wholesale ware-houses are usually availabe in sufficient quantity.

1. When sufficient samples are available:
   Select at random 12 sample units that are representative of an apparent or suspected spoilage condition (i.e., swollen containers or reports of abnormal appearance of contents) from each production code involved. Also select 12 contol sample units of sound product from a related code (same day, week). Analyze suspect and control sample units.

2. When sufficient samples are not available:
   If fewer than 12 are available from each production code involved, analyze all sample units representative of an apparent or suspected spoil-age condition. Analyze an equal number of sound control units from a related code. If only one or two sample units are available, it is advisable to request additional units while proceeding with the analysis of those on hand. Avoid testing very hard swells or buckled cans if a sufficient number of softer swells are available. Very hard swells or buckles may burst during examination and structural damage to cans may render the containers unsuitable for microleak testing and detailed container examination.

   Segregate samples by production code (if more than one code is present). Examine the label of each container for leakage stains, and if present, circle with a marking pen. Make a mark with waterproof ink on the bottom of the label and container to indicate the alignment of the label to the container. Carefully remove labels from containers and attach labels temporarily to the back of the data sheet for reference during the external examination of containers.

   Consecutively number each container on the side (body) with water-proof ink or copper sulfate solution;[27] take care not to write on the can side seam. Record container numbers, code(s), and can size(s) on the data sheet.

61.322   External examination

Examine the external condition of the containers for swelling of the ends (or lid). Examine containers for structural defects or damage to the following:

1. Cans[1, 18]
   a. End seams for evidence of crooked, excessively wide or narrow seams, "cutovers," and "sharp" seams, cracked or ruptured seams, "cable burns" (where the metal is abraded through the seam), and evidence of leakage.
   b. Side seam for possible solder or weld voids, pitting, rusting, or leakage.
   c. The embossed code on lid for possible fractures or perforations.

d. The can body for perforations, imperfections (particularly "inclusions" in the tinplate), or leakage.

e. Circle defects when they are found with waterproof ink. Also, mark an "X" on the end of the can exhibiting a defect(s) to show the end that *should not be opened during sampling of the container.* If no defects are found on either can end, save end with the code (usually the "cannery" end) and mark it with "X." Never open the lid end of two-piece aluminum or steel cans unless there is evidence of "leaker damage" on the body shell end.

f. Some canners apply a spot or stripe of heat-sensitive paint or "thermal-sensitive fluid" to the body of the container as a retort check. The paint contains suspended material and has the consistency of "house paint," whereas the fluid is a solution and has the consistency of coding ink. The choice of color may vary with different canners and with different types of products. For this reason, it may be necessary to confirm the specific color system used on the sample(s). Heat-sensitive paints and fluids in common use change color during retorting as follows:

Type	Color before retorting	Color after retorting
Paint	Red	White
	Blue	White
Fluid	Violet	Blue
	Black	Red
	Red	Yellow

A color change indicates only the product was retorted and does not show that the correct process temperature or time was achieved. Therefore, the possibility of insufficient processing cannot be discounted even though the color check conforms to the specified postretort color. No color change indicates that the can was not retorted.

Record observations on data sheet.

2. Glass containers
   a. The lid for possible misalignment, damage, or leakage.
   b. The glass container for "hairline" or small impact cracks or improper finish.
   c. The contents for gas bubbles and abnormal conditions (underfill, digestion, turbidity, etc.).

Record observations on data sheet.

3. Plastic retort trays[2, 30]
   a. The lid seal area for channel leakers, incomplete seals, uneven impression, evidence of severe delamination, severe seal width variation, or product inclusion involving loss of hermetic integrity.
   b. The lid and body for puncture, cuts, or evidence of leakage.
   c. The plastic container for swells, punctures, fractures, crush damage, cuts, or cracks involving evidence of leakage or loss of hermetic integrity.
   d. The contents for abnormal conditions including turbidity, digestion, underfill or lack of brine, uncharacteristic odor, etc.

4. Flexible pouches[2, 30]
   a. The seal area for blisters, severe wrinkles, channel leakers, contaminated seal, severely misaligned seal, notch leakers, pronounced seal creep, nonbonding, delamination in the sealed areas, product inclusion involving evidence of leakage or loss of hermetic integrity.
   b. The pouch body for swells, cuts, punctures, or evidence of fractures or malformation involving leakage or loss of hermetic integrity.
   c. The contents of abnormal condition including digestion, turbidity, uncharacteristic odor, frothing, etc.

61.323 Weight

Weigh each container to the nearest gram and record the weight on the data sheet. Subtract the average known tare weight of the empty container from each unit weight to determine the approximate net weight of each sample. Then look up the established net weight, as well as the maximum and minimum "permissible" net weights of the product. Following the disposition of contents and cleaning of container (Section 61.332), when the empty dried containers are available, weigh them to ensure that they fall within the average tare weight for the type of container.

If the net weights of the suspect sample units exceed the net weights of the controls and exceed the maximum permissible net weight, the suspect containers may be overfilled, causing reduced headspace and reduced or zero vacuum. In extreme cases of overfilling, the bulging of the lid gives the external appearance of a swell. Seafoods, e.g., sardines, because of their size and their packing in short-height cans, are often overfilled inadvertently.

If the suspect units have a lower net weight than controls and are below the minimum permissible net weight for the product, they may be underfilled or have leaked. Leakage also may be evidenced by stains or residues on the label or on the exterior areas of the container.

61.324 Vacuum measurement or gas analysis

Select a portion of the suspect flat containers for measurement of internal vacuum and swollen containers for analyses of headspace gas composition.

Also, select a portion of the control sample units for measurement of internal vacuum. Determine the number of units for vacuum or gas test as follows:

Number of suspect or control containers available	Number to select for vacuum or gas tests
6 to 12	2
2 to 5	1
1	None

When suspect samples consist of both flat and swollen containers, and only two to five are available, select a swell for gas analysis. If only one suspect unit is available, save it for aseptic sampling. A container punctured for gas or vacuum test should not be used for culturing because of the possibility of contamination.

1. Vacuum measurement (normal appearing containers)

Cool to room temperature any container that has been removed from incubation before measuring the vacuum. Use a puncture gauge with a rubber seal around the puncture needle to obtain the vacuum (in inches of mercury)(VWR Scientific, P.O. Box 7900, San Francisco, CA 94120). Take the vacuum through the lid, about ¾ in from the edge to avoid clogging the puncture needle. Record vacuum measurements on data sheet.

Flexible plastic retort trays are flushed with an inert gas and following processing contain a certain amount of headspace gas. Vacuum measurement, therefore, cannot be made on these packages. Some plastic containers for aseptically processed product are filled without having a vacuum and, therefore, also cannot be tested for vacuum.

2. Gas collection and analysis (swollen containers)

a. Qualitative test for hydrogen

When there is sufficient headspace gas in a swollen metal can, the lid may be punctured with a "Bacti-Disc Cutter" (Wilkens-Anderson Company, 425 West Division Street, Chicago, IL 60651) and the gas immediately collected in an inverted test tube that is held directly over the point of puncture. Immediately following collection of the gas, place the open end of the tube in a burner flame. This will result in a loud "pop" if the gas is mainly hydrogen. Usually hydrogen results from detinning of metal cans.

Sampling of plastic retort containers is often more difficult because of their flexibility. The plastic lid may be punctured with a sterile hypodermic needle and the gas immediately collected in an inverted tube. However, puncturing a plastic tray lid makes subsequent tests for microleaks difficult to perform. Hydrogen accumulation in plastic containers usually results from spoilage caused by thermophilic anaerobes.

b. Quantitative headspace gas analysis (hydrogen, carbon dioxide, nitrogen, and oxygen)

A gas sample from a swollen metal container can be collected by use of a rubber gasketed puncture needle connected to a syringe or a manometric device having a "gas-holding solution." In collecting a gas sample from a swollen plastic tray, care must be exercised because of the flexibility of the container and the lid; puncture the lid near its center.

Analyze the gas sample on a chemical gas analyzer or on a gas chromatograph fitted to a thermo conductivity detector (TCD).[33]

Gas from a sound product should contain mostly nitrogen with very small amounts (generally less than 1%) of hydrogen, carbon dioxide, and oxygen. A large percentage of carbon dioxide usually indicates microbial growth, or in some products such as vegetables it may indicate preprocessing product respiration. In high sugar products, carbon dioxide production may be due to the Maillard reaction. A large percentage of hydrogen may indicate metal corrosion or detinning (hydrogen swell), while in plastic retort trays a high concentration of hydrogen may indicate thermophilic anaerobic spoilage. A high concentration of both carbon dioxide and hydrogen may also be indicative of microbial growth, particularly of thermophilic anaerobes. Record results on the data sheet.

61.325 Preparation of area for tests

The area selected for examination should be clean, dust free, and located in an area where samples may be taken aseptically for microbiological examinations. A laminar air flow work station is ideal for providing an ultraclean working environment.[22] Anaylsts should wear clean protective laboratory garments. All sampling utensils and pipettes should be presterilized ready for use. The surface of the workbench used during examination procedures should be washed, sanitized with an effective disinfectant, such as 100 ppm chlorine solution, and wiped dry with clean paper towels.

These conditions are essential to minimize incidental microbial contamination during aseptic sampling, a problem which is most acute when no viable microorganisms are present in the product.[13, 14]

61.326 Preparation of containers

Wash all samples in warm soap and water to remove soil and grease. Rinse in clean running water and dry with clean paper towels. Arrange samples in numerical order (order to be opened) on the workbench. Place the unmarked end of the can to be opened in the upward position. Do not open container.

61.327   Aseptic sampling

For each sample unit, label two sterile large screw-cap test tubes (24 mm) with the sample unit number, product lot code, and date of examination. After aseptic sampling by the following procedure, retain each set of food samples obtained from each container for cultural tests.*

1. Sterilization of lid

Arrange all containers in numerical order, positioning the end to be opened in the upward position. The end to be saved should have been marked with an "X."

a. Flat to moderately hard swells

Flood the lid with a disinfecting agent, such as 100 ppm chlorine solution.[14] Do not use alcohol because it may not completely sterilize the lid surface.[16] Allow to stand 10 to 15 min and pour off excess sanitizing agent. Heat with a burner flame over the lid until visible moisture has evaporated. Do not overheat the lid if a canned sample is under positive pressure. Place side seam away from you during the flaming.

b. Hard swells, very hard swells, and buckled cans

It is advisable to chill sample containers having high positive pressure in a refrigerator for several hours prior to lid sterilization. This will minimize possible bursting of the container during flaming of the lid. When thermophilic anaerobes are suspected, do not chill, because chilling often kills the vegetative cells of TAs, and spores are rarely recoverable in thermophilic spoilage.

Note: Since it takes 10 to 15 min to disinfect a lid with the sanitizing agent, flood the lids of the next containers and let them stand while proceeding with opening and sampling. Once the lid has been flamed, aseptic opening and sampling must be conducted in one continuous operation for each sample unit.

2. Aseptic opening of lid

a. Flat container

Cut a hole slightly off center in the lid using a Bacti-Disc Cutter (Figure 4). A hole 2 in in diameter is usually sufficient for sampling; however, for a small can or jar, a smaller hole may be necessary. Always leave ½ to ¼ in of lid remaining in contact with rim for subsequent microleak testing and container examination.

Open plastic retort trays from the bottom or side to prevent damage to the seal area and lid. Following disinfection, lightly flame dry to avoid damage to the plastic container and cut a hole, large enough to remove a sample aseptically, using a small electric soldering iron with a sharp tip.

*Note: Sample units used for vacuum measurement or gas collection must not be used for aseptic sampling because of possible contamination from puncture devices.

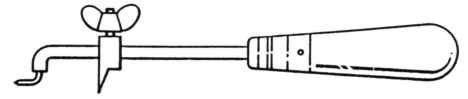

Figure 4—"Bacti-Disc Cutter" Can Opener[27]

b. Swollen container

Place the container on a large clean tray in case the contents under pressure spill over during opening. Invert a large sterilized plastic or metal funnel over the can, insert a sterile-tipped puncture rod through the funnel, and puncture the lid. Puncture a plastic container from the bottom, using a sterile sharp-tipped tool such as the tip of a knife that has been inserted through the funnel. (Resterilize or use a separate sterile funnel for each can.)

After venting has occurred, remove the funnel and open the container by the procedure described previously for a flat container (Section 61.327.2a).

3. Aseptic sampling of contents

Use sterile pipettes or utensils to transfer approximately 20 g of food to each of two labeled tubes. For potentially toxic materials, always use cotton plugged pipettes or pipettes fitted with a mechanical suction device such as a rubber bulb. The following procedures are suggested for transfer of various types of materials to the tubes:

Liquids:

Transfer 20 ml of liquid with sterile 20 ml pipettes.

Semiliquids (with or without small particulate material):

Transfer with sterile 20 ml pipettes having large bore tips.

Solids in liquids:

Pipette about 10 ml of liquid per tube with a sterile 20 ml pipette having a large bore tip. Transfer about 10 g of solids with sterile forceps (nonserrated tip type) or spatula.[11] (Do not reuse pipette or forceps without resteriling in an autoclave.)

Semisolid or solid materials:

Transfer about 20 g material with sterile forceps (nonserrated tin type) spatula or spoon. All transfer utensils must be wrapped and sterilized prior to use. Alcohol flaming of metal utensil must not be used because it is not an effective means of sterilization.[16] Retain all aseptically drawn samples for procedures in Section 61.34. Store tubes in the refrigerator unless microscopic examination reveals long rods indicating possible thermophilic anaerobes. (Vegetative cells of TAs often die under refrigeration.)

61.328   Odor and appearance

Never taste the contents of any container during a spoilage examination because of the potential presence of botulinum toxin!

1. Odor

    Compare the odor of the suspect samples to the odor of the control. (This procedure aids in the detection of an off-odor.)

    Generally, putrid odors suggest the presence of mesophilic, anaerobic sporeformers, and, if found, the samples should be tested for toxin. Fecal odors are generally from coliform bacteria and are indicative of leakage. (For reference to the putrefactive odor characteristic of anaerobic spoilage, smell a laboratory culture of nontoxic Putrefactive Anaerobe #3679 *C. sporogenes*, which may be obtained from the National Food Processors Association.) However, nonproteolytic, nonheat-resistant *C. botulinum* strains may be encountered that do not produce putrefactive odor.

    Sharp, sour odors are usually caused by acid production by bacteria. "Rotten egg" odor is caused by "sulfide stinker" spoilage, usually accompanied by dark discoloration of the product. These odors do not necessarily indicate the presence of toxin.

    Determine the odor characteristics of each opened sample unit. The following terms are commonly used in spoilage examinations:

acidic	hydrogen sulfide	rotten egg
butyric	medicinal	sharp
cheesy	metallic	sour
fecal	putrid	sweet

2. Appearance

    Compare the appearance of the suspect samples to that of the normal controls. Categorize appearance according to the following characteristics. Record the odor and appearance on the data sheet:

Off-color—cooked vs. uncooked
Texture—softening, digested, slimy
Consistency—fluid, viscous, ropy, liquified, coagulated
Clarity—cloudy (in clear liquids), frothy
Foreign materials—particles, mold

61.329   Microscopic examination

Examine the contents of each suspect and each control sample microscopically. With a flamed loop make a smear of the contents from each container on freshly cleaned microscope slides. Let the smear air dry, flame fix, stain with crystal violet (0.5% to 1% solution), and dry. Never gram stain a product because a gram stain result depends on the age of the culture. A gram stain should be made on an 18- to 24-hr culture only.

If a smear will not adhere to the slide during staining (sometimes encountered with fatty foods), rinse a second smear with xylol and allow to dry before staining with crystal violet.

If a phase microscope is available, examine a wet amount prepared by transferring a small drop of food slurry to a slide and overlaying it with a coverslip. Endospores appear brightly refractile under phase lighting.

Examine slides at about 1000× under the oil immersion objective, and record observations on the data sheet. Common results and interpretations are as follows:

1. A normal product may exhibit a few microbial cells in every microscopic field examined. The presence of more than a few cells per field, under 1000× magnification, usually indicates an excessive number of microorganisms. (Fermented foods, such as sauerkraut, are an exception because numerous dead cells will be present. Cultural recovery of viable microorganisms in fermented foods is necessary to confirm spoilage of microbial origin.)

2. Mixtures of rods, cocci, cocco-bacilli, and yeasts or molds usually indicate leakage, but also may indicate that the product missed the process or was grossly underprocessed.

3. Pure cultures of medium to long rods with or without detectable spores (directly or indirectly in subculture) may indicate leakage, especially if the morphology varies from sample to sample. If subsequent tests indicate that the container is structurally sound, and no postprocessing rough handling of wet cans was observed in the plant, insufficient processing may have occurred.

4. Pure cultures of medium to large rods having sporangia or free spores may indicate insufficient processing or leakage. If clostridial rods containing subterminal spores, or only free spores, are present, or if the odor of the product is putrid or "putrefactive," toxin tests by mouse inoculation should be done immediately (Chapter 36).

5. When mixed or pure cultures of cells are observed microscopically, but viable microorganisms are not recovered in subsequent cultural tests, "incipient spoilage" is indicated (except for fermented foods).
   Record results on the data sheet.

61.33   pH Determination

Determine the pH of each sample unit by insertion of the electrode(s) of a previously standardized pH meter, directly into the product in the container. Record pH on the data sheet. The procedure is described in 21 CFR 114.

After measuring the pH of each sample, clean the electrode(s) thoroughly. Use separate electrodes to measure the pH of foods that may be eaten and foods to be tested for spoilage.

Compare pH measurements of suspect and control samples. In addition, compare results to the normal pH range given for the particular food provided in Section 61.5.

61.331   Disposal of contents and cleaning of container

1. Samples suspected of having toxic spoilage

   When one or more sample units are suspected of containing meso-philic, anaerobic spoilage and/or toxin, autoclave the contents after transferring them to another container. Using rubber gloves, rinse the container with 100 ppm chlorine solution and air dry at 35° C. Auto-claving may change the container's lid sealing compound.

2. Low-acid foods (pH above 4.6) exhibiting no signs of toxic spoilage

   Empty contents into a metal tray and sterilize them in an autoclave before disposal. Use gloves when washing the container.

3. Acid food (pH 4.6 or lower)

   Empty contents into the appropriate disposal container without sterilization.

61.332   Cleaning of container

Wash the interior of the container with warm soap and water, using a bottle brush if necessary to remove food residues from interior seam surfaces. Rinse, soak cans in hot water for ½ hr, rinse the hot water, and drain. If available, an automatic dishwasher may be used to clean empty cans and bottles.

Prepare cans for container examination by shaking out excess water from the interior of the can, and placing the container, open end up, in an air incubator, and drying for 24 hr at 35°C. (Higher temperatures may cause lid sealing compound to seal leaks.) Containers must be dry before additional testing.

61.333   Container examination

1. Superficial examination

   Examine the interior of the can for patches of black or dark grey discoloration, especially along the side and end seams. Patches of dis-coloration indicate localized detinning and pitting that are due to chem-ical reaction of the can contents with the container, usually producing a hydrogen swell. Detinning may be due to leakage of oxygen into the can, faulty tin plate, abnormally corrosive contents, or excessive age of the product.

   In plain (unenameled) cans the tin may be completely corroded from the inner surface of the can and internal surfaces will be dark grey. Hy-drogen swells are not dependent on concurrent microbiological spoilage, but leaker spoilage may follow when corrosion has caused the con-tainer to perforate.

   For plastic trays and pouches, examine for seal imperfections, pinholes, and cracks or cuts. Flex cracks in the foil layer usually do not leak through the plastic.[2, 30]

2. Detailed examination

Detailed container examination is necessary when containers have not exhibited obvious defects, especially when leaker spoilage must be clearly differentiated from that caused by insufficient processing.

The detailed examination requires trained personnel and adequate facilities to conduct leakage testing, preferably by the "microleak" detection method,[7] followed by can teardown to evaluate seam and lap construction.[21]

When the expertise for conducting detailed container examinations is not available, it is advisable to seek assistance from the container manufacturer, the National Food Processors Association, or other container experts.

61.34 Microbiological Culture Procedures

Microbiological culture procedures are different for the examination of low-acid and acid foods. For this reason two separate examination sequences are provided: Section 61.341 for low-acid food samples having a normal product pH above 4.6, and Section 61.342 for acid food samples having a normal product pH of 4.6 or lower.

Each section contains a data sheet for recording results during the course of the microbiological examination (Figures 5 to 7). When microbiological tests are completed, compare the results, along with information from Sections 61.31 and 61.32, to the Spoilage Diagnosis Keys provided in Section 61.4.

Isolates obtained from microbiological tests, along with the reserve sample tube of product, always should be saved in case further work is necessary.

61.341   Cultural tests for low-acid foods having a normal pH above 4.6

1. Description of method

This method employs primary media for the recovery of spoilage microorganisms, and subculture media to identify growth characteristics and further characterize them into spoilage groups. Differentiation into spoilage groups is fundamentally dependent on the growth of isolates under aerobic or anaerobic conditions, growth response to 30° to 35°C and at 55°C, and morphological differentiation of vegetatitve and spore-forming cultures. Other determinative factors, including acid and gas production, odor of the culture, and specific cell morphology (cocci, rods, yeasts, etc.) are also utilized.

The purpose, description, and abbreviated designation for each medium employed is given in the following tables. In several instances, a choice of media is given for those in common use. These may be used interchangeably at the option of the investigator.

2. Primary recovery media

Purpose	Primary recovery media	Abbreviation
Aerobic recovery media	Dextrose tryptone bromcresol purple agar in poured plates	DTA[a]
	Alternate: Dextrose tryptone bromcresol purple broth in tubes (Omit agar.)	DTB[b]
Anaerobic recovery media	Peptone yeast extract broth containing bromcresol purple indicator and whole peas in tubes[14]	PE-2[c]
	Alternate: Cooked meat medium, consisting of liver or beef heart infusion broth in tubes	CMM[c]

[a]Growth on DTA plates indicates the presence of aerobic microorganisms. Acid production [bromcresol purple (BCP) turns from purple to yellow] may indicate a flat sour thermophilic isolate if growth occurs at 55°C. Isolates are characterized morphologically by microscopic examination of colonies. Prior to inoculation the surface of the agar should be free from excess moisture. Plates should be taped to prevent loss of moisture.

[b]Growth in DTB tubes is also indicative of aerobic growth; however, anaerobes may grow in the lower portion of the tube. Use of a larger food sample is the chief advantage of DTB.

[c]PE-2 may be used directly. CMM media must be exhausted prior to use by heating to 100°C for 20 min to remove oxygen and rapidly cooled without agitation to the *intended* incubation temperature (30° to 35°C or 55°C). After inoculation the surfaces of the medium may be layered (stratified) with sterile agar or vaspar to maintain anaerobic conditions. Gas production is evidenced by bubbles in the medium or gas accumulation under the agar or vaspar seal.

3. Subculture media

Purpose	Subculture media	Abbreviation
Growth and sporulation of aerobes.	Nutrient agar containing manganese in poured plates.[24]	NAMn[d]
Growth and sporulation of anaerobes (under strict anaerobic conditions).	Liver-veal agar in poured plates.[15]	LVA[e]

[d]NAMn supports growth and enhances spore production by aerobic sporeformers[10, 12, 24] and is used primarily to differentiate mesophilic from thermophilic *Bacillus* spp. When rod-shaped aerobes in pure culture are isolated on DTA (or DTB) and sporulation is not evident, but there is reason to believe sporeformers are involved in the spoilage, the isolates should be subcultured on NAMn at the temperature of initial isolation. After incubation up to 10 days, if spore production has taken place, the spores are heat shocked to destroy all vegetative cells and cultured again on NAMn at both 30° to 35°C and 55°C. The temperature at which outgrowth occurs from the spore state indicates whether the isolate is an obligate mesophile (growth at 30° to 35°C), an obligate thermophile (growth at 55°C), or a facultative thermophile (growth at 30° to 35°C

Sample No: _____ Code: _____ Date Received: _____

Culture stage	Medium	Number of tubes or plates per test	Incubation temperature (C)	Time period of incubation (days)	Results of cultural tests[a]			Cell morphology					Additional comments
					Growth	Acid	Gas[b]	Rods	Spores	Cocci	Yeast	Mold	
Recovery	DTA (or DTB)	2	30° to 35°C	4									
		2	55°C	4									
Subculture #1	NAMn	2	30° to 35°C	10									
		2	55°C	10									

Subculture #2 (Heat-shocked 85°C for 10 min)	NAMn	2	30° to 35°C	4
		2	55°C	4
Recovery	PE-2 (or CMM)	2	30° to 35°C	10
		2	55°C	4
Subculture	LVA (Aerobic)	2	30° to 35°C	4
	LVA (Anaerobic)	2	30° to 35°C	4

[a] 0 = Negative result, e.g., no growth, no acid, etc.
+ = Positive result, e.g., growth, acid, etc.
[b] Note odor of gas or culture in "Additional comments," particularly from PE-2/CMM and LVA cultures.

Figure 5—Cultural Tests on Low-Acid Food Sample Unit

and at 55°C). Further details are provided on the following cultural examination sequence diagram and in the procedure section.

ᵉLVA plates are used to differentiate anaerobes from aerobes. Isolates from PE-2 or CMM are streaked on LVA and incubated aerobically and anaerobically (in anaerobic jar or incubator). The medium supports sporulation of the anaerobic *Clostridium* sp., but it is a good growth medium and under aerobic conditions will grow a great variety of aerobes as well. Prior to inoculation, the surface of the agar should be free from moisture.

4. Cultural examination sequence

Figures 6A and 6B summarize the aerobic and anaerobic examination sequences for low-acid food samples. Review of these sequences prior to utilization of the stepwise testing procedure will aid in determining the extent of the examination. Often negative cultural results will preclude the need for further testing.

It should be noted that all tests starting with DTA or DTB media are designed to identify groups of aerobic microorganisms. All tests starting with PE-2 or CMM media are for identifying anaerobic microorganisms.

Maximum incubation periods are shown in the diagrams; usually growth will take place in a much shorter time and continued incubation is unnecessary (exception, NAMn). Detailed test results should be entered on the data sheet (Figure 5).

5. Procedure. Recovery methods

a. Select one of the two retained samples (taken aseptically in Section 61.327) for cultural testing. Choose samples that are representative of the various initial examination findings. Be sure to test all samples with putrid odor or elevated product pH. Save the other retained sample in the refrigerator in case additional cultural tests are necessary. For each retained sample selected for cultural tests, prepare a set of the following media. Note that duplicate media are listed for each test.

Label four DTA plates or DTB tubes with sample number and date. Mark two plates or tubes "30° to 35°C" and two "55°C."

Label four PE-2 or CMM tubes with sample number and date. Mark two tubes "30° to 35°C" and two tubes "55°C." CMM tubes must be exhausted by heating at 100°C for 20 min and cooled immediately before use.

b. Inoculate each DTA plate by transferring a small quantity of the food, via a flame-sterilized loop, to the surface of the plate. Streak to dilute out the inoculum across the surface of the plate. If DTB tubes are used, aseptically transfer about 1 ml or 1 g of food into the broth. Inoculate each tube of PE-2 (or CMM) by aseptically transferring about 1 ml or 1 g of food into the broth below its surface. Layer the surface of the four inoculated tubes with ½ in of sterile vaspar or agar to provide anaerobic conditions.

c. Incubate media as follows: Place DTA (or DTB) and PE-2 (or CMM) media, labeled "30° to 35°C" in an air incubator having a temperature ranging from 30° to 35°C. (This range is provided since different laboratories commonly use 30°C or 35°C as their preferred temperature of incubation.) Incubate DTA (or DTB) up to 4 days and PE-2 (or CMM) up to 10 days.

Place DTA plates labeled "55°C" in a 55°C incubator. If DTB tubes are used instead of DTA plates, heat the tubes in a water bath to 55°C before placing in the 55°C incubator. Incubate up to 4 days. Heat PE-2 (or CMM) tubes labeled "55°C to 55°C" in a water bath at 55°C before placing them in the 55°C incubator. (Prewarming is necessary to avoid growth and gas production by rapidly growing mesophiles before the tube contents reach the thermophilic temperatures in the incubator.) Incubate anaerobic media (PE-2 or CMM) up to 4 days.

d. Record detailed results on the data sheet in spaces provided for the recovery media (DTA/DTB; PE-2/CMM). Note: If high loads of organisms were observed during microscopic examination of the product, the cells seen in culture may result from carryover and not growth.

Growth in DTA or DTB: Record growth at the different temperatures based on acid production as indicated by bromcresol purple dye turning yellow or by visible growth when examined microscopically under oil immersion at about 1000× magnification (crystal violet stain or phase contrast microscopy). A gram stain may be made on 18- to 24-hr cultures only.

If growth consists of mixed cultures of rods, cocci, yeasts, or molds, then leakage or gross underprocessing is indicated and further culturing is unnecessary. Cocci, yeasts, or molds in pure culture also indicate leakage or gross underprocessing. Very short (tiny) rods are also an indication of leakage. Generally, rods of various widths also suggest leakage, but additional testing of them is necessary. If only rod-shaped bacteria are present, with or without spores, continue with subculture sequence given in Section 6a below.

Growth in PE-2 (or CMM): Record presence and temperature(s) of growth, acid production (in PE-2 medium only) and presence of gas under the seal. Remove the cap from each tube and note odor. Examine growth microscopically under oil immersion at about 1000× (crystal violet stain or phase microscopy). During microscopic examination observe for clostridial morphology, rod-shaped cells containing spores, and or free spores. Spores are brightly refractile, especially under phase microscopy.

If rod-shaped bacteria, with or without spores, are observed in PE-2 (or CMM) incubated at 30° to 35°C, continue with the subculture sequence given in Section 6b. Save the PE-2 (or CMM) culture tubes during the subculture procedure, because if anaerobic growth is observed in subculture, the PE-2 or CMM tubes must be tested for the presence of botulinum toxin (Chapter 36).

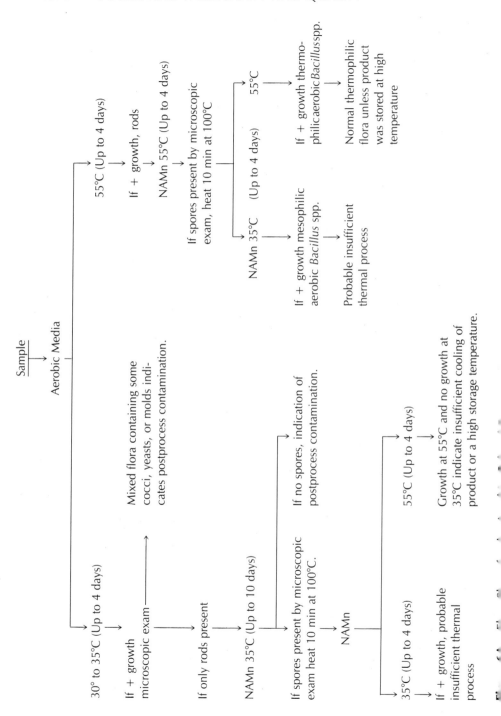

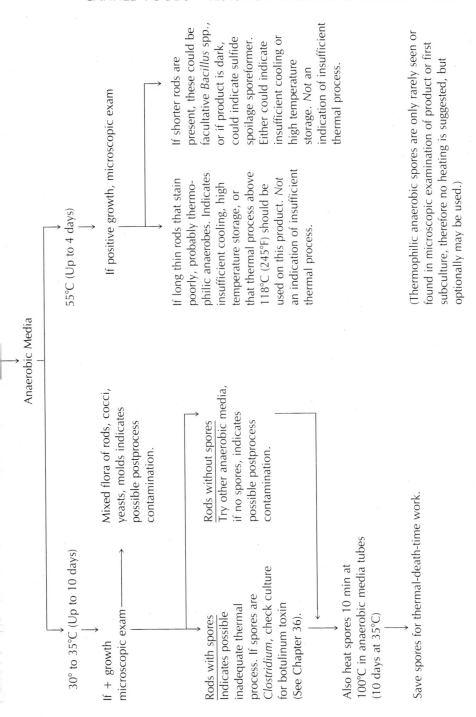

Anaerobic Media

30° to 35°C (Up to 10 days)

If + growth
microscopic exam

Mixed flora of rods, cocci, yeasts, molds indicates possible postprocess contamination.

Rods with spores
Indicates possible inadequate thermal process. If spores are Clostridium, check culture for botulinum toxin (See Chapter 36).

Rods without spores
Try other anaerobic media, if no spores, indicates possible postprocess contamination.

Also heat spores 10 min at 100°C in anaerobic media tubes (10 days at 35°C)

Save spores for thermal-death-time work.

55°C (Up to 4 days)

If positive growth, microscopic exam

If long thin rods that stain poorly, probably thermophilic anaerobes. Indicates insufficient cooling, high temperature storage, or that thermal process above 118°C (245°F) should be used on this product. Not an indication of insufficient thermal process.

If shorter rods are present, these could be facultative Bacillus spp., or if product is dark, could indicate sulfide spoilage sporeformer. Either could indicate insufficient cooling or high temperature storage. Not an indication of insufficient thermal process.

(Thermophilic anaerobic spores are only rarely seen or found in microscopic examination of product or first subculture, therefore no heating is suggested, but optionally may be used.)

Figure 6B—Flow Diagram for the Anaerobic Cultural Examination of Low-Acid Canned Foods for Spoilage Diagnosis

6. Procedure. Subculture methods

   a. The presence of mesophilic or thermophilic aerobic sporeformers (*Bacillus* spp.) may be established as follows:

     If only rod-shaped bacteria were observed on DTA or DTB media, they should be subcultured on NAMn plates as follows:

     (1) Streak cultures recovered at 30° to 35°C on DTA or DTB media onto two NAMn plates. Incubate the NAMn subculture at 30° to 35°C only.

     (2) Streak bacillus culture recovered at 55°C on DTA or DTB media onto two NAMn plates. Incubate the NAMn subculture at 55°C only.

     (3) If growth occurred on DTA or DTB media at 30° to 35°C and 55°C, test the 30° to 35°C culture(s) as in (1) and test the 55°C culture(s) as in (2).

     Allow NAMn subcultures to incubate up to 10 days to ensure sporulation. Verify spore formation by microscopic examination of all cultures before proceeding.

     Place two loopfuls of a colony containing spores from each NAMn plate incubated at 30° to 35°C and or 55°C into separate sterile 16 mm glass tubes containing 1 ml of sterile distilled water. Avoid touching the sides of the tubes with the loop. Swirl tubes gently to disperse culture. Place the tubes in a 85°C waterbath for 10 min to heat-shock mesophilic spores and to destroy vegetative cells. Heat-shocking thermophilic spores will require higher temperatures (Chapters 21, 22). The level of the spore suspension in the tube should be 1 in below the level of the water bath.

     Following heat-shock of the suspensions, streak a loopful from each tube onto each of four fresh NAMn plates. Incubate two plates at 30° to 35°C and two at 55°C. Incubate up to 4 days at each temperature and record presence or absence of growth on data sheet. Examine microscopically for spores and note this result also.

   b. The presence of mesophilic obligately anaerobic sporeformers (clostridia) may be established as follows:

     If rod-shaped bacteria occur in PE-2 or CMM broth incubated at 30° to 35°C, streak four LVA plates from each positive tube in a manner to dilute the inoculum. Incubate two of the LVA plates aerobically, in a 30° to 35°C incubator for up to 4 days. Incubate the other two plates in an anaerobic incubator at 30° to 35°C for up to 4 days. In the latter case, ensure that anaerobic conditions are maintained by use of a suitable oxidation-reduction indicator.

     After 2 to 4 days' incubation, examine the aerobic and anaerobic plates for growth. Examine the cultures microscopically and record cell morphology and presence or absence of spores. Note the odor of anaerobic culture and record if it is putrid, or otherwise describe the odor as in Section 61.328.1.

The following interpretations and tests are dependent on the results of subculture growth reactions in LVA plates incubated at 30° to 35°C under aerobic or anaerobic conditions.

(1) When growth occurs only on the aerobic LVA plates, an aerobe has been isolated. No further testing is necessary since anaerobic isolates were not recovered.

(2) When growth occurs only on the anaerobic LVA plates, a strict anaerobe has been isolated. A *Clostridium* species is indicated if microbiological examination reveals the presence of spore-forming cells having clostridial morphology (cells often shaped like tennis rackets, having terminal spores in swollen sporangia), and/or free spores.

Growth on the anaerobic LVA plate, particularly with a putrid odor, necessitates testing the 30° to 35°C PE-2 or CMM isolation media for the presence of *C. botulinum* toxin by the mouse inoculation procedure (Chapter 36). The proteolytic, heat-resistant spores isolated may be saved by heating them for 10 min at 100°C in anaerobic media tubes and incubating for 10 days at 35°C.

(3) Growth on both the aerobic and anaerobic LVA plates indicates the presence of an aerobe and an anaerobe, or a facultative anaerobe, or a mixture of all three.

Since toxic *C. botulinum* may be present on the anaerobic LVA plate, examine the culture microscopically and conduct the test for botulinum toxin (Chapter 36).

Growth on the aerobic and anaerobic LVA plates may consist of a pure culture of asporogenous facultatively anaerobic lactobacilli. Microscopically, these organisms appear as slender rods. They will be present in instances of container leakage and are nonpathogenic.

Note: The procedures in Section 6b are intended to confirm the presence of mesophilic obligately anaerobic microorganisms indicating the potential presence of *C. botulinum* and the need for conducting the toxin test. However, since mixtures of obligate and/or facultative anaerobes may be recovered, further identification and tests for heat resistance are recommended by methods presented elsewhere in the compendium. When *C. botulinum* is suspected, refer specifically to Chapter 36 for additional test methods.

61.342   Cultural tests for acid or acidified foods having a normal pH of 4.6 or lower

1. Method

Aciduric microorganisms are the only types capable of growing in a product having a pH of 4.6 or lower. For this reason, the subculture media must be selective for the spoilage type involved, i.e., must approach the normal pH of the food to eliminate the possibility of isolating viable organisms that are dormant in the product, but are capable of growing in a more neutral medium.[3]

The general media of choice for recovering most acid-tolerant microorganisms are orange serum broth acidified to pH 5.5,[4] or thermoacidurans agar plates acidified to pH 5.0.[26] It should be noted, however, that because the pH of these media are somewhat higher than 4.6, microorganisms may be recovered occasionally that are normally suppressed in the acid product. It is common to recover spoilage microorganisms from specific acid products when cultured in media consisting of the normal product that has been tubed and sterilized. Hence, when the investigator is dealing exclusively with spoilage diagnosis of a specific acid product, it is recommended that recovery of spoilage microorganisms in tubed and sterilized normal product be considered.

Other media are useful to recover specific types of spoilage organisms or to differentiate microorganisms in acid foods. Potato dextrose agar acidified to pH 3.5 or phytone yeast extract agar with streptomycin and chloramphenicol[6] are suitable for the recovery of yeasts and molds without the interference of bacteria. Thermoacidurans agar acidified to pH 5.0 is useful for recovery of *B. coagulans* and butyric anaerobes. Unacidified dextrose tryptone agar with bromcresol purple indicator may be employed to demonstrate acid producers and unacidified APT agar may be used to support growth of fastidious lactic acid bacteria.

The latter two media also support the growth of acid-intolerant microorganisms and should be used in conjunction with acidified media.

2. Procedure
   a. Select one of the two retained samples (taken aseptically in Section 61.327) for cultural testing. Save the other sample in the refrigerator in case specific cultural tests become necessary. For each retained sample selected for cultural tests, asesmble the following media (includes duplicate media per test):

   Four orange serum broth (OSB) tubes or thermoacidurans agar (TAA) plates

   Two thermoacidurans agar (TAD) deep tubes if butyric anaerobe spoilage is suspected

   Two potato dextrose agar (PDA) and phytone yeast extract agar (PYE) plates if yeast and/or mold spoilage is suspected

   Use PDA if spoilage from heat-resistant mold (*B. fulva*) is suspected in fruit and fruit products (Chapter 17)

   Two DTA plates if aerobic acid formers are suspected

   Two APT plates if fastidious lactobacilli are suspected, especially in flat cans

   Label tubes and plates with sample number and date.

b. Inoculate OSB tubes with about 1 g of food sample. (Record if the medium becomes turbid from the food at time of inoculation.) If TAA plates are used, streak each with a loopful of food as described.

c. Inoculate optional media by transferring a small amount of food to the plate using a flame-sterilized loop. Streak across media to dilute out the inoculum. Use a pipette for inoculation of TAD tubes; place 1 ml in bottom of melted 47° to 50°C agar, and cool rapidly.

d. Incubate all samples at temperatures indicated on the data collection form. Heat all tubed media intended for 55°C incubation at 55°C in a waterbath immediately after inoculation and before placing in the incubator.

e. If growth occurs after incubation, note the following conditions:

Presence of acid in media containing bromcresol purple indicator (purple to yellow)

Presence of gas in liquid media (bubbles) or in layered anaerobic media (gas under plug)

Prepare a crystal violet stain or a wet mount for phase microscopy as soon as growth is apparent. Look for the presence of refractile spores in sporangia and/or free spores, as well as the morphological forms of nonsporeforming microorganisms.

If DTA or APT medium was used, flood with a 3% solution of hydrogen peroxide. A positive catalase test is indicated by gas bubbles around the colonies; a negative catalase reaction is indicated by the absence of bubbles. Lactic acid bacteria are indicated by negative catalase reaction.

Enter results on worksheet (Figure 7) and compare to diagnostic keys in the following Section 61.4.

61.4   KEYS TO PROBABLE CAUSE OF SPOILAGE

Refer to Tables 1 and 2 to diagnose a spoilage condition. Each key categorizes possible spoilage conditions for food within a given pH range. The normal pH of the product being examined must be used when referring to the charts. Separate keys are provided for low-acid and acid food products.

61.51   Addresses for Firms Listed in References, Section 61.6

Association of Official Analytical Chemists (AOAC). 2200 Wilson Blvd., Arlington, VA 22201-3301

Food Processors Institute (FPI), 1401 New York Ave. NW, Washington, DC 20005

National Food Processors Association (NFPA), (previously NCA) 1401 New York Ave. NW, Washington, DC 20005

General Services Administration, Specifications Section, Room 6654, 7th and D Sts. SW, Washington, DC 20407

Microbiology, Metal Division Research and Development, Continental Can Co., Inc., 711 Jorie Blvd., Oak Brook, IL 60521

Sample No:	Code:		Date:										
			Results										
Medium	Incubation temperature (C) (Incubate up to 5 days)	Growth	Acid	Gas	Mold	Yeast		Bacterial			Catalase + or −
								Cocci	Rods	Spores	
OSB[a] or TAA	30° to 35°										
OSB[a] or TAA	55° 30° to 35°										
TAD	30° to 55°										
PDA or PYE	25° to 30°										
DTA[b] (opt)	30° to 35°										
APT[b] (opt)	30° to 35°										

[a]Note if OSB is layered to obtain anaerobic conditions.
[b]Incubation of DTA and/or APT in an anaerobic jar is useful when very poor growth is produced by aerobic incubation procedures. Permit plates to stand exposed to air for a minimum of 30 min before testing for catalase.

Figure 7—Cultural Test Results for Acid or Acidified Foods Having pH of 4.6 or Less

Cultural information

Purpose	Medium	Abbreviation	Incubation temperature
General recovery	Orange serum broth,[4] pH 5.5, in tubes.[c] *Alternative:* Thermoacidurans agar, pH 5.0, plates.[26]	OSB TAA	30° to 35°C
B. coagulans. Facultative thermophilic aerobes; aciduric flat sours	Orange serum broth,[4] pH 5.5, in tubes.[c] Thermoacidurans agar,[26] pH 5.0, plates.	OSB TAA	55°C 30° to 35°C
Butyric anaerobes	Thermoacidurans agar,[26] pH 5.0, deep tubes.	TAD	30° to 35°C
Yeasts and molds. Especially the heat-resistant mold *Byssochlamys fulva*	Potato dextrose agar, pH 3.5, plates. *Alternate:* Phytone yeast extract agar with streptomycin and chloramphenicol,[6] plates.	PDA PYE	25° to 30°C
Aerobes and acid formers	Dextrose tryptone agar with bromcresol purple indicator, plates.	DTA	30° to 35°C
Fastidious lactic acid bacteria	APT agar,[17] plates.[d]	APT	30° to 35°C

[c]If butyric anaerobes are indicated by a butyric odor of the product, or if spoilage by thermophilic anaerobes is indicated by high temperature storage conditions, carbon dioxide and hydrogen, and presence of sporeforming rods, layer the OSB with sterile vaspar or acidified agar to produce anaerobic conditions, or use thermoacidurans agar deep tubes.

[d]The test for catalase consists of flooding growth on this medium with a 3% solution of hydrogen peroxide. Catalase negative isolates belong to the lactic group (lactobacilli, streptococci, pediococci).

Figure 7—Cultural Test Results for Acid or Acidified Foods Having pH of 4.6 or Less (Continued)

Table 1—Low-Acid Foods—pH Above 4.6[28] Keys to Probable Cause of Spoilage

Condition of cans	Characteristics of material in cans						Diagnosis
	Odor	Appearance	Gas (CO_2 & H_2)	pH	Smear	Cultures	
Swells	Normal to "metallic"	Normal to frothy (Cans usually etched or corroded.)	More than 20% H_2	Normal	Negative to occasional organisms	Negative	Hydrogen swells
	Sour	Frothy; possibly ropy brine	Mostly CO_2	Below normal	Pure or mixed cultures of rods, coccoids, cocci, or yeasts	Growth, aerobically and/or anaerobically at 30°C, and possibly growth at 55°C	Leakage
	Sour	Frothy; possibly ropy brine; food particles firm with uncooked appearance	Mostly CO_2	Below normal	Pure or mixed cultures of rods, coccoids, cocci, or yeasts	Growth, aerobically and/or anaerobically at 30°C, and possibly growth at 55°C. (If product received high exhaust, only spore-formers may be recovered.)	No process given
	Normal to sour-cheesy	Frothy	H_2 and CO_2	Slightly to definitely below normal	Rods med., short to med., long, usually granular; spores seldom seen	Gas anaerobically at 55°C and possibly slowly at 30°C Negative: Thermophilic anaerobes often autosterilize	Inadequate cooling or storage at elevated temps. —thermophilic anaerobes
(Note: Cans are sometimes flat.)	Normal to cheesy to putrid	Normal to frothy with disintegration of solid particles	Mostly CO_2, possibly some H_2	Normal to slightly below normal	Rods; possibly spores present	Gas anaerobically at 30°C. Putrid odor	Insufficient processing—mesophilic anaerobes (possibly C. botulinum)

	Odor	Brine	Gas	Vacuum	Microscopic	Culture	Interpretation
No vacuum and/or cans buckled	Slightly off— possibly ammoniacal	Normal to frothy	CO_2	Slightly to definitely below normal	Rods; occasionally spores observed	Growth, aerobically and/or anaerobically with gas at 30°C and possibly at 55°C. Pellicle in aerobic broth tubes. Spores formed on agar and in pellicle	Insufficient processing or leakage— B. subtilis type
	Butyric acid	Frothy; large volume gas	H_2 and CO_2	Definitely below normal	Rods, bipolar staining; possibly spores	Gas anaerobically at 30°C. Butyric acid odor	Insufficient processing— butyric acid anaerobe
	Normal	Normal	No H_2	Normal to slightly below normal	Negative to moderate number of organisms	Negative	Insufficient vacuum caused by (1) Incipient spoilage, (2) Insufficient exhaust, (3) Insufficient blanch, (4) Improper retort cooling procedures, (5) Overfill
Flat cans (0 to normal vacuum)	Sour	Normal to cloudy brine		Slightly to definitely below normal	Rods possibly granular in appearance	Growth without gas at 55°C and possibly at 30°C	Inadequate cooling or storage at elevated temps.—thermophilic flat sours
	Normal to sour	Normal to cloudy brine; possibly moldy		Slightly to definitely below normal	Pure or mixed cultures of rods, coccoids, cocci, or mold	Growth, aerobically and/or anaerobically at 30°C, and possibly at 55°C	Leakage

Table 2—Acid Foods—pH 4.6 or Below, Keys to Probable Cause of Spoilage

Condition of cans	Odor	Appearance	Gas (CO_2 & H_2)	pH	Smear	Cultures	Diagnosis
					Characteristics of material in cans		
Swells	Normal to "metallic"	Normal to frothy. (Cans usually etched or corroded)	More than 20% H_2	Normal	Negative to occasional organisms	Negative	Hydrogen swells
	Sour	Frothy; possibly ropy brine	Mostly CO_2	Below normal	Pure or mixed cultures of rods, coccoids, cocci, or yeasts	Growth, aerobically and/or anaerobically at 30°C and possibly at 55°C	Leakage or grossly insufficient processing
	Sour	Frothy; possibly ropy brine; food particles firm	Mostly CO_2	Below normal	Pure or mixed cultures of rods, coccoids, cocci, or yeasts	Growth, aerobically and/or anaerobically at 30°C and possibly at 55°C. (If product received high exhaust, only spore-formers may be recovered.)	No process given
	Normal to sour-cheesy	Frothy	H_2 and CO_2	Normal to slightly below normal	Rods, med. short to med. long, usually granular; spores seldom seen	Gas anaerobically at 55°C and possibly slowly at 30°C	Inadequate cooling or storage at elevated temps.—thermo-philic anaerobes
	Butyric acid	Frothy; large volume gas	H_2 and CO_2	Below normal	Rods, bipolar staining; possibly spores	Gas anaerobically at 30°C. Butyric acid odor	Insufficient proc-essing, butyric acid anaerobes

No vacuum and/or cans buckled	Sour	Frothy	Mostly CO_2	Below normal	Short to long rods	Gas anaerobically; acid and possibly gas aerobically in broth tubes at 30°C. Possible growth at 55°C	Grossly insufficient processing—lactobacilli
	Normal	Normal	No H_2	Normal to slightly below normal	Negative to moderate number of organisms	Negative	Insufficient vacuum caused by (1) Incipient spoilage, (2) Insufficient exhaust, (3) Insufficient blanch, (4) Improper retort cooling procedure, (5) Overfill
Flat cans (0 to normal vacuum)	Sour to "medicinal"	Normal		Slightly to definitely below normal	Rods, possibly granular in appearance	Growth without gas at 55°C, and possibly at 30°C. Growth on thermoacidurans agar (pH 5.0)	Insufficient processing—*B. coagulans* (Spoilage of this type usually limited to tomato juice)
	Normal to sour	Normal to cloudy brine; possibly moldy		Slightly to definitely below normal	Pure or mixed cultures of rods, coccoids, cocci, or mold	Growth aerobically and/or anaerobically at 30°C and possibly at 55°C	Leakage, or no process given

61.5   NORMAL pH RANGES OF SELECTED COMMERCIALLY CANNED FOODS[18]

Kind of food	pH range (approximate)	Kind of food	pH range (approximate)
Apples, whole	3.4–3.5	Cherry juice	3.4–3.6
Apples, juice	3.3–3.5	Chicken	6.2–6.4
Asparagus, green	5.0–5.8	Chicken with noodles	6.2–6.7
Beans		Chop suey	5.4–5.6
baked	4.8–5.5	Cider	2.9–3.3
green	4.9–5.5	Clams	5.9–7.1
lima	5.4–6.3	Codfish	6.0–6.1
soy	6.0–6.6	Corn	
Beans, with pork	5.1–5.8	on the cob	6.1–6.8
Beef, corned, hash	5.5–6.0	cream style	5.9–6.5
Beets, whole	4.9–5.8	whole grain	
Blackberries	3.0–3.3	brine packed	5.8–6.5
Blueberries	3.2–3.6	vacuum packed	6.0–6.4
Boysenberries	3.0–3.3	Crab apples, spiced	3.3–3.7
Bread		Cranberry	
white	5.0–6.0	juice	2.5–2.7
date and nut	5.1–5.6	sauce	2.3
Broccoli	5.2–6.0	Currant juice	3.0
Carrots, chopped	5.3–5.6	Dates	6.2–6.4
Carrot juice	5.2–5.8	Duck	6.0–6.1
Cheese		Figs	4.9–5.0
Parmesan	5.2–5.3	Frankfurters	6.2
Roquefort	4.7–4.8	Fruit cocktails	3.6–4.0
Gooseberries	2.8–3.1	Potatoes	
Grapefruit		white	5.4–5.9
juice	2.9–3.4	mashed	5.1
pulp	3.4	Potato salad	3.9–4.6
sections	3.0–3.5	Prune juice	3.7–4.3
Grapes	3.5–4.5	Pumpkin	5.2–5.5
Hams, spiced	6.0–6.3	Raspberries	2.9–3.7
Hominy, lye	6.9–7.9	Rhubarb	2.9–3.3
Huckleberries	2.8–2.9	Salmon	6.1–6.5
Jam, fruit	3.5–4.0	Sardines	5.7–6.6
Jellies, fruit	3.0–3.5	Sauerkraut	3.1–3.7
Lemons	2.2–2.4	juice	3.3–3.4
juice	2.2–2.6	Shrimp	6.8–7.0
Lime juice	2.2–2.4	Soups	
Loganberries	2.7–3.5	bean	5.7–5.8
Mackerel	5.9–6.2	beef broth	6.0–6.2
Milk		chicken noodle	5.5–6.5
cow	6.4–6.8	clam chowder	5.6–5.9
evaporated	5.9–6.3	duck	5.0–5.7

Molasses	5.0–5.4	mushroom	6.3–6.7
Mushrooms	6.0–6.5	noodle	5.6–5.8
Olives, ripe	5.9–7.3	oyster	6.5–6.9
Orange juice	3.0–4.0	pea	5.7–6.2
Oysters	6.3–6.7	tomato	4.2–5.2
Peaches	3.4–4.2	turtle	5.2–5.3
Pears (Bartlett)	3.8–4.6	vegetable	4.7–5.6
Peas	5.6–6.5	Spinach	4.8–5.8
Pickles		Squash	5.0–5.3
dill	2.6–3.8	Strawberries	3.0–3.9
sour	3.0–3.5	Sweet potatoes	5.3–5.6
sweet	2.5–3.0	Tomatoes	4.1–4.4
Pimento	4.3–4.9	juice	3.9–4.4
Pineapple		Tuna	5.9–6.1
crushed	3.2–4.0	Turnip greens	5.4–5.6
sliced	3.5–4.1	Vegetable	
juice	3.4–3.7	juice	3.9–4.3
Plums	2.8–3.0	mixed	5.4–5.6
		Vinegar	2.4–3.4
		Youngberries	3.0–3.7

61.6 REFERENCES

1. AOAC/FDA. 1984. "Classification of Visible Can Defects (Exterior)." In "Bacteriological Analytical Manual," 6th ed. Food and Drug Admin./Assn. Off. Anal. Chem., Arlington, Va.
2. AOAC/NFPA/FDA. 1989. "Classification of Visible Flexible Package Defects (Exterior)." National Food Processors Assn./Food and Drug Admin./Assn. Off. Anal. Chem., Arlington, Va.
3. APHA. 1966a. Canned Foods. In "Recommended Methods for the Microbiological Examination of Foods," 2nd ed., ed. J. M. Scharf, p. 40. Am. Pub. Health Assn., New York.
4. APHA. 1966b. Appendix A, Culture Media, #48. Orange serum agar. In "Recommended Methods for the Microbiological Examination of Foods," 2nd ed., ed. J. M. Scharf, p. 178. Am. Pub. Health Assn., New York.
5. Ball, C. O. and Olson, F. C. W. 1957. "Sterilization in Food Technology: Theory, Practice and Calculations." McGraw-Hill Book Co., New York.
6. BBL. 1988. Phytone yeast extract agar. In "Manual of Products and Laboratory Procedures," 6th ed., p. 224. Becton Dickinson Microbiol. Systems, Cockeysville, Md.
7. Bee, G. R., DeCamp, R. A., and Denny, C. B. 1972. "Construction and Use of a Vacuum Micro-leak Detector for Metal and Glass Containers." Natl. Canners Assn./National Food Processors Assn., Washington, D.C.
8. Cameron, E. J. 1940. Report on canned vegetables. J. Assn. Off. Anal. Chem. 23: 607.
9. Cameron, E. J. and Esty, J. R. 1940. Comments on the microbiology of spoilage in canned foods. Food Res. 5: 549.
10. Charney, J., Fisher, W. P., and Hegarty, C. P. 1951. Manganese as an essential element for sporulation in the genus Bacillus. J. Bacteriol. 62: 145.
11. Corson, L. M., Evancho, G. M., and Ashton, D. H. 1973. Use of forceps in sterility testing: A possible source of contamination. J. Food Sci. 38: 1267.
12. Curran, H. R. and Evans, F. R. 1954. The influence of iron or manganese upon the formation of spores by mesophilic aerobes in fluid organic media. J. Bacteriol. 67: 489.

13. Denny, C. B. 1970. Collaborative study of procedure for determining commercial sterility of low-acid canned foods. J. Assn. Off. Anal. Chem. 53: 713.
14. Denny, C. B. 1972. Collaborative study of a method for the determination of commercial sterility of low-acid canned foods. J. Assn. Off. Anal. Chem. 61: 613.
15. Difco. 1984. Liver veal agar. In "Difco Manual of Dehydrated Culture Media and Reagents for Microbiological and Clinical Laboratory Procedures," 10th ed., p. 528. Difco Laboratories, Inc., Detroit, Mich.
16. Doyle, J. E. and Ernst, R. E. 1969. Alcohol. Alcohol flaming—a possible cause of contamination in sterility testing. Amer. Clin. Pathol. 51: 507.
17. Evans, J. B. and Niven, C. F. Jr. 1951. Nutrition of the heterofermentative lactobacilli that cause greening of cured meat products. J. Bacteriol. 62: 599.
18. FDA/AOAC. 1984. pH ranges. In "Bacteriological Analytical Manual," 6th ed., Chapter 23, p. 11. Food and Drug Admin., Div. of Microbiology/Assn. Off. Anal. Chem., Arlington, Va.
19. FPI. 1988a. "Canned Foods: Principles of Thermal Process Control, Acidification, and Container Closure Evaluation." Food Processors Institute, Washington, D.C.
20. FPI. 1988b. Food Container Handling. In "Canned Foods: Principles of Thermal Process Control, Acidification, and Container Closure Evaluation," p. 27. Food Processors Institute, Washington, D.C.
21. FPI. 1988c. Container Closure Evaluation. In "Canned Foods: Principles of Thermal Process Control, Acidification, and Container Closure Evaluation," p. 117. Food Processors Institute, Washington, D.C.
22. GSA. 1988. Clean room and work station requirements. Fed. Std. No. 209D, Specifications Section, Gen. Serv. Admin., Washington, D.C.
23. Hartwell, R. R. 1951. Certain aspects of internal corrosion in tin plate containers. Adv. Food Res. 3: 327.
24. Maunder, D. T. 1970. "Examination of Canned Foods for Microbial Spoilage." Microbiology, Metal Div. R. and D., Continental Can Co., Inc., Oak Brook, Ill.
25. NCA. 1962. Diagnosis of Canned Food Spoilage. NCA Research Information. Natl. Canners Assn. 62: February.
26. NCA. 1968a. Preparation of media for microorganisms. Thermoacidurans agar. In "Laboratory Manual for Food Canners and Processors," Vol. I, "Microbiology and Processing," p. 20. Natl. Canners Assn., AVI, Westport, Conn.
27. NCA. 1968b. Investigating spoilage problems. In "Laboratory Manual for Food Canners and Processors," p. 45. Natl. Canners Assn., AVI, Westport, Conn.
28. NCA. 1968c. Investigating spoilage problems. In "Laboratory Manual for Food Canners and Processors," p. 56–59. Natl. Canners Assn., AVI, Westport, Conn.
29. NCA. 1968d. Process calculations. In "Laboratory Manual for Food Canners and Processors," p. 220. Natl. Canners Assn., AVI, Westport, Conn.
30. NFPA. 1989. Flexible Package Integrity Bulletin. Bull. 41-L. Natl. Food Proc. Assn., Washington, D.C.
31. Stern, R. M., Hegarty, C. P., Williams, O. B. 1942. Detection of Bacillus thermoacidurans (Berry) in tomato juice and successful cultivation of the organism in the laboratory. Food Res. 7: 186.
32. Townsend, C. T., Yee, L., and Mercer, W. A. 1954. Inhibition of the growth of Clostridium botulinum by acidification. Food Res. 19: 536.
33. Vosti, D. C., Hernandez, H. H., and Strand, J. B. 1961. Analysis of headspace gases in canned foods by gas chromatography. Food Technol. 15: 29.

Chapter 62

MEDIA, REAGENTS, AND STAINS

Gary R. Acuff

62.1 CULTURE MEDIA, INTRODUCTION

This chapter contains the formulae for all non-commercially available culture media mentioned in the text of the "Compendium" and the directions for making and using media. Commercially available media that are listed are designated as commercially available by asterisks after the media names. Additional information is supplied for these media when requested by chapter authors. The names of the various media are those by which they are generally known in the literature, with a few exceptions where the name used was given by the author of the chapter referring to the medium. In the text the recommended medium is referred to by name, and the name is listed alphabetically in Section 62.3 of this chapter.

62.11 Forms of Media

In most cases, recommended media can be obtained in dehydrated form. The equivalent product of any manufacturer may be used and should be made in accordance with the manufacturer's instructions. Catalogs of media manufacturers contain descriptions of products with their formulations. Since it is difficult to define equivalency in objective terms, the user must test products in the laboratory as part of a routine laboratory quality assurance program to determine that the medium functions as expected. Dehydrated media should be employed unless the author specifically recommends that the user prepare the media from individual ingredients. In such cases, the laboratory should

---

This chapter has been revised from earlier editions and contains information previously provided by A.H. Schwab, H.V. Leininger, and E.M. Powers.

test the medium with sufficient cultures to determine that the performance of the preparation is satisfactory. In some instances, the name of a manufacturer is given to provide a source of the material mentioned in the formulation when that material is available from a single company or is not commonly employed in the laboratory.

62.111   Dehydrated media

Dehydrated media should be stored in sealed containers in a cool, dry place, protected from light, or as instructed by the manufacturer. If the environment is hot and humid, media may be stored in a refrigerator or freezer, as preferred. Properly stored, most dehydrated media should be stable for at least three years; however, purchases should be planned to permit a complete turnover within a year or two.

After the first usage, when the seal has been broken, quality of the dehydrated medium may depend on the storage environment. A suitable package size should be purchased to minimize repeated use of material from an unsealed container. Air and moisture entering an unsealed container can initiate reactions that reduce productivity by the medium.

Care should also be taken to avoid chemical or microbiological contamination that may take place if unclean spatulas are used to transfer the material.

62.112   Prepared media

The "life" of any prepared medium, whether in tubes, bottles, or plates, depends on the type of medium and the conditions of storage. Prepared media should not be stored unless protected against water loss. Cotton-plugged containers do not adequately protect against water loss. Prepared plates should be stored in moisture-proof containers, such as plastic bags, to minimize moisture loss. Because of the instability of prepared culture media, it is advisable in most cases to use prepared plates no more than one week old and media in screw-capped tubes no more than 6 months old. For exceptions (e.g., bismuth sulfite agar), the reader should refer to the formula and directions for making and using each medium found in this chapter and in catalogs and reference materials available from media manufacturers. If dehydration has occurred, media should be discarded. All prepared media, whether in plates or tubes, should be stored between 2° and 8°C unless recommended otherwise.

62.12   Basic Steps in Medium Preparation

1. Carefully weigh the proper amount of the dehydrated base medium or the correct proportion of constituent ingredients.
2. Place the requisite amount of microbiologically suitable (distilled, deionized, or otherwise appropriately treated) water into a suitable container (e.g., borosilicate glass or stainless steel).

3. Add the weighed material(s) to part of the water. Mix with a stirring rod. Add remaining water, and mix again.
4. Heat, if necessary, to effect complete solution by boiling while stirring on a hot plate/magnetic stirrer. Alternatively, heat the medium on an asbestos-centered wire gauze over a free flame or over an electric hot plate, agitating frequently to prevent burning of medium at the bottom of the container. A nonpressurized free-flowing steam unit may also be used. Media containing agar should be boiled to ensure dissolution of the agar. Prolonged boiling may cause undesirable foaming; this can be reduced by holding the flask in cold water for a few seconds after initial boiling has been accomplished. Restore water, if necessary, to compensate for loss by evaporation.
5. Determine the pH of the medium, and adjust if necessary.
6. Distribute the medium into suitable containers. This can be most easily accomplished for liquid media by dispensing with automatic pipettors available through laboratory supply houses. A hand-held adjustable pipettor is suitable for small numbers of test tubes; an electrically operated machine is more satisfactory for larger numbers. In each instance, before use, machines must be flushed with microbiologically suitable water, followed by medium until the water has been completely removed from the system. After use, the apparatus must be flushed with warm water, detergent solution, tap water, and distilled water. If residues accumulate, the apparatus should be disassembled and scrubbed. If the apparatus employs a syringe, a small amount of water should be left in the syringe to prevent drying out and subsequent "freezing" of the plunger and barrel.
7. The amount of medium distributed per container should be limited so that no point within the volume of medium is more than 2.5 cm from the top surface or walls of the container (to ensure rapid equilibration of temperature when placed in a waterbath).
8. Autoclave at 121°C for 15 min or according to the recommended procedures for each medium. For volumes larger than 500 ml, sterilization times should be increased to 20 to 30 min or more, as needed. When sterilizing media containing heat-stable carbohydrates, temperatures should not exceed 116° or 118°C. Heat-labile carbohydrates should be filtered, sterilized, and then added aseptically to cooled, autoclaved base medium. Recheck the pH before using the medium (62.13).
9. Overloading the autoclave or improper spacing of containers will greatly reduce autoclaving efficiency. For good results, separate containers by at least one-half inch in all directions, and do not use volumes of media in excess of 3% to 4% of the volume of the autoclave (see 62.151).
10. Melt only enough solid media necessary for use within three hours. Hold solid media at 44° to 46°C. If a precipitate forms, discard media. Do not remelt media.

Note a: Chemicals and substrates such as carbohydrates must be reagent grade unless otherwise specified. Follow the manufacturer's instructions for storing stock reagents. Discontinue use of chemicals showing any evidence (e.g., color change) of contamination, decomposition, or hydration.

Note b: Automatic agar makers with a complete sterilization cycle are available and may be of value to some laboratories.

62.13 Adjusting Reaction (pH)

Determine the hydrogen-ion concentration (pH) of culture media electrometrically at 25°C. This temperature is used in commercial production of media and should be used in the laboratory to determine the pH of media before use. Determinations made at 45°C to take advantage of the fluid state of agar are not accurate, differing significantly from those obtained at the recommended temperature.

Electrometric procedure (potentiometer): Allow electrodes of the instrument to equilibrate (some models may require 30 min) to the temperature at which the determination is to be made, and adjust the buffer solution to the same temperature before testing the instrument. Only buffers referenced to the National Bureau of Standards (NBS) are recommended. The pH of the buffer solution should be in the pH range of the medium to be tested. The temperature of test solution and buffer should be the same; room temperature (25°C) is generally used for convenience. For solid media, macerate a suitable aliquot thoroughly with a glass rod before inserting the electrodes. Surface electrodes, if available, are convenient for checking the pH of plated media. Be sure that the temperature is maintained until the reading is complete. If in doubt, repeat the determination. Do not dilute test solutions or buffers.

Note: Plating media are not highly buffered. This can cause confusion. Meters are designed only to show a difference in pH between two solutions at the same temperature. Completely anomalous observations will be obtained if the meter is used under other conditions. Temperature compensators of pH meters do not permit correction of a temperature difference between the test solution and reference buffer. The reason for this is that the H^+ concentration of the buffer changes with temperature. Temperature compensators should be set at the temperature at which measurement is made. Since the emf/pH ratio is less at 25°C than at 45°C, for example, a correction factor must be used; this is built into the instrument and makes it possible to determine the correct pH directly.

62.14 Redox Potential (Eh)

The growth of microorganisms in a biological medium depends on the redox potential (Eh) of that medium. Eh is of particular concern to those working with anaerobic microorganisms, since it provides the most useful scale for measuring the degree of anaerobiosis. It can be defined for our purpose as the possibility of a medium's giving up or taking electrons, in other words, its potential to be oxidized or reduced.

The Eh of a medium can be accurately measured electrometrically with most pH meters using the millivolt mode of the meter. Consult the manufacturer's pH meter instruction manual for the step-by-step procedure for taking Eh measurements on the meter. A measuring electrode normally made of platinum and a calomel reference electrode are used for determining Eh. The electrodes, after being placed at the bottom of the medium, are allowed to reach equilibrium, and the Eh value is then read in millivolts. Because oxygen plays an important role in Eh measurement, steps must be taken to avoid the introduction of oxygen into the medium. This can be done by passing nitrogen over the medium. Caution: Commercially available nitrogen should be purified before use because it is not always oxygen free. The nitrogen is purified by passing it through an alkaline solution of pyrogallol or an alkaline solution of sodium hydrosulfite. To remove oxygen from the medium, purified nitrogen can be passed through the medium; however, consider the effect of the Eh measurement if this is done.

Since redox potentials depend on pH, the pH values at which they are determined should be indicated. A more common practice in anaerobic microbiology is to measure Eh by estimating its value with the use of redox dyes. Methylene blue and resazurin are two of the most widely used of these dyes for estimating Eh. Where accurate Eh determinations are not required, the use of redox dyes is suggested; however, since some dyes are toxic to some bacteria, they should be tested before use.

62.15   Sterilization and Storage

Before sterilization, bring any medium containing agar to boiling temperature, stirring frequently. Restore lost water if necessary (62.124), and autoclave. Because the pH of a medium may change during sterilization and because of possible browning reactions, it is important not to exceed the recommended temperature and time. Reduce pressure with reasonable promptness (but in no less than 15 min) to prevent undue changes in the nutritional properties of the medium, and remove from the autoclave when atmospheric pressure is obtained. For a medium containing agar, autoclave the medium in flasks or bottles from which melted medium may be poured into plates. Optionally, use test tubes containing 15- to 20-ml amounts for pouring melted medium into plates.

Prepare medium in such quantities that, if stored, it will be used before loss of moisture through evaporation becomes evident. To prevent contamination and excessive evaporation of moisture from a medium in flasks and bottles during storage, optionally fit pliable aluminum foil, rubber, plastic, parchment, heavy kraft paper, or viscose caps securely over closures before autoclaving. Use of screw-cap or crown (cork-and-seal type) closures on containers appreciably reduces contamination and evaporation. If tubed media are used within a short time, commercially available polypropylene or stainless steel closures may be used. Media should be stored at 2° to 8°C in a dry, dust-free area and should not be exposed to direct sunlight.

62.151   Steam sterilization

Steam-sterilize media, water, and materials such as rubber, cork, cotton, paper, heat-stable plastic tubes, and closures by autoclaving at 121°C for not less than 15 min. Autoclave media and dilution blanks within an hour of preparation. Slightly loosen closures to allow passage of steam into and air from closed containers when autoclaved. Place one or more spore controls in the center of the load, preferably within a container similar to those being processed. Make certain that the load is loosely packed (62.129). Before allowing steam pressure to rise, automatically or manually expel all air from the sterilizer through an appropriate steam trap exhaust valve of suitable size. If expelling air manually, make sure air-free steam is being exhausted before pressurization begins. Because temperature obtained at a constant pressure of pressure-saturated steam varies according to atmospheric pressure, rely on a properly operating and calibrated mercury thermometer for temperature readings.

Avoid overloading autoclaves so that the rate of air exhaust and heating is not appreciably delayed (62.129). The autoclave should reach 121°C slowly but within 10 min after starting the air-exhaust operation. A rapid come-up time in an autoclave does not result in more efficient autoclaving. Inefficiency results from the failure of steam to replace air when steam enters the autoclave too quickly. A steam flow that is too slow also results in decreased efficiency because air-steam mixtures are forming.

Where nonliquid materials with slow heat conductance are to be sterilized, or where the packing arrangement or volume of materials otherwise retards the penetration of heat, allow extra time for materials to reach 121°C before beginning to time the sterilization period. If necessary, use longer periods to ensure sterility.

After sterilization, gradually reduce the pressure within the autoclave (using no less than 15 min) since liquids may be at temperatures above their boiling point at atmospheric pressure. If the pressure is lowered too rapidly, liquids may boil over and be lost. When sterilizing dry materials, such as sampling equipment or empty sample bottles, pressure may be released rapidly through exhaust valves at the end of the 15-min holding period at 121°C. Rapid exhaust through exhaust valves prevents collection of condensate and speeds drying of paper-wrapped equipment.

Used plates, pipettes, tubes, etc., should be routinely decontaminated in all microbiological laboratories. Dairy products, especially raw milk, may harbor potential pathogens such as *Staphylococcus* and *Streptococcus*. For decontamination, the same principles apply for loading the sterilizer and for sterilizing as for preparing media. Plastic Petri dishes are most conveniently sterilized by placing them in heat-resistant autoclavable bags. When large numbers of Petri dishes are autoclaved, sterilization time should be at least 30 min. Insufficient sterilizing of plastic Petri dishes is indicated when they retain some degree of their original shape; properly autoclaved plates become amorphous. Amorphousness by itself, however, is not proof of sterility.

62.152   Hot-air sterilization

Sterilize equipment with dry heat in hot-air sterilizers so that materials at the center of the load are heated to not less than 170°C for not less than 1 hr (this usually requires exposure for about 2 hr at 170°C). To ensure sterility, do not crowd the oven. When the oven is loaded to capacity, it may be necessary to use a longer time period or slightly higher temperature. Spore packs or thermocouples should be used to establish effective sterilization procedures.

62.16   Quality Control

This chapter generally constitutes a discussion of day-to-day quality control practices; however, specific mention should be made of the need to use simple quality control measures in standardized media preparation procedures. An extensive discussion of laboratory quality control that includes media and media preparation is provided in Chapter 1, specifically Section 1.8. The following are minimal quality control procedures used by laboratories meeting standard method requirements to analyze dairy products. Many of the procedures are mentioned elsewhere in this chapter, but they are summarized here to emphasize their contribution to quality control in media production. Some of the items were taken from a CDC publication.[3]

1. Date the label of each bottle of dehydrated medium to indicate when it was received and when it was first opened.
2. Store dehydrated media in tightly capped bottles in a cool, dry place protected from light, or in a refrigerator if necessary. Keep no more than a six- to twelve-month supply on hand, being sure to use older stocks first. Dehydrated media should be free-flowing powders; if a change is noted in this property or in color, discard.
3. Whenever possible, use commercial dehydrated media.
4. Complete mixing of medium to form a homogeneous solution in water is necessary before sterilizing and dispensing. Avoid unnecessary stirring, which causes foaming.
5. The performance of an autoclave should be monitored by either a continuous temperature-recording device calibrated with standards traceable to NBS in combination with properly placed indicator strips or discs, or spore strips or suspensions. The record for each "run" should be dated, numbered, and filed.

6. Limit heating of the medium to the minimum necessary to ensure sterilization. Open the autoclave immediately following a sterilization cycle (when atmospheric pressure has been reached and the medium is below boiling temperature). Avoid prolonged storage of the medium in a waterbath.

7. Check the final pH of each lot of medium after cooling to room temperature. The pH of agar is obtained using a slurry of the medium in a beaker.

8. Follow strict aseptic technique while dispensing sterilized material. Hands should not touch any part of the dispensing tubing that may come in contact with sterile material. During interruptions in a dispensing cycle, the spout of a dispenser train should be placed in a sterile glass container. If possible, a dispensing cycle should not be interrupted.

9. Moving parts of any dispensing apparatus should be oiled or greased as recommended by the manufacturer. Any leaks should be repaired immediately. The accuracy of the medium dispensed should be checked with a graduated container at the beginning and end of each batch dispensed.

10. Media containing dyes should be protected from light by storage in a dark room, in a dark glass bottle, or wrapped with brown paper.

11. Each container of autoclaved medium should be labeled with the name of the medium and the autoclave "run number."

12. Inclusive dates during which each lot and container of dehydrated medium were used should be recorded for possible future troubleshooting.

13. Each lot should be inspected visually before use for volume, tightness of closures, clarity, color, consistency, and completeness of label.

14. Balances should be checked with certified weights on a routine basis.

15. pH meters should be standardized before each use with standard buffers, and electrodes should be checked to see that they are properly filled and not cracked.

62.17   Suitability of Water for Microbiological Applications

Only water that has been treated to free it from traces of dissolved metals and bactericidal and inhibitory compounds should be used to prepare culture media, reagents, and dilution blanks. However, for routine use in dairy product analysis, the growth medium or dilution system prepared with the water is of concern, not the water itself. Culture media provide considerable protection from toxic agents present in water; therefore, the primary interest in quality of water for routine applications is in its use as a dilution fluid.

If special circumstances arise suggesting that the water itself should be examined, specific resistance in ohms may be determined as a rough indication of distilled water quality. Generally, between 400,000 and 500,000 ohms specific resistance is the breakpoint between acceptable and unacceptable distilled water. If organic contamination is suspected, an experienced chemist should make the determination.

Distillate from chlorinated water occasionally contains significant amounts of free chlorine, even when passed through an ion-exchange resin column before use. If distilled or treated water gives color with an orthotolidine test,[1] the chlorine should be neutralized with sodium thiosulfate before use for milk dilution blanks.

62.18 Testing of Dilution Water for Toxicity

The fifteenth edition of "Standard Methods for the Examination of Dairy Products" describes procedures for toxicity testing of dilution water in section 5.4.[2] Tests should be conducted on a regular basis to confirm the quality of laboratory diluents.

62.19 Cleaning Glassware and Testing for Detergent Residues

Modern detergents are very effective for cleaning laboratory glassware. Most of these are of the anionic type, usually with alkaline builders such as phosphates, carbonates, or silicates. Some detergents, especially the cationic type (quaternary ammonium compounds or "quats"), are highly bactericidal, and great care must be exercised to ensure their removal. Detergents and soaps have a great affinity for all surfaces, and because of this characteristic they displace dirt and allow it to be easily washed away. However, because of this same characteristic, they are difficult to remove completely.

62.191 Cleaning glassware

Most common detergents in laboratory use are satisfactory for general purposes; however, deposits of "milk stone" or calcium salts that resist cleaning by ordinary means are occasionally encountered. These salts must be removed by rinsing glassware in acid solutions for several minutes before effective cleansing can be achieved. A suitable solution for removing milk stone contains dichromate and sulfuric acid. This is prepared by dissolving 40.0 g of finely ground potassium dichromate in 150.0 ml of treated water. Place in a Pyrex vessel, and add 330.0 ml of sulfuric acid very slowly with continuous stirring. During the addition of acid the vessel containing the dichromate solution should be cooled by placing it in a cold waterbath (a stoppered sink will suffice). The laboratory worker should wear eye protection and protective clothing when making the cleaning solution because it is extremely corrosive. Each laboratory should devise safety procedures for preparing and handling this preparation.

The detergent wash is best done with hot water after preliminary rinsing with warm water to remove most of the debris. Soaking aids removal of stubborn residues. Glassware having residues that are not removed by the detergent action should be immersed for 24 hr in the acid-dichromate cleaning solution and then rinsed thoroughly in the tap and distilled water. Traces of acid on glassware can be detected with pH indicator paper after the last rinse. Six to 12 rinses with running tap water followed by several rinses with distilled water are necessary for complete removal of detergent.

62.192   Detergent residues

If doubt remains as to the effectiveness of rinsing, especially when quaternary ammonium compounds were used, the following procedure may be used to detect bactericidal residues:

Prepare glass Petri dishes in three ways: wash one set of three and sterilize by the usual method; wash a second set of three in the acid cleaning solution, then in castile soap, then rinse four times in tap water and six times in distilled water before sterilizing; dip a third set in the presently used detergent solution and sterilize without rinsing.

Place a sample of milk in triplicate in these dishes, and count colonies after two days' incubation at 32°C. No significant difference in counts should appear between the first and second sets of plates. A reduction in bacterial count or diminished size of colonies may be apparent in plates of group three if the detergent is bactericidal or bacteriostatic and residues remain.

62.2   EQUIPMENT

The following equipment and supplies are those most frequently used for the preparation of media, reagents, and stains. Their specifications, listed below, meet the specifications described in "Standard Methods for the Examination of Water and Wastewater,"[1] and "Standard Methods for the Examination of Dairy Products."[2]

62.21   Autoclave

The autoclave shall be large enough to prevent crowding of the interior and shall be constructed to provide uniform temperatures within the chamber up to and including the sterilizing temperature of 121°C. Additionally, it must be equipped with an accurate mercury-filled thermometer or bimetallic helix dial thermometer properly located to register minimum temperatures within the sterilizing chamber, a pressure gauge, and a properly adjusted safety valve. A temperature recording instrument is optional. A small, 5- to 10-quart pressure cooker, equipped with a thermometer for temperature control, may be substituted for an autoclave when proper temperatures are maintained and recorded and satisfactory results are obtained. The autoclave, and especially strainers to traps or vents, should be cleaned frequently and immediately after spills or malfunction of the equipment. The laboratory should have a maintenance program designed specifically to keep the equipment in good repair and working order, with checks at least annually by reputable repairmen. These checks should include thermocouple readings to determine temperatures throughout the autoclave.

62.22   Automatic Pipettors

Pipettors shall be capable of delivering a volume with an accuracy of $\pm 1\%$.

62.23   Balance

The balance shall be sensitive to 0.1 g with 200-g load; a 2-kg capacity single pan balance is preferred.

62.24   Dilution Bottles, Tubes

Bottles or tubes should be resistant glass, preferably borosilicate. Dilution bottles should have a capacity of about 150 ml and be closed with Escher type rubber stoppers or screw caps. Use friction-fit liners in screw caps, as required to make the closure leakproof. Liners that do not produce toxic or bacteriostatic compounds must be used. Be sure that each batch of dilution blanks is filled properly. Dilution bottles should be marked indelibly at 99 $\pm$ 1 ml graduation level. Plastic caps for bottles or tubes and plastic closures for sample containers must be treated when new to remove toxic residues if the manufacturer's information indicates them to be toxic or if no information is available. Treatment may be accomplished by autoclaving them twice while they are submerged in water or exposing them to two successive washings in water containing a suitable detergent at 82°C.

62.25   Hot-Air Sterilizing Oven

The oven should be large enough to prevent crowding of the interior, and should have vents suitably located to ensure prompt and uniform heat distribution for adequate sterilization. It should be equipped with a thermometer having a range of 0° to 220°C located to register the minimum temperature in the oven. In addition to the thermometer, a temperature recorder is desirable.

62.26   pH Meter

An electrometric pH meter with an accuracy of 0.1 pH unit shall be used.

62.27   Petri Dishes or Plates

Petri dishes or plates shall have bottoms of at least 85 mm inside diameter and shall be 12 mm deep, with interior and exterior surfaces of bottoms free from bubbles, scratches, or other defects. Petri dishes may be made of glass or of plastic and should have flat bottoms.

62.28   Petri Dish Containers

Containers should be of stainless steel or aluminum, with covers. Char-resistant sacks of high-quality sulfate-pulp kraft paper may be substituted. Disposable petri dishes may be stored in their original containers.

62.29   Pipettes, Glass and Plastic

Pipettes should be nontoxic, straight-walled, calibrated for bacteriological use, and conforming to APHA specifications, with tips ground or fire polished (glass). Pipettes having graduations other than those listed in the APHA specifications may be used provided they meet all the other APHA specifications: volume delivered in 4 sec maximum, last drop of undiluted milk blown out, or last drop of diluted milk touched out, 1 ml tolerance ± 0.025 ml. To allow for residual milk and dilutions on walls and in the tip of the glass pipette under the specific technique hereinafter described for rapid transfers, such pipettes shall be graduated to contain 1.075 ml of water at 20°C. In the case of styrene plastic, the pipette should be calibrated to contain 1.055 ml of water at 20°C. Use only pipettes with unbroken tips and having graduations distinctly marked so as to contrast sharply with the color of the fluid and dilutions being employed. Discard pipettes that are damaged in any way. Note: Do not pipette volumes 10% more than the pipette's delivery capacity.

62.210   Pipette Containers

Stainless steel or aluminum containers are preferred. Copper containers shall not be used. Char-resistant, high-quality sulfate-pulp kraft paper may be substituted.

62.211   Refrigerator

A refrigerator is required to cool and maintain the temperature of media between 0° and 4.4°C until used.

62.212   Thermometers

Use thermometers of appropriate range, mercury filled or having a distinctively colored fluid, with a freezing point lower than −1°C; or an adjustable type, with a graduation interval not to exceed 1°C unless otherwise specified and accuracy checked at least once a year with a thermometer certified by the National Bureau of Standards or to a secondary standard traceable to the NBS thermometer. Where a record is desired of temperatures in refrigerators, autoclaves, hot-air ovens, or incubators, automatic temperature-recording instruments may be used. Two general types of mercury thermometers are in use in laboratories: those calibrated for total immersion, and those designed to be partially immersed. Partial immersion thermometers have a line all the way around the stem of the thermometer at the point to which they should be immersed. If this line is not indicated, then the thermometer is designed for total immersion. As examples, a partial immersion thermometer should be used in a waterbath because only part of the thermometer is immersed in the medium (water, in this case) whose temperature is being measured. Conversely, a thermometer in an incubator or refrigerator is totally immersed in the warm or cold environment and should be of the complete immersion type.

The easiest way to check the calibration of laboratory thermometers is to put them in a waterbath, either partially or totally immersed in the water, according to the way they will be used in the laboratory. Also place in the waterbath a thermometer certified by the NBS. Most, but not all, such thermometers are calibrated for total immersion, so that they typically are totally immersed in the water of the waterbath. Vigorous stirring of the water in the bath is essential to ensure uniform temperature during thermometer calibration.

Check the calibration by comparing the temperature reading on the certified thermometer with that of the laboratory thermometer at or very near the temperature that the thermometer will be used to measure (e.g., an incubator thermometer should be checked at 32°C if this is the temperature of interest). If the thermometer is to be used for several purposes, it should be checked at three different temperatures at least. If there is a difference in the temperature reading of the laboratory thermometer and the certified thermometer after the reading of the certified thermometer has been corrected as indicated by the certificate, attach a tag to the laboratory thermometer to show the amount of correction that should be applied to obtain an accurate determination of temperature.

62.213   Waterbath

A waterbath of appropriate size and thermostatically controlled is needed for holding melted media at 44° to 46°C.

62.3   ALPHABETICAL LISTING OF CULTURE MEDIA

A-1 MEDIUM

Tryptone	20.0 g
Lactose	5.0 g
Sodium chloride	5.0 g
Triton X-100	1.0 ml
Salicin	0.5 g
Distilled water	1.0 L

Dissolve the ingredients listed above in 1.0 L of distilled water. Adjust the pH to 6.9 ± 0.1, and dispense 10-ml portions of single strength broth into 18- × 150-mm tubes containing inverted fermentation tubes. For double-strength broth, use 22- × 175-mm tubes containing inverted fermentation tubes. The medium may have a cloudy appearance before sterilization. Autoclave 10 min at 121°C. Store in the dark for up to 7 days.

ACETATE DIFFERENTIAL AGAR*

ACETOBACTER AGAR

Autolyzed yeast	10.0 g
CaCO$_3$	10.0 g
Agar	15.0 g
Distilled water	1.0 L
Glucose	3.0 g

Suspend the ingredients (except glucose) in distilled water and dissolve by heating to 100°C. Add 3.0 g of glucose, and then autoclave for 15 min at 121°C.

Note: When distributing the medium into tubes, distribute the CaCO$_3$ evenly among tubes. After autoclaving, the tubes should be shaken, then slanted and cooled quickly to keep the CaCO$_3$ in suspension.

ACID PRODUCTS TEST BROTH

Yeast extract	7.5 g
Peptone	10.0 g
Invert sugar†	10.0 g
Distilled water	1.0 L

†Invert sugar, catalog No. 758C, may be obtained from ICN Nutritional Biochemicals, 26201 Miles Road, Cleveland, OH 44128.

Suspend the yeast extract and peptone in distilled water. Slowly stir in the invert sugar, bring the mixture to a boil, and continue heating until all the ingredients are dissolved. Cool the broth, and adjust the pH to 4.0 ± 0.2, using tartaric acid 25% w/v. The broth should be distributed in 500-ml Erlenmeyer flasks (300.0 ml total volume of broth per flask) with screw-type closures or equivalent. Autoclave at 121°C for 15 min.

*Commercially available.

AGAR MEDIUM FOR DIFFERENTIAL ENUMERATION OF LACTIC STREPTOCOCCI

Tryptone	5.0 g
Yeast extract	5.0 g
Casamino acids	2.5 g
L-Arginine hydrochloride	5.0 g
Dipotassium phosphate	1.25 g
Calcium citrate	10.0 g
Carboxymethyl cellulose†	15.0 g
Agar	15.0 g

†Dupont CMC Grade P-754 at the rate of 0.6% may be substituted for CMC Cekol MV, Uddeholm, Sweden.

Suspend 15.0 g of agar in 500.0 ml of distilled water, and steam until dissolved. In another glass container suspend 10.0 g of calcium citrate and 15.0 g of CMC in 500.0 ml of distilled water. Stir while heating until a homogeneous, white, turbid suspension is formed. Mix the two portions in a stainless steel vessel containing the required amounts of tryptone, yeast extract, dipotassium phosphate, casamino acids, and arginine. Cover the mixture, and steam for 15 min. After steaming, adjust the pH to 5.6 ± 0.2 with 6 N hydrochloric acid. Dispense the agar medium into bottles in 100-ml quantities, and autoclave at 121°C for 15 min.

Just before pouring plates, add 5.0 ml of sterile, reconstituted nonfat milk (11% solids), 10.0 ml of sterile 3% (w/v) calcium carbonate in distilled water, and 2.0 ml of sterile 0.1% bromcresol purple in distilled water to 100 ml of the sterile agar medium (melted and tempered to 55°C). Mix to obtain homogeneity. Final pH should be 5.9 ± 0.2. Pour the mixture into previously chilled, sterile Petri dishes to obtain a layer of medium 4 to 5 mm thick. After solidification, dry the plates for 18 to 24 hr in an incubator at 37°C.

ALKALINE PEPTONE WATER (APW)

Peptone	10.0 g
Sodium chloride	10.0 g
Distilled water	1.0 L

Dissolve all ingredients in distilled water, and adjust the pH to 8.4 to 8.6. Dispense into tubes or bottles, and sterilize at 121°C for 10 min.

ANAEROBIC EGG YOLK AGAR

Fresh eggs (antibiotic free)	3.0
Yeast extract	5.0 g
Tryptone	5.0 g
Proteose peptone	20.0 g
Sodium chloride	5.0 g
Agar	20.0 g
Distilled water	1.0 L

Wash eggs with a stiff brush and drain. Soak in 70% alcohol for 10 to 15 min. Remove eggs and allow to air dry. Crack eggs aseptically, separate, and discard the whites. Add the yolks to an equal volume of sterile saline and mix thoroughly.

Combine the remaining ingredients, dissolve by heating, and adjust the pH to 7.0. Dispense the medium into appropriate containers, and sterilize at 121°C for 15 min. Melt 1.0 L of the sterile agar, cool to 45° to 50°C, and add 80.0 ml of the egg yolk emulsion. Mix thoroughly and pour plates immediately.

ANDERSEN'S PORK PEA AGAR

Pork infusion	800.0 ml
Pea infusion	200.0 ml
Peptone	5.0 g
Tryptone	1.6 g
Dipotassium phosphate	1.25 g
Soluble starch	1.0 g
Sodium thioglycollate	0.5 g
Agar	16.0 g
Distilled water	1.0 L

Prepare the pork infusion by adding 1 lb of fresh, lean, ground pork to 1.0 L of distilled water and steaming in flowing steam for 1 hr. Filter out the meat through cheesecloth. Chill to solidify, remove the remaining fat, centrifuge to remove the remaining solids, and use the infusion in the above formula.

Prepare the pea infusion by blending 1 lb of good-quality, fresh green peas or frozen peas with 450.0 ml of water, and steaming for 1 hr in flowing steam. Remove the solids by centrifugation, and clarify with celite (diatomaceous earth). Use the filtrate in the above formula.

Mix the pork infusion, pea infusion, and other ingredients, and adjust the pH to 7.2 ± 0.2. Autoclave the mixture for 5 min at 121°C, and clarify while hot by adding 25.0 g of celite. Filter the mixture through Whatman No. 4 filter paper with suction. Distribute into tubes, and store at 4°C. As needed, thaw and autoclave at 121°C for 12 min.

Prepare a 5% solution of sodium bicarbonate, sterilize by filtration, and keep refrigerated. Place 0.4 ml of bicarbonate into each plate, pour molten agar, mix thoroughly, and allow to solidify. When solid, pour a layer of thioglycollate agar over the surface and allow to harden.

(APT) AGAR/BROTH*

ASLA AGAR

$(NH_4)_2SO_4$	3.0 g
Sodium lactate	20.0 g
Na_2HPO_4	1.2 g
KH_2PO_4	1.2 g
$MnSO_4 \cdot 4H_2O$	0.05 g
$MgSO_4 \cdot 7H_2O$	0.2 g
$FeSO_4 \cdot 7H_2O$	0.04 g
Cysteine-HCl	0.5 g
Biotin	1.0 mg
Calcium pantothenate	1.0 mg
p-aminobenzoic acid	1.0 mg
Thiamin	1.0 mg
Davis agar	10.0 g
Distilled water	1.0 L

Dissolve all of the ingredients except for the vitamins in distilled water with gentle heat. Adjust the pH to 6.5 prior to autoclaving at 121°C for 15 min. Prepare a 100.0 mg per L stock solution of the vitamins, filter sterilize, and add 10.0 ml of this solution to each L of medium just before pouring into Petri plates. Store the vitamin stock solution in the freezer. Note: This medium is selective for the propionibacteria, but some strains may not grow.

ASPERGILLUS FLAVUS and *PARASITICUS* AGAR (AFPA)

Commercially available from Oxoid as AFPA Base (CM731) with a chloramphenicol supplement (SR78).

Yeast extract	20.0 g
Bacteriological peptone	10.0 g
Ferric ammonium citrate	0.5 g
Chloramphenicol	0.1 g
Agar	15.0 g
Distilled water to make	1.0 L
Dichloran (2,6-dichloro-4-nitroanaline), stock solution (0.2% in ethanol)	1.0 ml

*Commercially available.

Combine the listed ingredients and autoclave at 121°C for 15 min. The final pH should be 6.0 to 6.5. The medium may be used for pour plates or prepoured into sterile Petri dishes and allowed to solidify for use in surface plating. Do not invert the plates for incubation. Plate counts on this medium should be incubated at 30 ± 1°C for 42 hr. Plates may be incubated longer if necessary. Colonies exhibiting a bright yellow-orange reverse should be counted as *A. flavus* and *A. parasiticus* colonies.

BAIRD-PARKER AGAR*

BAIRD-PARKER AGAR CONTAINING RABBIT PLASMA-FIBRINOGEN

Prepare Baird-Parker agar by suspending in 900.0 ml of distilled water and boiling to dissolve completely. Dispense 90.0-ml portions in screw-capped bottles, and autoclave for 15 min at 121°C. Final pH should be 6.8 to 7.2 at 25°C.

Rabbit Plasma Fibrinogen Solution:

Mix 50.0 ml of rehydrated rabbit plasma-EDTA with 50.0 ml of 15% bovine fibrinogen (citrated, fraction I, type I, Sigma Chemical Co.). Add 20.0 mg of salt-free soybean trypsin inhibitor (Schwartz/Mann), and dissolve by mixing. Filter sterilize the mixture using sterile 1-μm millipore filters.

Preparation of Complete Medium:

Prepare filter-sterilized solutions of 1% potassium tellurite and 20% sodium pyruvate.

Mix 10.0 ml of prewarmed rabbit plasma-fibrinogen (45° to 50°C), 90.0 ml of melted and cooled (45° to 50°C) Baird-Parker agar medium, and 1.0 ml of 1% potassium tellurite. Avoid entrapping air bubbles. Pour 15.0 to 18.0 ml into sterile Petri dishes. After solidification store plates in plastic bags at 2° to 8°C. Plates can be stored for 4 weeks under these conditions. Just prior to use, spread 0.5 ml of sterile 20% sodium pyruvate solution on each plate, and allow to dry at 50°C or 35°C (2 or 4 hr, respectively) with agar surface upwards.

---

*Commercially available.

BAIRD-PARKER AGAR WITHOUT EGG YOLK*

BASE LAYER AGAR WITH NUTRIENT OVERLAY AGAR

Fat	50.0 g
Victoria Blue B (1:1500 aqueous solution)	200.0 ml
Agar	15.0 g
Distilled water	800.0 ml

Victoria Blue solution is not necessary if tributyrin is used as the fat substrate. If Victoria Blue is not used, add 200.0 ml of distilled water to the base layer medium. The fat used in this medium may consist of tributyrin, corn oil, soybean oil, any available cooking oil, lard, tallow, or triglycerides that do not contain antioxidant or other inhibitory substances. Free fatty acids (FFA) in the fat substrates are removed as described in Section 11.32. Sterilize the fat in the autoclave for 30 min at 121°C. Sterilize the Victoria Blue solution by membrane filtration (0.45 μm). Dissolve the agar in 800.0 ml of distilled water, and sterilize for 15 min at 121°C. Cool the sterile ingredients to 50°C, and mix together in a warm sterile blender for 1 min. Pour 3.0 to 4.0 ml of medium into the bottom of sterile Petri dishes (plastic Petri dishes may require a larger volume of medium because of the difficulty in wetting the surface of the plate with the fat-containing medium). Plates may be used immediately or stored for 3 to 4 days in the refrigerator.

The plates containing the base agar should be dried before use in a bacteriological safety hood (laminar flow) by partially opening the Petri dish lids (10 to 15 min). Dilutions of the food sample suspected of containing lipolytic microorganisms should be prepared, and 0.1 ml of each dilution should be spread onto the surface of plates containing the base agar. When the inoculum is dry (a few minutes), 10 to 12 ml of a nutrient overlay agar (nutrient agar, standard methods agar, or tryptic soy agar, listed in order of preference) should be poured over the base agar.

BC (*BACILLUS CEREUS*) MOTILITY MEDIUM

Trypticase	10.0 g
Yeast extract	2.5 g
Glucose	5.0 g
Disodium hydrogen phosphate	2.5 g
Agar	3.0 g
Distilled water	1.0 L

Dissolve the ingredients in distilled water, and heat to boiling to completely dissolve the agar. Mix thoroughly, and dispense 2.0 ml into 13 × 100-mm

*Commercially available.

tubes. Autoclave for 15 min at 121°C. Final pH should be 7.4 ± 0.2. Allow the medium to solidify, and store at room temperature for 2 or 3 days for best results.

BEEF HEART INFUSION BROTH

Beef heart infusion	500.0 g
Tryptose	10.0 g
Sodium chloride	5.0 g
Distilled water	1.0 L

Dissolve the ingredients in distilled water, distribute into tubes, and sterilize by autoclaving for 15 min at 121°C. The final pH of the medium should be adjusted to 7.4.

For best results, the medium should be freshly prepared. If it is not used the same day as sterilized, heat in boiling water or flowing steam for several minutes to remove absorbed oxygen, and cool quickly, without agitation, just prior to inoculation.

BILE ESCULIN AGAR*

BILE-OXALATE-SORBOSE (BOS) BROTH

Sodium phosphate dibasic	9.14 g
Sodium oxalate	5.0 g
Bile salts	2.0 g
NaCl	1.0 g
Magnesium sulfate·H_2O	0.01 g
Calcium chloride	0.01 g
Distilled water	659.0 ml

Dissolve the ingredients in distilled water, and adjust the pH to 7.6. Autoclave at 121°C for 15 min, cool, and add the following filter-sterilized solutions:

Sorbose (10%)	100.0 ml
Asparagine (1.0%)	100.0 ml
Methionine (1.0%)	100.0 ml
Yeast extract (2.5 mg/ml)	10.0 ml
Sodium pyruvate (0.5%)	10.0 ml
Metanil yellow (2.5 mg/ml)	10.0 ml
Sodium nitrofurantoin (1.0 mg/ml)	10.0 ml
Irgasan (0.4% in 95% ethanol)	1.0 ml

Mix thoroughly, and distribute in appropriate amounts.

*Commercially available.

BILE SALTS BRILLIANT GREEN STARCH (BBGS) AGAR

Proteose peptone	10.0 g
Lab-lemco powder (Oxoid)	5.0 g
Bile salts (Oxoid L55)	5.0 g
Soluble starch	10.0 g
Agar	15.0 g
Brilliant green (0.05% w/v solution)	1.0 ml
Distilled water	1.0 L

Suspend the ingredients in distilled water, and dissolve by heating while stirring. Autoclave for 15 min at 121°C. Final pH should be 7.2.

BISMUTH SULFITE (BS) AGAR*

BLOOD AGAR

Blood agar base (commercial, dehydrated)	40.0 g
Distilled water	1.0 L

Prepare the base according to the manufacturer's instructions. Temper the sterilized base at 45° to 50°C, and aseptically add 5% sterile, defibrinated, room temperature sheep blood. Mix thoroughly, avoiding incorporation of air bubbles, and pour into plates.

BLOOD AGAR BASE*

BRAIN HEART INFUSION (BHI) AGAR/BROTH*

BRILLIANT GREEN BILE (BGB) AGAR/BROTH*

BROMCRESOL PURPLE CARBOHYDRATE BROTH BASE WITH CARBOHYDRATES

Basal medium:

Peptone	10.0 g
Beef extract (optional)	3.0 g
Sodium chloride	5.0 g
Bromcresol purple	0.04 g
Distilled water	1.0 L

*Commercially available.

Combine the ingredients above with 5 g per L of the desired carbohydrate (glucose, adonitol, arabinose, mannitol, maltose, sucrose, lactose, sorbitol, cellobiose, salicin, or trehalose). Adjust the pH to 7.0 ± 0.2. Dispense 8-ml aliquots into 16- × 150-mm tubes containing inverted 12- × 75-mm fermentation tubes. Autoclave for 10 min at 121°C. Final pH should be 6.8 to 7.0.

BRUCELLA BROTH*

BRUCELLA-FBP AGAR/BROTH

Brucella broth	28.0 g
$FeSO_4$	0.25 g
Sodium metabisulfite (anhydrous)	0.25 g
Sodium pyruvate (anhydrous)	0.25 g
Distilled water	970.0 ml

Suspend the Brucella broth in 970.0 ml of distilled water, and boil for approximately 1 min to dissolve completely. Autoclave at 121°C for 15 min, and cool to 50°C. Prepare the FBP solution by dissolving $FeSO_4$, sodium metabisulfite, and sodium pyruvate together in 30 ml of distilled water, and sterilize by filtering through a 0.22-μm filter. Add the filter-sterilized FBP solution (ca. 30 ml) to the cooled medium, and distribute into tubes. Brucella-FBP agar and semi-solid medium are made in the same manner, but 15 g or 1.6 g of agar, respectively, is added to the Brucella broth before autoclaving.

BUFFERED GLYCEROL SALT SOLUTION

Glycerol (glycerin)	100.0 ml
Dipotassium phosphate (anhydrous)	12.4 g
Monopotassium phosphate (anhydrous)	4.0 g
Sodium chloride	4.2 g
Distilled water	900.0 ml

Dissolve the sodium chloride in part of the water, and make up to 900.0 ml. Add the glycerol and phosphates, and adjust the pH to 7.2. Autoclave for 15 min at 121°C. For double-strength (20%) glycerol solution, use 200.0 ml of glycerol and 800.0 ml of distilled water.

*Commercially available.

BUTZLER'S AGAR

Columbia agar base	39.0 g
Distilled water	930.0 ml
Defibrinated sheep blood	50.0 ml
Cefoperazone	15.0 mg
Rifampicin	10.0 mg
Colistin	10,000 IU
Amphotericin B	2.0 mg

Mix Columbia agar base (Oxoid CM331) in distilled water, and boil to dissolve completely. Autoclave at 121°C for 15 min. After cooling the medium to 50°C, add the blood (lysed horse blood is also acceptable) and a filter-sterilized (through a 0.22-μm filter) solution of the antibiotics dissolved in 20 ml of distilled water.

CAMPY-BAP (BLASER'S AGAR)

Brucella agar	43.0 g
Distilled water	925.0 ml
Lysed horse blood	50.0 ml
Vancomycin	10.0 mg
Polymyxin B	2,500 IU
Trimethoprim lactate	5.0 mg
Amphotericin B	2.0 mg
Cephalothin	15.0 mg

Dissolve the Brucella agar in distilled water, heat while stirring, and boil for approximately 1 min to dissolve the agar completely. Autoclave at 121°C for 15 min. Cool the medium to 50°C, and add the blood and filter-sterilized solutions of antibiotics. Defibrinated sheep blood may be used in lieu of horse blood; use 100.0 ml of sheep blood and only 875.0 ml of distilled water to prepare the Brucella agar base medium. Difficulties in dissolving the specified antibiotics are resolved by making the water alkali. Prepare solutions of each antimicrobial compound for 1.0 L of medium in 5.0 ml of Brucella broth; dissolve the amounts of each compound required for 10.0 L of medium in 50.0 ml of Brucella broth, filter through a 0.22-μm filter, dispense 5-ml portions in vials, and freeze until use. The combination of antimicrobials is also available commercially.

CAMPYLOBACTER CHARCOAL DIFFERENTIAL AGAR (CCDA)-PRESTON BLOOD-FREE MEDIUM

Nutrient broth No. 2 (Oxoid)	25.0 g
Bacteriological charcoal	4.0 g
Casein hydrolysate	3.0 g
Sodium deoxycholate	1.0 g
Ferrous sulfate	0.25 g
Sodium pyruvate	0.25 g
Agar	12.0 g
Sodium cefoperazone	32.0 mg
Distilled water	1.0 L

Dissolve all of the medium components except cefoperazone in 1.0 L of distilled water, and boil to dissolve completely. Autoclave at 121°C for 15 min. Cool to 50°C, and add filter-sterilized (through a 0.22-μm filter) cefoperazone. Mix well, and pour into sterile Petri plates.

CAMPY-THIO MEDIUM

Trypticase peptone	20.0 g
Sodium chloride	2.5 g
Dipotassium phosphate	1.5 g
Sodium thioglycollate	0.6 g
L-Cystine	0.4 g
Sodium sulfite	0.2 g
Agar	15.0 g
Distilled water	1.0 L

Suspend the ingredients in distilled water, and heat to boiling to dissolve completely. Alternatively, any commercially available thioglycollate broth medium without indicator may be used providing the final concentration of agar is 0.16%. Autoclave at 121°C for 15 min. After the mixture has cooled to 50°C, add the filter-sterilized antibiotic solutions described in Campy-BAP medium. For shipment of swab samples, dispense 3-ml amounts for 1.5-cm swabs or 5 ml for 3.0-cm swabs in screw-capped tubes (16- × 125-mm).

CARBOHYDRATE FERMENTATION BROTH

Peptone	10.0 g
Meat extract	3.0 g
NaCl	5.0 g
Andrade's indicator	10.0 ml
Distilled water	1.0 L

Dissolve the ingredients in distilled water, and adjust the pH to 7.1 to 7.2. Dispense the medium into tubes, and sterilize by autoclaving at 121°C for 15 min. If detection of gas formation is desired, include an inverted vial (Durham tube) before sterilization. The vial will fill with liquid upon slow cooling after autoclaving. Add each desired carbohydrate at a final concentration of either 0.5% or 1.0%. It is desirable to add the carbohydrates as filter-sterilized (0.22 μm pore size) solutions although some can be autoclaved without deleterious results. The filter-sterilized carbohydrate can be added as a 10% solution (e.g., 5.0 ml of basal broth plus 0.5 ml of 10% carbohydrate). A more accurate method is to prepare the basal broth as a 2X solution and add an equal volume of a 2X carbohydrate solution, which also eliminates problems of solubility that may be encountered at 10% concentrations.

CARY-BLAIR TRANSPORT MEDIUM*

CASAMINO ACIDS-YEAST EXTRACT (CAYE) BROTH

Casamino acids	30.0 g
Yeast extract	4.0 g
Potassium phosphate (dibasic)	0.5 g
Glucose	2.0 g
Distilled water	1.0 L

Dissolve all ingredients except glucose in distilled water. Adjust the pH to 7.2 ± 0.2 and sterilize at 121°C for 15 min. Cool and aseptically add 10 ml of a filter-sterilized 20% glucose solution in distilled water. After mixing, aseptically dispense into sterile tubes or bottles.

CASAMINO ACIDS-YEAST EXTRACT-LINCOMYCIN MEDIUM

Prepare casamino acids-yeast extract broth (Gorbach), and adjust the pH to 8.0. Autoclave at 121°C for 15 min and cool. Dissolve 45 mg of lincomycin in 5.0 ml of distilled water, and filter sterilize. Aseptically add 5.0 ml of the lincomycin solution to 1.0 L of CA-YE-S (Gorbach) broth.

CASAMINO ACIDS-YEAST EXTRACT-SALTS (CA-YE-S) BROTH (GORBACH)

Casamino acids	20.0 g
Yeast extract	6.0 g
Sodium chloride	2.5 g
K_2HPO_4	8.71 g
Trace salts solution (optional)	1.0 ml
Distilled water	1.0 L

*Commercially available.

Combine the ingredients above (except trace salts solution) with distilled water, and adjust the pH so that after autoclaving it is 8.5 ± 0.2. Autoclave at 121°C for 15 min.

Trace Salts Solution:

MgSO$_4$	50.0 g
MnCl$_2$	5.0 g
FeCl$_2$	5.0 g
Distilled water	1.0 L

Combine the ingredients above with distilled water, and add enough 0.1 N H$_2$SO$_4$ to dissolve. Sterilize by filtration through a 0.45-μm membrane. Add 1.0 ml of the trace salts stock solution to each 1.0 L of base medium. Dispense 10-ml portions into 50-ml flasks.

CEFSULODIN-IRGASAN-NOVOBIOCIN (CIN) AGAR

Special peptone (Oxoid)	20.0 g
Yeast extract	2.0 g
Mannitol	20.0 g
Pyruvic acid (Na salt)	2.0 g
NaCl	1.0 g
Magnesium sulfate·7H$_2$O	0.01 g
Sodium desoxycholate	0.5 g
Agar (Oxoid L11)	12.0 g
Distilled water	949.0 ml

Suspend all ingredients in distilled water, and bring to a boil with stirring to completely dissolve. Cool to approximately 80°C, and add 1.0 ml of 0.4% Irgasan (Ciba-Geigy) in 95% ethanol. Mix well, and cool to about 50° to 55°C. Add the following filter-sterilized (except NaOH, 0.22 μm pore size) solutions:

NaOH (5 N)	1.0 ml
Neutral red (3 mg/ml)	10.0 ml
Crystal violet (0.1 mg/ml)	10.0 ml
Cefsulodin (1.5 mg/ml)	10.0 ml
Novobiocin (0.25 mg/ml)	10.0 ml

Add 10.0 ml of a filter-sterilized 10% solution of strontium chloride slowly with stirring. Adjust the pH to 7.40, and pour the medium into sterile Petri plates. Note: Comparable formulations are available commercially as "*Yersinia* Selective Agar."

CELL GROWTH MEDIUM

Mix the following sterile solutions aseptically:

Minimal essential medium with Hank's salts (MEMH) ...	1.0 L
L-15 medium (Leibovitz), containing	
100 IU penicillin G,	
100 µg streptomycin, and	
50 µg gentamicin per ml	1.0 L

Mix the solutions on a magnetic stirrer, filter through a 0.20-µm membrane, and dispense into a sterile 2-L Erlenmeyer flask. Adjust the pH to 7.5, and cap and store at 5°C.

Just before use add:

Fetal bovine serum	200.0 ml
$NaHCO_3$ (7.5%)	50.0 ml

CELLOBIOSE POLYMYXIN COLISTIN (CPC) AGAR

Solution A:

Peptone (Difco)	10.0 g
Beef extract (Difco)	5.0 g
Sodium chloride	20.0 g
Bromthymol blue	0.04 g
Cresol red	0.04 g
Agar	15.0 g
Distilled water	900.0 ml

Adjust pH to 7.6, autoclave at 121°C for 15 min, and cool to 55°C.

Solution B:

Cellobiose	15.0 g
Colistin†	1,360,000 IU
Polymyxin††	100,000 IU
Distilled water	100.0 ml

†Colistin is available from Sigma Chemical Co., St. Louis, MO (Colistin Methane Sulfonate, stock number C-1511).

††Polymyxin B sulfate may also be purchased from Sigma Chemical Co. (stock number P-1004).

Filter sterilize Solution B, add to cooled Solution A, and dispense into sterile Petri dishes. When solidified, CPC agar is an olive-green to light brown color. Use within 7 days of preparation.

CHOPPED LIVER BROTH

Ground beef liver	500.0 g
Soluble starch	1.0 g
Peptone	10.0 g
Dipotassium phosphate	1.0 g
Distilled water	1.0 L

Add finely ground beef liver to the distilled water, and boil for 1 hr. Adjust the pH of the broth to 7.0 ± 0.2, and boil for another 10 min. Press through cheesecloth, and bring the broth to 1.0 L with distilled water. Add the peptone and dipotassium phosphate, and adjust the pH to 7.0 ± 0.2. Place liver particles from the pressed cake in the bottom of culture tubes (about 1 cm deep), cover with 8 to 10 ml of broth, and sterilize by autoclaving for 20 min at 121°C. Before use, exhaust the medium for 20 min in flowing steam.

CHRISTENSEN'S UREA AGAR*

CLOSTRIDIUM BOTULINUM ISOLATION (CBI) AGAR

Trypticase peptone	40.0 g
Na_2HPO_4	5.0 g
NaCl	2.0 g
$MgSO_4$ (5% aqueous solution)	0.2 ml
D-Glucose	2.0 g
Yeast extract	5.0 g
Agar	20.0 g
Distilled water	900.0 ml
Egg yolk suspension (50% in saline, Difco)	100.0 ml
Cycloserine	250.0 mg
Sulfamethoxazole	76.0 mg
Trimethoprim	4.0 mg

Combine the ingredients above, except for the egg yolk suspension and the antimicrobial agents, with distilled water, and dissolve by heating. Adjust the pH to 7.4, and autoclave at 121°C for 15 min. Cool the basal medium to 55°C.

Prepare separate stock solutions of the antimicrobial agents as described below.

Cycloserine: 1.0% solution in distilled water.

Sulfamethoxazole: 1.9% solution in distilled water and add enough 10% NaOH to put into solution.

Trimethoprim: 0.1% solution in distilled water and add enough 0.05 N HCl to put into solution (carry out procedure in a 55°C waterbath).

*Commercially available.

To the tempered (55°C) basal medium add the following (amounts listed per 1.0 L total volume of medium):

Egg yolk suspension (ambient temperature)	100.0 ml
Cycloserine stock solution.....	25.0 ml
Sulfamethoxazole stock solution............................	4.0 ml
Trimethoprim stock solution..	4.0 ml

If there has been a significant loss of volume on autoclaving, add enough sterile distilled water to bring the volume back to 1.0 L. Mix the medium thoroughly, and dispense into sterile Petri dishes in 20-ml quantities. Dry the plates at ambient temperature for several hours to avoid excess surface moisture. Store unused plates sealed in plastic bags at 4°C until used. Before using plates, hold under anaerobic conditions for 4 hr.

COLBECK'S EGG YOLK BROTH*

COLIFORM MEDIUM (CM)

Proteose peptone No. 3 (Difco)	10.0 g
Yeast extract...	6.0 g
Lactose	20.0 g
Bile salts No. 3 (Difco)	1.0 g
Sodium lauryl sulfate	1.0 g
Sodium desoxycholate	0.1 g
Bromcresol purple stock solution.............................	10.0 ml
Distilled water	1.0 L

Bromcresol purple stock solution:

Add 0.35 g of bromcresol purple to 2.0 ml of 0.1 N NaOH in a volumetric flask, and swirl until mixed. Bring the final volume of mixture to 100.0 ml by adding distilled water. Thoroughly mix and filter sterilize.

Combine the dehydrated ingredients, and dissolve in 1.0 L of distilled water (900.0 ml for cream). Add 10.0 ml of bromcresol purple stock solution and adjust the pH to 6.8 ± 0.1 with 0.1 N NaOH (or 12.0 ml of 1.0 N NH$_4$OH for yogurt, pH 7.0, or 90.0 ml of 1.0 N HCl for cream, pH 7.0 ± 0.1). Mix thoroughly, and dispense in 50-ml volumes (95-ml for yogurt and cream, 20-ml for raw milk) into dilution bottles adjusting for evaporation that may occur during autoclaving. Autoclave for 15 min at 121°C (25 min at 121°C for yogurt only).

*Commercially available.

COLUMBIA BLOOD AGAR BASE*

COLONIZATION MEDIUM

Brain heart infusion	0.5 g
Bile salts No. 3 (Difco)	0.1 g
Mannose	1.0 g
Dulbecco's phosphate-buffered saline	700.0 ml

Combine above ingredients, and sterilize by filtration through a 0.45-µm membrane.

CONGO RED ACID-MORPHOLINEPROPANESULFONIC ACID PIGMENTATION (CRAMP) AGAR

Galactose	2.0 g
Casamino acids	2.0 g
Congo red	5.0 mg
NaCl	2.9 g
Morpholinepropanesulfonic acid	8.4 g
Ammonium chloride	0.5 g
Sodium thiosulfate	0.6 g
Potassium phosphate dibasic	0.24 g
Magnesium sulfate	98.6 mg
Tricine	1.8 g
Agarose	14.0 g
Distilled water	1.0 L

Combine the ingredients, and adjust the pH to 5.3. Autoclave at 121°C for 15 min.

COOKED MEAT MEDIUM (CMM)*

CVP (CRYSTAL VIOLET PECTATE) MEDIUM

To 500.0 ml of boiling distilled water blending at very low speed in a preheated blender add:

Crystal violet solution (0.075% w/v aqueous solution)	1.0 ml
Sodium hydroxide (1N aqueous solution)	4.5 ml
Calcium chloride (fresh 10% w/v $CaCl_2 \cdot H_2O$ aqueous solution)	3.0 ml
Agar	2.0 g
Sodium nitrate	1.0 g

*Commercially available.

Blend at high speed for 15 sec. Continue blending at low speed and slowly add:

Sodium polypectate† ....   9.0 g

†For best results use polypectate from Ral Tech Sci. Services, Inc., 3301 Kingman Blvd., P.O. Box 7545, Madison, WI 53707.

Pour the incomplete medium into a 2-L flask, and add:

Sodium lauryl sulfate (10% w/
v aqueous solution).............   0.5 ml

Cap the flask with aluminum foil rather than cotton plug, and autoclave for 25 min at 121°C. Avoid foaming, and pour plates as soon as possible since the medium solidifies quickly and cannot be remelted. Since it is essential that the surface of the agar be free of water, allow the plates to dry for 48 hr at room temperature before use. The final pH of the medium is 7.2.

CZAPEK YEAST AUTOLYSATE (CYA) AGAR

Yeast extract	5.0 g
Sucrose	30.0 g
$NaNO_3$	3.0 g
KCl	0.5 g
K_2PO_4	1.0 g
$MgSO_4 \cdot 7H_2O$	0.5 g
$FeSO_4 \cdot 5H_2O$	0.01 g
Agar	15.0 g
Distilled water	1.0 L

Suspend the ingredients in distilled water, and heat the mixture to boiling while stirring to dissolve completely. Autoclave at 121°C for 15 min.

DECARBOXYLASE BROTH WITH ARGININE*

DECARBOXYLASE BROTH WITH LYSINE*

DECARBOXYLASE BROTH WITH ORNITHINE*

DECARBOXYLASE MEDIUM MOELLER PLUS LYSINE*

*Commercially available.

DECARBOXYLASE MEDIUM MOELLER PLUS ORNITHINE*

DEXTROSE AGAR/BROTH*

DEXTROSE TRYPTONE AGAR/BROTH*

DEXTROSE TRYPTONE BROMCRESOL PURPLE AGAR (DTA)/BROTH (DTB)

See Dextrose Tryptone Agar/Broth.

DEY-ENGLEY NEUTRALIZING MEDIUM*

DICHLORAN ROSE BENGAL CHLORAMPHENICOL (DRBC) AGAR*

Commercially available from Oxoid as DRBC Agar Base (CM727) with a chloramphenicol supplement (SR78).

DIFFERENTIAL BROTH FOR LACTIC STREPTOCOCCI

Tryptone	5.0 g
Yeast extract	5.0 g
Dipotassium phosphate	1.0 g
Arginine	5.0 g
Sodium citrate	20.0 g
Bromcresol purple	0.02 g
Distilled water to make	1.0 L

Suspend the ingredients in 800.0 ml of distilled water, add 35 ml of 11% reconstituted skim milk, and bring the total volume to 1.0 L. Steam the medium for 15 min, cool to 25°C, and adjust the pH to 6.2. Dispense 7.0-ml quantities into 10- × 126-mm screw-capped tubes containing Durham fermentation tubes. Autoclave at 121°C for 15 min. The final pH should be 6.2 ± 0.2. Do not open the autoclave door until the temperature has dropped below 75°C.

DNase TEST AGAR*

After 24 hr of incubation, the DNase medium is flooded with 0.1N HCl. DNase-positive colonies are surrounded by a clear zone. At 24 hr, DNase-positive colonies on the Toluidine Blue agar are surrounded by a purplish-pink precipitation formed by the reaction of hydrolyzed DNA with the dye.

*Commercially available.

DOYLE AND ROMAN ENRICHMENT MEDIUM

Brucella broth (Gibco)	29.0 g
Distilled water	910.0 ml
Sodium succinate	3.0 g
Cysteine hydrochloride	0.1 g
Lysed horse blood	70.0 ml
Vancomycin	15.0 mg
Trimethoprim lactate	5.0 mg
Polymyxin B	20,000 IU
Cycloheximide	50.0 mg

Dissolve by swirling the Brucella broth medium, sodium succinate, and cysteine hydrochloride in distilled water. Autoclave at 121°C for 15 min. Cool the medium to room temperature, and add the lysed horse blood and filter-sterilized (through a 0.22-μm filter) antibiotics. Dispense 90 or 100 ml into sterile side-arm flasks.

EAGLE'S MINIMAL ESSENTIAL MEDIUM (MEME)
(With Earle's salts and nonessential amino acids)

L-Alanine	8.9 mg
L-Arginine HCl	126.0 mg
L-Asparagine-H_2O	150.0 mg
L-Aspartic acid	13.3 mg
L-Cystine·2HCl	31.29 mg
L-Glutamic acid	14.7 mg
L-Glutamine	292.0 mg
L-Glycine	7.5 mg
L-Histidine HCl·H_2O	42.0 mg
L-Isoleucine	52.0 mg
L-Leucine	52.0 mg
L-Lysine HCl	72.5 mg
L-Methionine	15.0 mg
D-Phenylalanine	32.0 mg
L-Proline	11.5 mg
L-Serine	10.5 mg
L-Threonine	48.0 mg
L-Tryptophan	10.0 mg
L-Tyrosine (disodium salt)	52.1 mg
L-Valine	46.0 mg
D-Calcium pantothenate	1.0 mg
Choline chloride	1.0 mg
Folic acid	1.0 mg
Isoinositol	2.0 mg
Nicotinamide	1.0 mg

EAGLE'S MINIMAL ESSENTIAL MEDIUM (MEME) (Continued)

Pyridoxal HCl	1.0 mg
Riboflavin	0.1 mg
Thiamin HCl	1.0 mg
Glucose	1000.0 mg
$CaCl_2 \cdot 2H_2O$	265.0 mg
KCl	400.0 mg
$MgSO_4 \cdot 7H_2O$	200.0 mg
NaCl	6800.0 mg
$NaHCO_3$	2200.0 mg
$NaH_2PO_4 \cdot H_2O$	140.0 mg
Phenol red	10.0 mg
Distilled water	1.0 L

Dissolve ingredients in 1.0 L of distilled water. Sterilize by filtration, and adjust the pH to 7.2 ± 0.2. Store at 5°C.

EAGLE'S MINIMUM ESSENTIAL MEDIUM (MEME)*

EARLE'S BALANCED SALTS (ES) SOLUTION (PHENOL RED-FREE)

NaCl	6.8 g
KCl	400.0 mg
$CaCl_2 \cdot 2H_2O$	265.0 mg
$MgSO_4 \cdot 7H_2O$	200.0 mg
$NaH_2PO_4 \cdot H_2O$	140.0 mg
Glucose	1.0 g
$NaHCO_3$	2.2 g
Distilled water	1.0 L

Dissolve ingredients in 1.0 L of distilled water. Sterilize by filtration, and adjust the pH to 7.2 ± 0.2.

EC (*ESCHERICHIA COLI*) BROTH*

EGG YOLK EMULSION 50%*

EGG YOLK-FREE TRYPTOSE-SULFITE CYCLOSERINE (EY-FREE TSC) AGAR

Same as Tryptose-Sulfite Cycloserine Agar.

EOSIN METHYLENE BLUE (EMB) AGAR (LEVINE)*

*Commercially available.

EUGON AGAR*

FERMENTATION BASE FOR *CAMPYLOBACTER*

Enteric fermentation base (Difco)	18.0 g
Andrade's indicator	10.0 ml
Glucose	10.0 g
Distilled water	1.0 L

Dissolve the enteric fermentation base and glucose in 950.0 ml of distilled water. Add Andrade's indicator, and adjust the pH to 7.2. Add distilled water to a total volume of 1000.0 ml, and dispense in 3.0-ml amounts in 15- × 125-mm tubes with inverted vials. Autoclave at 121°C for 15 min.

FERMENTATION MEDIUM (SPRAY)

(For *Clostridium perfringens*)

Trypticase	10.0 g
Neopeptone	10.0 g
Agar	2.0 g
Sodium thioglycollate	0.25 g
Distilled water	1.0 L

Dissolve the ingredients except agar in distilled water, and adjust the pH to 7.4. Add the agar, and heat while stirring until the agar is dissolved. Mix well, and dispense 9.0-ml portions into 16- × 125-mm tubes. Autoclave for 15 min at 121°C. Before use, heat the tubed medium in boiling water or flowing steam for 10 min, and add 1.0 ml of 10% sterile carbohydrate solution to each tube.

FETAL BOVINE SERUM (FBS)*

fGTC AGAR

Trypticase soy agar	40.0 g
KH_2PO_4	5.0 g
Amylose azure†	3.0 g
Galactose	1.0 g
Thallous acetate (acetic acid, thallous salt)	0.5 g
Tween 80 (polyoxyethylene sorbitan monooleate)	0.75 ml
4-methylumbelliferyl-α-D-galactoside	100.0 mg
Gentamicin sulfate	2.5 mg
Distilled water	1.0 L

†Available from Calbiochem.
*Commercially available.

Prepare a gentamicin stock solution (1.0 mg/ml) in sterile water, and store in the refrigerator; use 2.5 ml per L of medium. Dissolve all of the ingredients listed above in distilled water, and autoclave at 121°C for 15 min. Cool to 55°C, and add 20 ml of 10% $NaHCO_3$ in water (made fresh daily and pasteurized by heating to boiling) to each L of medium. Mix and cool medium to 45°C before pouring into sterile Petri dishes.

FLUID THIOGLYCOLLATE MEDIUM*

FPA (FLUORESCENT PECTOLYTIC AGAR) MEDIUM

Proteose peptone No. 3	20.0 g
Dipotassium phosphate	1.5 g
Magnesium sulfate·7H₂O	0.73 g
Pectin	5.0 g
Agar	15.0 g
Distilled water	1.0 L

Dissolve ingredients in distilled water by boiling. Adjust to pH 7.1, and sterilize at 121°C for 15 min.

Add 1.0 ml ethanol to the following mixture of dry antibiotics, and allow to stand 30 min.

Penicillin G	75,000 units
Novobiocin	45.0 mg
Cycloheximide	75.0 mg

Dilute antibiotic solution with 9 ml sterile distilled water, and add 1.0 ml of the dilute solution to 100.0 ml of sterile and cooled basal medium before pouring into sterile Petri plates. After the plates are inoculated by a spread plate technique and incubated, the fluorescent bacteria are detected under long-wavelength ultraviolet light. Plates are then treated with the polysaccharide precipitant as described under MP-7 medium.

*Commercially available.

FRASER SECONDARY ENRICHMENT BROTH

Proteose peptone	5.0 g
Tryptone	5.0 g
Lab Lemco powder (Oxoid)	5.0 g
Yeast extract	5.0 g
NaCl	20.0 g
KH_2PO_4	1.35 g
Na_2HPO_4	12.0 g
Esculin	1.0 g
Nalidixic acid (2% in 0.1 M NaOH)	1.0 ml
Lithium chloride	3.0 g
Distilled water	1.0 L

Combine the ingredients in distilled water, mix well, and dispense in 10-ml aliquots in 20- × 150-mm test tubes. Autoclave at 121°C for 12 min. Note: Do not overheat; cool at once after removal from the autoclave. Store the sterilized medium under refrigeration. Immediately before use, to each 10-ml tube of medium add 0.1 ml of filter-sterilized acriflavin solution (2.5 mg/ml, Sigma) and 0.1 ml of filter-sterilized ferric ammonium citrate solution (5% stock solution in distilled water, Sigma).

GELATIN AGAR

Gelatin	30.0 g
Agar	15.0 g
Sodium chloride	10.0 g
Trypticase (pancreatic digest of casein)	10.0 g
Distilled water	1.0 L

Dissolve ingredients in distilled water by bringing to a boil. Dispense in tubes or bottles, and sterilize at 121°C for 15 min. Final pH should be 7.2 ± 0.2.

GELATIN PHOSPHATE SALT (GPS) AGAR/BROTH

Gelatin	10.0 g
Sodium chloride	10.0 g
Potassium phosphate (dibasic)	5.0 g
Agar	15.0 g
Distilled water	1.0 L

Dissolve all ingredients in distilled water by bringing to a boil. Dispense in tubes or bottles, and sterilize at 121°C for 15 min. Final pH should be 7.2 ± 0.2.

To prepare GPS broth, omit the agar.

GLUCOSE SALT TEEPOL BROTH (GSTB)

Beef extract	3.0 g
Peptone	10.0 g
Sodium chloride	30.0 g
Glucose	5.0 g
Methyl violet	0.002 g
Teepol†	4.0 ml
Distilled water	1.0 L

†Available from Particle Data Laboratories, Ltd., 115 Hahn Street, Elmhurst, Illinois 60126.

Dissolve ingredients in distilled water. Adjust pH to 8.8 ± 0.2, dispense in tubes or bottles, and sterilize at 121°C for 15 min.

GN-BROTH
Same as Gram-Negative Broth, Hajna.

GRAM-NEGATIVE (GN) BROTH, HAJNA*

GUM TRAGACANTH-ARABIC

Gum tragacanth	2.0 g
Gum arabic	1.0 g
Distilled water	100.0 ml

Dissolve the ingredients in distilled water, heating slightly. Autoclave at 121°C for 15 min.

HALOPHILIC AGAR (HA)/BROTH (HB)

Casamino acids	10.0 g
Yeast extract	10.0 g
Proteose peptone	5.0 g
Trisodium citrate	3.0 g
KCl	2.0 g
$MgSO_4 \cdot 7H_2O$	25.0 g
NaCl	250.0 g
Agar	20.0 g
Distilled water	1.0 L

Combine the ingredients with distilled water, and heat to boiling to dissolve completely. Autoclave at 121°C for 15 min. Final pH should be 7.2.

To prepare HB, omit the agar.

*Commercially available.

HAM'S F-10 MEDIUM
(With Glutamine and NaHCO$_3$)

L-Alanine	8.91 mg
L-Arginine-HCl	211.0 mg
L-Asparagine·H$_2$O	15.0 mg
L-Aspartic acid	13.3 mg
L-Cysteine-HCl	35.12 mg
L-Glutamine	146.2 mg
L-Glutamic acid	14.7 mg
Glycine	7.51 mg
L-Histidine HCl·H$_2$O	21.0 mg
L-Isoleucine	2.6 mg
L-Leucine	13.1 mg
L-Lysine HCl	29.3 mg
L-Methionine	4.48 mg
L-Phenylalanine	4.96 mg
L-Proline	11.5 mg
L-Serine	10.5 mg
L-Threonine	3.57 mg
L-Tryptophan	0.60 mg
L-Tyrosine	1.81 mg
L-Valine	3.5 mg
Glucose	1100.0 mg
Hypoxanthine	4.08 mg
Lipoic acid	0.2 mg
Phenol red	1.2 mg
Sodium pyruvate	110.0 mg
Thymidine	0.727 mg
Biotin	0.024 mg
Choline chloride	0.698 mg
Folic acid	1.320 mg
Isoinositol	0.541 mg
Niacinamide	0.615 mg
D-calcium pantothenate	0.715 mg
Pyridoxine-HCl	0.206 mg
Riboflavin	0.376 mg
Thiamin HCl	1.010 mg
Vitamin B$_{12}$	1.360 mg
CaCl$_2$·2H$_2$O	44.10 mg
CuSO$_4$·5H$_2$O	0.0025 mg
FeSO$_4$·7H$_2$O	0.83 mg
KCl	285.0 mg
KH$_2$PO$_4$	83.0 mg
MgSO$_4$·7H$_2$O	152.8 mg
NaCl	7400.0 mg
NaHCO$_3$	1200.0 mg
Na$_2$HPO$_4$·7H$_2$O	290.0 mg
ZnSO$_4$·7H$_2$O	0.028 mg
Distilled water	1.0 L

Dissolve ingredients in 1.0 L of distilled water, and sterilize by filtration. Adjust the final pH to 7.0 ± 0.2. Check sterility before use. Store at 2° to 8°C.

HC (HEMORRHAGIC COLI) AGAR

Tryptone	20.0 g
Bile salts No. 3	1.12 g
Sodium chloride	5.0 g
Sorbitol	20.0 g
4-Methylumbelliferyl-β-D glucuronide (MUG)	0.1 g
Bromcresol purple	0.015 g
Agar	15.0 g
Distilled water	1.0 L

Dissolve the ingredients listed above in distilled water by heating with stirring. Autoclave the medium for 15 min at 121°C. The final pH should be 7.2 ± 0.2.

Note: MUG is not essential for the enzyme-labeled monoclonal antibody procedure.

HEART INFUSION AGAR/BROTH*

HEKTOEN ENTERIC (HE) AGAR*

HHD MEDIUM

Fructose	2.5 g
KH_2PO_4	2.5 g
Trypticase peptone	10.0 g
Phytone peptone	1.5 g
Casamino acids	3.0 g
Yeast extract	1.0 g
Tween 80	1.0 g
Bromcresol green solution	20.0 ml
Agar (when desired)	20.0 g
Distilled water	1.0 L

Combine ingredients with 1.0 L of distilled water, and heat to boiling while stirring to dissolve the agar completely. Adjust the pH to 7.0 ± 0.02, and autoclave for 15 min at 121°C.

Bromcresol green solution is prepared by dissolving 0.1 g of bromcresol green in 30.0 ml of 0.01 N NaOH.

*Commercially available.

HL AGAR

Base Layer:

Prepare Columbia Blood Agar Base, and autoclave at 121°C for 15 min. Place 10.0 ml into Petri dishes as the base.

Top Layer:

Prepare Columbia Blood Agar Base, and autoclave at 121°C for 15 min. Add 5.0% horse blood to the tempered (46°C) medium, and mix thoroughly. Pour 5.0 ml of blood agar over the base layer while the base is still warm. HL agar may be stored under refrigeration in plastic bags; discard any plates that become discolored or show hemolysis.

HORIE ARABINOSE ETHYL VIOLET BROTH (HAEB)

Peptone	5.0 g
Beef extract	3.0 g
Sodium chloride	30.0 g
Bromthymol blue	0.03 g
Ethyl violet	0.001 g
Arabinose	5.0 g
Distilled water	1.0 L

Dissolve all ingredients except arabinose in 900.0 ml of distilled water. Adjust the pH to 9.0 ± 0.2, and sterilize at 121°C for 15 min. Cool and aseptically add 100.0 ml of a filter-sterilized 5% arabinose solution in distilled water. After mixing, aseptically dispense the medium into sterile tubes or bottles.

HYA AGAR

Beef extract	1.0 g
Proteose peptone No. 3	10.0 g
Glucose	2.5 g
Galactose	2.5 g
Lactose	5.0 g
Agar	15.0 g
Distilled water	1.0 L

Dissolve the ingredients except for the glucose, galactose, and lactose in distilled water with heat. Adjust the pH to 6.8 ± 0.2 before autoclaving in 90.0-ml aliquots at 121°C for 20 min. Add each of the sugars as cold, sterilized, 10% solutions (filter-sterilized) just prior to plating samples.

INDICATOR BROTH WITH VARIOUS SUGARS
(CARBOHYDRATE FERMENTATION MEDIA)*

INDOLE NITRITE MEDIUM*

INFECTION MEDIUM (IM)

Heat-inactivated fetal bovine serum (2 hr at 55°C)	20.0 ml
Brain heart infusion	0.125 g
Bile salts No. 3	0.05 g
Earle's balanced salts solution	80.0 ml

Combine the above ingredients and filter sterilize. Store at 4° to 10°C.

INOSITOL BRILLIANT GREEN BILE SALTS (IBB) AGAR

Peptone	10.0 g
Meat extract	5.0 g
Sodium chloride	5.0 g
Bile salts No. 3	8.5 g
Brilliant green	0.33 mg
Neutral red	25.0 mg
Inositol	10.0 g
Agar	15.0 g
Distilled water	1.0 L

Dissolve ingredients in distilled water, and adjust the pH to 7.2. Autoclave at 115°C for 15 min.

INOSITOL GELATIN DEEPS

Gelatin	120.0 g
Sodium phosphate (dibasic)	5.0 g
Yeast extract	5.0 g
Inositol	10.0 g
Phenol red	0.05 g
Distilled water	1.0 L

Heat to dissolve ingredients in distilled water, and adjust the pH to 7.4. Distribute the medium into tubes (5 ml per tube), and autoclave at 115°C for 15 min.

*Commercially available.

INTRACELLULAR GROWTH PHASE (IGP) MEDIUM

Minimal essential medium	72.0 ml
Fetal bovine serum	8.0 ml
Gentamicin sulfate	500.0 mg
Lysozyme†	30.0 mg
Dulbecco's phosphate-buffered saline	20.0 ml

†Available from Schwarz-Mann, Inc., Division of Mediscience, 2 Ram Ridge Road, Spring Valley, NY 10977.

Combine the above ingredients, and filter sterilize. Store at 4° to 10°C.

IRGASAN-TICARCILLIN-CHLORATE (ITC) BROTH

Tryptone	10.0 g
Yeast extract	1.0 g
Magnesium chloride·6H$_2$O	60.0 g
NaCl	5.0 g
Potassium chlorate	1.0 g
Malachite green (0.2%)	5.0 ml
Distilled water	1.0 L

Combine the ingredients with distilled water, and sterilize by autoclaving at 121°C for 15 min. Add the following after cooling the medium:

Ticarcillin (filter-sterilized)	1.0 µg/ml
Irgasan DP300 (stock solution in 95% ethanol)	1.0 µg/ml

KAPER'S MEDIUM

Proteose peptone (Difco)	5.0 g
Yeast extract (Difco)	3.0 g
Tryptone (Difco)	10.0 g
L-Ornithine·HCl	5.0 g
Mannitol	1.0 g
Inositol	10.0 g
Sodium thiosulfate	0.4 g
Ferric ammonium citrate	0.5 g
Bromcresol purple	0.02 g
Agar	3.0 g
Distilled water	1.0 L

Heat to dissolve all ingredients completely in distilled water and adjust the pH to 6.7. Dispense the medium into tubes (5 ml per tube) and autoclave at 121°C for 12 min.

KCN BROTH BASE*

KF STREPTOCOCCUS AGAR*

KIM-GOEPFERT (KG) AGAR

Preparation A:

Peptone	1.0 g
Yeast extract	0.5 g
Phenol red	0.025 g
Agar	18.0 g
Distilled water	900.0 ml

Preparation B - Colbeck's Egg Yolk Broth or Concentrated Egg Yolk Emulsion:

Concentrated Egg Yolk Emulsion is available commercially from Oxoid Limited or as Egg Yolk Enrichment 50% from Difco Laboratories.

Preparation C - Polymyxin B Sulfate:

This selective agent is obtainable in sterile powdered form (500,000 units, i.e., 50 mg per vial) from Pfizer, Inc. To use, aseptically add 5.0 ml of sterile distilled water with a sterile syringe. Mix to dissolve the powder.

Dissolve Preparation A ingredients in distilled water, heat to boiling to completely dissolve the agar, and adjust the pH to 6.8. Autoclave at 121°C for 20 min, cool to 50°C, and add 100.0 ml of Preparation B and 1.0 ml of Preparation C. Mix well, pour into Petri dishes, allow to solidify, and store in a manner to eliminate excess surface moisture. Plates may be stored at 4°C for up to 7 days.

KLIGLER IRON AGAR (KIA)*

KM AGAR

Nonfat milk	10.0 g
Milk protein hydrolysate	2.5 g
Glucose	5.0 g
Agar	15.0 g
Distilled water	1.0 L

*Commercially available.

Combine the ingredients in distilled water, and heat while stirring to dissolve the agar completely. Adjust the pH to 6.6 before autoclaving for 12 min at 115°C (10 lb/in²). Cool the medium to 45°C in a waterbath.

To each L of KM agar at 45°C add 10.0 ml of each of the following solutions which have been steamed (110°C) for 30 min:

Solution 1:

10% potassium ferricyanide

Solution 2:

1.0 g of ferric citrate and 1.0 g of sodium citrate in 40.0 ml of distilled water.

Gently swirl the medium and pour plates. Dry the plates in the dark for 24 hr at 30°C.

KOSER'S CITRATE MEDIUM*

L-15 MEDIUM (MODIFIED) LEIBOVITZ

D-Galactose	90.0 mg
Phenol red, Na	10.0 mg
Sodium pyruvate	550.0 mg
DL-α-Alanine	450.0 mg
L-Arginine (free base)	500.0 mg
L-Asparagine·H₂O	250.0 mg
L-Cysteine (free base)	120.0 mg
L-Glutamine	300.0 mg
Glycine	200.0 mg
L-Histidine (free base)	250.0 mg
L-Isoleucine	250.0 mg
L-Leucine HCl	125.0 mg
DL-Methionine	150.0 mg
L-Phenylalanine	250.0 mg
L-Serine	200.0 mg
DL-Threonine	600.0 mg
L-Tryptophan	20.0 mg
L-Tyrosine	300.0 mg
DL-Valine	200.0 mg
D-Calcium pantothenate	1.0 mg
Choline chloride	1.0 mg

*Commercially available.

L-15 MEDIUM (MODIFIED) LEIBOVITZ (Continued)

Folic acid	1.0 mg
i-Inositol	2.0 mg
Nicotinamide	1.0 mg
Pyridoxine HCl	1.0 mg
Riboflavin-5-phosphate, Na	0.1 mg
Thiamin monophosphate·2H$_2$O	1.0 mg
CaCl$_2$ (anhydrous)	140.0 mg
KCl	400.0 mg
KH$_2$PO$_4$	60.0 mg
MgCl$_2$ (anhydrous)	93.68 mg
NaCl	8000.0 mg
Na$_2$HPO$_4$ (anhydrous)	190.0 mg
Distilled water	1.0 L

Combine all ingredients, and filter through a 0.20-μm membrane. Dispense into a 2-L Erlenmeyer flask. The final pH should be 7.5. Cap the flask and store at 5°C.

LACTIC (ELLIKER) AGAR

Add 15.0 g of agar per L of commercially available Elliker broth.

LACTIC STREAK AGAR

Sodium carboxymethylcellulose	10.0 g
Yeast extract	5.0 g
Phytone peptone	5.0 g
Beef extract	5.0 g
Lactose	1.5 g
Calcium citrate	10.0 g
L-Arginine hydrochloride	1.5 g
Polypeptone	5.0 g
Agar	15.0 g
Bromcresol purple (0.1%)	2.0 ml
Distilled water	1.0 L

Suspend the agar in 800.0 ml of distilled water, and heat to dissolve completely. Add the other ingredients, with the exception of the sodium carboxymethylcellulose, calcium citrate, and bromcresol purple. Suspend the sodium carboxymethylcellulose and calcium citrate in 200.0 ml of water, disperse using a blender, and then add the mixture to the molten medium. Adjust the pH to 6.0, dispense in 100.0-ml amounts, and autoclave at 115°C for 10 min. Cool the sterilized medium to 50°C, and add 2.0 ml of a sterile 0.1% aqueous bromcresol purple solution. Pour plates and dry at 37°C for one hr. Discard plates if not used that day. Store bottles of agar at 5°C.

Note: If higher temperatures are used in autoclaving, the lactose will have to be sterilized separately to avoid sugar-amino acid reactions.

LACTOBACILLUS HETEROFERM SCREEN BROTH
(Modified MRS)

Bacto proteose peptone No. 3	10.0 g
Bacto yeast extract	5.0 g
Tween 80	1.0 ml
Ammonium citrate	2.0 g
Sodium acetate	5.0 g
Magnesium sulfate	0.1 g
Manganese sulfate	0.05 g
Dipotassium phosphate	2.0 g
Dextrose (Bacto)	20.0 g
Bromcresol green (Bacto)	0.04 g
2-phenylethyl alcohol (to inhibit gram-negatives)	3.0 g
Actidione (to inhibit yeasts)	4.0 mg
Distilled water	1.0 L

Combine the ingredients with distilled water, and stir to dissolve. Adjust the pH to 4.3 ± 0.01 (pH adjustment is critical for excluding CO_2-producing starter cultures such as *Leuconostoc* spp.) with concentrated HCl, and then dispense the medium into 16- × 125-mm tubes containing inverted Durham fermentation tubes. Autoclave for 15 min at 121°C.

Modifications for Salad Dressings:

MRS agar is prepared by adding 15.0 g of agar per L of medium. For lactobacilli detection in salad dressings, adjust the medium pH to 5.5 with glacial acetic acid after sterilization.

LACTOBACILLUS SELECTION (LBS) AGAR

Pancreatic digest of casein	10.0 g
Yeast extract	5.0 g
Monopotassium phosphate	6.0 g
Ammonium citrate	2.0 g
Dextrose	20.0 g
Sorbitan monooleate	1.0 g
Sodium acetate hydrate	25.0 g
Magnesium sulfate	0.575 g
Manganese sulfate	0.120 g
Ferrous sulfate	0.034 g
Agar	15.0 g
Distilled water	1.0 L

Mix the ingredients thoroughly in distilled water, and boil for 2 min. Use the medium without autoclaving (medium can be autoclaved when storage is necessary). Cool to 45°C, add 1.32 ml of glacial acetic acid, and pour as for plate counts. Final pH should be 5.4 ± 0.2. Overlay pour plates with the medium to permit earlier enumeration of colonies.

Note: 1.32 ml of glacial acetic acid must be added to the commercially available BBL product (LBS agar). Acetic acid is included in the Oxoid formulation, called Rogosa agar.

Modifications:

Add 1% fructose to LBS agar to ensure greater enumeration of certain lactobacilli. Add 200 ppm cycloheximide if needed to inhibit yeasts.

Adjust the pH to 5.4 ± 0.2 using acetic acid, and add 0.0075% sterile brilliant green prior to cooling. Mix, cool, and pour as above.

LACTOSE BROTH*

LACTOSE GELATIN MEDIUM

Tryptose	15.0 g
Yeast extract	10.0 g
Lactose	10.0 g
Gelatin	120.0 g
Phenol red (as solution)	0.05 g
Distilled water	1.0 L

Suspend the ingredients except the gelatin and phenol red in 400.0 ml of distilled water, and dissolve by heating gently while stirring. Suspend the gelatin in 600.0 ml of cold distilled water, and dissolve by heating in a water-bath at 50° to 60°C with frequent stirring. When the gelatin is dissolved, combine with the other dissolved ingredients and adjust the pH to 7.5 with 1 N sodium hydroxide. Add the phenol red, mix well, and dispense 10.0-ml portions into 16- × 125-mm screw-capped tubes. Sterilize by autoclaving for 10 min at 121°C. If the medium is not used within 8 hr, deaerate by holding in a waterbath at 50° to 70°C for 2 to 3 hr before use.

LAURYL TRYPTOSE BROTH or LAURYL SULFATE TRYPTOSE (LST) BROTH*

*Commercially available.

LB (*LACTOBACILLUS BULGARICUS*) AGAR

Tryptone	10.0 g
Yeast extract	5.0 g
Glucose	20.0 g
Dipotassium phosphate	2.0 g
Beef extract	10.0 g
Filtered tomato juice	40.0 ml
Tween 80	1.0 g
Distilled water	780.0 ml
Agar	20.0 g

Combine the ingredients with distilled water, and heat to dissolve. Adjust the pH to 6.8, and then add 80.0 ml of acetate buffer (113.55 g of sodium acetate and 9.90 g of acetic acid per L). Autoclave at 121°C for 15 min.

LBS (*LACTOBACILLUS* SELECTION) OXGALL AGAR

Prepare LBS agar and add 0.15% oxgall (BBL) before adjusting the pH to 5.4 ± 0.2 and heating.

LEE'S AGAR

Tryptone	10.0 g
Yeast extract	10.0 g
Lactose	5.0 g
Sucrose	5.0 g
Calcium carbonate	3.0 g
Dipotassium phosphate	0.5 g
Bromcresol purple solution (0.2%)	10.0 ml
Agar	18.0 g
Distilled water to make	1.0 L

Dissolve the ingredients except for the bromcresol purple in distilled water with gentle heating. Adjust the pH of the medium to 7.0 ± 0.2 before autoclaving 20 min at 121°C. Carefully mix the melted medium to suspend the calcium carbonate evenly. Just before pouring plates, add 10.0 ml of a sterile (121°C for 15 min) 0.2% bromcresol purple solution. Pour the medium into previously chilled sterile Petri dishes to obtain a layer of medium 4- to 5-mm thick. After solidification, dry the plates in a 30°C incubator for 18 to 24 hr.

*Commercially available.

LES ENDO AGAR*

LEVINE EOSINE METHYLENE BLUE (L-EMB) AGAR*

LISTERIA ENRICHMENT BROTH (LEB)-FDA

Acriflavin HCl (Sigma)	15.0 mg
Nalidixic acid (sodium salt, Sigma)	40.0 mg
Cycloheximide (Sigma)	50.0 mg
Trypticase soy broth-yeast extract (sterile)	1.0 L

Add the three supplemental ingredients aseptically to trypticase soy broth-yeast extract (TSB-YE) after autoclaving and just before use. Make acriflavin and nalidixic acid supplements as 0.5% stock solutions in distilled water. Make the cycloheximide supplement as 1.0% stock in 40% ethanol in water. Filter sterilize all three supplementary ingredients. Add 0.68 ml of acriflavin solution, 1.8 ml of nalidixic acid solution, and 1.15 ml of cycloheximide solution to 225.0 ml of TSB-YE to achieve the correct concentrations.

LITMUS MILK*

LIVER BROTH

Fresh beef liver	500.0 g
Distilled water	1.0 L
Tryptone	10.0 g
Soluble starch	1.0 g
Dipotassium phosphate	1.0 g

Remove the fat from 1 lb fresh beef liver. Grind the liver, mix with 1.0 L of distilled water, and boil slowly for 1 hr. Adjust the pH to 7.6, and remove the liver particles by straining through cheesecloth. Bring the volume of the broth back to 1.0 L with distilled water, and add the tryptone, dipotassium phosphate, and soluble starch. Refilter the broth. Dispense 15.0 ml of the broth into 20- × 150-mm tubes, and add previously removed liver particles to a depth of 1.0 in. in each tube. Autoclave 20 min at 121°C.

LIVER BROTH PLUS SALT

Prepare liver broth, and add 15% salt (or closely approximate the salt content of the sample to be examined).

---

*Commercially available.

LIVER VEAL AGAR (LVA)*

LIVER VEAL EGG YOLK AGAR

Fresh eggs (antibiotic free)	3.0
Liver veal agar	1.0 L

Wash eggs with a stiff brush, and drain. Soak eggs in 0.1% mercuric chloride solution for 1 hr. Pour off the mercuric chloride solution, and replace with 70% ethyl alcohol. Soak in 70% ethyl alcohol for 30 min. Crack the eggs aseptically, and discard the whites. Remove the yolk with a sterile 50-ml Luerlok syringe. Place in a sterile container, and add an equal volume of sterile saline (0.85% sodium chloride). Mix thoroughly. To each 500.0 ml of melted liver veal agar tempered to 50°C add 40.0 ml of the egg yolk-saline solution. Mix thoroughly and pour plates. Dry plates at room temperature for 2 days or at 35°C for 24 hr. Discard contaminated plates, and store sterile plates under refrigeration.

LPM (LITHIUM PHENYLETHANOL MOXALACTAM) AGAR

Phenylethanol agar	35.5 g
Glycine anhydride	10.0 g
Lithium chloride	5.0 g
Distilled water	1.0 L

Prepare as directed by the manufacturer, and autoclave at 121°C for 12 min. Cool the medium in a 46°C waterbath, and then add 2.0 ml of 1.0% filter-sterilized moxalactam per L of medium. Mix well, and pour 12.0 ml into 100-mm plates. Refrigerate LPM plates in plastic bags. The 1% moxalactam solution is prepared by dissolving 1.0 g of sodium or ammonia moxalactam in 100.0 ml of 0.1 M potassium buffer (0.1 M KH_2PO_4 into 0.1 M K_2HPO_4 until the pH reaches 6.0). Filter-sterilized moxalactam can be frozen until needed at $-60°C$ in 4.0-ml quantities.

LYSINE DECARBOXYLASE BROTH*

LYSINE IRON AGAR (LIA)*
(Edwards and Fife)

LYSOZYME BROTH

Nutrient Broth:

Prepare nutrient broth, and dispense 99.0-ml amounts in bottles or flasks. Autoclave for 15 min at 121°C.

*Commercially available.

Lysozyme Solution:

Dissolve 0.1 g of lysozyme in 65.0 ml of sterile 0.01 N hydrochloric acid. Heat to boiling for 20 min, and dilute to 100.0 ml with sterile 0.01 N hydrochloric acid. Alternatively, dissolve 0.1 g of lysozyme chloride in 100.0 ml of distilled water, and sterilize by filtration. Test solution for sterility before use.

Add 1.0 ml of sterile 0.1% lysozyme solution to each 99.0 ml of nutrient broth. Mix thoroughly, and aseptically dispense 2.5 ml of the complete medium into sterile 13- × 100-mm tubes.

M 16 AGAR
(A modification of Rogosa SL agar)

Beef extract	5.0 g
Yeast extract	2.5 g
Ascorbic acid	0.5 g
Phytone or soytone	5.0 g
Polypeptone or tryptose	5.0 g
Sodium acetate trihydrate	3.0 g
Lactose or dextrose	5.0 g
Agar	10.0 g
Distilled water	1.0 L

Dissolve all of the ingredients except for the lactose or dextrose in 950.0 ml of distilled water, and boil while stirring to dissolve the agar completely. Adjust the pH to 7.2 ± 0.2 with 2 N NaOH. Autoclave at 121°C for 15 min, and cool to 50°C. Add a sterile solution of lactose or dextrose (5.0 g in 50.0 ml of distilled water, autoclaved at 121°C for 15 min) to the medium.

M 17 AGAR

Phytone peptone	5.0 g
Polypeptone	5.0 g
Yeast extract	2.5 g
Beef extract	5.0 g
Lactose	5.0 g
Ascorbic acid	0.5 g
β-Disodium glycerophosphate	19.0 g
1.0 M MgSO$_4$·7H$_2$O	1.0 ml
Agar	10.0 g
Distilled water	1.0 L

Add 10.0 g of agar to 950.0 ml of distilled water, and heat to boiling to dissolve the agar completely. The remaining ingredients, except for the lactose, should be added to the dissolved agar, and the mixture should be auto-

claved at 121°C for 15 min. After cooling the sterile medium to 45°C in a temperature-controlled waterbath, add a sterile solution of lactose (5.0 g in 50.0 ml of distilled water, sterilized at 121°C for 15 min). Final pH should be 7.15.

M-BROTH*

MacCONKEY (MAC) AGAR*

MacCONKEY GLUCOSE AGAR

Same as Violet Red Bile Agar with 1% glucose.

MAGNESIUM OXALATE (MOX) AGAR

Trypticase soy agar	40.0 g
Sodium oxalate	2.68 g
Magnesium chloride·6H$_2$O	4.067 g
Distilled water	1.0 L

Combine the ingredients with distilled water, and boil while stirring to dissolve the agar completely. Sterilize by autoclaving at 121°C for 15 min. Final pH should be 7.4 to 7.6.

MALONATE BROTH*

MALONATE BROTH MODIFIED*

(With added glucose and yeast extract)

MALT AGAR*

MALT EXTRACT AGAR (MEA)*

Malt extract	20.0 g
Dextrose	20.0 g
Peptone (bacteriological)	1.0 g
Agar	20.0 g
Distilled water	1.0 L

Suspend the ingredients in distilled water, and heat the mixture to boiling while stirring to dissolve completely. Autoclave at 121°C for 15 min. Formulations of this medium are commercially available.

*Commercially available.

MALT EXTRACT YEAST EXTRACT 40% GLUCOSE (MY40G) AGAR

Malt extract powder	12.0 g
Yeast extract	3.0 g
Agar	12.0 g
Distilled water to make	600.0 g
Glucose, AR	400.0 g

Combine the ingredients except glucose with 550.0 ml of distilled water, and steam to dissolve the agar. Immediately make up to 600.0 g with distilled water. While the solution is still hot, add the glucose all at once, and stir rapidly to prevent the formation of hard lumps of glucose monohydrate. If lumps form, dissolve them by steaming for a few minutes. Steam the medium for 30 min. This medium is of sufficiently low a_w not to require autoclaving. The final pH of this medium is about 5.5, and the a_w is near 0.92.

MANNITOL YOLK POLYMYXIN (MYP) AGAR

Preparation A:

Beef extract	1.0 g
Peptone	10.0 g
D-Mannitol	10.0 g
NaCl	10.0 g
Phenol red	0.025 g
Agar	15.0 g
Distilled water	900.0 ml

Preparation B - Colbeck's Egg Yolk Broth or Concentrated Egg Yolk Emulsion:
   Concentrated Egg Yolk Emulsion is available commercially from Oxoid Limited or as Egg Yolk Enrichment 50% from Difco Laboratories.
Preparation C - Polymyxin B Sulfate:
   Dissolve 500,000 units of sterile polymyxin B sulfate (Burroughs Wellcome Co, Research Triangle Park, NC 27709) in 50.0 ml of sterile distilled water.

Mix the ingredients in distilled water, adjust the pH to 7.2 ± 0.1, heat to boiling to dissolve, and dispense 225.0-ml portions into 500-ml flasks. Autoclave at 121°C for 20 min, cool to 50°C in a waterbath, and add 12.5 ml of Preparation B and 2.5 ml of Preparation C to each flask containing 225.0 ml of medium. Mix well, pour into Petri dishes, allow to solidify, and dry for 24 hr at room temperature. Plates may be stored at 4°C for 7 days.

MD MEDIUM

L-Malic acid (Sigma)	20.0 g
Trypticase	10.0 g
D-(+)-Glucose (Sigma)	5.0 g
Casamino acids	3.0 g
Phytone	1.5 g
Yeast extract	1.0 g
Tween 80 (Atlas Chemical Ind.)	1.0 g
Bromcresol green solution	20.0 ml
Agar (when desired)	20.0 g
Distilled water	1.0 L

Combine ingredients with 1.0 L of distilled water. Heat to boiling while stirring to dissolve agar completely. Adjust the pH to 7.0 with 10 N KOH, and autoclave for 15 min at 121°C. Medium may be stored at room temperature.

Bromcresol green solution is prepared by dissolving 0.1 g of bromcresol green in 30.0 ml of 0.01 N NaOH.

MEME-FBS

Minimal essential medium, Earle's salts	90.0 ml
Fetal bovine serum	10.0 ml

MEME-FBS-PEN-STREP SOLUTION

Minimal essential medium, Earle's salts	90.0 ml
Fetal bovine serum	10.0 ml
Penicillin-streptomycin solution	1.0 ml

Penicillin-Streptomycin Stock Solution:

Penicillin G	500,000.0 IU
Streptomycin	500,000.0 μg
Distilled water	100.0 ml

The antibiotic stock solution should be prepared by dissolving the antibiotics in water and sterilizing by filtration. Store at 5°C until needed to prepare the MEME-FBS-PEN-STREP solution.

M-ENDO MEDIUM (AGAR OR BROTH)*

m-ENTEROCOCCUS AGAR*

(Difco)

M-FC*

Same as Modified Fecal Coliform Agar.

MF ENDO BROTH*

m-HPC AGAR*

MINERALS MODIFIED GLUTAMATE AGAR

Lactose	10.0 g
Sodium formate	0.25 g
L(−)-Cystine	0.02 g
L(−)-Aspartic acid	0.024 g
K_2HPO_4	0.9 g
Thiamin	0.001 g
Nicotinic acid	0.001 g
Pantothenic acid	0.001 g
$MgSO_4 \cdot 7H_2O$	0.1 g
Ferric ammonium citrate	0.01 g
$CaCl_2 \cdot 2H_2O$	0.01 g
L(+)-Arginine	0.02 g
Bromcresol purple	0.01 g
Ammonium chloride	2.5 g
Sodium glutamate	6.35 g
Agar	15.0 g
Distilled water	1.0 L

Combine all ingredients, and heat to boiling to dissolve agar. Autoclave for 10 min at 116°C. The final pH should be 6.7 ± 0.2. Dispense 20-ml portions into 15- × 100-mm Petri dishes.

MINIMAL ESSENTIAL MEDIUM WITH EARLE'S SALTS (MEME)*

*Commercially available.

MINIMAL ESSENTIAL MEDIUM WITH HANK'S SALTS (MEMH)

L-Arginine HCl	126.4 mg
L-Cystine Na	28.42 mg
L-Glutamine	292.3 mg
L-Histidine HCl·H_2O	41.90 mg
L-Isoleucine	52.50 mg
L-Leucine	52.50 mg
L-Lysine HCl	73.06 mg
L-Methionine	14.90 mg
L-Phenylalanine	33.02 mg
L-Threonine	47.64 mg
L-Tryptophan	40.20 mg
L-Tyrosine	36.22 mg
L-Valine	46.90 mg
D-Calcium pantothenate	1.0 mg
Choline chloride	1.0 mg
Folic acid	1.0 mg
i-Inositol	2.0 mg
Nicotinamide	1.0 mg
Pyridoxal HCl	1.0 mg
Riboflavin	0.1 mg
Thiamin HCl	1.0 mg
$CaCl_2·2H_2O$	140.0 mg
KCl	400.0 mg
KH_2PO_4	60.0 mg
$MgSO_4$	97.7 mg
NaCl	8000.0 mg
Na_2HPO_4	47.5 mg
Dextrose	1000.0 mg
Phenol red, Na†	17.0 mg
$NaHCO_3$ (filter sterilized and added to final medium)†	1875.0 mg
Distilled water	1.0 L

†MEMH used for extraction lacks phenol red and $NaHCO_3$.

Combine all ingredients, and sterilize by filtration through a 0.2-μm filter. Dispense into a 2-L Erlenmeyer flask. The final pH should be 7.2 ± 0.2. This medium is available in a commercial formulation.

MODIFIED (AEA) SPORULATION MEDIUM

Polypeptone	10.0 g
Yeast extract	10.0 g
Sodium phosphate (dibasic)	4.36 g
Potassium phosphate (monobasic)	0.25 g
Ammonium acetate	1.5 g
Magnesium sulfate (heptahydrate)	0.2 g
Distilled water	1.0 L

Dissolve the ingredients in distilled water, and adjust the pH to 7.5 ± 0.1 with 2 M sodium carbonate. Dispense the medium in 15-ml portions in 20- × 150-mm screw-capped tubes, and sterilize by autoclaving for 15 min at 121°C. To prepare the final medium, add 0.6 ml of separately sterilized 10% raffinose and 0.2 ml each of filter-sterilized 0.66 M sodium carbonate and 0.32% cobalt chloride ($CoCl_2 \cdot 6H_2O$) dropwise to each 15 ml of base medium. Check the pH of one or two tubes. The pH should be near 7.8 ± 0.1. Just before use, steam the medium for 10 min, and, after cooling, add 0.2 ml of filter-sterilized 1.5% sodium ascorbate (prepared that day) to each 15-ml tube of medium.

MODIFIED COLIFORM MEDIUM (mCM)

Proteose peptone No. 3 (Difco)	10.0 g
Yeast extract	6.0 g
Lactose	20.0 g
Bile salts No. 3 (Difco)	1.0 g
Sodium lauryl sulfate	1.0 g
Sodium desoxycholate	0.1 g
Bromcresol purple stock solution	10.0 ml
Tris (hydroxymethyl) amino methane	12.1 g
Distilled water	1.0 L

Bromcresol purple stock solution:

Add 0.35 g of bromcresol purple to 2.0 ml of 0.1 N NaOH in a volumetric flask and swirl until mixed. Bring the final volume of mixture to 100.0 ml by adding distilled water. Thoroughly mix and filter sterilize.

Combine the dehydrated ingredients, and dissolve in 1.0 L of distilled water (900.0 ml for cream). Add 10.0 ml of bromcresol purple stock solution, and adjust the pH to 6.8 ± 0.1 with 0.1 N NaOH (or 12.0 ml of 1.0 N NH_4OH for yogurt, pH 7.0, or 90.0 ml of 1.0 N HCl for cream, pH 7.0 ± 0.1). Mix thoroughly, and dispense in 50-ml volumes (95-ml for yogurt and cream, 20-ml for raw milk) into dilution bottles, adjusting for evaporation that may occur during autoclaving. Autoclave for 15 min at 121°C (25 min at 121°C for yogurt only).

MODIFIED DUNCAN STRONG (DS) MEDIUM

Yeast extract	4.0 g
Proteose peptone	15.0 g
Sodium thioglycollate	1.0 g
Sodium phosphate (dibasic heptahydrate)	10.0 g
Raffinose	4.0 g
Distilled water	1.0 L

Combine the ingredients with distilled water, and mix thoroughly. Sterilize by autoclaving for 15 min at 121°C. Adjust the pH to 7.8 using filter-sterilized 0.66 M sodium carbonate, and then dispense into tubes. Check the pH of one or two of the tubes; it should be near 7.8 ± 0.1.

MODIFIED FECAL COLIFORM (mFC) AGAR*

Tryptose	10.0 g
Proteose peptone No. 3	5.0 g
Yeast extract	3.0 g
Sodium chloride	5.0 g
Lactose	12.5 g
Bile salts No. 3	1.5 g
Aniline blue (water blue)	0.1 g
Agar	15.0 g
Distilled water	1.0 L

Combine all ingredients, and dissolve by heating to boiling. Do not autoclave. Temper to 50°C, and adjust the pH to 7.4. Pour the medium into sterile Petri plates in 20-ml aliquots, and allow to dry thoroughly. The medium may be stored for 4 weeks at 4°C.

MODIFIED LACTIC AGAR FOR YOGURT BACTERIA

Aseptically add 7.0% (v/v) sterile (121°C for 12 min) reconstituted nonfat dry milk (11% solids, w/w) to melted lactic (Elliker) agar. To avoid partial solidification of the agar, the milk should be prewarmed to 47°C before the addition. After pouring into sterile Petri dishes, dry the plates for 18 to 24 hr at 28° to 30°C.

MODIFIED McBRIDE AGAR

Phenylethanol agar (Difco)	35.5 g
Glycine anhydride	10.0 g
Lithium chloride	0.5 g
Distilled water	1.0 L

Combine the ingredients listed, and dissolve with heat while stirring. Autoclave at 121°C for 15 min, and cool to 46°C. Add filter-sterilized cycloheximide to obtain a concentration of 200.0 mg per L of medium.

*Commercially available.

MODIFIED NICKELS AND LEESMENT AGAR

Part 1:

Tryptone	20.0 g
Yeast extract	5.0 g
Gelatin	2.5 g
Lactose	10.0 g
NaCl	4.0 g
Sodium citrate	2.0 g
Distilled water	750.0 ml

Dissolve the ingredients in distilled water, and adjust the pH to 6.65.

Part 2:

Incubate 10% reconstituted nonfat milk inoculated with lactic starter at 20°C for 24 hr. Centrifuge the incubated milk to remove the precipitated curd, and collect the clear supernatant. Autoclave the supernatant at 121°C for 15 min, and store at 4°C.

Part 3:

Grind 13.3 g of calcium citrate and 0.8 g of carboxymethylcellulose, and slowly add to 100.0 ml of hot water. Mix well, and filter through a cotton cloth.

Part 4:

Dissolve 8.0 g of calcium lactate in 50.0 ml of distilled water with gentle heating.

Prepare each of the four parts separately and autoclave at 121°C for 15 min. After autoclaving, mix the four parts in the following amounts to make up 1.0 L of medium:

Part 1	750.0 ml
Part 2	100.0 ml
Part 3	100.0 ml
Part 4	50.0 ml

Pour plates with periodic mixing of the agar.

MODIFIED OXFORD (MX) AGAR*

Commercially available from Oxoid (CM856); however, commercial formulations may deviate from the original formula.

*Commercially available.

MODIFIED PLATE COUNT AGAR

Yeast extract	20.0 g
Tryptone	20.0 g
Glucose	4.0 g
Agar	10.0 g
Distilled water	1.0 L

Dissolve the ingredients in 1.0 L of distilled water by stirring while heating. Dispense the medium into bottles, and autoclave at 121°C for 15 min. The final pH should be 7.0 ± 0.1.

MODIFIED RAPPAPORT (RAP) BROTH

Solution A:

Tryptone	10.0 g
Distilled water	1.0 L

Solution B:

Sodium phosphate dibasic	9.5 g
Distilled water	1.0 L

Solution C:

Magnesium chloride·6H$_2$O	40.0 g
Distilled water	100.0 ml

Sterilize by autoclaving at 121°C for 15 min.

Solution D:

Malachite green	0.2 g
Distilled water	100.0 ml

Do not sterilize Solution D.

Solution E:

Carbenicillin	10.0 mg
Distilled water	10.0 ml

Combine carbenicillin with distilled water and filter sterilize.

To make 250.0 ml of medium, mix 155.0 ml of Solution A and 40.0 ml of Solution B. Sterilize the mixture by autoclaving at 121°C for 15 min. Cool to 50°C, and add 53.0 ml of Solution C. Add 1.6 ml of Solution D and 0.6 ml of Solution E, and mix thoroughly. No final pH adjustment is necessary.

MODIFIED SA AGAR (LACHICA'S MEDIUM)

Heart infusion agar (Difco)	40.0 g
Amylose azure†	3.0 g
Ampicillin	0.01 mg
Distilled water	1.0 L

†Available from Calbiochem, San Diego, CA.

Suspend the ingredients in distilled water, and dissolve by heating while stirring. Autoclave for 15 min at 121°C. Pour sterilized and tempered medium into sterile Petri dishes.

Colonies of the *Aeromonas hydrophila* group appear surrounded by a light halo on a light blue background.

MODIFIED SODIUM LACTATE AGAR

Trypticase soy broth	10.0 g
Yeast extract	10.0 g
Sodium lactate (60% syrup)	20.0 ml
Agar	15.0 g
Distilled water	1.0 L

Dissolve the ingredients in distilled water with gentle heating. Adjust the pH to 7.0 before autoclaving at 121°C for 15 to 20 min. This formulation contains dextrose in the trypticase soy broth and thus is not as selective as sodium lactate agar.

MODIFIED V-P BROTH
(Smith, Gordon, and Clark)

Proteose peptone	7.0 g
Glucose	5.0 g
NaCl	5.0 g
Distilled water	1.0 L

Dissolve the ingredients in distilled water, and dispense 5.0 ml into 20-mm test tubes. Autoclave for 15 min at 121°C. This is a modified medium and must be formulated in the laboratory.

MOTILITY-NITRATE MEDIUM (BUFFERED)

(For *Clostridium perfringens*)

Beef extract	3.0 g
Peptone	5.0 g
Potassium nitrate	1.0 g
Disodium phosphate	2.5 g
Agar	3.0 g
Galactose	5.0 g
Glycerol	5.0 g
Distilled water	1.0 L

Dissolve the ingredients, except agar, in distilled water, and adjust the pH to 7.4. Add the agar, and heat to boiling with stirring to dissolve completely. Dispense 11-ml portions into 16- × 125-mm tubes. Sterilize the dispensed medium by autoclaving for 15 min at 121°C, and cool quickly in cold water. If the medium is not used within 4 hr after preparation, heat for 10 min in boiling water or flowing steam and chill in cold water before use.

MOTILITY TEST MEDIUM*

MP-5 (MINERAL PECTIN 5) MEDIUM

Prepare 500.0 ml of double-strength (without agar) MP-7 medium, and adjust the pH to 5 to 6 with 1N hydrochloric acid. Also prepare 500.0 ml of 3% agar solution, and heat to dissolve. Sterilize the double-strength MP-7 medium and the 3% agar solution at 121°C for 15 min, and then cool both to 48°C. Mix the two sterile solutions, and pour plates immediately to prevent hydrolysis.

MP-7 (MINERAL PECTIN 7) MEDIUM

Basal medium:

Pectin (citrus or apple)	5.0 g
Monopotassium phosphate	4.0 g
Disodium phosphate	6.0 g
Yeast extract	1.0 g
Ammonium sulfate	2.0 g
Agar	15.0 g

Mix the dry ingredients prior to placing in liquid for better dispersion, and add 500.0 ml distilled water.

*Commercially available.

Prepare separate mineral solutions as described below.

Ferrous sulfate.....................	0.2 g plus 200.0 ml distilled water
Magnesium sulfate...............	40.0 g plus 200.0 ml distilled water
Calcium chloride	0.2 g plus 200.0 ml distilled water
Boric acid	0.002 g plus 200.0 ml distilled water
Manganese sulfate	0.002 g plus 200.0 ml distilled water
Zinc sulfate........................	0.014 g plus 200.0 ml distilled water
Cupric sulfate	0.010 g plus 200.0 ml distilled water
Molybdenum trioxide...........	0.002 g plus 200.0 ml distilled water

Mix 1.0 ml of each of the above salt solutions in 492.0 ml of distilled water, producing 500.0 ml of mineral solution. Add the 500.0 ml of the mineral salt solution to the 500.0 ml of basal medium to bring the volume of the mixture to 1.0 L. Adjust the pH to 7.2 ± 0.2. Dissolve the ingredients with gentle heating, and sterilize at 121°C for 15 min. Temper medium to 48°C, and pour into sterile petri plates.

After colonies have grown, preferably on spread plates, pour the polysaccharide precipitant (described in the Reagents Section) over the surface of the plate, taking care not to dislodge the colonies. Zones of pectin hydrolysis will appear quickly, usually within a few minutes, and can best be viewed against a black background. The reagent precipitates intact pectin, and pectinolytic colonies are seen surrounded by a halo in an otherwise opaque medium.

MRS AGAR/BROTH*

Commercially available as lactobacilli MRS broth. For agar, add 15.0 g of agar per L of commercially available lactobacilli MRS broth.

MR-VP BROTH
(BUFFERED GLUCOSE BROTH)*

MUELLER-HINTON AGAR*

NEUTRALIZING BUFFER*

NITRATE BROTH*

*Commercially available.

NITRATE BROTH
(Campylobacter)

Heart infusion broth (Difco)	25.0 g
Potassium nitrate	2.0 g
Distilled water	1.0 L

Dissolve the heart infusion broth and potassium nitrate in the distilled water, and adjust the pH to 7.0. Dispense 4.0-ml amounts of the medium into 15- × 125-mm tubes with inverted vials, and autoclave at 121°C for 15 min.

NITRATE REDUCTION MEDIUM

Nutrient broth (Difco)	8.0 g
Potassium nitrate	1.0 g
Distilled water	1.0 L

Dissolve the nutrient broth and potassium nitrate in the distilled water, and dispense into tubes. Autoclave at 121°C for 15 min.

NONFAT DRY MILK (RECONSTITUTED)

Nonfat dry milk	100.0 g
Distilled water	1.0 L

Combine 100.0 g of dehydrated nonfat dry milk with 1.0 L of distilled water, and swirl until dissolved. Dispense 225-ml portions into 500-ml Erlenmeyer flasks, and autoclave at 121°C for 15 min. Aseptically adjust the final volume to 225 ml just before use. Add 0.45 ml of a 1.0% aqueous brilliant green dye solution to the medium-sample mixture after adjusting the final pH.

NUTRIENT AGAR*

If this medium is to be used as a blood agar base, add 8.0 g of sodium chloride per L to make the medium isotonic so that red cells will not rupture, and adjust the pH to 7.3 ± 0.2.

NUTRIENT AGAR WITH MANGANESE (NAMn)

Preparation A:

Prepare commercially available nutrient agar as indicated.

*Commercially available.

Preparation B:

Dissolve 3.08 g of manganese sulfate in 100.0 ml of distilled water. Add 1.0 ml of Preparation B to Preparation A (nutrient agar), and autoclave at 121°C for 15 min.

NUTRIENT BROTH*

NUTRIENT OVERLAY AGAR

Same as Base Layer Agar with Nutrient Overlay Agar.

ORANGE SERUM AGAR (OSA)/BROTH (OSB)*

OXIDATION-FERMENTATION MEDIUM FOR *CAMPYLOBACTER*

Basal medium without carbohydrate:

Bacto casitone	0.2 g
Agar	0.3 g
Phenol red, 1.0% aqueous	0.3 ml
Distilled water	100.0 ml

Dissolve the casitone in the distilled water and add the phenol red. Adjust the pH to 7.4, add the agar, and heat to boiling for 1 min to dissolve completely. Autoclave at 121°C for 15 min, and dispense 6 ml of the basal medium into 15- × 125-mm tubes. Cool tubes in an upright position.

Basal medium with carbohydrate:

Carbohydrate (glucose) - 1% final concentration
10% glucose in distilled water.................................. 10.0 ml

Filter sterilize (0.22-μm filter) the carbohydrate. When the sterile basal medium is tempered, add the carbohydrate aseptically (10 ml of 10% carbohydrate to 100 ml of basal medium) and dispense.

OXYTETRACYCLINE GLUCOSE YEAST EXTRACT* (OGY) AGAR

Available commercially from Oxoid as Oxytetracycline-Glucose-Yeast Extract Agar (O.G.Y.E. Agar, CM545) with an oxytetracycline supplement (SR73).

*Commercially available.

PARK AND SANDERS ENRICHMENT BROTH

<u>Basal Medium:</u>

Brucella broth (dehydrated)	29.0 g
Sodium pyruvate	0.25 g
Distilled water	950.0 ml
Lysed horse blood	50.0 ml

<u>Supplement A:</u>

Vancomycin	0.01 g
Trimethoprim lactate	0.01 g

<u>Supplement B:</u>

Cefoperazone	0.032 g
Cycloheximide	0.1 g

Dissolve the Brucella broth and sodium pyruvate in distilled water, and autoclave at 121°C for 15 min. Cool to room temperature, and add the blood and Supplement A. Dispense 50- or 100-ml portions in a cotton-plugged 250-ml Erlenmeyer flask. After a resuscitation period of approximately 4 hr at 31° to 32°C (to recover injured cells), add Supplement B to each flask, and incubate at 37°C for 2 hr, then at 42°C under a microaerobic atmosphere for an additional 40 to 42 hr with agitation at 100 rpm. Both the resuscitation and enrichment culture must be performed in a microaerobic environment. Solutions of each antimicrobial compound for 1 L of medium preparation may be dissolved in 5 ml of Brucella broth; dissolve the amounts of each compound required for 10 L of medium in 50 ml of Brucella broth, filter through a 0.22-μm filter, dispense in 5-ml portions in vials, and freeze until use.

PE-2 MEDIUM

Yeast extract	3.0 g
Peptone	20.0 g
Bromcresol purple (2% ethanol solution)	2.0 ml
Distilled water	1.0 L

Dissolve the ingredients in distilled water by heating, if necessary, and dispense 19-ml portions into 18- × 150-mm screw-capped culture tubes. Add 8 to 10 untreated Alaska seed peas (Rogers Bros. Co., Seed Division, P.O. Box 2188, Idaho Falls, ID 83401, catalog No. 423, or Northrup King Seed

Co., 1500 N.E. Jackson St., Minneapolis, MN 55413, or W. Atlee Burpee Co., Warminster, PA 18974). Allow ingredients to stand 1 hr to permit hydration. Autoclave at 121°C for 15 min. Prepare bromcresol purple 2% ethanol solution by adding 2.0 g of the dye to 10.0 ml of ethanol, and dilute to 100.0 ml with distilled water. Add 2.0 ml of the solution to 1.0 L of medium.

PENTACHLORONITROBENZENE ROSE BENGAL YEAST EXTRACT SUCROSE (PRYES) AGAR

Yeast extract	20.0 g
Sucrose	150.0 g
Pentachloronitrobenzene (PCNB)	0.1 g
Chloramphenicol	0.05 g
Chlortetracycline	0.05 g
Rose Bengal	0.025 g
Agar	20.0 g
Distilled water to make	1.0 L

PCNB is sparingly soluble in water. A fine wettable powder should be used and the medium should be agitated very thoroughly during preparation. A combination of chloramphenicol (50 mg/L) and chlortetracycline hydrochloride (50 mg/L) is more effective in inhibiting bacteria than 100 mg/L of chloramphenicol alone. Chlortetracycline hydrochloride should be added to molten, heat-sterilized base medium that has been cooled to 45° to 50°C. The pH of the medium should be adjusted to 5.6 with tartaric acid before and after autoclaving. This medium may be used to prepare pour plates or prepoured into sterile Petri dishes and allowed to solidify for use in direct plating. Do not invert plates. Incubate at 20° to 25°C for 5 to 7 days or until colonies develop. Colonies exhibiting a violet brown pigment on the reverse are counted as potential ochratoxin- and citrinin-producing strains of *P. viridicatium*. Colonies exhibiting a yellow reverse and obverse are counted as potential xanthomegnin- and viomellein-producing strains of *P. viridicatium* and *P. aurantiogriseum* (*P. cyclopium*).

PEPTONE BROTH (1.0%)

Peptone	10.0 g
Distilled water	1.0 L

Dissolve peptone in distilled water by stirring. Autoclave at 121°C for 15 min.

PHENOL RED CARBOHYDRATE BROTH*

PHENOL RED DEXTROSE BROTH*
(Difco)

PHYTONE YEAST EXTRACT (PYE) AGAR*
(BBL)

PHYTONE YEAST EXTRACT AGAR WITH STREPTOMYCIN AND CHLORAMPHENICOL

Phytone or soytone	10.0 g
Yeast extract	5.0 g
Dextrose	40.0 g
Streptomycin	0.03 g
Chloramphenicol	0.05 g
Agar	17.0 g
Distilled water	1.0 L

Suspend the ingredients listed above in distilled water, and dissolve by boiling gently. Dispense the medium into suitable containers, and autoclave at 118°C for 15 min. Final pH should be 6.6 ± 0.2.

PL AGAR

Peptone	5.0 g
Sodium chloride	5.0 g
Yeast extract	2.0 g
Mannitol	7.5 g
L-Arabinose	5.0 g
Inositol	1.0 g
Lysine	2.0 g
Bile salts No. 2	1.0 g
Phenol red	0.08 g
Agar	15.0 g
Distilled water	1.0 L

Dissolve ingredients in distilled water, and adjust the pH to 7.4. Autoclave at 115°C for 15 min.

PLATE COUNT AGAR (PCA)*

*Commercially available.

PLATE COUNT AGAR WITH ANTIBIOTIC

Plate count agar... 1.0 L
Chloramphenicol.. 100.0 mg

To 1.0 L of commercially available plate count agar add 100.0 mg of chloramphenicol. Mix thoroughly, and autoclave at 121°C for 15 min.

POLYPECTATE GEL MEDIUM

Sodium polypectate .... 70.0 g
Peptone.. 5.0 g
Dipotassium phosphate.. 5.0 g
Monopotassium phosphate .... 1.0 g
Calcium chloride·2H$_2$O.. 0.6 g
Distilled water .... 1.0 L

Source of polypectate: Raltech, the previous source for sodium polypectate, has been sold. The remaining polypectate stock that Raltech owned was sold to someone else, but it was destroyed by mistake over a year ago. Currently, there is no known source of suitable commercial polypectate for plate assays and viscosity assays.

Heat 500.0 ml of distilled water, and place all ingredients except the polypectate in a blender with the heated water to dissolve. Add the polypectate last, in small amounts per addition, with slow stirring to diminish occluded air. Adjust the pH to 7.0, and then add the remainder of the distilled water. Sterilize by autoclaving at 121°C for 15 min, temper the medium to 48°C, and then pour into sterile Petri plates.

PORK PLASMA-FIBRINOGEN OVERLAY AGAR

Grind bovine fibrinogen (BFG) fraction I (Calbiochem, San Diego) in a mortar to a fine powder, and dissolve 8.0 mg/ml in 0.05 M sodium phosphate buffer of pH 7.0 by stirring for 30 min on a magnetic stirrer. Filter the solution through Whatman No. 41 paper and filter sterilize.

Dissolve trypsin inhibitor (Soya; Sigma Chemical Co., St. Louis, MO) in 0.05 M sodium phosphate buffer of pH 7.0 at a concentration of 3 mg/ml and filter sterilize.

Obtain fresh or rehydrated commercial pork plasma-EDTA and filter sterilize.

Prepare sterile 1.4% agar in distilled water. Melt and temper the agar to 45°C prior to use.

Mix gently and thoroughly the following amounts of prewarmed (45°C) solutions to prepare the overlay agar:

Pork plasma	2.5 ml
BFG	47.5 ml
Trypsin inhibitor	0.5 ml
Agar	50.0 ml

This mixture should be kept at 45° to 50°C and used within 1 hr. Use 8.0 ml of the overlay mixture per plate of Baird-Parker agar without egg yolk but containing potassium tellurite.

POTATO DEXTROSE AGAR (PDA)*

POTATO DEXTROSE AGAR (ACIDIFIED)

As plating medium for yeasts and molds, melt previously sterilized potato dextrose agar (commercially available) in flowing steam or boiling water, cool, and acidify to pH 3.5 with sterile 10% tartaric acid solution. Mix thoroughly, and pour into plates. To preserve the solidifying properties of the agar, do not heat the medium after the addition of tartaric acid.

POTATO DEXTROSE AGAR (WITH ANTIBIOTICS)

Prepare an antibiotic solution containing 500.0 mg each of chlortetracycline HCl and chloramphenicol in 100.0 ml of sterile phosphate buffered distilled water and mix. (Not all material dissolves; therefore the suspension must be evenly dispersed before pipetting into the medium.) Add 2.0 ml of this solution per 100.0 ml of tempered potato dextrose agar, giving a final concentration in the medium of 100.0 mg/L of each of the antibiotics. After being swirled to mix, the medium is ready to use.

POTATO DEXTROSE AGAR 2% GLUCOSE 60% SUCROSE

Potato dextrose agar	39.0 g
Glucose, AR	20.0 g
Sucrose	600.0 g
Distilled water to make	1.0 L

Add potato dextrose agar to approximately 400.0 ml of distilled water, and heat while stirring until completely dissolved. Further heat the solution, and add the glucose and sucrose until all the sugar is dissolved. Make up to a total volume of 1.0 L with distilled water. Dispense the medium into smaller containers, and autoclave at 121°C for 15 min. The final a_w of this medium is 0.92.

*Commercially available.

PRE-ENRICHMENT MEDIUM (PEM)

Sodium phosphate dibasic	7.1 g
NaCl	1.0 g
Potassium chloride	1.0 g
Special peptone (Oxoid)	10.0 g
Yeast extract	20.0 g
Distilled water	1.0 L

Adjust the pH to 8.3, and sterilize by autoclaving at 121°C for 15 min. Cool the medium, and add the following filter-sterilized (0.22-μm pore size) solutions to give the final concentrations indicated per L:

Magnesium sulfate·7H$_2$O	10.0 mg
Calcium chloride	10.0 mg

PRESTON ENRICHMENT BROTH

Nutrient broth No. 2 (Oxoid)	25.0 g
Distilled water	910.0 ml
Lysed horse blood	50.0 ml
Polymyxin B	5,000 IU
Rifampicin	10.0 mg
Trimethoprim lactate	10.0 mg
Cycloheximide	100.0 mg

Dissolve the nutrient broth No. 2 in distilled water, heat with frequent agitation, and boil for approximately 1 min to dissolve completely. Autoclave at 121°C for 15 min. Cool to 50°C, and add the blood and filter-sterilized (0.22-μm filter) antibiotics.

PROTEOSE AGAR

Proteose peptone No. 3	15.0 g
Yeast extract	7.5 g
Casamino acids	5.0 g
Starch, soluble	1.0 g
K$_2$HPO$_4$	5.0 g
(NH$_4$)$_2$SO$_4$	1.5 g
Agar	15.0 g
Distilled water	1.0 L

Combine all ingredients, and heat with agitation to dissolve agar. Dispense 10-ml portions into 16- × 150-mm test tubes. Autoclave for 15 min at 121°C. The final pH should be 9.0 ± 0.2. Incline while cooling to obtain a long slant.

PURPLE CARBOHYDRATE BROTH*

R2A AGAR*

RMW AGAR*

Commercially available as Rogosa SL agar.

ROSE BENGAL CHLORAMPHENICOL (RBC) AGAR*

Commercially available from Oxoid as Rose-Bengal Chloramphenicol Agar (CM549) with a chloramphenicol supplement (SR78).

SA AGAR

Phenol red agar base	31.0 g
Soluble starch, reagent grade	10.0 g
Distilled water	1.0 L

Suspend the ingredients in distilled water, and dissolve by heating while stirring. Autoclave for 15 min at 121°C. After sterilizing and tempering, 10 mg of ampicillin (A-9393, Sigma) should be dissolved in a very small quantity of sterile distilled water and added to 1 L of the medium before pouring into sterile Petri dishes.

The presence of *A. hydrophila* group organisms can be verified by the addition of approximately 5 ml of Lugol's iodine solution to each plate.

SABOURAUD DEXTROSE AGAR*

SALMONELLA SHIGELLA (SS) AGAR*

SALT POLYMYXIN BROTH (SPB)

Trypticase (pancreatic digest of casein)	10.0 g
Yeast extract	3.0 g
Sodium chloride	20.0 g
Polymyxin B	250,000 IU
Distilled water	1.0 L

Dissolve all ingredients in distilled water. Adjust the pH to 8.8 ± 0.2, dispense into tubes or bottles, and sterilize at 115°C for 10 min.

*Commercially available.

SEA WATER AGAR (SWA)

Yeast extract	5.0 g
Peptone	5.0 g
Beef extract	3.0 g
Agar	15.0 g
Synthetic sea water	1.0 L

Dissolve the ingredients in synthetic sea water with heat while stirring. Autoclave the medium at 121°C for 15 min. The final pH should be 7.5.

SELENITE CYSTINE (SC) BROTH*

SEMISOLID BRUCELLA-FBP MEDIUM

See Brucella-FBP Agar/Broth.

SEMISOLID BRUCELLA (ALBIMI) MEDIUM

(With cysteine, glycine, or NaCl for *Campylobacter*)

Brucella broth (Gibco)	29.0 g
Agar	1.6 g
Distilled water	1.0 g

The following are added individually before sterilization:

L-Cysteine hydrochloride	0.2 g
Glycine	10.0 g
Sodium chloride	3.5 g

Dissolve the ingredients completely, adjust the pH to 7.0, and dispense 10 ml of the medium in 16- × 150-mm screw-capped tubes. Autoclave at 121°C for 15 min. Cool tubes in an upright position.

SIMMONS CITRATE AGAR*

SINGLE LAYER AGAR

Nutrient agar, standard methods agar, or tryptic soy agar (amount recommended by manufacturer to prepare 1.0 L of medium)	
Fat	50.0 g
Victoria Blue B (1:1500 aqueous solution)	200.0 ml
Distilled water	800.0 ml

*Commercially available.

Victoria Blue solution is not necessary if tributyrin is used as the fat substrate. If Victoria Blue is not used, use 1.0 L of distilled water to prepare the agar base medium. The fat in this medium may consist of tributyrin, corn oil, soybean oil, any available cooking oil, lard, tallow, or triglycerides that do not contain antioxidant or other inhibitory substances. Free fatty acids (FFA) in the fat substrates are removed as described in Section 11.32. Sterilize the fat in the autoclave for 30 min at 121°C. Sterilize the Victoria Blue solution by membrane filtration (0.45 μm). Dissolve the agar base medium in 800.0 ml of distilled water, and sterilize for 15 min at 121°C. Cool the sterile ingredients to 50°C, and mix together in a warm sterile blender for 1 min. Prepare dilutions of samples, and pour plates with 12 to 15 ml of this medium.

SKIM MILK AGAR

Standard methods agar	1.0 L
Reconstituted skim milk (10% solids)	100.0 ml

Melt standard methods agar, cool to 50°C, and add 100.0 ml of sterile skim milk. Mix well, and pour into sterile petri dishes.

SKIRROW'S AGAR

Blood agar base (Oxoid No. 2)	40.0 g
Distilled water	935.0 ml
Lysed horse blood	50.0 ml
Vancomycin	10.0 mg
Polymyxin B	2,500 IU
Trimethoprim lactate	5.0 mg

Dissolve the blood agar base in distilled water, heat while stirring, and boil for approximately 1 min to dissolve the agar completely. Autoclave at 121°C for 15 min. Cool the medium to 50°C, and add the blood and filter-sterilized (through a 0.22-μm filter) antibiotics (contained in 15 ml of distilled water). The combination of antibiotics is available commercially.

SODIUM DODECYL SULFATE POLYMYXIN SUCROSE AGAR (SDS)

Proteose peptone (Difco)	10.0 g
Beef extract (Difco)	5.0 g
Sucrose	15.0 g
Sodium chloride	20.0 g
Sodium dodecyl sulfate (sodium lauryl sulfate)	1.0 g
Bromthymol blue	0.04 g
Cresol red	0.04 g
Agar	15.0 g
Distilled water	1.0 L

Dissolve all ingredients by boiling, and dispense in 100-ml aliquots. Autoclave for 15 min at 121°C. The final pH should be 7.6 ± 0.2. The basal medium is good for 3 months if stored at room temperature. To use, melt the needed 100-ml aliquots, cool to 45° to 50°C, and add 10,000 IU of polymyxin B sulfate to each 100-ml aliquot. Pour plates immediately. Upon solidification the agar will be a red-brown color.

SODIUM LACTATE AGAR

Trypticase	10.0 g
Yeast extract	10.0 g
Sodium lactate	10.0 g
Dipotassium phosphate	0.25 g
Agar	15.0 g
Distilled water to make	1.0 L

Dissolve the ingredients in distilled water with gentle heating. Adjust the medium to pH 7.0 ± 0.2 before autoclaving for 20 min at 121°C.

SOFT AGAR GELATIN OVERLAY*
(Basal Medium)

Peptone	5.0 g
Beef extract	3.0 g
Sodium chloride	5.0 g
Manganese sulfate	0.05 g
Agar	15.0 g
Distilled water	1.0 L

Dissolve the ingredients in distilled water with gentle heating. Adjust the pH to 7.0, and autoclave at 121°C for 15 min. The soft overlay is the same as the basal medium except that 0.8% agar and 1.5% gelatin are used for the overlay.

SORBITOL-MacCONKEY AGAR*
(Difco)

SS AGAR
See Salmonella Shigella Agar

---

*Commercially available.

SS-DESOXYCHOLATE (SSDC) AGAR

SS Agar	60.0 g
Sodium desoxycholate	10.0 g
Calcium chloride	1.0 g
Distilled water	1.0 L

Combine the ingredients with distilled water, and boil while stirring for 2 to 3 min to dissolve the agar completely. Do not autoclave.

This medium is available from E. Merck AG, Darmstadt, Germany, as "*Yersinia*-Agar."

ST (*STREPTOCOCCUS THERMOPHILUS*) AGAR

Tryptone	10.0 g
Yeast extract	5.0 g
Sucrose	10.0 g
Dipotassium phosphate	2.0 g
Agar	15.0 g
Distilled water	1.0 L

Add the ingredients to distilled water, heat to dissolve the agar, and autoclave at 121°C for 15 min. The final pH should be 6.8.

STANDARD METHODS AGAR*
(Plate Count Agar)

STANDARD METHODS CASEINATE AGAR

Pancreatic digest of casein (tryptone or trypticase)	5.0 g
Yeast extract	2.5 g
Glucose	1.0 g
Agar	15.0 g
Sodium caseinate	10.0 g
Trisodium citrate hydrated (0.015 M solution)	1.0 L
Calcium chloride (1.0 M solution)	20.0 ml

Prepare a 0.015 M solution of trisodium citrate by placing 4.41 g of trisodium citrate (dihydrate) into a volumetric flask, bring to 1.0 L volume with distilled water, and mix thoroughly. Dissolve the pancreatic digest of casein, yeast extract, glucose, and agar in 500.0 ml of the 0.015 M trisodium citrate with gentle heating.

*Commercially available.

SULFITE AGAR*

SYNCASE BROTH

Casamino acids	20.0 g
Yeast extract	6.0 g
Sodium chloride	2.5 g
K_2HPO_4	8.71 g
Distilled water	1.0 L

Combine all ingredients, and adjust the pH with 0.1 N NaOH so that the value after autoclaving (15 min at 121°C) is 8.5. Note: It is normal for a precipitate to form upon standing.

SYNTHETIC SEA WATER (SW)

NaCl	24.0 g
KCl	0.7 g
$MgCl_2 \cdot 6H_2O$	5.3 g
$MgSO_4 \cdot 7H_2O$	7.0 g
$CaCl_2$	0.1 g
Distilled water	1.0 L

Suspend the ingredients in distilled water, and dissolve. Adjust the pH to 7.5 with 1 N NaOH. Dispense, and autoclave at 121°C for 15 min.

TETRATHIONATE BROTH*

TETRATHIONATE BROTH (WITHOUT IODINE)*

THERMOACIDURANS AGAR (TAA)*

THIN-LAYER ENZYME ASSAY (TEA) PLATE

Dissolve 10 mg of bovine serum albumin (BSA) or another protein substrate in 1.0 ml of distilled water. Mix 1.0 ml of this solution with 9.0 ml of distilled water in a polystyrene Petri dish that has been previously cleaned with ethanol and dried with sterile compressed air. After 1 min, decant the protein solution, wash the surface with distilled water, and blow dry. The plate may be stored at 4°C for up to 6 months. Prepare agar medium with the protein-coated Petri dish in the usual manner.

*Commercially available.

THIOGLYCOLLATE AGAR

Fluid Thioglycollate medium (commercial, dehydrated) ..   29.5 g
Agar...   20.0 g
Distilled water ....   1.0 L

Suspend the ingredients in distilled water, and heat to boiling while stirring to dissolve completely. Distribute the medium into tubes or flasks, and autoclave at 121°C for 15 min. This medium should be used within 1 week of preparation.

THIOSULFATE CITRATE BILE SALTS SUCROSE (TCBS) AGAR*

T_1N_1 AGAR/BROTH

Trypticase (pancreatic digest of casein)........................   10.0 g
Sodium chloride..   10.0 g
Agar...   15.0 g
Distilled water ....   1.0 L

Dissolve the ingredients in distilled water by bringing to a boil. Dispense in tubes, and sterilize at 121°C for 15 min. Allow to solidify in an inclined position (long slant). Final pH should be 7.2 ± 0.2. To prepare T_1N_1 broth, omit the agar.

TOLUIDINE BLUE AGAR

Nutrient broth ....   8.0 g
Sodium chloride...   5.0 g
Toluidine blue ....   0.083 g
Deoxyribonucleic acid (DNA) ....   0.3 g
Agar...   20.0 g
Distilled water ....   1.0 L

Add the DNA to cold distilled water, and heat slowly while stirring. When the DNA is in solution, add the rest of the components and sterilize by autoclaving at 121°C for 15 min.

*Commercially available.

TOLUIDINE BLUE DNA AGAR

Deoxyribonucleic acid (DNA)	0.30 g
Calcium chloride (anhydrous)	5.5 mg
NaCl	10.0 g
Agar	10.0 g
Tris (hydroxymethyl) aminomethane	6.1 g
Toluidine blue	0.083 g
Distilled water	1.0 L

Suspend the ingredients in 1.0 L of distilled water, adjust the pH to 9.0, and boil to dissolve completely. Cool to 45° to 50°C, and add 0.083 g of Toluidine Blue-O. Mix the medium, and dispense in small portions into screw-capped storage bottles. This medium need not be sterilized and can be stored at room temperature for 4 months even with several melting cycles. Prepare plates by dispensing 10-ml portions into 15- × 100-mm Petri dishes, and store melted agar at 2° to 8°C. Prior to use cut 2-mm wells in the agar plates with a metal cannula, and remove the agar plugs by aspiration.

TRIMETHYLAMINE N-OXIDE (TMAO) MEDIUM

Nutrient broth No. 2 (Oxoid CM67)	25.0 g
Yeast extract (Difco)	1.0 g
New Zealand agar (Oxoid)	2.0 g
Trimethylamine N-oxide (Sigma)	1.0 g
Distilled water	1.0 L

Dissolve the nutrient broth, yeast extract, and TMAO in the distilled water. Add the agar, and heat to dissolve. Dispense 4 ml in 13- × 100-mm screw cap tubes, and autoclave at 121°C for 15 min. Cool the tubes in an upright position, and store under refrigeration.

TRIPLE SUGAR IRON (TSI) AGAR*

TRYPTICASE NOVOBIOCIN (TN) AGAR/BROTH

Trypticase soy broth	30.0 g
Bile salts No. 3	1.5 g
Dipotassium phosphate	1.5 g
Novobiocin	20.0 mg
Distilled water	1.0 L

*Commercially available.

Dissolve the ingredients, except novobiocin, in distilled water by heating while stirring. Autoclave the medium for 15 min at 121°C. Adjust the pH to 7.2 ± 0.2. Prepare a stock solution of novobiocin in distilled water and filter sterilize. Add enough of the novobiocin solution to equal 20.0 mg per L of medium.

To prepare TN agar, include 15.0 g of agar per L of medium.

TRYPTICASE PEPTONE GLUCOSE YEAST EXTRACT BROTH (BUFFERED)

(For Clostridium perfringens)

Trypticase or tryptone	50.0 g
Peptone	5.0 g
Yeast extract	20.0 g
Glucose	4.0 g
Disodium phosphate	5.0 g
Sodium thioglycollate	1.0 g
Distilled water	1.0 L

Dissolve the ingredients in distilled water, adjust the pH to 7.3, and dispense 15 ml into 20- × 150-mm culture tubes. Sterilize the dispensed medium by autoclaving at 121°C for 8 min (15 min for larger volumes), and refrigerate until used.

TRYPTICASE PEPTONE GLUCOSE YEAST EXTRACT (TPGY) BROTH
and
TPGY WITH TRYPSIN (TPGYT)

Trypticase or tryptone	50.0 g
Peptone	5.0 g
Yeast extract	20.0 g
Glucose	4.0 g
Sodium thioglycollate	1.0 g
Distilled water	1.0 L

Dissolve solid ingredients in distilled water, adjust the pH to 7.0, and dispense into tubes in appropriate volumes. Sterilize the dispensed medium at 121°C for 8 min (15 min for large volumes), and refrigerate until used.

If trypsin is to be added, prepare a 1.5% aqueous solution of trypsin. Sterilize by filtration through a Millipore (or compatible) 0.45-μm filter, and refrigerate until needed. After steaming TPGY broth to drive off oxygen and cooling, add the trypsin to the TPGY broth immediately before inoculating to give a final concentration of 0.1%.

TRYPTICASE SOY AGAR (TSA)/BROTH (TSB)*

TRYPTICASE SOY AGAR PLUS 3% NaCl (TSA-NaCl)

Trypticase peptone	15.0 g
Phytone peptone	5.0 g
NaCl	5.0 g
Agar	15.0 g
Distilled water	1.0 L

Combine the ingredients, and heat with agitation to dissolve the agar. Boil the medium for 1 min and then dispense into suitable tubes or flasks. Autoclave for 15 min at 121°C. The final pH should be 7.3 ± 0.2.

TRYPTICASE SOY AGAR-YEAST EXTRACT (TSA-YE)

Trypticase soy agar (dehydrated, TSA, BBL)	40.0 g
Yeast extract	6.0 g
Distilled water	1.0 L

Suspend the dehydrated TSA and yeast extract in 1.0 L of distilled water, and stir while heating to dissolve completely. Autoclave at 121°C for 15 min, and then temper the medium to 45° to 50°C before pouring into sterile Petri dishes.

TRYPTICASE SOY BROTH-YEAST EXTRACT (TSB-YE)

Trypticase soy broth (dehydrated, TSB, BBL)	30.0 g
Yeast extract	6.0 g
Distilled water	1.0 L

Suspend the dehydrated TSB and yeast extract in 1.0 L of distilled water, and stir while heating to dissolve completely. Dispense into tubes, and autoclave at 121°C for 15 min.

TRYPTICASE SOY POLYMYXIN BROTH

Preparation A:

Trypticase peptone	17.0 g
Phytone peptone	3.0 g
Sodium chloride	5.0 g
Dipotassium phosphate	2.5 g
Dextrose	2.5 g
Distilled water	1.0 L

*Commercially available.

Preparation B - Polymyxin B sulfate:

This selective agent is obtainable in sterile powdered form (500,000 units, i.e., 50 mg per vial) from Pfizer, Inc. To use, aseptically add 33.3 ml of sterile distilled water with a sterile syringe to give a 0.15% solution. Mix to dissolve the powder, and store at 4°C until used.

Suspend Preparation A ingredients in water, and mix thoroughly. Warm the mixture slightly if necessary to complete the solution. Dispense 15.0 ml into 20- × 150-mm culture tubes, and sterilize by autoclaving for 15 min at 121°C. Just before use, add 0.1 ml of sterile 0.15% polymyxin B sulfate solution (Preparation B) to each tube and mix thoroughly.

TRYPTICASE-SOY-SHEEP BLOOD AGAR

Prepare trypticase (tryptic) soy agar, and cool to 48°C in a waterbath. Add 5.0 ml of sterile defibrinated sheep blood for each 100.0 ml of medium, mix well, and dispense 18.0 ml into 15- × 100-mm culture dishes. Allow plates to dry for 24 to 48 hr at room temperature before use.

TRYPTICASE-SOY-SHEEP BLOOD (TSB) AGAR
(For *Clostridium perfringens*)

Trypticase peptone	15.0 g
Phytone peptone	5.0 g
NaCl	5.0 g
Agar	15.0 g
Distilled water	1.0 L

Suspend the ingredients in distilled water, mix thoroughly, and heat to boiling while stirring for 1 min. Autoclave the medium for 15 min at 118° to 121°C, and cool to approximately 45°C in a waterbath. Final pH should be 7.3 ± 0.1. Add 50.0 ml of defibrinated sheep blood to each L of base medium. Thoroughly mix and dispense 18 to 20 ml in 15- × 100-mm petri dishes. Commercially prepared plates are satisfactory.

TRYPTIC SOY AGAR/BROTH*

*Commercially available.

TRYPTIC SOY AGAR-MAGNESIUM SULFATE (TSAM)
(For *E. coli*)

Tryptone	15.0 g
Soytone	5.0 g
Sodium chloride	5.0 g
$MgSO_4 \cdot 7H_2O$	1.5 g
Agar	15.0 g
Distilled water	1.0 L

Dissolve by boiling, and autoclave at 121°C for 15 min. Temper the medium to 50°C. The final pH should be 7.3. Pour 20 ml per plate, and allow to dry thoroughly. The medium can be prepared from commercial tryptic soy agar by the addition of 1.5 g $MgSO_4 \cdot 7H_2O$ to 1.0 L of medium. The medium may be stored for 4 weeks at 4°C.

TRYPTIC SOY AGAR-MAGNESIUM SULFATE-NaCl (TSAMS)
(For *Vibrio*)

Tryptone	50.0 g
Soytone	5.0 g
Sodium chloride	30.0 g
$MgSO_4 \cdot 7H_2O$	1.5 g
Agar	15.0 g
Distilled water	1.0 L

Dissolve by boiling, and autoclave at 121°C for 15 min. Temper the medium to 50°C. The final pH should be 7.3. Pour 20 ml per plate, and allow to dry thoroughly. The medium can be prepared from commercial tryptic soy agar by the addition of 25 g sodium chloride and 1.5 g $MgSO_4 \cdot 7H_2O$ to 1.0 L of medium. The medium may be stored for 4 weeks at 4°C.

TRYPTIC SOY-FAST GREEN AGAR (TSFA)

Trypticase soy agar (commercial, dehydrated)	40.0 g
Fast Green FCF (CI No. 42053)	0.25 g
Distilled water	1.0 L

Suspend the ingredients in distilled water, and heat to boiling while stirring to dissolve completely. Dispense the medium into flasks, and autoclave for 15 min at 121°C. Temper the sterile medium to 50°C, and adjust the pH to 7.3. Pour 20 ml of medium per plate, and allow to dry thoroughly. This medium may be stored for 4 weeks at 4°C. Fast Green FCF is available from Sigma (F7252).

TRYPTONE BILE AGAR*

TRYPTONE BROTH

Tryptone or trypticase	10.0 g
Dextrose	5.0 g
Dipotassium phosphate	1.25 g
Yeast extract	1.0 g
Bromcresol purple (2% alcoholic solution)	2.0 ml
Distilled water	1.0 L

Combine the ingredients with distilled water, and dissolve with gentle heat if necessary. To prepare a 2% bromcresol purple solution, add 2.0 g of bromcresol purple to 10.0 ml of ethyl alcohol, and dilute to 100.0 ml with distilled water. Add 2.0 ml of the solution to each L of medium. Dispense 10-ml portions into 20- × 150-mm screw-capped culture tubes, and autoclave for 20 min at 121°C. Do not exhaust before using.

TRYPTONE (1%) BROTH FOR INDOLE*

TRYPTONE GLUCOSE EXTRACT AGAR*

TRYPTONE GLUCOSE YEAST AGAR*
(Plate Count Agar)

TRYPTONE-GLUCOSE-YEAST EXTRACT AGAR*
(Plate Count Agar)

TRYPTONE PHOSPHATE-BRAIN HEART INFUSION-YEAST EXTRACT AGAR (TPBY)

Tryptone	20.0 g
NaCl	5.0 g
K_2HPO_4	2.0 g
KH_2PO_4	2.0 g
Brain heart infusion	1.0 g
Yeast extract	1.0 g
Tween 80	1.5 ml
Oxgall	0.5 g
Agar	15.0 g
Distilled water	1.0 L

*Commercially available.

Combine ingredients, and boil with stirring to dissolve the agar. Adjust the final pH to 7.0 ± 0.2, and autoclave for 15 min at 121°C.

TRYPTONE PHOSPHATE BROTH

Tryptone	20.0 g
Tween 80	1.5 ml
K_2HPO_4	2.0 g
KH_2PO_4	2.0 g
NaCl	5.0 g
Distilled water	1.0 L

Dissolve the ingredients in distilled water, and sterilize by autoclaving for 15 min at 121°C. Adjust the final pH to 7.0 ± 0.2.

TRYPTOPHAN BROTH

Same as Tryptone Broth.

TRYPTOSE AGAR*

TRYPTOSE CYCLOSERINE DEXTROSE AGAR

Tryptose	15.0 g
Soytone	5.0 g
Yeast extract	5.0 g
Ferric ammonium citrate	1.0 g
Agar	20.0 g
Distilled water	1.0 L

Dissolve the ingredients in distilled water, and adjust the pH to 7.6 ± 0.2. Autoclave the medium for 10 min at 121°C, and cool to approximately 50°C in a waterbath. To each L of cooled medium add 10.0 ml of a filter-sterilized solution of 4.0% D-cycloserine to give a final concentration of 400 μg/ml.

TRYPTOSE-SULFITE CYCLOSERINE (TSC) AGAR

Tryptose	15.0 g
Soytone	5.0 g
Yeast extract	5.0 g
Sodium bisulfite (meta)	1.0 g
Ferric ammonium citrate	1.0 g
Agar	20.0 g
Distilled water	1.0 L

*Commercially available.

Dissolve the ingredients in distilled water, adjust the pH to 7.6 ± 0.2, and autoclave the medium for 10 min at 121°C. To each L of autoclaved medium cooled to 50°C, add 10.0 ml of a 4.0% filter-sterilized solution of D-cycloserine to give a final concentration of approximately 400 μg per ml. Also add 80.0 ml of a sterile 50% egg yolk in saline emulsion per L of medium, with the exception of medium to be used to overlay the plates. Egg yolk enrichment 50% may be obtained from Difco Laboratories, Detroit, MI. Dispense the medium in standard Petri dishes for surface plating. Before use, air dry the plates at room temperature for 24 hr or until the surface of the agar is somewhat dry. Prepare plates fresh each time they are to be used. Note: SFP agar base available commercially from Difco Laboratories is the same as the above basal medium.

TYROSINE AGAR

Preparation A:

Prepare nutrient agar, and dispense 100.0 ml into bottles. Autoclave 15 min at 121°C, and cool to 48°C in a waterbath.

Preparation B:

Add 0.5 g of L-tyrosine to a 20- × 150-mm culture tube, and suspend in 10.0 ml of distilled water using a Vortex mixer. Sterilize the suspension by autoclaving for 15 min at 121°C.

Mix Preparation A (100.0 ml) with sterile Preparation B (10.0 ml), and aseptically dispense 3.5 ml of complete medium into sterile 13- × 100-mm tubes. Slant tubes, and cool rapidly to prevent separation of the tyrosine.

UREA BROTH*

UREA R(APID) BROTH*

UVM (UNIVERSITY OF VERMONT) BROTH*

Commercially available from BBL; however, the commercial formulation may deviate from the original formula.

VEAL INFUSION AGAR AND BROTH*

*Commercially available.

VIBRIO PARAHAEMOLYTICUS SUCROSE AGAR (VPSA)

Tryptose	5.0 g
Tryptone	5.0 g
Yeast extract	7.0 g
Sucrose	10.0 g
Sodium chloride	30.0 g
Bile salts No. 3	1.5 g
Bromthymol blue	0.025 g
Agar	15.0 g
Distilled water	1.0 L

Dissolve ingredients and sterilize by boiling. Temper the medium to 50°C, and adjust the pH to 8.6. Pour 20 ml per plate, and allow to dry thoroughly. The medium may be stored for 4 weeks at 4°C.

VIOLET RED BILE AGAR (VRBA)*

Modification:

Add 1% glucose for pour-plate enumeration of total *Enterobacteriaceae* in brined vegetables.

WAGATSUMA AGAR

Peptone	10.0 g
Yeast extract	3.0 g
Dipotassium phosphate	5.0 g
Sodium chloride	70.0 g
Mannitol	10.0 g
Crystal violet	0.001 g
Agar	15.0 g
Distilled water	1.0 L

Suspend ingredients in distilled water, and dissolve by boiling gently. Adjust the pH to 8.0. Do not autoclave. Wash rabbit or human erythrocytes three times in physiological saline, and reconstitute to original blood volume. Add 2.0 ml of washed erythrocytes to 100.0 ml of agar cooled to 50°C just prior to pouring into sterile Petri dishes.

WANG'S TRANSPORT/STORAGE MEDIUM

Brucella broth	28.0 g
Agar	4.0 g
Defibrinated sheep blood	100.0 ml
Distilled water	900.0 ml

*Commercially available.

Dissolve the Brucella broth and agar in distilled water, and boil for 1 min to dissolve the agar completely. Autoclave at 121°C for 15 min, and cool to 50°C before adding the blood. Lysed horse blood may be used in lieu of sheep blood; 50 ml of horse blood and an additional 50 ml of sterile distilled water will replace the sheep blood. Dispense in 4.0-ml portions in sterile 15- × 125-mm screw-capped test tubes, and solidify in an upright position.

WESLEY BROTH

Basal medium:

Tryptose	20.0 g
Yeast extract	2.5 g
NaCl	5.0 g
Ferrous sulfate	0.25 g
Sodium metabisulfite	0.25 g
Sodium pyruvate	0.25 g
Bicine	10.0 g
Agar	1.0 g
Distilled water	1.0 L

Supplements:

Rifampin	25.0 mg
Cefsulodin	6.25 mg
Polymyxin B sulfate	20,000 IU
Alkaline hematin solution	20.0 mg

The basal medium is prepared by dissolving the listed ingredients in distilled water. Heat to boiling to dissolve the agar completely, and then autoclave at 121°C for 15 min. Temper the basal medium to 50°C.

Dissolve the rifampin, cefsulodin, and polymyxin B sulfate in a minimal amount of distilled water, and filter sterilize. Add each antimicrobial to the basal medium to achieve the concentration listed above. Alkaline hematin solution is prepared by dissolving 32.0 mg of bovine hemin (Sigma) in 10 ml of 0.15 N NaOH followed by autoclaving for 30 min at 5.0 lbs/in^2. Add 6.25 ml of the cooled alkaline hematin solution to each L of the basal medium to achieve 20.0 mg of hemin per L.

The medium should be used immediately or stored overnight in the dark under refrigeration before use.

XYLOSE-LYSINE-DESOXYCHOLATE AGAR (XLD)*

*Commercially available.

Y-1 CELL MEDIUM

Ham's F-10 medium with glutamine and NaHCO$_3$ .... 85.0 ml
Fetal bovine serum, sterile virus-screened,
    mycoplasma free .... 15.0 ml
Penicillin G-streptomycin stock solution...................... 1.0 ml

Penicillin G-streptomycin stock solution:

Penicillin G.. 500,000.0 IU
Streptomycin.. 500,000.0 μg
Distilled water... 100.0 ml

Prepare the antibiotic stock solution by dissolving the antibiotics in water and sterilizing by filtration. Store at 5°C until needed to prepare the Y-1 Cell Medium.

YERSINIA AGAR*
See SS-desoxycholate (SSDC) agar.

YERSINIA SELECTIVE AGAR*

62.4 ALPHABETICAL LISTING OF REAGENTS, DILUENTS, AND INDICATORS

This section contains the formulae for preparation of all reagents, diluents, and indicators used throughout this book, with the exception of a few complex preparations listed in specific chapters. Reagents, diluents, and indicators that are commercially available are indicated by asterisks. Reagents should be prepared using chemicals of only the highest purity and double-distilled water. The reagents may be heat-sterilized or sterilized by membrane filtration when necessary.

ABTS SUBSTRATE SOLUTION

Stock solution 1 (0.5 M hydrogen peroxide):

Hydrogen peroxide, 30%... 5.7 ml

Add double-distilled water to make 100.0 ml. Store in refrigerator.

*Commercially available.

Stock solution 2 (40 mM ABTS):

2,2′-azino-di-(3-ethyl benzthiazoline-6-sulfonate) (ABTS)   0.54 g

Add double-distilled water to make 25.0 ml.

0.05 M citric acid, pH 4.0:

Citric acid (monohydrate) .... 9.6 g

Dissolve citric acid in 900.0 ml of double-distilled water. Adjust pH to 4.0 with 6 M NaOH, and dilute to 1.0 L. Store in refrigerator.

Substrate solution:

Stock solution 1 .... 0.24 ml
Stock solution 2 .... 1.0 ml

Add stock solutions 1 and 2 to 90.0 ml of 0.05 M citric acid, and then bring volume to 100.0 ml. Prepare fresh on day of use.

Caution: Substrate solution is light sensitive. Protect from light as much as possible.

ALPHA-NAPHTHOL SOLUTION

Dissolve 5.0 g of fresh α-Naphthol in 100.0 ml of 99% isopropyl alcohol. Store in brown bottles under refrigeration.

ANDRADE'S INDICATOR

Acid fuchsin.. 2.0 g
Sodium hydroxide, 1 N.. 160.0 ml
Distilled water.. 1.0 L

Dissolve the acid fuchsin in the distilled water, and add the sodium hydroxide. If the fuchsin is not sufficiently decolorized after several hours, add an additional 1 to 2 ml of alkali. The dye content of each lot of acid fuchsin varies, and the amount of alkali to use with each lot should be specified on the label. The reagent improves somewhat on aging and may be prepared in sufficient quantity to last for several years.

0.1 M BICARBONATE BUFFER, pH 9.6

Na_2CO_3 .... 1.59 g
$NaHCO_3$... 2.93 g
Distilled water.. 1.0 L

Dissolve ingredients in distilled water, and store at room temperature for not more than 2 weeks.

BRILLIANT GREEN DYE SOLUTION, 1.0%

Brilliant green dye..	1.0 g
Distilled water (sterile)...	100.0 ml

Dissolve 1.0 g of brilliant green dye in sterile distilled water, and then dilute to 100.0 ml. Before use, test all batches of the dye for toxicity with known positive and negative test microorganisms.

BROMCRESOL PURPLE DYE SOLUTION, 0.2%

Bromcresol purple dye	0.2 g
Distilled water (sterile)...	100.0 ml

Dissolve 0.2 g of bromcresol purple dye in sterile distilled water, and then dilute to 100.0 ml.

BUTTERFIELD'S PHOSPHATE BUFFERED DILUTION WATER

See Phosphate Buffer (Butterfield).

CALF THYMUS DNA (10 mg/ml)

Purified calf thymus DNA.......................................	1.0 g
Distilled water	100.0 ml

Combine ingredients, and stir several hours to dissolve. The solution should be viscous. Sonicate until average molecular weight is 500 to 800 base pairs. Begin by sonicating for 5 min in 10- to 30-second bursts. Monitor the molecular weight by agarose gel electrophoresis with appropriate size standards. Dispense into screw-capped tubes (1 ml/tube). Store frozen at 20°C or lower.

CATALASE TEST

Flood plates with 3.0% hydrogen peroxide solution. Observe for bubble formation using a hand lens or wide-field binocular microscope. Colonies exhibiting no evidence of gas formation are catalase negative. Alternative method: Transfer a loopful of colony to a slide, mix with 2.0 to 5.0% hydrogen peroxide, and observe as above.

0.05 M CITRIC ACID (pH 4.0)

Citric acid (monohydrate) .... 9.6 g
Double-distilled water to make .... 1.0 L

Dissolve citric acid in 900.0 ml of double-distilled water. Adjust the pH to 4.0 with 6 M NaOH, and dilute to 1.0 L. Store at 4°C.

COAGULASE PLASMA CONTAINING EDTA*

CYTOCHROME OXIDASE REAGENT

N,N,N,N-tetramethyl-p-phenylenediamine .... 5.0 g
Distilled water .... 1.0 L

Combine ingredients, and store in dark glass bottle at 5° to 10°C. Storage life is 14 days. To perform test, add 0.3 ml of the reagent to an 18-hr blood agar base slant. Positive reaction is development of a blue color within 1 min.

DENHARDT'S SOLUTION

Ficoll (M.W. ~ 400,000) .... 5.0 g
Polyvinyl pyrrolidone (average M.W. 360,000) .... 5.0 g
Bovine serum albumin (nuclease-free) .... 5.0 g
Distilled water to make .... 100.0 ml

Combine all ingredients, and filter sterilize. Store in small aliquots at −20°C.

DIASTASE STOCK SOLUTION

Diastase (Sigma No. A6880 or equivalent) .... 10.0 g
Tris buffer 1.0 M, pH 7.0 .... 100.0 ml

Warm the Tris buffer to room temperature, and then dissolve the enzyme in the buffer, warming to 35°C if necessary. Filter sterilize the solution using a 0.45-μm membrane filter, and dispense into test tubes in 1- or 2-ml volumes. Store up to 1 week at 4° to 6°C or up to 3 months at −18°C.

*Commercially available.

DULBECCO'S PHOSPHATE-BUFFERED SALINE (DPBS)

NaCl	8.0 g
KCl	200.0 mg
Na_2HPO_4	1.15 g
KH_2PO_4	200.0 mg
$CaCl_2$	100.0 mg
$MgCl_2 \cdot 6H_2O$	100.0 mg
Distilled water	1.0 L

Combine ingredients, and dissolve in distilled water. Sterilize by filtration. Final pH should be 7.2.

DULBECCO'S PHOSPHATE-BUFFERED SALINE (CALCIUM- AND MAGNESIUM-FREE)

NaCl	8.0 g
KCl	200.0 mg
Na_2HPO_4	1.15 g
KH_2PO_4	200.0 mg
Distilled water	1.0 L

Combine ingredients, and dissolve in distilled water. Sterilize by filtration.

0.5 M EDTA

Na_2EDTA	186.12 g
Distilled water	1.0 L

Dissolve in 800 to 900 ml of distilled water. Adjust the pH to 8.0 with 10 N NaOH, and bring the volume to 1.0 L with distilled water.

ELISA (ENZYME-LINKED IMMUNOSORBENT ASSAY) BUFFER

Bovine serum albumin	1.0 g
Sodium chloride	8.0 g
KH_2PO_4	0.2 g
Na_2HPO_4	2.9 g
Potassium chloride	0.2 g
Distilled water	1.0 L

Dissolve ingredients in distilled water, adjust pH to 7.4, and add 0.5 ml of Tween 20. Store frozen, and thaw before use.

FORMALINIZED PHYSIOLOGICAL SALINE SOLUTION

Formaldehyde solution (36% to 38%)	6.0 ml
NaCl	8.5 g
Distilled water	1.0 L

Dissolve 8.5 g of NaCl in 1.0 L of distilled water, and autoclave for 15 min at 121°C. Cool to room temperature, and add 6.0 ml of formaldehyde solution. Do not autoclave after the addition of formaldehyde.

GELATINASE SOLUTION, 5%

Gelatinase	5.0 g
Distilled water	100.0 ml

Suspend gelatinase in distilled water, centrifuge for 10 min at 9500 rpm, and then sterilize by filtration through a 0.45-μm membrane. Dispense 100-ml portions into sterile bottles.

GEL PHOSPHATE BUFFER

Gelatin	2.0 g
Na_2HPO_4	4.0 g
Distilled water	1.0 L

Dissolve ingredients by heating gently in 800.0 ml of distilled water. Adjust the pH to 6.2 with HCl. Add the remaining water (200.0 ml minus the volume of HCl added), and sterilize at 121°C for 20 min.

HANK'S PHOSPHATE-BUFFERED SALINE

(Calcium- and Magnesium-free)

NaCl	8.0 g
KCl	400.0 mg
$Na_2HPO_4 \cdot 7H_2O$	90.0 mg
KH_2PO_4	60.0 mg
Glucose	1.0 g
$NaHCO_3$	350.0 mg
Distilled water	1.0 L

Dissolve all ingredients in distilled water, and sterilize by filtration.

HORSERADISH PEROXIDASE (HRP)

(Color Development Solution)

Solution A:

4-chloro-1-naphthol	60.0 μg
Methanol (ice cold)	20.0 ml

Solution A should be stored in the dark.

Solution B:

Tris buffered saline (TBS)	100.0 ml
30% H_2O_2	60.0 μl

Solution B should be prepared just before use.
Combine Solutions A (ice cold) and B (room temperature), and use within 10 min on antibody-soaked filters (10 ml/HGMF).

HORSERADISH PEROXIDASE (HRP)-PROTEIN A CONJUGATE

Same as Protein A Peroxidase Conjugate.

HYBRIDIZATION MIXTURE B

Distilled water	28.9 ml
20X standard saline citrate (SSC)	15.0 ml
50X Denhardt's solution	5.0 ml
0.5 M EDTA, pH 8.0	0.1 ml

Combine the above ingredients and dissolve. Final volume is 49 ml.

HYDROCHLORIC ACID (1 N)

Hydrochloric acid (concentrated)	86.0 ml
Distilled water to make	1.0 L

INDOLE OXIDANT-ACCELERATED REAGENT

Solution A:

4-dimethylaminobenzaldehyde	2.5 g
Ethanol (95%)	90.0 ml
Concentrated HCl	10.0 ml

Solution A can be stored for 4 weeks at 4°C if protected from light.

Solution B:

Potassium persulfate	1.0 g
Distilled water	100.0 ml

Solution B can be stored for 3 months at 4°C.
Mix equal volumes of Solution A and Solution B just before use.

(KOH) FOR VOGES-PROSKAUER (VP) REACTION*

KOVAC'S REAGENT (INDOLE)

p-Dimethylaminobenzaldehyde	5.0 g
Amyl alcohol	75.0 ml
Hydrochloric acid (concentrated)	25.0 ml

Dissolve p-dimethylaminobenzaldehyde in the amyl alcohol, and then slowly add the hydrochloric acid. To test for indole, add 0.2 to 0.3 ml of reagent to 5.0 ml of a 48-hr culture of bacteria in tryptone broth. A dark red color in the surface layer constitutes a positive test for indole.

LEAD ACETATE PAPER STRIP

Soak a filter paper strip (5- × 70-mm) in saturated lead acetate solution. Dry and sterilize the filter paper strip in an oven at 70°C for 2 to 3 hr.

LUGOL'S IODINE SOLUTION

Iodine	1.0 g
Potassium iodide	2.0 g
Distilled water	300.0 ml

LYSIS MIXTURES C AND D

Mixture C:

10 N NaOH (400.0 g/L)	50.0 ml
5.0 M NaCl (292.25 g/L)	300.0 ml
Distilled water	650.0 ml

*Commercially available.

Mixture D:

2.0 M Tris-HCl buffer, pH 7.0	50.0 ml
5.0 M NaCl (292.25 g/L)	400.0 ml
Distilled water	550.0 ml

MacFARLAND STANDARDS

Make suspensions of barium sulfate as follows:

1. Prepare v/v 1.0% solution of sulfuric acid.
2. Prepare w/v 1.0% solution of barium chloride.
3. Prepare 10 standards as follows:

MacFarland Standard No.	1% Barium Chloride (ml)	1% Sulfuric Acid (ml)	Approximate Bacterial Suspension $\times$ 10^6/ml
1	0.1	9.9	300
2	0.2	9.8	600
3	0.3	9.7	900
4	0.4	9.6	1200
5	0.5	9.5	1500
6	0.6	9.4	1800
7	0.7	9.3	2100
8	0.8	9.2	2400
9	0.9	9.1	2700
10	1.0	9.0	3000

4. Seal about 3 ml of each standard in a small test tube. Select tubes carefully for uniformity of absorbance.

METHYL RED INDICATOR FOR MR TEST

Methyl red	0.10 g
Alcohol, 95% (ethanol)	300.0 ml
Distilled water to bring volume to	500.0 ml

Dissolve methyl red in 300.0 ml of ethanol, and add distilled water to make a total volume of 500.0 ml. Incubate test cultures 5 days at 30°C. Alternatively, incubate at 37°C for 48 hr. Add 5 or 6 drops of reagent to cultures. Do not perform tests on cultures incubated for less than 48 hr. If results are equivocal, repeat tests on cultures incubated for 4 or 5 days. Duplicated tests should be incubated at 22° to 25°C.

NESSLER'S REAGENT*

NITRATE REDUCTION REAGENTS

Method 1

Solution A:

Sulfanilic acid	0.5 g
Glacial acetic acid	30.0 ml
Distilled water	120.0 ml

Solution B:

N (1-naphthyl) ethylenediamine dihydrochloride (Marshal's reagent)†	0.2 g
Glacial acetic acid	30.0 ml
Distilled water	120.0 ml

†Cleve's acid (5-amino-2 naphthalene sulfonic acid) may be substituted for Marshal's reagent.

To 3.0 ml of an 18-hr culture in indole-nitrate broth, add 2 drops of Solution A and 2 drops of Solution B. A red violet color that develops within 10 minutes indicates that nitrate has been reduced to nitrite. If the reaction is negative, examine for residual nitrate since conceivably the nitrite may have been reduced to another state. Add a few grains of powdered zinc. If a red violet color does not develop, nitrate has been reduced. Perform tests on uninoculated medium as a control.

Method 2

Solution A:

Sulfanilic acid	2.0 g
Glacial acetic acid	60.0 ml
Distilled water	150.0 ml

Solution B:

α-Naphthol	1.0 g
Absolute alcohol	200.0 ml

Add 0.2 ml of Solution A followed by 0.2 ml of Solution B to a culture incubated 24 to 48 hr in nitrate broth. Development of an orange color within 10 min indicates that nitrate has been reduced to nitrite.

*Commercially available.

NITRATE REDUCTION REAGENTS
(For *Campylobacter*)

Solution A:

Glacial acetic acid	286.0 ml
Distilled water	714.0 ml
Sulfanilic acid	7.01 g

Slowly add the glacial acetic acid to the distilled water. Mix carefully. Add the sulfanilic acid, and mix well to dissolve. Store under refrigeration.

Solution B:

Glacial acetic acid	286.0 ml
Distilled water	714.0 ml
Dimethyl-α-naphthylamine	5.01 ml

Slowly add the glacial acetic acid to the distilled water. Mix carefully. Add the dimethyl-α-naphthylamine, and mix well to dissolve. Store under refrigeration.

O157 MONOCLONAL ANTIBODY SOLUTION
(*E. coli* O157)

E. coli O157 ascitic fluid	10.0 µl
Tris buffered saline (TBS) with 1% gelatin	11.0 ml
Horseradish peroxidase (HRP)-protein A conjugate	3.0 µl

Dispense 10 µl of *E. coli* O157 ascitic fluid (National Research Council, Ottawa, Ontario, Canada) into 1.0 ml of TBS 1% gelatin. Add 3.0 µl HRP-protein A conjugate, and stir the mixture at 4°C for 1 hr. Dilute to 10.0 ml with TBS 1% gelatin. This amount is sufficient for one hydrophobic grid membrane filter (HGMF).

OXIDASE REAGENT
(Kovac's Modification)

Tetramethyl-p-phenylenediamine dihydrochloride	50.0 mg
Distilled water	5.0 ml

Dissolve powder in distilled water. Store up to 1 week at 4°C in dark brown container or covered tube to protect from light.

PENICILLIN-STREPTOMYCIN SOLUTION
(Antibiotic Concentrate)

Penicillin G	500,000.0 IU
Streptomycin	500,000.0 μg
Distilled water	100.0 ml

Dissolve the antibiotics in distilled water, and sterilize by filtration. Store at 5°C.

PENICILLIN-STREPTOMYCIN-GENTAMICIN SULFATE SOLUTION

Penicillin G	500,000.0 IU
Streptomycin	500,000.0 μg
Gentamicin sulfate	500,000.0 μg
Distilled water	100.0 ml

Dissolve the antibiotics in distilled water, and sterilize by filtration through a 0.20-μm membrane. Store at 5°C.

PEPTONE/TWEEN 80 DILUENT (PT)

Peptone	1.0 g
Tween 80	10.0 g
Distilled water	1.0 L

Suspend the ingredients in distilled water, and heat if necessary to dissolve completely. Dispense the diluent into bottles in desired volumes, and autoclave 15 min at 121°C.

PEPTONE TWEEN SALT DILUENT (PTS)

Peptone	1.0 g
Tween 80	10.0 g
Sodium chloride	30.0 g
Distilled water	1.0 L

Dissolve ingredients in distilled water, and dispense into bottles of desired volume. Autoclave 15 min at 121°C.

PEPTONE WATER DILUENT (0.1%)

Peptone	1.0 g
Distilled water	1.0 L

Dissolve peptone in distilled water. Adjust pH to 7.0 ± 0.1. Prepare dilution blanks with this solution, dispensing a sufficient quantity to allow for loss during autoclaving. Autoclave at 121°C for 15 min.

PHOSPHATE BUFFER (BUTTERFIELD)

Stock solution:

KH_2PO_4	34.0 g
Distilled water...	500.0 ml

Combine the above ingredients, and adjust the pH to 7.2 with about 175 ml 1 N sodium hydroxide solution; dilute to 1.0 L. Sterilize at 121°C for 15 min, and store in refrigerator.

Diluent:

Dilute 1.25 ml of stock solution to 1.0 L with distilled water. Prepare dilution blanks in suitable containers. Sterilize at 121°C for 15 min.

PHOSPHATE BUFFERED SALINE (PBS)*

PHOSPHATE BUFFERED SALINE (PBS)
(For *Clostridium perfringens*)

Sodium phosphate (dibasic)......................................	8.09 g
Potassium phosphate (monobasic)	2.44 g
NaCl..	4.25 g
Double-distilled water to make	1.0 L

Combine the ingredients, and adjust the pH to 7.2. Store at 4°C. The addition of 0.1 g of thiomersal (merthiolate) per L is recommended unless sediment from feces is to be cultured.

PHOSPHATE BUFFERED SALINE-MERTHIOLATE 0.01% (PBS-M)

Na_2HPO_4...	8.09 g
KH_2PO_4	2.44 g
NaCl..	4.25 g
Merthiolate	0.1 g
Double-distilled water to make	1.0 L

*Commercially available.

Dissolve ingredients in double-distilled water to make a total volume of 1.0 liter. Adjust the pH to 7.2.

PHOSPHATE BUFFERED SALINE-MERTHIOLATE, 0.01%; GELATIN, 0.3% (PBS-M-GEL)

Gelatin..	3.0 g
Phosphate buffered saline-merthiolate (PBS-M)	1.0 L

Dissolve ingredients in buffer, and adjust the pH to 7.2. Filter through a 0.45-μm membrane.

PHOSPHATE BUFFERED SALINE-MERTHIOLATE, 0.01%; RABBIT SERUM ALBUMIN, 0.5% (PBS-M-RSA)

Rabbit serum albumin...	5.0 g
Phosphate buffered saline-merthiolate (PBS-M)	1.0 L

Dissolve ingredients in buffer, and adjust the pH to 7.2. Filter through a 0.45-μm membrane.

PHYSIOLOGICAL SALINE SOLUTION 0.85% (STERILE)

NaCl..	8.5 g
Distilled water	1.0 L

Dissolve NaCl in distilled water, and autoclave for 15 min at 121°C. Cool to room temperature.

POLYSACCHARIDE PRECIPITANT

Dissolve 1.0 g hexadecyltrimethylammoniumbromide in 100.0 ml of water. Solution may be sterilized by autoclaving if desired. Flood plates with the solution. Clear zones indicative of pectic enzymes should be visible within 15 min.

POTASSIUM HYDROXIDE SOLUTION, 40%

Potassium hydroxide...	40.0 g
Distilled water to make	100.0 ml

Combine the ingredients, and stir until dissolved.

POTASSIUM HYDROXIDE 40% + CREATINE

Potassium hydroxide	40.0 g
Creatine (reagent grade)	0.3 g
Distilled water to make	100.0 ml

Combine the ingredients, and stir until dissolved. Do not store over 3 days at 2° to 8°C nor more than 21 days at -17.8°C.

PROTEIN A PEROXIDASE CONJUGATE*

SALINE SOLUTION, 0.5% AQUEOUS SOLUTION

NaCl	5.0 g
Distilled water	1.0 L

Dissolve NaCl in distilled water, and autoclave for 15 min at 121°C. Final pH should be 7.0.

SALINE-TWEEN-MERTHIOLATE (STM)

NaCl	9.0 g
Tween-20	0.5 g
Merthiolate	0.1 g
Double-distilled water to make	1.0 L

SALTS-PHOSPHATE BUFFERED SALINE SOLUTION (SALTS-PBS)

NaCl	121.0 g
KCl	15.5 g
$MgCl_2$	12.7 g
$CaCl_2 \cdot 2H_2O$	10.2 g
$NaH_2PO_4 \cdot H_2O$	2.0 g
$NaH_2PO_4 \cdot 7H_2O$	3.9 g
Distilled water	1.0 L

Dissolve ingredients in distilled water, and adjust the pH to 7.4.

*Commercially available.

SODIUM CHLORIDE 3%

NaCl	30.0 g
Distilled water	1.0 L

Dissolve NaCl in distilled water, dispense into suitable containers, and autoclave at 121°C for 15 min.

SODIUM CHLORIDE, PHYSIOLOGICAL (0.85% NaCl)

See Physiological Saline Solution 0.85%.

SODIUM HYDROXIDE SOLUTION (0.02 N)

Sodium hydroxide	0.8 g
Distilled water to make	1.0 L

SODIUM HYDROXIDE SOLUTION (1 N)

Sodium hydroxide	40.0 g
Distilled water to make	1.0 L

SPICER-EDWARDS EN COMPLEX ANTIBODY SOLUTION

Spicer-Edwards EN complex (Difco)	0.1 ml
Horseradish peroxidase (HRP)-protein A conjugate	0.07 ml
Tris buffered saline (TBS) 1% gelatin	41.0 ml

Add 0.1 ml of Spicer-Edwards EN Complex to 0.07 ml of HRP-protein A conjugate in 1.0 ml of TBS 1% gelatin, and stir at 4°C for 1 hr. Dilute to 40.0 ml with TBS 1% gelatin. Use within a few hours. This amount is sufficient for four HGMFs.

STANDARD SALINE CITRATE (SSC) SOLUTION (20X)

NaCl	175.4 g
Sodium citrate	88.2 g
Distilled water to make	1.0 L

Dissolve ingredients in distilled water to make a total volume of 1.0 L. Prepare 5X and 2X SSC by diluting this stock solution with distilled water.

STOPPING REAGENT (ELISA)

Stock solution A:

Hydrofluoric acid, 48%	3.47 ml
1 M NaOH	6.0 ml
Double-distilled water to make	1.0 L

Add ingredients individually to 900.0 ml of double-distilled water and dilute to 1.0 L. Store at 4°C.

Stock solution B:

Na$_4$EDTA	38.0 g
Double-distilled water to make	100.0 ml

Add ingredients to 90.0 ml of double-distilled water, and then dilute with double-distilled water to make 100.0 ml. Store at 4°C.

TERGITOL ANIONIC 7*

This reagent is a sodium sulfate derivative of 3,9-diethyl tridecanol-6. Tergitol-7™ is an anionic wetting agent manufactured by Union Carbide Corp., Chemicals and Plastics, 270 Park Avenue, New York, NY 10017.

TRIPHENYLTETRAZOLIUM CHLORIDE (TTC)

Triphenyltetrazolium chloride	1.0 g

Add distilled water to bring the total volume to 100.0 ml, and dissolve. Filter sterilize before use.

TRIS BUFFER 1.0 M

Tris (hydroxymethyl) aminomethane	121.1 g
Distilled water	1.0 L

Dissolve the Tris in 500 ml of distilled water, and adjust to the desired pH with 5 N hydrochloric acid. Bring the total volume to 1.0 L with distilled water, and store at 4° to 6°C.

TRIS BUFFERED SALINE (TBS)

Tris	2.42 g
NaCl	29.24 g
Distilled water	1.0 L

*Commercially available.

Dissolve ingredients in distilled water by heating and stirring. Autoclave for 15 min at 121°C. Final pH should be 7.5 ± 0.2.

TRIS BUFFERED SALINE (TBS) 1% GELATIN

Tris	2.42 g
NaCl	29.24 g
Gelatin	10.0 g
Distilled water	1.0 L

Dissolve ingredients in distilled water by heating and stirring. Autoclave for 15 min at 121°C. Final pH should be 7.5 ± 0.2.

TRIS BUFFERED SALINE (TBS) 3% GELATIN

Tris	2.42 g
NaCl	29.24 g
Gelatin	30.0 g
Distilled water	1.0 L

Dissolve ingredients in distilled water by heating and stirring. Autoclave for 15 min at 121°C. Final pH should be 7.5 ± 0.2.

TRIS BUFFERED SALINE (TBS) TWEEN

Tris	2.42 g
NaCl	29.24 g
Tween 20	0.5 ml
Distilled water	1.0 L

Dissolve ingredients in distilled water by heating and stirring. Autoclave for 15 min at 121°C. Final pH should be 7.5 ± 0.2.

TRITON X-100*

This reagent is the registered trademark for octylphenoxy polyethoxy ethanol. Triton X-100 is a nonionic preparation manufactured by Rohm and Haas Company, Independence Mall West, Philadelphia, PA 19105. It is also sold by Fisher Scientific Company.

TRYPSIN STOCK SOLUTION

Trypsin (Difco No. 0152 or equivalent)	10.0 g
Tris buffer 1.0 M, pH 7.0	100.0 ml

*Commercially available.

Warm the Tris buffer to room temperature, and then dissolve the enzyme in the buffer, warming to 35°C if necessary. Filter-sterilize the solution using a 0.45-μm membrane filter, and dispense into test tubes in 1- or 2-ml volumes. Store up to 1 week at 4° to 6°C or up to 3 months at −18°C.

VASPAR

Combine one part mineral oil with two parts petroleum jelly, and sterilize in an oven at 191°C for 3 hr.

VEROCYTOTOXIN ANTISERUM

Grow *E. coli* O157:H7 in tryptic soy broth at 37°C for 18 hr, add 0.5% formalin, and keep at 37°C for 2 weeks. Inoculate formalized culture into rabbits through ear veins. Give a total of 5 inoculations (0.5, 1.0, 2.0, 4.0, and 4.0 ml); one each at 5-day intervals. Remove blood after 6 weeks, and obtain the serum. Heat the serum at 56°C for 30 min, and adsorb the antiserum 6 times with about 10^{12} cells of heat-treated (121°C for 1 hr) *E. coli* O157:H7, in the proportion of 1 ml of packed cells to 20 ml of antiserum. Use the antibody solution at a 1:5000 dilution.

VIBRIOSTATIC AGENT O/129*

(Sigma #D0656)

VOGES-PROSKAUER (V-P) TEST REAGENTS

Solution A:

α-Naphthol	5.0 g
Ethanol (absolute)	100.0 ml

Solution B:

Potassium hydroxide	40.0 g
Distilled water to make	100.0 ml

Perform Voges-Proskauer (V-P) test at room temperature by transferring 1 ml of a 48-hr culture to a test tube and adding 0.6 ml of α-Naphthol (Solution A) and 0.2 ml of 40% potassium hydroxide (Solution B). Shake after addition of each solution. To intensify and speed reactions, add a few crystals of creatine to the test medium. Read results 4 hr after adding reagents. Positive V-P test indication is the development of an eosin pink color.

*Commercially available.

VRACKO-SHERRIS REAGENT

ρ-Dimethylaminobenzaldehyde (DABA)......................	5.0 g
1 N HCl to make	100.0 ml

Bring volume to 100 ml with 1 N HCl. Keep from light. DABA may take overnight to go into solution. The solution will keep for 1 week.

Y-1 PHOSPHATE SALINE SOLUTION

Na_2HPO_4...	1.07 g
NaH_2PO_4...	0.24 g
NaCl...	8.9 g
Distilled water...	1.0 L

Dissolve ingredients in distilled water, and adjust the pH to 7.5. Autoclave for 15 min at 121°C, and store at 5°C.

62.5   ALPHABETICAL LISTING OF STAINS

This section contains directions for preparation of all stains used throughout this book. Dyes employed should be from batches certified by the Biological Stain Commission or dyes of equal purity. (No batch is approved by the Commission unless it meets chemical and physical tests and has been found to produce satisfactory results in the procedures for which it is normally used.)

Control organisms should be employed frequently, preferably with every batch of slides stained, to assure the analyst that the completed preparations and techniques employed are producing appropriate results.

BASIC FUCHSIN STAIN

Dissolve 0.5 g of basic fuchsin in 20.0 ml of 95% ethanol. Dilute to 100.0 ml with distilled water. Filter if necessary to remove any excess dye particles. Note: Carbol-fuchsin ZN stain may be substituted.

CRYSTAL VIOLET STAIN
(0.5 to 1% solution)

Crystal violet (90% dye content)	0.5 to 1.0 g
Distilled water..	100.0 ml

Dissolve the crystal violet in distilled water, and filter through coarse filter paper. Prepare smear, air-dry, heat-fix, and stain for 20 to 30 sec. Rinse with tap water, air-dry, and examine.

ERYTHROSIN STAIN

Stock Solution:

Erythrosin B (certified)	1.0 g
Distilled water	100.0 ml

Dissolve the dye in the distilled water, and store under refrigeration.

Buffer Solution:

Dissolve equal parts of 0.2 M disodium phosphate and 0.2 M monosodium phosphate in distilled water

Make a 1:5000 concentration of the stain by diluting 1.0 ml of the stock solution with 50.0 ml of the buffer solution. To 1.0 ml of liquid sample add 1.0 ml of the 1:5000 erythrosin solution in a small serum tube. Shake to obtain an even suspension of organisms, and transfer a drop of solution to the hemacytometer with a 3-mm platinum loop.

GIEMSA STAIN

Giemsa stain	
(Matheson Coleman & Bell, Norwood, OH 45212)........	1.0 g
Glycerol	66.0 ml
Methanol (absolute)...	66.0 ml

Dissolve stain in glycerol by heating 1.5 to 2.0 hr at 55° to 60°C. Add methanol, and store in tightly stoppered bottle at 22°C for at least 2 weeks. Dilute stock solution with distilled water (1 + 9) before use.

GRAM STAIN (HUCKER)

Hucker Crystal Violet

Solution A:

Crystal violet (85% dye content)	2.0 g
Ethyl alcohol 95%	20.0 ml

Solution B:

Ammonium oxalate monohydrate...............................	0.2 g
Distilled water	20.0 ml

Prepare the following four solutions:

a. Ammonium oxalate-crystal violet solution: Mix equal parts of Solutions

A and B. (Sometimes the crystal violet is so concentrated that gram-negative organisms do not properly decolorize. To avoid this difficulty, the crystal violet solution may be diluted as much as tenfold prior to mixing with equal parts of Solution B.)

b. Lugol's solution, Gram's modification: Dissolve 1.0 g of iodine crystals and 2.0 g potassium iodide in 300.0 ml of distilled water.

c. Counterstain: Dissolve 2.5 g safranin dye in 100.0 ml of 95% ethyl alcohol. Add 10.0 ml of the alcohol solution of safranin to 100.0 ml of distilled water.

d. Ethyl alcohol: 95%.

Staining Procedure: Stain the heat-fixed smear for 1 min with the ammonium oxalate-crystal violet solution. Wash the slide in water; immerse in Lugol's solution for 1 min.

Wash the stained slide in water; blot dry. Decolorize with ethyl alcohol for 30 sec, using gentle agitation. Wash with water. Blot and cover with counterstain for 10 sec, then wash, dry, and examine as usual.

Cells that decolorize and accept the safranin stain are gram-negative. Cells that do not decolorize but retain the crystal violet stain are gram-positive.

Preferably stain vigorously growing 24-hour cultures from nutrient or other agar free of added carbohydrates. Use positive and negative culture controls.

GRAM STAIN (HUCKER MODIFICATION) FOR *CAMPYLOBACTER*

Crystal Violet:

Solution A:

Crystal violet (90% dye content)	2.0 g
95% ethyl alcohol	200.0 ml

Solution B:

Ammonium oxalate	8.0 g
Distilled water	800.0 ml

Prepare Solutions A and B, and then mix. Let the solution stand overnight or for several days until the dye goes into solution. Filter through coarse filter paper.

Gram's Iodine:

Iodine crystals	1.0 g
Potassium iodide	2.0 g
Distilled water	300.0 ml

Decolorizer:

95% ethyl alcohol

0.3% Carbol Fuchsin Counterstain:

Solution A:

Basic fuchsin	0.3 g
Ethyl alcohol	10.0 ml

Solution B:

Phenol (melted crystal)	5.0 ml
Distilled water	95.0 ml

Prepare Solutions A and B, and mix.

Staining Procedure:

1. Prepare a thin smear in a drop of water on a clean glass slide.
2. Air-dry, and gently fix with heat.
3. Stain for 1 min with crystal violet.
4. Wash the slide with tap water.
5. Add iodine for 1 min.
6. Wash the slide with tap water.
7. Decolorize with ethyl alcohol until alcohol wash is clear.
8. Wash the slide with tap water.
9. Counterstain with carbol fuchsin for 10 to 20 sec.
10. Wash the slide with tap water, dry, and examine.

GRAM STAIN (KOPELOFF AND COHEN MODIFICATION)

Methyl Violet:

Crystal violet or methyl violet 6B (1% aqueous)	30.0 ml
Sodium bicarbonate solution (5%)	8.0 ml

Allow the solution to stand at room temperature for 5 min or more before using.

Iodine:

Iodine	2.0 g
Sodium bicarbonate solution (1 N)	10.0 ml
Distilled water	90.0 ml

Dissolve 2.0 g of iodine in 10 ml of the sodium hydroxide solution, and then add 90.0 ml of distilled water.

Decolorizer:

Ethyl alcohol (95%)	50.0 ml
Acetone	50.0 ml

Counterstain:

Basic fuchsin	0.1 g
Distilled water	100.0 ml

Staining Procedure:

1. Prepare a thin smear in a drop of water on a clean glass slide.
2. Air-dry, and gently fix with the least amount of heat necessary.
3. Flood the smear with crystal violet or methyl violet for 5 min.
4. Flush the smear with iodine solution for 2 min.
5. Drain without blotting, but do not allow the smear to dry.
6. Add the decolorizer dropwise until the runoff is colorless (10 sec or less).
7. Air-dry the slide.
8. Counterstain with basic fuchsin for 20 sec.
9. Wash the excess stain from the slide by short exposure to tap water, and then air-dry. If the slide is not clear, immerse in xylol.
10. Cells that decolorize and accept the basic fuchsin stain are gram-negative. Cells that do not decolorize but retain the crystal violet or methyl. violet stain are gram-positive.

LIPID GLOBULE STAIN

(Burdon's Method)

Solution A:

Sudan black B	0.3 g
Ethyl alcohol 70%	100.0 ml

To prepare Solution A, dissolve 0.3 g of Sudan black B (C.I. 26150) in 70% ethanol. After the bulk of the dye has dissolved, shake solution at intervals during the day and allow to stand overnight. Filter if necessary to remove undissolved dye. Store in a well-stoppered bottle.

Solution B:

Safranin O	0.5 g
Distilled water	100.0 ml

Procedure:

1. Prepare smear, and let dry thoroughly in air. Heat-fix with minimal flaming.
2. Flood entire slide with Solution A, and leave undisturbed for 10 to 20 min.
3. Drain off the excess stain, and blot dry.
4. Wash the slide for 5 to 10 sec with chemically pure xylene, and blot dry.
5. Counterstain with Solution B for 10 to 20 sec.
6. Wash slide with tap water, blot dry, and examine.

MAY-GRUNWALD STAIN

May-Grunwald stain (Matheson Coleman & Bell, Norwood, OH 45212)	2.5 g
Methanol (absolute)	1.0 L

Weigh stain into 50 ml of methanol, dissolve by grinding, and dilute to 1.0 L with methanol. Stir for 16 hr at 37°C. Hold stain for 1 month at 22°C (room temperature). Filter before use.

MODIFIED LEVOWITZ-WEBER STAIN

Methylene blue chloride (certified)	0.5 g
Ethanol (95%)	56.0 ml
Xylene	40.0 ml
Glacial acetic acid	4.0 ml

Add 0.5 g of methylene blue chloride to 56.0 ml of 95% ethanol and 40.0 ml of xylene in a 200-ml flask. Swirl to dissolve, and then let stand for 12 to 24 hr at 4.4° to 7.2°C. Add 4.0 ml of glacial acetic acid, and filter through Whatman No. 42 paper or equivalent. Store the stain in a tightly closed bottle having a cap that will not be affected by the reagents.

NORTH ANILINE OIL-METHYLENE BLUE STAIN

Mix 3.0 ml of aniline oil with 10.0 ml of 95% ethanol, and then slowly add 1.5 ml of HCl with constant agitation. Add 30.0 ml of saturated alcoholic methylene blue solution, and then dilute to 100.0 ml with distilled water. Filter before use.

RYU FLAGELLA STAIN*

(Kodaka Modification)

Solution A:

5% phenol	10.0 ml
Powdered tannic acid	2.0 g
Saturated aluminum potassium sulfate 12-hydrate (crystal)	
(14 g potassium alum in 100 ml distilled water)	10.0 ml

Solution B:

Saturated alcoholic solution of crystal violet
(12 g crystal violet in 100 ml 95% ethyl alcohol)

Mix 10 parts of Solution A (mordant) with 1 part of Solution B (stain). Store at room temperature indefinitely. Does not require filtration before use.

Procedure:

1. With an inoculating needle, pick a colony, and lightly touch the needle in the center of 2 drops of distilled water on a new, precleaned slide.
2. Air-dry the slide at room temperature.
3. Cover the smear with the staining solution, and stain for 5 min. Stain time may vary with each lot of stain.
4. Thoroughly wash the slide in running tap water.
5. Dry the slide, and examine.

The stain is available commercially from Carr Scarborough Microbiologics, Inc., P.O. Box 1328, Stone Mountain, GA 30086.

SPORE STAIN (ASHBY'S)

Solution A:

Malachite green	5.0 g
Distilled water	100.0 ml

Solution B:

Safranin O	0.5 g
Distilled water	100.0 ml

*Commercially available.

Procedure:

1. Prepare smear, and heat-fix with minimal flaming.
2. Place slide over boiling waterbath until definite drops of water collect on the bottom of the slide.
3. Flood the slide with Solution A.
4. After 1 or 2 min, wash the slide thoroughly in cool tap water.
5. Counterstain with Solution B for 20 to 30 sec.
6. Rinse slide thoroughly in cool water, dry without blotting, and examine.

ZIEHL-NEELSEN'S CARBOL FUCHSIN STAIN*
(TB CARBOL FUCHSIN ZN)

62.6   REFERENCES

1. APHA. 1975. "Standard Methods for the Examination of Water and Wastewater," 14th ed. Am. Pub. Health Assn., Washington, D.C.
2. APHA. 1985. "Standard Methods for the Examination of Dairy Products," 15th ed. Am. Pub. Health Assn., Washington, D.C.
3. CDC. 1974. "Manual of Quality Control Procedures for Microbiological Laboratories," Centers for Disease Control, Atlanta, Ga.
4. Stamer, J.R. and Stoyla, B.O. 1967. Growth response of *Lactobacillus brevis* to aeration and organic catalysts. Appl. Microbiol. 15:1025.

INDEX

RDER FORM

(Please print)

Please send me _____ copies of

Compendium of Methods for the Microbiological Examination of Foods

3rd edition (1100 pages, hardcover, Stock No. 032K) at $90.00 each for nonmembers and $63.00 for APHA members.

U.S.—Add $9.00 per book for shipping and handling.
Non-U.S.—Add $11.50 per book for shipping and handling.
For orders over $200.00, call (202) 789-5667 for shipping and handling charges.

_____ **Total** dollars including shipping and handling.

☐ Payment enclosed (make check payable to APHA). All checks and money orders must be in US dollars and drawn on US banks.

☐ Visa ☐ Mastercard

Credit Card No. _____ Expiration Date _____

Cardholder's Signature _____

Name _____

Member No. _____

Organization _____

Address _____

City/State/Zip _____

Country _____

Phone ( ) _____

Is this a business address? ___ Yes ___ No

Mail order form to: **American Public Health Association**
Publication Sales
Department 5037
Washington, DC 20061-5037

To order or charge by phone, call (202) 789-5636. Prices subject to change without notice. After 8/92, please call (202) 789-5667 to confirm prices.